IRIS CHECK LIST

of

Registered Cultivar Names

1990–1999

Edited by Keith Keppel

The American Iris Society, Inc
Hannibal, New York
2001

PUBLISHED BY THE AMERICAN IRIS SOCIETY
2001

Printed in the United States of America
by
Edwards Brothers Incorporated • Ann Arbor, Michigan

Iris Check List

THIS BOOK IS DEDICATED TO

THE MEMORY OF

KATHLEEN KAY NELSON

...WHO ASSISTED HER REGISTRAR FATHER FOR SEVEN YEARS BEFORE BECOMING REGISTRAR HERSELF FOR AN ADDITIONAL TWENTY-TWO YEARS

...WHO EDITED THE 1969, 1979, AND 1989 CHECK LISTS

...AND WHO WAS STILL PROCESSING REGISTRATION REQUESTS SIX HOURS BEFORE LOSING HER BATTLE WITH CANCER, AUGUST 7, 1994.

Contents

Preface

No compilation of this size is without error, which we sadly acknowledge. Typographical errors will always be with us, but as informational errors are detected, the Registrar welcomes notification of corrections with documentation as appropriate. We look forward to the day when all the records will be on computer and corrections/additions can be made the instant they are detected. The Registrations Committee is already accumulating non-published parental and introductory data pertaining to previous decades with this in mind!

As Editor, I wish to express thanks to Bruce Filardi, David Silverberg, and Mike Lowe for assistance in proofreading text, and to Sara Marley and David Silverberg for assembling the Awards listing. Special thanks to Mike Lowe for formatting the book and working with the printer. Also of incomparable assistance have been our Associate Registrars in other countries, for help in gathering and interpreting data on foreign originations. The bottom line, of course, is the help given by the registrants and introducers themselves, furnishing the information to be compiled.

In 1929 the first hardbound Check List was published by the American Iris Society, and the issuance of a new Check List each ten years has become a tradition. Beginning with the 1949 Check List, each ten-year book incorporates the information contained in the annual Registrar's reports for that decade. Information in this Check List does vary somewhat from that previously published. Some descriptions have been reworded or reformatted slightly for clarity and consistency, and we have tried to eliminate inconsistencies in the way a particular firm or individual is listed from year to year. The coding for bloom season has been modified slightly. At the request of the Russian associate registrar, the spelling of a few names transliterated from the Cyrillic alphabet has been changed. Minor typographical corrections have been made, and when additional parental information has been made available, some parentages have been augmented or restated. Some registrations appearing in annual reports have been deleted if the hybridizer has stated that no stock was distributed, stock of the plant destroyed, and the name does not appear in later breeding records. When discrepancies appear between what was printed in an annual Registrations and Introductions reports and what appears in the Check List, the Check List entries should be presumed more accurate.

Again, we wish to thank the Associate Registrars and the co-operating societies around the world that have appointed them. As of 1999, these societies and individuals were as follows:

British Iris Society: Jennifer Hewitt, Haygarth, Cleeton St. Mary, Cleobury Mortimer, Kidderminster DY14 0QU, England, U.K.
Gesellschaft der Staudenfreunde E.V.: Gisela Dathe, Tannenring 57, 65207 Wiesbaden, Germany
Iris Society of Australia: Helen Reid, 16 Farnsworth St., Sunshine, Victoria 3020, Australia
Middle-European Iris Society: Zdeněk Seidl, Vinohradská 57, 748 01 Hlučín, Czech Republic
New Zealand Iris Society: Dr. H. J. Manning, Jolendale Park, 9 Peterson Place, Bridge Hill, Alexandra, New Zealand
Russian Iris Society: Sergey Loktev, P. O. Box 54, 129226 Moscow, Russia
Societá Italiana dell'Iris: Prof. Paolo Gambassini, Lungarno C. Colombo 18, 50136 Firenze, Italy
Societe Francaise des Iris et Plantes Bulbeuses: Jean Peyrard, 101 ave. de la Republique, 38170 Seyssinet, France

American Iris Society Registrar-Recorder, Keith Keppel, P. O. Box 18154, Salem, OR 97305, U.S.A.

HOW TO USE THIS CHECK LIST

REGISTRATION information is given in the following order:

NAME OF CULTIVAR – listed in alphabetical order

NAME OF HYBRIDIZER AND/OR REGISTRANT

YEAR OF REGISTRATION (R.)

SEEDLING NUMBER – (information optional)

CLASS OF IRIS – see list of Abbreviations for explanation of individual entries

HEIGHT –listed in inches, followed by centimeters

SEASON – normal season of bloom relative to other cultivars of the same class. Normal bloom season for a particular class is divided into thirds: E (early), M (midseason) and L (late). The initials are listed for one (or more) thirds wherein the described cultivar blooms. Bloom outside the normal range for the class is indicated by VE (very early) or VL (very late). RE indicates remontancy, a tendency to rebloom at an entirely different season.

DESCRIPTION

PARENTAGE

INTRODUCER AND DATE OF INTRODUCTION – if the cultivar is in commerce

PRIOR REGISTRATIONS WITH ADDITIONAL INFORMATION:

NAME OF CULTIVAR

NAME OF HYBRIDIZER AND/OR REGISTRANT

CLASS OF IRIS

YEAR OF REGISTRATION (R.)

ADDITIONAL DATA – usually Introducer and date of Introduction, but may be correction of description, parentage, etc.

#PRIOR REGISTRATIONS, NAMES RELEASED:

NAME OF CULTIVAR, preceded by #

NAME OF HYBRIDIZER AND/OR REGISTRANT

CLASS OF IRIS

YEAR OF REGISTRATION (R.)

ADDITIONAL DATA – explanation of name release.

ABBREVIATIONS and REFERENCES

The following abbreviations will be found throughout the book:

AB - arilbred. (Use of + or - marks in conjunction with a subgroup listing indicate more (+) or (-) less than one half aril content.)

AR - aril

BB - border bearded

CA - californicae (also known as Pacific Coast Natives, PCNs, or pacificas)

dip. - diploid

E - early (relative time of bloom)

F - falls (sepals)

HCC - Horticultural Colour Chart

IB - intermediate bearded

inv. - involving, or involved

JI - japanese

L - late (relative time of bloom)

LA - louisiana

M - midseason (relative time of bloom)

M&P - Maerz & Paul, Dictionary of Color

MDB - miniature dwarf bearded

MTB - miniature tall bearded (also known as table irises)

Munsell - Nickerson Color Fan, Munsell Hue coding

NEGS - Fischer Color Chart, New England Gladiolus Society

OB - oncobred (oncocyclus and bearded hybrid)

OG - oncogelia (oncocylcus - regelia hybrid)

OGB - oncogeliabred (oncocyclus, regelia and bearded hybrid)
OH - oncocyclus hybrid
Pantone - Pantone Color Chart
R. - registered
RB - regeliabred (regelia - bearded hybrid)
RE - remontant (reblooming)
RH - regelia hybrid
RHS - Royal Horticultural Society Colour Chart
S. - standards (petals)
Sdlg. - seedling
sib - sibling
SIB - siberian
SDB - standard dwarf bearded
SPEC - species
SPEC-X - species hybrid
SPU - spuria
TB - tall bearded
tet. - tetraploid
VE - very early (relative time of bloom)
VL - very late (relative time of bloom)

PARENTAGES

All parentages contain one large **X**, which indicates the final cross made; everything to the left of the **X** pertains to the pod (female) parent, everything to the right pertains to the pollen (male) parent.

Each set of parentheses **( )** represents <u>one</u> cross of <u>two</u> parents. Thus – (A x B) represents a cross of Plant A as the pod parent, plant B as the pollen parent. (C x (A x B)) represents Plant C as pod parent, <u>a seedling</u> (A x B) as pollen parent.

Additional information may be included, such as: 91-42A: (Entourage x Vanity). This means that seedling 91-42A is from (or =) a cross of Entourage (pod) x Vanity (pollen).

81-131H, sib to Snowbrook, would mean that seedling 81-131H is a sibling of Snowbrook, and that its parentage can be found by checking the registration for Snowbrook (which may be in a prior Check List).

As parentages become ever more complicated, occasionally you may find something similar to – W 170-1, pod parent of Devil's Lake. This means you must go to the registration for Devil's Lake and find the parentage of W 170-1 as indicated <u>within</u> the Devil's Lake parentage.

THE AMERICAN IRIS SOCIETY
1999 CHECK LIST

An alphabetical compilation of registrations and introductions,
1990 through 1999.

AAH SO GLORIOSO (C. Zurek, TB, R. 1988). Rancho de la Flor de Lis 1990.

AARDVARK ANTICKZ (Brad Kasperek, R. 1998). Sdlg. 94B-52A. IB, 21" (53 cm), M. Lightly ruffled gold and tan blend tinged greyed yellow (RHS 160B), lightly peppered greyed purple (184A), with white (155C) inclusions; style arms yellow, midrib purple; beards orange; broken color pattern; pronounced musky fragrance. Quicken X Gnus Flash. Zebra 1999.

AARON'S BLUEBELLS (G. Poole, TB, R. 1988). Redbud Lane 1990.

AARON'S BONUS (George Sutton, R. 1998). Sdlg. F-186. TB, 37" (94 cm), EM. Greyed white, F. veined yellow green to gold at shoulders; beards dark yellow, pale yellow at end; ruffled, edges creped. Elizabeth Poldark X Fine China. Sutton 1999.

AARON'S CHILD (George Sutton, R. 1997). Sdlg. G-86. IB, 26" (66 cm), EM & RE. S. and style arms orient pink (RHS 36A); F. white, 1/2" orient pink edge; beards pinkish orange, 1/2" bright violet blue horn; ruffled; slight sweet fragrance. Aaron's Dagger X Chanted.

AARON'S DAGGER (George Sutton, R. 1995). Sdlg. TW-BU. TB, 37" (94 cm), EM. Red violet self; beards orange and violet, 3/4" fuzzy violet horn; slight sweet fragrance. Twice Thrilling X Bubble Up. Sutton 1995.

AARON'S DREAM (George Sutton, R. 1994). Sdlg. B-331-AR. TB, 37" (94 cm), EML & RE. Pale blue (near white) self; beards medium blue; slight sweet fragrance. B-178: (Faithfulness x Scented Nutmeg) X Baldwin 8241A: (Jolimont x Velvet Vista). Sutton 1994.

AARON'S ROD (George Sutton, R. 1997). Sdlg. G-74. TB, 37" (94 cm), ML. Ruffled bluebird blue (RHS 94A) self, F. veined darker; beards blue, tipped mustard, short horn; slight sweet fragrance. Busy Being Blue X Deity. Sutton 1998.

AARON'S SHIELD (Lois Rich by James Whitely, R. 1994). Sdlg. R69-88. AR (RC), 14" (36 cm), E. S. orchid violet, violet veins and midrib, white orchid edge; self style arms elevated over beards; F. orchid, light orchid veins, darker orchid violet from mulberry violet signal to edge; bright yellow orange beards. Persian Pansy X Austin 58A-O-25C. Aril Patch 1994.

ABBA ALIAS ABBA (Allan Ensminger, R. 1993). Sdlg. 188-8. SDB, 13" (33 cm), ML. S. hyacinth blue (HCC 40/1); F. mimosa yellow (602/1); beards blue. 85-13: (People Pleaser x 183-4: ((Tantara x Jungle Shadows) x *pumila* x (Miss Region Twenty-One x Tumwater)))) X 285-13, sib. Varigay 1994.

ABBEY CHANT (George Sutton, R. 1997). Sdlg. H-86. IB, 25" (64 cm), VE & RE. S. and style arms bright yellow (RHS 7A); F. white, hafts and 1/2" edge lighter yellow (7C); beards violet (83B) at end, spanish orange (26) in throat, all hairs tipped cream, beard ending with violet blue horn; ruffled; pronounced musky fragrance. Aaron's Dagger X Chanted. Sutton 1998.

ABBEY ROAD (David Silverberg, R. 1994). Sdlg. 85-34C. TB, 35" (89 cm), M. S. creamy yellow; F. warm white, creamy yellow shoulders; beards yellow, tipped cream. Pleated Gown X Ganges Moon. Stockton 1994.

ABDALLAH PARK (George Slade, R. 1997). Sdlg. 91M1. TB, 38" (97 cm), L. Ruffled medium red violet self; beards orange, tipped violet; sweet fragrance. Helen With Love X seedling, parentage unknown.

ABIDING JOY (George Sutton, R. 1996). Sdlg. G-15-B. TB, 38" (97 cm), ML. Ruffled sea lavender (RHS 85A), amethyst (84C) at base of S.; beards sea lavender; slight sweet fragrance. Winterscape X Sky Hooks. Sutton 1997.

ABIGAIL ANN (Carl Jorgensen, R. 1995). Sdlg. 84-P-4D. TB, 34" (86 cm), L-VL. S. azalea pink (HCC 618/3); style arms azalea pink, large, lacy; F. light azalea pink (618/5) edge, paling toward shrimp red (616) beards; ruffled; slight sweet fragrance. Cozy and Warm X Summit Love. Long 1995.

ABIGAIL LIND (Richard Goula, R. 1992). Sdlg. G-78-L1. LA, 32" (81 cm), EM. S. pale lavender; F. full lavender violet, yellow green signal; ruffled; slight spicy fragrance. Lavender Ruffles X Clara Goula.

ABIGAIL NICOLE (Darlene Pinegar, R. 1999). Sdlg. DS-5B. TB, 30" (76 cm), M. S. and style arms medium yellow; F. white ground, dark gold haft marking, overall dark purplish blue veining

1

becoming near-solid by 3/8" greyed plum edge; beards medium yellow, white at end, dark yellow in throat; lightly ruffled. Double Scoop X Glitz 'n Glitter.

ABILENE (Jim Hedgecock, R. 1993). Sdlg. C-84-25-1. BB, 25" (64 cm), M. Heavily laced and ruffled pale red, F. with large violet blaze below golden yellow beard; slight sweet fragrance. Hilow X 73-13, inv. Quadros sdlgs. Comanche Acres 1994.

ABILITY (Joseph Ghio, R. 1998). Sdlg. LA-93. LA, 30" (76 cm), EM. Rosy red, F. with overall cream veining. Sdlg., parentage unknown, X Margaret Lee. Bay View 1999.

ABINGTON PURPLE (R. J. Blakeway-Phillips, R. 1993). SPEC (*unguicularis*), 12" (30 cm), EML. Purple with orange signal; slight fragrance. Selection of *I. unguicularis*, probably from *angustifolia*. Broadleigh 1987.

ABORIGEN (Viacheslav Gavrilin, R. 1999). Sdlg. 6-4-2-94. TB, 34" (86 cm), VE. Ruffled lilac, edged lighter; style arms lilac; beards orange; slight fragrance. Eagle's Flight X unknown. Gavrilin 1999.

ABOUT LAST NIGHT (Paul Black, R. 1999). Sdlg. B137A. TB, 30" (76 cm), M. S. purplish black; style arms deep purplish black, black midline and tan edges; F. black, hafts veined cream; beards bright yellow gold, wide; pronounced sweet fragrance. Witches' Sabbath X Oklahoma Crude. Mid-America 1999.

ABOUT TOWN (Barry Blyth, R. 1996). Sdlg. B160-1. TB, 40" (102 cm), EM. S. silvery mauve lilac; F. red violet, 1/8" silvery mauve lilac edge; beards tangerine; ruffled, laced. Bubble Up X Electrique. Tempo Two 1996/97.

ABRACO (Sterling Innerst, R. 1992). Sdlg. 2812-2. JI (6 F.), 36-40" (91-102 cm), M. White ground heavily sanded fuchsia red-maroon, 1/4" blue rim, yellow signal. Jocasta X 1540-7, Iapetus sib. Iris Pond 1993.

ABREK (Viktor Koroliov, R. 1999). Sdlg. S81-94K. TB, 35" (90 cm), M. S. yellow, tinted brown; style arms yellow; F. claret red edged color of S., hafts marked yellow wine; beards bright yellow; pronounced spicy fragrance. "Borokko" X Vitafire. Koroliov 1999.

ABSALOM (Sterling Innerst, R. 1994). Sdlg. 3693-1. JI (6 F.), 38" (97 cm), M. Medium blue, mottled white, yellow signals; blue style arms; slight fragrance. 2462-3: ((Stranger in Paradise x Yusho) x Anytus) X 3244-1: ((Frostbound x Fringed Cloud) x Hegira). Iris Pond 1995.

ABSALOM'S TREACHERY (Pete McGrath, R. 1998). Sdlg. McAB 93-21 PP. AB (OGB), 26" (66 cm), M. S. spectrum violet, slightly darker veining; style arms honey, striped violet, crests rose violet; F. dark rose violet with smoky wash, gold toned throat, dark violet signal; beards dark. Turkish Herald X Heart Stealer. Aril Society 1998.

ABSOLUTE DELIGHT (Robert Dunn, R. 1999). Sdlg. B1058B. TB, 35" (89 cm), EM. White ground plicata, small grape violet veins and lines; style arms grape violet; beards yellow, tipped blue; slight sweet fragrance. Eagle's Flight X Trace.

ABSTRACT ART (Keith Keppel, TB, R. 1989). Keppel 1990.

ABUZZ (Allan Ensminger, R. 1993). Sdlg. 288-36. SDB, 15" (40 cm), L. Pastel violet; poppy red beards. Raspberry Rose X Pink Capers. Varigay 1994.

ABYSS (Donovan Albers, SDB, R. 1989). Redbud Lane 1990.

ACACIA RHUMBA (Heather Pryor, R. 1994). Sdlg. 46/90-1. LA, 28" (71 cm), E. S. soft lemon (RHS 20B), chartreuse line signal; green styles, lemon border and crests; F. slightly darker lemon (13C) veined green, chartreuse line signal; finely serrate. Jazz Ballet X Rosebery. Rainbow Ridge 1995/96.

ACADIANA SUNSET (Richard Goula, R. 1992). Sdlg. G-87-R3. LA, 30" (76 cm), EM. S. medium violet red; F. medium dark red with trace of violet iridescence, large bright yellow signal; slight spicy fragrance. Ann Chowning X Mrs. Ira Nelson. Gatewood 1993.

ACAPULCO SUNSET (Hooker Nichols, TB, R. 1988). Hillcrest 1993.

ACE (Lynda Miller, R. 1999). Sdlg. 4094B. MTB, 22" (56 cm), M. S. white ground, deep violet overlay; style arms white, violet midrib; F. white ground, deep violet center line, dots and solid border; beards pale violet, hairs tipped golden bronze; slight musky fragrance. Cherry X Manisses. Miller's Manor 1999.

ACE OF DIAMONDS (Fred Gadd by Lynn Markham, selector, R. 1995). Sdlg. 16-87C. TB, 35" (89 cm), ML. Lightly frilled white self, faint pinkish lavender cast, F. slightly texture veined; beards pink at end, shading to deep orange red in throat, near-white base. Marjie K X Wish. Markham 1996.

ACE OF LACE (Tom Burseen, TB, R. 1989). T.B.'s Place 1990.

ACE ROYALE (Barry Blyth, R. 1997). Sdlg. B162-3. TB, 38" (97 cm), M. S. opalescent pinkish cream-white, slightly deeper basal flush; style arms pinkish cream white, lavender midline; F. rich plum burgundy; beards rich chocolate bronze; slight sweet fragrance. Crimson Snow X Electrique. Tempo Two 1997/98.

ACEY DEUCEY (Allan Ensminger, R. 1993). Sdlg. 88-9. SDB, 13" (33 cm), EM. S. white; F. yellow; yellow beards tipped white. 85-13 sib X 85-13: (People Pleaser x 83-4: ((Tantara x Jungle Shadows) x (*pumila* x (Miss Region Twenty-One x Tumwater)))). Varigay 1994.

ACID PRINT (Barry Blyth, R. 1991). Sdlg. X44-A. SDB, 14" (36 cm), EML. S. cream, overlaid rose in muted tones; F. bright lemon, bright rose plicata markings on hafts and halfway down; bright tangerine beard. Logo X ((Sniffs 'n' Sneezes x Hammered Copper) x Ashanti). Tempo Two 1991/92.

ACK-COMMODATE (William Ackerman, JI, R. 1988). Nicholls Gardens 1995.

ACK-COUNTABLE (William Ackerman, JI, R. 1988). Nicholls Gardens 1991.

ACK-SCENT PINK (William Ackerman, JI, R. 1988). Nicholls Gardens 1994.

ACOMA (Tom Magee, TB, R. 1987). Long 1990.

ACQUA DI ROSA (Augusto Bianco, R. 1999). Sdlg. 411-95. TB, 38" (96 cm), EM. S. mallow rose; style arms rose; F. medium rose, lighter center; beards tangerine; slight spicy fragrance. (Champagne Elegance x Winterscape) X Collector's Art.

ACSTEDE NINE-HUNDRED (B. Price, IB, R. 1986). British Iris Society 1990.

ACTIVE AYR (Graeme Grosvenor, R. 1993). JI (6 F.), 54" (137 cm), E. Heavily ruffled and fluted white self. Snowy Hills X Hagoromo. Rainbow Ridge 1993/94.

ACTIVE DUTY (Harold Stahly, R. 1999). Sdlg. 92-36. SIB, 37" (94 cm), M. Deep wine red (deeper than RHS 89A), F. with green throat, white signal with slight blue halo; style arms slightly lighter wine red, midrib deeper. Temper Tantrum X unknown. Stahly 1999.

ACT THREE (Barry Blyth, R. 1995). Sdlg. Z47-1. TB, 34" (86 cm), EM. S. lemon buff, slight violet midrib flush; F. bright blue violet; beards lavender, old gold in throat; pronounced sweet fragrance. Edith Wolford X Soaring. Tempo Two 1995/96.

ADA MARIE (Harry Wolford, R. 1993). Sdlg. P9C6-1. TB, 32-34" (81-86 cm), EM. S. bright gold; F. orange red with blue infusion, bright gold edge; orange beards; slight fragrance. Prancing Pony X Carolina Gold.

ADAM CONERLY (James R. Allen, TB, R. 1987). Comanche Acres 1995.

ADA MORGAN (Richard Morgan, R. 1997). Sdlg. L275-A. LA, 30" (76 cm), EM. S. light pinkish violet; style arms green; F. slightly deeper pinkish violet. L29-A: (Clyde Redmond x Sidney Conger) X Marie Caillet.

ADDED ELEGANCE (Chet Tompkins, R. 1990). Sdlg. 86-4. TB, 36" (91 cm), EML. S. white, faintly edged blue; F. white with blended heliotrope and blue stitched edge; beards white, tipped pale blue; ruffled; pronounced spicy fragrance. Inv. plic lines X 80-13C: ((Bandera Waltz sib x Rippling Rose) x Calliope Tune). Fleur de Lis 1990.

ADDED VALUE (Paul Black, R. 1997). Sdlg. A33B. TB, 33" (84 cm), ML. S. salmon buff, midrib pale violet; style arms amber, center orchid pink; F. blended light dusty rose violet, dusty rose edge, hafts light amber; beards orange; slightly ruffled; slight musky sweet fragrance. Robusto X Ruth Black. Mid-America 1997.

ADD IT UP (O. D. Niswonger, R. 1996). Sdlg. SDB 4-95. SDB, 12" (31 cm), M. Light canteloupe orange; beards tangerine, blue at end. Candy Queen X That's Pink. Cape Iris 1997.

ADEPT (Joseph Ghio, R. 1997). Sdlg. PD-245N2. CA, 14" (36 cm), EM. S. mahogany rose; F. apricot rose, deep maroon signal. Local Girl X PG-172A, Charter Member sib. Bay View 1997.

ADMETUS (Sterling Innerst, R. 1992). Sdlg. 3045-5. JI (6 F.), 36-40" (91-102 cm), M. White, flushed fuchsia red in center, yellow signal. Geisha Gown X Tamatsushima. Iris Pond 1993.

ADORABLE DIVA (A. & D. Willott, R. 1993). Sdlg. 92-220. TB, 36" (91 cm), EM. Ruffled light apricot pink, slightly deeper haft; beards bright orange. Beverly Sills X Master Gardener. Willott 1994.

ADORABLE ROSE (Opal Brown by Margaret McCrae, R. 1998). Sdlg. 90-2B4. TB, 35" (89 cm), M. S. blended red violet (M&P 45-I-1 to 44-I-3); style arms lighter blended red violet (near 44-H-1); F. blended corinth purple (46-J-2 to 44-J-2), slight cattleya (42-H-6) blaze; beards bright chrome orange (10-K-12); lightly ruffled; pronounced sweet fragrance. Dualtone sib X 81-4E8: (77-1A8, Pearls and Gold sib, x 79-3F10, Persian Gown sib).

ADORING GLANCES (O. D. Niswonger, R. 1992). Sdlg. SDB 18-88. SDB, 12" (30 cm), M. S. light grey with chartreuse infusion; F. same, with deeper chartreuse spot around blue beard. Chubby Cheeks X unknown. Cape Iris 1992.

ADRIAN ROGERS (Robert Fabel-Ward, R. 1990). LA, 30" (76 cm), EM. Very dark violet with golden veins, prominent crest to tip of F. Black Gamecock X Chowning FC77/9: (Mockers Song x Ann Chowning).

ADRIATIC BLUE (O. D. Niswonger, R. 1995). Sdlg. Sp 3-93. SPU, 42" (107 cm), M. S. and style arms deep blue; F. gold, rimmed deep blue. Missouri Rivers X -- probably Russian Blue. Cape Iris 1996.

ADRIATIC SHORES (Eric & Bob Tankesley-Clarke, R. 1994). SPEC, 18" (46 cm), M. Deep purple, slightly darker F.; beards ice white; pronounced sweet fragrance; purple leaf base. Collected; distributed as *I. germanica* U56 and in commerce prior to 1985.

ADVANCE DESIGN (Bennett Jones, R. 1992). Sdlg. 447-11. SDB, 12" (30 cm), M. S. blended peach pink; F. rust, widely banded lemon yellow; beards carrot red. Live Jazz X Pink Caper. Bennett Jones 1994.

AD VANTAGE (Chet Tompkins, R. 1990). Sdlg. 83-11. TB, 37" (94 cm), ML. Cranberry violet with reddish undertone, picoteed edge; beards red violet; pronounced musky fragrance. ((Daguerrotype x Genesis) x Grant Gordon) X ((Grant Gordon x Grand Waltz) x (Cranberry Ice x Grant Gordon)). Fleur de Lis 1990.

AEGEAN STORM (Hooker Nichols, TB, R. 1989). Hillcrest 1994.

AEGIDIENTURM (Harald Moos, R. 1993). Sdlg. 88/811Z. TB, 36" (91 cm), E. Intensely frilled light pink; beards red orange. Flaming Victory X (Laced Cotton x Precious Moments). Schoeppinger 1993.

AELITA (Adolph Volfovich-Moler, R. 1995). Sdlg. V-34. TB, 51" (130 cm), L. S. cream white; F. lilac, edges paler; beards orange; ruffled, laced. Rippling Waters X Pipes of Pan. Volfovich-Moler 1992.

AESTHICA (Tom Burseen, R. 1991). Sdlg. 7-286E. TB, 36" (91 cm), E. S. toasted light red (RHS 41C); F. slightly darker, with tannish brown overlay; beards tangerine; ruffled, heavily laced; slight fragrance. Exhilaration X Copper Lace. T.B.'s Place 1992.

AFFAIRE (Barry Blyth, R. 1992). Sdlg. Y3-1. TB, 36" (91 cm), EM. S. lavender to blue grey; F. greenish mustard, slight tan overlay; beards mustard yellow. ((Alpine Journey x Beachgirl) x (Beachgirl x ((Tranquil Star x Coral Strand) x (Persian Smoke x Chimbolam)))) X Behold a Lady. Tempo Two 1993/94.

AFFIRMATION (Glenn Corlew, TB, R. 1988). Cooley 1992.

AFLOAT (John C. Taylor, R. 1998). Sdlg. UL 8-1. LA, 43" (110 cm), M. S. and style arms blue violet; F. blue violet, darker in center, very prominent yellow signal; heavily fluted. C'est La Mote X First Favorite.

AFRICAN COAST (R. & F. Walster, R. 1991). Sdlg. 3-1986B. TB, 34" (86 cm), ML. S. soft rosy mahogany; F. dark mahogany, white hafts veined dark mahogany; beards yellow, tipped white. Pink Taffeta X Distant Fire. Walsterway 1991.

AFRICAN SUNSET (Schreiner, R. 1991). Sdlg. K 939-M. TB, 35" (89 cm), L. S. orange (RHS 21A); F. orange brown (24A); beards tangerine. E 766-A: ((Marilyn C x Celestial Glory) x Flaming Dragon) X G 1519-A, Burnt Toffee sib. Schreiner 1991.

AFRICAN WINE (Brad Kasperek, R. 1998). Sdlg. 94M-64A. MDB, 8" (20 cm), M. S. cabernet (RHS 185C); style arms wine and tan; F. deep chrysanthemum crimson (185A) edged lighter (185B); beards burnt orange, hairs tipped lavender at end; ruffled; slight fragrance. Orange Tiger X 92M-6T: (Snow Cub x Flea Circus). Zebra 1999.

AFROSIAB (Adolf Volfovich-Moler, R. 1998). Sdlg. V-184. AB (RB), 39" (100 cm), E. S. light purple, veined violet and brown, broad brown edge; style arms purple, crests brown; F. cherry purple veined darker, rim brown; beards orange yellow, purple at end; waved form; pronounced fragrance. *I. stolonifera* X Mary Frances.

AFTER EIGHT (Harold Stahly, R. 1995). Sdlg. 86-5. TB, 34" (86 cm), M. Deep blackish violet self; style arms deep violet; beards near-black; ruffled. Superstition X Black Flag. Stahly 1995.

AFTER ROMANCE (Akihiko Terada, R. 1998). Sdlg. S095-89-11. TB, 36" (91 cm), M. Ruffled and laced red purple, F. with white spot around yellow beard; pronounced musky fragrance. Mary Frances X Master Touch. Roris 1998.

AFTERSHOCK (Joseph Ghio, R. 1990). Sdlg. PJ-180A2. CA, 14" (36 cm), ML. Deep brassy gold, mahogany brown signal. PL-226A2: (Peanut Gallery x (((Pacific Moon x California Native) x San Vicente sib) x Mission Santa Cruz)) X (Moraga sib x ((Simply Wild x Camp Capitola sib) x (Big Wheel x California Mystique))). Bay View 1991.

AFTER THE BALL (Ben Hager, R. 1991). Sdlg. T4393DpVLcVyLa. TB, 35" (89 cm), VL.

4

Laced clear dark violet, lighter around pale blue beards, inconspicuous brown haft veining. T3965LcLvVyLa: ((T2590A: ((Babson M131-4 x Morning Breeze) x Dream Time) x Grand Waltz) x T3323BlWh: (Igloo x T2590A)) X T4098TlLcV: (Silver Flow x Irene Nelson). Melrose 1992.

AFTER THE DAWN (Richard Ernst, R. 1994). Sdlg. G102-1. TB, 36" (91 cm), M. S. blended violet peach, darker violet midrib; style arms peach yellow; F. creamy peach yellow, light caramel shoulders, white center wash; ruffled; slight sweet fragrance. St. Helens' Wake X Hula Dancer. Cooley 1995.

AFTER THE STORM (Sterling Innerst, R. 1991). Sdlg. 3169-4. TB, 36" (91 cm), ML. Medium blue; beards white, tipped lemon; slight sweet fragrance. Silent Morn X Swirling Seas. Innerst 1992.

AGAIN AND AGAIN (Sterling Innerst, R. 1999). Sdlg. Re4619-1. TB, 36" (91 cm), M & RE. Medium yellow; beards white; slight fragrance. Renown X Anxious. Innerst 1999.

AGATHA CHRISTIE (George Sutton, R. 1996). Sdlg. F-315. IB, 24" (61 cm), VE-EM. S. greyed wistaria blue (RHS 92D); style arms wistaria blue; F. white ground, veined and edged bluebird blue (94A); beards wistaria blue; ruffled. C-24: (Momentum x 4-33: ((Heavenly Harmony x Petite Posy) x French Gown)) X Le Flirt. Sutton 1998.

AGELESS (Allan Ensminger, R. 1993). Sdlg. 190-7. SDB, 15" (40 cm), ML. Salmon pink; beards red. 88-33: (Pink Caper x 81-56: (78-21 x (((64-12 x Stepping Out) x (Faydy Girl x sib)) x Rancho Rose))) X Tiny Cherub. Varigay 1994.

AGE OF CHIVALRY (Joseph Ghio, R. 1991). Sdlg. PI-192-G2. CA, 17" (43 cm), ML. Medium to dark blue with glowing purple cast, deep blue signal. Idylwild X PM-240-Z2: (Zayante Creek x Miramar). Bay View 1992.

AGE OF INNOCENCE (Frederick Kerr by Stockton Iris Gardens, R. 1994). Sdlg. 88-03-02. TB, 38" (97 cm), M. S. pure white; F. white, edged blue (RHS 92A); beards golden yellow (21A); ruffled; slight fragrance. Edith Wolford X Condottiere. Stockton 1994.

AGGIE BELLE (Kirk Strawn, R. 1993). Sdlg. EE-1985. LA, 48" (122 cm), M. S. greyed purple (RHS 185D); style arms greyed red (181C), yellow cast; F. greyed purple (184B), yellow orange (15A) signal. Kirk Strawn X Count Pulaski.

AGGRESSIVELY FORWARD (Sterling Innerst, R. 1994). Sdlg. 3104-1. TB, 36" (91 cm), M. Full yellow ground plicata, F. trimmed blue purple; black dart under bronze yellow beard; musky fragrance. Point Made X 2238-11: ((Osage Buff x Spinning Wheel) x Burgundy Brown). Innerst 1995.

A GOGO (Lawrence Ransom, R. 1992). Sdlg. U1. MDB, 4" (10 cm), VE-E. Pale yellow self; beards white. Parentage unknown. Iris au Trescols 1993.

AHMID BEY (E. S. Fankhauser, R. 1998). Sdlg. AB.9.87.A. AB (OGB-), 24" (60 cm), M & RE. Light blue self; beards white, hairs tipped yellow, pale blue at end. Blue Sapphire X AB.84.3.A.: (AB.16.68.B., C. G. White type seedling, parentage lost, x Capitola). Tempo Two 1998/99.

AICHI-NO-KAGAYAKI (Shinnosuki Osugi/Ryuichi Osugi by Society for Japanese Irises, R. 1993). SPEC-X, 22" (56 cm), E. S. light yellow; F. slightly darker yellow, darker yellow signal patch with many distinct brown markings around edge. I. pseudacorus X I. ensata, white. Osugi 1962.

AÏDA ROSE (Jean Segui, R. 1998). TB, 35" (90 cm), ML. S. and style arms orient pink (RHS 36A); F. cadmium orange (23D); beards marigold orange (28B); 1-6 trumpet-shaped parts like extra styles. Princess X Buffy. Iris de Thau 1988. (Introduced as Aïda.)

AINDLING GOLDAUGE (Artur Winkelmann, R. 1992). Sdlg. F2 N3 87. SPEC-X (sib/vers), 23½" (60 cm), ML. Dark violet, large yellow signal with thin white inner band. Neidenstein X unknown.

AINDLING LIBELLE (Artur Winkelmann, R. 1992). Sdlg. FWhN4. SPEC-X, 23½" (60 cm), L. Violet self, yellow signal, veined white and violet; style arms light violet; foliage yellow in spring. Fourfold White X Neidenstein.

AINDLING MORGENSTIMMUNG (Artur Winkelmann, R. 1992). Sdlg. F2N7 87Ha. SPEC-X (sib/vers), 27½" (70 cm), VL. Medium violet blue self. Neidenstein X unknown.

AINDLING ROHRSAENGER (Artur Winkelmann, R. 1992). Sdlg. F2 N16. SPEC-X (sib/vers), 20" (50 cm), E. Violet self, yellow white signal; style arms light violet. Neidenstein X unknown.

AIN'T MISBEHAVIN' (Richard Ernst, R. 1994). Sdlg. JF169-11-11. TB, 37" (94 cm), M. S. blended red violet and blue violet (RHS 84B/C, 85C); style arms violet (84B); F. violet (84C), blended whiter (76C) from beard tip to rim, faint bluish center stripe; beards orange, bluish at end; ruffled; pronounced sweet fragrance. F169-11: (Afternoon Delight x (Ringo x (Cranberry Ice x Grand Waltz))) X F123-2: (Afternoon Delight x Edna's Wish). Cooley 1995.

AIRBRUSHED (Connell Marsh, TB, R. 1989). C. Marsh 1990.

AIR BUBBLES (Chet Tompkins, R. 1990). Sdlg. 84-148. TB, 39-40" (99-102 cm), EML. Pale golden cocoa with lilac and silver blue overtone in center; style arms matching, centerline lilac; beards blue, tipped lilac; pronounced fragrance. 81-114, inv. sdlgs., X Wayward Angel. Fleur de Lis 1990.

AIRLINE (Graeme Grosvenor, R. 1998). Sdlg. V103-A. TB, 40" (102 cm), ML. S. pale blue; F. white, edged blue violet; beards orange yellow, tipped blue; slight fragrance. T9-1: (Marriage Vows x Snowbrook) X S86-3: (Momentum x Snowbrook). Rainbow Ridge 1998/99.

AIRS ABOVE GROUND (Nora Scopes, R. 1992). Sdlg. 5/158C. TB, 35" (89 cm), M. Ruffled palest icy blue fading white, crystalline texture; beards grey to white; sweet fragrance. Forbidden X Cobweb Morning.

AIR SHOW (Lois Belardi, R. 1995). Sdlg. SDTI-1. CA, 13" (33 cm), M. S. white, medium blue flush and veining at midrib; style arms white; F. white, light purple veining radiating from small yellow line signal to within 1/2" of edge. Idylwild X SDT-0: ((Pacific High x Del Rey) x (Spring Daze x California Mystique)). Bay View 1996.

AIR UP THERE (Tom Burseen, R. 1995). Sdlg. 92-126C. TB, 36" (91 cm), M. S. creamy lemon, narrow yellow rim; style arms creamy lemon; F. cream, edged lemon, lavender center streak; beards tangerine, cream flounces and tatters, sometimes spooned; ruffled; spicy fragrance. Mesmerizer X 9-149-A: (Mystic Magic x Fifth Dimension). T.B.'s Place 1996.

AJAX THE LESS (Allan Ensminger, R. 1993). Sdlg. 87-17. SDB, 10" (25 cm), L. White with hyacinth blue (HCC 40/1) spot. 84-17: (Pied Pretty x unknown) X 185-3: (Do-Si-Do x 83-6: (Pied Pretty x Sno Jo)). Varigay 1994.

AKADEMIK KOROLIOV (Irina Driagina, R. 1996). Sdlg. 5-01. TB, 43" (110 cm), L. Light blue self; beards orange. Parentage unknown. Driagina 1973.

AKADEMIK VAVILOV (Viktor Sheviakov, R. 1995). Sdlg. 215-L. TB, 33" (85 cm), ML. Ruffled violet blue self; beards light blue, bright orange in throat. Violet Harmony X Blue Sapphire. Sheviakov 1991.

AKATUY (Galina Zinoviyeva, R. 1998). Sdlg. 588-1. BB, 26" (65 cm), ML. S. and style arms yellow; F. claret edged yellow, brown veining on whitish cream hafts and around orange beard. Pipes of Pan X Kangchenjunga. Zabaykalski 1998.

AKEBONO (Society for Japanese Irises, R. 1994). JI (6 F.), 36" (91 cm), EM. Pink, darker at edge, yellow signal; style arms white, crests pink. Unknown hybridizer and parentage. Introduced prior to 1980.

AKE NARUMI (Toyokazu Ichie by Society for Japanese Irises, R. 1995). JI (3 F.), 35" (90 cm), M. S. and style arms medium violet, silvery edge; F. deep to medium violet, veined deeper over silvery ground, distinct silver edge. Parentage unknown. Introduced in Japan, 1980.

AKIAMA (Ivar Schmidt, R. 1995). Sdlg. ENB 89/5. JI (3 F.), 27" (69 cm), M. S. and style arms white, edged lavender purple; F. vibrant lavender purple, white around small yellow ochre signal, heavy white veining. Time and Tide X unknown. Iris Acres 1995/96.

AKI-NO-NISHIKI (Isaburo Hayashi, by Society for Japanese Irises, R. 1995). JI (3 F.), 36" (90 cm), M. S. and style arms white, edged deep red violet; F. deep red violet, prominent white halo and veins; drooping form. Parentage unknown. Introduced in Japan prior to 1890. (Reinstatement of variety marked as obsolete in 1939 Check List.)

AKIRA HORINAKA (Tony Huber, R. 1999). Sdlg. 95-184. SPEC-X (reensata), 38" (96 cm), ML. S. violet to red purple (RHS 88B to 74C), rather short, rounded; style arms violet (88C/D), edged white to lilac (92C); F. violet (88B) to mallow purple (73A/B), bright yellow signal. Versata 92-143: (*I. versicolor* MAG-PK-85 x magenta *I. ensata* sdlg.) X Raspberry Rimmed.

AKKORD (Viktor Sheviakov, R. 1995). Sdlg. 8 S 10 (358). TB, 33" (85 cm), ML. Ruffled dark purple violet, F. slightly deeper; beards dark purple violet. Rippling Waters X Matinata. Sheviakov 1997.

ALABASTER UNICORN (George Sutton, R. 1995). Sdlg. G-16ARSA. TB, 36-38" (91-97 cm), ML. Ruffled white self (whiter than RHS 155B); beards yellow (12B), white horns. A-92-ASA: (Dauber's Delight x Sky Hooks) X Honky Tonk Blues. Sutton 1996.

ALADDIN'S FLAME (Virginia Messick, R. 1993). Sdlg. M88-128. SDB, 14" (36 cm), M. Old gold self; beards deep blue. Hushpuppy X (Toy x Mandy). Messick 1993.

ALADDIN'S TREASURE (Darlene Pinegar, R. 1993). Sdlg. CSS-1-2. AB (OGB-), 28" (72 cm), EM. S. and style arms deep bronze, toned greenish, splashed red; F. deep bronze, heavily veined red, turning solid red toward bronze edge, dark red spot below dark gold beard. Cairo Sands X unknown. Spanish Fork 1994.

ALAN M. TURING (Mitch Jameson, R. 1996). Sdlg. 1-93-A. TB, 30" (76 cm), L. S. and style arms glistening red purple; F. smooth deep purple, edged S. color; beards purple, hairs tipped gold. Emanations X Mavis Waves.

ALAN'S APOGEE (Alan Johnson by Jean Johnson, R. 1994). Sdlg. AJ 72-4. TB, 36" (91 cm), L. S. violet (RHS 88C); F. purple violet (80 B); beards pale yellow, tipped pastel violet; slight spicy fragrance. Parentage unknown.

ALASCAPE (George Bush, R. 1997). Sdlg. 12-0-8. JI (6 F.), 38" (97 cm), M. Pure white, lightly veined orchid, F. with lemon signal; style arms white, tipped orchid; globular form. Parentage unknown -- seed from Japan. Bush 1998.

ALASKAN SEAS (James McWhirter, R. 1991). Sdlg. J85-5-2. TB, 34" (86 cm), EM. S. pale blue; F. deep marine blue; beards blue; heavily ruffled; pronounced fragrance. Blues on Parade X Hilo Shore. Cottage 1992.

ALASKAN SUNRISE (Sharol Longaker, R. 1992). TB, 38" (97 cm), M. Pure white, F. with yellow throat; beards yellow, tipped white; lightly laced; sweet fragrance. Lovely Kay X Laced Cotton. Anderson Iris 1992.

ALATELY (Richard Sparling, R. 1994). Sdlg. MTB 93-1. MTB, 20" (51 cm), L. S. yellow (RHS 6D); F. purple (77A), yellow (6D) rim and veins from haft, slight yellow strip; beards bright yellow; purple based foliage. Parentage unknown. Miller's Manor 1995.

ALDINGA (Ivar Schmidt, R. 1995). Sdlg. PC 89-AK. CA, 14" (36 cm), VE. S. lemon cream, midribs honey brown; style arms lemon cream; F. pale lemon cream, golden yellow signal bleeding to form wash, heavy honey brown veining; ruffled. Nayook X unknown. Iris Acres 1995/96.

ALDRIDGE RUBY (Philip Allery, R. 1999). Sdlg. WY5. JI (3 F.), 37" (95 cm), ML. S. chalk white (RHS 155C) splashed violet (87B); style arms white (155B); F. chalk white, canary yellow (9A) signal; S. near-vertical, F. strongly flared. H6/83AY white, seed from S. Hirao, X Kozasa Gawa. Payne's Japanese Irises 1999.

ALDRIDGE SNOW MAIDEN (Philip Allery, R. 1999). Sdlg. WY1. JI (3 F.), 37" (94 cm), ML. S. chalk white (RHS 155C); style arms white, cream rib; F. chalk white, canary yellow (9A) signal; S. near-vertical, F. flared and arched. H6/83AY white, seed from S. Hirao, X self.

ALDRIDGE VISITOR (Currier McEwen by Philip Allery, R. 1999). Sdlg. 84/66(3). JI (6 F.), 35" (89 cm), ML & RE. Inner 3 F. violet blue (RHS 89A) tinged purple (77A); outer 3 F. violet purple (77A), violet blue (89A) halo surrounding bright lemon yellow (13A) signal with deeper (14A) rib; style arms violet blue (89C); lightly ruffled. Sib to Exuberant Chantey.

ALEKSANDRA (Viktor Sheviakov, R. 1995). Sdlg. 10V 15A. TB, 30" (75 cm), L. S. pinkish cream yellow, tinted light brown on edge; F. pinkish cream yellow, pinkish brown haft markings; beards yellow, orange in throat; ruffled. "Solnechny" X Chinquapin. Sheviakov 1995.

ALEKSANDR CHERKASOV (Galina Zinoviyeva, R. 1998). Sdlg. 550-1. TB, 35" (90 cm), EM. S. pale blue violet; style arms light blue; F. light blue violet, hafts brownish violet; beards yellow, blue at end. "Starinny Romans" X Maroon Caper. Zabaykalsi 1998.

ALEKSANDR NEVSKI (V. & N. Gordodelovy, R. 1995). Sdlg. 58. TB, 39" (100 cm), M. S. white, light blue base; F. white, brown haft striations; beards bright orange. Parentage unknown. Gordodelovy 1987.

ALEKSANDR PUSHKIN (V. & N. Gordodelovy, R. 1995). Sdlg. 210. TB, 33" (85 cm), ML. S. cherry; F. dark cherry, white striations around brown beard. Parentage unknown. Gordodelovy 1983.

ALENE'S NEW LOVE (Walt Dean, R. 1996). SDB, 10-11" (25-28 cm), M. Light rose purple (RHS 75A), small white dart below bright lavender beard; slight musky fragrance. Alene's Other Love X Chanted.

ALENE'S OTHER LOVE (Walt Dean, R. 1993). Sdlg. T-8. SDB, 10-11" (25-28 cm), M. S. top and edge pink blending to lavender in center, purple at base; style arms pink; F. greyed orange, small white starburst under lavender beard; slight musky fragrance. Triplicate X Third Charm. Stockton 1994.

ALENKI TSVETOCHEK (Nataliya Khimina, R. 1999). Sdlg. 96-63. TB, 33" (85 cm), EM. S. coral pink; style arms white; F. bright pink; beards white. Sky Blue Pink X Pink Memories.

ALENTEJO (Cy Bartlett, R. 1999). Sdlg. C92-103. IB, 20" (51 cm), M. S. white, blended pale yellow, midrib veined yellow, inner base dotted brown; style arms white, blended yellow; F. yellow, sanded, dotted and veined brown; beards bright golden yellow; heavily ruffled; sweet fragrance. Eyebright X Brandy Sipper.

ALESSANDRA (Ladislav Muska, R. 1996). Sdlg. SMVA-01. TB, 36" (91 cm), EM. Ruffled, heavily laced pinkish self; beards tangerine. (Sweet Musette x "Valassko": (Pink Angel x (Buffy x Silver Shower))) X Fontanone. Muska 1996.

ALETHEIA (John Knaus, R. 1995). Sdlg. 9033. TB, 36" (91 cm), E. S. white, edges tinted pale blue (RHS 92C); style arms white; F. medium violet (87A), blending to wistaria blue (92A), fading to white near beard, leaving 3/4" colored band; beards white, gold (24A) tipped hairs and gold in throat; ruffled, lightly laced; slight sweet fragrance. 87-67: (Aachen Prince x (((Melodrama x Allegiance) x Actress) x Grand Waltz)) X 87-03: ((Flamingo Blues x Firewater) x (Grand Waltz x Ruffled Ballet)). Knaus 1996.

ALEXANDER'S RAGTIME BAND (Larry Gaulter by Bob Brown, R. 1993). Sdlg. G86-14. TB, 37" (94 cm), M. S. purple, veined; F. darker velvety purple; white beards over white eyelash area; ruffled. Titan's Glory X His Lordship. Stockton 1994.

ALEXANDRA BETH (Bee Warburton, IB, R. 1987). Correction of spelling (ALEXANDER BETH) in 1989 Checklist.

ALEXANDRA ROSY MORN (Helen Falconer, R. 1998). Sdlg. 1/95. SDB, 10" (25 cm), M. S. rose; style arms gold, midrib maroon; F. rose, velvety red spot; beards pale lavender; flared; slight fragrance. Parentage unknown.

ALEXANDRA SPRING SONG (Helen Falconer, R. 1998). Sdlg. 2/95. IB, 16" (41 cm), M. S. lemon, pale lavender marginal flush; style arms gold, midrib lavender; F. antique gold; beards lavender, gold in throat; slight sweet fragrance. Parentage unknown.

ALEXANDRA'S SONG (Helen Falconer, R. 1997). Sdlg. 1/89. TB, 36" (91 cm), E. S. cream, light blue flush when fresh; style arms gold; F. ivory cream, gold wash on hafts and edge; beards gold, blue tip; ruffled; slight fragrance. Song of Norway X Leda's Lover. Waimate 1999/2000.

ALEXANDRA TWILIGHT (Helen Falconer, R. 1997). Sdlg. 1/90. SDB, 11" (27 cm), E. S. plum; style arms orange, streaked plum; F. deeper plum, plum black thumbprint spot; beards purple; ruffled; slight fragrance. Cherry Garden X Barnstormer. Waimate 1999/2000.

ALEX SUMMERS (Shuichi Hirao by Clarence Mahan, R. 1994). JI (3 F.), 30" (76 cm), EM. S. lilac pink; F. light violet, greenish yellow signal. Draycott 1997.

ALICE DAVIS (Ed Matheny III, R. 1994). Sdlg. 08-01-93. TB, 35" (89 cm), M. S. pink (RHS 36B); F. creamy white (155B), edged pink (36B), honeydew (32) shoulders; beards bright orange; ruffled, lightly laced; slight musky fragrance. Wet on Wet X Autumn Blush. Ed's Iris 1995.

ALICE FOSS (Jack Worel, R. 1994). Sdlg. 10-14-2. TB, 35" (89 cm), M. S. white; F. sky blue, turning to white at edge; beards yellow; ruffled; slight fragrance. Condottiere X Ruffled Ballet. Holly Lane 1994.

ALICE MARIE JUZAN (Bob Thomason, R. 1992). Sdlg. BT 8901A. MDB, 5" (13 cm), EM. S. lilac; F. lilac, brown hafts, dark lavender spot around beard; beards white, tipped orange in throat, fuzzy; slight sweet fragrance. Dream Stuff X Ditto. Okie Iris 1999.

ALICE'S DREAM (Jim Hedgecock, R. 1994). Sdlg. 85-unk-1. TB, 34" (85 cm), M. Medium yellow, lighter area near bright golden yellow beards; ruffled, laced; slight sweet fragrance. Parentage unknown. Comanche Acres 1995.

ALICIA ANN (Darlene Pinegar, R. 1992). Sdlg. VF-1-4. BB, 26" (66 cm), EML. S. medium blue; F. medium blue, fading to light blue with near-white center; beards deep yellow, tipped light blue; ruffled. Victoria Falls X Cloud Fire. Spanish Fork 1993.

ALICIA CLARE (Bernard Pryor, R. 1996). Sdlg. 35/92-H. LA, 30" (76 cm), M. S. and F. soft lemon, golden veining intensifying to lime green near styles, lime green signal; style arms soft butter yellow; heavily ruffled. Volcanic Wildfire X Spanish Ballet.

ALIEN MIST (Cy Bartlett, R. 1998). Sdlg. HD-IQ 1. TB, 37" (94 cm), M. Ruffled very pale blue self; beards bright medium blue violet, horned; slight sweet fragrance. Howdy Do X Inca Queen. Sutton 1998.

ALIENOR D'AQUITAINE (Lawrence Ransom, R. 1991). Sdlg. 87/17-5. IB, 19" (48 cm), ML. S. pale cream yellow (RHS 4D); F. same, yellow (10A) halo; beards cream, brushed yellow; lightly ruffled; pronounced sweet fragrance. I Do X Baby Blessed. Iris au Trescols 1992.

ALI KHAN (Howard Shockey, R. 1995). Sdlg. 90-133-BA. AB (OGB), 28" (71 cm), M. S. white, midrib yellow; F. yellow, extra large crescent signal maroon brown; beards light bronze; slight sweet fragrance. Queen Sheba X Red Sands. Arilian Acres 1996.

ALINTA (Barry Blyth, R. 1998). Sdlg. E1-1. SDB, 10" (25 cm), EM. S. light burgundy, deepening toward midrib; F. creamy white, allover pattern of rich burgundy deepening to plush burgundy at haft; beards bright brick red, 1/8" lavender end; pronounced spicy fragrance. C31-1: (A31-3, Cherry Child sib, x A25-11, Cavort sib) X C28-1, Echoes sib. Tempo Two 1998/99.

ALIONKA (Viktor Koroliov, R. 1995). Sdlg. S-1-86K. TB, 37" (95 cm), M. White ground plicata, dotted and stitched red violet edge; beards yellow; lightly ruffled; slight sweet fragrance. Siva Siva X unknown. Koroliov 1992.

ALISON TAYLOR (John D. Taylor by Carilla Taylor, R. 1998). Sdlg. D30K. IB, 18" (45 cm), ML. S. yellow ground, brown speckling heaviest toward edge; style arms yellow; F. yellow, brown speckling; beards cream; lightly waved and ruffled; slight musky fragrance. Eyebright X Flamenco.

ALISSONE (Ladislav Muska, R. 1997). Sdlg. AFLM-06. TB, 36" (91 cm), M. Heavily ruffled, lightly laced peach self; style arms pinkish peach; beards tangerine, white at end; fragrant. (Aphrodisiac x Lady Madonna) X Peach Boom. Muska 1997.

ALIZARINE (Lawrence Ransom, R. 1993). Sdlg. 87/66-10. TB, 37" (94 cm), M. Lightly ruffled magenta red, dark cream hafts with magenta markings; dark orange beards. Coup de Coeur X Lady Friend. Iris au Trescols 1994.

ALIZES (Jean Cayeux, R. 1991). Sdlg. 7706 C. TB, 33" (84 cm), EM. S. pure crystalline white; F. medium blue with white center; beards yellow. (6507 A: ((Palomino x Emma Cook) x Tahiti Sunrise) x Pink Taffeta) X Condottiere. Cayeux 1987.

ALIZE WINGS (A.R.J. Bailey, R. 1994). Sdlg. M/KM93/3. JI (6 F.), 30" (76 cm), E. White with blue veining, yellow signal; short mauve blue styles. Moonlight Waves X Katy Mendez sdlg.

ALKHIMIK (Nina Miroshnichenko, R. 1999). TB, 28" (72 cm), M. S. claret, yellowish base; style arms yellow, claret midrib and crests; F. lilac, inner rim lemon yellow, outer rim light brown; beards yellow, lilac at end; slight fragrance. Parentage unknown. Miroshnichenko 1993.

ALL AFLUTTER (Monty Byers by Phyllis Dickey, R. 1994). Sdlg. G63-1. TB, 36" (91 cm), M. Bright white; beards red orange with long, very pale blue flounce turning up at end; slight sweet fragrance. Conjuration X Mesmerizer. Misty Hill 1994.

ALL AMERICAN (Monty Byers, R. 1991). Sdlg. G39-2. TB, 31" (79 cm), M & RE. S. light blue; F. glacial white; beards bright red; pronounced sweet fragrance. Eternal Bliss X Pacific Tide. Moonshine 1992.

ALL CERULEAN (George Bush, R. 1997). Sdlg. 1-3-5. JI (6 F.), 36" (91 cm), ML. Sky blue, yellow signal; style arms sky blue tipped lilac; flared. Parentage unknown -- seed from Japan.

ALL CHAT (Barry Blyth, R. 1998). Sdlg. E57-1. IB, 25" (63 cm), VE-EML. S. iridescent magenta, lightly shot burgundy; F. shot brighter burgundy, deeper at hafts; beards bronze with lavender base, tangerine in throat; slight fragrance. It Is X Dawn Sky. Tempo Two 1998/99.

ALL DAY SMILE (Lois O'Brien, R. 1993). Sdlg. 85-308A. TB, 37" (94 cm), EM. Ruffled feminine pink, fluted and laced F.; beards coral pink. Cheesecake X Frisco Follies. O'Brien Iris 1995.

ALL DOLLED UP (Austin Morgan, R. 1990). TB, 36" (91 cm), EM. S. deep bronze; F. wine red bleeding evenly into wide rose band, narrow light brown outer rim, rose violet streak extending from yellow beard. Stunning X Round and Round. Iris Test Garden 1983.

ALL DRESSED UP (James Gibson by Cooley's Gardens, R. 1998). Sdlg. 35-82C. TB, 36" (91 cm), M. S. and style arms pink; F. pink, deeper shoulders with pale honey cast, center with deeper pink veining; beards tangerine red; slight sweet fragrance. Edna's Wish X 125-79A, unknown. Cooley 1998.

ALL HEART (Ben Hager, R. 1992). Sdlg. T4340TWhWbds. TB, 33" (84 cm), M. Deeply fluted pure white, laciniated edges; beards tangerine red. T3628TWh: ((Carved Cameo x Picture Pink) x (Carved Cameo x Vanity)) X Christmas Rubies. Melrose 1992.

ALL IN WHITE (Donald Delmez, R. 1995). Sdlg. WTGSN-1. JI (3 F.), 36" (91 cm), E. White self, yellow green signals; ruffled, creped. Parentage unknown.

ALLISON ELIZABETH (Darlene Pinegar, R. 1995). Sdlg. VF-1-2-2D. BB, 26" (66 cm), ML. Dark lavender, lightening with age, F. with rosy orchid hafts carrying darker marking, lighter near coral orange beard; heavily ruffled; slight sweet fragrance. VF-1-2: (Victoria Falls x Cloud Fire) X GR-1-8: (Gypsy Rings x Moon Mistress). Spanish Fork 1996.

ALLISON RODERIQUE (Charles Rhodes, R. 1997). Sdlg. CC-1B. TB, 29" (74 cm), M. S. and style arms indian yellow (RHS 17B); F. white, 1/2" lemon yellow (13A) border; beards lemon yellow; laced; slight sweet fragrance. Summer Promise X Lemon Fever.

#ALL LIT UP (Monty Byers, TB, R. 1986). Name transferred 1991.

ALL LIT UP (Monty Byers, R. 1991). Sdlg. G23-101. TB, 33" (84 cm), EM & RE. S. white; F. brilliant gold; beards tangerine orange. Borderline X Blazing Sunrise. Moonshine 1992.

ALL RHYTHM (Barry Blyth, R. 1998). Sdlg. E84-2. TB, 38" (96 cm), M. S. orchid magenta; F.

rosy plum; beards soft apricot. C101-3: (A63-10, Plume d'Or sib, x A153-13, Cafe Risque sib) X About Town. Tempo Two 1998/99.

ALL SHOOK UP (Joseph Ghio, R. 1990). Sdlg. PJ-166Q2. CA, 12" (30 cm), ML. S. blue lavender, gold midrib; F. bright gold, deep blue lavender plicata markings. (Tunitas x (Lighthouse Point x Mission Santa Cruz)) X Grand Design. Bay View 1991.

ALL SILENT (Barry Blyth, R. 1995). Sdlg. A77-1. TB, 38" (97 cm), EM. Silvery blue to blue white self; beards matching; pronounced sweet fragrance. Silverado X Blues Brothers. Tempo Two 1995/96.

ALL THAT GLITTERS (Sharon McAllister, R. 1992). Sdlg. 84-5A-16. AB (OGB), 28" (72 cm), EM. S. ivory, soft yellow veins; F. apricot yellow ground blushed orange rust; throat distinctly veined rust (overall effect near RHS 163B), orange rust linear signal; beards orange rust. Promise to Elizabeth X Koko Knoll. McAllister 1992.

ALL TOGETHER (Joseph Gatty, R. 1991). Sdlg. S26-1. TB, 36" (91 cm), M. S. reed yellow (M&P 10-G-1 to 10-I-1), faint flush of pink on midrib at times; F. yellow (11-G-1), mimosa (10-J-2) hafts, near-white center patch; beards dandelion (9-L-4) tipped cadmium yellow (9-L-8). Lovely Glow X Hollywood Blonde. Keppel 1992.

ALLURING PINK (William Simon by Elizabeth Simon, R. 1993). TB, 36" (91 cm), M. Pale pink, F. with white center; beards orange, tipped white. Parentage unknown. Stahly 1994.

ALLUVIAL GOLD (John C. Taylor, R. 1991). Sdlg. OL 139-1. LA, 43" (110 cm), ML. Lightly ruffled yellow (RHS 13C), midribs deeper. Dazzling Star X Watch Out. Rainbow Ridge 1991/92.

ALMADEN (William Maryott, R. 1990). Sdlg. K12A. TB, 36" (91 cm), M. Lightly ruffled dark smooth red maroon (RHS 187A); beards dark maroon red; slight sweet fragrance. F7: (Brandy x Coffee House) X H70: ((Brandy x (Caliente x Pink Angel)) x Royal Premiere). Maryott 1990.

ALMOST CAMELOT (Ronald Mullin by Mary Dunn, selector, R. 1994). Sdlg. 84-49-X. TB, 36" (91 cm), EM. S. ruffled pale lilac; F. magenta plum, pale lilac area around golden beard; ruffled. Galore X Theatre. M.A.D. Iris 1995.

ALMOST DARK (Barry Blyth, R. 1994). Sdlg. A72-1. TB, 38" (97 cm), EM. S. rich violet; F. velvety rich violet; beards violet. Blues Brothers X Blackout. Tempo Two 1994/95.

ALMOST EDEN (Duane Meek, R. 1999). Sdlg. 91-1-1. TB, 36" (91 cm), ML. S. rose tan; style arms lighter rose tan; F. ivory, blushed rose tan when fresh, rose tan narrow rim and darker hafts; beards rose tan, blue violet at end; ruffled, laced. Awakening X Hamblen 85-50B. D & J Gardens 1999.

ALMOST HEAVEN (O. D. Niswonger, R. 1996). Sdlg. 58-92. TB, 38" (97 cm), M. Mauve pink self; beards blue. Blue Chip Pink X Fontaine. Cape Iris 1997.

ALMOST LOST (C. R. King, R. 1994). Sdlg. 5 CRK 93. TB, 48" (122 cm), M. S. dark rose with many veins; F. dark burgundy; beards yellow, ruffled. Parentage unknown.

ALMOST PARADISE (Richard Ernst, R. 1993). Sdlg. HR85-45J. TB, 35" (89 cm), M. S. creamy pink; F. raspberry purple and light purple blend; beards bright orange; ruffled, laced; slight sweet fragrance. T602-1: (Cranberry Ice x (Sumptuous x Sandberry)) X Tracy Tyrene. Cooley 1993.

ALMOST PERSUADED (Eugene Hunt by Sharon McAllister, R. 1992). Sdlg. ORB 90-3. AB (OGB), 28" (72 cm), EM. S. smooth grey violet (near RHS 88D) with few darker veins at edge; F. cream ground washed smoky grey violet (near 83C), very heavily veined and dotted, signal area veined deep burgundy; beards mustard in heart tipped violet. (Esther the Queen x Dove Song) X Almost. McAllister 1992.

ALMOST RICH (O. D. Niswonger, R. 1993). Sdlg. 31-88. TB, 34" (86 cm), M. S. light blue; F. white ground with blue violet plicata markings; beards yellow, pale blue in throat. 48-85: (Everything Plus x La Zanzara) X Charmed Life. Cape Iris 1994.

ALOHA CARNIVAL (Cleo Palmer, R. 1992). Sdlg. 8999. SDB, 13" (33 cm), L. S. very pale peach to near-white; F. white, overlaid with light orange spot over most of F., white edge, light orange hafts and shoulders, orange veining throughout hafts and spot, white area around beard; beards red orange, near-white tip. Dorothy Howard X 8614, Pink Jubilee sib. Palmer's Iris 1992.

ALOHA MOON (Cleo Palmer, R. 1992). Sdlg. 8972. SDB, 14" (36 cm), M. S. pale lime yellow, near-white edge; F. pale lime yellow, paler center and edge; beards yellow, near-white tip. Luxurious X unknown. Palmer's Iris 1992.

ALON (David Shahak, R. 1992). Sdlg. S.T.77-44 III. AB (OGB+), 29½" (75 cm), M. S. purple (RHS 78D); F. red purple (71A), lightly dotted near base, dark purple signal; beards yellow. *I. samariae* X OGB sdlg. from A. Houck seed. Aril Society, Tira Nurseries 1993.

ALONE AT LAST (Eric & Bob Tankesley-Clarke, R. 1999). Sdlg. 602A. TB, 38" (97 cm), VL. Soft mimosa yellow, F. blending to ivory in center; style arms soft yellow; beards dark yellow; ruffled; slight sweet fragrance. Pleated Gown X Big Dipper. Adamgrove 1997.

ALONG THE WAY (Tom Burseen, R. 1990). Sdlg. 7-128A. TB, 36" (91 cm), EM. S. red purple (RHS 59D); F. darker red purple (59A), light area around tangerine beard; ruffled; slight spicy fragrance. 5-117: ((Curtain Call x Galen) x Lady Friend) X Laredo. T.B.'s Place 1991.

A L'ORANGE (Lilly Gartman, R. 1990). Sdlg. 85-24A. TB, 40" (102 cm), ML. S. tangerine orange with deeper pink flush; F. tangerine orange; beards orange red. Smooth Talk X 82-2A: (Preface x Lady Friend). Roris 1994.

ALOUETTE (Mary Dunn, R. 1990). Sdlg. L112-2. LA, 32" (81 cm), ML. S. alabaster pink, ivory buff cast; style arms green; F. alabaster pink buff, large yellow signal, ruffled and serrate. Handmaiden X Monument. Bay View 1990.

ALPHA GNU (Brad Kasperek, R. 1998). Sdlg. 94-13-20. SPEC-X, 22" (56 cm), VE. Red violet (RHS 88A/B) streaked silver white (155C); style arms violet lavender; beards light yellow; broken color pattern; slight fragrance. Batik X Ostry White. Zebra 1999.

ALPHASPU (B. Charles Jenkins, R. 1992). Sdlg. B1-9A. SPU, 34" (86 cm), VE. Ruffled bright yellow self. Ada Perry X SP85A: (Dawn Candle x unknown). Shepard Iris 1992.

ALPINE MAJESTY (J. T. Aitken, R. 1997). Sdlg. 88J9. JI (6 F.), 48" (122 cm), ML. White self. Parentage unknown. Aitken's Salmon Creek 1997.

ALPINE REGION (Barry Blyth, R. 1996). Sdlg. B148-1. TB, 34" (86 cm), ML. S. lemon; F. creamy white; beards lemon; sweet fragrance. Billows X Z62-2, Harmonics sib. Tempo Two 1996/97.

ALPINE SONG (Jim Hedgecock, R. 1992). Sdlg. 84-85-9. TB, 34" (86 cm), M. Heavily laced and ruffled blue white; beards blue white; pronounced sweet fragrance. Emmanuel X Lacy Snowflake. Comanche Acres 1993.

ALPINE SPRING (Frederick Kerr, R. 1999). Sdlg. 947001. TB, 32" (81 cm), ML. S. blue white, base infused darker; F. light blue, haft and edge darker, stripe from end of beard to lower margin; beards white, hairs tipped yellow, blue at end; ruffled, flared. Swing and Sway X Glacier Spring.

ALPINE STORM (Paul Black, R. 1999). Sdlg. 89116B. TB, 32" (81 cm), M. Heavily ruffled ice white; beards yellow gold, violet white at end; slight sweet fragrance. Victorian Frills X 8631A: (Extravagant x Copyright). Mid-America 1999.

ALPINE SUMMIT (Lyle Fort, R. 1991). Sdlg. 86-141B. TB, 35" (89 cm), M. Ruffled white; beards white; slight sweet fragrance. Paradise X Wide Hips. Fort Iris 1992.

ALPINE TWILIGHT (John Durrance, R. 1996). Sdlg. 86-151. TB, 36" (91 cm), L. S. and style arms pink (RHS 65C); F. violet pink (66C) washed pink, gradually spreading from center outward as flower ages; beards pink, pinkish orange in throat; ruffled, lightly laced. Sostenique X Heavenly Harmony. Long 1996.

ALRIGHT ALREADY (Gustav Seligmann by Sharon McAllister, R. 1994). Sdlg. 84-7C-3. AB (OGB), 29" (74 cm), EM. S. iridescent royal blue (near RHS 90A); F. slightly darker, reddish violet signal; beards yellow orange. Bionic Burst X Prince Thou Art. McAllister 1995.

ALSTER-ARKADEN (Lothar Denkewitz, R. 1995). Sdlg. M-85-hbl 1. IB, 16" (40 cm), M. S. clear light french blue, deeper at base; style arms clear blue; F. clear oriental blue, some olive haft veining; beards blue, tipped cream; slight spicy fragrance. Secret Society X Eiswurfel. Von Zeppelin 1997.

ALTAR BOY (Joseph Ghio, R. 1998). Sdlg. PC-190A. CA, 12" (31 cm), VE. Blended mother-of-pearl, F. with stronger orchid at shoulders. PE-197M2: (PG-178apr-pk: (PI-MIX-A, unknown, x (Black Eye sib x Herald sib)) x PG-172big-pk, Charter Member sib) X (PG-172A x Rainbow Connection). Bay View 1998.

ALTAR FIRES (Bernice Miller, R. 1990). Sdlg. AF 90. BB, 27" (69 cm), EM & RE (Sept./AL). Flaming rusty red orange; beards bronze; slight fragrance. Gideon Victorious X Samaritan Child. Garden of the Enchanted Rainbow 1990.

ALTERED STATES (Tom Burseen, R. 1997). Sdlg. 1-70A. TB, 36" (91 cm), M. S. white ground, heavily washed and streaked purple; style arms dark purple; F. white, dotted, blotched and sometimes streaked purple; unstable pattern; beards purple black, hairs tipped mustard; ruffled; spicy fragrance. 8-454: ((Flower Show x Mandolin) x ((Rancho Rose x Tiburon) x (In Tempo x Roundup))) X 9-356: (Villa Splendor x ((Summer Sunshine x Joy Ride) x Mountain Melody)). T.B.'s Place 1997.

ALTOGETHER LOVELY (Sharon McAllister, R. 1995). Sdlg. 86-6-6. AB (OGB), 28" (71 cm), EM. S. ivory, flushed pale pinkish lilac; style arms yellowish buff; F. buff ground, flushed pale pinkish lilac giving blended flesh pink effect, heavy burgundy dotting and veining around mustard brown beard. Granted Wish X Sunrise in Glory. McAllister 1995.

ALVA (Alva Hickerson by Rilla Hickerson, R. 1990). Sdlg. 811-32-3. BB, 27" (70 cm), M. S. greyed brown (RHS 199B); F. cream, lightly speckled and stitched brown on edge; beards brown purple; slight fragrance. 77-8-1: (unknown x Woodwine) X Picayune. Rillalva Iris 1991.

ALVATON ANGEL (Betty Wilkerson, R. 1996). Sdlg. E28-1. TB, 35" (89 cm), EM. White (RHS 155D) self; beards white, yellow in throat; slight sweet fragrance. Lemon Duet X Heavenly Angels. Bridge in Time 1996.

ALWAYS REMEMBER (Ronald Mullin, R. 1999). Sdlg. 511W. TB, 40" (102 cm), ML. Coral pink, F. with powder pink overlay; beards light orange, tipped white. Coral Satin X Custom Made.

ALWYN'S ARTISTRY (Alwyn Cox by Mrs. A. B. Cox, R. 1994). Sdlg. 72-7-1. TB, 42" (107 cm), ML. S. chartreuse cream (RHS 18C), narrow warm white edge; F. violet blue (92A), 1/4" light beige edge, lighter area around light yellow beard; slight spicy fragrance. Parentage unknown.

ALYOSHA K. (David Shannon, R. 1999). MTB, 17" (43 cm), M. S. white, diamond-dusted, base touched yellow; style arms white and yellow; F. smooth deep blue violet, bright white rim, small spray of white lines near light yellow beard. Bumblebee Deelight X Tyke. Shannon Gardens 1997.

ALYSHEBA (Dorothy Guild, MTB, R. 1987). Guild 1990.

AMADORA (R. E. Nichol, R. 1991). Sdlg. K67. TB, 38" (97 cm), M. S. pale blue; F. ruffled blue violet (RHS 93C), paling slightly toward edge; beards pale blue. Morwenna X Warleggan. Sutton 1992.

AMAIN (Lloyd Zurbrigg, TB, R. 1983). Correction of data shown in 1989 Checklist: White with golden hafts, some gold in S. and F.; beards yellow. I Do X Jean Guymer. Avonbank 1983.

AMANDA HOPKINS (Bob Thomason, R. 1993). Sdlg. BT 8714C. TB, 28" (71 cm), ML. Lightly ruffled blue white, darker area around beard; beards orange, tipped yellow; slight fragrance. Snowy Wonderland X Good Morning America. Okie Iris 1999.

AMANDA'S CHARM (Joan Kepf, R. 1992). Sdlg. 111884-A. TB, 37" (94 cm), L. White, edged pale lilac; beards bright yellow orange; slight sweet fragrance. Foolish Pleasure X Startler.

AMANDSA (Alphonse Van Mulders, R. 1991). Sdlg. 366/89. TB, 30" (76 cm), M. Amethyst violet; beards white. Parentage unknown. Jardinart Van Mulders 1992.

AMARETTO (Viktor Sheviakov, R. 1995). Sdlg. 20V 15. TB, 33" (85 cm), ML. S. light brick red; F. brick red, yellow spots on hafts, light lilac blaze below beard; beards yellow brown; musky fragrance. Latin Lover X Rippling Waters. Sheviakov 1997.

AMARYLLIS (Ruth Goebel, TB, R. 1989). Long 1995.

AMAZING (Ed Matheny III, R. 1997). Sdlg. 27-02-91. TB, 32" (81 cm), M. S. frosty walnut, light purple at center; F. purple; beards yellow orange. Mariachi Music X Porta Villa. Ed's Iris 1998.

AMAZONKA (Viktor Sheviakov, R. 1995). Sdlg. 22S 10. TB, 30" (75 cm), ML. Ruffled greenish cream, F. with greenish brown hafts; beards greenish brown. Allegiance X Pink Taffeta. Sheviakov 1995.

AMBER AMBUSH (Mary Ann Heacock, R. 1991). Sdlg. H80-19. SDB, 13" (33 cm), EM. S. deep tangerine pink; self style arms, some magenta rose shading; F. deep tangerine pink, some magenta haft veining; beards tangerine. H72-6: (H60-8: (Cretica sdlg. x pink TB) x H67-19: (Lenna M x H60-8)) X H77-23: ((Pink Cushion x H60-8) x H67-19). Long 1993.

AMBER AMULET (Frederick Kerr, R. 1999). Sdlg. 9385A. TB, 39" (99 cm), EML. S. and style arms amber orange; F. white, edged amber orange; beards tangerine red. Quick Pick X 902303: (Blazing Sunrise x Guadalajara). Rainbow Acres 1999.

AMBER ARTISAN (Bryce Williamson, R. 1993). Sdlg. A-11-K. TB, 32" (81 cm), ML. S. smooth buff, tan, amber and gold blend; F. buff, tan and amber blend, washed golden tan on shoulders, blazed milky violet below yellow orange beard; heavily ruffled; slight fragrance. Armistice X Fan Club. Stockton 1994.

AMBER CHALICE (B.L.C. Dodsworth, R. 1995). Sdlg. EB 89A. TB, 41" (105 cm), M. Ruffled coral; beards tangerine; sweet fragrance. Tangerine Sunrise X Sanderling. British Iris Society 1999.

AMBER ELEGANCE (Lowell Baumunk, R. 1998). Sdlg. 92RuHK-2. TB, 34" (86 cm), L. Bright amber gold, lighter below bright gold beards. Rustler X Harvest King.

AMBER GLEAM (B. Charles Jenkins, R. 1992). Sdlg. C7-14A. SPU, 35-45" (89-114 cm), L. Glowing amber self. Crow Wing X Forty Carats. Shepard Iris 1993.

AMBER JEWEL (Kevin Nilsen, R. 1996). Sdlg. 35-90-2. TB, 31½" (80 cm), VE-E. S. amber brown, veined deeper; style arms amber brown; F. medium brown, deeper toward heart; beards burnt orange. 15-84: (Bicentennial x San Jose) X Gigolo.

AMBER MARIE (Louise Smith, R. 1992). BB, 26½" (67 cm), EM. Lightly ruffled yellow; beards dark yellow; slight sweet fragrance. Parentage unknown.

AMBER SPREE (Barry Blyth, R. 1994). Sdlg. Z46-1. TB, 34" (86 cm), M. S. russet brown tinged gold; F. russet brown with deeper overlay of red brown, deepening toward hafts, white ray pattern radiating from mustard yellow beard to haft; slight musky fragrance. Rustler X Swain. Tempo Two 1994/95.

AMBER TAMBOUR (Richard Ernst, R. 1991). Sdlg. F125-22. TB, 34" (86 cm), L. Ruffled deep amber; beards amber orange; slight spicy fragrance. Edna's Wish X Wild Jasmine. Cooley 1991.

AMBROISIE (Richard Cayeux, R. 1997). Sdlg. 89146 A. TB, 33" (85 cm), L. Raspberry pink self; beards bronze pink. Enchanting X Helene C. Cayeux 1997.

AMBROSIAL PINK DONAMAE (Louise Smith, R. 1991). Sdlg. 80-145. TB, 34" (86 cm), EM. Ruffled pink; beards pink, tipped orange; slight sweet fragrance. 76-171-4: (Pink Horizon x unknown) X unknown.

AMBROSSIANA (Ladislav Muska, R. 1997). Sdlg. RIGE-09. TB, 35" (89 cm), ML. S. vanilla amber; style arms cream; F. light reddish lilac; beards tangerine; heavily ruffled, lightly laced; spicy fragrance. (Ringo x Geniality) X Se-Seque. Muska 1997.

AMEILA BEDEILA (Sterling Innerst, R. 1991). Sdlg. 3379-4. IB, 27" (69 cm), M. Cream white, green spot on F.; beards cream; slight musky fragrance. Scented Nutmeg X 2815-1: (Little Episode x Pippi Longstockings). Innerst 1992.

AMELIA CHYNOWETH (R. E. Nichol by Jean Nichol, R. 1998). Sdlg. S 278-15. TB, 36" (91 cm), M. S. white, midrib infused pale lilac (RHS 76C); style arms pale lilac (75B); F. deep purple black; beards dull gold; ruffled; slight fragrance. N 195: (Pascoe x Warleggan) X N 185-2: (K 84-6: (Cardew x Warleggan) x Bluebird Wine).

AMELIA MUELLER (A. Theodore Mueller, R. 1990). Sdlg. 76-210-3. TB, 28-34" (71-86 cm), ML. S. tan, orange rib fading to yellow; F. yellow tan blending to creamy yellow, few light haft marks at near-white center, edge yellow tan; beards orange, lighter tip; ruffled, crinkled. Niswonger 71-7: (Denver Mint x Meghan) X West Coast. Mueller's Iris 1993.

AMELIA'S ANGEL (A. Theodore Mueller, R. 1990). Sdlg. 84-58. TB, 28-36" (71-91 cm), M. Light pink, some blending; beards red pink. Pink Angel X Vanity. Mueller's Iris 1993.

AMELIA'S CANARY (A. Theodore Mueller, R. 1996). Sdlg. 91-62-7. TB, 30-36" (76-91 cm), M. S. canary yellow; style arms canary to lemon yellow; F. blue, shoulders brighter yellow, blending into blue; beards yellow, hairs tipped light blue; ruffled. Edith Wolford X -- probably Amelia's Dove. Mueller's Iris 1997.

AMELIA'S DOVE (A. Theodore Mueller, R. 1990). Sdlg. 80-221. TB, 28-34" (71-86 cm), ML. Dark dove self; beards deep orange. Unknown X Saber Dance. Mueller's Iris 1993.

AMELIA'S ORCHID (A. Theodore Mueller, R. 1992). Sdlg. 86-21-1. TB, 30" (76 cm), M. S. near-white blending to light pink at edge; F. light pink blending to slightly lighter around wavy edge; beards light pink, spooned; slight fragrance. Latin Lover X Spoon Time. Mueller's Iris 1993.

AMERICAN CLASSIC (Schreiner, R. 1996). Sdlg. DD 975-1. TB, 36" (91 cm), EML. S. white ground, 1" violet blue edge; style arms violet blue; F. white, 1/2" violet blue plicata edging; beards light blue white, hairs tipped yellow; heavily ruffled. Y 491-1: (Lorilee x Raspberry Frills) X T 405-2: (Titan's Glory X K290-A: ((Rococo x Belray) x Navy Strut)). Schreiner 1996.

AMERICAN EAGLE (George Sutton, R. 1998). Sdlg. G-84. TB, 37" (94 cm), M. Ruffled white self; beards yellow, hairs tipped white, with 2½" wide white spoon; slight sweet fragrance. Mesmerizer X Silverado. Sutton 1998.

AMERICAN GREETINGS (Joyce Meek, R. 1991). Sdlg. G86-5-9. TB, 36" (91 cm), ML. S. white; F. powder blue; beards coral red; lightly ruffled. Diva X Candace sib. D & J Gardens 1991.

AMERICAN PATRIOT (Cy Bartlett, R. 1996). Sdlg. C92-123. IB, 21" (53 cm), M. S. white; F. blue purple, edged white; beards red. Fierce Fire sib X (Wychwood x Battle Fury). Sutton 1997.

AMERICAN STYLE (Ed Roberts, R. 1992). Sdlg. 889. TB, 34" (86 cm), M. S. deep pumpkin, burnt orange overlay; F. deep pumpkin, small yellow signal; beards red orange; laced. Speculator X Far Corners. Ed Roberts 1993.

AMERICA'S SONG (Jack Worel, R. 1994). Sdlg. 17-18-4. TB, 35" (89 cm), M. Very light blue self; beards medium blue. Good Morning America X Song of Norway. Holly Lane 1994.

AMERICA'S TEAM (Walter Moores, R. 1997). Sdlg. 91-14-CRE. TB, 32" (81 cm), M & RE. S. and

13

style arms light lavender, aging cool white; F. purple violet; beards dark violet, base mustard; ruffled; slight spicy fragrance. Best Bet X Hawaiian Surf. Moores 1998.

*AMETHYST CRYSTAL (N. Earnshaw-Whittles, CA, R. 1981). V. H. Humphrey 1993.

AMETHYST DANCER (Richard Ernst, R. 1996). Sdlg. M101-2. TB, 34" (86 cm), M. S. cream pink, violet midrib infusion, blended honey rim on inside; style arms cream pink; F. deep amethyst berry, pink rim, striped hafts extending 1/3 way down; beards tangerine red; lightly ruffled; slight sweet fragrance. Liaison X F169-23: (Afternoon Delight x Tracy Tyrene sib). Cooley 1997.

AMETHYST DELIGHT (Elyse Hill, R. 1995). Sdlg. EJ 2-13-93. TB, 36" (91 cm), EM. S. amethyst; style arms amethyst blended orange; F. amethyst, lacy buff edge; beards orange; ruffled; slight sweet fragrance. Pagan Pink X EJ 2-17-91: (Deep Fire x Briar Rose). O'Brien Iris 1998.

AMETHYST SMILE (Ladislav Muska, R. 1995). Sdlg. BRCK-03. TB, 38" (97 cm), ML. Heavily laced deep amethyst self; beards light gold; sweet fragrance. ("Bile Roucho": (Laced Cotton x Miss Dolly Dollars) x "Cipkovana Krinolina": (After All x Grand Waltz)) X "Charmante": (Glory Bound x 80-SRGW-9). Muska 1996.

AMETHYST TRIM (Terrell Taylor, R. 1999). Sdlg. 93-85. TB, 32" (81 cm), L. S. and style arms light naples yellow (RHS 11B); F. light naples yellow, 1/2" brushed grape (79D) edge; beards yellow; lightly ruffled; sweet fragrance. Gypsy Woman X Glitz 'n Glitter.

AMETHYST WINGS (William Ackerman, JI, R. 1989). Nicholls Gardens 1990.

AMETHYST WINTER (Richard Richards, R. 1998). Sdlg. 6011. TB, 36" (91 cm), ML & RE. Ruffled amethyst violet (RHS 83A) self; style arms paler violet; beards pale yellow; slight sweet fragrance. Feedback X Star Master. Cal-Dixie 1998.

AMETISTOVOYE ZAREVO (Viktor Sheviakov, R. 1995). Sdlg. 21 A 12. TB, 30" (75 cm), L. Amethyst violet self; beards orange, amethyst violet at end; musky fragrance. "Solnechny" X Amethyst Flame. Sheviakov 1997.

AMETISTOVY BRASLET (Viktor Sheviakov, R. 1999). Sdlg. 7A7A. TB, 32" (80 cm), M. Lightly ruffled dark amethyst violet, F. with light violet hafts; beards white at end, yellow midsection, orange in throat; slight sweet fragrance. Amethyst Flame X Rippling Waters.

AMETISTOVYYE SERGI (Adolf Volfovich-Moler, R. 1995). Sdlg. V-3. TB, 35" (90 cm), M. S. light golden brown; F. lilac, light brown edge; beards yellow; ruffled. Dancers Veil X Siva Siva. Volfovich-Moler 1992.

AMHERST (Thelma Naylor, SDB, R. 1981). British Iris Society 1995.

AMHERST BLUEBEARD (Thelma Naylor, R. 1997). Sdlg. 87/2/3. SDB, 9" (23 cm), EM. S. pale yellow; F. pale yellow, deeper near blue beard; slight fragrance. Queen's Ivory X Kentucky Bluegrass.

AMHERST COLORS (John Durrance, R. 1993). Sdlg. D89-1. TB, 35" (89 cm), ML. Lightly ruffled violet blue; beards violet blue. Blue Maxx X Bubbling Over. Long 1993.

AMHERST GLACIER (Thelma Naylor, R. 1999). Sdlg. 74/6/5. IB, 18" (46 cm), ML. Ice blue; style arms pale mauve, blue midrib; beards pale blue, gold in throat; musky fragrance. J. D. Taylor J 42/3, white with yellow-lined F., X Little Vanessa.

AMHERST GOLD (Thelma Naylor, R. 1997). Sdlg. 77/8/2. MDB, 8" (20 cm), E. Buttercup yellow self; beards white; sweet fragrance. 74/10/6: (72/3/3, from J. Taylor sdlgs., x 71/1/5: (Taylor yellow sdlg. x Brannigan)) X Mairi.

AMHERST KNIGHTRIDER (Thelma Naylor, R. 1999). Sdlg. 74/6/8. IB, 18" (46 cm), ML. S. medium blue; style arms medium blue, edge paler; F. medium blue (RHS 90B), brown and white patterning around beard; beards white, gold in throat; musky fragrance. Sib to Amherst Glacier.

AMHERST MOON (Thelma Naylor, R. 1997). Sdlg. 85/12/2. SDB, 10" (25 cm), ML. White self opening from very pale ice blue bud; beards white. 74/6/5: (Taylor J42/3 white x Little Vanessa) X 82/3/1: (Jeremy Brian x 77/8/3, Amherst Gold sib).

AMHERST SUN (Thelma Naylor, R. 1997). Sdlg. 85/6/1. SDB, 11½" (29 cm), E. S. pale yellow; F. deep yellow, pale yellow edge, dark brown at haft; beards gold; sweet fragrance. Amherst X 80/27/1: ((Vista x (Taylor yellow sdlg. x Brannigan)) x (Taylor J42/3 white x (Widecombe Fair x unknown))).

AMOENIDO (Izidor Golob, R. 1997). Sdlg. 8931-25. TB, 33" (85 cm), ML. S. milky white; style arms white; F. medium blue; beards yellow; slight sweet fragrance. Margarita X River Hawk. Peroma 1997.

AMONG FRIENDS (W. Terry Varner, R. 1999). Sdlg. S-306. MTB, 18" (46 cm), E. S. pure white; F. white, large solid dark purple spot, pure white edge; beards white; flared. O-363: (Valiant Warrior x Parakeet) X P-331: (Consummation x M-310: (K-305: (Consummation x Desert Quail) x K-311: (((First Call x Colonial Lady) x Lavender Doll) x Welch T-201))).

AMPHONE'S STORY (Zdeněk Seidl, R. 1997). Sdlg. 91-LKŠl/1. TB, 36" (90 cm), M. S. and style arms light cadmium orange (RHS 23D); F. light naples yellow (11C); beards yellow orange; ruffled. "Lososová Kadeř": (Beaux Arts x Miss Dolly Dollars) X "Šlahačka": (Buffy x Silver Shower).

AMPLE CHARM (Tom Burseen, R. 1995). Sdlg. 8-123D. TB, 36" (91 cm), E. S. and style arms pinkish orange (RHS 29B); F. light orange (29C), veined light red brown, white ray pattern from orange beard; ruffled; musky fragrance. 5-179: (Flower Show x Mandolin) X Pulse Rate Date. T.B.'s Place 1995.

AMPLIFIED (Joseph Ghio, R. 1999). Sdlg. 95-18P2. TB, 36" (91 cm), L-VL. S. yellow orange, red infusion; F. bright yellow orange; beards red, white base. 92-102Y4: ((Quito x (85-199L, Mogul sib, x 85-27bo, Bogota sib)) x Forbidden Fruit) X 93-109H3, Cordoba sib.

AMUR-BATIUSHKA (Nina Miroshnichenko, R. 1996). BB, 26" (65 cm), M. Ruffled dark blue, tinted violet; beards light blue; slight sweet fragrance. Parentage unknown. Miroshnichenko 1988.

AMURSKIYE VOLNY (V. & N. Gordodelovy, R. 1995). Sdlg. 101. TB, 33" (85 cm), E. S. pale blue; F. light blue, hafts striated; beards light blue at end, cream, changing to yellow in throat; lightly ruffled. Parentage unknown. Gordodelovy 1982.

AMURSKI ZALIV (Sergey Butiukov by Liudmila Mironova, R. 1999). JI (6 F.), 33-37" (85-95 cm), M. Light blue lilac, signal yellow; style arms white, crests light blue. Vasili Alfiorov X unknown. DVO RAN 1990.

AMUSEMENT (Hooker Nichols, TB, R. 1988). Roris 1991.

AMY ARISTO (J. Owings Rebert, R. 1999). Sdlg. CB-97-11. SIB, 30" (76 cm), M. Lavender blue, F. with ivory to rust signal. Parentage unknown.

AMY'S BLUSHING (Barry Blyth, R. 1998). Sdlg. D57-3. TB, 36" (91 cm), ML. S. mauve pink, creamy influence; F. mauve pink with silvery white overlay, 1/4" edge matching S.; beards apricot, white at end; pronounced sweet fragrance. Hostess Royale X Spring Tidings. Tempo Two 1998/99.

ANACONDA LOVE (Brad Kasperek, R. 1998). Sdlg. 94B-43B. BB, 24" (61 cm), ML. S. light pink (RHS 63D), lightly splashed beetroot purple (71A); style arms beetroot purple and pink, lightly laced; F. beetroot purple, streaked silver white (155C), occasionally streaked pink; beards orange; broken color pattern; ruffled; slight fragrance. 92B-56R: (Baboon Bottom x 89B-42E: (Rustic Dance x Maria Tormena)) X Tanzanian Tangerine. Zebra 1999.

ANACRUSIS (Harald Mathes, R. 1992). Sdlg. 88-MD-16. AB (OGB), 20" (50 cm), E. Oxblood red, signals and beards red black. Dresden Gold X T-IA-M: ((*I. iberica* x *I. auranitica*) x *I. mellita*). Aril Society 1992.

ANAGRAM (Keith Keppel, R. 1990). Sdlg. 84-1V. IB, 22" (56 cm), EM. S. near apricot (M&P 10-F-5/6); F. slightly greyer apricot (11-G-5), mauve (45-F-1) flush and blended spot, tawny (13-D-10) haft flush, small off-white spot; beards bittersweet orange (3-B-12); slight sweet fragrance. Nazette X 79-84B: ((Anon x Prediction sib) x (Flamenco sib x (Roundup sib x April Melody))). Keppel 1991.

ANA MERCEDIS (J. Owings Rebert, R. 1996). Sdlg. UG-4. SIB, 28" (71 cm), M. S. light blue; F. light blue, dark blue veining through slight ivory signal, shoulders light yellow. Parentage unknown.

ANCASTER BLUE RUFFLE (Jim McMillen, R. 1993). TB, 36" (91 cm), EM. S. frosted light blue, darker midrib, fading to near-white at edge; F. deep blue violet, 1/4" frosted light blue edge; beards tangerine, brushed blue, white at end; lightly ruffled. Ringo X unknown. McMillen's Iris 1993.

ANCIENT ART (George Sutton, R. 1997). Sdlg. E-45. BB, 26" (66 cm), M. S. and style arms chrome yellow; F. chrome yellow blended and veined red brown (RHS 180), edged antique gold; beards antique gold; ruffled. (Dazzling Gold x Taco Belle) X Gypsy Wings. Sutton 1998.

ANCIENT ECHOES (Barry Blyth, R. 1997). Sdlg. A166-1. TB, 34" (86 cm), ML. S. old gold to antique gold; F. plush red black, 1/4" tan edge; beards bronze, tipped old gold; sweet fragrance. Town Gossip X Supreme Sultan. Tempo Two 1997/98.

ANCIENT SCROLLS (Lois Rich by James Whitely, R. 1990). Sdlg. R75-69B. AB (OGB), 29" (74 cm), ML. S. white ground with diamond dusting, mulberry veins, fluted; style arms honey tan, finely veined mulberry, light tan rust lip; F. white, veined rust, rust signal; beard dark gold to orange. R72-73B: (R64-12B x (GM15 CGW x Jebel Jehar)) X R73-176O: ((R69-108A x Welcome Reward) x (Welcome Reward x RR64-23A)). Aril Patch, Aril Society 1990.

ANDALOU (Jean Cayeux by Richard Cayeux, R. 1995). Sdlg. 86219 A. TB, 33" (85 cm), EML. S. bright yellow; F. clear velvety red; beards golden yellow. 84188: (Irish Spring x 7155 D: ((Snowline x Silver Sands) x (Postscript x Orange Parade))) X Gypsy Caravan. Cayeux 1995.

ANDIAMO (Harold Stahly, R. 1997). Sdlg. 92-7. TB, 38" (96 cm), EM. Ruffled medium peach, F. with light red wash extending from orange tangerine beard to near margin. Capricious X Halo in Orange. Stahly 1997.

ANDOUILLE (Patrick O'Connor, R. 1999). Sdlg. 94-22. LA, 32" (81 cm), ML. Cherry red rimmed white, F. with yellow spear signal; style arms cherry red, white tips. 82-12: (Deneb x Mac's Blue Heaven) X R. Morgan L-113-B. Bois d'Arc 1999.

ANDRE (Hilmary Catton, R. 1996). Sdlg. C 8611. MDB, 7" (18 cm), E. S. cream, greenish midrib; F. pale lime green, deep purple ray pattern; beards pale blue, hairs tipped gold in throat. Making Eyes X Sapphire Jewel.

ANDREANA (Jayne Ritchie, R. 1998). Sdlg. 92-24-11. IB, 20" (51 cm), M. S. pale lavender; style arms lavender, tipped buff; F. lilac pink, blended buff, hafts buff; beards lavender at end, tangerine in throat; ruffled. Silk Sari X 89-29-6: (82-28-2: (Inscription x (Latin Lover x White Mite)) x Lankow 2A28-3: (Spring Bonnet x Wright L85: (Blue Trinket x Cotton Blossom))). Ritchie 1999.

ANDREY RUBLIOV (V. & N. Gordodelovy, R. 1995). Sdlg. 133. TB, 30" (75 cm), M. S. brown; F. violet, edged brown, brown haft striations; beards orange; ruffled. Parentage unknown. Gordodelovy 1994.

ANDREY TUPOLEV (Viacheslav Gavrilin, R. 1999). Sdlg. 1-16-3-94. TB, 34" (86 cm), EM. Ruffled terracotta; beards red; slight fragrance. Darkside X Gypsy Caravan. Gavrilin 1999.

ANDRINA (Jean Witt, R. 1990). Sdlg. 86-05-RP. MTB, 21" (53 cm), M. S. white, trace of violet as wire edge; style arms white, lavender midrib and stigma; F. dark red violet (darker than Munsell 7.5P 3/9), white hafts lined violet; beards yellow, tipped brown; slight fragrance. Little Lucy X (Delicata x "Mrs. Andrist").

AND ROYAL (Barry Blyth, R. 1990). Sdlg. V100-1. TB, 36" (91 cm), VE-EM. S. off-white to oyster shell; F. rosy violet; beards bright gold; ruffled, waved. Street Dancer X Shine on Wine. Tempo Two 1990/91.

ANECDOTE (Ben Hager, R. 1991). Sdlg. SD5129YPc. SDB, 13" (33 cm), M. S. yellow overlaid maroon brown; F. yellow, edged maroon brown; beards yellow. SD4920Y/TnOrBds: (((Dainty Royal x Zip) x (Marinka x ((Knotty Pine x Grace Note) x Zip))) x (Noisemaker x Pepper Mill)) X SD4455RsBiPc: (Gigglepot x SD4024PkPc, pollen parent of Software). Adamgrove 1992.

ANETT (Manfred Beer, R. 1991). Sdlg. MB 8/81D. TB, 41" (105 cm), M. Raspberry pink; beards mandarin. Fond Wish X Falbala. Gartencenter Kania 1991.

ANGELA'S JOY (Loleta Powell, R. 1994). TB, 29" (74 cm), ML. S. and style arms white; F. white, edged violet blue, horizontal; beards white, tipped gold; slight sweet fragrance. Parentage unknown. Powell's Gardens 1996.

ANGEL BABY (Hooker Nichols, SDB, R. 1978). Additional information: Puppet X Copy Cat.

ANGEL BLUE SKY (Cloyd McCord, R. 1997). Sdlg. 0106. TB, 36" (91 cm), M. Light blue; beards orange; pronounced fragrance. Princess Maxine X Sexton's Girl. McCord 1997.

ANGEL FIRE (Cleo Palmer, R. 1991). Sdlg. 89117. IB, 18" (46 cm), E. S. near-white, tinted pink, ruffled; F. same, yellowish shoulders, pink flush to either side of reddish pink beard; spicy fragrance. Miss Dolly Dollars X 8549: ((Miss Oklahoma x (Dove Wings x 7259: ((Wilma V. x unknown) x Little Titan))) x (Show Baby x (Lenna M x (Prophecy x Dove Wings)))). Palmer's Iris 1991.

ANGEL GIRL (Francis Rogers, R. 1998). Sdlg. C308-X. TB, 31" (78 cm), L. S. and style arms bluebird blue (RHS 94C); F. wistaria blue (92D), flushed darker (92C) over most of area; beards wistaria blue (92C) end, white center, yellow in throat; ruffled; sweet fragrance. Honky Tonk Blues X Kathy's Joy. Meadowbrook 1999.

ANGEL HEART (J. T. Aitken, R. 1996). Sdlg. 90M35. IB, 25" (64 cm), M & RE (Sept./WA). S. white; F. white, hafts yellow; beards orange. Coral Charmer X Be Happy. Aitken's Salmon Creek 1996.

ANGELIC CHARM (Richard Morgan, R. 1997). Sdlg. L116-A. LA, 24-28" (61-71 cm), M. Very pale orchid to white, F. with green yellow signal; style arms green and cream. Winter's Veil X Vested Ways.

ANGELIC GLOW (Loleta Powell, R. 1994). Sdlg. 91-3. TB, 36" (91 cm), EML. Lightly ruffled creamy white; beards rich gold. Carolina Angel X Eastertime. Powell's Gardens 1996.

ANGELIC MIST (Barry Blyth, R. 1994). Sdlg. A24-1. SDB, 12" (30 cm), ML. S. shell pink-white; F. creamier shell pink-white, very faint plicata edge; beards white, tangerine in throat. Cupfull X Chanted. Tempo Two 1994/95.

ANGELIC SMILE (Cleo Palmer, R. 1992). Sdlg. 8940. SDB, 14½" (37 cm), M. S. white; F. white, edged full yellow, yellow shoulders; beards red. 8621: ((7607: (Dove Wings x 7259((Wilma V. x unknown) x Little Titan)) x ((Baria x Carpathia) x Dove Wings)) x 8254) X 8254: ((Lenna M. x Little Titan) x 7607). Palmer's Iris 1992.

ANGELIC WINGS (Bernice Miller, R. 1991). Sdlg. AW91. TB, 35" (89 cm), EM & RE (Aug.-Nov./AL). Lightly ruffled pale blue, fading white; beards white, yellow and red in throat; slight sweet fragrance. Radiant Angel X English Cottage. Garden of the Enchanted Rainbow 1991.

ANGELI DI LUCE (Frederick Kerr, R. 1999). Sdlg. 931901. TB, 36" (91 cm), ML. S. pale pinkish lavender, lighter center; style arms pinkish lavender; F. white, wide pinkish lavender plicata edge, stripe below beard; beards tangerine orange, base white; slight sweet fragrance. Ballerina Girl X Pink Froth. Rainbow Acres 1999.

ANGEL OF LOVE (Cloyd McCord, R. 1996). Sdlg. 85-10. TB, 36" (91 cm), E. S. pallid blue; style arms pale blue; F. pallid blue, pale green reverse; beards lavender, base orange; spicy fragrance. 82-1: (Chorus Girl x Custom Made) X 83-5: (Evening Mist x (Beauty Crown x Homecoming Queen)). McCord 1996.

ANGEL'S BLUSH (Darlene Pinegar, R. 1994). Sdlg. VF-1-2-2B. TB, 30" (76 cm), EML. S. and style arms light chamois peach; F. chamois peach, creamy center; beards deep orange; slight sweet fragrance. VF-1-2: (Victoria Falls x Cloud Fire) X GR-1-8: (Gypsy Rings x Moon Mistress). Spanish Fork 1995.

ANGEL'S CALL (Barry Blyth, R. 1995). Sdlg. Z62-6. TB, 36" (91 cm), EML. S. white, infused very pale blue; F. white, 1/2" pale blue border; beards lemon; slight sweet fragrance. W56-1: (Lipstick Lies x Light Beam) X Snowbrook. Tempo Two 1995/96.

ANGEL'S FANCY (Fred Crandall by Marie Ingersoll, R. 1990). TB, 38" (97 cm), M. Mauve self; beards pink tipped white; pronounced fragrance. (76-10 x 77-16) X 77-15. Ingersoll's Iris 1990.

ANGEL'S HALO (Lynda Miller, SDB, R. 1989). Miller's Manor 1991.

ANGELS IN FLIGHT (Virginia Messick, R. 1995). Sdlg. M87-39. TB, 37" (94 cm), M. White, with blue wash up S. and in middle of F.; beards cream; ruffled. Olympiad X Breakers. Messick 1995.

ANGEL'S WALTZ (Lynn Markham, R. 1999). Sdlg. 92-17E. TB, 27-30" (69-76 cm), L-VL. Ruffled white with slight blue cast, slightly greenish S. midrib, faint greenish texture veining in F.; beards blue white end, blended midsection, gold in throat; crystalline finish; pronounced spicy fragrance. Angel Feathers X Pops Concert.

ANGEL'S WINK (Libby Cross, R. 1997). Sdlg. 91-EE-3. MDB, 5" (13 cm), ML. White self; beards white. Blue Pools X unknown. Crosspatch 1998.

ANGELUS ANGEL (Chet Tompkins, R. 1997). Sdlg. 93-42. TB, 38" (97 cm), ML-VL. Heavily ruffled bright laelia to rhodonite pink; beards bright rhodonite pink. (Wanda Wood x ((Pagoda Goddess x Beverly Sills) x (Ming Porcelain x (Courtin' Time sib x (Bonbon x Painted Clouds))))) X ((Facsimile x Ovation) x Angel's Touch). Fleur de Lis 1997.

ANGELUS CHIMES (Donald Sorensen, R. 1994). Sdlg. S-91-33-1. TB, 33" (84 cm), ML. S. lemon yellow (RHS 8B); style arms yellow gold, flushed cream; F. white, heavily ruffled 3/8" lemon yellow edge; beards yellow gold; slight sweet fragrance. Blushing Diana X Winter White. Birchwood 1997.

ANGIE'S NIKO (Ruth Goebel, R. 1995). Sdlg. A.N. TB, 33" (84 cm), M. S. greyed red (RHS 182B); F. violet (84B) edge on off-white; beards bright tangerine. Parentage unknown.

ANGLESEY (Harry Foster, SIB, R. 1986). V. H. Humphrey 1995.

ANH VAN NGUYEN (Bob Thomason, R. 1991). Sdlg. 8625B. TB, 28" (71 cm), M. Soft medium fuchsia violet, darker stripe down center of F., white hafts veined brown; beards deep gold tipped lavender; slight fragrance. Annikins X Autumn Blush. Okie Iris 1994.

ANIMAL CRACKERS (Bryce Williamson, R. 1996). Sdlg. 1791-1. TB, 34" (86 cm), EM. S. medium ginger brown, few yellow lines at base of midrib; style arms ginger brown; F. lemon gold ground heavily dotted and stitched medium to dark ginger brown, wide canary yellow (RHS 9B) band; beards lemon; ruffled; slight musky fragrance. Parquet X Jitterbug. Stockton 1999.

ANITA (Manfred Beer, R. 1991). Sdlg. MB 8/83A. TB, 39" (100 cm), L. Lightly pleated warm white; beards orange. Peach Frost X Salmon Dream. Gartencenter Kania 1991.

ANNA AND HERMAN (Louise Smith, R. 1991). Sdlg. 78-21. TB, 36" (91 cm), EM. S. medium yellow; F. and beards dark yellow; slight sweet fragrance. Unknown yellow sdlg. X pink sdlg.

ANNA ANGELWINGS (Anna Rettig, R. 1997). Sdlg. AR-011. JI (3 F.), 40" (102 cm), ML. S. pure white; style arms white; F. pure white, canary yellow (RHS 9A) signal large and radiating slightly. Numazu X unknown. A & M Perennials 1998.

ANNA BARTENEVA (Piotr Hattenberger, R. 1995). SDB, 12-14" (30-35 cm), E. Orange self; beards light orange. Seed from Altaiski Botanical Garden. Stockholm X unknown.

ANNA COOK (Harry Turner, R. 1992). Sdlg. 5-86-1. TB, 33½" (86 cm), M. S. yellow ochre (HCC 07/2); F. same, ruffled edge speckled tan, white signal; beards orange. Fresno Calypso X (Happy Bride x Rancho Rose). Snellville 1993.

ANNA LOU (Jack Worel, R. 1996). Sdlg. TTB. TB, 30" (76 cm), M. S. and style arms light blue (RHS 97D); F. light purple (83C); beards red orange; ruffled; slight sweet fragrance. Condottiere X Scintillation. Holly Lane 1996.

ANNA PAULINE (Sandra Underwood by Louise Smith, R. 1991). Sdlg. 85-10. TB, 34" (86 cm), EM. Pale yellow; beards yellow orange; slight sweet fragrance. Parentage unknown.

ANN BLOCHER (Clarence Blocher, TB, R. 1986). Iris Country 1990.

ANNE GADDIE (Gene Gaddie, TB, R. 1989). Gaddies' Gardens 1991.

ANNELIES (Manfred Beer, R. 1991). Sdlg. MB 2/81A. TB, 39" (100 cm), M. Gold brown, F. with veined shoulders; beards yellow. Carolina Honey X ((Bang x Martel) x pink sdlg.). Gartencenter Kania 1991.

ANNE-MARIE CHESNAIS (Jean-Jacques Francois, R. 1998). Sdlg. 3-18(95). TB, 32" (80 cm), EM. S. and style arms yellow, striated violine in center; F. violet blue lightening near edge, beige shoulders veined brown; beards orange yellow; ruffled; slight sweet fragrance. Edith Wolford X Ringo.

ANNE MORGAN (Graeme Morgan, R. 1997). Sdlg. J.36. TB, 34" (87 cm), ML. S. smoky lemon, midrib lilac; F. lilac violet, darkening toward lower edge, cream and light brown at haft; beards lilac, lighter at end; sweet fragrance. Mother Earth X Mountain Violet.

ANNE MURRAY (Michael Moller, R. 1992). Sdlg. 82-C-1. TB, 36" (91 cm), ML. S. light lilac blue, darker midrib flush; F. light blue white, veined darker blue; beards yellow, tipped white; ruffled; slight sweet fragrance. Solid State X Avis. Long 1996.

ANNE'S CHOICE (Ed Attenberger, R. 1995). Sdlg. 90-03-33. TB, 37" (94 cm), ML. Rose pink self, hafts suffused darker rose tan; beards orange; ruffled, lightly laced; slight sweet fragrance. Buffy X "Ribbons Royal".

ANN FAITH (M. D. Faith, R. 1998). Sdlg. 69646. LA, 30" (76 cm), M. White, yellow signal with lime green lines; flat, slightly cupped form. Bit of Blue X self.

ANN HORDERN (Heather Pryor, R. 1997). Sdlg. 57/90-9. LA, 40" (102 cm), ML. Pale lemon, pink blush to petal rim, darker pink veining, F. with bright yellow raised steeple signal; style arms lemon; entire flower changing to pink after second day; scalloped, ruffled. Desert Jewel X Noble Planet. Iris Haven 1997/98.

ANNIE-LEIGH (Henry Thomas by Mr./Mrs. T. Nisbet, R. 1994). Sdlg. LCHW-1. TB, 32" (81 cm), ML. S. medium red violet (RHS 79C); F. ruffled medium grey violet (87A) edged S. color, violet stripe below burnt tangerine beard; slight spicy fragrance. Lime Crystal X Harbour Watch.

ANNIE Mc (David Miller, R. 1990). Sdlg. DM 83-3A. BB, 24" (61 cm), ML. Laced white, hafts yellow; beards red, tipped white; slight fragrance. Valentina X Tipperary. Long 1991.

ANNIE'S DRESS (O. D. Niswonger, R. 1990). Sdlg. SDB 11-85. SDB, 10" (25 cm), M. Dark red violet; beards pale blue. Tarheel Elf X 2-82: (Little Black Belt x Ruby Contrast). Cape Iris 1990.

ANNORAH LYNN (Jim Hedgecock, R. 1999). Sdlg. F-16-1. TB, 36" (91 cm), M. Heavily laced and ruffled medium purple, slightly lighter near beards; beards silver with purple base, yellow in throat; slight sweet fragrance. Blue Chip Pink X Rebecca Anne.

ANOKA ANGEL (David Johnson, R. 1992). SDB, 12" (31 cm), M. Ruffled, flared white, gold halo pattern around bushy blue-white beard; slight spicy fragrance. Lima Colada X Flirty Mary. Riverdale 1992.

ANON PRIDE (Cloyd McCord, R. 1992). Sdlg. ANON 05. TB, 36" (91 cm), E. S. light rose lavender; F. yellow, 1/4" edge stitched light lavender, light lavender veining on hafts, white area around bright orange beard; laced, ruffled; sweet fragrance. Anon X 82-3A: (Beauty Crown x Homecoming Queen).

ANOTHER SUN (Chun Fan, R. 1995). Sdlg. F87-135-G. TB, 38" (97 cm), M. S. pale yellowish cream; F. pure white, 1/8" yellow (RHS 5A) rim; beards orange yellow; ruffled; slight sweet fragrance. Commander in Chief X Carved Marble.

ANSWERED PRAYERS (Keith Keppel, R. 1994). Sdlg. 88-11A. TB, 36" (91 cm), EM. S. light pink (M&P 9-A-2/3); F. pinkish white (9-A-1) deepening to pink (9-A-2) edge, buff (9-F-4) hafts; beards capucine red (9-E-12), white at tip; heavily ruffled; slight fragrance. Classmate X 86-23A: ((Goddess x 77-137F: (74-35C, Mistress sib, x 74-52A: ((Joy Ride x Roundup) x (April Melody x (((Irma Melrose x Tea Apron) x ((Full Circle x Rococo) x Tea Apron)) x April Melody))))) x (Goddess x 77-137F)). Keppel 1995.

ANTARCTIQUE (Richard Cayeux, R. 1993). Sdlg. 8708 B. IB, 18" (46 cm), M. S. pure white; F. light lavender blue; beards light yellow. Boo X Spinning Wheel. Cayeux 1993.

ANTHOLOGY (Barry Blyth, R. 1999). Sdlg. E84-1. TB, 37" (94 cm), VE-EM. S. lavender cattleya, slightly muted; F. magenta cattleya; beards dusky tangerine, end lavender and white; pronounced musky fragrance. C101-3: (A63-10, Plume d'Or sib, x A153-13, Cafe Risque sib) X About Town. Tempo Two 1999/2000.

ANTICIPATION ORANGE (Lorena Reid, R. 1994). Sdlg. 8S23-2J. SIB (sino-sib), 24-30" (61-76 cm), L. S. pale orange crush, slightly deeper gold midrib; style arms deep gold, edged pale orange crush; F. pale orange crush, large deep gold signal shading paler into orange crush area. Clear yellow sdlg.: (*I. chrysographes* sdlg., maroon with white signal, x unknown) X self. Laurie's Garden 1994.

ANTICOSTI DISCOVERY (Tony Huber, R. 1998). Sdlg. Ex AC 05. SPEC (*versicolor*), 49-59" (125-150 cm), EM. S. violet (RHS 88B) veining on white; style arms violet, bordered white and light pink; F. deeper violet (86A/B), haft and signal bright yellow surrounded by large white zone veined violet; slight sweet fragrance. Collected, Anticosti Island, Quebec.

ANTIGUA SOLEIL (Laure Anfosso, R. 1991). Sdlg. L 83 10D. TB, 36" (90 cm), M. Ruffled light lemon, paler in center of F.; beards lemon, white horn. Beverly Sills X Sky Hooks. Iris en Provence 1990.

ANTIQUE DOLL (John C. Taylor, R. 1996). Sdlg. UL 14-2. LA, 39" (100 cm), ML. S. cadmium orange (RHS 23D); style arms orange buff (22D); F. apricot (24D), yellow signals bordered orange. Dancing Vogue X Watch Out.

ANTIQUE LACE (Donald Sorensen, R. 1996). Sdlg. S-91-35-12. TB, 37" (94 cm), M. S. light yellow (RHS 7D); style arms light yellow (7C); F. white, light yellow (7D) blended edge, dark yellow (7A) hafts; beards cadmium orange (23A); heavily ruffled and laced; pronounced sweet fragrance. Easter Finery X Perfect Interlude. Birchwood 1999.

ANTJE (Manfred Beer, R. 1992). Sdlg. EWMB 47/69B. TB, 28" (71 cm), E. S. brown with red brown touch; F. red brown, edged S. color; beards gold brown; waved; spicy fragrance. Bang X Martel. Beer 1994.

ANTON CHEKHOV (V. & N. Gordodelovy, R. 1996). Sdlg. 411. TB, 39" (100 cm), M. Ruffled light pink, brown shading on hafts and base of S.; style arms cream; beards red; slight fragrance. Parentage unknown. Gordodelovy 1990.

ANTONINA VIATKINA (Nina Miroshnichenko, R. 1996). TB, 39" (98 cm), ML. Ruffled pinkish lilac self; beards yellow, paler at end; slight sweet fragrance. Parentage unknown. Miroshnichenko 1976.

ANVIL OF DARKNESS (Sterling Innerst, R. 1998). Sdlg. 3936-10. TB, 29½" (75 cm), M. Black self; beards black; slight fragrance. 2336-3: (By Night x Swazi Princess) X Before the Storm. Innerst 1998.

ANXIOUS (Ben Hager, R. 1992). Sdlg. RE5076Lv. TB, 35" (89 cm), EML & RE. Pale lilac; beards pale yellow. Bonus Mama sib X Hallowed Thought. Melrose 1992.

ANXIOUSLY AHEAD (Sterling Innerst, R. 1999). Sdlg. 3961-5. TB, 34" (86 cm), EM. S. deep rose to fuchsia pink; style arms lavender blue; F. dark lavender blue purple; beards orange; slight sweet fragrance. Different Approach X Old Loyalties.

ANYTHING GOES (Ben Hager, R. 1995). Sdlg. T5504Fcy. TB, 35" (89 cm), EM. S. rosy pink; F. deeper rose, veined from throat 2/3 way down petal; beards tangerine. T5235Pk: (T4836CrSh: ((Peach Tree x (Vanity x Pink Persian)) x Silver Flow) x Falling in Love) X T5240WWPk/Oc: (Presence x ((Catalyst x Perfect Accent) x Flaming Victory)). Cooley 1998.

ANYWAY (Barry Blyth, R. 1998). Sdlg. E11-2. SDB, 12" (30 cm), VE-EM. Bright yellow, F. with light reddish brown veined pattern halfway down, white around beard; beards white, tangerine in throat. B62-1, Moustache sib, X Little Bev. Tempo Two 1998/99.

AOSHI BAGAKI (Shuichi Hirao by Society for Japanese Irises, R. 1993). JI (6 F.), 30" (76 cm), M. Ruffled blue violet (RHS 93C) with silver blue veining which stops 1/2" from edge; signal yellow. Parentage unknown. Hirao 1970.

APACHE RUFFLES (Jim Hedgecock, R. 1997). Sdlg. 84-6-R. TB, 36" (91 cm), M. Ruffled, lightly laced medium orange, F. with slightly lighter area by bright red orange beard; pronounced sweet fragrance. Sun Fire X Mandolin. Comanche Acres 1998.

APLOMB (Joseph Ghio, R. 1991). Sdlg. 86-115K2. TB, 40" (102 cm), ML. S. mulberry plum; F. deep mulberry plum, deeper shoulders; beards brick. 83-10V2: ((Act of Love x Lady Friend) x Caption) X Stratagem. Bay View 1992.

APOLLONIAN (Akihiko Terada, R. 1998). Sdlg. S255-89-21. TB, 38" (97 cm), ML. Pink, lightly infused yellow, F. with prominent deeper veining; beards reddish orange; slight musky fragrance. Elegant Answer X Lady Friend. Roris 1998.

APOLLO ONE (George Sutton, R. 1995). Sdlg. G-31A. TB, 34" (86 cm), EM. S. white ground, sanded and edged spiraea red (RHS 63A); style arms white and burgundy; F. white, striped and edged spiraea red; beards bronze gold, hairs tipped light burgundy, spiraea red horn; ruffled; pronounced sweet fragrance. Point in Time X Sky Hooks. Sutton 1997.

APOLLO'S SONG (John C. Taylor, LA, R. 1989). Rainbow Ridge 1990/91.

APOLLO'S TOUCH (Hooker Nichols, R. 1990). Sdlg. 8812E. IB, 18" (46 cm), EML. S. ivory, creamy yellow midrib and base; F. smooth yellow, edged white; beards orange yellow, tipped white; ruffled. Academy Awards X Marmalade Skies. Hillcrest 1991.

APPARE (Nobutsune Nishida by Walter Marx, JI, R. 1951). Correction/expansion of information in 1939 and 1959 Checklists. JI (6 F.). Bright red violet, large white central area with white lines radiating to margin. Introduced in Japan, 1938.

APPLEBLOSSOM DAYS (Bernard Hamner by Shepard Iris Garden, R. 1992). Sdlg. 82-25. TB, 35" (89 cm), M. S. peach pink; F. same, pink-toned eggshell wash over center area, apricot orange (RHS 23C) hafts; beards coral pink; heavily laced. (80-47 x Jaime Lynn) X Melissa Sue. Hamner Iris, Shepard Iris 1992.

APPOINTER (Tomas Tamberg, R. 1993). SPEC-X, 27" (70 cm), ML. S. blue violet; F. blue violet with some yellow veining. Berlin Tiger X Mysterious Monique. Schoeppinger 1994.

APPROACHABLE (Richard Ernst, R. 1998). Sdlg. JF120-16A-1. TB, 35" (89 cm), M. S. creamy peach, midrib infused pink, rim honey; style arms creamy peach; F. creamy peach, with faint blue violet cast, shoulders mauve, rim honey; beards tangerine orange. F120-16: (Afternoon Delight x Gaulter 81-17, inv. Irene Nelson) X F104-1: (B119-1: (Irene Nelson x Sun Fire) x Friday Surprise). Cooley 1998.

APPROACH ME (Tom Burseen, R. 1990). Sdlg. 5-57X. TB, 35" (89 cm), EM. Ruffled and laced very light pink (RHS 69C); beards tangerine. Pink Divinity X Wings of Dreams. T.B.'s Place 1991.

APPROVAL (Graeme Grosvenor, R. 1995). Sdlg. T 8-5. TB, 38" (97 cm), EM. S. and style arms pale blue; F. white, edged pale blue, darker blue hafts; beards yellow, tipped blue; ruffled. Kiss of Gold X Armada. Rainbow Ridge 1995/96.

APRICORANGE (Cy Bartlett, R. 1996). Sdlg. MS-PF-BOF. TB, 33" (84 cm), ML. S. pale apricot; F. slightly deeper orange apricot; beards orange; ruffled. (Marmalade Skies x Peachy Face) X Blaze of Fire.

APRICOTA (Doris Greenwood by J. T. Aitken, TB, R. 1985). Correction of parentage. (Summer Love x Bright Butterfly) X (Kimberlina x Gypsy Dream).

APRICOT AMBROSIA (Opal Brown, R. 1995). Sdlg. 91-4D. TB, 30" (76 cm), M. Ruffled apricot self; beards deeper orange. Fun Fest X Malaguena. Brown's Sunnyhill 1995.

APRICOT CANDY (Akihiko Terada, R. 1995). Sdlg. 228-6. TB, 36" (91 cm), M. Ruffled and laced orange self; F. tinted white in center; beards deep orange. Hindenburg X Good Show. Roris 1996.

APRICOT DANISH (Barry Blyth, R. 1996). Sdlg. A63-C. TB, 38" (97 cm), ML. Dusky apricot, slightly lighter area below tangerine orange beard; sweet fragrance. Dance Man X Rembrandt Magic. Tempo Two 1996/97.

APRICOT DROPS (J. T. Aitken, R. 1995). Sdlg. 91M9. MTB, 18" (46 cm), VE-EM. Apricot orange, F. with deeper spot; beards yellow, tipped orange. Abridged Version X Pele. Aitken's Salmon Creek 1995.

APRICOT FIZZ (D. L. Shepard, R. 1996). Sdlg. 89099-8435. TB, 40" (107 cm), EM. S. rich apricot sherbet; style arms apricot, white center veined apricot; F. apricot, apricot-veined white central blaze; beards dark yellow. Charming Rose X Orange Empire. Shepard Iris 1996.

APRICOT FLUSH (Art Blodgett, R. 1992). Sdlg. 86-53. TB, 32" (81 cm), EM. Ruffled buttercup yellow (HCC 5/2); tangerine beards. 82-22: (Peach Champagne x Lighted Within) X 286: (Frills x Lighted Within). Blodgett 1993.

APRICOT FROSTY (O. D. Niswonger, R. 1992). Sdlg. BB 30-89. BB, 23" (58 cm), M. S. white; F. deep apricot; beards apricot. Beachgirl X Champagne Elegance. Cape Iris 1992.

APRICOT GIANT (Loleta Powell, R. 1992). Sdlg. 91-2. TB, 36" (91 cm), VE-EML. Apricot self; beards apricot orange. Tarlatin X Jelly Roll. Powell's Gardens 1993.

APRICOT PARTY (A. & D. Willott, R. 1995). Sdlg. 88-115. SDB, 13" (33 cm), M. S. rosy apricot; F. apricot, deeper haft lines; beards red orange tipped blue; ruffled. 84-91: (79-105, Coral Wings sib, x Coral Wings) X unknown. Willott 1995.

APRICOT SKIES (Richard Brook, R. 1995). Sdlg. A 18/1. BB, 27" (69 cm), M. S. creamy apricot pink (RHS 23D) edged buffy cream (11B); F. golden apricot orange (13B), deeper (13A) on shoulders, small veined cream patch; beards fiery orange red (28A). Marmalade Skies X Peachy Face. Zephyrwude 1996.

APRICOT TOPPING (Paul Black, R. 1997). Sdlg. 8924A. BB, 25" (64 cm), M. S. apricot orange, slight violet midrib infusion; style arms apricot orange; F. blended wine red darkest in center, apricot to white rays around orange beard, apricot rim and petal reverse; ruffled, lightly laced; slight sweet fragrance. Spiced Cider X Glitz 'n Glitter. Mid-America 1997.

APRIL AIR (Polly Black, R. 1992). Sdlg. EG2-4-ORC. TB, 40" (102 cm), E. Lightly ruffled orchid touched white beside yellow beards; slight fragrance. Parentage unknown. Polly Black 1992.

APRIL ANGEL (Hooker Nichols, R. 1990). Sdlg. 8815A. SDB, 12" (30 cm), EML S. eggshell white; end of style arms faintly stitched violet; F. ivory, flared and ruffled; beards yellow and white. Court Magician X (Pink Kitten x (Happy Mood x Kiss)). Hillcrest 1991.

APRIL BLIZZARD (A. & D. Willott, R. 1993). Sdlg. 92-45. MDB, 4½" (12 cm), EM. S. white; F. white, hafts tinted green; beards white. Pastel Delight X 79-13: (Greenlee GX-2: ((White Mite x self) x (I. pumila alba x Hanselmayer)) x Buttons). Willott 1994.

APRIL FOG (Hooker Nichols by O. D. Niswonger, R. 1989). Sdlg. IB 31-87. IB, 20" (51 cm), M. S. blue; F. very pale blue; beards blue white. Captured Spirit X Mystique. Cape Iris 1990.

APRIL ICE (A. & D. Willott, R. 1993). Sdlg. 91-10. MDB, 4" (10 cm), E. S. cool white; F. same, trace of turquoise halo; beards white. Buttons X 79-13: (Greenlee GX-2: ((White Mite x self) x (I. pumila alba x Hanselmayer)) x Buttons). Willott 1995.

APRIL IN PARIS (Vernon Wood, R. 1991). Sdlg. 86-41. TB, 34" (86 cm), M. Lightly ruffled and laced medium pink (RHS 55D); beards tangerine red. Vision in Pink X 82-38: ((Mais Oui x Carved Pink) x Blushing Pink). Cottage 1992.

APRIL JEWEL (Larry Lauer, R. 1999). Sdlg. 443-5. TB, 34" (86 cm), M. S. venetian pink, edged orange buff; style arms orange buff; F. orange buff with slight pink cast, yellow ochre shoulders; beards red tangerine, small horn; ruffled, lightly laced; pronounced sweet fragrance. 91-221: (Orange Treat x L88-56-1: (Chickasaw Sue x Role Model)) X Pagan Pink.

APRIL'S BIRTHDAY (B. Charles Jenkins, R. 1994). Sdlg. BF13E. SPU, 38-50" (97-127 cm), VE. White self, large yellow signal. Bali Bali X Cinnamon Stick. Shepard Iris 1994.

APRY ECHO (Glenn Bowers, R. 1997). Sdlg. B38-L. TB, 34" (86 cm), EM & RE. Ruffled peach apricot self; beards deep apricot; slight sweet fragrance. Remember Spring X Uriah the Hittite.

AQUAMARINE DREAM (Frederick Kerr, R. 1999). Sdlg. 900102. TB, 38" (97 cm), M. Aquamarine blue self; beards aquamarine blue. 8715A: (Dream Lover x Breakers) X Scandia Delight. Rainbow Acres 1999.

AQUATIC ALLIANCE (Lorena Reid, R. 1994). Sdlg. 8VL18-1. SPEC-X, 24" (61 cm), M. Light violet, large gold signals edged white, veined dark purple. I. versicolor alba X Regal. Laurie's Garden 1994.

AQUILIFER (G. F. Wilson, R. 1991). Sdlg. 4-89MSO-A. AB (OGB), 29½" (75 cm), EM. S. oyster white veined gold, gold yellow rib; F. pale gold veined slightly darker at hafts, large round well-defined red brown signal; beards mustard yellow, wide; sweet fragrance. Mainstream X Onlooker. Pleasure Iris 1993.

ARABESQUE CHARM (Ladislav Muska, R. 1999). Sdlg. RSAF-09. TB, 38" (97 cm), M. S. white, midrib base washed pink; style arms white; F. rosy violet, narrow lavender rim; beards burnt tangerine vermilion; ruffled, heavily laced; sweet fragrance. ((Ringo x Sweeter Than Wine) x Alessandra) X Fontana di Trevi. Muska 1999.

ARABIAN ARCHER (Lois Rich by James Whitely, R. 1992). Sdlg. R84-65A. AB (OGB), 31" (79 cm), E. S. lavender, veined darker, electric blue midrib; F. oxblood with self veins, black signal with 15 darker lines; beards yellow. R80-119J: (R75-169J: ((R71-109C: ((Bagdad Beauty x Pink Formal) x Welcome Reward) x R69-107K: (Welcome Reward x ((Bagdad Beauty x Orchid and Flame) x Kalifa Hirfa))) x sib) x (R75-66B: ((Judean Charmer x Judean Cream) x White Lightning) x R75-169A)) X R80-124G: (((W83-0 x Pink Formal) x (R71-109C x R69-107K)) x (R75-66B x R75-169A)). Aril Patch 1992.

ARABIAN STORY (Barry Blyth, R. 1998). Sdlg. D46-3. TB, 34-36" (86-91 cm), EM. S. bright mustard yellow; F. red brown, slightly lighter near mustard beard; ruffled; sweet fragrance. B157-1: (Imprimis x Bubble Up) X Aura Light. Tempo Two 1998/99.

ARACHNEPHOBIA (Kevin Vaughn, R. 1997). Sdlg. F-60-1. LA, 36-38" (91-97 cm), EM. Bright cherry red, veined slightly darker; F. with tiny signal obscured by style arm; all floral parts narrow, separated, spidery. Black Widow X Cajun Cookery.

ARAISO (Bungo Miyazawa by Society for Japanese Irises, R. 1994). JI (3 F.), 38" (97 cm), M. S. violet, tiny white edge; style arms violet; F. pale blue (almost white), thin violet veins, signal yellow. Parentage unknown. Miyazawa between 1945 and 1952.

ARASHIYAMA (Shuichi Hirao by Society for Japanese Irises, R. 1994). JI (3 F.), 27½" (70 cm), E. S. red violet veined and flecked white; style arms white, red violet crests flecked white; F. red violet, veined and flecked white, white halo. Parentage unknown. Hirao 1962.

ARC DE TRIOMPHE (Frederick Kerr, R. 1995). Sdlg. 90-39-03. TB, 32" (81 cm), M. S. white, infused yellow; F. yellow, darker veining and hafts; beards gold; ruffled; slight sweet fragrance. Echo de France X Little Much. Rainbow Acres 1995.

ARCHANGEL WINGS (Rob Stetson, R. 1997). Sdlg. TB95J1. TB, 36-38" (91-97 cm), L. Heavily ruffled white self; beards white, hairs tipped orange, large white flounce; slight spicy fragrance. Elizabeth Poldark X Art School Angel.

ARC OF COLOURS (Barry Blyth, R. 1998). Sdlg. D64-3. TB, 36" (91 cm), M. Brownish blend infused electric lavender; F. tan, brilliant electric violet blaze, 1/4" edge matching S.; beards bronze; slight fragrance. Plume d'Or X A153-5, Cafe Risque sib. Tempo Two 1998/99.

ARCTIC AGE (Schreiner, R. 1999). Sdlg. EE 282-1. TB, 38" (97 cm), ML. Ruffled clean white (RHS 155D); beards lemon yellow. AA 1099-1: (Silverado sib x Song of Angels sib) X W 630-A: (R 11-A: (Last Hurrah sib x Laced Cotton sib) x Lady Madonna). Schreiner 1999.

ARCTIC BLAST (George Shoop, R. 1994). Sdlg. 89-47. SDB, 9" (23 cm), M. Ruffled pure white self; beards white. Spring Dancer X Pink Caper. Keppel 1995.

ARCTIC BLISS (Larry Johnson, R. 1999). Sdlg. J089-24. TB, 36" (91 cm), EM. Light blue; beards yellow. Many Thanks X Fair Dinkum. Cooley 1999.

ARCTIC EXPRESS (Joseph Gatty by Keith Keppel, R. 1995). Sdlg. X60-3. TB, 38" (97 cm), EM. Ruffled pure white self; beards white, pale lemon in throat tipped orange yellow. Christmas X Ocean Pacific. Keppel 1996.

ARCTIC FLURRY (C. M. Anderson, R. 1990). TB, 30" (76 cm), M. Pristine white; beards white; lightly waved, flaring. Skywatch X Laced Cotton.

ARCTIC FOX (Vernon Wood, R. 1997). Sdlg. 93-104. TB, 32" (81 cm), ML. White self; beards very dark burnt red. Skyblaze X Silver Fox. Stockton 1998.

ARCTIC GOLDHEART (Lorena Reid, R. 1994). Sdlg. S.A.G.H. SPEC *(setosa)*, 30" (76 cm), M. S. none; style arms deep gold midrib, lighter edge, creamy crests; F. pale cream to white, round gold signal, gold in throat. *I. setosa alba* X unknown. Laurie's Garden 1994.

ARCTIC LAVENDER (Lorena Reid, R. 1995). SPEC *(setosa)*, 24" (61 cm), E. F. light lavender veined deeper rosy lavender, signal yellow paling to indistinct white border, deeper yellow veins; style arms white, midrib very light warm gold. *I. setosa alba* X unknown. Laurie's Garden 1995.

ARCTIC REBLOOMER (Carla Lankow, R. 1992). SPEC *(setosa)*, 37" (94 cm), M & RE. S. (virtually none) blue violet; F. blue violet. Parentage unknown. Laurie's Garden 1994.

ARCTIC SPRING (Allan Ensminger by Tim Stanek, R. 1991). Sdlg. 180-63. BB, 24" (61 cm), VL. White, 1/4" light green (lighter than RHS 145D) rim on F.; beards white. 76-23: (Angel Choir x Fuji's Mantle) X Bridal Wreath. Eight Mile Grove 1991.

ARCTIC TERN (B.L.C. Dodsworth, TB, R. 1984). British Iris Society 1987.

ARDEN (John D. Taylor, R. 1983). Change of classification from IB to BB. British Iris Society 1989.

ARIL REVERIE (Walter Moores, AB, R. 1988). Hillcrest, Moores 1990.

ARITHA TYRESSA (Francis Brenner, R. 1992). Sdlg. B-78. TB, 28" (71 cm), ML. Aureolin yellow (RHS 12A) self; beards cadmium orange (23A); slight fragrance. Parentage unknown.

ARIZONA BIG RED (D. L. Shepard, R. 1996). Sdlg. 89506-85P. LA, 38" (97 cm), ML. S. soft ruby red; style arms soft ruby red, lined gold on back; F. dark ruby red, spear-shaped golden yellow signal. Charlie's Ginny X Bajazzo. Shepard Iris 1996.

ARIZONA BYWAYS (Robert Annand, R. 1990). Sdlg. 88-61A. TB, 37" (94 cm), M. S. glistening rosy beige; style arms lavender; F. earthtones washed over purple blaze, lacy gold edge; beards gold. 81-9: (77-10: (Butterscotch Trim x (Rippling Waters x Kiss of Fire)) x Butterscotch Trim) X Harlem Hussy. Milwood Nursery 1993.

ARIZONA CITRUS (D. L. Shepard, R. 1998). Sdlg. 94017-0* 90143. TB, 42" (107 cm), ML. S. bright canary yellow, veined dark yellow; style arms canary yellow; F. canary yellow, white blaze veined yellow, heavy golden orange haft veining; beards orange; ruffled. Splash of Blue X Chosen One. Shepard Iris 1998.

ARIZONA REDHEAD (D. L. Shepard, R. 1998). Sdlg. 95044-8941. TB, 43" (109 cm), ML. S. sandy red; style arms sandy red, edged golden red; F. ruby red, hafts heavily veined, sand red center stripe, lower portion of F. red black; beards rusty orange; ruffled. 89004: (Chief Redskin x 85015: (Mirror Mirror x Burgundy Brown)) X Chief Redskin. Shepard Iris 1998.

ARIZONA SANDSTONE (Terrell Taylor, R. 1999). Sdlg. 95-5. TB, 36" (91 cm), M. Dark sandstone red (RHS 178B), edges lighter, violet central infusion; beards burnt orange; ruffled; pronounced spicy fragrance. Bygone Era X Macho Hombre.

ARIZONIQUE (B. Charles Jenkins, R. 1998). Sdlg. AY86F. SPU, 40" (107 cm), ML. S. lavender, blending to yellow at base; style arms lavender, midrib yellow; F. yellow, blending to wavy lavender margin; flared. B3-5B: (Crow Wing x Equality) X A15-0E: (Forty Carats x unknown). Shepard Iris 1998.

ARMAGEDDON (Chet Tompkins, R. 1992). Sdlg. 87-35. TB, 36" (91 cm), ML. S. vivid blend of clover and amaranth pink; F. deep red maroon, 1/4" picoteed amaranth pink edge; beards shrimp red; ruffled. Reverse sib to Heavenly Body X ((Dusky Dancer x Camelot Rose) x ((Kin-na-Zin x Camelot Rose) x (Crystal Ribbon sib x Cimbay))). Fleur de Lis 1992.

AROMAT SIRENI (Viktor Sheviakov, R. 1995). Sdlg. 12A 7. TB, 30" (75 cm), ML. S. violet and brown blend; F. violet, light blue area near yellow orange beard, violet brown and cream haft markings. Cloudcap X Professor Chayanov. Sheviakov 1997.

AROUND MIDNIGHT (Schreiner, R. 1995). Sdlg. AA 285-1. TB, 39" (99 cm), ML. S. and style arms dark purple (RHS 89A); F. dark black (187A); beards black; heavily ruffled. T 393-1: (J124-1: ((Matinata x Nightside) x G 393-1) x Titan's Glory) X T 315-1: (K 398-1: ((V 781-CC x (Toll Gate x After Dark)) x ((Dazzling Delight x Vitafire) x (V 270-4 x War Lord))) x P 273-B: (Morning Hymn x Louisiana Lace)). Schreiner 1995.

ARRIVAL (Jim & Vicki Craig, R. 1996). Sdlg. C25V8. SDB, 15" (37 cm), VL. Palest blue, quickly fading to white; beards yellow. (9N2: ((En Route x Pink Taffeta) x (New Moon x 6H1: (Sacred Mountain x *I. aphylla* "Werckmeister"))) x Little Sunrise) X (Star Child x 6H1). J. & V. Craig 1996.

ARROWS (Mary Dunn by Joseph Ghio, R. 1998). Sdlg. 240-10. LA, 34" (86 cm), ML. Lavender, green line signal; style arms green. Lina X Makebelieve World. Bay View 1998.

ART AND SOUL (Barry Blyth, R. 1998). Sdlg. A186-1. SPU, 38" (96 cm), ML. S. blue lavender over lemon white, veining whiter at base; F. lemon, long gold signal, 1/8" blended blue lavender edge; heavily ruffled. Niswonger Sp 4-81: (Cinnamon Stick x Redwood Supreme) X unknown. Tempo Two 1998/99.

ART DECO (Schreiner, R. 1997). Sdlg. DD 1300-1. TB, 33" (84 cm), VE. S. dark blue violet (RHS 89A), white center marks; style arms blue violet; F. white (155D) ground, 1/2" stitched dark blue violet edge; beards yellow, blue at end; slight fragrance. Momentum X 1983 #1, unknown. Schreiner 1997.

ART FAIRE (Schreiner, R. 1993). Sdlg. Y 902-1. TB, 35" (89 cm), EM. Near-white (RHS 155D); F. banded deep violet (82B); beards yellow. Gypsy Woman X N 502-E, pollen parent of Peach Picotee. Schreiner 1993.

ARTFUL DODGER (Joseph Ghio, R. 1997). Sdlg. PD-219V4. CA, 14" (36 cm), ML. Golden tan self, small maroon signal. PF-159H: (PI-MIX-B2, unknown, x PH-231bo: ((Bubbly x (Solid Citizen x (Lighthouse Point x Mission Santa Cruz))) x National Anthem)) X School Boy. Bay View 1997.

ARTIFICE (Pierre Anfosso, R. 1990). Sdlg. P 82 20A. TB, 36" (91 cm), ML. S. rose pink; F. amber pink, amber hafts; beards tangerine. Carmen X X Beverly Sills. Iris en Provence 1990.

ARTISTIC DREAMS (Clarence Protzmann, TB, R. 1989). Protzmann 1990.

ARTISTIC SONG (Terrell Taylor, R. 1997). Sdlg. 94-9. TB, 32" (80 cm), EM. S. bright medium gold (RHS 20A); F. primrose yellow (4B) ground, cardinal red (53A) markings; beards bronze; musky fragrance. Thunder Echo X Jitterbug. Bonita Gardens 1997.

#ART NOUVEAU (Virginia Messick, TB, R. 1979). Name transferred, 1991.

ART NOUVEAU (Virginia Messick, R. 1991). Sdlg. M86-6. TB, 37" (94 cm), M. Ruffled deep rose pink, lighter area around beard, tiny white signal; beards matching, tipped white. Lorilee X Gaulter sdlg. inv. Foolish Pleasure. Cottage 1992.

ART PROJECT (Lloyd Zurbrigg, TB, R. 1989). Avonbank, Landsend Gardens 1990.

ART QUAKE (Carol Lankow by J. T. Aitken, R. 1994). Sdlg. 7H-118. BB, 25" (64 cm), ML. Gold, with amber hafts, blue blaze below orange beards. 7579-2: (Andi x (((Sunray x Top Flight) x Fleeta) x Yellow Dresden)) X 8C94-2: (M. Wright H13, yellow BB, x Maroon Bells). Aitken's Salmon Creek 1994.

ART SHOW (Keith Keppel, TB, R. 1989). Roris 1990.

ARVELLABEN (Joseph Grant, R. 1993). Sdlg. JG-563-88-JAP. JI (3 F.), 46" (117 cm), ML. S. deep burgundy with very fine deep grape, fine white edge; F. white ground heavily veined deep purple, purple halo around yellow signal. "Aioi" X Haru-no-Umi.

ASAHIMARU (Society for Japanese Irises, R. 1992). JI (3 F.), 39" (100 cm), EM. Deep red violet, yellow signal. Parentage unknown. Introduced and in commerce in Japan prior to 1940.

ASAHI-NO-YUKI (Shuichi Hirao, by Society for Japanese Irises, R. 1995). JI (7-9 F.), 35" (90 cm), M. White, brushed soft violet, giving light pastel violet effect; style arms white, soft violet markings. Parentage unknown. Introduced in Japan ca. 1970.

ASATO BIRAKI (Shuichi Hirao, by Society for Japanese Irises, R. 1993). JI (3 F.), 31½" (80 cm), M. S. deep blue violet with white center; style arms white, broadly edged blue violet; F. deep blue violet. Parentage unknown. Hirao 1969.

ASCENSION CROWN (Gary Middleton, R. 1999). Sdlg. 96/CA 1. TB, 39" (99 cm), M. S. clear pale yellow, midrib faintly infused sky blue; style arms creamy apricot, violet midrib; F. amethyst violet blending to pale misty blue lilac edge, centerline misty sky blue, hafts marked brown and overlaid faint lemon yellow; beards bright orange; ruffled; pronounced sweet fragrance. Carnaby X Amadora.

ASCENSION DAY (Ernest Naylor by Thelma Naylor, R. 1998). Sdlg. D3/3. IB, 24" (60 cm), M. White ground plicata edged pale blue; style arms pale blue; beards white. A3/1: ((Dancers Veil x Rococo) x Brannigan) X Foggy Dew.

ASCENT OF ANGELS (Mike Bernard, R. 1995). Sdlg. T120A. TB, 36" (91 cm), M. S. wistaria blue (RHS 92D), midrib deeper; F. wistaria blue washed violet (87A); beards light lavender, gold deep in throat; heavily ruffled; pronounced sweet fragrance. Honky Tonk Blues X Voodoo Blues. Maryott 1996.

ASCII ART (Walter Moores, R. 1995). Sdlg. 87-15PL. TB, 32" (81 cm), M. S. white; style arms blue violet; F. white, narrow blue violet stitched edge, wider at hafts; beards white; ruffled; slight sweet fragrance. Victoria Falls X Fall Spotlight. Moores 1997.

ASHFIELD CLEMENTINE (Anne Watson, R. 1994). Sdlg. AW1. SIB, 32" (81 cm), M. S. violet blue, ultramarine veining, white signal; style arms near medium prussian blue on ribs, shading to lilac violet blue edge; F. violet blue, ultramarine veining, gold signal edged white; flat form. Parentage unknown.

ASHI-NO-UKIFUNE (Yoshio Mitsuda by Society for Japanese Irises, R. 1993). JI (6 F.), 36" (90 cm), M. Large ruffled white to light violet ground veined blue violet, deep blue purple halo, yellow signal; style arms purple, numerous. Parentage unknown. Mitsuda 1969.

ASHLEIGH LEMONLIME (John Beal, R. 1993). Sdlg. 84SP1. SPU, 38" (97 cm), E. Tailored lemon yellow self. Parentage unknown.

ASHLEIGH NICOLE (Darlene Pinegar, R. 1993). Sdlg. V-1-2. TB, 28" (71 cm), M. S. and style arms medium light pink; F. creamy white, edged medium light pink, apricot shoulders; beards dark coral; ruffled; slight sweet fragrance. Vanity X Marmalade Skies. Spanish Fork 1994.

ASHLEY (J. D. Stadler, R. 1992). Sdlg. J25/05. TB, 33" (83 cm), M. S. muted yellow; F. blended grey and tan with lavender flush; beards orange; ruffled; slight fragrance. Loudoun Cameo X Sheer Poetry.

ASHTON DREAM (William Ackerman, R. 1997). Sdlg. A4-4-86. JI (3 F.), 33" (84 cm), E. S. pale lobelia blue (RHS 91C), edged dark hyacinth blue (91A); style arms white with violet blue lips, broad; F. pale lobelia blue, shading to white around golden yellow (14A) signal; margins crinkled. Gosho Asobi X self.

ASHTON PRIDE (William Ackerman, R. 1997). Sdlg. AW2-6. JI (6 F.), 36" (91 cm), EM. F. violet blue (RHS 90B/C) veins on lighter (90D) ground; style arms near-white midrib, pale violet blue (90C) lips and edge. A33-6-177: (F-7 x P-19) X Gosho Asobi.

ASHTON SNOW (William Ackerman, R. 1997). Sdlg. B5-5. JI (3 F.), 30" (76 cm), M. S. chalk white, narrow purple (RHS 90B) rim; style arms white, lips blushed pale purple; F. chalk white, aureolin yellow (12A) signal. M91-55: (Double Cream x Enduring Pink Frost) X Double Cream.

ASHTON VELVET (William Ackerman, R. 1997). Sdlg. B1-14. JI (3 F.), 28" (71 cm), M. S. deep pansy violet (RHS 83A) with narrow white margin; style arms pansy violet, rimmed white; F. veined deep violet (86A), heaviest near aureolin yellow (12A) signal, pale methyl violet to sea lavender violet (85C/D) ground. M91-62: (DS(11-33) irradiated seed x self) X Taffeta and Velvet.

ASIAN ALLIANCE (Jean Witt, SPEC-X, R. 1988). Laurie's Garden 1990.

ASIAN WARRIOR (J. T. Aitken, R. 1993). Sdlg. 86J-1-9. JI (3 F.), 36" (91 cm), ML. S. raspberry red with white flash; style arms white, brushed red; F. velvety raspberry red with white area around yellow signal. Stranger in Paradise X King's Court. Aitken's Salmon Creek 1993.

AS IS (Sharon McAllister, R. 1998). Sdlg. 87-7-1. AB (OGB-), 30" (76 cm), ML. S. buff; style arms yellow, crest buff; F. golden apricot center blending through rust to smoky grey edge, burgundy area around beard; beards yellow, hairs tipped burgundy. Chapeau X 84-9A-3: ((Martha Mia x Expert Advice) x -- probably Rose of Sharon). McAllister 1998.

ASKIYA (Adolf Volfovich-Moler, R. 1995). Sdlg. V-56. TB, 47" (120 cm), E. S. light brown; F. dark red, light brown rim; beards orange yellow; ruffled, laced. Broadway Star X Rippling Waters. Volfovich-Moler 1992.

ASKOMIL (Revie Harvey, SPEC-X (evansia), R. 1986). Hilmary Catton 1991.

ASLAN (Sterling Innerst, R. 1996). Sdlg. 3613-4. SDB, 14" (36 cm), M. S. red violet; F. blue, large purple spot; beards blue; slight musky fragrance. 2875-1: ((Betsey Boo x Cherub Tears) x (Soft Air x Pink Cushion)) X Dash sib.

ASPECT (John C. Taylor, R. 1997). Sdlg. UL 22-8. LA, 35" (90 cm), ML. Fluted and ruffled light yellow, green center, yellow line-effect signal. Gladiator's Gift X Dural Dreamtime. Rainbow Ridge 1998/99.

ASPECTS OF LOVE (Oscar Schick, R. 1998). Sdlg. 91-17B06. TB, 36" (91 cm), M. Heavily ruffled light coral pink, F. with darker coral pink shoulders, lighter center; beards coral pink; slight spicy fragrance. Fortunata X Vision in Pink. Stockton 1998.

ASPEN (Monty Byers, TB, R. 1989). Moonshine 1991.

ASPIRE (Barry Blyth, R. 1997). Sdlg. C75-A. IB, 18" (46 cm), VE-EM. S. pink with lilac flush, honey glow; F. pink with lilac flush, slightly lighter below beard, deeper mid-stripe, pinkish brown hafts; beards white, tipped tangerine; pronounced sweet fragrance. Z10-14, Rockabye sib, X Aztec Burst. Tempo Two 1997/98.

ASSIGNMENT (Sterling Innerst, R. 1990). Sdlg. 3235-6. SDB, 14" (36 cm), M. S. light green; F. dark green; beards green. Rain Dance X 1583-2: ((Gentle Smile x Mystic Symbol) x (Gentle Smile x Stockholm)). Innerst 1991.

ASTEROID ZONE (George Sutton, R. 1995). Sdlg. F-62. TB, 35" (89 cm), M. S. bright yellow (RHS 2A); style arms bright yellow and white; F. bright yellow, white around beard; beards lemon gold (near 13A), upwardly curved fuzzy yellow and white horn; ruffled, lightly laced. Come To Me X Candlegleam. Sutton 1996.

ASTRA GIRL (W. Terry Varner, MTB, R. 1989). Ohio Gardens 1990.

ASTRA LADY (W. Terry Varner, R. 1998). Sdlg. U-300. MTB, 22" (56 cm), EM. Lightly ruffled pure white self; beards light yellow; lightly ruffled. Baby Bibs X Astra Girl. Ohio Gardens 1998.

ASTRID CAYEUX (Jean Cayeux by Richard Cayeux, R. 1995). Sdlg. 7981 A. TB, 33" (85 cm), M. S. pure white; F. white, lilac flush intensifying toward edge; beards bright orange. Heavenly Harmony X Metropolitan. Cayeux 1991.

ASTROLOGER (William Plotner, R. 1992). Sdlg. 83-325-2. TB, 40-42" (102-107 cm), EM. Toga purple with small white star surrounding orchid-tipped yellow beards. NX-131: (Night Owl x Stepping Out) X 104: (Exotic Star x Diplomat). Wildwood Gardens 1992.

ATALA (Pierre-Christian Anfosso, R. 1990). Sdlg. PC 81 12. TB, 33½" (85 cm), M. S. bright yellow; F. black maroon with small white spot around beard. Sostenique X Study in Black. Iris en Provence 1990.

ATCHAFALAYA (Farron Campbell, R. 1998). Sdlg. 94-275-A. LA, 34-36" (86-91 cm), EM. Velvety very dark red violet, slight silver halo; yellow signal and green crest on all petals; style arms red violet; lightly ruffled cartwheel form. John's Lucifer X Jeri. Lone Star 1998.

AT FIRST SIGHT (Larry Lauer, R. 1999). Sdlg. 373-6. SDB, 12" (31 cm), E. Lightly ruffled light wistaria blue self; beards white, tipped light blue, yellow in throat; pronounced sweet fragrance. Pacific Destiny X Chicory Charm.

ATLANTA BELLE (Tom Magee, TB, R. 1989). Long 1992.

ATLANTIC MIST (Jim Hedgecock, R. 1990). Sdlg. 84-56. TB, 34" (86 cm), M. Ruffled blue violet; beards blue violet, tipped silver; slight fragrance. Navy Strut X Pacific Mist. Comanche Acres 1991.

AT LAST (Sharon McAllister, R. 1993). Sdlg. 89-12-8. AB (OGB-), 28" (72 cm), E. S. white ground with fine lilac veins around edge; F. buff ground with intense netting of fine mulberry veining around mulberry beard, fading out toward edge. Casa Vicente X Joint Venture. McAllister 1993.

ATOMIC FLAME (Chet Tompkins, R. 1994). Sdlg. 88-7A. TB, 39" (99 cm), M. S. deep orange yellow, slightly flecked and speckled on edge; style arms orange yellow; F. deep orange yellow, speckled cayenne red border; beards orange. Fun and Games X Laredo. Fleur de Lis 1994.

ATONEMENT (Kevin Nilsen, R. 1991). Sdlg. 2-85-1. TB, 39" (99 cm), EM. Fringed and heavily ruffled white, green midrib and veins; beards light red. Loudoun Charmer X Mandolin. Iridescence 1991/92.

ATTEN (Howard Shockey, R. 1993). AB (OGB), 27" (69 cm), M. S. orchid violet; F. light ground with rose orchid overlay, near-black signal; beards bronze. 86-138-R: ((79-105-C: (Stars Over Chicago x Welcome Reward) x Desert Princess) x Syrian Moon) X 86-140-T: (((79-105-H x Syrian Moon) x (Heart Stealer x 79-105-C)) x Onlooker). Arilian Acres 1993.

ATTENSUN (Tom Burseen, R. 1993). Sdlg. 8-9A. TB, 34" (86 cm), E. S. bright golden yellow (RHS 24B); F. gold ground washed maroon, netted and veined white, lacy gold edge; beards gold; spicy fragrance. 8-158A: (Burning Desire x Rustic Dance) X 5-233: (Michigan Pride x Dazzling Gold). T.B.'s Place 1994.

ATTENTION GETTER (Cleo Palmer, R. 1994). Sdlg. 8872. SDB, 13" (33 cm), L. S. white, rims lightly marked with light violet streaks and dark vertical edge markings; F. white, heavy dark violet veining on hafts and shoulders to just beyond beard tip, dark violet vertical edge; beards yellow to white, tipped violet. Jenny Grace X Muchacha. Palmer's Iris 1994.

AT THE BALLET (Calvin Helsley, R. 1993). Sdlg. 93-1. SIB, 28" (71 cm), M. Ruffled lavender violet (RHS 85C), 3/16" lighter (85D) edge, veined and dotted slightly deeper overall, brown in throat; style arms lavender violet (85D). Temper Tantrum X Silver Illusion. Helsley 1998.

AUDITION (John C. Taylor, R. 1998). Sdlg. SL50-1. LA, 47" (120 cm), M. S. red purple; style arms red purple, yellow base; F. deeper red purple, edged buff, signal yellow. Gladiator's Gift X Margaret Lee sib. Rainbow Ridge 1999/2000.

AUDLEY BUTTERSCOTCH (A. J. Trinder, BB, R. 1991). Change of name to SALLY JANE.

AU GRATIN (Lawrence Ransom, R. 1991). Sdlg. 85/23-1. IB, 20" (50 cm), EM. S. yellow (RHS 9B); F. same, whiter toward center, brown ray pattern around tip of orange yellow beard. Debby Rairdon X Eyebright. Iris au Trescols 1992.

AULD ROSE (Stan Dexter by Marie Ingersoll, R. 1994). Sdlg. A18-6-78-A. TB, 38" (97 cm), EM. S. old rose; F. red, edged old rose, with near-white centerline; beards yellow. Afternoon Delight X Wish. Ingersoll's Iris 1995.

AUNT AGATHA (R. E. Nichol, TB, R. 1989). British Iris Society 1999.

AUNT HANK (Jim Hedgecock, R. 1999). Sdlg. JM 85-11-1. TB, 36" (91 cm), M. S. medium pink; F. dark pink, medium pink marginal band and centerstripe, pale pink haft marking; beards pale pink at end, to bright red orange in throat; ruffled, laced. Cloud Fire X Sangre de Cristo.

AUNT JOSEPHINE (Donald Spoon, R. 1990). Sdlg. 89-11. TB, 35" (89 cm), M. Fluted white; beards yellow. Lively Lemon X Mandolin. Winterberry 1997.

AUNT LUCY (Gerald Richardson, R. 1992). Sdlg. 86-9-2. TB, 33" (84 cm), M. S. heavily flushed violet, fading to pale blue violet toward edge; F. pale blue violet with deeper violet flush radiating from beard; beards violet, tipped light bronze; slight fragrance. Cosmic Dance X Olympiad. Rainbow's End 1994.

AUNT SHIRLEY (Joseph Mertzweiller, R. 1990). Sdlg. 78-50. LA, 34-36" (86-91 cm), M. Coral pink, medium yellow signal; musky fragrance. Deneb X Press Release. Cordon Bleu 1992.

AU PAIR (Lawrence Ransom, R. 1994). Sdlg. 87/66-14. TB, 37" (94 cm), M. Rose carmine, F. with light rose violet fan pattern in center, shoulders tinted beige brown; beards orange red with whiter base; ruffled, lightly laced and serrate; slight sweet fragrance. Coup de Coeur X Lady Friend. Iris au Trescols 1995.

AURA LIGHT (Barry Blyth, R. 1993). Sdlg. A106-4. TB, 34" (86 cm), EM. S. pure white; F. brilliant gold; beards mustard; ruffled. Imprimis sib X Chocolate Vanilla. Keppel 1996, Tempo Two 1996/97.

AURIC (Kevin Nilsen, R. 1990). Sdlg. 1-86-1. TB, 36" (91 cm), EM. S. golden yellow; F. white area below yellow beard, red maroon edge with yellow underlay and some fine yellow pencil edging; ruffled. Ken Ware X Light Beam. Iridescence 1990/91.

AURIC DREAMS (Stan Dexter by Marie Ingersoll, R. 1994). Sdlg. 141-83-283-B. TB, 38" (97 cm), M. S. blushed orange; F. tan orange with lighter flash; beards tangerine. Custom Made X Marmalade. Ingersoll's Iris 1995.

AURORALITA (John Weiler, R. 1980). Sdlg. 85-32-2. SDB, 10" (25 cm), EM & RE. S. light yellow, stippled and edged silvery lavender; F. pale yellow, darker yellow edge stippled very light silvery lavender; beards pale lavender; slight sweet fragrance. 82-23-1: (Twink x Third Charm) X Muchacha. Rialto 1990.

AURORA'S BLUSH (A. & D. Willott, R. 1993). Sdlg. 92-169. IB, 25" (63 cm), EM. Lightly ruffled raspberry pink, violet flush at end of beards; beards light coral, tipped light red violet. Pastel Delight X Deloris Clark. Willott 1993.

AURORA SEA (Jayne Ritchie, R. 1998). Sdlg. 91-27-53. MDB, 7" (18 cm), ML. S. hyacinth blue (RHS 91B) in center, blending to lightly greyed edge; style arms hyacinth blue, tipped antique gold; F. luminata pattern, hyacinth blue center edged tuscan yellow (162B), hafts tuscan yellow; beards gold. Chubby Cheeks X 87-1-5: (Sam x Auburn Valley). Ritchie 1998.

AURORA'S GOWN (Barbara Roberts, R. 1999). Sdlg. JA 24-15. TB, 32-34" (81-86 cm), M. S. pale cream; style arms deep lemon yellow; F. ivory; beards lemon yellow, pale cream at end; ruffled; slight lemon fragrance. Jaunty Aire X Crystal Glitters.

AURORA'S VEIL (Carole Vossen, R. 1992). Sdlg. 2-56. AB (OGB+), 16" (41 cm), EM. S. palest lilac, veined slightly darker, rose buff midrib; style arms golden tan; F. buff with inconspicuous veining rosier in center, maroon black lance-shaped signal; beards gold. Macedonia X Bethlehem Star. Aril Society 1992.

AUSPICIOUS (Jim & Vicki Craig, R. 1994). Sdlg. C38V36. IB, 26" (67 cm), L. S. light blue blending to medium purple in center, bronzy midrib area; F. dark grape purple center blending to medium purple edge; beards bronze, tipped medium purple; ruffled. ((Odyssey x Maroon Caper) x (Chapeau x (Sacred Mountain x *I. aphylla* "Werckmeister"))) X 11R4, Reformation sib. J. & V. Craig 1994.

AUSSIE CHALLENGE (Graeme Grosvenor, R. 1996). Sdlg. R5-3. TB, 36" (91 cm), ML. Purple self; beards blue violet. Silverado X Dusky Challenger. Rainbow Ridge 1996/97.

AUSTRIAN GARNETS (William Maryott, R. 1991). Sdlg. L120BST. TB, 39" (99 cm), M. S. reddish black (RHS 187A) with metallic sheen; F. same with lighter (77A) metallic center; self beards tipped brown; ruffled. F89B: (Seeing Red x Maroon Bells) X J61BST: (F89B x G144A: ((Malaysia x San Jose) x Ghio 76-241P: ((Louise Watts sib x ((((Commentary x Claudia Rene) x Claudia Rene) x Ponderosa) x (Ponderosa x New Moon))) x Homecoming Queen))). Maryott 1991.

AUSTRIAN VIOLET (Eric & Bob Tankesley-Clarke, R. 1994). SPEC, 10" (25 cm), E. Dark reddish violet self; beards blue; slight sweet fragrance. Collected; distributed by Hanselmayer prior to 1960 and in commerce as *I. aphylla* H10.

AUTUMN ACCENT (Schreiner, R. 1996). Sdlg. Z 720-A. TB, 37" (94 cm), ML. Golden yellow (RHS 14A) self; beards deep golden yellow orange; lightly ruffled. S 946-B: (Tut's Gold x N 364-1: ((New Moon x E 1451-A: (Sunsite x ((M708-1 x Trim) x (Autumn Brown x Brass Accents sib)))) x ((Sun Miracle sib x Kingdom) x Moon River))) X Golden Ecstasy. Schreiner 1996.

AUTUMN CIRCUS (Ben Hager, R. 1990). Sdlg. RE4889StpPc. TB, 34" (86 cm), E & RE (Sept.-Oct./CA). S. white, lightly peppered blue violet to solid edge; style arms deep violet; F. white, bold lines radiating from white beard, blue violet plicata edge. T3711Pc: (Space Odyssey x Socialite) X Earl of Essex. Melrose 1990.

AUTUMN CLOUDS (Ben Hager, R. 1990). Sdlg. RE4384BlWh. TB, 45" (114 cm), M & RE (Sept.-Oct./CA). Lightly ruffled pale blue, fading to blue white; beards blue white. T3532LtBl: (White Elephant sib x Avalon Bay) X Welcome Aboard sib. Melrose 1990.

AUTUMN EMBERS (Chuck Chapman, R. 1996). Sdlg. 89-4-2. SDB, 12" (31 cm), L & RE. S. clear bright yellow; style arms yellow; F. red brown, yellow throat, thin yellow edge and streak below yellow beard. Sunstrip X Triplicate. Chapman Iris 1996.

AUTUMN GRANDEUR (Ben Hager, R. 1992). Sdlg. RE4839WBl. TB, 36" (91 cm), M & RE. Medium violet blue; beards blue white. Tinted Crystal X T3532LtBl: (T3085Bl: (Geometrics x Ice Sculpture) x Avalon Bay). Melrose 1993.

AUTUMN HARBOR (George Sutton, R. 1996). Sdlg. 4-128. TB, 37" (94 cm), EM & RE. S. and style arms wistaria blue (RHS 92C); F. gentian blue (94D); beards wistaria blue faintly tipped yellow; ruffled; slight spicy fragrance. Scented Nutmeg X Faithfulness. Sutton 1997.

AUTUMN HARVEST (Graeme Grosvenor, R. 1999). Sdlg. V53-7. TB, 36" (91 cm), EM. S. golden buff, lightly veined red; F. red brown, golden buff rim; beards tangerine. Rustler X Bogota.

AUTUMN MAPLE (John Weiler, R. 1992). Sdlg. 88-22-7RE. SDB, 11" (28 cm), EM & RE. S. medium pinkish orange; F. slightly darker; beards dark orange; slight sweet fragrance. Rainbow Sherbet X Blitz. Rialto 1992.

AUTUMN PAGEANT (Franklin Carr, R. 1990). Sdlg. 86-6. TB, 38" (97 cm), EM. S. light brown with yellow infusion, light violet midrib; F. white ground, light brown and yellow halo with light violet plicata markings, light yellow brown edge, darker yellow brown on shoulders, violet line from tip of yellow brown beard to edge; slight sweet fragrance. Burgundy Brown X Sterling Prince. Carr 1993.

AUTUMN PRINCE (Ron Busch, R. 1991). Sdlg. 8391/2. TB, 36" (91 cm), M. S. white blushed lavender, copper gold center veining; F. tan, deeper toward hafts, violet blush below yellow beards. Parentage unknown. Busch 1992.

AUTUMN SONG (Adolf Volfovich-Moler, R. 1997). Sdlg. V-162. TB, 43" (110 cm), EM. Ruffled and laced orange self; beards yellow orange; slight fragrance. Fresno Calypso X Askiya. Volfovich-Moler 1999.

AUTUMN THUNDER (George Sutton, R. 1999). Sdlg. H-88. TB, 37" (94 cm), EML & RE. S. and style arms violet blue (RHS 85A); F. deep blue violet (86C), darker toward edge; beards methyl violet (85C); ruffled; slight musky fragrance. Star Master X Stingray.

AUTUMN TRYST (John Weiler, R. 1993). Sdlg. 86-118-1RE. TB, 34" (86 cm), EM & RE. S. white, shot, stippled and edged rosy lavender; F. white, edged rosy lavender; beards pale yellow; slight sweet fragrance. Lilac Stitchery X Earl of Essex. Rialto 1993.

AUTUMN YEARS (Allan Ensminger, R. 1995). Sdlg. 90-47. TB, 33" (84 cm), M. S. egyptian buff (HCC 407/3), streaked and splashed rhodamine purple (29/3); style arms chrome yellow (605/1); F. egyptian buff with chrome yellow hafts, rhodamine purple streaks and splashes; beards chrome yellow (605). Isn't This Something X Goodbye Heart. Varigay 1996.

AVAILABLE (Mary Dunn, R. 1995). Sdlg. M939X. TB, 36" (91 cm), M. S. white ground, wide lilac violet plicata band; style arms pastel lilac violet; F. white ground, wide heavy lilac band; beards pale yellow. Go Around X Fiction. M.A.D. Iris 1996.

AVALANCHE EXPRESS (Chad Harris, R. 1999). Sdlg. 91JA1. JI (9 F.), 44" (112 cm), M. Bone white, signal yellow (RHS 2C); style arms heavy cream yellow (2D). Frosted Pyramid X Hagoromo.

AVALON SUNSET (Schreiner, R. 1994). Sdlg. DD 833-1. TB, 36" (91 cm), ML. Ruffled orange (RHS 23A); beards tangerine. Fresno Flash X Z 403-A: (S 656-1: ((Pink Pinafore x (Oraglow x unknown)) x (Something Else x (G 1212-A: ((Golden Ice x Celestial Glory) x Flaming Star) x Gold Trimmings))) x S 494-C: (Vanity x (G 1292-B: (((N364-1 x Whole Cloth) x Prairie Clover) x Distant Chimes) x Loudoun Charmer))). Schreiner 1994.

AVE (Chet Tompkins, R. 1997). Sdlg. 93-82. TB, 38-39" (96-99 cm), ML-VL. Heavily ruffled white self, F. with enamel finish; beards white. (inv. Ave Maria, One Clear Call x ((Frost Alert x Fine China) x (Cynthia Ann x Winter Watch))) X Cloud Kingdom. Fleur de Lis 1997.

AVELLINE (John C. Taylor, R. 1997). Sdlg. UL 15-4. LA, 39" (100 cm), ML. S. marble purple, darker central line; style arms purple and greyed red; F. purple, edge fading to lighter purple, signal yellow. Dancing Vogue X Dural Dreamtime. Rainbow Ridge 1997/98.

AVENGING WARRIOR (Bryce Williamson, R. 1995). Sdlg. WKAA-1. TB, 38" (97 cm), EM. S. mahogany red, shaded mahogany brown; style arms mahogany red; F. mahogany red with big cherry red-black highlights, hafts mahogany brown; beards bronze, yellow at end; lightly ruffled. Warrior King X Avenging Angel.

AVOCA MIST (Heather Pryor, R. 1999). Sdlg. 38/90-1. LA, 48" (122 cm), E. S. white, mauve line signal; style arms white; F. lavender pink, white rim, darker mauve veining, orange line signal; ruffled. Dural White Butterfly X Jet Ace.

AWAJISHIMA (Yoshio Mitsuda by Society for Japanese Irises, R. 1994). JI (6 F.), 36" (90 cm), M. Red violet veined white; style arms white, tinted red violet, red violet crests. Parentage unknown. Mitsuda 1962.

AWAKENING (Duane Meek, R. 1994). Sdlg. 287-1-7. TB, 35" (89 cm), ML. S. deep pink with slight lavender infusion; F. pink, lightening to ivory from beard to slightly above lower rim, soft tan hint at hafts; beards henna, lavender blue at end; ruffled; slight sweet fragrance. Silver Fox X 307-2-2: (Blushing Pink x Beverly Sills). D & J Gardens 1994.

AWAKENING DREAMS (Barry Blyth, R. 1999). Sdlg. D69-8. TB, 35" (89 cm), ML. S. pastel pink; F. lighter, shading to pinkish white center; beards white, white and tangerine in throat. Letter From Paris X Spring Tidings. Tempo Two 1999/2000.

AWESOME (Chet Tompkins, R. 1990). Sdlg. 85-14. TB, 39-40" (99-102 cm), ML-VL. Heavily ruffled lilac rose; beards geranium red; slight sweet fragrance. (((Christmas Time x Emissary) x (Sky Kissed x Easy Grace)) x (Scintillating Lady x Karen)) X (Angel's Touch x Extravagant). Fleur de Lis 1990.

AZAU (Sergey Loktev, R. 1999). Sdlg. 94-L15E-L38. SDB, 13" (33 cm), ML-VL. S. light yellow; style arms pale violet, crests pale yellow; F. mustard yellow, veined darker, hafts and below beard marked white; beards orange, end pale blue with hairs tipped yellow. Jade Stone X unknown.

AZIAT (Adolf Volfovich-Moler, R. 1995). Sdlg. V-6. TB, 39" (100 cm), M. S. light orange; F. purplish crimson, edged orange; beards yellow; ruffled, laced. Rippling Waters X Broadway Star. Volfovich-Moler 1993.

AZTEC BURST (Barry Blyth, R. 1993). Sdlg. Z63-1. TB, 38" (97 cm), VE-EM. S. white; F. apricot to light orange; beards apricot tangerine. W117-1: ((Alpine Journey x Beachgirl) x (Beachgirl x ((Tranquil Star x Coral Strand) x (Persian Smoke x Chimbolam)))) X Chocolate Vanilla. Tempo Two 1993/94.

AZUMA KAGAMI (Kamo Nursery by Society for Japanese Irises, R. 1999). JI (6 F.), 36" (91 cm), M. White with violet veining; style arms violet, crests edged lighter. Parentage unknown. Kamo Nursery 1987.

AZURE ANGEL (Graeme Grosvenor, R. 1993). Sdlg. R6-2. TB, 36" (91 cm), EM. S. light blue, violet midrib; F. dark blue, light blue rim; beards white; ruffled. Silverado X Snowbrook. Rainbow Ridge 1993/94.

AZURE HEAVEN (Donald Delmez, R. 1996). Sdlg. DB-1. JI (6 F.), 33" (84 cm), M. Ruffled sky blue, small yellow signal; style arms white, blue-tipped, multiple. "Sakuraku" X self. Delmez Gardens 1996.

AZURE ICICLE (Bernard Hamner by Shepard Iris Garden, R. 1993). Sdlg. 87-06. TB, 40" (102 cm), E. S. icy blue white; F. blue white, ruffled deep blue edge; beards white, tipped blue. Dutch Girl X Glistening Icicle. Hamner Iris, Shepard Iris 1993.

AZURE PUFF (A. & D. Willott, R. 1990). Sdlg. 89-19. SDB, 11½" (29 cm), EM. Lightly ruffled pale blue; beards light blue. 84-150: (Blue Surf x Cindy Mitchell) X Pilgrims' Choice.

AZURE REPRISE (Walter Moores, R. 1994). Sdlg. 88-16. TB, 34" (86 cm), EM & RE (Oct./ MS). Sky blue, yellow hafts; beards white, tipped yellow; slight sweet fragrance. Desiderata X White Reprise. Moores 1999.

AZURE SEA (Chet Tompkins, R. 1993). Sdlg. 115C. TB, 34" (86 cm), ML. Smooth deep dark azure blue; beards mustard. (((Fleet Admiral x Babbling Brook) x Radiant Bride) x (Sapphire Shore x Restless Waves)) X Sheer Bliss. Fleur de Lis 1993.

AZURE WHIR (John Durrance, R. 1992). Sdlg. D83-3. TB, 35" (89 cm), E. Ruffled light blue grey; beards light yellow, tipped blue. Lady X X Betty Simon. Long 1992.

AZZURRA (Augusto Bianco, R. 1994). Sdlg. 114. TB, 37" (93 cm), M. S. medium azure blue; style arms clear blue; F. medium azure blue; beards clear blue, strong yellow in throat; lightly ruffled; slight sweet fragrance. Olympiad X Shipshape. Contemporary 1996.

BAANAPE (Ladislav Muska, R. 1999). Sdlg. 98-QGCM-02. TB, 35" (89 cm), M. S. pale lavender orchid; style arms light amber, washed lilac; F. vanilla, deeper lavender orchid plicata markings; beards yellow; ruffled, lightly laced; pronounced fragrance. ((Queen in Calico x Graffiti) x Colortart) X Mezzotinto. Muska 1999.

BAB BABBILI (Ladislav Muska, R. 1995). Sdlg. HLMP-09. TB, 37" (94 cm), ML. S. pastel creamy cinnamon; F. lilac lavender, cocoa brown rim; beards orange; heavily laced; sweet fragrance. Honey Lace X Michigan Pride. Muska 1992.

BABBLING BROOK (Keith Keppel, TB, R. 1965). Correction of introductory data: Keppel 1966.

BABIYE LETO (Adolf Volfovich-Moler, R. 1995). Sdlg. 139. TB, 35" (90 cm), M. S. light orange blended pale violet; F. crimson, pale orange edge; beards yellow; heavily ruffled, laced. Pink Sleigh X Vostochny Ornament. Volfovich-Moler 1997.

BABOON BOTTOM (Brad Kasperek, R. 1993). Sdlg. 89-44T. BB, 26" (66 cm), M. S. streaked and swirled medium pink (RHS 39C) and old rose (72D); F. light pink (39D) ground, streaked medium pink and old rose with random swirls of off-white (155C), red purple (72B) dotting on edge of shoulders; beards tangerine, tipped rose pink; ruffled, laced; slight fragrance. Date Bait X Maria Tormena. Zebra 1994.

BABS BARNETTE (Farron Campbell, R. 1997). Sdlg. 93-124B. LA, 36-42" (91-107 cm), M. S. light rose pink to mauve pink, light rose veining; style arms creamy yellow heavily flushed and tipped rose; F. rose pink to mauve rose, rose veining, yellow crest; lightly ruffled; stalks slightly zig-zag; slight fragrance. Dural White Butterfly X "Lynn Hantel". Lone Star 1997.

BABY BELLE (Larry Lauer, R. 1998). Sdlg. 92-204-3. SDB, 10" (25 cm), E & RE. S. white ground, heavy blue violet markings; style arms blue violet, lighter crest; F. light yellow to white ground, blue violet marginal markings, brown haft markings; beards blue violet at end, white and burnt orange in center, orange in throat; slight sweet fragrance. Chubby Cheeks X Bountiful Harvest. Lauer's Flowers 1998.

BABY BENGAL (George Sutton, BB, R. 1989). Sutton 1990.

BABY BLANKET (Joseph Ghio, R. 1998). Sdlg. PC-179#. CA, 16" (41 cm), M. Deep pink, F. with large blue signal spot. PE-189M: (PG-177G: (PI-MIX-A, unknown, x Valet sib) x PG-154, Spanish Don sib) X PE-190N: (Greeting Card x PG-185Y: (PI-MIX-Y, unknown x PI-MIX-A, unknown)). Bay View 1998.

BABY BOOM (Monty Byers, SDB, R. 1989). Moonshine 1990.

BABY BROWN EYES (Darlene Pinegar, R. 1993). Sdlg. SSP-1-7. SDB, 9" (23 cm), EM. S. yellowish brown, edged brown; style arms yellowish brown; F. velvety rust red edged yellow brown, deep yellow hafts; beards dark orange, tipped yellow; ruffled, flared. Sunstrip X unknown. Spanish Fork 1994.

BABY CHICK (B. Charles Jenkins, R. 1992). Sdlg. C35-24A. SPU, 28-35" (71-89 cm), E. Ruffled yellow self. Struttin' X Ping and Pang (lavender blue). Shepard Iris 1992.

BABY CRYSTAL (A. & D. Willott, R. 1993). Sdlg. 91-13. MDB, 6" (15 cm), EM. S. white; F. white, aqua flush below white beard. Buttons X 79-13: (Greenlee GX-2: ((White Mite x self) x (*pumila alba* x Hanselmayer)) x Buttons).

BABY DOE TABOR (Tom Magee, R. 1999). Sdlg. 925A. SDB, 11" (28 cm), E. S. fawn tan; style arms fawn tan, blue basal shadow; F. fawn tan, slightly darker haft veins; beards pale blue tipped russet at end, russet in throat; slight musky fragrance. Billy Boy X 884B: (811C: (Sea Change x Nazette) x 854A: (Marmalade Skies x Sun Sparkle)).

BABY GRAND (Duane Meek, R. 1994). Sdlg. 69A-1-4. BB, 20-25" (51-64 cm), ML-VL. S. blue violet, midrib flushed deeper; F. white; beards blue; ruffled, heavily textured; sweet fragrance. Edge of Winter X ((Apropos x Rococo) x Blue Luster). D & J Gardens 1994.

BABY IGUANA (Hugh & Mary Thurman, R. 1995). Sdlg. 91-3-2. SDB, 10" (25 cm), M. S. and style arms light creamy green (RHS 130D); F. light creamy green (129D), chartreuse (150A) area near beard, overlaid and veined dark olive (148A); beards bronze, light purple at end; ruffled. Tiger Print X unknown. Kickapoo 1996.

BABYLONIAN FIRES (Lois Rich by James Whitely, R. 1992). Sdlg. R79-151C. AB (OGB), 31" (79 cm), ML. S. rose lavender with gold midrib; F. rosy tone of orange mahogany, black mulberry signal; beards yellow. R75-160B: (((K55-9A x (*I. lortetii* x *I. auranitica*) x (W83-O x *I. barnumae*))) x Campus Flirt) x ((Kerr 56-4-0 x (*I. susiana* x OY40)) x Snoqualmie) X R73-175F: (R71-84M: ((Kelita Adah x JGA-AM) x (Welcome Reward x ((Bagdad Beauty x Orchid and Flame) x Kalifa Hirfa))) x R71-84D, sib). Aril Patch 1992.

BABY PRINCE (Lloyd Zurbrigg, R. 1994). Sdlg. KK 20A. SDB, 10" (25 cm), VE & RE (fall). Violet self; beards violet, tipped yellow. Plum Wine X Baby Blessed. Friendship 1995.

BABY'S NOOK (Lloyd Zurbrigg, R. 1999). Sdlg. NN 32B Last. TB, 29" (74 cm), VL. Apricot self; beards tangerine apricot, large apricot flounce. Flying X Godsend.

BABY TALK (Chet Tompkins, R. 1997). Sdlg. 94-78-3. BB, 22" (56 cm), ML. S. and style arms bisque white, allover flush of lilac peach and gilt; F. blended peach, gilt, lilac and pink over bisque; beards blue, tipped mustard yellow. Courtin' Time X inv. Punch, Judy, Cat Nap, Intermission. Fleur de Lis 1997.

BABY VENUS (A. & D. Willott, R. 1996). Sdlg. 91-23. MDB, 5" (13 cm), EM. S. and style arms pale yellow; F. light yellow blending to pale yellow edge; beards cream, yellow in throat; lightly ruffled. Gold Canary X Buttons. Willott 1996.

BACHELOR BOY (Barry Blyth, R. 1998). Sdlg. D90-2. BB, 24" (61 cm), ML. S. soft mushroom to oyster, fine cream veining; F. light burgundy magenta, 1/8" mushroom to oyster edge; beards blackish bronze. A165-1: (U83-A: (Edge of Winter x London Lord) x X70-A: (Magharee x Shoop 80-2: (So Rare x (Ringo x Color Bash)))) X B162-3, Foreign Knight sib. Tempo Two 1998/99.

BACHELOR PARTY (Paul Black, R. 1999). Sdlg. A500-XX. TB, 34" (86 cm), ML. S. and style arms medium pink; F. white center, with pink hafts, band and texture veining; beards tangerine; heavily ruffled; slight sweet fragrance. Sensuality X Romantic Mood. Mid-America 1999.

BACI (Barry Blyth, R. 1996). Sdlg. D21-7. SDB, 14" (36 cm), EM. Bright yellow, F. with soft olive signal around beard; beards lavender white, burnt tangerine in throat. Celsius X B34-2, Say Hello sib. Tempo Two 1996/97.

BACK HOME (T. J. Betts, R. 1993). Sdlg. 826JB. LA, 45" (114 cm), E. Ruffled blue violet (RHS 88B), green and yellow signals; style arms silvery green, lacy violet crests. Ila Nunn X tan sdlg.

BACK STREET AFFAIR (Sterling Innerst, R. 1996). Sdlg. 3973-6. TB, 34" (86 cm), M. S. medium yellow; F. coffee to milky brown, narrow yellow border; beards brilliant gold; slight sweet fragrance. Springhouse X Mixed Doubles. Innerst 1997.

BACKWATER BLUES (Harold Stahly, R. 1999). Sdlg. 94-17. TB, 35" (89 cm), EM. Medium blue violet (RHS 88A), white vein network extending to 1/4" marginal band of deeper color; style arms medium blue violet; beards blue, bronze in throat. Baltic Star X Painted Plic. Stahly 1999.

BACKYARD KISSES (Michael Moller, R. 1999). Sdlg. LO/LO/RB-1. SDB, 13" (33 cm), M. Light tangerine orange self; beards bright red. Obligato X Orange Tiger.

BAD CAD (Tom Burseen, R. 1991). Sdlg. 7-31A. TB, 33" (84 cm), EM. S. bright rusty orange (RHS 170B); F. cream yellow ground, heavily marked and streaked dark maroon red (184A), more concentrated at edge; beards gold; ruffled; musky fragrance. 4-74: (Prosperity x Sun Toasted) X 3-214: (Pencil Sketch x Porta Villa). T.B.'s Place 1992.

BAD GUYS (Chet Tompkins, R. 1995). Sdlg. 90-14. TB, 38" (97 cm), ML-VL. S. deep creamy chamois, greenish infusion; style arms orchid; F. orchid cerise, shoulders deeper; beards yellow lemon, tipped orchid. (Spring Sharing x Heavenly Body) X Revival Meeting sib. Fleur de Lis 1995.

BAGDAD'S FOLLY (Lois Rich by James Whitely, R. 1992). Sdlg. R80-141B. AB (OGB), 30" (76 cm), M. S. off-white with pale orchid veining, faint bright yellow brushing on midrib; style arms cream; F. cream ground heavily veined brown, orange rust signal; beards dark tan. Ancient Scrolls X R74-119B: (((Kerr 59-9A x (I. atrofusca x Kerr 53-44DF)) x Marx 633A) x (Welcome Reward x ((Bagdad Beauty x Orchid and Flame) x Kalifa Hirfa))). Aril Patch 1992.

BAGHWAN (Chet Tompkins, R. 1990). Sdlg. 83-81. TB, 38" (97 cm), EML. White, pale lemon tint deep in throat; beards pale lemon over white; slight sweet fragrance. (((Tinsel Town x Sterling Silver) x (Radiant Bride x Coco)) x (Radiant Bride x Angel Unawares)) X (((Radiant Bride x Angel Unawares) x (Sterling Silver x Wedding Vow)) x (Crown Sterling x Wedding Vow)). Fleur de Lis 1990.

BAHAMA MAMA (James McWhirter by Abram Feuerstein, R. 1999). Sdlg. 94F. TB, 32" (81 cm), M. Bright orange self; beards bright orange. Gratuity X Voltage. Stockton 1999.

BAIKALSEE (Vera Matthe, R. 1990). Sdlg. VM 76-28-1. TB, 36" (91 cm), M. Ruffled violet blue (RHS 93A) blending to darker (89A) in center of F.; beards violet blue (93D); slight sweet fragrance. VM 74-1-4: (Music Maker x Emerald Fountain) X Shipshape.

BAKHCHISARAISKI FONTAN (Nina Miroshnichenko, R. 1999). TB, 29" (74 cm), EML. S. and style arms pale lilac; F. blended white, lemon and lilac; beards orange, end lilac with yellow tip. Parentage unknown. Miroshnichenko 1996.

BAKLAVA (Paul Black, R. 1998). Sdlg. C 133K. SDB, 14" (36 cm), M. S. medium yellow ground, medium brown wide band, midrib and central area dotting; style arms light gold, medium brown midrib and crests; F. medium yellow, medium plum brown edge, brown haft veining; beards white at end, shading to orange gold in throat; pronounced sweet fragrance. 91260A: ((Gentle Air x Chubby Cheeks sib) x (85418A: (Caesura x (Betsey Boo x (Antique Satin x Encanto))) x 84207A: (Gigglepot x Oriental Blush))) X (Chubby Cheeks x (Gentle Air x Chubby Cheeks sib)). Mid-America 1998.

BALANÇOIRE (Jean Segui, R. 1998). TB, 35" (90 cm), E. S. greenish yellow (RHS 154D); F.

wistaria blue (RHS 92B), edged paler; beards chinese yellow (16A), white at end, with small horn. Ghio sdlg. inv. *I. balkana* X self. Iris de Thau 1981.

BALCH SPRINGS (Hooker Nichols, R. 1992). Sdlg. 8856B. TB, 36" (91 cm), ML. S. light blue; F. slightly deeper, edged lighter; beards yellow and blue; lightly ruffled; sweet fragrance. Sea of Galilee X Titan's Glory. Hillcrest 1993.

BALI NIGHTS (Kirk Strawn, R. 1993). Sdlg. 55-1985. LA, 35" (89 cm), L. Violet (RHS 83B), yellow orange signal; style arms violet. #1, unknown, X Black Gamecock. Bois d'Arc 1996.

BALLALAIKA MUSIC (Harald Mathes, R. 1992). AR (RC), 20" (51 cm), EM. S. plum ground flushed violet along midrib; F. plum ground, violet central flush intensifying in violet signal area; beards bronze; pronounced sweet fragrance. Werckmeister's Beauty X Dunshanbe. Aril Society 1992.

BALLERINA GIRL (Frederick Kerr, R. 1998). Sdlg. 901701. TB, 36" (91 cm), M. S. and style arms pink, tinted red violet; F. pink ground, lighter center, red violet plicata edge, tannish red violet hafts and veins by beard; beards tangerine salmon, white at end and base; ruffled. Anna Belle Babson X Shopper's Holiday. Rainbow Acres 1998.

BALLERINA PRINCESS (J. D. Stadler, R. 1990). Sdlg. H18/81. BB, 26" (66 cm), ML. Heavily ruffled white, 1/2" blue violet edge on F.; beards yellow; slight sweet fragrance. Celestial Dream X Dream Romance. Celestial Gardens 1991.

BALLET ANGEL (Cloyd McCord, R. 1997). Sdlg. 707. TB, 36" (91 cm), M. S. and style arms pink; F. white, 1/4" lavender marginal band; beards orange, white at end; sweet fragrance. Ballet Dreamer X Princess Maxine. McCord 1997.

BALLET DREAMER (Cloyd McCord, R. 1991). Sdlg. 85-7. TB, 36" (91 cm), E. S. light pink; F. light lavender, light pink signal; beards yellow; slight fragrance. 82-1: (Chorus Girl x Custom Made) X 84-1: (Last Call x American Sweetheart). McCord 1991.

BALLET LESSON (O. D. Niswonger, R. 1992). Sdlg. SDB 36-91. SDB, 12" (30 cm), M. Peachy pink, intensified color around beards; beards white, tipped pink. Straw Hat X Ballet Slippers. Cape Iris 1993.

BALLET MUSIC (Bryce Williamson, R. 1993). Sdlg. A-10-A. TB, 38" (97 cm), ML. Heavily ruffled dark raspberry violet; beards tangerine red; slight fragrance. Love Poem X Extravagant. Bryce Williamson 1995.

BALLET ROYALE (Vernon Wood, R. 1998). Sdlg. 92-65. TB, 32-34" (81-86 cm), M. Heavily ruffled pink self; beards tangerine. Sib to Pink Quartz. Stockton 1999.

BALLETTAENZERIN (Eberhard Fischer, R. 1993). Sdlg. 2. TB, 36" (90 cm), M. Waved, flared medium violet blue; beards violet; slight sweet fragrance. Prince Indigo X Demetria. A. Weinreich 1993.

BALLINA (Ian Barry, R. 1990). Sdlg. 87-25. TB, 35" (90 cm), M. Light orange; beards tangerine. Georgia Girl X Spanish Gift.

BAL MASQUE (Jean Cayeux, R. 1993). Sdlg. 84109 L. TB, 34" (86 cm), ML. S. pure white; F. bright pansy violet, small white flash below tangerine red beard. (Condottiere x Delphi) X (Alizes x (Condottiere x Lunar Rainbow)). Cayeux 1991.

BALOO (Mary Dunn, R. 1992). Sdlg. M87-1010A. TB, 38" (97 cm), M. Pale sky blue; self beards fading white with age. Precious Moments X Crystalyn. M.A.D. Iris 1993.

BALTIC BLUE (O. D. Niswonger, R. 1998). Sdlg. SDB 4-97. SDB, 14" (36 cm), M. Light blue, F. with olive green hafts; beards dark blue. SDB 22-91: (SDB 27-87: (Oriental Blush x unknown) x Ballet Slippers) X SDB 72-91: (Star Dancer x unknown). Cape Iris 1998.

BALTIC STAR (Harold Stahly, R. 1994). Sdlg. 88-28. TB, 34" (85 cm), M. S. deep purple black (deeper than RHS 79A), lighter area around midrib; F. same, with white wash beginning at beard and blending to solid purple black rim, hafts touched deep brown; beards deep brown violet. Wagontrail Night X Night Lady. Stahly 1994.

BAMA BABY (Frank Foster, R. 1995). Sdlg. 8784W. IB, 23" (58 cm), EM. White self; beards cream white; ruffled, flared; slight musky fragrance. Mint Ice X Alabama Bound. Long 1998.

BAMBA (Barry Blyth, R. 1994). Sdlg. A17-5. SDB, 10" (25 cm), VE-EM. S. apricot flushed pink; F. same with bluish rose violet overlay, deepening to light tan at hafts, lavender flash below burnt tangerine beard; pronounced sweet fragrance. Thundercat X X32-B: (Yipee x sib). Tempo Two 1994/95.

BANANA FRAPPE (Richard Ernst, R. 1991). Sdlg. R85-12. TB, 38" (97 cm), M. Ruffled yellow; beards yellow orange; slight sweet fragrance. Gold Cadillac X Sunday Sunshine. Cooley 1991.

BANANAS FOSTER (Kevin Vaughn, R. 1998). Sdlg. F-17-4. LA, 25-27" (63-69 cm), ML. S. bright amber, thin cinnamon edge; style arms amber, infused cinnamon, base green; F. amber, color deepening toward broad (1/2" to 3/4") cinnamon edge, rose-outlined gold signal. Heavenly Glow X Kelley's Choice.

BANBURY PAGEANT (Marjorie Brummitt, CA, R. 1976). V. H. Humphrey 1997.

BANDED ROGUE (Carl Boswell, BB, R. 1988). Adamgrove 1990.

BAND OF ANGELS (Robert Hollingworth, R. 1996). Sdlg. 91Y1A1. SIB (tet.), 31" (79 cm), ML. S. and style arms medium blue violet, reddish tinge; style arms broad, short; F. medium blue violet, large cream to gold blaze, clear cream marginal band. 84X7B2: (81A3C5: (induced tet. 79F1(T): (Dreaming Spires x unknown) x induced tet. 78G2(T): (Cambridge x unknown)) x 80X2C11 induced tet.: (Forrest McCord x 78H3, sib)) X 8706B9, Strawberry Fair sib. Windwood Gardens 1996.

BANGLES (Lynda Miller, R. 1993). Sdlg. 3791. MTB, 21" (53 cm), EM. S. medium amethyst, aging light amethyst; F. medium sapphire blue, aging light blue violet, amethyst signal; beards gold. Lucky Mistake X Rosemary's Dream. Miller's Manor 1995.

BANISH MISFORTUNE (Marty Schafer/Jan Sacks, R. 1999). Sdlg. S92-85-12. SIB, 45" (114 cm), EML. S. medium light bluebird blue (RHS 94C), veined darker (94B); style arms lighter, with dark midrib; F. lobelia blue (91B) on lower portion, veined darker, remainder covered by large signal of dark mimosa yellow (8A) on haft paling (8D) on blade, with deep purple (93A/B) veins; slight fragrance. S89-23-4: (S85-6-6: (Star Cluster x Ruffled Velvet) x Isabelle) X Snow Prince. Joe Pye Weed 1999.

BANKO-NO-KOE (Nobutsune Nishida by Society for Japanese Irises, R. 1993). JI (3 F.), 36" (90 cm), M. S. rose purple, large white center; style arms white, edged rose purple; F. rose purple, purple splashed white ground toward white halo, yellow signal. Parentage unknown. Nishida 1930.

BANTAM PRINCE (Chuck Chapman, R. 1999). Sdlg. 90-51-11. SDB, 10" (25 cm), E. Dark royal purple, F. with large black cherry spot, radiating lines; beards purple. Mary's Lamb X Bantam. Chapman Iris 1999.

BARBARA MANN (Labriano Anaya/Julian Wells by Santa Fe Iris Society, R. 1996). TB, 32" (81 cm), M. S. cream, midrib suffused light peach; F. cream to white, peach haft markings; beards gold, white at end; ruffled; pronounced sweet fragrance. Beauty Crown X Pink Riot. Iris Ranch 1992.

BARBARA MY LOVE (William Maryott, R. 1998). Sdlg. X194A. TB, 36" (91 cm), M. S. pale salmon (RHS 27A); style arms deep gold; F. white, 3/8" spanish orange (26D) band; beards yellow, orange in throat; slight sweet fragrance. S198B: (N110Yel: (Chief Redskin x Bronco Brown) x Speculator) X S216C: (Oktoberfest x Good Show). Maryott 1999.

BARBARA'S BLUE (Connell Marsh, TB, R. 1987). C. Marsh 1990.

BARBARA'S LACE (George Sutton, R. 1998). Sdlg. J-117A. TB, 36" (91 cm), ML. S. blended orient pink (RHS 36B/C), deeper on midrib; style arms orient pink; F. white, flushed orient pink (36C), deeper (36A) on shoulders; beards carrot red, orient pink at end, extending as petaloid ending in 1/2" spoon; ruffled, heavily laced; slight sweet fragrance. Tiffany Time X G-19: (Sweet Musette x Twice Thrilling).

BARBARELLA (Harald Mathes, R. 1991). Sdlg. AP-BSF. AB (OGB), 12" (30 cm), E. S. smooth gold, flushed darker at midrib; F. same, large dark mahogany signal spot and veining; beards bright yellow. Unknown regeliocyclus sdlg. X "Schokoladenherz", yellow *pumila*. Aril Society 1991.

BARCOO (John C. Taylor, R. 1997). Sdlg. UL 17-1. LA, 43" (110 cm), ML. S. and style arms rosy pink; F. rosy pink, lighter edge, yellow dagger signal. Dancing Vogue X Dural White Butterfly. Rainbow Ridge 1997/98.

BAREKET (David Shahak, R. 1992). Sdlg. S-5-81-127 III. AR (OH), 25½" (65 cm), M. S. purple violet (RHS 80C); F. red purple (71A), dark brown signal; beards black purple. *I. samariae* X (*I. mariae* x *I. hermona*). Aril Society, Tira Nurseries 1993.

BARELY THERE (Tom Burseen, R. 1993). Sdlg. 8-355A. TB, 36" (91 cm), ML. S. lemon cream (RHS 162C); style crests yellow; F. diamond dusted pale lemon white (155A) edged pale violet (85D); beards bright gold; ruffled; sweet fragrance. Planned Treasure X 5-73: (Shoreline x Capricious). T.B.'s Place 1994.

BARLEY GREEN (Evelyn Robarts, R. 1990). Sdlg. 82-55. TB, 35" (89 cm), M. Ruffled cool light straw yellow (pale green effect), greenish yellow area around medium yellow beards; slight sweet fragrance. Starfrost Pink X Winter Panorama. Stahly 1991.

BARN DANCE (Monty Byers, R. 1990). Sdlg. E45-100. TB, 35" (89 cm), EM & RE. S. medium light yellow; F. pale straw yellow, slightly deeper yellow hafts and border peppered and sanded rose brown, small white area under bright yellow beard; ruffled; slight sweet fragrance. Broadway X Spirit of Fiji. Moonshine 1991.

BARNEY'S CHOICE (Richard Kindermann, R. 1992). Sdlg. K-1019. TB, 34" (86 cm), M. S. ruffled gold; F. gold, brushed bronze; beards gold; fluted; spicy fragrance. Triple Play X (Wild Apache x Wild Jasmine). Mill Creek 1995.

BARNEY'S DELIGHT (A. & D. Willott, R. 1990). Sdlg. 84-142. SDB, 12" (31 cm), ML. Ruffled apricot, lighter around end of beard, darker hafts; beards orange, blue at tip. Oh Katz X Coral Wings. Willott 1990.

BARNUM'S WORLD (William Simon, TB, R. 1986). Stahly 1990.

BAROQUE GARDEN (Harald Moos, R. 1991). Sdlg. 87/728A. TB, 36" (90 cm), EM. S. glossy red brown; F. dark red brown; beards copper; frilled. Samurai Warrior X Queen in Calico. Schoeppinger 1992.

BAROQUE MELODY (Connell Marsh, BB, R. 1984). C. Marsh 1990.

BARR PURPLE EAST (Barr & Sons by Jennifer Hewitt, R. 1999). JI (3 F.), 47" (120 cm), M. S. bishops violet (RHS 81A) veined deep purple (83B); style arms violet (86A); F. bishops violet veined deep purple and vivid violet (89A), signal bright lemon yellow (13A/B), slightly speckled deep purple; S. spatulate, floppy; F. circular, horizontal to drooping. Parentage unknown. Barr & Sons 1938; in commerce in Britain as *I. ensata* Purple East.

BARRY J (Louise Smith, R. 1991). Sdlg. 86-33. IB, 21" (53 cm), EM. Blue lavender; beards orange, tipped white; slight sweet fragrance. Parentage unknown.

BARRY'S CHOICE (James McWhirter by Abram Feuerstein, R. 1999). TB, 34" (86 cm), M. Topaz orange, S. slightly darker, F. with pale blue white area under butterscotch orange beard. Arabian Tapestry X Role Model. Stockton 1998.

BARYSHNIA (Viacheslav Gavrilin, R. 1998). Sdlg. 6-27-3-94. TB, 34" (86 cm), ML. S. pinkish yellow; style arms yellow; F. light raspberry edged darker, narrow yellow stripes from orange red beard to edge; ruffled; slight fragrance. Fiesta Time X Starcrest. Gavrilin 1999.

BAS-BLEU (Lawrence Ransom, R. 1991). Sdlg. 86/61-2. IB, 18" (46 cm), E. Ruffled violet blue; beards blue, brushed mustard brown. Mystique X Double Lament. Iris au Trescols 1992.

BASHFUL BELLE (Mabel Framke, R. 1990). Sdlg. 85-28FM. TB, 37" (94 cm), ML. S. blended creamy beige overtoned greenish beige and copper; F. brassy beige undertoned lemon lime and deep copper; beards coppery tan. (((Mint Meringue x Cosmopolitan) x (Mint Meringue x Song Fest)) x (Emerald Echo x Exotic Wings)) X (((Aqualette x Fairy Magic) x (Song Fest x Wild Melody)) x Mauna Loa Magic). Fleur de Lis 1990.

BASHO (Shuichi Hirao by Society for Japanese Irises, R. 1993). JI (3 F.), 33" (85 cm), ML. Royal violet, yellow signal. Parentage unknown. Hirao 1956.

BASSO (Allan Ensminger, IB, R. 1989). Varigay 1990.

BASTILLE DAY (Patrick O'Connor, R. 1992). Sdlg. 81-16. LA, 42" (107 cm), M. Red violet, yellow signal; style arms light red. Ann Chowning X unknown.

BAT BOY (Joseph Ghio, R. 1995). Sdlg. PF-153R. CA, 14" (36 cm), M. S. brassy gold; F. brassy gold, mahogany signal and red watermark area over top 1/3 of petal. PI-MIX-B, unknown, X PH-242R2: (Temblor sib x ((San Gregorio x (Montara sib x Mission Santa Cruz sib)) x Villa Branciforte sib)). Bay View 1995.

BATTLE ALERT (Joseph Ghio, R. 1995). Sdlg. PF-170Z. CA, 15" (38 cm), M. Orange red, F. with near-black watercolor signal. Mission Santa Clara sib X PI-MIX-S, unknown. Bay View 1995.

BATTLE ROYAL (Joseph Ghio, R. 1993). Sdlg. 88-79-I. TB, 38" (97 cm), EM. Cherry red over apricot base; beards bronze. 85-44X: (((Praline x Lady Friend) x (Lady Friend x (Act of Love x (Ballet in Orange x 73-122Z: (Hi Top x ((Ponderosa x Travel On) x Peace Offering)))))) x ((Lady Friend sib x ((Malaysia x Carolina Honey) x 73-122Z)) x ((Entourage x Homecoming Queen) x Mulled Wine))) X 85-111V: ((((((Ponderosa x Honey Rae) x ((((Commentary x Claudia Rene) x Claudia Rene) x Ponderosa) x (Ponderosa x New Moon))) x Homecoming Queen) x ((Ballet in Orange x 73-122Z) x Blaze of Fire)) x Impressionist sib) x 83-110 red, Olden Days sib). Bay View 1994.

BAUBLES AND BEADS (Lynda Miller, R. 1996). Sdlg. 400293. MTB, 25-26" (63-66 cm), ML. S.

bright gold; style arms golden yellow; F. red black, slight haft stippling; beards dark gold; slight musky fragrance. Disco Jewel X Manisses. Miller's Manor 1997.

BAWDY HOUSE (John Marchant, R. 1992). Sdlg. 7987. CA, 14" (36 cm), ML. S. buffy yellow tan; F. same, with red purple wash within 1/16" of edge, diffused signal; ruffled. Sdlg. X sdlg.

BAYBERRY BABY (Sharon McAllister, R. 1992). AB (OGB), 16" (42 cm), EM. S. pale chartreuse; F. chartreuse, lightly washed brown, giving olive green effect overall; beards rich brown. Gene's Little Secret X Rose of Sharon. Aril Society 1992.

BAY CITY (Robert Dunn, R. 1996). Sdlg. B2126A. TB, 36" (91 cm), EML. Dark violet blue self; beards light violet, deeper tips. Larry Gaulter X B1003A: (Allstar x Busy Being Blue). M.A.D. Iris 1999.

BAYOU ANGEL (Frank Chowning by Henry Rowlan, R. 1990). Sdlg. 85-FC-17. LA, 32" (81 cm), ML. S. rose pink with ray signal pattern; F. rose pink, green lancehead signal edged yellow; ruffled. This I Love X unknown. Comanche Acres 1991.

BAYOU BANDIT (Jeff Weeks by Farron Campbell, R. 1998). SPEC (*fulva*), 28-36" (71-91 cm), EM. Light chocolate, pink and lavender tones, silvery glaze; F. with bright yellow crest signal; style arms soft yellow, flushed chocolate. Collected near Denham Springs, LA. Lone Star 1998.

BAYOU BLUEBIRD (Henry Rowlan by Comanche Acres, R. 1999). Sldg. 88-LA-16. LA, 34" (86 cm), M. Lightly ruffled bluebird blue, F. with large yellow steeple signal with green center. Parentage unknown. Comanche Acres 1999.

BAYOU BORSCH (Kevin Vaughn, R. 1996). Sdlg. E-18-1. LA, 38-40" (97-102 cm), ML. S. and style arms dark beetroot purple; F. same, velvety texture, tiny obscure orange yellow line signal; ruffled; slight musky fragrance. Extraordinaire X Red Velvet Elvis.

BAYOU DAWN (Henry Rowlan, R. 1992). Sdlg. 89LA40. LA, 34" (86 cm), EM. S. spinel red (RHS 54C); style arms and crests yellow; F. darker spinel red (54A), inconspicuous yellow line signal; ruffled. Bronze Trophy X Amber Dawn. Comanche Acres 1993.

BAYOU FOUNTAIN (Patrick O'Connor, R. 1992). Sdlg. 81-1. LA, 36" (91 cm), EM. Blue purple with some white streaking near signal; signals yellow on white ground; style arms dark red purple. Parentage unknown. Bois d'Arc 1994.

BAYOU TIGER (Kirk Strawn, R. 1993). Sdlg. BB1984. LA, 35" (89 cm), L. S. red purple (RHS 71A); style arms yellow (3C); F. greyed orange (163C) veined brown (166B), orange (24A) signal. Charles Arny III X Counterpoise. Bois d'Arc 1996.

BAY WATCH (Robert Dunn, R. 1995). Sdlg. B1058-A. TB, 37" (94 cm), M. S. white, pale blue stain at extreme top, slight midrib stain; F. white, tiny plum purple rim; beards white, barely tipped violet. Eagle's Flight X Trace. M.A.D. Iris 1997.

BEACH BABY (Richard Tasco, R. 1994). Sdlg. 91-18. SDB, 12" (30 cm), ML. Yellow, with red wash extending halfway down F.; beards lavender blue, gold in throat; slight musky fragrance. Bisbee X Tender Tears. Superstition 1995.

BEACHES (Frank Foster, R. 1995). Sdlg. 8412CY. TB, 34" (86 cm), EM. S. cream to pale yellow, slightly darker edge; F. cream, 1/2" medium yellow border; beards cream yellow; ruffled; slight sweet fragrance. Entourage X Winter White.

BEACH SAMBA (Akihiko Terada, R. 1998). Sdlg. S101-89-1. TB, 36" (91 cm), ML. Lightly ruffled light orange self; beards bright orange; slight musky fragrance. Fireside Glow X Good Show. Roris 1998.

BEACHWOOD BUZZ (A. & D. Willott, R. 1998). Sdlg. W91-117. MDB, 6" (15 cm), M. Ruffled butterscotch gold, F. with small red brown spot; style arms butterscotch; beards light blue at end, yellow in throat. Poet Laureate X Buzz Bee. Willott 1998.

BE A DREAM (O. D. Niswonger, R. 1992). Sdlg. 77-89. TB, 35" (89 cm), ML. Warm white, F. with golden hafts; beards yellow; rippled, waved. Coral Light X 47-83: (Premonition x Coral Beauty). Cape Iris 1992.

BEADWORK (Sharon McAllister, R. 1995). Sdlg. 91-21-13. AB (OGB-), 30" (76 cm), M. S. variegated white and yellow, dotted and veined soft mulberry; style arms soft yellow, crest and midrib mulberry; F. color of S., with heavy rust veining radiating from yellow orange beard and linear violet signal. Anon X Boaz. McAllister 1995.

BEAKY WIT (Ladislav Muska, R. 1999). Sdlg. 98-MGSC-03. TB, 34" (86 cm), L. S. bright cream; style arms bright gold; F. white, striped and edged cream; beards orange, orchid horn; ruffled, lightly laced; sweet fragrance. (Mys Horn x (Geniality x Sky Hooks)) X "Cream Secrets". Muska 1999.

BEALE STREET (Kevin Vaughn, R. 1996). Sdlg. D-45-1. LA, 40-44" (102-112 cm), EML. Ruffled intense dark blue (RHS 96B), F. texture-veined deeper (96A), pale primrose yellow (4A) signal outlined black; slight musky fragrance. Bellevue Coquette X Marie Dolores. Contemporary 1997.

BEARDED WONDER (Evelyn Robarts, R. 1996). Sdlg. 531. TB, 30-32" (76-81 cm), M. S. and style arms greyed pale yellow; F. greyed pale yellow, horizontal to slightly cupped; beards pale yellow, violet midsection, bright coral in throat, ending in variably colored elevated flounce; ruffled; slight sweet fragrance. Trendy X Sky Hooks. Stahly 1997.

BEATRICE CHERBUY (Jean Cayeux, R. 1991). Sdlg. 8006 D. TB, 36" (91 cm), M. S. white lilac; F. sparkling lilac; beards tangerine red. Condottiere X Lunar Rainbow. Cayeux 1987.

BEAT THE HEAT (Tom Burseen, R. 1995). Sdlg. 1-17B. TB, 35" (89 cm), EM. S. and style arms light lavender blue, darker midrib; F. violet (RHS 87A); beards mustard; ruffled. Polar Seas X 9-358A: ((Bubble Bath x Titan's Glory) x Bluid). T.B.'s Place 1996.

BEAUMARIS (Harry Foster, SIB, R. 1988). V. H. Humphrey 1995.

BEAUSOLEIL (Patrick O'Connor, R. 1999). Sdlg. 82-11. LA, 40-42" (102-107 cm), M. S. light pink, broad white lengthwise band; style arms cream with darker pink band along lighter midrib, tips pink; F. pink, white veining more pronounced around small yellow line signal. Cajun Caper X unknown.

BEAUTIFUL ACCENT (Donald Delmez, R. 1994). Sdlg. MBSW-1. JI (6 F.), 33" (84 cm), M. Medium blue splashed white, deep yellow signal; style arms tipped blue, splashed white, white midrib. Kontaki-On X "Sakuraku". Delmez Gardens 1994.

BEAUTIFUL BABY (Chet Tompkins, R. 1990). Sdlg. 85-7. IB, 24-26" (61-66 cm), EML. Ruffled lemon to icy yellow with white F. blaze; beards yellow. (Dearly Do x (Grace Note x Indeed)) X Elegant Era. Fleur de Lis 1990.

BEAUTIFUL FORTY (Tomas Tamberg, R. 1993). Sdlg. SSTT39. SIB (sino-sib), 28-36" (70-90 cm), M. Near-white, uniformly veined darker. SSTT9: (Mirza Citronella x unknown) X SSTT20: (*I. clarkei* x unknown). Schoeppinger, Tamberg 1993.

BEAUTIFUL VISION (Schreiner, TB, R. 1989). Schreiner 1990.

BEAUTY CIRCLE (Mary Dunn by Robert Dunn, R. 1999). Sdlg. M2148-D. TB, 36" (91 cm), EM. S. and style arms orchid; F. white ground, hafts and narrow edge of orchid dotting; beards tangerine; heavily ruffled, laced; slight sweet fragrance. Patterns X Power Surge.

BEAUTY SLEEP (Kevin Nilsen, R. 1992). Sdlg. 26-87-1. TB, 34" (87 cm), EM. S. cream with light yellow veining; style arms white and light yellow; F. white with light yellow edge; beards yellow; heavily ruffled. Cloudburst X Wings of Dreams. Iridescence 1992/93.

BECALMED (Barry Blyth, R. 1993). Sdlg. Z35-1. IB, 24" (61 cm), ML. Soft pastel apricot, slightly deeper F. overlay; beards tangerine, outer 1/2" white. (Precious Moments x London Lord) X Chanted. Tempo Two 1993/94.

BECKY'S BONNET (Sandra Lemmer, R. 1995). Sdlg. T911. TB, 35" (89 cm), EM. S. lemon yellow; F. grape purple, grey white marginal band, white haft rays; beards orange. Merry Madrigal X Noon Siesta. Lemmer 1998.

BEDECKED NETS (Ladislav Muska, R. 1999). Sdlg. QCFG-02. TB, 36" (91 cm), M. S. yellow ground sanded cinnamon brown; style arms light cinnamon brown; F. yellow, maroon plicata washing; beards orange; slight fragrance. (((Queen in Calico x Zuzana) x (Calicoball x Rei Momo)) x (Funny Bird x Graffiti)) X Casbah. Muska 1998.

BEDEVIL (Barry Blyth, R. 1998). Sdlg. E74-4. IB, 25" (63 cm), EM. S. pinkish mushroom, infused soft burgundy; F. rich plush burgundy; beards burnt tangerine, 3/8" lavender end; pronounced sweet fragrance. Hold Me X B164-1: (Chocolate Vanilla x Electrique). Tempo Two 1998/99.

BEDFORD LILAC (Bennett Jones, R. 1990). Sdlg. 362-1. SDB, 11" (28 cm), M. Flax blue (HCC 642/1), deeper blended F. spot; self beards. Sapphire Jewel X 297-1: ((Blithe Blue x ((Meadow Moss x 175) x (Gingerbread Man x Meadow Moss))) x ((Gingerbread Man x Meadow Moss) x (Meadow Moss x Kentucky Bluegrass))). Bennett Jones 1991.

BED IN PEPPERING (Ladislav Muska, R. 1999). Sdlg. GQCZ-03. TB, 38" (97 cm), M. S. light cream vanilla; style arms cream yellow; F. cream vanilla, edged and peppered cinnamon; beards light orange; slight fragrance. Graffiti X ((Queen in Calico x Zuzana) x Change of Pace). Muska 1998.

BEDROOM EYES (Joseph Ghio, R. 1998). Sdlg. PC-185F4. CA, 12" (31 cm), ML. Peach self, F. with neon violet signal. PE-190N: (Greeting Card x PG-185Y: (PI-MIX-Y, unknown, x PI-MIX-A, unknown)) X PE-205W2: (PG-185bo x PG-172, Charter Member sib). Bay View 1998.

BEE FLAMENCO (Monique Dumas-Quesnel, R. 1992). Sdlg. 91-X-versata-O. SPEC-X (versata),

43" (110 cm), M. S. light mauve (RHS 76A); F. light mauve (86C), purple (83B) halo around deep yellow-veined signal; slight sweet fragrance. EX-CO-MR-14 *versicolor* X purple *ensata* sdlg. Dominion Seed House, Horticlub 1999.

BEE MUSED (Paul Black, R. 1997). Sdlg. A504A. SDB, 11" (28 cm), M. Medium purple, F. with white area around large lavender beard; slight sweet fragrance. Parentage unknown. Mid-America 1997.

BEESEA (B. Charles Jenkins, R. 1993). Sdlg. BJ27F. SPU, 45" (114 cm), EM. Purple with large creamy signal patch blending to purple. Lively One X Now This. Shepard Iris 1993.

BEE'S KNEES (Barry Blyth, R. 1994). Sdlg. A44-20. SDB, 12" (30 cm), ML. S. medium pink with lavender flush, fine wire edging of gold glitter; F. creamy white, blended pink plicata stitching with lavender flush, brown tones and line radiating from beard; beards white, burnt bronze on outer 1/2"; slight sweet fragrance. V7-5, Gigolette sib, X Chanted. Tempo Two 1994/95.

BEFRIEND (Barry Blyth, R. 1998). Sdlg. E124-2. TB, 40" (102 cm), M. S. cream to tan; F. deeper tan, rose influence, 3/8" light creamy tan inner edge, 1/8" deeper tan outer edge; beards tangerine; sweet fragrance. Plume d'Or X About Town. Tempo Two 1998/99.

#BEGINNER'S LUCK (Mrs. W. A. Gates, TB, R. 1948). Not introduced; name released.

BEGINNER'S LUCK (John Pozniak by Maryott's Gardens, R. 1998). Sdlg. B16. TB, 37" (94 cm), M. Orchid (RHS 85A) self; beards orchid; slight sweet fragrance. Skating Party X Orchidarium. Maryott 1998.

BEGINNINGS (Joyce Meek, R. 1992). Sdlg. 473-1-3. TB, 36" (91 cm), M. S. almost solidly stitched rosy lavender; F. white, narrow rosy violet plicata band; beards white, tipped rusty orange; ruffled; slight fragrance. Deanna Darcy X Candace. D & J Gardens 1992.

BEG TO DIFFER (Frederick Kerr, R. 1999). Sdlg. 9493B. TB, 36" (91 cm), M. S. usually absent, lemon yellow if present; style arms lemon yellow suffused blue violet; F. medium blue violet; beards blue; ruffled, flared. Stairway to Heaven X Cosmic Wave. Rainbow Acres 1999.

BE HAPPY (J. T. Aitken, R. 1990). Sdlg. 82M12-9. SDB, 9" (23 cm), ML & RE. S. pale blue white; F. medium yellow; beards pale blue white; slight fragrance. Windbeam X Dixie Pixie. Aitken's Salmon Creek 1990.

BEHIND CLOSED DOORS (Sterling Innerst, R. 1996). Sdlg. 4034-5. TB, 36" (91 cm), M. S. hot pink; style arms pink; F. hot pink, irregular color application, purplish shoulder stripes; beards pink, tipped white; slight spicy fragrance. Jitterbug X 3348-2: ((Capricious x Colortart) x Queen in Calico). Innerst 1997.

BEHOLD YOUR MUSE (Richard Ernst, R. 1998). Sdlg. NG106-1A-2. TB, 38" (97 cm), M. S. and style arms medium blue violet; F. near-white with faint violet cast, very pale yellow rim; beards deep yellow. G106-1A: (Hula Girl x self) X JF168-2-6, Gentle Fellow sib. Cooley 1998.

BEIKOKU (Robert Fabel-Ward, R. 1990). JI (3 F.), 37" (94 cm), L. S. white; F. light violet, veined white. Yuki-no-Yama X self.

BEING BUSY (Ben Hager, R. 1992). Sdlg. SD4978Y/MrSp. SDB, 10-15" (25-38 cm), ML. S. bright yellow; F. deep maroon red, narrowly edged greyed mauve; beards blue. SD4447: (Combo x April Fool) X Rabbit's Foot. Adamgrove 1993.

BELAYA DAMA (V. & N. Gordodelovy, R. 1996). Sdlg. 79. TB, 28" (72 cm), EM. White, tinted light blue, hafts shaded brown; beards orange, yellow at end. Parentage unknown. Gordodelovy 1996.

BELAYA OLIMPIADA (Viktor Sheviakov, R. 1995). Sdlg. 10D 10A. TB, 34" (87 cm), ML. White with diamond finish; beards bright yellow. Latin Lover X Golden Years. Sheviakov 1997.

BEL AZUR (Richard Cayeux, R. 1993). Sdlg. 8713 C. IB, 23" (58 cm), M. Pure light blue self; beards white. Open Sky X Swirling Seas. Cayeux 1993.

BELGIUM SKY (Willy Hublau, R. 1996). Sdlg. B1. JI (6 F.), 35" (90 cm), M. Light blue (RHS 91D), dark violet halo around dark yellow signal, light yellow rays; style arms 4-6, silvery white edged blue, stamens crested. Sdlg. X Lady in Waiting.

BELLA ISABELLA (William Maryott, R. 1998). Sdlg. L156N. TB, 37" (94 cm), M. S. and style arms lavender blue (RHS 88C); F. lavender blue paling to light wistaria blue (92B), slight gold haft marking; beards yellow, prominent; lightly laced; pronounced sweet fragrance. Sib to Temperence. Maryott 1998.

BELLA VEE (Kenneth Fisher, R. 1990). Sdlg. 88-3. MTB (dip.), 21" (53 cm), M. Light yellow; beards light orange fading yellow. 25-24-H: ((Spring Bells x New Idea) x Blue Bisque) X 82-1B: (Consummation x 79-32, unknown). Aitken's Salmon Creek 1991.

BELLE AUDE (Jean Segui, R. 1998). TB, 32" (80 cm), M. S. and style arms azalea pink (RHS 38B);

F. paler coral pink (38D); beards dark azalea pink (41C), lighter at end; slight fragrance. Orinda X One Desire. Iris de Thau 1982.

BELLE DE NUIT (Cayeux, R. 1999). Sdlg. 89199 C. TB, 33" (85 cm), M. S. pale blue; F. bluish pansy violet, lighter margin; beards tangerine, white at end. In Town X Rebecca Perret.

BELLENDER BLUE (Bob Bauer/John Coble, R. 1993). Sdlg. J82A-25. JI (3 F.), 50" (127 cm), E. Dark blue violet, yellow signal; style arms dark blue violet. Prairie Chief X unknown. Ensata Gardens 1993.

BELLE PROMESSE (Tony Huber, R. 1993). Sdlg. DOM-F2-08. SPEC-X, 36" (90 cm), E. S. violet blue (RHS 90B); F. velvety deep violet (near 83B), darkening around dark yellow signal, sanded dark purple. Oriental Touch X *I. versicolor*.

BELLEVUE'S MATT (Neil Bertinot, R. 1997). Sdlg. 92-18D. LA, 40" (102 cm), M. S. wine red (Exotica 34), underside yellow, narrow yellow partial edging; style arms light mimosa yellow (2), light green tinge, slight garnet lake streaking; F. light garnet lake (35-), most of F. edged yellow, underside yellow, yellow sunburst signal; ruffled; slight fragrance. President Hedley X 84-2: (Alibi x Clara Goula).

BELLS ARE RINGING (James McWhirter, R. 1992). Sdlg. J85-29-2. TB, 36" (91 cm), M. Ruffled deep sky blue; beards blue, tipped white; slight fragrance. Winterscape X Ramona Howard. Cottage 1993.

BELO (Mary Dunn, R. 1990). Sdlg. M75-557-3. BB, 22" (51 cm), M. S. pastel orchid, edge slightly deeper; F. pastel orchid, slightly deeper ruffled edge; beards matching. Grand Waltz X Whirling Ruffles. M.A.D. Iris 1991.

BELORUSSKI ETIUD (Viktor Koroliov, R. 1997). Sdlg. S38-94K. TB, 45" (115 cm), M. Light blue, tinted lilac, F. with hafts streaked brown; style arms white, crests light blue; beards white at end, yellow, to orange in throat; slight sweet fragrance. South Pacific X New Snow. Koroliov 1997.

BELOW STAIRS (Mary Tubbs, TB, R. 1987). British Iris Society 1993.

BELY ANGEL (Viktor Sheviakov, R. 1997). Sdlg. 18a12a. TB, 32" (80 cm), M. White, hafts yellow; beards bright yellow; slight spicy fragrance. Winter Olympics X Christmas Angel. Sheviakov 1997.

BELY SFINKS (Nina Miroshnichenko, R. 1996). TB, 39" (100 cm), L. Ruffled white self; beards yellow, paler at end; slight sweet fragrance. Parentage unknown. Miroshnichenko 1989.

BELYYE NOCHI (Nina Miroshnichenko, R. 1997). TB, 30" (77 cm), ML. Pure white self; beards white, yellow in throat; slight spicy fragrance. Parentage unknown. Miroshnichenko 1997.

BE MY ANGEL (Barry Blyth, R. 1998). Sdlg. E14-1. SDB, 12" (30 cm), ML. S. soft beige pink, slight lilac infusion at base, open form; style arms beige pink, flushed light violet; F. lighter beige pink, slightly deeper 1/8" edge, darker crescent, small white area around beard; beards bright lavender at end, tangerine in throat; slight fragrance. Celsius X B25-1: (Z7-2, Toy Kingdom sib, x Z24-1, Volts sib). Tempo Two 1998/99.

BEN AHDEM (Cedric Morris, AB (RB), R. 1951). R. Wallace & Co. 1950.

BENGALSKI OGON (Sergey Loktev, R. 1999). Sdlg. 94-R11-9A. BB, 26" (67 cm), EM. S. blue lilac, midrib lighter; style arms light lilac, darker midrib and crests; F. blue lilac to white around beard, hafts creamy lemon; beards white, hairs tipped dirty yellow. Roseplic X Victoria Falls. Loktev 1999.

BEN HAROUN (E. S. Fankhauser, R. 1998). Sdlg. AB.10.82.C. AB (OGB), 24" (60 cm), M. S. dark red purple; style arms brown, purple midrib; F. dark red purple, black signal; beards brown. AB.18.68.A.: (Ben Hassan x ABA.21.60.A.: ((Jallah Effendi x Kalifa Baltis) x (Ahmed Aga x Beisan Aga))) X Beisan Aga. Tempo Two 1998/99.

BENI KOSHI (Zensaku Makino by Society for Japanese Irises, R. 1995). JI (3 F.), 36" (90 cm), M. S. white, edged red violet; style arms white; F. light lilac with large red violet center radiating 2/3 way to edge, white veins. Parentage unknown. Introduced in Japan, 1973.

BENIN (Nora Scopes, R. 1994). Sdlg. 9S 79A. TB, 36" (91 cm), L. Flaring deep red brown self; beards brown. (Spartan x (Tarot x unknown)) X Cracklin Burgundy.

BENI RENGE (Shuichi Hirao by Society for Japanese Irises, R. 1993). JI (6-9 F.), 28-31" (70-80 cm), M. Deep red violet, paling toward edge, prominent white veins, yellow signal; style arms white. Parentage unknown. Hirao 1985.

BENI TSUBAKI (Shuichi Hirao by Society for Japanese Irises, R. 1993). JI (6 F.), 27½" (70 cm), M. Rose violet deepening toward center, white pencil veining, yellow signal; style arms white. Parentage unknown. Hirao 1970.

BENJAMIN (Cedric Morris, AB (RB), R. 1951). R. Wallace & Co. 1950.

BENNERUP BLUE (Dorothy Rogers, R. 1993). SIB, 38-40" (97-102 cm), EM. Rich cobalt blue; style arms pale blue. Parentage unknown; sdlg. purchased from Sunny Border Nurseries, CT. Caprice Farm 1991.

BEN SALAH (E. S. Fankhauser, AB, R. 1989). Tempo Two 1991/92.

BENTON BLUEJOHN (Cedric Morris, TB, R. 1951). R. Wallace & Co. 1950.

BENTON BURGUNDY (Cedric Morris, TB, R. 1951). R. Wallace & Co. 1950.

BENTON CORONET (Cedric Morris, TB, R. 1951). R. Wallace & Co. 1950.

BENTON IMARI (Cedric Morris, TB, R. 1951). R. Wallace & Co. 1950.

BENTON MINUET (Cedric Morris, TB, R. 1951). R. Wallace & Co. 1950.

BENTON VIKING (Cedric Morris, TB, R. 1951). R. Wallace & Co. 1950.

BERA (Joseph Mertzweiller, R. 1996). Sdlg. 87-9. LA, 30-34" (76-86 cm), M. S. medium purple, narrow silvery white edge; style arms purple; F. slightly darker purple, veined, with narrow 1/16"-1/8" silvery white edge, narrow triangular yellow signal; slight musky fragrance. Acadian Miss X Easter Tide. Lone Star 1996.

BERIT STRAWN (Kirk Strawn, R. 1993). Sdlg. 60-1984. LA, 36" (91 cm), ML. S. and style arms yellow (RHS 7D); F. darker yellow (7A), yellow orange (17B) signal. Ila Nunn X Sun Fury. Bois d'Arc 1996.

BERLIN BLUE MOON (Tomas Tamberg, R. 1990). SIB (dip.), 24" (60 cm), M. Clear light medium blue. Parentage unknown. Friesland Staudengarten 1990.

BERLIN-CAPE CONNECTION (O. D. Niswonger, R. 1997). Sdlg. CS 1-93. SPEC-X, 36" (91 cm), M. S. medium blue; style arms light blue; F. light blue, venation spreading from small yellow signal. (Starting Calsibe x converted yellowish cal-sib sdlg., parentage unknown) X unknown. Cape Iris 1997.

BERLIN CHRYTOSA (Tomas Tamberg, R. 1993). SPEC-X, 43" (110 cm), M. Light blue violet, darker blue violet signal. Berliner Riesen X *I. setosa*. Tamberg 1993.

BERLIN DARK MANTLE (Tomas Tamberg, R. 1996). SIB (sino-sib), 24" (60 cm), M. Dark violet; large flowers with wide falls, short hafts. Berliner Riesen X dark violet sdlg. from L. Reid seed. Laurie's Garden 1988.

BERLINER RUNDE (Tomas Tamberg, R. 1990). Sdlg. SSTT171. SIB (dip), 20" (50 cm), M. Medium greyish blue. ((Cambridge x self) x self) X Blue Rosebud. Schoeppinger 1989.

BERLINER WEISSE (Tomas Tamberg, R. 1995). SIB, 28" (70 cm), M. White self; wide form. (Wide White x unknown) X Creme Chantilly. Schoeppinger 1996.

BERLIN GLOW (Tomas Tamberg, R. 1993). BB, 26" (65 cm), M. Orange self; beards red. Flaming Light X orange sdlg. Schoeppinger 1993.

BERLIN LANCE (Tomas Tamberg, R. 1993). SIB (tet.), 36" (90 cm), M. S. white; F. white, yellowish throat. C. McEwen sdlg. X (Wide White x unknown). Schoeppinger 1991. Introduced as "White Lance".

BERLIN LITTLE BLUE (Tomas Tamberg, R. 1993). Sdlg. 8371. SIB (dip.), 21½" (55 cm), M. Light blue self. SSTT152: (white sdlg. x blue sdlg.) X Berlin Delft. Schoeppinger, Tamberg 1993.

BERLIN PURPLE WINE (Tomas Tamberg, R. 1993). SIB (tet.), 36" (90 cm), M. S. wine red; F. velvety wine red, bluish hue on signal area. 8256: (Lake Niklas x (Cambrita x Tealwood)) X Teal Velvet. Schoeppinger, Tamberg 1993.

BERLIN RUFFLES (Tomas Tamberg, R. 1993). Sdlg. 8256-2. SIB (tet.), 39" (100 cm), M. S. medium blue; F. velvety medium blue; ruffled. Lake Niklas X 7643C: (Cambrita x Tealwood). Schoeppinger, Tamberg 1993.

BERLIN SEVIGATA (Tomas Tamberg, SPEC-X, R. 1988). Schoeppinger 1991.

BERLIN SKY (Tomas Tamberg, R. 1993). Sdlg. SSTT182. SIB (tet.), 29½" (75 cm), M. Light blue, darker blue in heart. Cambridge X SSTT108: ((Tycoon x Limeheart) x Limeheart). V. H. Humphrey 1995.

BERLIN TIGER (Tomas Tamberg, SPEC-X, R. 1988). Schoeppinger 1990.

BERMUDA TRIANGLE (A. & D. Cadd, R. 1999). Sdlg. 82-93-1. BB, 27" (69 cm), M. S. and style arms old gold, midribs touched lavender; F. old gold, triangular fluorescent lavender purple wash from beard to edge, darkest at top; beards bronze, small fuzzy lavender horn; slight sweet fragrance. Marsh Light X Branching Out.

BERNICE CARLAN (Fred Burr, R. 1999). TB, 28" (71 cm), EM. S. yellow, flushed rose; F. ivory to yellow ground, wide rose plicata margin; beards orange. Parentage unknown.

BERNICE IKINS (Kirk Strawn, R. 1993). Sdlg. 4-1983. LA, 33" (84 cm), M. S. imperial purple (RHS

78B), frilled cream edge; style arms light yellow (8C); F. beetroot purple (71A), frilled cream edge, yellow orange (17A) signal. Charlie's Michele X Just for Joe. Bois d'Arc 1996.

BERNICE'S LEGACY (Bernice Miller by Richard Richards, R. 1999). TB, 32" (81 cm), EML & RE. S. garnet (RHS 182A); style arms greyed orange (163B), oxblood (183A) midrib; F. garnet (180A), brown (165B) hafts with inconspicuous markings; beards bronze yellow (163A). Parentage unknown.

BERNSTEINDOM (Eberhard Fischer, R. 1993). Sdlg. 1. TB, 36" (90 cm), M. Amber yellow, F. with white area around light yellow beard; slight spicy fragrance. Amethyst Flame X Rusticana. A. Weinreich 1993.

BEROWRA (Graeme Grosvenor, R. 1994). Sdlg. S87-1. TB, 36" (91 cm), EM. Dark violet, F. veined darker; beards white; ruffled; slight sweet fragrance. Silverado X Tinted Crystal.

BERRY CLASSIC (Gary Sides, R. 1998). Sdlg. D44-F43A. TB, 36" (91 cm), ML. Boysenberry purple, F. with white area around beard, insignificant white haft striations; beards blue violet, hairs tipped white; heavily ruffled. B78-D29C: (Late Lilac x Royal Viking) X Titan's Glory. Sides 1999.

BERRY ME NOT (James Gibson by Cooley's Gardens, R. 1998). Sdlg. 7-82A. TB, 36" (91 cm), EM. Blue violet plicata markings on cream, darker on hafts; style arms blue violet; beards burnt orange. 10-79B: (((Going My Way x ((29-65B: (((Blue Rim x Lucy Lee) x Rococo) x April Melody) x Casino Queen sib) x (29-65D x Casino Queen sib))) x Chestnut Beauty sib) x (CoCo Mocha x Summer Sunshine sib)) X Mountain Melody. Cooley 1998.

BERRY NICE (A. & D. Willott, R. 1999). Sdlg. W 94-44. MDB, 4" (10 cm) E. Lightly ruffled creamy white, F. with large red violet spot; beards cream. W 92-3: (W 79-13: (Greenlee X-2 x Buttons) x Daring Eyes) X unknown.

BERRY SHERBERT (Ken Mohr, R. 1990). TB, 36" (91 cm), EM. S. medium blue pink infused rose violet at midrib; F. rose violet; beards coral orange. Exotic Flare X Heather Blush. Pacific Coast Hybridizers 1990.

BERTHA HOLMES THOMASON (Bob Thomason, R. 1992). Sdlg. BT 8936E. TB, 36" (91 cm), ML. S. medium blue violet, darker at edge; F. medium blue violet, lighter hafts veined brown plum; beards blue, orange in throat; ruffled; pronounced sweet fragrance. Titan's Glory X Praise the Lord.

BERTIE JEFFRIES (Robert Jeffries, R. 1991). Sdlg. J81-2-A. TB, 40" (102 cm), ML. S. white tinted pale violet, darker imperial purple midrib; F. imperial purple (HCC 33/2), lighter hafts; beards saturn red (13/1); ruffled, lightly laced; slight sweet fragrance. L. Rogers B18 X J79-1: (J70-14-A: ((Lovely Letty x Whole Cloth) x Cloverdale) x Flaming Arrow). Bar K Iris, Kansas Rainbow Iris 1991.

BERTWISTLE (Sterling Innerst, R. 1990). Sdlg. 2187-13. TB, 36" (91 cm), ML. S. white; F. white, 1/2" medium yellow edge; beards white; slight spicy fragrance. Eastertime X Beverly Sills. Innerst 1990.

BERYL JEAN (Kevin Nilsen, R. 1995). Sdlg. 48-87-1. TB, 35" (90 cm), EM. Lavender blue self; beards light yellow, white base. Leda's Lover X 48-84: (Prized Possession x Mary Frances). Iridescence 1995/96.

BESOTTED (Berry Blyth, R. 1997). Sdlg. B113-3. BB, 20" (51 cm), EM. S. vibrant lavender lilac, wide open; F. lilac, 2/3 covered with burgundy signal, small white area around bronze beard; sweet fragrance. Zing Me X Knight Templar. Tempo Two 1997/98.

BEST OF TIMES (George Slade, R. 1990). Sdlg. 85-28-K. TB, 37" (94 cm), M. Orchid pink; beards bright shrimp pink. Frosty Jewels X Helen's Pick. Wyle Wynde 1990.

BEST VALUE (Graeme Grosvenor, R. 1998). Sdlg. U58-1. TB, 40" (101 cm), M. Sky blue self; beards white. G'Day Mate X Scandia Delight. Rainbow Ridge 1999/2000.

BETTER BELIEVE IT (John C. Taylor, R. 1996). Sdlg. UL 20-6. LA, 47" (120 cm), ML. S. yellow spray pattern, border red; style arms yellow, blushed red; F. yellow spray pattern, red border, green-ribbed yellow signal. Desert Jewel X Margaret Lee. Rainbow Ridge 1998/99.

BETTER HALF (Pat Otterness, R. 1999). Sdlg. 9697-12X34-018. TB, 33" (84 cm), EM. S. pale amber yellow (near RHS 18C/D); F. purple (near 77) lightening with age; beards gold. Edith Wolford X Silverado.

BETTER WATCH OUT (John C. Taylor, R. 1994). Sdlg. RL 33-1. LA, 25" (63 cm), EM. S. light pink veined darker pink; style arms carmine rose edged yellow; F. dark carmine pink edged light pink, yellow signal; ruffled. Watch Out X Margaret Lee. Rainbow Ridge 1996/97.

BET TWICE (O. D. Niswonger, R. 1997). Sdlg. 53-95. TB, 34" (86 cm), M. Pinkish mauve self;

beards dark blue, hairs tipped tangerine. 96-91: (Pink Blue Genes x 58-88: (Matinee Idol x Pink Ballerina)) X 46-92: (Pink Blue Genes x Fontaine). Cape Iris 1998.

BETTY BLOCKBUSTER (John C. Taylor, R. 1994). Sdlg. RL 35-D. LA, 50" (127 cm), M. S. violet pink; F. carmine red pink, yellow signal; fluted. Wine and Dine X Margaret Lee. Rainbow Ridge 1995/96.

BETTY CHRISTINE (Elyse Hill, R. 1995). Sdlg. EJ 27-1-91. TB, 34" (86 cm), M. S. and style arms buff peach, midribs wine; F. wine, veined darker, 1/4" buff edge; beards orange; ruffled; slight sweet fragrance. Ringo X EJ 3-7-89: (Liaison x Lightning Ridge). O'Brien Iris 1998.

BETTY DUNN (O. D. Niswonger, R. 1995). Sdlg. 36-89. TB, 33" (84 cm), M. S. near-white, slight pink basal flush; style arms white, pink center streak; F. salmon pink, white rim; beards tangerine. 7-81: (Coral Strand x Lisa Ann) X Champagne Elegance. Cape Iris 1995.

BETTY JUNE (Glenn Bowers, R. 1998). Sdlg. A75-2. TB, 30" (76 cm), M. Ruffled and laced old rose (Pantone 1945U) self; beards brilliant orange (021C). Mulled Wine X Joe Vial.

BETTY KNIGHT (Stephen Stevens, R. 1992). Sdlg. 82-15-1. TB, 34" (86 cm), M. S. violet blue (RHS 93C) with lighter (93D) area at midrib; F. violet blue (93C), lighter area (93D) and veining around violet (93D) beard; ruffled; slight fragrance. 79-1-1: (77-5-13: (Lilac Dimples x (After All x sdlg.)) x Ruffled Ballet) X Star Wars. Hahn's Rainbow 1993.

BETTY LOU BLUE (Louise Smith, R. 1992). TB, 33" (84 cm), EM. Light blue; beards white; pronounced sweet fragrance. Parentage unknown.

BETTY TUCKER (Ed Matheny III, R. 1999). Sdlg. L:01-02-96. LA, 40" (102 cm), ML. S. grape; style arms light raspberry; F. raspberry, yellowish green signal. Rosebery X unknown.

BETWEEN THE LINES (Marty Schafer/Jan Sacks, R. 1991). Sdlg. SP85-2-4. SPEC (*versicolor*), 22" (56 cm), M. White ground veined violet (RHS 93B/C/D) throughout giving light blue effect, yellow signal blending to green in heart; style arms with violet midrib, pearly edge. S. Tiffney sdlg. X unknown. Joe Pye Weed 1991.

BEURON (Eckard Berlin, SPEC, R. 1979). British Iris Society 1995.

BEVERLY CULLERS (Sandra Underwood by Louise Smith, R. 1991). Sdlg. 86-101. TB, 32" (81 cm), EM. S. magenta plicata; F. white ground, magenta trim; beards orange, tipped white; pronounced sweet fragrance. Parentage unknown.

BEVERLY IN WHITE (Jared Harris, R. 1994). TB, 36" (91 cm), M. White self; style arms white, touched yellow; beards coral red, lighter in throat; slight musky fragrance. Sport of Beverly Sills found in Pinegar garden, Spanish Fork, UT. Zebra 1999.

BEVFRA'S GEM (Stan Dexter by Marie Ingersoll, R. 1991). Sdlg. 142-83-283-B. TB, 36" (91 cm), M. S. pale orchid violet; F. white, dark orchid violet midrib and rim, violet thumbprints; beards yellow, tipped white. 80/10B: (Vanity x Focus) X Coral Surf. Ingersoll's Iris 1992.

BEWARE (John C. Taylor, R. 1998). Sdlg. UL 25-1. LA, 43" (110 cm), M. S. purple violet; style arms light purple violet; F. purple violet, yellow signal. Jazz Ballet X Rachel's Request.

BEWDLEY (John D. Taylor, IB, R. 1986). V. H. Humphrey 1997.

BEWILDERBEAST (Brad Kasperek, R. 1994). Sdlg. 91B-2A. TB, 30" (76 cm), M. S. streaked light mauve (RHS 61A) and silver white (155C); F. dark mauve (61A) with silver white streaking, sunshine yellow shoulders with mauve veining; beards golden brown; laced, lightly ruffled; slight fragrance. Tiger Honey X Rustic Dance. Zebra 1995.

BEWITCHING TWILIGHT (Chad Harris, R. 1999). Sdlg. 89JE6. JI, (6+ F.), 41" (104 cm), M. White ground, heavily brushed light blue (RHS 101C) fading to pastel blue (101D), signal yellow (2B) radiating veins extending halfway length of F.; style arms heavy cream yellow. Knight in Armor X Marx sdlg.

BEYOND BEAUTY (David Shahak by Arnold Ferguson, selector, R. 1997). Sdlg. RxPM#4. AR (OH), 19" (48 cm), L. S. light blue (RHS 91D), veined darker blue; style arms ribbed rose red; F. grey brown, overlaid with maroon veining from dime-sized black signal; beards black, wide; slight fragrance. Ravid X Princess Maya. Grandview Iris Patch 1998.

BIALA NOC (Lech Komarnicki, R. 1997). Sdlg. 93/4-62B. TB, 32" (80 cm), ML. Clean white self, F. with green veining in center; beards light lavender blue, hairs tipped white; ruffled; pronounced sweet fragrance. Song of Norway X Heaven's Best.

BIBBITY BOBBITY BOO (Chet Tompkins, R. 1997). Sdlg. 94-78-1. BB, 23" (58 cm), EML. S. and style arms coppery wine, flushed and edged grass green; F. dark plum, brown and wine blend, greenish edge and throat area; beards mustard purple. Punch X inv. Cat Nap, Judy, Angel's Touch, Ivory Faun. Fleur de Lis 1997.

BIG BIRD (Tom Magee, TB, R. 1988). Long 1992.

BIG BOSS (Bernard Hamner, R. 1995). Sdlg. 89-30-5. TB, 40" (102 cm), E. Ruffled violet blue (RHS 92A), edge of F. slightly lighter (92B); beards white, yellow in throat. Breakers X Quintessence. Hamner Iris 1995.

BIG BUCK (Joseph Hoage, R. 1990). Sdlg. H 80-5A. TB, 38" (97 cm), ML. Medium blue, beards very dark blue. Song of Norway X Evening Echo. Long 1991.

BIG BUSINESS (Lilly Gartman, R. 1990). Sdlg. 86-2A. TB, 38" (97 cm), ML. S. chartreuse yellow; F. same, deeper rim and shoulders; beards gold. Critic's Choice X Status Seeker. Roris 1994.

BIG COUNTRY (Sharon McAllister, R. 1995). Sdlg. 83-5-4. AB (OGB), 30" (76 cm), M. S. pallid lobelia blue (near RHS 91D); style arms bright yellow (near 18A); F. pale mimosa yellow (between 8D, 158A), V-shaped area of fine reddish brown dotting and veining around beard; beards gold, brown at base. Boaz X Jean Ralls. McAllister 1996.

BIG EASY (Mary Dunn, R. 1995). Sdlg. L209-1. LA, 36" (91 cm), ML. Luminous fuchsia, F. with large golden signal; style arms lighter fuchsia. Plantation Beau X Wine Country. Bay View 1996.

BIGGI (Manfred Beer, R. 1992). Sdlg. MB 65/750. TB, 36" (90 cm), M. Dark violet blue; beards violet, tipped cream yellow; slight sweet fragrance. Pacific Panorama X (Grand Alliance x Matinata). Beer 1994.

BIG IDEAS (Labriano Anaya/Julian Wells, R. 1991). Sdlg. 84-4AA. TB, 40" (102 cm), M. Ruffled bright yellow, white signal; beards bright yellow; sweet fragrance. Leda's Lover X Fresno Calypso. Rancho de la Flor de Lis 1991.

BIG ISSUE (James Burch, R. 1993). Sdlg. 45-2. BB, 18" (46 cm), E. S. maroon (RHS 187D); F. maroon black (187A); beards bronze (163B). 38-16: (Steinhauer 7305 x Dark Ritual) X Merry Monarch. Burch Iris, Comanche Acres 1994.

BIG MELT (Tom Burseen, R. 1991). Sdlg. 6-91A. TB, 37" (94 cm), ML. Ruffled, flared, lightly laced cool violet white (lighter than RHS 85D), darker at center; beards gold tipped lavender blue; spicy fragrance. Local Motion X 5-236C: (Lacy Snowflake x Silver Peak). T.B.'s Place 1992.

BIG MOVE (Graeme Grosvenor, R. 1999). Sdlg. V91-A. TB, 36" (91 cm), M. Apricot self; beards tangerine; slight sweet fragrance. Move On sib X Bogota.

BIG'S CHILD (Tomas Tamberg, R. 1993). Sdlg. 8414-2. SIB (tet.), 36" (90 cm), M. Medium blue self. Dear Dianne X SSTT183: (Cambridge x ((Tycoon x Limeheart) x Limeheart)). Schoeppinger 1995.

BIG SKY (Ben Hager, TB, R. 1989). Melrose 1990.

BIG SMILE (Joseph Ghio, R. 1997). Sdlg. PD-204B. CA, 12" (31 cm), EM. Medium gold self; slightly lighter signal. PF-154R: (PI-MIX-R, unknown, x Eagle Eyes) X School Boy. Bay View 1997.

BIG SQUEEZE (Paul Black, R. 1999). Sdlg. A59F. TB, 33" (84 cm), L. S. peach pink, crystalline gold rim; style arms medium orange; F. medium orange, inconspicuous white haft veining; beards bright orange; heavily ruffled, lightly laced; pronounced sweet fragrance. Victorian Frills X Good Show. Mid-America 1999.

BIG THUNDER (William Simon by Elizabeth Simon, R. 1991). Sdlg. ML-26-38. TB, 34" (86 cm), ML. Deep red-toned brown; beards golden brown. Parentage unknown. Stahly 1992.

BIG TIGER (Cyril Field, R. 1992). Sdlg. CF10. TB, 28" (70 cm), L. S. golden yellow; F. red tiger lines from hafts to within 1/2" of edge, 1/2" yellow band; beards yellow. (Golden Zebra x yellow sdlg.) X Golden Zebra.

BIG 'UN (George Slade, R. 1991). Sdlg. 87-19-A. TB, 35" (89 cm), M. S. pale blue white; F. dark violet blue (RHS 89B); beards pale blue; pronounced sweet fragrance. River Hawk X Morgan Trader.

BIG VICTORY (James Burch, BB, R. 1989). Burch Iris 1990.

#BIJOU (JI, not reg.). Listed in 1939 Checklist without hybridizer or description. Name released.

BIJOU (George Sutton, R. 1999). Sdlg. L-78-A. SDB, 10" (25 cm), VE-E. S. blue pink (RHS 73D); style arms neyron pink; F. glacier blue, edged pink; beards midnight blue; ruffled; slight sweet fragrance. G-85: (Sigh x Chanted) X Little Blue Eyes.

BILBAO BEAUTY (Kevin Nilsen, R. 1995). Sdlg. 64-87-2. TB, 35" (90 cm), M. S. light apricot, blushed rose pink; F. apricot, overlaid reddish pink, apricot edge; beards red. 59-84: ((Golden Brilliance x Lisa Ann) x Entourage) X Chief Hematite.

BILLIE THE BROWNIE (John Burton, R. 1991). Sdlg. 85-P-3. MTB, 23" (58 cm), ML. S. golden brown blend (near RHS 199C/D); F. golden brown blend (near 199B/C), gold at hafts, iridescent purple overlay in center; beards bright gold; slight fragrance. Blue Twinkle X -- probably Spanish Coins. Burton 1992.

BILL NEILL (Kirk Strawn, R. 1993). Sdlg. 8-1985. LA, 36" (91 cm), E. S. greyed purple (RHS 186A); style arms greyed red (182C); F. red purple (59A), yellow (13B) signal. Grace Scott X Kirk Strawn. Bois d'Arc 1996.

BILLOWING CLOUDS (B. Charles Jenkins, R. 1998). Sdlg. CA72G. SPU, 30-40" (76-107 cm), EM. S. and style arms white; F. white, prominent yellow signal blended onto 1/3 of petal; rounded, waved form. BJ08G: (Lively One x Diminuendo) X BG34C: (Lively One x C7-21A: (Crow Wing x Medallion)).

BILLOWING DAWN (Chet Tompkins, R. 1998). Sdlg. 95-76. TB, 36-38" (91-97 cm), ML. S. and style arms ice white; F. butter yellow; beards yellow, base white. (Burning Bright x Soaring Spirit) X (Justin Tyme x Candle Power). Fleur de Lis 1998.

BILLOWS (Barry Blyth, R. 1991). Sdlg. W62-A. TB, 32-34" (81-86 cm), EM. S. creamy white, smoky rose tan infusion; F. bright white, 1/4" smoky rose stitching on edge; beards pale lemon; slight fragrance. Rain Flurry X Bama Berry. Tempo Two 1991/92.

BILL'S PRIDE (William Phillips by Francis Scott Key Iris Society, R. 1992). Sdlg. 88-8. TB, 36" (91 cm), M. S. grey-white, violet midrib; F. violet, bronze haft markings; beards deep yellow, tipped blue. Skyline Drive X New Moon. Francis Scott Key Iris Society 1993.

BILLY BLUE JAY (Duane Meek, R. 1992). Sdlg. 842-1-6. CA, 14" (36 cm), ML. Medium blue self. ((I. tenax x I. innominata) x Abell blue sdlg.) X Rio del Mar. D & J Gardens 1992.

BILLY McKEE (Chet Tompkins, R. 1993). Sdlg. 87-49A. TB, 36" (91 cm), ML. Glittering sky blue self; beards yellow, tipped blue. (((Curly McQ x White Waters) x (Sapphire Shore x Babbling Brook)) x ((Radiant Bride x Sterling Silver) x (Tinsel Town x Sterling Silver))) X Land o'Lakes. Fleur de Lis 1993.

BINALONG (Kevin Nilsen, R. 1992). Sdlg. 32-88-1. TB, 30" (77 cm), EM. S. deep brown, lighter midrib; F. ruffled claret red to black, darker edge, pale yellow hafts; beards orange yellow. 8-86: (Beachgirl x Lady Friend) X 15-84-1: (Bicentennial x San Jose). Iridescence 1992/93.

BIONIC FOCUS (Henry Danielson by Luella Danielson, R. 1990). Sdlg. HD-9. AB (OGB), 28" (71 cm), M. S. light rose lavender, veined darker, yellow hafts; style arms yellow; F. light red blend, maroon signal; beards maroon. Summer Set X Bionic Burst. Pleasure Iris 1991.

BIRGIT (Manfred Beer, R. 1991). Sdlg. MB 22/83A. TB, 39" (100 cm), L. Medium brown, small violet F. spot. Malaysia X Carolina Honey. Gartencenter Kania 1991.

BIRTHDAY GREETINGS (Joseph Ghio by Maryott's Gardens, R. 1994). Sdlg. 85-153-BO. TB, 37" (94 cm), M. Coral pink (RHS 49A), F. with deeper coral (31B) shoulders; beards tipped tangerine; slight sweet fragrance. Newlywed X 82-156-H2, Winning Smile pollen parent. Maryott 1994.

#BIRTHDAY SURPRISE (Ben Hager by Marilyn Harlow, TB, R. 1986). Stock destroyed, name released.

BIRTHDAY SURPRISE (William Maryott, R. 1991). Sdlg. L183A. TB, 35" (89 cm), M. S. pinkish tan with trace of raspberry; F. pink ground with diffused raspberry rim; beards rusty brick; ruffled. J52B: ((Orange Plush x Anon) x Queen in Calico) X Gigolo. Maryott 1991.

BISCHOFSHOL (Harald Moos, R. 1991). Sdlg. 81/50H. TB, 31½" (80 cm), M. Lightly ruffled light orange, white area below tangerine beard. Flaming Light X Fresno Calypso. Schoeppinger 1992.

BISOU (Lawrence Ransom, R. 1994). Sdlg. 90/458-1. MDB, 8" (15 cm), ML. Cream white, S. suffused with yellow veining, F. with dark yellow halo; beards bluish white, hairs tipped yellow to orange; pronounced sweet fragrance. Willowmist X Tiny Cherub. Iris au Trescols 1995.

BISTRO (Joseph Gatty by Keith Keppel, R. 1998). Sdlg. Y8-6. IB, 27" (69 cm), EML. S. and style arms goldenrod (M&P 10-L-5); F. goldenrod ground, almost complete buckthorn brown (13-L-8) overlay, shaded henna (6-J-12) toward center, fine goldenrod edge; beards mustard, orange with tan tips in throat; ruffled; pronounced sweet fragrance. Quote X Keppel 87-40D: (82-43B, Foreign Accent sib, x ((Morocco x Santana) x Phoenix)). Keppel 1999.

BIT OF ENVY (Louise Bellagamba, R. 1995). Sdlg. D-193. SDB, 9" (23 cm), ML. S. and style arms greenish white; F. greenish white, green veins and spot below greenish white beard. Unknown green and white MDB X Wilma Greenlee.

BIT OF GOSSIP (Barry Blyth, R. 1997). Sdlg. D34-5. SDB, 15" (38 cm), EM. S. pink, fine gold wire edge, lighter violet midrib; F. white, 1/4" blended pinkish lavender edge with deeper dotting and centerline; beards white and tangerine; slight fragrance. Bee's Knees X A7-1: (Merry Dance x Mini Song). Tempo Two 1997/98.

43

BIT O'MAGIC (Lynda Miller, BB, R. 1988). Miller's Manor 1991.

#BITSY (Ben Hager, BB, R. 1986). Not introduced; name released.

BITSY (Ben Hager, R. 1991). Sdlg. AMD4940TyTyDpY. MDB, 5-7½" (13-19 cm), EML. Deep bright yellow; self beards. AMD4468: (3800: (((Shrinking Violet x Timmie Too) x ((Star Child x (Norah x Thisbe)) x sib)) x (unknown x ((Norah x Thisbe) x (Frenchi x Pagoda)))) x 3384: ((Atomic Blue x *I. binata*) x (Roberts 51-38 x Little Charmer))) X AMD3829: (Tiny Apricot x (((Prodigy x ((Red-Lilli x Pogo) x Regards)) x (Buttercup Charm x (Pink Amber x Pink Cushion))) x (Buttercup Charm x 2562))). Adamgrove 1991.

BITSY BLUE (Lynda Miller, R. 1991). Sdlg. 487. MDB, 4" (10 cm), E. Creamy white, small turquoise F. spot; beards white, yellow in throat. 584: ((What Not x Sky Dot) x unknown) X 384, unknown. Miller's Manor 1992.

BITTERSWEET JOY (Lynda Miller, R. 1993). Sdlg. 4787A. TB, 34" (86 cm), M. Medium orange with soft golden glow around burnt tangerine beards; slight sweet fragrance. Can't Elope X 3185A: (Sultan's Palace x Marmalade). Miller's Manor 1994.

BLACK ACCENT (Chet Tompkins, R. 1995). Sdlg. 89-13. TB, 34" (86 cm), M. Black red self; beards black red, tinted violet. (Royal Rage x Black Dragon) X (Catawba Ruby x Darkside). Fleur de Lis 1995.

BLACK ANDROMEDA (Chet Tompkins, R. 1994). Sdlg. 91-11. TB, 38" (97 cm), ML. S. azure wine; F. very dark wine; beards red. Armageddon X Sweeter Than Wine. Fleur de Lis 1994.

BLACK AS NIGHT (Duane Meek, R. 1992). Sdlg. 202-1-5. TB, 37" (94 cm), ML. S. red black, flushed red at midrib; F. darker; beards black, tipped brown mustard; ruffled; slight fragrance. Harlem Hussy X Black Pearl. D & J Gardens 1992.

BLACK BANDIT (Duane Meek, R. 1998). Sdlg. 3-1-4. SDB, 10" (25 cm), E. Ruffled red black, F. deeper; beards brown, purple at end. Chanted X Chubby Cheeks. D & J Gardens 1998.

BLACKBEARD'S GHOST (Sharon McAllister, R. 1992). Sdlg. 85-4-8. AB (OGB), 28" (72 cm), EM. S. very pale wistaria violet, slightly darker veins; F. pale wistaria ground, washed burgundy, finely veined deeper burgundy, signal area intensely veined deep burgundy; beards burgundy black. Bold Sentry X Whither Thou Goest. McAllister 1992.

BLACKBERRY JAM (A. & D. Willott, R. 1995). Sdlg. 92-124. SDB, 12" (30 cm), ML. S. dark red violet; F. very dark red violet; beards orange brown; lightly ruffled. Nachos X Pilgrims' Choice. Willott 1995.

BLACKBERRY JUBILEE (Marty Schafer/Jan Sacks, R. 1997). Sdlg. S90-38-2. SIB, 36" (91 cm), ML. S. dappled red violet, veined darker; style arms pearly blue, red violet flush and crest edge, aqua midrib, semi-upright; F. color of S., small signal white, yellow green at center, blue violet veining; ruffled. Trim the Velvet X S87-10-1: (Mad Magenta x Percheron). Joe Pye Weed 1997.

BLACKBERRY LAKE (John Marchant, R. 1990). Sdlg. 2787. CA, 10" (25 cm), M. S. slightly smoky lilac purple (HCC 31/2); F. lilac purple (31/2) flushed pansy violet (33/2), diffused ray signal, lightly ruffled. Sdlg. X sdlg. Portable Acres 1990.

BLACK BUTTE (Schreiner, R. 1999). Sdlg. AA 426-A. TB, 36" (91 cm), ML. S. and style arms dark purple black (RHS 89A); F. deep obsidian black (202A); beards purple black, yellow in throat. T 255-E: (((Seven Leagues x Sailor's Dance) x Virginia Squire) x Titan's Glory) X V 73-1: (((Night Song x (Black Swan x Tuxedo sib)) x Navy Strut) x Black Dragon). Schreiner 1999.

BLACK CHERRY DELIGHT (O. D. Niswonger, R. 1992). Sdlg. SDB 20-89. SDB, 11" (28 cm), M. S. white; style arms hint of tangerine on crest; F. dark fuchsia, edged white, beards white, tipped tangerine. Splash of Red X Slap Bang. Cape Iris 1992.

BLACKCURRANT (Marky Smith, R. 1998). Sdlg. 93-31A. IB, 25" (64 cm), EM. S. plum purple (RHS 79A) blending to primrose yellow wire edge; style arms clear yellow, midrib and style crests brushed violet; F. redder than S., primrose yellow wire rim and veins, blue violet toward center, pure yellow surrounding beard; beards cream at end, yellow in midsection, orange in throat; ruffled; slight sweet fragrance. Fancy Woman X Gemstar. Aitken's Salmon Creek 1999.

BLACK EYE (Joseph Ghio, CA, R. 1989). Bay View 1990.

BLACK FALLS (Don Nebeker, R. 1995). Sdlg. 1135-17. TB, 38-40" (97-107 cm), M. S. dark spectrum violet (HCC 735); style arms dark violet purple (733); F. black (darker than 0001060); beards spectrum violet, hairs tipped saffron yellow; ruffled. Blackout X 1076-10: (Graduation x (Fancy Tales x Planned Treasure)). Zebra 1996.

BLACK GARNET (Lorena Reid, R. 1996). Sdlg. 8S72-2G. SIB (sino-sib), 54-60" (137-152 cm), M.

S. dark maroon; style arms near black, deep red center ridge; F. dark maroon, large black signal, single white centerline. Enbee Deeaych X Berlin Dark Mantle. Laurie's Garden 1996.

BLACK GRAPES (Bernard Hamner by Shepard Iris Garden, R. 1993). Sdlg. 87-17. Black purple self; dark purple beards. Holy Night X Purple Pirouette. Hamner Iris, Shepard Iris 1993.

BLACK HARMONY (Reuben David, R. 1993). Sdlg. A-B. TB, 34" (86 cm), ML. Dark purple self; beards dark purple; slight sweet fragrance. Navy Strut X unknown. Holly Lane 1993.

BLACKLEG (Anne Blanco White, R. 1995). SPEC-X, 48" (120 cm), M. S. and F. yellow; stems aubergine. Chance Beauty X self. British Iris Society 1997.

BLACKLIGHT (John Marchant, R. 1990). Sdlg. 5787. CA, 12" (30 cm), M. S. smoky lilac purple (HCC 31/2); F. ruby red (827/3), blacklight blue spot. Sdlg. X sdlg. Portable Acres 1990.

BLACK NIGHT (A. Theodore Mueller, R. 1999). Sdlg. 78-26. IB, 16-20" (41-51 cm), E. Very velvety black; beards dark, slightly tipped yellow; waved; slight fragrance. Moondella X Tawny Tone. Mueller's Garden 1999.

BLACK SUEDE (A. & D. Willott, R. 1995). Sdlg. 88-117. SDB, 11" (28 cm), M. S. dark red violet; F. very dark red violet; beards yellow and violet; ruffled. Nachos X Pilgrims' Choice. Willott 1995.

BLACK SUITED (Sterling Innerst, R. 1999). Sdlg. 4736-1. TB, 36" (91 cm), ML. Black self; beards black; slight musky fragrance. Before the Storm X Black Tie Affair.

BLACK TEDDY BEAR (Donald Spoon, R. 1995). Sdlg. 90-3C. BB, 27" (69 cm), ML. S. and style arms purple black; F. slightly darker purple black; beards lighter purple black. Baby Blessed X Little Blackfoot. Winterberry 1997.

BLACK TIE AFFAIR (Schreiner, R. 1993). Sdlg. AA 273-B. TB, 36" (91 cm), M. Velvety inky black (RHS 202A); beards black. T 392-A: (Black Dragon x Titan'sGlory) X T 315-A: (K 398-1: (B 302-G: (((Broadway Star x Whole Cloth) x Blue Mountains) x (Toll Gate x After Dark)) x H 296-A) x P 273-B: (Morning Hymn x Louisiana Lace)). Schreiner 1993.

BLACKY (Manfred Beer, R. 1991). Sdlg. MB 11/83A. TB, 36" (90 cm), M. Black blue, F. velvety; beards dark blue. Swazi Princess X By Night. Gartencenter Kania, Von Zeppelin 1992.

BLAEBERRY PIE (B.L.C. Dodsworth, R. 1998). Sdlg. EB 98 AA. TB, 41" (104 cm), L. Ruffled mulberry self; beards mulberry; sweet fragrance. Whernside X Mulberry Punch.

BLAKIT (Oleg Amekhin, R. 1996). Sdlg. B-3. SPEC (*versicolor*), 24" (60 cm), M. Light blue self, white spot. Parentage unknown. Amekhin 1996.

BLANEY MARLOW (Donald Spoon, R. 1995). Sdlg. 89-144. TB, 43" (109 cm), ML. S. pink (RHS 36D); style arms rose pink center, pink edge; F. palest rose pink, stitched rose pink (68C) darkening at hafts; beards red (40B). Poet X Sweet Anita. Winterberry 1995.

BLANKETY BLANK (Tom Burseen, R. 1997). Sdlg. 92-148A. TB, 36" (91 cm), EM. S. white ground, heavily washed cherry (RHS 71A); style arms red violet; F. creamy apricot, marked and dotted cherry, solid at edge; beards lemon; ruffled; slight musky fragrance. 90-23A: (Say Okay x (Rosy Cloud x Mountain Melody)) X Power Surge. T.B.'s Place 1998.

BLARING GALE (Wanda Dow, TB, R. 1988). T & H Garden 1992.

BLAST (Ben Hager, R. 1992). Sdlg. IB5109Var. IB, 21" (53 cm), ML. S. bright apricot orange; F. bright magenta; beards fiery tangerine. Shenanigan X SD4455Pk/Rs: (Gigglepot x SD4024PkPc, pollen parent of Software). Adamgrove 1993.

BLATANT (Monty Byers, TB, R. 1989). Moonshine 1990.

BLAUER MONTAG (Anne-Ruth Brehm, R. 1997). Sdlg. 552. BB, 24-27" (60-70 cm), L. Lavender self; beards lavender. Breakers X Titan's Glory. Brehm 1998.

BLAUE WELLE (Eberhard Fischer, R. 1993). Sdlg. 3. TB, 36" (90 cm), EM. S. medium violet blue; F. slightly darker medium violet blue; beards blue; waved; slight sweet fragrance. Prince Indigo X Demetria. G. Mattuschka 1993.

BLAUKAEPPCHEN (Claus Goldbeck by Lothar Denkewitz, R. 1995). SDB, 10" (26 cm), M. S. clear lavender; style arms pale lavender; F. aster violet to brown; beards clear blue; pronounced spicy fragrance. Regards X unknown. Von Zeppelin 1997.

BLAUMACHER (Tomas Tamberg, R. 1997). Sdlg. SSTT259. SIB (tet.), 30" (76 cm), M. Light medium blue; falls wide. Lady of Quality X converted sdlg.: (SSTT152 x Berlin Delft). Schoeppinger 1997.

BLEACHED BLONDE (Perry Dyer, R. 1998). Sdlg. 94-71A. SDB, 10" (25 cm), M. S. ivory to cream, midrib flushed butter yellow, light blue stitching deeper and heavier toward base; style arms ivory, flushed butter yellow; F. ivory lightly banded yellow, unmarked, with warm yellow shoulders; beards light yellow. Chubby Cheeks X Gigolette. Contemporary 1999.

BLENHEIM ROYAL (Schreiner, R. 1990). Sdlg. V 62-A. TB, 38" (97 cm), M. Ruffled medium blue

(RHS 96A); beards cream. R 35-1: ((D 1147-A, Miriam Steel sib, x Sailor's Dance) x (Navy Strut x Full Tide)) X R 214-B: (Master Touch x unknown). Schreiner 1990.

BLESSED ASSURANCE (Lloyd Zurbrigg, R. 1994). Sdlg. LL 24 #1. IB, 16" (41 cm), E & RE (fall). S. light daffodil yellow; style arms light yellow; F. deep daffodil yellow; beards yellow. I Bless X Marmalade Skies. Friendship 1995.

BLESSINGS GALORE (George Slade, TB, R. 1989). Wyle Wynde 1990.

BLINK (Lynda Miller, R. 1995). Sdlg. 191CA. MDB, 5½" (14 cm), ML. S. creamy yellow; style arms cream, veined light blue; F. russet brown edged medium yellow; beards pale blue, tipped orange in throat. 487: (Bee Early x 384, unknown) X 1087: (Copper Chief x unknown). Miller's Manor 1996.

BLISSED OUT (Barry Blyth, R. 1997). Sdlg. D6-1. SDB, 12" (30 cm), VE-EM & RE. S. pastel pink, slight violet midrib flush; style arms pink; F. pastel pink, whitish area near beard, slightly deeper hafts; beards tangerine, vivid purple at end. Volts X B34-2, Say Hello sib. Tempo Two 1997/98.

BLITZEN (Marky Smith, R. 1998). Sdlg. 95-34A. IB, 24" (61 cm), EM. S. greyed tuscan yellow (RHS 162C) blending to lavender midrib wash; style arms clear primrose yellow; F. primrose yellow ground washed soft violet (near 90D), sides redder, butter yellow shoulders, primrose wire rim and veins at sides, cream white surrounding and long point below beard; beards cream at end, yellow midsection, orange in throat; ruffled; slight musky fragrance. Low Spirits X Gemstar.

BLIZZARD BAY (Chet Tompkins, R. 1998). Sdlg. 93-15A. TB, 34" (86 cm), EML. Antique pearl to skim milk white self; beards antique pearl. Sheer Bliss X Honky Tonk Blues. Fleur de Lis 1998.

BLONDE BOMBSHELL (Joseph Ghio, R. 1996). Sdlg. 92-12X3. TB, 40" (102 cm), ML. S. coral, blending to cream apricot edge; F. white, banded creamy apricot; beards coral. 90-21Y: ((Romantic Mood x 82-198F3: (((Louise Watts x (Ghost Story x Ponderosa)) x (Ballet in Orange x (Hi Top x ((Ponderosa x Travel On) x Peace Offering)))) x Caption)) x 87-28N, pod parent of Winning Edge X 90-24T2: (((Winning Note x Caption) x 82-198F3) x (((Just Married x Fortunata) x (Just Married x Exhilaration)) x (Designer Gown x Divinity))). Bay View 1997.

BLONDIE (R. W. Broomfield, R. 1994). Sdlg. RB02. SPEC (*pseudacorus*), 24" (60 cm), M. Yellow; foliage cream early in season before turning green. *I. pseudacorus* "variegata" X unknown.

BLONDINKA (V. & N. Gordodelovy, R. 1995). Sdlg. 218. TB, 32" (80 cm), M. S. cream, striated brown at base; F. white, rim cream, brown haft striations, purple spot below beard; beards orange, purple on end; ruffled. Parentage unknown. Gordodelovy 1994.

BLOOD COVENANT (Hooker Nichols, R. 1990). Sdlg. 8602E. SDB, 12" (30 cm), EML. S. light garnet brown with tan undertone; F. garnet brown edged S. color; beards brown gold. Pony Express X Sheer Energy. Hillcrest 1991.

BLOTA HUNKA (L. J. Duffy, R. 1992). Sdlg. WI-54-84. SPEC (*setosa*), 24-36" (47-91 cm), E. Wine with white streaking at base of F., some red overtones; style arms pale rose, wine mid-streak; dark maroon buds. Selection of *I. setosa interior* collected near Fairbanks, Alaska, 1984.

BLOUSY (Tom Burseen, R. 1990). Sdlg. 6-22D. TB, 37" (94 cm), M. S. very light buff pink (RHS 159B); F. light greenish sand (164D), texture-veined; beards buff, tipped tangerine; sweet fragrance. Somsee Somsigh sib X Lady Friend. T.B.'s Place 1991.

BLOW UP (Tom Burseen, R. 1993). Sdlg. 9-215D. TB, 38" (89 cm), EM. S. dark chocolate brown (RHS 166A); F. bright lemon yellow ground peppered chocolate brown to solid chocolate brown edge; beards bronze; ruffled; slight fragrance. Point Made X 6-146: (Rio de Oro x Noon Siesta). T.B.'s Place 1994.

BLUE AGAIN (Duane Meek, R. 1997). Sdlg. 33-1-7. TB, 37" (94 cm), M. Lightly ruffled medium blue, slightly lighter area beside white beard. French Kiss X St. Louis Blues. D & J Gardens 1997.

BLUE ANEW (Ben Hager, R. 1990). Sdlg. RE4384RndBl. TB, 32" (81 cm), M & RE (Aug.-Nov/CA). Medium blue; beards blue white. T3532LtBl: (White Elephant sib x Avalon Bay) X Welcome Aboard sib. Melrose 1990.

BLUE BALLET (Keith Keppel, TB, R. 1989). Keppel 1990.

BLUEBERRIES AND CREAM (Darlene Pinegar, R. 1990). Sdlg. AM-1-2. TB, 29" (74 cm), EML. S. medium blueberry, white center, blueberry midrib; F. creamy yellow aging to creamy white, blueberry edge, gold hafts with blueberry markings; beards deep yellow gold; ruffled; pronounced sweet fragrance. April Melody X Spinning Wheel. Spanish Fork 1991.

BLUEBERRY FAIR (Robert Hollingworth, R. 1996). Sdlg. 92K2B1. SIB (tet.), 32" (81 cm), M. S.

light blue violet; style arms broad, short, multi-shaded blue violet to light blue; F. medium blue violet, veined white signal area; ruffled, flared. Coronation Anthem X 82J2C7(T), Jewelled Crown sib. Windwood Gardens 1997.

BLUEBERRY FILLY (Brad Kasperek, R. 1998). Sdlg. 94-13-67. IB, 23" (58 cm), VE. Blue violet (RHS 89B/C), silver white streaking; style arms violet blue; beards light yellow; broken color pattern; slight fragrance. Batik X Ostry White.

BLUEBERRY ICE (Jim & Vicki Craig, R. 1997). Sdlg. 41W25. TB, 42" (107 cm), EML. S. white, washed and dotted violet, 1/4" solid deep violet edge, midrib violet; style arms deep violet; F. white, violet 1/2" stitched edge, scattered dotting heavier near beard, 1/2" dart below beard; beards light blue at end, changing to dark yellow in throat; heavily ruffled; slight sweet fragrance. Gentle Rain X (Odyssey x (Odyssey x Deborah Suzanne)). J. & V. Craig 1997.

BLUEBIRD'S MELODY (Beryl Pederick, R. 1994). Sdlg. 10. TB, 35" (89 cm), VE. S. bluebird blue (HCC 042/1) veined mauve; F. violet purple (733), narrowly edged bluebird blue; beards gold, tipped white; slight fragrance. Lady Vera X Bluebird Wine.

BLUEBIRD SPECIAL (Jean Stallcop by Don Delmez, R. 1998). JI (6 F.), 38" (97 cm), M. Ruffled white, veined blue; signal yellow. Parentage unknown. Delmez Gardens 1998.

BLUE BLAZER (John Clive Russell, R. 1999). TB, 32" (81 cm), M. Ruffled red, tan and brown blend, F. with blue blaze below beard; style arms red to tan; beards white, tipped yellow; slight fragrance. Parentage unknown. Iris Garden 1999.

BLUEBLOOD YELLOW (Nathan Rudolph by Loleta Powell, R. 1991). TB, 32" (81 cm), ML. Heavily ruffled and laced light yellow, edged gilt; beards electric blue. Parentage unknown. Powell's Gardens 1992.

BLUE BUBBLES (Bernard Hamner, R. 1990). Sdlg. 85-779. BB, 27" (69 cm), M. Ruffled violet blue (RHS 91B); self beards. Bubbling Over X Classic Profile. Hamner Iris 1990.

BLUE BY ME (Udo & Rudolph Wilkeneit, R. 1996). Sdlg. EW 1/1/94. MDB, 6" (15 cm), E. S. sky blue, blue heart; F. sky blue; beards blue. Parentage unknown.

BLUE CANDLE (Cloyd McCord, R. 1996). Sdlg. 79-2-C. TB, 35" (89 cm), M & RE. S. dark blue; F. dark blue, light blue blaze; beards light orange; ruffled, laced; sweet fragrance. Princess Maxine X self. McCord 1996.

BLUE CHEER (Larry Lauer, R. 1997). Sdlg. 87-59. TB, 35" (89 cm), M. Ruffled blue, shoulders white; beards light blue, hairs tipped white; slight sweet fragrance. Breakers X Denney 81-5-1: ((Regents Row sib x Winterscape) x Midnight Love Affair). Stockton 1997.

BLUE CHIP PINK (O. D. Niswonger, TB, R. 1989). Cape Iris 1990.

BLUE CHIP STOCK (Paul Black, R. 1998). Sdlg. B195B. MTB, 22" (56 cm), E. S. light to medium blue, darker midrib; style arms light to medium blue; F. dark violet blue paling toward edge; beards blue, old gold in throat; ruffled; slight musky fragrance. Echo Pond X Privileged Character. Mid-America 1998.

BLUE COCKATIEL (John Weiler, R. 1990). Sdlg. CAW 3. CA, 13" (33 cm), M. Light cockatiel blue, circular white signal. Roving Eye X Claremont Bluebird.

BLUE COVE (A. Theodore Mueller, R. 1994). Sdlg. 87-4. TB, 30-32" (76-81 cm), EM. Slightly blended light blue self; style arms very light blue; beards yellow. Lord Jeff X Entourage. Mueller's Garden 1994.

BLUE CREPE (Lucille Kavan, SDB, R. 1976). Ennenga Iris 1992.

BLUE CREVASSE (B.L.C. Dodsworth, R. 1997). Sdlg. EB 94F. TB, 42" (107 cm), L. S. pale blue, deep blue center; F. medium blue, deep blue center; beards blue; ruffled. Clemency X Swaledale.

BLUE CRUSADER (Schreiner, R. 1998). Sdlg. CC 163-2. TB, 42" (107 cm), L. Heavily ruffled deep blue violet (RHS 93A) self; beards blue violet. Honky Tonk Blues X Riverboat Blues. Schreiner 1998.

BLUE DELPH (Nora Scopes, SDB, R. 1984). British Iris Society 1987.

BLUE EMBERS (Bob Bauer/John Coble, R. 1993). Sdlg. J83J-1. JI (3 F.), 38" (97 cm), VE. S. light blue, edged violet; style arms white, crests edged blue; F. light blue violet, white halo and short rays, yellow signal. Parentage unknown, seed from bee pod, Ackerman garden. Ensata Gardens 1993.

BLUE EPAULETTES (Cy Bartlett, TB, R. 1985). British Iris Society 1989.

BLUE-EYED MAIDEN (A. & D. Willott, R. 1992). Sdlg. 88-7. SDB, 10" (25 cm), E. Lightly ruffled pink, F. with apricot hafts; beards bright blue. 84-88: (Oh Katz x Coral Wings) X Poet Laureate. Willott 1992.

BLUE-EYED SUSAN (Larry Lauer, R. 1998). Sdlg. 91-258-6. TB, 38" (97 cm), ML. S. light yellow; style arms yellow; F. white, yellow rim; beards blue, mustard in throat, with short horn; ruffled. 86-20-1: (Nancy Glazier x Brandy) X Triple Whammy. Stockton 1998.

BLUE EYES CRYING (Jim Hedgecock, R. 1999). Sdlg. 1-D-26-1. SDB, 12" (31 cm), M. Ruffled pale blue, F. with dark blue and green striations by beard; beards pale blue, orange in throat. Novemberfest X unknown.

BLUE FIN (George Sutton, R. 1997). Sdlg. G-20ARSA. TB, 38" (97 cm), ML & RE. S. pale wistaria blue (RHS 92D), midrib veined deeper; style arms pale wistaria blue; F. pale wistaria blue, fine darker veining; beards dark blue violet (93), 1" bald wistaria blue horn; lightly ruffled; slight spicy fragrance. Chico Maid X Sky Hooks. Sutton 1998.

BLUE FIRE (Darlene Pinegar, R. 1994). Sdlg. GR-1-8-1A. TB, 35" (89 cm), ML. S. and style arms medium blue; F. medium blue, aging paler, darker center wash, lighter edge and dark blue centerline; beards deep yellow, tipped light blue; heavily ruffled; pronounced sweet fragrance. GR-1-8-1: (Gypsy Rings x Moon Mistress) X Olympiad. Spanish Fork 1995.

BLUE FOR SUE (A. & D. Willott, R. 1998). Sdlg. 88-1. SDB, 10" (25 cm), EM. Lightly ruffled light violet blue; beards light violet blue. Sapphire Gem X Pilgrims' Choice. Willott 1998.

BLUE FOR YOU (Barry Blyth, R. 1997). Sdlg. C118-A. TB, 36" (92 cm), EML. Light silvery iridescent blue with shot silk effect; beards navy, tipped white; pronounced sweet fragrance. A72-2, Almost Dark sib, X Born at Dawn. Tempo Two 1997/98.

BLUE HEELER COUNTRY (Graeme Grosvenor, R. 1998). Sdlg. V39-B. TB, 36" (91 cm), L. S. pale blue; F. dark blue, light blue rim; beards blue, hairs tipped mustard; slight sweet fragrance. Proud Tradition X Riverboat Blues. Rainbow Ridge 1998/99.

BLUE HOOKS (Ladislav Muska, R. 1995). Sdlg. SHBS-03. TB, 37" (94 cm), M. Ruffled deep purplish blue lilac self; beards yellow, deep blue horns. (Sky Hooks x "Belase Striebo") X (Glory Bound x Sky Hooks). Muska 1994.

BLUE IT UP (Richard Ernst, R. 1991). Sdlg. F116-925A. TB, 38" (97 cm), EM. Ruffled deep medium blue, white zone at tip of beard; beards light blue, tipped white. B205-1: (Dover Beach x Navy Strut) X Swirling Seas. Cooley 1991.

BLUE JAY WAY (Larry Lauer, R. 1998). Sdlg. 91-206-1. TB, 36" (91 cm), EM. Ruffled blue, F. with white area around beard; beards white, yellow in throat; slight sweet fragrance. Speed Limit X Kathleen Kay Nelson. Stockton 1998.

BLUE LAMP (Cy Bartlett, R. 1999). Sdlg. (PA-CM)B. TB, 36" (91 cm), M. Ruffled medium blue self; style arms blue, touched cream; beards blue to cream; slight sweet fragrance. (Pledge Allegiance x Chico Maid) X Breakers.

BLUE LARK (Cloyd McCord, R. 1996). Sdlg. 74-08. TB, 36" (91 cm), E. Ruffled pale blue; beards white, yellow base; sweet fragrance. Princess Maxine X 83-5: (Evening Mist x (Beauty Crown x Homecoming Queen)).

BLUELIGHT YOKOHAMA (Akihiko Terada, R. 1995). Sdlg. 116-89-14. TB, 36" (91 cm), M. Ruffled medium blue self; beards yellow, tipped white. Memphis Blues X Welcome Aboard. Roris 1996.

BLUE MOMENT (Duane Meek, R. 1992). Sdlg. P24-1-7. CA, 15" (38 cm), ML. Medium to dark blue, hint of violet. T. Abell blue sdlg. X ((*I. tenax* x *I. innominata*) x Native Warrior). D & J Gardens 1992.

BLUE MONTANA SKY (Roger Nelson, R. 1994). Sdlg. RN88-8CWA. TB, 31-32" (79-81 cm), M. S. wistaria blue (near RHS 93C/D); F. softer blue (near 93A/B); beards blue white, slightly tipped gold; sweet fragrance. Electric Avenue X Full Tide. Iris Country 1994.

BLUE MORNING DAWN (Henry Millhorn, R. 1998). SIB, 40-46" (102-117 cm), M. Deep damask blue purple self, inconspicuous signal; very slight fragrance. Parentage unknown. Glasshouse Works 1995.

BLUE MOUND (Nadine Yunker, R. 1992). Sdlg. ST-1-6. SIB, 36" (91 cm), ML. S. violet blue (RHS 94B), F. same, greyed yellow throat with white at bottom. Dreaming Yellow X unknown. Yunker 1992.

BLUE NOTE BLUES (Richard Ernst, R. 1996). Sdlg. 9-194 BL. TB, 37" (94 cm), M. Ruffled medium blue (RHS 96B to 100D), F. with blended lighter area near beard; beards pale yellow (near 4D); pronounced sweet fragrance. From sdlgs. inv. Navy Strut, Dover Beach, Swirling Seas, Nights of Gladness. Cooley 1997.

BLUE PHARAOH (Oscar Schick, R. 1995). Sdlg. 90-04C21. TB, 36" (91 cm), M. S. medium blue (RHS 105D), white underside; style arms medium blue; F. medium blue, white underside apparent in beard area; beards cool white; ruffled; slight spicy fragrance. Tide's In X Blue Maxx. Stockton 1996.

BLUE QUILL (George Sutton, R. 1997). Sdlg. G-6. TB, 38" (97 cm), M. S. and style arms medium sky blue blended hyacinth blue; F. medium sky blue veined hyacinth blue; beards white, tipped yellow, 2" medium sky blue horn arched upward, ending in flounce; ruffled; slight sweet fragrance. Busy Being Blue X Dauber's Delight.

BLUE RAIN (Kevin Nilsen, R. 1991). Sdlg. 8-84-2. TB, 30" (76 cm), EM. Ruffled and waved white ground plicata, stitched dark violet blue, five distinctive blue lines adjacent to light violet beard. Gentle Rain X Blue Petticoats. Iridescence 1991/92.

BLUE RECALL (Raymond Smith, R. 1991). Sdlg. 8823BR. TB, 30" (76 cm), M & RE. Medium blue (Nickerson 10PB 5/9); yellow beard tipped light blue. Bethany Claire X 8606A: ((Winter Olympics sdlg. x Winter Olympics sdlg.) x Victoria Falls).

BLUE REVIEW (Raymond Smith, R. 1991). Sdlg. 8805AR. TB, 29" (71 cm), M & RE. Brilliant violet (Nickerson 10PB 5/9), white area around beard; beards orange, tipped white. Olive Reflection X 8606JR: ((7311C, Winter Olympics sdlg., x 7610B, Winter Olympics sdlg.) x Victoria Falls). R. G. Smith 1994.

BLUE RIDGE BEAUTY (Donald Spoon, R. 1999). Sdlg. 93-73A. TB, 34" (86 cm), M. S. smoky lavender white, midrib and base darker; style arms smoky lavender white; F. smoky violet blend (RHS 84A to 85A), lighter edges, darker venation; beards smoky violet to lavender white; ruffled, flared. Silverado X Lord Fairfax.

BLUE RILL (Bennett Jones, R. 1999). Sdlg. 569-4. SDB, 12" (31 cm), M. Ruffled gentian blue; beards pale blue white; slight fragrance. Stardate X Bay Ruffles. Aitken's Salmon Creek 1999.

BLUES CHASER (Duane Meek, R. 1991). Sdlg. 505-2-2. TB, 37" (94 cm), EM. Ruffled ice blue; beards blue. Song of Norway X Winterscape. D & J Gardens 1991.

BLUE SKIRT WALTZ (Schreiner, R. 1999). Sdlg. CC 94-1. TB, 39" (99 cm), ML. Ruffled light blue (RHS 97A) self; beards yellow, white at end. Silverado X Oregon Skies. Schreiner 1999.

BLUE SPARKLER (W. W. Steinhauer, TB, R. 1989). Cottage 1993.

BLUE SPRITZ (Donald Delmez, R. 1996). Sdlg. DWSAP. JI (6 F.), 35" (89 cm), M. Blue white, veined blue purple, edge white, signal yellow green; style arms multiple, dark blue lined white; ruffled. Caprician Butterfly X Warai-Hotei. Delmez Gardens 1996.

BLUE STREAKER (Donald Spoon, R. 1997). Sdlg. 91-40A. TB, 34" (86 cm), ML. Translucent lavender blue self, darker S. midrib and prominent F. center stripe; beards lavender blue, hairs tipped gold; ruffled, flared. Honky Tonk Blues X Silverado.

BLUE SUEDE SHOES (Schreiner, R. 1996). Sdlg. AA 105-1. TB, 39" (99 cm), ML. Ruffled medium blue (RHS 93A) self; beards yellow, tipped white at end. Breakers X T 283-1: (Land o' Lakes x Pledge Allegiance). Schreiner 1996.

BLUEVAIL OF NIGHT (Glenn G. Stoneking-Jones, R. 1998). Sdlg. CIR6-50240-07-25-1998. TB, 28" (71 cm), EM. S. dark violet blue; F. light blue, edges dark blue; beards dark blue, hairs tipped white; slight sweet fragrance. San Francisco X Blue Rhythm. Orin 1999.

#BLUE ZEBRA (William Ackerman, JI, R. 1981). Stock destroyed, name released 1996.

BLUE ZULU (B.L.C. Dodsworth, R. 1997). Sdlg. EB 90ZA. TB, 40" (102 cm), M. Ruffled pale blue self; beards white. Sullom Voe X High Peak.

BLUID (Tom Burseen, R. 1990). Sdlg. 5-322-A. TB, 33" (84 cm), M. Ruffled and flared medium violet blue (RHS 91A); beards yellow. Soap Opera X Swirling Seas. T.B.'s Place 1990.

BLUSETTE (Gustav Seligmann by Sharon McAllister, R. 1992). Sdlg. 84-7C-1. AB (OGB), 28" (72 cm), EM. Hoogiana blue (opens near RHS 106A, aging 106D); beards orange yellow. Bionic Burst X Prince Thou Art. McAllister 1992.

BLUSHING BALLERINA (A. & D. Willott, R. 1995). Sdlg. 92-187. SDB, 13½" (34 cm), ML. S. pale apricot, edge blended ceam; F. creamy white, tinted apricot, light apricot spots around creamy white beard; ruffled. Barney's Delight X Lucky Duck.

BLUSHING CRIMSON (Lois Rich by Ensata Gardens, R. 1995). Sdlg. K72-3F. JI (6 F.), 36" (92 cm), M. White halo, rays and edges, areas between rays sanded dark rose (RHS 80A), lightening toward edge; signals yellow; style arms pure white, crests large. Parentage unknown. Ensata Gardens 1995.

BLUSHING DUCHESS (George Shoop, R. 1990). Sdlg. 82-33-1. TB, 34" (86 cm), M. Lightly ruffled deep pink; beards tangerine red; slight fragrance. 79-30: ((Social Climber x Pink Pleasure) x (((Ole x Gypsy Rings sib) x Bright Sunset) x (Bright Sunset x Gay Image))) X Today's Fashion. Shoop 1990.

BLUSHING PRINCESS (William Ackerman, R. 1990). Sdlg. A4-6-122. JI (3 F.), 33" (84 cm), L. S. white with narrow dark purple (RHS 77A/B) margin; style arms white, pale purple lip; F. white blending to medium purple (77C/D) margin, green yellow (1B) signal. D5-12-115, inv. sdlgs. from Seiko-en Nursery, X D5-12-133. Nicholls Gardens 1993.

BLUSHING RADIANCE (Graeme Grosvenor, R. 1999). Sdlg. V31-T. TB, 34" (86 cm), EM. S. blue pink, heavy mauve flush; F. lighter pink, paling near beard; beards tangerine, tipped white; slight sweet fragrance. Move On X Spring Tidings.

BLUSHING ROSE (Darlene Pinegar, R. 1997). Sdlg. PNS-3-2. TB, 35" (89 cm), ML. S. and style arms medium pink; F. rosy pink mauve, darker haft marks extending to overall veining, hafts peach, white by beard; beards dark coral orange; lightly ruffled; slight musky fragrance. Earlirose X Rancho Rose. Spanish Fork 1997.

BLUSHING SNOWMAIDEN (Chad Harris, R. 1999). Sdlg. 91JA3. JI (9+ F.), 40" (107 cm), M. White, randomly brushed rose (RHS 80C) with white rays, signal yellow (2C); style arms white. Frosted Pyramid X Hagoromo.

BLUSH OF YOUTH (Glenn Corlew, R. 1996). Sdlg. 1303-2A. TB, 34" (86 cm), ML. Off-white, blushed pink, F. with rose brown on shoulders; beards tangerine orange, slight tip crest. V. Wood sdlg.: ((Mais Oui x Carved Pink) x Blushing Pink) X Elsiemae Nicholson. Cooley 1997.

BLUTIQUE (Virginia Messick, R. 1998). Sdlg. M 89-52. TB, 36" (91 cm), M. Bright medium blue on white, broken color pattern; style arms blue; beards blue. (Purple Pepper x Breakers) X Batik. Messick 1998.

BOBBIE ALLEN (J. R. Allen, TB, R. 1987). Allen Irises 1992.

BOBBY DAZZLER (Nora Scopes, TB, R. 1986). British Iris Society 1987.

BOBBY LEE EVANS (Alice Bouldin, R. 1990). Sdlg. 81-1. SIB, 28" (71 cm), M. Deep violet blue self. Swank X unknown.

BOB NICHOL (R. E. Nichol by Jean Nichol, R. 1998). Sdlg. N172. TB, 36" (91 cm), M. Ruffled dark buttercup yellow (RHS 15B), F. with tiny white splash at tip of dark yellow beard; style arms yellow. Elizabeth Poldark X Doctor Behenna.

BODY AND SOUL (Harold Stahly, R. 1999). Sdlg. 93-9. TB, 37" (94 cm), EM. S. apricot yellow (RHS 19A), orange pink central suffusion; style arms apricot yellow; F. slightly lighter (16B), shoulders touched pink; beards bright nasturtium red (30A); slight sweet fragrance. 84-44: (Sun Fire x (Orange Chariot x Barcelona)) X Esmeralda. Stahly 1999.

BOEHEMIAN HIGHWAY (Gerard Knehans Jr., R. 1999). Sdlg. KI.001. TB, 33" (84 cm), EM. Heavily ruffled deep purple violet (darker than RHS 89A); beards dark violet at end, light blue midsection, burnt gold in throat; slight sweet fragrance. Orbiter X Star Wars.

BOERDESCHNEE (Eberhard Fischer, R. 1999). Sdlg. 9. TB, 39" (100 cm), M. Waved warm white, F. with yellow hafts; beards pale yellow, white at end, dark yellow in throat. Azucena X Leda's Lover.

BOGART (George Sutton, R. 1996). Sdlg. 4-151. TB, 37" (94 cm), EM. Ruffled imperial purple (RHS 78A), F. with plum purple veining; beards pale violet, hairs tipped bronze orange to bronze except at end. Skiers' Delight X Lilac Wine.

BOG OGNIA (V. & N. Gordodelovy, R. 1995). Sdlg. 275. TB, 37" (95 cm), E. S. orange; F. bright orange; beards orange. Parentage unknown. Gordodelovy 1993.

BOGOTA (Joseph Ghio, TB, R. 1989). Bay View 1990.

BOISTEROUS (Paul Black, R. 1998). Sdlg. 91-78A. BB, 26" (66 cm), M. S. pearl lavender, veined gilt gold, gilt gold central area overlay; style arms pearl lavender, deeper lavender center, gilt gold notch; F. brick red blending to russet edge, white hafts sanded and veined brick red, small violet dart extending to faint central line; beards light violet white at end, yellow central area, yellow orange in throat; heavily ruffled; pronounced musky fragrance. Latin Hideaway X Dream of Gold sib. Mid-America 1998.

BOLD AND BEAUTIFUL (Sharon McAllister, R. 1990). Sdlg. AS-TOJ-1. AB (OGB), 29" (74 cm), EM. S. creamy lilac (near RHS 76D) splashed darker violet (near 84B); style arms bright yellow; F. golden yellow splashed shades of orange and brown, terracotta (172A) signal; beards brown. C.G. White arilbred X Tribe of Judah. Aril Society 1990.

BOLD BLAZER (Currier McEwen by Harry Kuesel, R. 1992). Sdlg. T(2)69-68. SIB (tet.), 24" (61 cm), M. Bright violet blue (RHS 93C) with prominent 5/8" circular white signal veined violet blue. T(1)61/Cas 2(1): (Violet Flare x unknown) X T(1)61/Cas 15(5): (Pirouette x unknown).

BOLD CRYSTAL (Jim & Vicki Craig, R. 1995). Sdlg. C2V6. BB, 26" (66 cm), E. Ruffled vivid blue, F. with darker blue haft marks; beards medium blue, pale yellow in throat; pronounced sweet fragrance. 17L3: (Odyssey x Maroon Caper) X 42N12: (41L14: (Odyssey x Deborah Suzanne) x 82L13: (((High Above x Lhasa) x High Life) x ((High Above x Lhasa) x Stepping Out))). J. & V. Craig 1995.

BOLDER BOULDER (Tom Magee, R. 1999). Sdlg. 911A. TB, 30" (76 cm), E & RE. S. pinkish grey; style arms grey, lilac lip; F. purplish lilac; beards bittersweet; slight sweet fragrance. Acoma X Champagne Elegance.

BOLD FASHION (Schreiner, R. 1998). Sdlg. CC 760-C. TB, 37" (94 cm), ML. S. and style arms egyptian buff (RHS 19D); F. white, 1½" violet purple (77A) rim; beards tangerine. AA 674-A: (M 1176-C, unknown, x S 885-1: (Cut Crystal x ((Glazed Orange sib x Orange Chariot) x Lacy Snowflake))) X AA 1315-B: (Gypsy Woman x (Gypsy Woman x Nearpass 81-11: ((Touche x (Country Music x Lady of Loudoun)) x Sea of Stars))). Schreiner 1998.

BOLD IMP (Ken Fisher, R. 1993). Sdlg. 91-13. MTB, 22" (56 cm), L. S. red brown; F. deep red; beards orange. 81-25-24A: ((Baby Lace x Sherwin-Wright) x Blue Bisque) X 83-4: (Consummation x (Hunson 70-11 x Buttercup Charm)). Aitken's Salmon Creek 1994.

BOLD LOOK (Schreiner, R. 1993). Sdlg. 1984-503. TB, 36" (91 cm), L. Heavily ruffled bright deep radiant yellow (RHS 12A), yellow signal; beards gold. Parentage unknown. Schreiner 1993.

BOLD STRIPES (John Weiler, R. 1992). Sdlg. 82-152-1. TB, 36" (91 cm), ML. Lightly ruffled pale yellow; beards medium yellow; foliage variegated green and ivory; slight sweet fragrance. 75-40-2A: (Goodnight Irene x Blue Luster) X Rumba Ruffle. Rialto 1992.

BOLD STROKE (Evelyn Jones, R. 1992). Sdlg. I-88-1-7. IB, 24" (61 cm), ML. French blue self; beards blackish blue; slight fragrance. Blue Line X Codicil. Bennett Jones 1993.

BOLD SUN (William Plotner, R. 1994). Sdlg. 86-341-1. TB, 36" (91 cm), M. S. lemon yellow (RHS 7B), green midrib approximately halfway up; style arms sunflower yellow (12A/B); F. lemon yellow bleeding to wide golden yellow (15C) edge, yellow ochre midstripe from beard tip to edge; beards golden glow. Bold Logic X Sunshine Maker. Wildwood Gardens 1994.

BOLD VIOLET (O. D. Niswonger, R. 1994). Sdlg. SDB 48-91. SDB, 12" (30 cm), ML. Violet with deeper violet spot; beards white, tipped very pale blue. SDB 20-87: (C. Palmer 72-59: ((Wilma V. x unknown) x Little Titan) x H. Nichols 81-9A: (April Anthem x Passport)) X Adoring Glances. Cape Iris 1994.

BOLD VISION (Frederick Kerr, R. 1999). Sdlg. 936307. TB, 29" (74 cm), EML. S. dark yellow; F. dark yellow, lighter around gold beard, wide brownish red band; ruffled, flared. Citoyen X 9111A, Dear Jean sib.

BOLLINGER (B.L.C. Dodsworth, R. 1995). Sdlg. BS 1. TB, 38" (97 cm), E. S. white infused purple; F. white, stitched purple; beards purple; ruffled; sweet fragrance. Blue Staccato X Stitch in Time. British Iris Society 1997.

BOMBAY GOLD (Francis Rogers, R. 1998). Sdlg. C-309-Y. TB, 34" (86 cm), M. Laced lemon yellow (RHS 13A), F. with lighter area beside and below beard; beards cadmium orange (23A); pronounced fragrance. Throb X C-52-A: (Royal Johnson 0-31, unknown, x Joyce Diane). Meadowbrook 1999.

BONAPARTE (Mary Dunn, R. 1993). Sdlg. L155-12. LA, 36" (91 cm), M. S. russet brown; style arms green, streaked russet; F. russet brown, large yellow signal. Southerner X L96-15: (Charlie's Michele x Rhett). Bay View 1993.

BONET (Augusto Bianco, R. 1998). Sdlg. 501. TB, 33" (85 cm), EM & RE. S. plum violet; style arms blended plum violet; F. violet, edge plum; beards gold to orange in throat, lilac at end; slight musky fragrance. Inca Queen X Soap Opera. Iride 1998.

BONFIRE NIGHT (Nora Scopes, R. 1991). Sdlg. 8/156. TB, 48" (122 cm), ML. Deep blackish red; beards yellow. 6/84: ((Spartan x 8/55: (Tarot x unknown)) x unknown) X Tintinara.

BONNE FILLE (Carl Boswell, R. 1998). Sdlg. 135-89-B. BB, 22" (56 cm), E. S. and style arms lilac white; F. creamy white, blue cast; beards cream; lightly laced and ruffled; slight spicy fragrance. Show Me X Lady Cream. Adamgrove 1998.

BONNE TERRE (Ruth Goebel, R. 1995). Sdlg. G-P. SDB, 12" (31 cm), E. S. beech brown (RHS 165A); F. oxblood (183A); beards blue. Gingerbread Man X sdlg. inv. Betsey Boo, Riches, Dancing Damsel.

BONNIE BELLE (Sharol Longaker, R. 1993). TB, 34" (86 cm), ML. Laced, flared lilac, white spot on hafts; beards orange. Lovely Kay X Laced Cotton. Anderson Iris 1993.

BONNIE DAVENPORT (Tom Burseen, R. 1997). Sdlg. 93-363B. TB, 36" (91 cm), M. Greyed lemon, edged lemon tan, F. with golden brown hafts; style arms lemon; beards purple, hairs tipped bronze, ending in cream spoon or flounce; ruffled. Thornbird X Green Prophecy. T.B.'s Place 1997.

BONNIE GLEASON (Bob Thomason, TB, R. 1987). Okie Iris 1999.

BONNIE'S BLUEBIRD (Donald Spoon, R. 1995). TB, 34" (86 cm), M. S. white, veined light cornflower blue; style arms white, edged light cornflower blue; F. cornflower blue; beards white, yellow in throat; ruffled, flared. Parentage unknown. Winterberry 1996.

BONUS BUCKS (George Sutton, R. 1996). Sdlg. B-401. TB, 35" (89 cm), ML. Ruffled diamond-dusted ethyl blue (RHS 112D), hyacinth blue (91A) spot inside base of S.; beards cobalt blue (101C), bronze in throat; pronounced spicy sweet fragrance. Ice Castle X Touch of Bronze. Sutton 1997.

BONUS LITE (George Sutton, R. 1997). Sdlg. D-112BR. TB, 37" (94 cm), ML & RE. S. white; style arms white, tinted yellow; F. white, shoulders gold; beards yellow orange, yellow with white base at outer end; ruffled; slight sweet fragrance. C-114: (Skating Party x White Lightning) X C-113: (Skiers' Delight x White Elephant). Sutton 1998.

BONUS MAMA (Ben Hager, R. 1990). Sdlg. RE4184Wh#6. TB, 30" (76 cm), E & RE (Aug.-Nov./CA). S. warm white; F. same, hint of yellow in throat; beards light yellow. T3030Wh: (Ice Sculpture x Geometrics) X I Do. Melrose 1990.

BOOGIE WOOGIE (Hooker Nichols, TB, R. 1988). Hillcrest 1993.

BOOM BOOM BUNNY (Lynda Miller, R. 1994). Sdlg. 2489. SDB, 10" (25 cm), EML. S. and style arms medium pink; F. pale pink veined medium pink, small medium pink spot around tangerine-tipped white beard; slight musky fragrance. 985A: (380: (Dove Wings x unknown) x Cherub Tears) X 1085: (Pink Pixie x Oriental Blush). Miller's Manor 1995.

BOOMERANG (William Maryott, R. 1991). Sdlg. K24C. TB, 37" (94 cm), M & RE. S. light pastel apricot; F. light apricot flushed light maroon; beards peach; lightly ruffled. G32A: ((Carved Cameo x Wings of Dreams) x Keppel 74-32E: ((Roundup x Artwork sib) x Osage Buff)) X H50A: (E31D: ((Dream Fantasy x Pink Sleigh) x Heather Blush) x F154E: ((Latin Lover x Victorian Days) x Keppel 74-32E)). Maryott 1992.

BOOM TOWN (Vernon Wood, R. 1991). Sdlg. 90-44. CA, 8-10" (20-25 cm), M. S. off-white (RHS 11D) ground, heavily lined and flushed red (53C), 1/4" off-white edge; style arms yellow; F. yellow (13A), heavily lined red (45C), 1/8" to 1/4" off-white (11D) edge, 1/2" red (45C) inner band. 88-76: (Big Money x Mimsey) X 88-68: (Long Shot x Mimsey). Portable Acres 1992.

BOOP EYES (Lorena Reid, R. 1995). Sdlg. 90S16-8F. SIB (sino-sib), 30-36" (76-91 cm), ML. S. and style arms medium lavender; F. medium lavender, large white signal bordered navy, with black lines at top in throat. Sino-sib sdlg.: (Beautiful Forty x unknown) X Butterfly Mode. Laurie's Garden 1995.

BOOT HILL (Paul Black, R. 1999). Sdlg. C100B. BB, 26" (66 cm), EM. S. charcoal purple; style arms paler, edged gold; F. dark grape purple center paling slightly toward edge, distinct cream haft veining; beards bright old gold; ruffled; pronounced sweet fragrance. Red Zinger X Tom Johnson. Mid-America 1999.

BORDEAUX PEARL (O. D. Niswonger, R. 1998). Sdlg. SDB 2-96. SDB, 14" (36 cm), M. S. and style arms burgundy; F. burgundy plicata markings, white central area with deeper burgundy streak; beards light blue. Chanted X Chubby Cheeks. Cape Iris 1998.

BORDER MUSIC (George Sutton, R. 1997). Sdlg. E-36RBB. BB, 26" (66 cm), EML. S. blended yellow ochre and pale methyl violet; style arms yellow ochre; F. pale methyl violet (RHS 85C) veined darker, 1/4" yellow edge at end of F., dark yellow ochre shoulders; beards yellow, methyl violet base; ruffled; slight sweet fragrance. Berry Rich X Miss Nellie. Sutton 1998.

BORDER RUFFIAN (Ray Lyons, TB, R. 1989). Long 1993.

BORDIURNY SINI (Irina Driagina, R. 1995). Sdlg. 78-03. BB, 24" (60 cm), VE. S. light blue; F. dark blue; beards light blue; ruffled. "Chernomorets" X Sable. Driagina 1989.

BOREALIS REX (Marvin Granger, R. 1991). Sdlg. FB-Self-91-11. LA, 28-30" (71-76 cm), M. S. light lavender pink; style arms deep green at base, cream white below light lavender pink claw; F. light lavender pink, white rays emerging below styles, lower half deep lavender purple, deep orange yellow signal; slight fragrance. FB-Self-88-8: (Freddie Boy x self) X self. Faggard 1994.

BORN A KING (Ed Roberts, R. 1992). Sdlg. 922. TB, 32" (81 cm), M. S. light lavender, white midrib touch; F. lavender, small white signal; beards yellow, tipped white; slight fragrance. Carriage Trade X Grand Waltz. Ed Roberts 1993.

BORN AT DAWN (Barry Blyth, R. 1995). Sdlg. A145-1. TB, 34-36" (86-91 cm), ML. Iridescent silvery blue, deepening on S. midribs and hafts of F.; matching beards. Just Magic X Blues Brothers. Tempo Two 1995/96.

BORN BEAUTIFUL (Paul Black, R. 1991). Sdlg. 88109B. TB, 37" (94 cm), ML. S. violet blue (RHS 92B to 87B at rib); style arms yellow orange, edged violet; F. violet (87A), smoky flesh violet rim; beards orange, blue at end; ruffled, laced; slight musky fragrance. Adventuress X Undersea Adventure. Mid-America 1992.

BORN TO EXCEED (Roger Nelson, R. 1992). Sdlg. RN 86-82BD. TB, 36" (91 cm), ML. S. icy violet blue (near RHS 92B), diamond-dusted finish; F. blue violet (near 87A to 89A), paling (88B/C) with age; beards grey orange (163A/B) tipped lavender; heavily ruffled, flared; sweet fragrance. Song of Spring X RN 82-93F: (Royal Regency x Metropolitan). Iris Country 1993.

BOSA SVETLANA (Ladislav Muska by Sergey Loktev, R. 1999). SDB, 12" (30 cm), EML. S. yellow olive, brownish base; style arms yellow olive, light blue midrib; F. brown, edged olive; beards yellow, light blue at end. ((Laced Lemonade x Bit of Chocolate) x ((Laced Lemonade x Little Annie) x ((Angelic Inspiration x Laced Lemonade) x Laced Lemonade))) X (Rangerette x Boo). Muska 1996. Introduced as "Chic Dee".

BOSS TWEED (James McWhirter, R. 1992). Sdlg. J88-22-1. TB, 38" (97 cm), M. Ruffled honey tan brown, white area under gold beards; slight fragrance. Arabian Tapestry X Role Model. Cottage 1993.

BOSTON BEAUTY (Colin Fidock, R. 1997). Sdlg. F96-2. AB (OGB), 24" (60 cm), E. S. icy lavender; style arms pale lavender, tinged gold; F. pale honey, large light burgundy signal; beards pale burgundy, tipped gold. Turkish Pendant X Close Contact.

BOSTON TOWN (Colin Fidock, R. 1999). Sdlg. F98-3. AB (OGB), 20" (51 cm), E. S. pale icy lavender; style arms gold; F. pale gold, milk chocolate signal shot dark raspberry; beards dark gold. Turkish Pendant X Close Contact.

BOTTLED SUNSHINE (Hooker Nichols, R. 1994). Sdlg. 91-04A. IB, 22" (56 cm), EML-VL. S. aureolin; F. white, deeper aureolin on edge and each side of gold beards; ruffled; pronounced fragrance. Highborn Kinsman X Joyce Terry. Hillcrest 1995.

#BOUDOIR (Joseph Ghio, TB, R. 1988). Not introduced. Name transferred.

BOUDOIR (Joseph Ghio, R. 1996). Sdlg. 91-35N2. TB, 32" (81 cm), ML. S. pure pink; F. lavender blue, shoulders pink; beards coral. 88-41T: (Honeymoon Suite x (((Homecoming Queen x 76-110BB: ((Malaysia x Carolina Honey) x (Hi Top x ((Ponderosa x Travel On) x Peace Offering)))) x ((Act of Love x Lady Friend) x (76-110BB x Toastmaster)))) X 89-73Q: (Birthday Greetings x Presence). Bay View 1997.

BOUND FOR GLORY (Heather Pryor, R. 1999). Sdlg. 5/94-A. LA, 48" (122 cm), M. Ruffled spanish orange (RHS 26A), S. with red line signal, F. with yellow steeple signal, red edging and line; style arms green at center, yellow midrib, orange tips. Bushfire Moon X Hot and Spicy.

BOUNTIFUL BLUE (Horace M. Hill by Philip Edinger, R. 1999). IB, 18" (46 cm), E & RE. Dark violet blue, beards yellow. Parentage unknown. Hill's Iris & Peony Farm 1942.

BOUNTIFUL HARVEST (Ben Hager, R. 1991). Sdlg. RE4889WPc. TB, 34" (86 cm), E & RE (June-frost/ CA). S. white ground, edged and lightly peppered violet overall, narrow purple line up midrib; F. white, stitched purple edge, faint purple center stripe; beards pale yellow, tipped purple; deeply fluted. (Space Odyssey x Socialite) X Earl of Essex. Melrose 1991.

BOUQUET MAGIC (Jim & Vicki Craig, R. 1993). Sdlg. 39X16. TB, 30" (76 cm), E. S. light blue, green at midrib base; F. maroon purple shading to lilac at edge; beards dark yellow; heavily ruffled; pronounced sweet fragrance. Payoff X Takeoff. J. & V. Craig 1993.

BOURNE ELEGANT (J. R. Ellis by A. Bailey, SPEC-X, R. 1988). British Iris Society 1987.

BOURNE GRACEFUL (J. R. Ellis, SPEC, R. 1975). British Iris Society 1990.

BOUTIQUE FASHION (Richard Ernst, R. 1999). Sdlg. MG106-1-9. TB, 35" (89 cm), M. Crinkle-textured blended purple, S. golden yellow at base, F. with gold shoulders; beards gold. Dawn of Change X Rainbow Goddess. Cooley 1999.

BOXWINK'S GOLDEN DREAM (W. W. Steinhauer, R. 1992). Sdlg. 85-5. TB, 36" (91 cm), ML. Yellow self, slightly flared F.; beards yellow. Dutch Treat X Entrepreneur. Cottage 1993.

BOXWINK'S HAPPY SMILES (W. W. Steinhauer, R. 1994). Sdlg. S-93-3. TB, 36" (91 cm), EML. Very light blue self, tinted lavender; beards reddish orange to pink. Vivien X Triumphant.

BOXWINK'S HELZA POPPIN (W. W. Steinhauer, R. 1994). Sdlg. S-93-1. TB, 36" (91 cm), ML. S. and style arms orange; F. orange with red blush; beards red; lightly ruffled. Orange Burst X Gigolo.

BOXWINK'S IDITAROD (W. W. Steinhauer, R. 1992). Sdlg. S-90-2. TB, 34" (86 cm), ML. White self; beards yellow tipped white. First Impression X Turbulence. Stockton 1995.

BOXWINK'S LEMON TREE (W. W. Steinhauer, R. 1994). Sdlg. S-85-12. TB, 34" (86 cm), EML. Clear light yellow self; matching beards. Dutch Treat X Entrepreneur. Stockton 1995.

BOXWINK'S PLEASANT ESCAPADE (W. W. Steinhauer, R. 1994). Sdlg. S-90-3. TB, 36" (91 cm), ML. Ruffled deep purple self, reddish undertone; beards purple. Evelyn's Echo X Titan's Glory.

BOXWINK'S ROYAL COURTSHIP (W. W. Steinhauer, R. 1994). Sdlg. S-90-4. TB, 36" (91 cm), ML. Ruffled very dark purple self; beards purple. Evelyn's Echo X Titan's Glory.

BOXWINK'S SNOW FOX (W. W. Steinhauer, R. 1994). Sdlg. S-93-5. TB, 36" (91 cm), ML. S. white; style arms yellow; F. white, yellow near end of yellow beard; heavily ruffled, flared. First Impression X Turbulence.

BOXWINK'S THUNDERGUST (W. W. Steinhauer, R. 1992). Sdlg. S-90-1. TB, 34" (86 cm), ML. Heavily ruffled deep purple; beards deep purple; pronounced fragrance. Titan's Glory X Evelyn's Echo.

BOY CRAZY (Mary Dunn, R. 1994). Sdlg. L 110-1. LA, 34" (86 cm), M. Deep red purple, darker texture veining, F. with bright yellow line signal; style arms with pinkish edge; wide form. C'est Chic X Easter Tide. Bay View 1995.

BOY NEXT DOOR (Paul Black, R. 1993). Sdlg. 88185C. TB, 36" (91 cm), M. S. caramel, slight violet midrib infusion; style arms old gold; F. violet center flash blending lighter toward edge, caramel edge and hafts; beards old gold, violet horn; ruffled; slight musky fragrance. Sky Hooks X 8636A: (Frances Gaulter x Sky Hooks). Mid-America 1993.

BOYSENBERRY BUTTERCUP (Larry Lauer, R. 1997). Sdlg. 89-7-1. TB, 37" (94 cm), EM. S. light creamy yellow, purple midrib shading; style arms creamy yellow, base purple; F. lavender, rim lighter; beards white end, mustard midsection, yellow in throat; ruffled; pronounced sweet fragrance. Best Bet X 87-29: (Edith Wolford x Denney 81-5-1: ((Regents Row sib x Winterscape) x Midnight Love Affair)). Stockton 1997.

BOZRAH (Fred Gadd, AB, R. 1988). Wild Mountain Thyme 1990.

BRADFORD PROMISE (Lois O'Brien, R. 1993). TB, 37" (94 cm), ML. S. creamy white, aging white; F. saffron yellow green, white wire edge; beards deep gold; ruffled; slight sweet fragrance. B7737-K: (Lemon Mist x Chartreuse Ruffles) X Sublime. O'Brien Iris 1995.

BRAEMER (John C. Taylor, R. 1997). Sdlg. UL 14-4. LA, 39" (100 cm), M. S. smoky pink (red purple); style arms smoky pink, center white; F. smoky pink, signals yellow with pink halo; lightly ruffled. Dancing Vogue X Watch Out. Rainbow Ridge 1997/98.

BRAGGADOCIO (Keith Keppel, R. 1996). Sdlg. 91-244E. TB, 30" (76 cm), ML. S. honey beige (M&P 11-C-6); style arms golden beige (11-G-6), center flushed lavender; F. blended dahlia purple (55-J-12) to port wine (56-J-12), center blended plum (47-J-9), rim shaded old mauve (46-I-5); beards dark burnt orange (4-H-12); lightly ruffled; slight sweet fragrance. 88-144A: (Gallant Rogue x (Ever After x Impressionist)) X 88-140A: ((Tomorrow's Child x Gatty K41-1: (Show Biz x Villain)) x Gallant Rogue). Keppel 1997.

BRAIN CHILD (Ben Hager, R. 1994). Sdlg. BB5611-Oc. BB, 20" (51 cm), M. Orchid self; beards tangerine. Pink Bubbles X ABB5013SmPk: (Audacious x (((Flaming Light x (2022B: (A66: (Norah x Thisbe) x Glittering Amber) x Glittering Amber sdlg.) x Picture Perfect)) x Fresno Calypso) x ((Louise Hopper x ((New Idea x 2271B) x 2271A: ((Seventh Heaven sdlg. x (Frenchi x Pagoda) x 1242F: (666D x 666B)))) x (((New Idea x 1242) x 2022B) x ((A666 x (Frenchi x Pagoda)) x 1242F))))). Adamgrove 1997.

BRAMBLEBERRY (Marky Smith, R. 1997). Sdlg. 91-23A. MDB, 7½" (19 cm), ML. S. rich red violet (RHS 83B), edge slightly paler; style arms mauve violet, edges cream; F. strong red violet, edge paler, shoulders darker, blacker area around beard, white in throat near beard; beards white, strong yellow in throat; lightly ruffled; slight spicy fragrance. Rosie Lulu X Privileged Character. Aitken's Salmon Creek 1998.

BRASH (Joseph Gatty by Keith Keppel, R. 1994). Sdlg. Y7-2. SDB, 15" (38 cm), EML. S. light chrome yellow (M&P 10-L-4) flushed metallic grey (46-B-1), deeper in center; style arms aureolin (10-L-2); F. sunflower (9-L-4) suffused greyed mauve (46-G-1), washed deeper in center, flecked darker; beards deep chrome yellow (9-L-7). Sam X Quote. Keppel 1995.

BRASS BEAUTY (Eleanor McCown, R. 1991). Sdlg. 84-0. SPU, 45" (114 cm), M. S. greenish gold; F. brassy gold overlaid with brown veins, ruffled hairline green gold edge, green gold signal. Adobe Sunset X Crow Wing. Cordon Bleu 1991.

BRASS HORN (Leo Barnard, R. 1995). Sdlg. L-88-9A. TB, 30" (76 cm), EM & RE. S. brass; F. brass, shaded antique brass; beards brass ending in antique brass horn; ruffled; slight sweet fragrance. Sky Hooks X Copper Capers. Paradise Iris 1995.

BRASS KNOCKER (Pauline Evans, R. 1997). Sdlg. 93/16. SPU, 50" (127 cm), M. S. creamy white; F. creamy white, some blending of gold from gold signal. Airy Fancy X Missouri Blue. Tempo Two 1997/98.

BRASSY CHAP (Stan Dexter by Marie Ingersoll, R. 1991). Sdlg. 103-83-142. TB, 32" (81 cm), M. Brassy orange, F. with rose purple flash; beards orange; laced. 80-97A: (Distant Light x Mabel Helland) X Hombre. Ingersoll's Iris 1992.

BRATISLAVSKÁ NOC (Zdeněk Seidel, R. 1997). Sdlg. 91-ThBo/1. TB, 39" (100 cm), EM. Ruffled dark violet (RHS 83A) self; beards violet blue, mustard in throat; slight spicy fragrance. Thriller X Blackout. Seidl 1996.

BRATR NOCI (Zdeněk Seidl, R. 1998). Sdlg. ThBo/13. TB, 39" (100 cm), ML-VL. S. and style arms deep blue purple; F. velvety purple black; beards mustard, hairs tipped blue purple; slight spicy fragrance. Thriller X Blackout.

BRAUTNACHT (Frank Kathe, R. 1993). Sdlg. 19/1-88. SDB, 9½" (23 cm), M. Heavily ruffled inky blue, black-blue spot around ink blue beards. 404-88 X Lilli-Var. Kathe 1993.

BRAVE NEW WORLD (Abram Feuerstein, R. 1996). Sdlg. 92-414/96-1. TB, 34" (86 cm), ML. Ruffled lavender-tinted white; beards yellow orange in throat, white to lavender, ending in lavender horn; slight sweet fragrance. Gaulter light blue 81-110 X Wondrous. Stockton 1996.

BRAZEN BEAUTY (Duane Meek, R. 1994). Sdlg. 66-1-5. TB, 35-36" (89-91 cm), M. S. ivory with wide raspberry pink rim; F. ivory, precise darker raspberry pink plicata rim; beards brick red; laced, heavily ruffled. Lingering Love X Queen in Calico. D & J Gardens 1994.

BRAZENBERRY (Sterling Innerst, R. 1999). Sdlg. 4346-1. TB, 36" (91 cm), M. Ruby berry-wine; beards maroon bronze; slight fragrance. Silverado X Rosette Wine. Innerst 1999.

BRAZEN HUSSY (Gene Gaddie, TB, R. 1988). Gaddies' Gardens 1991.

BRAZILIAN HOLIDAY (Schreiner, R. 1997). Sdlg. EE 293-1. TB, 36" (91 cm), ML. S. lavender white (RHS 85D); style arms white and yellow; F. plum purple (79A); beards yellowish apricot; ruffled; slight fragrance. AA 1382-1: (S 320-2: ((Gay Parasol x Bold Hour sib) x Bristo Magic) x Sweeter Than Wine) X Mulberry Punch. Schreiner 1997.

BRAZOS ABUNDANCE (Kirk Strawn, R. 1993). Sdlg. 7-1985. LA, 40" (102 cm), M. S. and style arms yellow (RHS 10D); F. slightly darker (8B), bright yellow (9A) signal. Southerner X President Hedley. Bois d'Arc 1996.

BRAZOS ANGELICA (Kirk Strawn, R. 1993). Sdlg. 38-1985. LA, 36" (91 cm), M. S. purple (RHS 76B), hint of yellow on edge and center; style arms yellow (8C) with purple (76B) blush; F. purple (76C) blushed yellow (8D), yellow (7A) signal. Sun Fury X Easter Tide. Bois d'Arc 1996.

BRAZOS CHARMER (Kirk Strawn, R. 1993). Sdlg. 1-1985. LA, 36" (91 cm), M. S. red purple (RHS 72B); style arms yellow (3C); F. red purple, yellow orange (14A) signal. Charlie's Ginny X Charles Arny III. Bois d'Arc 1996.

BRAZOS DELIGHT (Kirk Strawn, R. 1993). Sdlg. 11-1985. LA, 45" (112 cm), M. S. purple (RHS 78D); style arms purple (77B); F. darker purple (78A), yellow orange (17B) signal. Carmen X Charjoy's Jan. Bois d'Arc 1996.

BRAZOS EARLY (Kirk Strawn, R. 1997). LA, 39" (99 cm), VE. S. violet (RHS 83C); style arms and F. slightly deeper violet (83B); slight musky fragrance. Parentage unknown.

BRAZOS GOLD (Kirk Strawn, R. 1993). Sdlg. 6-1985. LA, 33" (84 cm), E. S. bright yellow orange (RHS 14B); F. slightly darker yellow orange (14A), golden orange (21B) signal. Southerner X President Hedley. Bois d'Arc 1996.

BRAZOS KNOCKOUT (Kirk Strawn, R. 1993). Sdlg. 57-1985. LA, 36" (91 cm), L. S. red purple (RHS 71A to 77A); style arms purple (77A); F. red purple (71A), yellow (7A) signal. Sdlg., unknown, X Black Gamecock. Bois d'Arc 1996.

BRAZOS PEPPERMINT (Kirk Strawn, R. 1993). Sdlg. 51-1984. LA, 33" (84 cm), M. S. purple (RHS 77C); style arms yellow orange (19B); F. greyed purple (86C), yellow (12B) signal. Merry Whirl X Sun Fury. Bois d'Arc 1996.

BRAZOS PRIZE (Kirk Strawn, R. 1993). Sdlg. 13-1985. LA, 42" (107 cm), EM. S. pale yellow (RHS 4D); style arms yellow (3D); F. slightly darker yellow (3C), yellow orange (14B) signal. Clara Goula X President Hedley. Bois d'Arc 1996.

BRAZOS SHRIMP (Kirk Strawn, R. 1993). Sdlg. 72-1984. LA, 30" (81 cm), L. S. greyed red (RHS

181D); style arms greyed red (82B); F. greyed red (181A), yellow orange (14A) signal. Sun Fury X Shrimp Louis. Bois d'Arc 1996.

BRAZOS WINE (Kirk Strawn, R. 1993). Sdlg. K-1985. LA, 31" (81 cm), L. Purple (RHS 77A), yellow green signal. Sdlg., unknown, X Black Gamecock. Bois d'Arc 1996.

BREAKAWAY PHENOMENON (Austin Morgan, R. 1990). TB, 36" (91 cm), EML. S. bronzy tan rose; F. with olive tan hafts and precise narrow rim, variable rose and white bands; beards tan. Iris Test Gardens 1983. Introduced as "Breakaway".

BREAKFAST CREEK (Kevin Nilsen, R. 1992). Sdlg. 16-86-1. TB, 36" (91 cm), EM. Ruffled white with sky blue infusion giving fluffy blue effect; beards white, tipped yellow. Beachgirl X (Cherished Memory x Starfrost Pink). Iridescence 1992/93.

BREAK THE ICE (Graeme Grosvenor, R. 1995). Sdlg. T 17-Y. TB, 38-40" (97-102 cm), ML. Ruffled white self; beards white; slight sweet fragrance. Silverado X Scandia Delight. Rainbow Ridge 1995/96.

BREATHCATCHER (Chet Tompkins, R. 1994). Sdlg. R8117. TB, 39" (99 cm), ML. Pure white self; beards white. Winter Watch X Cynthia Ann. Fleur de Lis 1994.

BREATHE EASY (Mary Dunn by Joseph Ghio, R. 1998). Sdlg. 240-7. LA, 34" (86 cm), EM. Lime yellow self, green signal. Lina X Makebelieve World. Bay View 1999.

BREEZES (Barry Blyth, R. 1991). Sdlg. Y4-7. TB, 38" (96 cm), VE-EM. S. pure white; F. citron yellow; beards yellow; slight fragrance. ((Alpine Journey x Beachgirl) x ((Beachgirl x (Tranquil Star x Coral Strand)) x (Persian Smoke x Chimbolam))) X ((Inca Queen x (Tranquil Star x (Love Chant x Festive Skirt))) x Amber Snow). Tempo Two 1992/93.

BREKEKE (Ladislav Muska, R. 1996). Sdlg. CSGE-08. TB, 36" (91 cm), ML. S. pinkish lilac; F. light reddish lilac; beards orange, red brown horns; heavily ruffled; pronounced fragrance. ("Cipkovana Krinolina": (After All x Grand Waltz) x Sky Hooks) X Geniality. Muska 1996.

BRENDA HYATT (Cyril Field, R. 1992). Sdlg. CF5. TB, 28" (71 cm), L. S. orange red and yellow, faint orange streak down center; style arms yellow; F. mostly red random pattern; beards yellow. (Quivering Flame x Golden Zebra) X flat yellow sdlg.

BRETFORTON (John D. Taylor, CA, R. 1986). Correction of spelling in 1989 Checklist from BRETFROTON.

BRIAN RAY (Clyde Hahn, R. 1995). Sdlg. 92-1-C. SIB, 27" (69 cm), M. S. light purple; F. bright purple, white signal veined light purple; slight sweet fragrance. Parentage unknown. Hahn's Rainbow 1995.

BRIAN'S BAUBLE (Richard Sparling, R. 1991). Sdlg. RCS 22. SDB, 9" (23 cm), M. Yellow green (RHS 148D), few scattered maroon markings; beards yellow green. Parentage unknown. Green Box 1991.

BRIAR PATCH (O. D. Niswonger, R. 1995). Sdlg. SDB 29-92. SDB, 13" (33 cm), ML. S. and style arms light brown; F. light brown, dark brown area around beards and in center; beards purple, lightly tipped bronze. SDB 8-88 sib: (Hooligan x unknown) X SDB 16-88: (Hoodwink x unknown). Cape Iris 1996.

BRIDAL JIG (Marty Schafer/Jan Sacks, R. 1993). Sdlg. S86-45-1. SIB, 35" (89 cm), M. White, small crescent-shaped deep yellow signal; style arms white; slight fragrance. S83-2-1: (Sky Mirror x George Henry) X Creme Chantilly. Joe Pye Weed 1993.

BRIDESMAID IN PINK (Virginia Messick, R. 1999). Sdlg. M91-1. TB, 37" (94 cm), M. S. white with pink tinge, pale pink wash on lower midsection; F. rose pink tinged lavender, pale area at haft; beards tangerine, white at end. Winifred Ross X M89-92: ((Lingering Love x G40: (Art Center x Persian Berry)) x (G40 x G40)).

BRIDESMAID'S APPAREL (Luella Danielson, R. 1992). Sdlg. LD 4-09. AB (OGB), 30" (76 cm), M. S. orchid lavender; style arms light yellow, dark lavender midrib, orchid lavender crests with light blue lines; F. yellow green, sparsely veined blue from raspberry maroon eyelash signal, pink glow around beards and on hafts; beards maroon black; fragrant. (A86-2 x Dee Mouse) X For Pleasure. Pleasure Iris 1993.

BRIDGEFORD PINK (B.L.C. Dodsworth, TB, R. 1989). British Iris Society 1990.

BRIDGE IN TIME (Betty Wilkerson, R. 1995). Sdlg. C24-1 Re. TB, 32" (81 cm), M & RE. Ruffled white self; beards white, tipped yellow in throat; slight sweet fragrance. Glistening Icicle X Immortality. Bridge in Time 1995.

BRIDGE OF DREAMS (Shuichi Hirao by Society for Japanese Irises, R. 1991). Sdlg. SH-3. JI (3 F.), 32" (81 cm), M. S. purple (RHS 82A) veined darker, narrowly edged white; style arms cream to white, sanded and veined blue violet (93B); F. white, blue halo, heavy sanding, veining and center streak of blue violet, yellow signal. Parentage unknown. Society for Japanese Irises 1992.

BRIDGWATER BLUE (Richard Lay by Mary Tubbs, TB, R. 1982). British Iris Society 1990.

BRIELLE (Franklin Carr by Margaret Carr, R. 1995). Sdlg. 87-96S. TB, 38" (97 cm), M. Pale whitish blue, deeper blue in heart; beards blue, yellow in throat; slight sweet fragrance. Edge of Winter X Chico Maid.

BRIGHT AND SUNNY (Joan Roberts, R. 1997). Sdlg. MIX 9. BB, 25" (64 cm), M. Ruffled white, deep yellow hafts; beards yellow; slight sweet fragrance. Parentage unknown.

BRIGHT BUTTERCUP (Beryl Pederick, R. 1994). Sdlg. 1. TB, 40" (102 cm), M. Buttercup yellow (RHS 15A) self; beards gold to orange; slight fragrance. Joan McClemens X Sarfraz.

BRIGHT CHIC (George Shoop, R. 1990). Sdlg. 84-38. SDB, 9" (23 cm), E. Ruffled yellow; beards tangerine red; slight fragrance. Sunny Honey X dwarf sdlg. Shoop 1990.

BRIGHT CHILD (Keith Keppel, R. 1998). Sdlg. 92-10A. SDB, 10" (25 cm), E. Clear lemon yellow (M&P 10-K-3) to chrome yellow (10-L-4) glaciata, F. with hidden oyster white strip beside beard; style arms oyster white, crest lemon yellow; beards intense cadmium yellow (9-L-8), white-based dandelion yellow (9-4-L) at end; pronounced sweet fragrance. Firestorm X Gatty W37-4, Quote sib. Keppel 1999.

BRIGHTEN THE CORNER (Allan Ensminger, R. 1994). Sdlg. 89-33. BB, 26" (66 cm), ML. S. and style arms lemon yellow (HCC 4/2); F. lemon yellow with bright white area around lemon yellow beard. 85-40: ((Peachy Creamy x Fresno Calypso) x L. Michel 120-2: (Bride's Halo x Joyce Terry)) X sib. Varigay 1995.

BRIGHTEN UP (Ben Hager, IB, R. 1989). Melrose 1990.

BRIGHT 'N BREEZY (Paul Black, R. 1993). Sdlg. 89U18. TB, 34" (86 cm), L. S. light lemon yellow; style arms yellow; F. violet blue with three darker veins down center from beard to 1/2" blended grey edge, small white patch at beard; beards yellow tipped cream; waved; slight musky fragrance. Probably --- Edith Wolford X Sparkling Fountain. Mid-America 1993.

BRIGHT NIGHTS (Mary Dunn by Robert Dunn, R. 1998). Sdlg. M2010-3. TB, 36" (91 cm), E. Ruffled lilac, rose and blue blend, F. with smoky rose edge; style arms copper; beards old gold; slight sweet fragrance. Delirious X Kamora. M.A.D. Iris 1999.

BRIGHT PARASOL (Peter Jackson, R. 1999). Sdlg. LDV2. LA, 35" (90 cm) M. Ruffled deep rose pink (RHS 64B, aging 64C), yellow gold raised spear signal on all petals; style arms cream, washed light rose; umbrella form. Dancing Vogue X Valera. Iris Acres 1999/2000.

BRIGHT PROSPECTS (Sharon McAllister, R. 1993). Sdlg. 88-16-5. AB (OGB-), 16" (42 cm), E. S. yellowish ivory; F. soft yellow, large rust brown spot surrounding yellow orange beard. Hidden Talents X (Lillibright x unknown). McAllister 1993.

BRIGHT SPARKS (Ben Hager, R. 1999). Sdlg. AMT5624YOrBds. MTB (tet.), 23" (58 cm), EM. Yellow, F. deeper; beards bright orange tangerine. Sib to Devotee. Adamgrove 1999.

BRIGHT WATER (Lynn Markham, R. 1997). Sdlg. APH-1B. SPEC (*aphylla*), 12-14" (31-36 cm), M. S. smooth red purple (RHS 74B), deeper (74A) midline; style arms pale lavender, red purple midline and crests, very elongate, with crests split and recurved; F. red purple (74B), deeper midline, haft markings relatively inconspicuous; beards pale blue at end, warm yellow in thoat. Seed from SIGNA. *I. aphylla* purple X unknown. Markham, Ohio Gardens 1997.

BRILANTINE (Ladislav Muska, R. 1995). Sdlg. SKCK-01. TB, 39" (99 cm), ML. Ruffled light lavender bitone; beards gold with blue horn. (Sky Hooks x "Cipkovana Krinolina": (After All x Grand Waltz)) X Sky Hooks. Muska 1994.

#BRILLIANT DISPLAY (Mary Dunn, TB, R. 1967). Stock destroyed and name transferred.

BRILLIANT DISPLAY (Mary Dunn, R. 1995). Sdlg. M1015-V. TB, 37" (94 cm), M. S. bright yellow; style arms golden yellow; F. creamy yellow, deeper edge, light central area; beards bright orange yellow. California Classic X Vision in Pink. M.A.D. Iris 1996.

BRINDABELLA (John C. Taylor, R. 1997). Sdlg. UL 44-1. LA, 39" (100 cm), ML. Ruffled light yellow, darker around yellow signal blending to green center; style arms light yellow. Noble Planet X Dural White Butterfly.

BRINDLED BEAUTY (Allan Ensminger, R. 1993). Sdlg. 88-54. TB, 34" (86 cm), ML. S. white with campanula splashes; F. white with campanula streaks and splashes; beards nasturtium red; slight fragrance. Peach Jam X Maria Tormena. Varigay 1994.

BRISTOL (Susan Pav, R. 1995). Sdlg. 94-14HE. TB, 31" (79 cm), EM. S. deep purple; style arms purple midrib, white base; F. deep purple with double white spot; beards white base, violet midlayer, yellow tip at end, changing to yellow in throat; slight sweet fragrance. Hello Darkness X Exotic Isle.

BRITE BIT (Ben Hager, R. 1998). Sdlg. SD5653OrFlmBds. SDB, 13" (33 cm), M. Orange self; beards bright flame. SD4997B-DpYOrBds: (My Sheba sib x (Hooligan x ((Bongo x Double Lament) x Just Dandy))) X SD5119BrtYOrBds: (SD4749: (SD4027: (3769: (2885: (Blonde Doll x 2562: (Pink Amber x Pink Cusion)) x Solar Flight) x 3520: (2888: (2562 x Buttercup Charm) x 2885)) x 4034: ((((Buttercup Charm x 2562) x 2888) x Hammered Copper) x ((2562 x (Frosty Lemonade x Pink Cushion)) x 2888))) x SD4748: ((3769 x (2888 x Solar Flight)) x 4027)).

BRITHDIR (Maureen Foster, R. 1990). Sdlg. 6H10. TB, 32" (81 cm), EML. S. sand; style arms sand; F. white below mustard beard, shading to lemon to sand edge, deep tan speckled shoulders; lightly ruffled. Desert Echo X Flamenco.

BRIZZIE (Jim & Lucy Fry, R. 1990). Sdlg. 75-F-6. SDB, 9" (23 cm), M. S. yellow; F. pale yellow with green gold spot, yellow rim; beards orange tipped white; pronounced sweet fragrance. Pretty Face X Funny Face. J & L Iris 1991.

BROADCAST (John C. Taylor, R. 1998). Sdlg. UL 5-10. LA, 43" (110 cm), M. Ruffled purple violet, signals yellow. 'Bout Midnight X Rachel's Request. Rainbow Ridge 1998/99.

BROADLEIGH CAROLYN (Broadleigh Gardens, R. 1993). CA, 18" (46 cm), M. S. pale blue, deeper blue veining shading to purple; F. pale blue, purple eye, deep purple red veins. Parentage unknown.

BROADLEIGH DOROTHY (Broadleigh Gardens, R. 1993). CA, 14" (36 cm), M. S. cream washed brownish violet with blue lines; F. brownish red, golden eye, dark red veins. Parentage unknown. Broadleigh 1985.

BROADLEIGH ELIZABETH (Broadleigh Gardens, R. 1993). CA, 18" (46 cm), M. S. pale purple with deeper veins; F. bright purple with dark purple veins. Parentage unknown.

BROADLEIGH JOAN (Broadleigh Gardens, R. 1993). CA, 14" (36 cm), M. S. pale yellow; F. pale yellow, dark yellow eye, brown veining. Parentage unknown. Broadleigh 1979.

BROADLEIGH JOYCE (Broadleigh Gardens, R. 1993). CA, 24" (61 cm), M. S. pale lilac with deeper center, veined blue and purple; F. violet, pale blue rim, white eye, dark violet center marking. Parentage unknown.

BROADLEIGH LAVINIA (Broadleigh Gardens, R. 1993). CA, 18" (46 cm), M. S. pale cream veined purple; F. purple wash over cream ground, dark red purple eye, purple veins. Parentage unknown. Broadleigh 1977.

BROADLEIGH MITRE (Broadleigh Gardens, R. 1993). CA, 24" (61 cm), M. S. lilac; F. lilac, deepening toward center, white eye, pronounced yellow central midrib, deep violet veins. Parentage unknown. Broadleigh 1978.

BROADLEIGH NANCY (Broadleigh Gardens, R. 1993). CA, 14" (36 cm), M. S. pale blue, veined purple; F. pale blue, washed purple, white eye, purple veins. Parentage unknown. Broadleigh 1980.

BROADLEIGH SYBIL (Broadleigh Gardens, R. 1993). CA, 14" (36 cm), M. S. biscuit with purple veins; F. biscuit shaded purple, yellow eye, deep purple veins. Parentage unknown. Broadleigh 1973.

BROADLEIGH VICTORIA (Broadleigh Gardens, R. 1993). CA, 18" (46 cm), M. S. biscuit shaded lilac, purple veins; F. reddish purple, paling toward rim, white eye, pronounced yellow ring and central midrib, dark violet veins. Parentage unknown. Broadleigh 1983.

BROADMOOR (Lyle Fort by Dona Fort, R. 1997). Sdlg. 89-445-E. TB, 40" (107 cm), M. Ruffled blue white self; beards white, hairs tipped blue; slight sweet fragrance. Chico Maid X Wide Hips.

BROADWAY BABY (Joseph Gatty, IB, R. 1989). Keppel 1990.

BROADWAY BEAUTY (Art Blodgett, R. 1994). Sdlg. B21-88. BB, 26" (66 cm), M. Salmon pink self; beards tangerine. Pink Graces X B20-83: (Fuchsia Frills x (Peach Festival x Favorite's Daughter)). Blodgett 1994.

BROADWAY DOLL (Herbert Holk, R. 1995). Sdlg. 829. BB, 20" (51 cm), EM & RE. S. and style arms old gold, infused burgundy; F. white, burgundy band, heavily stippled burgundy; beards gold, tipped bronze; ruffled, fluted; slight spicy fragrance. Grenadine Pacesetter X Broadway. Cal-Dixie 1995.

BROADWAY DREAM (Hooker Nichols, SDB, R. 1988). Hillcrest 1992.

BROADWAY JOE (Robert Dunn, R. 1992). Sdlg. B87-1021-A. TB, 36" (91 cm), M. S. deep buckskin tan; F. velvety dark maroon, burgundy hafts and upper third; beards bronze; ruffled. B80-744-A: (Tarde x P. T. Barnum) X M80-706-A: (Charro x Cavalier). M.A.D. Iris 1995.

BROCADE BLUE (William Ackerman, R. 1990). Sdlg. A3-10-62. JI (6 F.), 32" (81 cm), E. Violet (RHS 93A) near yellow signal, blending to brighter shades of violet blue near ruffled edge; style arms occasionally 4. D4-7-128: (D5-11-33, irradiated seed, x Double Cream) X self. Nicholls Gardens 1991.

BROKEN DREAMS (Keith Keppel, R. 1997). Sdlg. 92-97E. TB, 34" (86 cm), M. S. opera pink (M&P 1-B-8); style arms peach (9-A-5); F. peach, yellower (9-C-3) haft overlay, small paler area; beards indian orange (1-E-12), paler at end; irregular white color breaking in petals, style arms and beards; heavily ruffled, faintly laced. 89-29A: (Social Event x Femme Fatale) X 90-113A: (Social Event x Bubble Up). Keppel 1998.

BROKEN HALO (Paul Black, R. 1991). Sdlg. 87134A. SDB, 14" (36 cm), M. S. warm white, edge heavily stitched violet; style arms white, brassy olive fringed tip; F. warm white, brassy olive hafts turning into violet plicata edge which in turn breaks into chartreuse plicata edge around lower half; beards cream in throat, tipped pale blue; ruffled. Chubby Cheeks X 84238F: (Oriental Blush x Sniffs 'n' Sneezes). Mid-America 1991.

BRONCHO BILLY (John Gass, TB, R. 1989). Change of spelling to BRONCO BILLY.

BRONCO BILLY (John Gass, TB, R. 1989). Rainbow Chasers 1997.

BRONCO DOWN (Tom Burseen, R. 1995). Sdlg. 0-152A. TB, 35" (89 cm), M. S. dark brown orange (RHS 167C); style arms tan, washed brown; F. yellow ground heavily stitched and washed dark red brown (187A); beards mustard; ruffled; spicy fragrance. 7-317: ((Wild Berry x Medieval) x Oh Babe) X 6-130: ((Pencil Sketch x Pinwheel) x (Bronco Brown x Theatre)). T.B.'s Place 1995.

BRONZAIRE (Cy Bartlett, R. 1991). Sdlg. D/WAT.1. IB, 20" (51 cm), EM. Lightly waved golden bronze; beards golden bronze with greenish cast. Diligence X Warm and Toasty. Sutton 1993.

BRONZE AGE (Lois Rich by James Whitely, R. 1992). Sdlg. R84-66E. AB (OGB), 30" (76 cm), M. S. tan bronze blend; style arms bronze yellow; F. bronze, dark brown signal, lined darker; beards bronze. R79-45A: (((((I. lortetii x I. auranitica) x W83-0) x Welcome Reward) x ((R73-176L: (((Bagdad Beauty x Pink Formal) x Welcome Reward) x (Welcome Reward x ((Bagdad Beauty x Orchid and Flame) x Kalifa Hirfa))) x Hf17A) x R73-176D)) X R79-149E: (Sand Etching x ((W83-0 x Pink Formal) x R73-176H)). Aril Patch 1992.

BRONZE ART (B. Charles Jenkins, R. 1992). Sdlg. B10-8B. SPU, 54-60" (137-152 cm), EM. Bronze self. Yellow Wings X Medallion. Shepard Iris 1992.

BRONZED VIOLET (Leslie Donnell, R. 1992). Sdlg. 87-3-7. TB, 30" (76 cm), M. Bronze violet (RHS 80B) with blue flash on F.; beards orange. Speculator X Tintinara. Tempo Two 1993/94.

BRONZE LACE (Bernard Hamner by Shepard Iris Garden, R. 1993). Sdlg. 83-13. TB, 38" (97 cm), M. Laced brassy copper, very slight cream blaze at base of copper beards. Good Earth X Homecoming Queen.

BRONZE SPRITE (Jean Witt, R. 1990). Sdlg. 85-02-45. MTB, 18" (46 cm), M. S. medium brown over yellow, nearly solid plicata dotting, plicata pattern also on inner surface; style arms yellow gold, tan midrib; F. white, edged in brown plicata markings, yellow hafts and reverse; beards yellow orange. Spanish Coins X unknown. Aitken's Salmon Creek 1991.

BRONZETTE STAR (Evelyn Kegerise, R. 1990). Sdlg. 83-401-1. TB, 36-38" (91-97 cm), M. Ruffled bright rusty brown, soft violet blaze on F. aging golden; beards orange gold; slight spicy fragrance. Lady Friend X Steady Pace. Evelyn Kegerise 1992.

BRONZOVY VEK (Nina Miroshnichenko, R. 1996). TB, 31" (79 cm), M. S. henna brown, copper yellow base; F. henna brown, darker hafts, small lilac spot under yellow beard; ruffled; pronounced sweet fragrance. Parentage unknown. Miroshnichenko 1994.

BRONZY MARVEL (Lorena Reid, R. 1998). Sdlg. 92S44-7F3B. SIB (sino-sib), 18" (46 cm), ML. S. warm pale lavender; style arms light gold, maroon base and partial midrib; F. light gold overlaid light magenta maroon giving bronze effect, large dark maroon signal with jagged edge, several dark gold central lines. Cascade Creme X clear yellow albino sdlg.: (I. chrysographes hybrid with bee signal x unknown). Laurie's Garden 1998.

BROOKSIDE (Ron Busch, R. 1997). Sdlg. 8673/4. TB, 40" (102 cm), M. S. robins-egg blue; F. light violet, widely edged robins-egg blue; beards orange; ruffled, flared; slight fragrance. 77204/2: ((Tea Apron x Wine and Roses) x (Siva Siva x Tuxedo)) X 7789: ((Rippling Waters x Velvet Robe) x Black Swan).

BROSELEY (John D. Taylor, TB, R. 1986). V. H. Humphrey 1992.

BROTHER JOHN (Ed Attenberger, R. 1996). Sdlg. 92-01-10. TB, 38" (97 cm), M. S. and style arms medium buff pink; F. light orchid, tan edge, whitish area around red orange beard; ruffled; slight sweet fragrance. Peach Picotee X Entourage.

BROWNIE POINTS (Joseph Ghio, R. 1999). Sdlg. PB-254K3. CA, 18" (46 cm), ML. Mocha, F. with deeper edge, maroon brown signal. Parentage unknown. Bay View 1999.

BROWN'S MUTANT (Clarence Mahan, R. 1993). MTB, 26" (66 cm), M. S. rich yellow; F. yellow, veined and dotted red; beards yellow; slight sweet fragrance. Sport of Kaleidoscope originating in the Rex and Alta Brown garden, ca. 1967.

BROWNSTONE (Joseph Ghio, R. 1992). Sdlg. SP-90-1. SPU, 40" (102 cm), ML. Deep mahogany self. Burnt Toast X (Border Town x Purple Profundo). Bay View 1993.

BROWN TO VIOLET (Austin Morgan, R. 1990). TB, 36" (91 cm), EML. S. deep brown; F. deep violet, brown hafts; beards brown. Parentage unknown. Iris Test Gardens 1990.

BROXTED CEDRIC (Ellis Carpenter, R. 1996). Sdlg. 88BB1. BB, 22" (56 cm), ML. S. light pink; style arms slightly deeper pink; F. very pale pink, flushed lilac toward edge, hafts pale lemon, light brown stitching; beards orange; slight fragrance. 85BB1, inv. Morris sdlg., X 85.6.6 peach: (Benton Berenice x self).

BROXTED CERULEAN (Ellis Carpenter, R. 1990). Sdlg. 76-5-1. TB, 40" (102 cm), ML. S. pale blue, lilac flush at base; F. very pale blue (almost bluish white); beards orange, tipped blue; slight musky fragrance. Gilston Gwyneth X Jeffs sdlg.: (Esther Fay x Rippling Waters).

BROXTED ISIS (Ellis Carpenter, R. 1990). Sdlg. 73-31. TB, 38" (97 cm), EM. Deep medium blue, slightly veined; beards medium blue. Lady Mohr X Morris B67/8, light blue.

BRUNEAU JASPER (Lucille Pinkston, R. 1996). Sdlg. 88-1-B. TB, 32" (81 cm), M. S. white, edge tinted light orchid; style arms white, tinged orchid; F. wine red, white washed ray pattern and wire rim; beards medium yellow; slight fragrance. Wild Jasmine X unknown. Sand Hollow 1997.

BRYNGWYN (Maureen Foster, R. 1990). Sdlg. 4E2. TB, 40" (102 cm), ML. Ruffled, flared white; beards white. Millrace X Song of Norway. V. H. Humphrey 1995.

BRYNMAWR (Harry Foster, SIB, R. 1989). V. H. Humphrey 1995.

BUBBLE DANCER (Joseph Ghio, R. 1993). Sdlg. 88-115G3. TB, 34" (86 cm), ML. Pure coral pink self; beards tangerine. 85-153T3: (Newlywed x 82-156H2, pod parent of Bubbling Along) X 85-107L2: (82-156H2 x Romantic Mood). Bay View 1994.

BUBBLE GUM BALLERINA (Dorman Haymon, LA, R. 1989). Deep South Garden 1990.

BUBBLING ALONG (Joseph Ghio, R. 1992). Sdlg. 87-122U. TB, 42" (107 cm), EM. Pure pink; beards coral tangerine. 82-156H: (Winning Note sib x (Blushing Pink x 76-176Y: (((Ponderosa x Debby Rairdon) x (Show Time x San Leandro)) x ((New Moon x ((Gracie Pfost x Ponderosa) x Ponderosa)) x Valentina)))) X Bubble Up. Bay View 1993.

BUCHHOLZER CHARM (Harald Moos, R. 1996). Sdlg. 91/103Y. TB, 34" (85 cm), M. Ruffled medium pink self; beards pink. (Vanity x Heimann sdlg.) X Buchholzer Traeumerei. Moos 1997.

BUCHHOLZER FLIEDER (Harald Moos, R. 1999). Sdlg. 93/B44D. TB, 32" (80 cm), M. Ruffled violet pink, F. with orange pink hafts; beards orange. Mulled Wine X Beverly Sills.

BUCHHOLZER GLUT (Harald Moos, R. 1993). Sdlg. 86/6007C. TB, 31½" (80 cm), M. Violet purple; beards red orange. Matinee Idol X Mulled Wine. Schoeppinger 1993.

BUCHHOLZER HIMMEL (Harald Moos, R. 1995). Sdlg. 91/A48y. TB, 31" (80 cm), M. S. and F. white, tinted blue; beards dark blue, tipped yellow; waved. Leineufer X Tide's In. Schoeppinger 1996.

BUCHHOLZER NACHT (Harald Moos, R. 1999). Sdlg. 94/27A. TB, 35" (90 cm), M. Waved blackish blue self; beards pale blue. Titan's Glory X Dusky Challenger.

BUCHHOLZER PRACHT (Harald Moos, R. 1996). Sdlg. 90/36D. TB, 34" (85 cm), M. Ruffled creamy orange; beards orange red. (Lilac Treat x Silver Shower) X Pretty Lady. Moos 1997.

BUCHHOLZER ROMANTIC (Harald Moos, R. 1992). Sdlg. 84/437C. TB, 33½" (85 cm), M. Heavily frilled whitish pink, hafts salmon pink; beards red orange. Buffy X Vanity. Schoeppinger 1993.

BUCHHOLZER ROYAL BLUE (Harald Moos, R. 1996). Sdlg. 91/127A. TB, 36" (90 cm), L. Heavily ruffled blue violet, F. with white zone around orange beard. Winifred Ross X Memphis Blues. Moos 1997.

BUCHHOLZER SONNE (Harald Moos, R. 1999). Sdlg. 84/487A. TB, 35" (90 cm), E. Waved lemon yellow, F. with white center; beards lemon yellow. Well Endowed X Precious Moments.

BUCHHOLZER SONNENAUFGANG (Harald Moos, R. 1995). Sdlg. 88/865 B. TB, 34" (86 cm),

M. Ochre yellow; beards orange; waved. Warrior King X 77/701 B: (Laced Cotton X Precious Moments). Schoeppinger 1996.

BUCHHOLZER TRAEUMEREI (Harald Moos, TB, R. 1986). Schoeppinger 1990.

BUCHHOLZER YELLOW (Harald Moos, R. 1991). Sdlg. 87/737A. TB, 31½" (80 cm), M. Golden yellow; beards gold yellow. Sommernachtstraum X Vanity. Schoeppinger 1993.

BUCKEYE BELLE (A. & D. Willott, R. 1990). Sdlg. 84-155. IB, 18" (46 cm), ML. Ruffled light yellow, red brown halo; beards yellow orange. (Ohio Belle x Prosperity) X Coral Wings. Willott 1990.

BUDDY BOY (Paul Black, R. 1999). Sdlg. B299A. SDB, 14" (36 cm), M. S. and style arms pastel violet; F. medium orchid lighter toward edge, pastel violet wire rim, short white haft veins; beards orange, light violet at end; pronounced sweet fragrance. Tweety Bird X 91321-sib blue: (87149B, Unpretentious sib, x 86382A: ((Oriental Blush x Gigglepot) x Stardate sib)). Mid-America 1999.

BUDJIK HILL (Geoff Austin, R. 1998). Sdlg. EWS-1595. TB, 28" (72 cm), ML. S. and style arms light blue; F. mauve; beards lemon; ruffled. Edith Wolford X Silverado. Austland 1998/99.

BUENOS AIRES REVISITED (John Durrance, R. 1990). Sdlg. D82-28. TB, 36" (91 cm), ML. S. orange; F. red. Anon X Taco Belle. Long 1990.

BUFFER ZONE (Sterling Innerst, R. 1998). Sdlg. 3911-5. TB, 34" (86 cm), M. Medium brown; beards golden brown; slight fragrance. 2116-1: (Coffee House x 1016-2, Gingeruffle sib) X 3277-1: (Glazed Gold x Catalyst). Innerst 1998.

BUGLEBOY BLUES (George Sutton, R. 1995). Sdlg. G-65A. TB, 38" (97 cm), ML. Ruffled sky blue (RHS 109C) mottled french blue (100); style arms blended sky blue (109B/C); beards sky blue, base white, gold in throat, ending in sky blue spoons; slight sweet fragrance. Dauber's Delight X Honky Tonk Blues. Sutton 1996

BUGLES AND HORNS (George Sutton, R. 1996). Sdlg. G-79-A. TB, 38" (97 cm), ML. Ruffled white self; style arms serrate; beards yellow, white at end, with white horns and flounces; slight sweet fragrance. Dauber's Delight X Kuniko. Sutton 1997.

BUGSY (Ben Hager, R. 1992). Sdlg. MD5494BkVar. MDB, 5-7" (13-18 cm), M. S. yellow; F. near-black maroon, edged yellow; beards orange yellow. AMD4942CrBrSp: ((Abridged Version sib x (Inca Toy x (sdlg. x Atomic Blue))) x ((Curio (Prodigy x ((Red-Lilli x Pogo) x Regards))) x ((1997A: (Rickshaw x Lilli-Var) x Bongo) x (Russet Dot x 1997G)))) X Ditto. Adamgrove 1993.

BUILDER QUEEN (Robert Jeffries, TB, R. 1989). Kansas Rainbow 1990.

BUISSON DE ROSES (Richard Cayeux, R. 1997). Sdlg. 8972 A. TB, 32" (80 cm), ML. Light salmon pink self; beards salmon. Paradise X Helene C. Cayeux 1998.

BULLWINKLE (George Sutton, R. 1994). Sdlg. HF-T-BBA. BB, 26" (66 cm), M. S. bright medium yellow, burgundy midrib; style arms yellow, washed burgundy; F. lighter yellow ground, burgundy plicata haft patterning, burgundy midrib, 1/8" light yellow outer rim, 1/3" burgundy (RHS 83A) inner rim; beards golden orange. GW-HF-T-A: ((Gypsy Wings x Heat Flare) x Tulare) X Baby Bengal. Sutton 1994.

BUMBLE BOOGIE (Riley Probst, R. 1997). Sdlg. 90RJX39D1. MTB, 22" (56 cm), M. S. gold; F. lavender, rimmed gold; beards orange, ending with slight projection; flared; slight fragrance. Real Jazzy X Bumblebee Deelite.

BUNGLEBERRY DEANE (C. R. King, R. 1994). Sdlg. 3 CRK 93. TB, 48" (122 cm), E. S. light mauve; F. burgundy, veined slightly deeper; beards yellow; ruffled; musky fragrance. Parentage unknown.

BUNGO-NO-KAGAYAKI (Kiyoro Yoshie by Society for Japanese Irises, R. 1995). JI (6 F.), 37" (95 cm), M. White with white venation; style arms white, very large. Parentage unknown. Introduced in Japan, 1966.

BUNNICULA (Sterling Innerst, R. 1990). Sdlg. 3377-2. IB, 25" (64 cm), M. S. white, light yellow base; F. full yellow; beards yellow. Image Maker X Dash Away. Innerst 1991.

BUNTY (Revie Harvey, SPEC, R. 1986). Hilmary Catton 1991.

BUONGIORNO APRILE (Valeria Romoli, R. 1996). Sdlg. 25D-90. TB, 36" (91 cm), M. Laced peach pink self; beards coral red, paler at end and base; slight musky fragrance. 4G-87: (18D-85 x Risque Pink) X Sweet Musette.

BUOYANT (John C. Taylor, R. 1997). Sdlg. UL 22-3. LA, 35" (90 cm), M. S. white, center blending to yellow; style arms lemon to light yellow; F. light yellow, yellow green signal; ruffled, fluted. Gladiator's Gift X Dural Dreamtime. Rainbow Ridge 1998/99.

BURANO (Augusto Bianco, R. 1999). Sdlg. 710. SDB, 11" (28 cm), M. S. caramel apricot; style arms beige and lilac; F. caramel apricot, wine lilac spot, yellow hafts; beards lavender, hairs tipped carrot; pronounced sweet fragrance. (Court Magician x Small Flash) X (Leprechaun's Gold x Logo).

BURGUNDELOVELY (George Bush, R. 1997). Sdlg. 19-20-21. JI (3 F.), 34" (86 cm), ML. Wine red, S. and style arms tipped black, F. with gold signal; arched, flared form. Parentage unknown; seed from Japan. Bush 1998.

BURGUNDY FIZZ (George Sutton, R. 1995). Sdlg. B-486A. TB, 39" (99 cm), ML. S. light violet burgundy; F. dark burgundy, edged silver white; beards burgundy; ruffled, laced. 2-33: (Silver Flow x Ringo) X Adventuress. Sutton 1995.

BURGUNDY PARTY (Bernard Hamner by Shepard Iris Garden, R. 1994). Sdlg. 89-59. TB, 38" (97 cm), M. S. light pinkish burgundy; F. rich dark burgundy, 1/8" pinkish burgundy fluted edge; beards lavender pink. Gay Parasol X Space Shadows. Hamner Iris, Shepard Iris 1994.

BURNING BRIGHT (Chet Tompkins, R. 1992). Sdlg. 87-5B. TB, 39" (99 cm), ML-VL. Ruffled and flared vivid chrome sulphur yellow glaciata; self beards. Fun and Games X Laredo. Fleur de Lis 1992.

BURNT CRISP (Tom Burseen, R. 1994). Sdlg. 6-81A. TB, 34" (86 cm), M. S. tan-brown; F. very dark brown, cream spray pattern at gold beard; laced; spicy fragrance. Rio de Oro X 4-52: (West Coast x Pencil Sketch). T.B.'s Place 1994.

BURRA SAHIB (Ben Hager, AB, R. 1989). Melrose 1990.

BURR SCENE (Tom Burseen, TB, R. 1989). T.B.'s Place 1990.

BURST (Barry Blyth, R. 1993). Sdlg. Z81-1. TB, 36" (91 cm), EM. S. golden butterscotch; F. butterscotch with red infusion halfway down; beards bright mustard yellow; sweet fragrance. Swain X (Mountain Melody x Polished Amber). Tempo Two 1993/94.

BURST OF BLUE (A. & D. Willott, R. 1998). Sdlg. W 94-30. MDB, 5" (13 cm), E. Lightly ruffled white, F. with medium-size full blue spot; beards white. W 91-85: (Pittance x W 79-13: (Greenlee GX-2 x Buttons)) X W 92-6: (Kuban *pumila* 205 x Daring Eyes). Willott 1998.

BUSHFIRE MOON (Heather Pryor, R. 1994). Sdlg. 40/90-7. LA, 30" (76 cm), EM. Ruffled orange yellow (RHS 23B) with fine green line signal on all petals. Alluvial Gold X Gladiator's Gift. Rainbow Ridge 1995/96.

BUSH GOSSIP (Barry Blyth, R. 1994). Sdlg. A53-3. IB, 22" (56 cm), VE-EM. S. mushroom pink, faint lavender midrib flush; F. darker mushroom to rose tan; beards bronze, bright lavender on outer 1"; pronounced musky fragrance. X25-5, Impish sib, X Electrique. Tempo Two 1994/95.

BUSHI (Ed Matheny III, R. 1995). Sdlg. J:00-01-93. JI (6 F.), 41" (104 cm), EM. Purple, splashed and etched cream, erratically marked; blue blaze at tip of yellow signal; style arms purple, greyed midrib. Geisha Gown X Glitter and Glamour. Ed's Iris 1996.

BUSINESS TYCOON (Hooker Nichols, SDB, R. 1988). Hillcrest 1990.

BUSY BEING BLUE (Don Denney by James McWhirter, TB, R. 1989). Cottage 1990.

BUSY LIZZIE (Nancy Burrows, TB, R. 1989). Stornoway Gardens 1990.

BUSY SIGNAL (Larry Lauer, R. 1992). Sdlg. L86-7-7. TB, 38" (97 cm), M. S. brown; F. darker velvety brown with gold plicata markings near gold beard; ruffled; slight fragrance. Chocolate Shake X Cinnamon. Cottage 1993.

BUT BEAUTIFUL (Barry Blyth, R. 1998). Sdlg. E118-2. TB, 38" (96 cm), VE-E. S. icy blue white, tangerine tan at base; F. coffee tan, dusted rose overlay deepening at hafts, near-violet by beard; beards rich tangerine, prominent; slight sweet fragrance. B209-1: (Y6-5, Imprimis sib, x Z63-4, Aztec Burst sib) X Yes. Tempo Two 1998/99.

BUTTER AND CREAM (Currier McEwen, R. 1995). Sdlg. T(8)-87/175. SIB (tet.), 30" (75 cm), EML. S. pale yellow (RHS 4D), edges deeper (4C); style arms creamy yellow (10D), deeper (10C) on midrib and outer third; F. rich yellow (12B), deeper (12A) crimped edge, paling (10D) with age except at edges; hafts yellow green (154A); ruffled. T(7)-84/118(1): ((Ruffles Plus sib x Happy Event) x Happy Event) X T(7)-84/106-(11): (Ivory Cream x T(3)-79/126-(1): inv. Dreaming Yellow sdlgs.). Eartheart 1999.

BUTTER CREAM (Opal Wulf, R. 1998). Sdlg. 19-93-1. BB, 23" (58 cm), EML. S. pale chartreuse yellow (RHS 2D), edged near-white; style arms pale yellow; F. pale primrose yellow (4D) flushed darker (4C), edges near-white, pale green gold shoulder veining; beards yellow, tipped white; ruffled, flared; pronounced sweet fragrance. Divine X Lichen. Wulf's Backachers 1998.

BUTTERED CLOUD (Ed Matheny III, R. 1991). Sdlg. 01-03-87. TB, 33" (84 cm), M. S. yellow; F. white, 1/4" yellow edge; beards orange; slight fragrance. Truly Yours X unknown. Ed's Iris 1992.

BUTTERFINGERS (Larry Lauer, R. 1997). Sdlg. 88-55-5. TB, 34" (86 cm), ML. S. and style arms yellow; F. white ground changing to yellow, patterned brown edge, light purple center streak; beards yellow; ruffled; slight sweet fragrance. Hot to Trot X (Gigolo x Captured Beauty). Stockton 1997.

BUTTERFLIES IN FLIGHT (J. T. Aitken, R. 1991). Sdlg. 85J2. JI (6 F.), 42" (107 cm), ML. White ground delicately veined blue violet, intensifying around yellow signal; style arms dark violet. Knight in Armor X Flying Tiger. Aitken's Salmon Creek 1991.

BUTTERFLY BRIGHT (William Ackerman, R. 1998). Sdlg. B4-16. JI (3 F.), 48" (122 cm), ML. S. red purple (RHS 72A), narrow white margin, small; style arms white, light mallow purple (72D) margin; F. white, narrow red purple veins radiating from bright yellow (7A) signal. Edged Delight X Emperor's Bride. Nicholls Gardens 1999.

BUTTERFLY DANCE (A. & D. Willott, R. 1999). Sdlg. W 93-92B. MTB, 25" (63 cm), M. S. full violet (RHS 86B), midrib slightly lighter; style arms light violet (86C); F. velvety deep violet (86A), white haft pattern; beards maize yellow (21B); lightly ruffled. Dunderman HH236 X unknown.

BUTTERFLY FESTIVAL (J. Owings Rebert, R. 1996). Sdlg. FR-C-1. SIB, 28" (71 cm), M. Light blue, F. with ivory and tan signal. Flight of Butterflies X unknown.

BUTTERFLY HOUSE (Evelyn Robarts, R. 1998). Sdlg. 91/34. TB, 33-35" (84-89 cm), M. Warm white self; style arms pale yellow; beards tangerine, ending in large, upturned white flounce; slight fragrance. Barley Green X Bearded Wonder. Stahly 1999.

BUTTERFLY MODE (Lorena Reid, R. 1991). Sdlg. BtFl 407. SIB (sino-sib), 42" (107 cm), ML. S. violet blue (RHS 95C); bright violet blue (95A) styles; F. violet blue (97C), white signal striated with almost black lines, rimmed violet blue (95A). Parentage unknown. Laurie's Garden 1992.

BUTTERFLY OF LOVE (Mary Dunn, R. 1994). Sdlg. 159-9. LA, 36" (91 cm), M. S. french lilac; F. french lilac, large white area around yellow line signal. Elusive Butterfly X L96: (Charlie's Michele x Rhett). Bay View 1994.

BUTTERMAKER (Art Cronin, R. 1990). Sdlg. F-27. SIB, 29" (74 cm), M. S. white, 3 yellow lines at midrib; style arms white, 2 yellow lines at midrib; F. yellow (RHS 6B), 3 deeper yellow lines at midrib, 1 cm. white edge at hafts widening to 2½ cm. at end of blade; signal yellow. Floating Island X Dreaming Yellow.

BUTTERMAKER'S BRIDE (Art Cronin, R. 1991). Sdlg. F-28. SIB, 38" (97 cm), L. S. and style arms white, midrib cream; F. pale yellow, yellow signal. Floating Island X Dreaming Yellow.

BUTTERMILK BLUSH (Jim Hedgecock, R. 1993). Sdlg. C-83-12-5. TB, 32" (81 cm), ML. S. pale cream white, midrib touched pink; F. pale cream white, hafts touched apricot; beards tangerine; ruffled, heavily laced; pronounced sweet fragrance. Peach Tree X Entourage. Comanche Acres 1994.

BUTTER ON ICE (Donald Sorensen, R. 1999). Sdlg. S-91-36-1. MTB, 23" (59 cm), M. S. light primrose yellow (RHS 4C); style arms paler (4D); F. white (155A), medium primrose yellow (4A) hafts; beards dark lemon (14A); flared; slight sweet fragrance. Fair Haldis X unknown.

BUTTER RINGS (J. T. Aitken, R. 1998). Sdlg. 91M29. SDB, 12" (31 cm), M. S. butter yellow; F. deeper yellow, butter yellow 1/8" rim; beards yellow. Lankow 0H9: (Flirty Mary x Loveshine) X Tickled Peach. Aitken's Salmon Creek 1998.

BUTTER RIPPLES (B. Charles Jenkins, R. 1998). Sdlg. AZ68D. SPU, 42-48" (107-122 cm), M. Heavily ruffled yellow self. Candle Lace X A19-0D: (Highline Honey x unknown). Shepard Iris 1999.

BUTTERSCOTCH BABY (Sharon McAllister, R. 1992). Sdlg. 88-16-1. AB (OGB-), 16" (42 cm), EM. S. greyed yellow orange (near RHS 161C); F. darker, greyed red (182B) signal; beards dark yellow, tangerine in throat. Hidden Talents X (Lillibright x unknown). Aril Society 1992.

BUTTERSCOTCH BLUES (Norma Barnard, R. 1996). Sdlg. N 91-93. TB, 32" (81 cm), M. S. and style arms butterscotch; F. ivory, banded butterscotch, variable pale blue center wash; beards gold; ruffled; slight sweet fragrance. Evening Magic X Bohemian. Paradise Iris 1996.

BUTTERSCOTCH CANDY (Cleo Palmer, R. 1994). Sdlg. 8834. SDB, 12" (30 cm), M. S. light tannish yellow, paler rim; F. light tannish yellow, tannish yellow rim, large brownish yellow spot; beards yellow, tipped pale blue violet; ruffled. Parentage unknown. Palmer's Iris 1994.

BUTTERSCOTCH CARPET (Chuck Chapman, R. 1994). Sdlg. 87-16-2. SDB, 10" (25 cm), L. S. light butterscotch tan; F. dark butterscotch, narrow yellow tan edge and lines in throat; beards yellow orange, yellow at end. Be Dazzled X Mister Roberts. Chapman Iris 1994.

BUTTERSCOTCH QUEEN (B. Charles Jenkins, R. 1992). Sdlg. C17-OS. SPU, 35-40" (80-102 cm), M. Burnt orange to butterscotch yellow self. Highline Honey X unknown. Shepard Iris 1991.

BUTTERSCOTCH ROUNDUP (Jim Hedgecock, R. 1991). Sdlg. C-84-25-3. TB, 34" (86 cm), M. Ruffled golden orange brown; beards golden orange; slight spicy-sweet fragrance. Hilow X 73-13, inv. sdlg. lines. Comanche Acres 1996.

BUZZ ME (Barry Blyth, R. 1992). Sdlg. X11-1. SDB, 12" (31 cm), EML. S. lemon yellow; F. lemon yellow, white spot with gold halo below bushy pastel lavender beard. Oladi X (Capricornia x (Helter Skelter x Real Coquette)). Tempo Two 1992/93

BYE BYE BIRDIE (Lynn Bausch, R. 1995). Sdlg. R 35-5. SDB, 10½" (26 cm), EM. S. cream (RHS 19D), midrib and border medium yellow (18A); style arms medium yellow blending to light violet toward base; F. creamy medium yellow border, darker yellow beside beard; beards medium blue violet (93C); ruffled; slight sweet fragrance. J6-2: (Angelic x Ivory Shimmer) X Azure Gem. Garden of the East Wind 1996.

BYE BYE BLACKBIRD (George Sutton, R. 1996). Sdlg. F-271. TB, 36" (91 cm), EM & RE. Ruffled black, violet-infused edge; beards purple black; slight spicy fragrance. B-379: ((Night Affair x (Black Flag x Ringo)) x (Black Flag x (Holy Night x Black Flag))) X B-381: (Holy Night x Recurring Ruffles).

BYE BYE BLUES (George Sutton, R. 1996). Sdlg. G-15-AR. TB, 37" (94 cm), M. S. blended hyacinth blue (RHS 91A) to wistaria blue (91C); style arms pale blue; F. wistaria blue (91 C/D); beards wistaria blue (91C), orange in throat, pale blue base, ending in hyacinth to wistaria spoon; ruffled; slight sweet fragrance. Dauber's Delight X Honky Tonk Blues. Sutton 1997.

BY GEORGE (George Slade, TB, R. 1988). Wyle Wynde 1990.

BYGONE DAYS (Chet Tompkins, R. 1992). Sdlg. 83-57. TB, 36" (91 cm), ML. Cool pink self; beards red. ((Char-Maize x Emissary) x (Maudie Marie x Deep Devotion)) X ((Ovation x Chanteuse) x (Paradise x Easy Grace)). Fleur de Lis 1992.

BYGONE ERA (Joseph Ghio, TB, R. 1989). Bay View 1990.

BY SURPRISE (H. C. Mohr by Bryce Williamson, R. 1993). TB, 34" (86 cm), EM. S. creamy white, flushed and banded lemon yellow; F. white, banded lemon yellow; beards lemon; ruffled, lightly laced; slight fragrance. Parentage unknown.

BY YOUR LEAVE (Richard Ernst, R. 1998). Sdlg. MHS 902-3. TB, 36" (91 cm), ML. Violet blue self; beards blue white. Raven's Quote X Clear Morning Sky. Cooley 1998.

BYZANCE (Pierre-Christian Anfosso, R. 1990). Sdlg. PC 81 13. AB (OGB), 31½" (80 cm), M. Gold yellow; raspberry spot under dark beards. Moon Star X Bethlehem Star. Iris en Provence 1990.

CABARET ACT (Bryce Williamson, R. 1995). Sdlg. A-12-1. TB, 36" (91 cm), M. S. valencia orange, midrib shaded amber orange tan; F. valencia orange, blended and shaded amber orange tan from shoulders; beards vivid tangerine red; lightly ruffled. Hindenburg X Baroque.

CABO DE NUOVO (Ladislav Muska, R. 1999). Sdlg. 98-BRDW-05. TB, 34" (86 cm), L. S. honey amber; style arms lighter amber; F. deep burgundy red; sweet fragrance. ((Brilantine x Ringo) x (Concorde With Hooks x Sweeter Than Wine)) X Decory Win. Muska 1999.

CABOT COVE (Larry Lauer, R. 1994). Sdlg. 86-28-1. TB, 35" (89 cm), M. S. blue orchid, washed white; F. blue orchid, washed white, aging to show sanded pepper pattern on shoulders and margins; beards white, tipped lavender; slight fragrance. Cocktail Hour X Go Around. Stockton 1994.

CABRIOLE (John Gass, R. 1997). Sdlg. G-85-6. TB, 36" (91 cm), M. Ruffled and laced white self; beards red; sweet fragrance. Valentina X Risque. Rainbow Chasers 1998.

CACHE (Barry Blyth, R. 1997). Sdlg. D24-1. SDB, 12" (30 cm), VE-EM. Bright orange; beards orange, tipped tangerine. Flitters X Carats. Tempo Two 1997/98.

CACHE CREEK (Colin Rigby, R. 1993). Sdlg. PCN 54. CA, 12-14" (30-36 cm), M. White with pale blue cast, small light yellow signal. Canyon Snow X sdlg. Portable Acres 1993.

CACOPHONY (Barry Blyth, R. 1995). Sdlg. A162-1. TB, 32" (81 cm), ML. S. bright apricot; F. plush burgundy, 1/8" bright apricot edge; beards bright tangerine; ruffled. Curacao X U83-B: (Edge of Winter x London Lord). Tempo Two 1995/96.

CADDO GAP (Richard Morgan, R. 1992). Sdlg. L439-V. LA, 32" (81 cm), M. Red violet (RHS 83B), orange yellow steeple signal; style arms lighter red violet. Strange Romance X L4-A: (Trail of Tears x Bayou Comus). Redbud Lane 1993.

CADMAN (Keith Fillmore, R. 1991). Sdlg. 8605-41B. IB, 22" (56 cm), M. S. light yellow; F. white, mustard yellow hafts radiating halfway down, yellow edge; beards orange to yellow, tipped white; ruffled; pronounced sweet fragrance. Drummer Boy X unknown. Bar K Iris 1992.

64

CAESAR'S NEPHEW (J. Owings Rebert, R. 1995). Sdlg. SR-2. SIB, 32" (81 cm), M. Medium violet self, F. with white blaze, gold haft. Caeser's Brother X unknown. Draycott 1998.

CAFEINE (Pierre Anfosso, R. 1990). Sdlg. P 81 S 11A. SPU, 47" (120 cm), E. Dark brown, gold in center of F. Proverb X sdlg. Iris en Provence 1990.

CAFE OLE (Joseph Ghio, R. 1991). Sdlg. 86-71E2. TB, 37" (94 cm), ML. Cocoa melon; beards tangerine. Memoirs X 83-82M: ((((Creme de Creme x Financier) x (Ballet in Orange x Coffee House)) x Cinnamon sib) x Cafe Society). Bay View 1992.

CAFE RISQUE (Barry Blyth, R. 1996). Sdlg. A153-8. TB, 30" (76 cm), VE-EM. S. iced grey, suffused orchid; F. dark plush burgundy, 1/8" blended edge of lilac burgundy; beards deep bronze. And Royal X Electrique. Tempo Two 1996/97.

CAHOOTS (Barry Blyth, R. 1998). Sdlg. E4-1. SDB, 12-14" (30-36 cm), EML. Sunset to burnt apricot, F. with deeper hafts; beards burnt tangerine, 1/4" lavender end; sweet fragrance. Little Bev X Desert Country. Tempo Two 1998/99.

CAILET (Kerryn Turner, R. 1996). Sdlg. KH91-29-1. TB, 40" (102 cm), ML. S. antique cream, gilt edge, cream texture-veining; beards white, hairs tipped gold in throat; sweet fragrance. Fragrant Lilac X Dance Man. Tempo Two 1996/97.

CAIRO LADY (Ray Lyons, R. 1990). Sdlg. 82-15-2. BB, 20-24" (50-60 cm), ML. S. bronze; F. blackish royal purple; beards brown bronze; ruffled. Brown Lasso X Cairo Lyric. Long 1991.

CAITLIN'S SMILE (James Waddick by Kevin Morley, R. 1993). Sdlg. M/T91A. SPEC (*typhifolia*), 33" (84 cm), VE. S. blue violet (darker, richer than RHS 89C) veined dark blue violet (richer than 90A); style arms medium blue violet, blue ridge; F. blue violet edge, lighter blue violet center (lighter than 89B) veined dark blue violet (richer than 90A), white flush radiating from signal; signal yellow in center, bronze on sides, veined dark blue violet (90A). Sdlg. X sdlg.

CAJUN ANGEL (Henry Rowlan, R. 1992). Sdlg. 89LA58. LA, 34" (86 cm), ML. S. spiraea red (RHS 63C); F. darker spiraea red (63B), cream area surrounding green line signal edged yellow; ruffled; slight musky fragrance. Bold Copy X Chowning red brown sdlg. Comanche Acres 1993.

CAJUN BEAUTY (Schreiner, R. 1992). Sdlg. V 624-A. TB, 36" (91 cm), ML. Slightly ruffled red (RHS 59A) self; beards old gold. Commando X Samurai Warrior. Schreiner 1992.

CAJUN BELLE (Henry Rowlan, R. 1991). Sdlg. 89-LA-38. LA, 35" (89 cm), ML. S. magnolia purple (RHS 70C); style arms lilac purple (70A); F. lilac purple, large green signal, cream rayed border; lightly ruffled; slight sweet fragrance. Monument X Crisp Lime. Comanche Acres 1993.

CAJUN COOKERY (Ben Hager, LA, R. 1989). Melrose 1990.

CAJUN COOKING (Francis Rogers, R. 1999). Sdlg. C-106-K. TB, 30" (76 cm), M. S. greyed orange (RHS 173A); style arms greyed orange (165B); F. greyed purple (187A), 1/8" greyed orange (172B) rim; beards greyed orange (167C); ruffled; sweet fragrance. Chippewa Brave X Gallant Rogue.

CAJUN LACE (Kirk Strawn, R. 1993). Sdlg. 44-1985. LA, 38" (97 cm), L. S. red purple (RHS 70B); style arms red (54C) over yellow (5C); F. red purple (61A), yellow (8A) signal. Lafitte's Retreat X Charles Arny III.

CAJUN LOVE (Henry Rowlan, LA, R. 1989). Comanche Acres 1990.

CAJUN LOVE STORY (Dorman Haymon, R. 1999). Sdlg. 81-92-1. LA, 39" (99 cm), M. Pallid flesh pink, slight mauve overlay, small olive veins; signals green gold, small; style arms pink; tailored; slight sweet fragrance. Charlie's Karen X All Agaze.

CAJUN MERRY (Mary Dunn, R. 1995). Sdlg. L174-1. LA, 36" (91 cm), M. Ecru mauve, F. with tiny red brown lines at edge of green signal. Fat Tuesday X Cammeray. Bay View 1997.

CAJUN PINSTRIPE (Kevin Vaughn, R. 1997). Sdlg. E-49-1. LA, 38-41" (97-104 cm), ML & RE. White, allover lavender blue (RHS 91B) veining except 1/4" unmarked edge; small F. signal mostly hidden by style arm; style arms white, veined and infused lavender blue, green at base; tight small ruffles. Dural White Butterfly X Malibu Magic.

CAJUN QUEEN (Lynda Miller, R. 1995). Sdlg. 5291A. TB, 33" (84 cm), L. S. light caramel gold, red violet midrib; style arms golden caramel and violet; F. brick red, rose violet center wash; beards old gold, base violet; slight sweet fragrance. 12487A: ((Spartan x unknown) x Lady Friend) X Graduation. Miller's Manor 1996.

CAJUN RHYTHM (Schreiner, R. 1996). Sdlg. CC 946-A. TB, 36" (91 cm), L. S. and style arms spanish orange (RHS 26B); F. bright ochre orange wash splashed white in center, 1" orange apricot (26A) outer band; beards tangerine; ruffled; slight fragrance. New Direction X W 725-2: (S 656-1: (M 437-2: (Pink Pinafore sib x (Oraglow x unknown)) x M 755-1: (Something Else x

((((L 59-3 x Glittering Amber) x Celestial Glory) x Flaming Star) x Gold Trimmings))) x N 720-1: (((Fairy Fable x Christmas Time) x Party Look) x Flaming Light)). Schreiner 1996.

CAJUN SPICES (William Maryott, R. 1994). Sdlg. S187A. TB, 36" (91 cm), ML. Sunfast copper self; beards yellow. M154A: (J5-SMOOTH: (Ghio 80-#5, unknown, x G208A: (Ghio 76-175, Paris Original sib, x Ghio 76-257X: (Entourage x Homecoming Queen))) x Lady Friend) X L120C, Austrian Garnets sib. Maryott 1994.

CAJUN SUNRISE (Joseph Mertzweiller, R. 1992). Sdlg. 74-22. LA, 34-36" (85-90 cm), EM. S. red, narrow yellow edge; style arms intense yellow; F. red, yellow sunburst blending to red, narrow yellow edge, yellow line signal. MacMillan yellow sdlg. X 60-87: (58-69: ((Bayou Sunset x Peggy Mac) x Upstart) x Belle Lou). Cordon Bleu 1993.

CAJUN SUNSET (Marvin Granger, R. 1990). Sdlg. 75-Y1. LA, 15" (38 cm), M. S. light yellow; F. deep greenish yellow; slight fragrance. 67-2: (Gypsy Moon x Queen o' Queens) X G. W. Holleyman. Faggard 1994.

CAJUN WEDDING (Kevin Vaughn, R. 1997). Sdlg. E-4-3. LA, 36-41" (91-104 cm), ML. S. white, veined greenish yellow (RHS 151C); style arms cream (162D); F. white, greenish yellow veins and signal, petal edge often gold; heavily ruffled, laciniated. Alluvial Gold X C-9-1: (Gourmet x Koorawatha).

CALAMARI (Jill Copeland, R. 1990). Sdlg. 86-1. JI (3 F.), 36" (91 cm), EM. S. purple violet (RHS 80A) rimmed white (155B); style arms violet (87D); F. white (155B) veined and sanded purple violet (80A), yellow (5A) signal. Parentage unknown. Ensata Gardens 1992.

CALCULATED GRACE (Sterling Innerst, R. 1998). Sdlg. 3987-3. TB, 36" (91 cm), M. Pewter white, light yellowish and lavender highlights; style arms cream; beards cream white; slight fragrance. Silverado X Missy Yorktowne. Innerst 1998.

CALDRON FIRE (James Gibson by Cooley's Gardens, R. 1994). Sdlg. 62-4B. TB, 36" (91 cm), EM. S. reddish copper, midrib infused warm yellow; F. deep yellow with white zone around orange red beard, red copper and burgundy plicata edge, shoulder and center stripe; slight sweet-spicy fragrance. Probably -- Honey Lace X Plum Gleam. Cooley 1995.

CALICOBALL (Ladislav Muska, R. 1995). Sdlg. QCCK-03. TB, 40" (102 cm), M. Heavily laced reddish blue lilac plicata; beards orange; sweet fragrance. (Queen in Calico x "Cipkovana Krinolina": (After All x Grand Waltz)) X "De Leone": (80-SRGW-9 x Chartreuse Ruffles). Muska 1996.

CALICO CLASSIC (George Slade, R. 1990). Sdlg. 83-8-1. TB, 36" (91 cm), M. S. dark red brown; F. tawny brown plicata markings on white ground; beards orange. Morocco X Fox Hound. Ed Als Iris 1992.

CALICO KID (Allan Ensminger, R. 1992). Sdlg. 85-19. BB, 18" (46 cm), ML. Venetian pink (HCC 420/3) striped bishops violet (34/1); beards red. Happy Song X 81-56: (78-21: ((Little Mark x 73-47) x 76-14, variegated sdlg.) x 77-54: (75-18: ((64-12 x Stepping Out) x (Faydy Girl x sib)) x Rancho Rose)). Varigay 1993.

CALICO KITTEN (Chet Tompkins, R. 1995). Sdlg. 84-64. BB, 26" (66 cm), EM. S. pale lemon, minute sandy lilac flecking; F. same, flecking heavier; beards yellow bronze. ((Peccadillo x Laredo) x Palace Lantern) X Beautiful Baby. Fleur de Lis 1995.

CALICO RUFFLES (Walter Moores, R. 1991). Sdlg. 85-30. TB, 34" (86 cm), EM. S. violet purple, base lighter; F. violet purple, lavender plicata hafts and veining extending to edge; beards yellow white, tipped purple; heavily ruffled; sweet fragrance. 82-12: (Barletta x Scrimshaw) X Pandora's Purple. Moores 1992.

CALIFE (Pierre Anfosso, R. 1990). Sdlg. P 82 S 5. SPU, 36" (90 cm), ML. S. purple with brown veining; F. gold yellow with brown veining, bright mauve edge. Sarong X Just Reward. Iris en Provence 1990.

CALIFORNIA DREAMER (John Marchant, R. 1990). Sdlg. 187. CA, 12" (30 cm), M. S. creamy white, methyl violet (HCC 39/1) stain on midrib; F. lightly ruffled methyl violet (39) fading to creamy white edge, diffused signal. Sdlg. X sdlg.

CALIFORNIA QUEEN (John Marchant, R. 1990). Sdlg. 4687. CA, 14" (36 cm), M. S. ruby red (HCC 827); F. ruby red (827/2) with violet blue spot. Sdlg. X sdlg.

CALIFORNIA SESQUICENTENNIAL (Glenn Stoneking-Jones, R. 1999). Sdlg. CIR6-5335-06-02-1999). TB, 28" (71 cm), M. S. chrome yellow; style arms chrome yellow veined tan; F. chrome yellow ground, upper half with tan plicata markings; beards orange; slight musky fragrance. Mostest X Desert Echo.

CALIFORNIA SISTER (John Marchant, R. 1990). Sdlg. 4187. CA, 12" (30 cm), ML. Spiraea red (HCC 25/2), tyrian purple (727) halo and veins around diffused yellow signal. Sdlg. X sdlg. Portable Acres 1990.

CALIFORNIA SKIES (Teresa Sage, R. 1994). Sdlg. GS90-2. CA, 18" (46 cm), EM. S. white, very light orchid serrate edges; F. light orchid blue with deeper orchid veining, light yellow signal with deep orchid halo, turquoise center blaze from signal to white edge. Parentage unknown; seed from Joe Ghio.

CALIFORNIA STYLE (Bennett Jones, R. 1989). Sdlg. 85-3-3. IB, 22" (56 cm), M. S. white, infused light orange at midrib base; F. bright orange, white rim and centerline; beards tangerine; lightly ruffled. Color Bash X Orange Tiger. Bennett Jones 1990.

CALITRIX (Ladislav Muska, R. 1996). Sdlg. QBSE-11. TB, 36" (91 cm), EM. S. light lavender blue; F. deep burgundy red, light amethyst lavender rim; beards orange; heavily laced; sweet fragrance. (Queen in Calico x "Bila Neha": (Lavender Petticoat x Silver Shower)) X Se-Seque. Muska 1996.

CALIZONA (B. Charles Jenkins, R. 1995). Sdlg. Quad-7. SPU, 37" (94 cm), VE. S. light violet blue (RHS 93D); F. bright yellow orange (15A), washed to edges with light violet blue. Parentage unknown. Shepard Iris 1996.

CALLING CARD (Virginia Messick, R. 1990). Sdlg. M85-39. IB, 20" (51 cm), M. S. bluish white; F. greenish cream; beards blue. Jack R. Dee X Azure Gem. Cottage 1991.

CALLIOPE MAGIC (Kerryn Turner, R. 1995). Sdlg. KH 90-18-1. TB, 42" (107 cm), EML. S. and style arms apricot; F. apricot with creamy white area below bright tangerine beard; slight sweet fragrance. Close Your Eyes X Dance Man. Tempo Two 1995/96.

CALLIOPE'S DREAM (Ladislav Muska, R. 1996). Sdlg. FGGR-05. TB, 40" (102 cm), M. S. light amethyst lavender; F. deep burgundy red, light amethyst rim; beards tangerine; heavily ruffled, laced; sweet fragrance. French Gown X (Geniality x Red Tornado). Muska 1996.

CALL RIPLEY'S (Tom Burseen, R. 1990). Sdlg. 5-17A. TB, 36" (91 cm), EM. S. light orange salmon (RHS 29D); F. velvety dark burgundy (187A) with black sheen, lighter margin; beards burnt orange; ruffled; slight fragrance. Lilac Wine X Tropical Tempo. T.B.'s Place 1990.

CALL WAITING (Harold Stahly, R. 1998). Sdlg. 93-10. TB, 35" (88 cm), M. S. and style arms medium tangerine orange (RHS 24B); F. light to medium brown (165B), paling slightly with age; beards tangerine; ruffled. (Sun Fire x (Orange Chariot x Barcelona)) X Esmeralda. Mill Creek, Stahly 1998.

CALM SEA (Ben Hager, R. 1992). Sdlg. T4654LtBl#1. TB, 35" (89 cm), M. Ruffled clear light blue; beards light blue. T4229LaCobBl: (((Geometrics sib x Ice Sculpture) x Avalon Bay) x Ron) X Welcome Aboard. Melrose 1992.

CALM STREAM (Cy Bartlett, R. 1998). Sdlg. W(CM-SP)1. TB, 38" (97 cm), ML. S. white, washed very pale lavender; F. medium blue lavender; beards light lavender, yellow in throat; heavily ruffled; slight sweet fragrance. Wensleydale X (Cherished Memory x Soul Power). Sutton 1998.

CALORIFIC (Allan Ensminger, R. 1992). Sdlg. 286-42. BB, 24" (61 cm), L. S. white; F. mauve (HCC 633/1), edged white; beards saturn red (13). 81-39: ((Almost Gladys x Foolish Pleasure) x Almost Gladys) X 84-64: (Almost Gladys x Crandall bicolor sdlg.). Varigay 1993.

CALVIN'S ROBE (T.J. Betts, R. 1999). Sdlg. 008C. LA, 38" (96 cm), M. S. mallow purple (RHS 72C), pale rim, darker veining; style arms pale magnolia purple (70D); F. lilac purple (70A), pale rim, darker veining, gold spear signal; ruffled. Sun Dream X Nick's Nugget.

CAMBROSA (Jean Witt, R. 1995). Sdlg. 94-03-ZY. SPEC-X (sib-tosa), 23" (58 cm), M. Clear medium blue, F. with golden yellow signal rimmed white; style arms medium blue; S. short, spoon- to paddle-shaped. Cambridge X *I. setosa* "Alaska Blue".

CAMEO BELLE (Stan Dexter by Marie Ingersoll, R. 1990). Sdlg. 1981/33. TB, 36" (91 cm), ML. Ruffled whitish pink to yellow; beards pale orange tipped white. 1977/20E, unknown, X Paradise. Ingersoll's Iris 1991.

CAMEO BLUSH (John Weiler by Joan Roberts, R. 1998). Sdlg. 89-180-1-E. BB, 25" (63 cm), EML & RE. Soft cameo pink, lightly blushed salmon; beards peachy yellow. Eternal Bliss X Reiterate. Friendship 1998.

CAMEO CUTIE (A. & D. Willott, R. 1990). Sdlg. 88-61. MDB, 7½" (19 cm), L. S. light apricot pink; F. pale pink, apricot hafts; beards pale pink. 84-88: (Oh Katz x Coral Wings) X Pastel Delight. Willott 1995.

CAMEO KITTEN (A. & D. Willott, R. 1999). Sdlg. W 95-143. SDB, 9" (23 cm), ML. Pale pink, F. with apricot hafts; beards pale blue. W 92-126: (Pink Panther x Fresh Face) X Cameo Cutie.

67

CAMEO ROSE (William Simon, TB, R. 1984). Stahly 1991.

CAMERA SHY (Vernon Wood, R. 1990). Sdlg. 87-55. TB, 36" (91 cm), M. Pale to light red (pink) self; beards bright red tangerine. 82-35: (79-26: ((Princess x Pink Taffeta) x Carved Pink) x ((Flaming Arrow x Gaulter sdlg.) x Carved Angel)) X 85-33: (Pink Belle x ((Pink Attire x Pink Persian) x 79-26)). Cottage 1991.

CAMILLE DURAND FORET (Dorman Haymon, R. 1994). Sdlg. 87-88-2. LA, 30" (76 cm), M. Ruffled bright yellow gold, darker gold signal; green in heart extending out to signal. 29-85-1: (Teresa Margaret x (Uptight x Lucile Holley)) X 111-86-1: (Easter Tide x Swamp Flame). Lone Star 1994.

#CAMP FIRE (Lena Lothrop, TB, R. 1930). Not introduced, name released.

CAMP FIRE (Howard Shockey, R. 1995). Sdlg. 92-208-X. TB, 34" (86 cm), M. S. purple violet; F. purple violet, large off-white area surrounding beard; beards bright red, large, bushy; slight spicy fragrance. 89-213-1: (Gift of Dreams x ((81-225-W: ((Chartreuse Ruffles x Orchid Flash) x (Starfrost Pink x Startler) x 82-232-4A: (Mimi x ((Carved Cameo x Summer Love) x (Lilac Mist x Fond Wish)))) x 81-225-K)) X 88-232-B: ((((Startler x Starfrost Pink) x Mimi) x 82-232-4A) x (Pearls and Gold x (Mimi x (Chartreuse Ruffles x High Life)))). Arilian Acres 1996.

CANADIAN BORDER (Chuck Chapman, R. 1997). Sdlg. 89-278-A. BB, 25" (64 cm), EML. Lightly ruffled white self; beards red. Victorian Frills X Coral Beauty. Chapman Iris 1997.

CANADIAN STREAKER (Chuck Chapman, R. 1997). Sdlg. 88-364-E. TB, 31" (79 cm), M. Ruffled light blue self; beards light blue; foliage heavily streaked cream, base dark red purple. Cup Race X Laced Cotton. Chapman Iris 1997.

CANALETTO (Tony Huber, R. 1992). Sdlg. AIS Rosea. SPEC (*versicolor*), 29½" (75 cm), E. S. washed light purple (RHS 77B); F. bright purple (80B), white and yellow center, purple veining. Seed from SIGNA Seed Exchange.

CANARY DELIGHT (Joan Roberts, R. 1997). Sdlg. 573-1. TB, 36" (91 cm), M. S. white; F. canary yellow, white rim; beards bright deep gold; lightly ruffled; slight sweet fragrance. Rose Princess X 326RE-2: (Immortality x Coral Chalice). Friendship 1997.

CANARY DUET (Heather Pryor, R. 1998). Sdlg. 55/90-8. LA, 47" (120 cm), EM. S. pale creamy lemon; style arms and F. lemon peel yellow; olive green line signal on all petals; heavily ruffled. Gladiator's Gift X Designer's Dream. Iris Haven 1999/2000.

CANARY FEATHERS (Walt Dean, R. 1996). TB, 36" (91 cm), M. Yellow, slight rosy central blush in F.; beards yellow, canary yellow feathery flounces. Too Many Flounces X unknown. Stanley Iris 1997.

CANARY JEWEL (Donovan Albers, R. 1990). Sdlg. 8408B. SDB, 10" (25 cm), M. Canary yellow (HCC 2/3), veined deep green gold around gentian blue (42/2) beard; slight fragrance. Little Bill X Mrs. Nate Rudolph. Redbud Lane 1991.

CANARY WHARF (Mary Tubbs, R. 1992). Sdlg. MT-3. TB, 34" (86 cm), M. S. yellow; F. yellow, deeper yellow throat; beards pale orange; lightly ruffled. Sun King X Wartime.

CANAVERAL (George Sutton, R. 1999). Sdlg. H-126-A. TB, 34" (86 cm), ML. S. and style arms white, faint methyl violet shading; F. methyl violet (RHS 85B) hafts and centerline blending to sea lavender violet (85D); beards lavender, hairs tipped yellow, methyl violet and white horn; ruffled, serrate; slight spicy fragrance. G-65-A, Eagle Control sib, X G-65-B, sib.

CANCAN BLUES (George Sutton, R. 1999). Sdlg. H-186. TB, 36" (91 cm), ML. S. and style arms hyacinth blue (RHS 91B); F. wistaria blue (92D) deepening to hyacinth blue at centerline and edges; beards hyacinth blue, base yellow, wistaria blue horn; ruffled; slight sweet fragrance. G-74: (Busy Being Blue x Deity) X Star Master.

CAN CAN DANCER (Larry Lauer, R. 1997). Sdlg. 91-195. TB, 36" (91 cm), M. S. and style arms yellow; F. purple, edged brown, shoulders yellow; beards mustard; ruffled; slight sweet fragrance. (Edith Wolford x Ragtime) X ((Edith Wolford x Ragtime) x M. Dunn M78-657, Personal Friend sib). Stockton 1997.

CANDID (Joseph Ghio, R. 1995). Sdlg. PF-153W2. CA, 15" (38 cm), M. S. mauve pink; F. mauvewood, lighter edge, maroon signal. PI-MIX-B, unknown, X PH-242R2: (Temblor sib x ((San Gregorio x (Montara sib x Mission Santa Cruz sib)) x Villa Branciforte sib)). Bay View 1995.

CANDLE LACE (B. Charles Jenkins, SPU, R. 1989). Shepard Iris 1990.

CANDLELIGHT MOOD (Richard Ernst, R. 1996). Sdlg. KF125-K. TB, 34" (86 cm), EM. S. solid medium lemon yellow, slight butter yellow cast; style arms yellow; F. white ground, almost solidly plicata patterned yellow; beards yellow; lightly ruffled. (Edna's Wish x Wild Jasmine) X (Edna's Wish x Wild Jasmine). Cooley 1996.

CAN DO (Allan Ensminger, R. 1992). Sdlg. 86-55. BB, 22" (56 cm), ML. S. sea lavender violet (HCC 637/1); F. white, 3/8" sea lavender violet (637) border; beards chinese yellow, tipped black. Everything Plus X 81-18: (Spinning Wheel x Bouree). Varigay 1993.

CANDY APPLE CLASSIC (William Maryott, R. 1998). Sdlg. X257A. TB, 36" (91 cm), EM. S. and style arms beetroot red to maroon (darker than RHS 72A); F. bright metallic candy red violet (80A), dark brown shoulders, slight brown band; beards dark bronze. U159A: (S168B: (red purple sdlg. x Houdini sib) x S179B: (En Garde x Houdini)) X U162A: (Cherry Glen x S195red: (Mariachi Music x Twice Told)). Maryott 1999.

CANDY FLOSS (Keith Keppel, IB, R. 1989). Keppel 1990.

CANDY QUEEN (O. D. Niswonger, R. 1992). Sdlg. SDB 12-91. SDB, 13" (33 cm), M. Salmon pink; beards white, tipped tangerine in throat. SDB 27-87: (Oriental Blush x unknown) X Ballet Slippers. Cape Iris 1992.

CANDY ROCK (George Sutton, R. 1999). Sdlg. G-36-K. IB, 26" (66 cm), EM & RE. S. and style arms rose purple (RHS 75A); F. imperial purple (78A) veined violet blue (93A); beards violet blue, hairs tipped lighter at end, light violet blue horn; ruffled. Aaron's Dagger X Chanted.

CANDYSTRIPER (Bee Warburton, R. 1991). Sdlg. V-22. SPEC (*versicolor*), 25" (64 cm), M. S. white with pale rose veining which fades toward edge, yellow in heart; style arms white flushed pale rose, narrow rose midline, yellow in heart; F. white, heavily veined rose (RHS 72A/B), inconspicuous yellow signal striped dark rose. Parentage unknown. Joe Pye Weed 1991.

CANDY WINE (Floyd Dyer, R. 1996). Sdlg. D-3-91-D. SDB, 13" (33 cm), M. S. dark wine-tinted red; F. dark red, blended yellow hafts with yellow veins; beards brown tan; slight sweet fragrance. D-34-85-D: ((Pink Cushion x Lenna M) x Peach Jewel) X Battle Shout. Dyer's Garden 1996.

CANNATELLA (Franklin Carr, TB, R. 1986). Carr 1990.

CANNINGTON APRICOT (Cy Bartlett, R. 1992). Sdlg. PK.L.2. SDB, 14" (36 cm), M. Pale apricot pink; beards orange. Pink Kitten X Alta Brown sdlg.

CANNINGTON BALLET (Cy Bartlett, R. 1993). Sdlg. CM/SP. TB, 35" (89 cm), M. S. blue white; F. light sky blue; beards white; ruffled; slight sweet fragrance. Cherished Memory X Soul Power. Sutton 1993.

CANNINGTON BLUEBIRD (Cy Bartlett, TB, R. 1987). Sutton 1992.

CANNINGTON CREAMERY (Cy Bartlett, TB, R. 1987). British Iris Society 1989.

CANNINGTON DELIGHT (Cy Bartlett, R. 1993). Sdlg. MS-PF-1. BB, 26" (66 cm), M. S. parchment white; F. apricot pink; beards reddish orange; ruffled; slight sweet fragrance. Marmalade Skies X Peachy Face. Sutton 1993.

CANNINGTON FLAIR (Cy Bartlett, R. 1991). Sdlg. QL-F-FP. SDB, 14" (36 cm), M. Greyed wedgwood blue, deeper patch below grey white beard. (Quiet Lagoon x Faraway) X Faraway Places.

CANNINGTON LASSO (Cy Bartlett, R. 1991). Sdlg. BL/SAS. BB, 24" (61 cm), M. S. gold infused brown on midrib; F. blue, purple, brown blend, 1/4" golden rim; beards yellow. Brown Lasso X Sand and Sea.

CANNINGTON OCHRE (Cy Bartlett, R. 1993). Sdlg. SD.ST.C. SDB, 12" (30 cm), M. S. yellow ochre; F. slightly darker; beards blue; lightly waved. (Silver Down x Sarah Taylor) X Capricornia. British Iris Society 1999.

CANNINGTON PEACH (Cy Bartlett, R. 1991). Sdlg. MS-PF-W. IB, 20" (51 cm), M. S. palest lemon (almost white); F. peachy orange; beards orange. (Marmalade Skies x Peachy Face) X Winkieland.

CANNINGTON SWEET PUFF (Cy Bartlett, R. 1990). Sdlg. C-IT-RW. TB, 39" (99 cm), L-VL. S. soft mallow pink; F. pale magenta; beards red; lightly ruffled. Carnaby X (In Tempo x Roman Walk). Iris Garden 1993.

CANNONBALL (Schreiner, R. 1994). Sdlg. W 902-2. TB, 41" (104 cm), ML. S. red wine; F. deeper velvety red wine (RHS 59A); beards yellow; ruffled. Warrior King X T 1576-F: (Gypsy Caravan x Cayenne Pepper). Schreiner 1994.

CAN'T ELOPE (Lynda Miller, R. 1990). Sdlg. 7085A. TB, 33" (84 cm), ML. Ruffled cantaloupe orange with lighter markings around tangerine beards; slight sweet fragrance. Gold Trimmings X Marmalade. Miller's Manor 1992.

CANTICLE OF PRAISE (Calvin Helsley, R. 1990). Sdlg. 85-14. TB, 34" (86 cm), M. S. light yellow, deep butter yellow at base; F. creamy white; beards deep butter yellow. Jubiloso X 8-80: (Golden Sensation x Jubiloso). Helsley 1991.

CANTINA (Monty Byers, TB, R. 1989). Moonshine 1990.

CANTO DI GIOIA (Ladislav Muska, R. 1996). Sdlg. GFGE-01. TB, 40" (102 cm), ML. S. creamy yellow; F. light red, light creamy cocoa band; beards mustard; ruffled, heavily laced; sweet fragrance. French Gown X Geniality. Muska 1995.

CANTRELL'S RAIDERS (Jim Hedgecock, R. 1999). Sdlg. F-5-1. TB, 34" (86 cm), EM. Heavily ruffled dark purple, F. with tiny silver streak below silver beard; pronounced sweet fragrance. Orbiter X J. R. Allen X-4-D. Comanche Acres 1999.

CANYON DE CHELLY (John Durrance, R. 1991). Sdlg. D84-49. BB, 26" (65 cm), M. S. sunburst gold; F. yellow brown blend; beards gold. Gold Galore X Brown Lasso. Long 1991.

CAPED CRUSADER (J. D. Stadler, R. 1992). Sdlg. J25/07. TB, 35" (89 cm), M. Smoky purple, F. with brown haft overlay; beards burnt sienna; slight fragrance. Loudoun Cameo X Sheer Poetry.

CAPE HORN (Monty Byers, TB, R. 1989). Moonshine 1991.

CAPITAL CITY JAZZ (Schreiner, R. 1997). Sdlg. AA 94-B. TB, 37" (94 cm), M. Ruffled medium blue (RHS 89B) self; beards white, yellow in throat; slight fragrance. T 283-1: (Land o' Lakes x Pledge Allegiance) X Breakers. Schreiner 1997.

CAPITOL DANDY (William Ackerman, JI, R. 1981). Nicholls Garden 1992.

CAPTAIN GATES (Heather Pryor, R. 1998). Sdlg. 25/91-B. LA, 39" (100 cm), ML. S. violet (RHS 83A), white rim and reverse; style arms white, violet tips and midrib blush; F. slightly deeper violet, white rim and reverse, yellow signal with raised golden yellow steeple; ruffled. Koorawatha X Sea Lord. Lone Star 1998.

CAPTAIN INDIGO (Cy Bartlett, R. 1998). Sdlg. C94-1. IB, 24" (60 cm), E. S. white, very heavily washed deep indigo blue; F. khaki; beards light khaki; lightly waved; slight fragrance. ((Chartreuse Babe x Indigo Crown) x Capricornia) X Warm and Toasty. Sutton 1999.

CAPTAIN'S JOY (Schreiner, R. 1994). Sdlg. W 26-A. TB, 38" (97 cm), ML. S. marine blue; F. darker navy blue; beards yellow, tipped blue; ruffled. Stormy Night X Pledge Allegiance. Schreiner 1994.

CAPTAIN TUN (Lothar Denkewitz, R. 1990). Sdlg. M-85-mbl-7. SDB, 13½" (35 cm), M. S. medium blue violet; F. deep blue violet; beards medium blue. Jan Maat X Annikins. Von Zeppelin 1992.

CAPTIVATING (George Sutton, R. 1997). Sdlg. G-29BR. TB, 38" (97 cm), ML. Heavily ruffled diamond-dusted light lavender self; beards light lavender, hairs tipped light yellow. Winterscape X Twice Thrilling. Sutton 1998.

CAPTIVE (Barry Blyth, R. 1999). Sdlg. F85-2. IB, 22" (56 cm), ML. S. pink to pinkish mushroom, slightly deeper midrib; F. rosy pink washed lavender, slight violet signal; beards white, tipped tangerine; pronounced sweet fragrance. Say Hello X C225-2, Gala Greetings sib. Tempo Two 1999/2000.

CAPTIVE SUN (Bennett Jones, R. 1993). Sdlg. 456-10. SDB, 10" (25 cm), M. S. white; F. canary yellow, precise white edge; lightly ruffled. Favorite Angel X 428: (Oregold x Loveshine). Bennett Jones 1994.

CARACAS (Joseph Ghio, R. 1990). Sdlg. 85-27M. TB, 38" (97 cm), EML. Full orange; beards tangerine. 83-82M: ((((Creme de Creme x Financier) x (Ballet in Orange x Coffee House)) x Cinnamon sib) x Cafe Society) X Guadalajara. Bay View 1991.

CARATS (Barry Blyth, R. 1994). Sdlg. A15-4. SDB, 8-10" (20-25 cm), ML. S. mango orange; F. with 1/4" mango orange edge, 3/8" paler mango halo, and deeper mango orange spot pattern around beard; beards pale lavender to white, tangerine in throat; slight fragrance. X16-A, Thundercat sib, X X23-A, Moondawn sib. Tempo Two 1994/95.

CARDEW (R. E. Nichol, R. 1990). Sdlg. D16-4. TB, 39½" (100 cm), M. S. very pale blue with heavy bleeding of F. color at midrib; style arms cream; F. red violet (RHS 77B) with considerable haft marking; beards pale tan blending to white at tip. Annabel Jane X Dialogue. V. H. Humphrey 1995.

CARDINALE C. (Ladislav Muska, R. 1995). Sdlg. TGGB-12. TB, 38" (97 cm), M. Ruffled purplish blue self; beards black blue; sweet fragrance. Titan's Glory X Glory Bound. Muska 1990.

CARELESS SALLY (Marty Schafer/Jan Sacks, R. 1996). Sdlg. 90-60-6. SIB, 26" (66 cm), M & RE. S. ground pearly white, pale reddish violet shading, blue violet veining; style arms pearly white, red violet wire edge, aqua blue (RHS 107B/C) veining, wide, ruffled and curled, held semi-upright; F. washed reddish violet (83C), heavy veining and dappling at shoulders, large signal deep yellow to cream, speckled dark purple; ruffled. S87-10-1: (Mad Magenta x Percheron) X Sailor's Fancy. Joe Pye Weed 1996.

CARENZA (Robert Nichol by Jean Nichol, R. 1997). Sdlg. M154. BB, 26" (66 cm), M. S. pale gold (RHS 163C); F. white ground, 3/8" copper brown (175A) edge, fine red brown centerline; beards deep gold; lightly ruffled. J43-2: (((Kilt Lilt x Autumn Leaves) x Show Biz) x (Limerick x Roundup)) X Doctor Behenna.

CARIBBEAN AHOY (Lloyd Zurbrigg, R. 1995). Sdlg. KK 41-3-2. TB, 40" (102 cm), M. S. and style arms yellow; F. white, yellow border; beards bright yellow gold, violet horns. F. Stephenson 82-14-01: (Song of Norway x Miss Jupiter) X unknown. Friendship 1998.

CARIBBEAN DEEP (Donald Spoon, R. 1997). Sdlg. 90-50A. TB, 32" (81 cm), ML. S. and style arms light blue; F. deep marine blue; beards dark blue, hairs tipped gold; ruffled, flared. Son of Dreams X Best Bet.

CARIBBEAN DREAM (Schreiner, R. 1990). Sdlg. V 35-A. TB, 36" (91 cm), ML. Ruffled blue (RHS 101C); beards white. Sea of Joy X N 59-A: (((Cup Race x Tufted Cloud) x Sailor's Dance) x (Sapphire Hills x D 136-G: (Parisian Blue x ((Blue Linen sib x (J 274-A x Violet Harmony)) x (Swan Ballet x Snowy Heron))))). Schreiner 1990.

CARIBEE (Ben Hager, TB, R. 1988). Roris 1990.

CARILLA (John D. Taylor, SDB, R. 1965). Orpington Nurseries 1966.

CARL REBERT (J. Owings Rebert, R. 1997). Sdlg. FY-C1. SIB, 36" (91 cm), M. Solid purple self; F. with greenish tan throat and ivory signal. Pansy Purple X unknown.

CARMEL GEM (B. Charles Jenkins, R. 1992). Sdlg. B4-32A. CA, 14" (36 cm), M. S. and style arms light purple; F. purple, elongated yellow center surrounded by ivory border with deep purple radial lines. Californian X Spring Daze. Portable Acres 1992.

CARMEL MISSION (Joseph Ghio, R. 1993). Sdlg. PG-166-02. CA, 12" (30 cm), ML. Burnt orange, deep orange ray signal. PI-MIX-U, unknown, X PJ-178D: ((Peanut Gallery x Villa Branciforte sib) x (San Gregorio x (Montara sib x Mission Santa Cruz sib))). Bay View 1994.

CARMEN JEANNE (Calvin Helsley, R. 1993). Sdlg. 89-5. SIB, 28" (71 cm), EM. S. violet blue (RHS 89C); style arms blue violet (89C/D); F. violet blue (89B), large white signal changing to gold in throat, large white spot on reverse; heavily ruffled; slight sweet fragrance. Mabel Coday X S. Varner S060: (Marlya x Steve). Helsley 1996.

CARMEN KNEPPER (Manfred Beer, R. 1991). Sdlg. MB 14/80B. TB, 37" (95 cm), M. Clear pink; beards red. Fond Wish X Pink Taffeta. Gartencenter Kania 1991.

CARNIVAL NIGHT (Adolf Volfovich-Moler, R. 1995). Sdlg. 121. TB, 32" (80 cm), EM. S. purple; F. blended purple; beards violet blue. Karmen Dance X Victoria Falls. Volfovich-Moler 1997.

CARNIVAL SONG (Schreiner, R. 1994). Sdlg. AA 217-A. TB, 36" (91 cm), EM. S. buff pink, midrib infused violet; F. peach (RHS 29D) ground with rich magenta (70A) plicata edge; beards tangerine. Y 252-1: (R 932-A: (Cozy Calico x Grape Accent) x Capricious) X Gigolo. Schreiner 1994.

CARNIVAL SUNSET (Hugh & Mary Thurman, R. 1995). Sdlg. 92-2-17. TB, 37" (94 cm), ML. S. pumpkin, edge slightly darker; style arms yellow orange; F. dark pumpkin; beards fire orange; ruffled; slight spicy fragrance. Good Show X American Style. Kickapoo 1997.

CAROLE'S CHOICE (B. Charles Jenkins, R. 1998). Sdlg. BH98C. SPU, 44" (112 cm), M. S. smoky brown blending to creamy yellow with prominent veining; style arms smoky brown, fringed; F. cream yellow fringed smoky brown, prominently veined; signal yellow, ribbed. Finally Free X Cinnamon Stick. Shepard Iris 1998.

CAROLINA DARKNESS (Loleta Powell, R. 1999). TB, 35" (89 cm), ML-VL. Blue black self; beards blue; slight fragrance. Blue Again X Black Tie Affair. Powell's Gardens 1999.

CAROLINE GIBBS (Monty Byers, TB, R. 1989). Moonshine 1990.

CAROLINE PENVENON (R. E. Nichol, TB, R. 1989). Iris Garden 1993.

CAROL'S DREAM (Mary Louise Dunderman, MTB, R. 1989). Ohio Gardens 1990.

CAROL'S JOY (Stan Dexter by Marie Ingersoll, R. 1991). Sdlg. 86-205X. TB, 34" (86 cm), EM. Pale orchid blue; beards yellow, tipped orchid blue. Parentage unknown. Ingersoll's Iris 1992.

CAROLYN MARY (Barry Blyth, R. 1992). Sdlg. W130-1. TB, 38-40" (97-102 cm), ML. S. icy blue, tinged grey; F. light lavender; beards lavender, tipped yellow; sweet fragrance. Divine Duchess X ((Embassadora x Evening Echo) x Touch of Bronze). Tempo Two 1992/93.

CAROUSEL WALTZ (Calvin Helsley, R. 1992). Sdlg. 88-3. BB, 26" (66 cm), M. S. light brown, medium red violet flush up midrib; style arms light violet, crests honey gold; F. pale violet, 1/2" honey gold edge; beards honey gold; slight sweet fragrance. Dave's Dazzler X Brown Lasso. Helsley 1996.

CARPACCIO (John Marchant, R. 1990). Sdlg. 7587. CA, 8" (20 cm), M. Clear garnet lake (HCC 28/2), cream wire rim on F., diffuse blue and yellow signal. Sdlg. X sdlg. Bay View 1992.

CARRARA LACE (Ladislav Muska, R. 1995). Sdlg. RUBS-02. TB, 40" (102 cm), ML. Heavily laced pure white; beards tangerine; spicy fragance. Ruching X ("Belase Striebo" x Silver Shower). Muska 1994.

CARRIE ALLEN (J. R. Allen, TB, R. 1987). Allen Iris 1997.

CARRIE CRISCOLA (Bob Thomason, R. 1992). Sdlg. BT 8803A. TB, 28" (71 cm), ML. S. white; F. white with pale lavender infusion, 1/4" violet edge; beards orange tipped white; ruffled; slight spicy fragrance. Snowy Wonderland X Violet Classic.

CARRIE REBEKAH (Melba Hamblen, TB, R. 1988). Roris 1990.

CARRIWITCHED (Sterling Innerst, R. 1992). Sdlg. 3828-4. IB, 19" (48 cm), M. White ground purple plicata; beards bluish, tipped bronze; slight fragrance. 2237-15: (Burgundy Brown x 1655-1: (Osage Buff x Spinning Wheel)) X 3529-1: (Jeepers x Muchacha). Innerst 1993.

CARROT TOP (Duane Meek, R. 1992). Sdlg. P-6-9. CA, 10" (25 cm), EM. Golden orange self. (*I. tenax* x *I. innominata*) X Fairy Chimes. D & J Gardens 1992.

CARTE BLANCHE (Schreiner, R. 1996). Sdlg. AA 1774-2. TB, 38" (97 cm), ML. Laced white (RHS 155C) self; beards tangerine-tipped white at end, tangerine in throat; slight fragrance. Sentimental Mood X Y 304-1: (R11-1: (Last Hurrah sib x Laced Cotton) x P 74-A: (Mt. Olympus x (St. Louis Blues x (G 1517-B x Neptune's Pool)))). Schreiner 1996.

CARTEL (Chet Tompkins, R. 1998). Sdlg. 94-55C. TB, 38" (97 cm), ML-VL. Renaissance red self; beards chocolate. ((Time Lord x Short Cut) x War Chief) X Short Cut sib. Fleur de Lis 1998.

CARTOON (Graeme Grosvenor, R. 1998). Sdlg. V80-1. TB, 34" (86 cm), M. S. light blue, lightly patterned blue violet; F. white, heavy blue violet plicata markings; beards tangerine, tipped white. Work Ethic X R6-5: (Silverado x Snowbrook). Rainbow Ridge 1999/2000.

CASCADE BUTTERCUP (Lorena Reid, R. 1998). Sdlg. 92S43-4J6. SIB (sino-sib), 36-40" (91-107 cm), ML. S. light buttercup yellow, edge crimped; style arms bright buttercup yellow; F. buttercup yellow, medium-sized deeper gold signal with few dark dashed lines. Cascade Creme X Anticipation Orange. Laurie's Garden 1998.

CASCADE CREME (Lorena Reid, R. 1991). Sdlg. Btfl 40#8(aw 40). SIB (sino-sib), 42" (107 cm), ML. S. white; style arms white; F. white, pale yellow cream in center with barest hint of grey lines; insignificant gold signal. Parentage unknown. Laurie's Garden 1991.

CASCADE MIST (Dana Borglum, R. 1999). Sdlg. VS1. SPEC (*versicolor*), 30" (76 cm), M. S. light blue; style arms pearly white; F. white, veined blue, yellow gold signal. Seed from SIGNA. Parentage unknown.

CASCADE RAPTURE (Hooker Nichols, R. 1991). Sdlg. 82115A. TB, 36" (91 cm), ML. S. white, dotted and edged light azure; F. white, narrowly stitched and dotted dark purple, hafts solid; beards orange and violet; ruffled. Odyssey X Crystal Ball. Hillcrest 1992.

CASCADE SPRING DRESS (Lorena Reid, R. 1991). Sdlg. D552-4. JI (6 F.), 36-42" (91-107 cm), M. Ruffled white ground, edged and flecked violet (RHS 87B/C), lemony signal; style arms white, tipped violet (87D). A116-5: (dark magenta sdlg. x white sdlg.) X Mystic Buddha. Laurie's Garden 1991.

CASCADE SPRINGS (Schreiner, R. 1994). Sdlg. AA 110-A. TB, 39" (99 cm), M. S. blue lavender (RHS 96D) wash; F. blue white with blue lavender (97C) washed center; beards light blue, frost tipped; ruffled. Sea of Joy X Memphis Blues. Schreiner 1994.

CASCADE STORM (Lorena Reid, R. 1991). Sdlg. D608-4/7. JI (6 F.), 36-42" (91-102 cm), L. Slightly ruffled violet blue (RHS 95A), veined slightly darker; large yellow (13A) signal. A106-2: (striped sdlg. x Rose Tower) X A123-3: (striped sdlg. x blue sdlg.). Laurie's Garden 1991.

CASCADE VELVET (Joe Halinar, R. 1994). Sdlg. PS-1. SPEC-X, 20" (51 cm), M. S. lavender purple; F. lavender purple, slightly darker veining, yellow eye zone. 40-chr. sino-sib sdlg. X *I. tenax*. Cascade Bulb and Seed 1995.

CASCADE WATERS (Chet Tompkins, R. 1995). Sdlg. 90-133A. TB, 39" (99 cm), ML. White self; beards white. ((Winter Watch x Lady Cynthia) x (Skating Party x Lace Ballet)) X (Lace Ballet x Frost Alert). Fleur de Lis 1995.

CASCADING RAINBOW (Paul Black, R. 1997). Sdlg. A33D. BB, 24" (61 cm), ML. S. peach salmon, midrib medium lilac; style arms apricot, orchid pink center; F. blended dusty rose violet, dusty rose edge, hafts light amber, texture-veined; beards red orange; ruffled, lightly laced; pronounced sweet fragrance. Robusto X Ruth Black. Mid-America 1997.

CASSEZ UNE JAMBE (Robert Fabel-Ward, R. 1995). Sdlg. BW 42/1 H. LA, 39" (100 cm), E. Rose pink self; signal yellow. Jerry Clower X Bayou St. John.

CASSIS (Lawrence Ransom, R. 1998). Sdlg. 90/189-1. SDB, 10" (25 cm), M. S. medium purple madder; style arms light naples yellow, purple madder midrib and crests; F. dark purple madder; beards dark cobalt violet brushed dark brown. 88/20-4: (Third Charm x Cherry Garden) X Two Rubies. Iris au Trescols 1999.

CASS WHITE (Robert Turley, R. 1996). SPEC (*hexagona*), 30-36" (76-91 cm), E. S. and style arms white; F. white, yellow signal; slight spicy fragrance. *I. hexagona*, collected at Olga, Lee County, Florida.

CAST ASHORE (Chuck Chapman, R. 1998) SPEC-X, 30" (76 cm), ML. S. white, rosy lavender lines running lengthwise; style arms white, rosy lavender lines; F. white, rosy lavender lines, small yellow signal. Natural hybrid: collected Bruce Peninsula, Ontario; presumed to be *I. versicolor-I. virginica* cross. Chapman Iris 1998.

CAST A SPELL (Barry Blyth, R. 1996). Sdlg. A106-2. TB, 36-38" (91-97 cm), VE-EM. S. lilac mauve, slight brown midrib veining; F. bright reddish brown, slight tan blending and white spraying near deep bronze beard; sweet fragrance. Tempo Two 1996/97.

CASTAWAY (Barry Blyth, R. 1993). Sdlg. X140-A. TB, 34" (86 cm), EM. S. light to medium metallic orange, pinkish midrib area; F. metallic orange; beards orange tangerine. Latin Lark X (Edna's Wish x Orangerie). Tempo Two 1993/94.

CASUAL JOY (Randall Moore, R. 1999). Sdlg. 92-C. TB, 38" (97 cm), EM. S. lavender-toned light blue; style arms light blue; F. light blue, some light lavender veining; beards yellow orange, lavender base, medium lavender horn; ruffled. Sky Hooks X Lurid.

CASUAL LOVE (Barry Blyth, R. 1999). Sdlg. E48-2. IB, 24" (61 cm), ML. S. lavender, white infusion at midrib and base; style arms lavender, rosy flush; F. purple, white area with deeper purple veining to end of beard; beards white, hairs faintly tipped bronze; slight fragrance. C29-Y: (A30-5, Imbue sib, x A14-8, Noble Toff sib) X B146-2: (Larkabout x Divine). Tempo Two 1999/2000.

CATALUMYA (Barry Blyth, R. 1992). Sdlg. X38-1. IB, 24" (61 cm), EM. Antique gold, F. overlaid brown; beards deep chocolate bronze-black. Honey Behold X ((Inca Queen x (Tranquil Star x (Love Chant x Festive Skirt))) x Amber Snow). Tempo Two 1992/93.

CATAWBA CAMOUFLAGE (B. J. Brown, R. 1992). Sdlg. 0189. TB, 30" (76 cm), EM. S. tan with violet basal infusion; F. tan, violet haft infusion; beards yellow. French Vanilla X Field Day. B. J. Brown 1993.

CATAWBA FRILLS (B. J. Brown, TB, R. 1989). Vine & Branch 1990.

CATAWBA HONEY (B. J. Brown, TB, R. 1989). Vine & Branch 1990.

CATAWBA MAIDEN (B. J. Brown, TB, R. 1989). Vine & Branch 1990.

CATAWBA PEACH (B. J. Brown, TB, R. 1989). Vine & Branch 1990.

CATAWBA POTTERY (B. J. Brown, R. 1992). Sdlg. 0289. TB, 32" (81 cm), EM. S. medium brown; F. medium brown, violet in center; beards brown, tipped gold; spicy fragrance. French Vanilla X Field Day. B. J. Brown 1993.

CATAWBA QUEEN (B. J. Brown, R. 1989). Vine & Branch 1990.

CATAWBA WARRIOR (B. J. Brown, TB, R. 1989). Vine & Branch 1990.

CATCH A CLOUD (Barry Blyth, R. 1999). Sdlg. C172-A. TB, 37" (94 cm), M. Pure white; beards white, lemon yellow in throat; slight fragrance. Sky Dancing X All Silent. Tempo Two 1999/2000.

CATCH A WAVE (Roger Nelson, R. 1995). Sdlg. RN 86-3BCF. TB, 36" (91 cm), ML. S. hazy violet blue (near RHS 92A); style arms deeper violet blue; F. hazy violet blue, with gilt edge, mulberry rose haft flush; beards gold orange, tipped lavender; slight musky fragrance. Pieces of Eight X Graduation. Iris Country 1995.

CATCH THE SUNSET (Wilford James, R. 1998). Sdlg. 93-3. TB, 41" (104 cm), E. S. and style arms light orange; F. deeper orange; beards bright orange; ruffled. Chickasaw Sue X Wedding Candles. Cuyahoga Valley 1998.

CATCH THE WIND (Roger Nelson, R. 1992). Sdlg. RN 86-53BM. TB, 36" (91 cm), M. S. ruffled icy blue; F. blue white; beards lavender at end, lavender gold middle, gold orange deep in throat; sweet fragrance. Pledge Allegiance X RN 84-26M: (Jean Hoffmeister x Windstar).

CATHERINE HOWARD (Mary Tubbs, R. 1992). Sdlg. H-DK. SIB, 36" (91 cm), M. Medium dark blue, blue signal. Parentage unknown.

CATHY DAVIS (Thelma Naylor, SDB, R. 1977). British Iris Society 1995.

CATHY'S SUNSHINE (Louise Smith, R. 1992). TB, 33" (84 cm), EM. S. medium yellow; F. pale yellow, edged darker yellow; beards yellow; slight sweet fragrance. Parentage unknown.

CATS REIGN (David Miller, R. 1996). Sdlg. 88-3A. SDB, 13" (33 cm), EM. S. and style arms dark pansy violet (RHS 83A); F. velvety plum purple (79A), dark pansy violet rim; beards light sky blue; slight sweet fragrance. Michael Paul X Little Bishop. Long 1997.

CATWALK IDOL (Heather Pryor, R. 1997). Sdlg. 18/93-E. LA, 32" (81 cm), EM. S. hot cerise, rim white, pale reverse; style arms beige with cerise blush; F. deeper hot cerise, rim white, pale reverse, raised orange steeple signal; ruffled. Stylish Socialite X Fashion World. Iris Haven 1999/2000.

CAUTION SIGN (George Sutton, R. 1995). Sdlg. E-13. SDB, 11" (28 cm), EM & RE. S. and style arms pale yellow (RHS 3D); F. yellow gold (13B); beards yellow gold (20A), base white. Blitz X Jazzamatazz. Sutton 1996.

CAVALIER'S CAPE (Lynda Miller, R. 1991). Sdlg. 6087A. TB, 34" (86 cm), M. Smoky plum red violet, blue blaze on F.; beards bronze; slight musky fragrance. 5384: (Spartan x unknown) X Mulled Wine. Miller's Manor 1992.

CAVORT (Barry Blyth, R. 1994). Sdlg. A25-3. SDB, 12" (30 cm), VE-EM. Smooth light orange self; beards orange. Cupfull X X20-A: (Camarilla x Yipee). Tempo Two 1994/95.

CEDAR BAYOU (Kirk Strawn, R. 1993). Sdlg. R1985. LA, 32" (81 cm), EM. S. violet blue (RHS 89C); style arms lighter violet blue (90D); F. violet blue (89C), yellow (13B) signal. Acadian Miss X Easter Tide. Bois d'Arc 1996.

CEE CEE (Sterling Innerst, R. 1995). Sdlg. 4070-5. TB, 36" (91 cm), ML & RE. S. ice blue; F. and style arms dark blue; beards blue black. Codicil X Best Bet. Innerst 1996.

CEE JAY (Carol Lankow by J. T. Aitken, R. 1992). Sdlg. 4G35-1. IB, 24" (61 cm), E. Ruffled white ground plicata with deep blue violet rim; beards violet. Chubby Cheeks X Jesse's Song. Aitken's Salmon Creek 1992.

CELEBRATION SONG (Schreiner, R. 1993). Sdlg. AA 1540-1. TB, 37" (94 cm), EML. S. apricot pink (RHS 36C); F. blue lavender (91D); beards tangerine. Lullaby of Spring X Frances Gaulter. Schreiner 1993.

CELESTE AIDA (Valeria Romoli, R. 1999). Sdlg. 33L-91. TB, 32" (80 cm), ML. Laced clear sky blue; beards sky blue, paler base and midsection, deep orange in throat; pronounced fragrance. 7-P-88: (unknown blue x Titan's Glory) X Skyblaze.

CELESTIAL CHOIR (Barry Blyth, R. 1998). Sdlg. D88-2. TB, 38" (96 cm), EM. Ruffled silvery blue white, hafts slightly deeper; beards lemon yellow; slight fragrance. Vanda Song X Some Are Angels. Tempo Two 1998/99.

CELESTIAL GEM (Margaret Adams, R. 1993). SPEC (*verna*), 4-5" (10-13 cm), M. Blue violet self; slight fragrance. *I. verna*, collected clone purchased from dealer at Beersheba, TN.

CELESTIAL GLEAM (Stan Dexter by Marie Ingersoll, R. 1993). Sdlg. A24-6-168A. TB, 38" (97 cm), ML. S. creamy white; F. light blue grey infused green in center; beards red. American Beauty X Elegant Addition. Ingersoll's Iris 1994.

CELESTIAL PINK (Currier McEwen, R. 1990). Sdlg. 80/168(4). JA (3 F.) dip., 32" (80 cm), EM. S. soft light pink (lighter than RHD 75D); style arms white, pink (69C) tufts; F. light pink (75C) with small central white area around soft yellow signal; ruffled. 76/17(3): (Sakurajishi x Mitzu Sakura) X unknown.

CELESTIAL PURITY (Terrell Taylor, R. 1998). Sdlg. 93-44. TB, 36" (91 cm), M. Ruffled white (RHS 155C) self; beards yellow, tipped white; pronounced fragrance. Precious Moments X Scandia Delight. Gormley Greenery 1998.

CELESTIAL SUNSHINE (Bernice Miller, TB, R. 1989). Garden of the Enchanted Rainbow 1989. Introduced as "Heavenly Sunshine".

CELSIUS (Barry Blyth, R. 1995). Sdlg. B117A-1. SDB, 14" (36 cm), VE-EM. S. lemon gold; F. 3/8" lemon gold edge around deep red brown signal; beards navy blue, bronze in throat. Zing Me X Chanted. Tempo Two 1995/96.

CELTIC HARP (Harold Stahly, R. 1998). Sdlg. 92-13. TB, 39" (98 cm), M. Ruffled medium cadmium orange (RHS 23A), F. slightly lighter at tip of tangerine beard. (Sun Fire x (Orange Chariot x Barcelona)) X Esmeralda. Mill Creek, Stahly 1998.

CELTIC PRINCE (Bryce Williamson, R. 1992). TB, 36-38" (91-97 cm), M. S. full buff butter infused with ochre and green tints; F. same, sanded and striped rusty sienna brown, white patch around lemon yellow beard; slight spicy fragrance. Pencil Sketch X Dixie Desert. Pacific Coast Hybridizers 1991.

CELTIC SKIES (George Sutton, R. 1998). Sdlg. H-154. TB, 35" (89 cm), ML-VL. Ruffled wistaria blue (RHS 92D), F. lighter on lower half; style arms wistaria blue (92C); beards lobelia blue (91C), hairs tipped yellow in throat; serrate petal edges; slight sweet fragrance. Winterscape X Tinted Crystal. Sutton 1999.

CENTENNIAL CHILD (Ben Hager, R. 1991). Sdlg. T4879TlPkBch. TB, 35" (89 cm), M. Deep coral pink; beards tangerine. T4331DpPk: ((((Vanity x Liz) x (Ice Sculpture x Liz)) x (Kindness x (Carved Cameo x Vanity))) x ((Ice Sculpture x Liz) x Vanity)) X Anna Belle Babson. Melrose 1991.

CENTENNIAL HALL (Graeme Grosvenor, R. 1999). Sdlg. V49-B. TB, 38" (97 cm), M. Soft apricot pink self; beards tangerine; slight fragrance. Ribands X Romantic Mood.

CENTERING POINT (Joseph Ghio, SPU, R. 1989). Bay View 1990.

CENTURION (Jesse Wills, TB, R. 1949). Correction of parentage. ((Rameses x Jean Cayeux) x Conestoga) X Tobacco Road.

CERDAGNE (Jean Segui, R. 1998). TB, 29" (75 cm), M & RE. S. and style arms yellow (RHS 14A); F. red purple (60A), edged yellow, with yellow rays on shoulders; beards orpiment orange (25A). Cinco de Mayo X Autumn Leaves. Iris de Thau 1989.

CEREMONIUM (Ken Mohr, R. 1993). Sdlg. 9-216-C. TB, 34" (86 cm), M. Heavily ruffled white infused blue orchid in heart; beards lemon, tipped white. K. Mohr 1332-1 X D. Mohr J-161-1. Pacific Coast Hybridizers 1993.

CERULEAN FIRE (Cleo Palmer, R. 1994). Sdlg. 9046A. IB, 23" (58 cm), M. S. very pale blue (near white); F. pale blue; beards red. Starfrost Pink X Pink Jubilee. Palmer's Iris 1994.

C'EST FANTASTIQUE (Mary Dunn, R. 1990). Sdlg. L135-2. LA, 37" (94 cm), M. S. light magenta burgundy; F. smooth light magenta burgundy, small yellow signal; lightly ruffled. Fantastique X Plantation Beau. Bay View 1991.

CEZANNE (Tony Huber, R. 1992). Sdlg. 88-VY-06. SPEC (*versicolor*), 29½" (75 cm), M. S. violet (RHS 93D); F. violet (93B), deep yellow signal veined purple, purple zone with purple veining and few white lines near signal. EX-CO-MR-04, wild collected *I. versicolor*, X EX-CO-TJ-02, wild collected *I. versicolor*.

CHAGALL (Monique Dumas-Quesnel, R. 1992). Sdlg. 90-PL-060. SPEC (*versicolor*), 27½" (70 cm), M. S. lilac (RHS 85B) veined purple; F. lilac (85B) near margins, darkening to deep violet (83A) near center; slight sweet fragrance. Parentage unknown.

CHAGRIN (Larry Harder, R. 1990). Sdlg. 85-1. IB, 23" (58 cm), M. S. yellow ochre (RHS 160A); F. brown blend (161A, 166D); beards yellow ochre; slight spicy fragrance. Love X Jubilee Trail. Maple Tree 1991.

CHAIFA (Oscar Schick, R. 1999). Sdlg. 93-07-B02. TB, 38" (97 cm), M. S. cream, light peach basal infusion; style arms cream; F. cream, pastel buff peach shoulders; beards tangerine, light peach at end; laced; slight musky fragrance. 90-12-F1: (Sue Ellen x Exhilaration) X Chantilly Lace. Stockton 1999.

#CHAMPAGNE AND CAVIAR (Roger Nelson, TB, R. 1987). Not introduced; name transferred.

CHAMPAGNE AND CAVIAR (Roger Nelson, R. 1995). Sdlg. RN 88-114CNO. TB, 31" (79 cm), M. S. and style arms blue white; F. silvery white; beards bluish white, soft yellow in throat; slight sweet fragrance. Yellow Flounce X RN 84-139L: ((Electric Avenue x Latitude) x Pink Sleigh). Iris Country 1996.

CHAMPAGNE ENCORE (J. T. Aitken, R. 1997). Sdlg. 92T94. IB, 24" (61 cm), M & RE. S. white; F. orange, greenish cast; beards orange. Champagne Elegance X Joe Cool. Aitken's Salmon Creek 1997.

CHAMPAGNE FROST (Keith Keppel, R. 1996). Sdlg. 92-59C. TB, 35" (89 cm), M. S. blue white (M&P 33-A-3) faintly flushed very pale pink (1-AB-7); style arms blue white, crests brushed buff peach; F. peach buff (10-CD-3) flushed peach (9-AB-3), hafts suffused corn (10-I-5); beards princeton orange (9-K-11), base and end white; ruffled; slight sweet fragrance. Lucky Lemon X Overjoyed. Keppel 1997.

CHAMPAGNE GIRL (Duane Meek, R. 1993). Sdlg. 611-7-2. TB, 36" (91 cm), EM. S. white with slight pink midrib flush; F. deep pink; beards tangerine; ruffled, slightly picoteed. Infinite Grace X 62-2-3: (Corduroy and Lace x Snowline). D & J Gardens 1993.

CHAMPAGNE GLITTERS (Daniel Thruman, R. 1997). Sdlg. 97-37B. TB, 37" (94 cm), L. S.

pink, midrib lined green; style arms pinkish white; F. white, speckled glistening gold, some green speckles; beards gold; ruffled; sweet fragrance. Gypsy Woman X Outrageous Fortune.

CHAMPAGNE JUNIOR (O. D. Niswonger, R. 1994). Sdlg. BB 28-89. BB, 26" (66 cm), M. S. lilac, touched pink; F. creamy apricot; beards white, tipped tangerine. Ambling X Champagne Elegance. Cape Iris 1994.

CHAMPAGNE LADY (Ray Lyons, R. 1992). Sdlg. 82-43-A. TB, 34" (86 cm), ML. Ruffled and laced amber self; beards gold. Carved Cameo X Mattie Silks. Long 1995.

CHAMPAGNE MOMENTS (Barry Blyth, R. 1998). Sdlg. D64-4. TB, 33" (84 cm), M. Antique cream, shot cream effect, hafts lemon yellow; beards gold; slight fragrance. Plume d'Or X A153-5, Cafe Risque sib. Tempo Two 1998/99.

CHAMPAGNE ON ICE (Tim Stanek, R. 1993). Sdlg. IRV4. TB, 36" (91 cm), ML. S. champagne yellow; style arms same, fringed, stigmatic lip infused lavender; F. mother-of-pearl with lavender midrib streak, 1/4" champagne yellow edge; beards champagne yellow, base lavender; ruffled, lightly laced; slight sweet fragrance. Cher X Lavender Ribbon. Eight Mile Grove 1993.

CHAMPAGNE TASTE (H. C. Mohr, R. 1990). TB, 36" (91 cm), M. S. soft tint of buff apricot pink; F. cream white, 1/4" edge of S. color; beards white, tipped coral red. Trevi Fountain X Exuberant. Pacific Coast Hybridizers 1990.

CHAMPAGNE WALTZ (Schreiner, 1994). Sdlg AA 1027-C. TB, 36" (91 cm), M. S. apricot yellow (RHS 17D); F. ruffled creamy white, 1/4" apricot yellow edge; beards tangerine. V 381-A: (Bright Reflection x S 658-5: ((Skyfire sib x J 571-B) x (Something Else x J 571-A: (((Golden Ice x Celestial Glory) x Flaming Star) x Gold Trimmings)))) X S 659-1, Outrageous Fortune sib. Schreiner 1994.

CHAMPAGNE WISHES (Keith Keppel, R. 1991). Sdlg. 85-10A. TB, 36" (91 cm), M. S. peachblow (M&P 10-B-5 to 2-C-8); F. light salmon (10-A-6); beards firecracker (1-H-12) shaded lilac pink (41-F-1); slight sweet-musky fragrance. Custom Made X 79-47A: (Goddess x 77-137F: (Mistress sib x ((Joy Ride x Roundup) x (April Melody x 68-40B: (((Irma Melrose x Tea Apron) x ((Full Circle x Rococo) x Tea Apron)) x April Melody))))). Keppel 1992.

CHAN (Ladislav Muska, R. 1996). Sdlg. S-DQMQ-01. SDB, 14" (36 cm), E. S. light lilac blue; F. deep lilac burgundy red, light lilac rim; beards yellow, blue at end; slight fragrance. (Demon x Queen's Pawn) X (Monkey x Queen's Pawn). Muska 1993.

CHANCE BEAUTY (J. R. Ellis, SPEC-X, R. 1988). British Iris Society 1990.

CHANCE ENCOUNTER (Duane Meek, R. 1996). Sdlg. 66-3-5. TB, 34" (86 cm), M. S. ivory white ground, wide mulberry rose plicata border; style arms mulberry rose; F. ivory, wide mulberry dotted line border and hafts, minute ivory outer rim; beards red orange, white at end; ruffled, lightly laced. Lingering Love X Queen in Calico. D & J Gardens 1996.

CHANCES (Barry Blyth, R. 1998). Sdlg. E31-1. SDB, 12-14" (30-36 cm), EM. Coral apricot, F. with large white spot, deeper orange apricot area beside beard; beards bright tangerine, base white; open S., slight sweet fragrance. Scion X Little Bev. Tempo Two 1998/99.

CHANDLER'S CHOICE (Currier McEwen, R. 1994). Sdlg. ST(6)78/134. SIB (tet.), 32" (81 cm), EML. S. and style arms dark red purple (RHS 77A); F. red violet (80A) with near-black (79A) veins, giving overall effect darker than (77A); pale yellowish white signals with 1/2" violet (87A) halo. Hubbard X Happy Event. Eartheart, Seaways 1995.

CHANGELING (William Plotner, R. 1992). Sdlg. 85-365-1. TB, 36-38" (91-97 cm), EM. S. indian tan veined and lightly bordered wistaria violet, aging to light mustard yellow lightly flushed orchid with faint orchid border; F. wistaria violet edged amber brown, aging to orchid white edged mustard yellow. Counterpart X ((Dualtone x Valvouche) x Gold Ring). Wildwood Gardens 1992.

CHANGE OF MILLENNIUM (A. & D. Cadd, R. 1999). Sdlg. 85-91-2. TB, 38" (97 cm), ML. S. light blue, lavender cast darker on midrib; style arms lavender blue; F. velvety dark reddish purple, whiter zonal area, dark purple shoulder markings and lines radiating from beard blending with surrounding color; beards blue purple, mustard yellow in throat; ruffled; pronounced spicy fragrance. Royalist X unknown.

CHANGE OF PACE (Schreiner, R. 1991). Sdlg. Z 549-A. TB, 35" (89 cm), EM. S. delicate pink (RHS 73D); F. white ground, deep rose violet (71A) plicata markings and peppering on edge; beards yellow. Eagle's Flight X Cinnamon Girl. Schreiner 1991.

CHANGE YOUR WAYS (Richard Ernst, R. 1994). Sdlg. JF169-25-2. TB, 37" (94 cm), ML. S. light blue violet, overlaid copper, with light violet veining, copper rim; F. light blue violet, copper rim, brassy reverse; beards yellow; ruffled; slight sweet fragrance. F169-25: (Afternoon Delight x (Ringo x (Cranberry Ice x Grand Waltz))) X F106-2: (Syncopation x (Irene Nelson x Honest Pleasure)). Cooley 1995.

CHANGING WINDS (Chet Tompkins, R. 1994). Sdlg. 88-14. TB, 38-39" (97-99 cm), ML. S. rosy vervain violet; F. manganese violet with cream ground showing in striped network pattern; beards tangerine red; ruffled. (Jet Fire x April Lost) X (April Lost X Gibson plicata line). Roris 1994.

CHANTED (Barry Blyth, R. 1990). Sdlg. X10-3. SDB, 12-14" (31-36 cm), M. Pink with smoky cast; beards lavender blue, tangerine in throat. Oladi X (Peach Eyes x Kandi Moon). Tempo Two 1990/91.

CHANTELLE (Frances Love, R. 1991). MTB, 18" (46 cm), E. S. white; F. cream, mahogany yellow thumbspot; beards white. Gingerbread Man X Picayune.

CHANTILLY DANCER (Barry Blyth, R. 1994). Sdlg. A44-11. SDB, 12-14" (30-36 cm), ML. S. lavender pink with light violet midrib infusion; F. creamy white, light pink overlay on lower 2/3, 1/4" lavender pink plicata stitching; beards white, tipped burnt tangerine. V7-5, Gigolette sib, X Chanted. Tempo Two 1994/95.

#CHANTILLY LACE (Nellye Ewing, TB, R. 1966). Not distributed or introduced; name released.

CHANTILLY LACE (William Maryott, R. 1992). Sdlg. L129B. TB, 36" (91 cm), M. Ruffled, heavily laced yellow cream (RHS 11A, 159B) with hint of purple (70D); beards yellow; slight sweet fragrance. G27A: ((Carved Cameo x Wings of Dreams) x Ghio 76-257: (Entourage x Homecoming Queen)) X H99B: ((Sharlee sib x Foolish Pleasure) x (Fantasy Faire x Ghio 76-115: (Veneer sib x San Jose))). Maryott 1992.

CHAOS (Lynda Miller, SDB, R. 1989). Miller's Manor 1990.

CHAPTER TWO (Colin Rigby, R. 1999). Sdlg. 9516-CS. SPEC-X (cal-sib), 14-16" (36-41 cm), M. S. red violet, veined darker; style arms red violet, edge slightly lighter; F. red violet, heavily veined darker, near-black thumbprint with few white and gold signal veins at base. L. Reid blue sino-sib sdlg. X Herald.

CHARABIA (Lawrence Ransom, R. 1994). Sdlg. 90/383-1. SDB, 11" (28 cm), ML. S. light yellow, darker gold frosted edge; style arms light yellow; F. blackcurrant purple spot, greyed violet middle halo blending to smoky greenish yellow edge; beards yellow, cream base; ruffled; slight spicy sweet fragrance. Pippi Longstockings X Small Flash. Iris au Trescols 1995.

CHARDONNAY (Marky Smith, R. 1992). Sdlg. 89-21A. SDB, 12" (31 cm), EM. S. bright yellow (RHS 11A); F. lighter yellow (11B) with darker shoulders, hafts and rim; beards strong yellow; heavily ruffled. 87-27M: (Cotton Blossom x Laced Lemonade) X B. Jones 392-1: (Sun Doll x Dixie Pixie). Aitken's Salmon Creek 1996.

CHARGE D'AFFAIRE (Mary Dunn, R. 1990). Sdlg. L119-3. LA, 36" (91 cm), M. S. light plum, lighter serrate edge; style arms green, tipped purple; F. velvety deeper plum, lighter serrate and ruffled edge, signal yellow. Clara Goula X L40-10: (Charlie's Michele x Carmen). Bay View 1992.

CHARGED UP (Lynda Miller, R. 1996). Sdlg. 100791. TB, 34" (86 cm), L. S. light rose over pale orange ground; style arms dark apricot; F. rose magenta over dark apricot, apricot center stripe; beards tangerine; slight musky fragrance. 4385D: (Far Corners x Marmalade) X unknown. Miller's Manor 1999.

CHARIVARI (Nora Scopes, R. 1991). Sdlg. 6/140. TB, 48" (122 cm), ML. S. chartreuse stippled maroon; F. cream infused chartreuse, edged maroon; beards brownish yellow. Lucky Dip X Capricious.

CHARLATAN (Janet Hutchinson, R. 1996). Sdlg. MSDWB6. LA, 47" (120 cm), M. S. yellow buff, mulberry veining heavier in center; style arms mulberry and buff; F. medium purplish mulberry, deeper centerline, pink buff marginal line, wide short yellow signal, deeper centerline; lightly ruffled; slight fragrance. Marsha Sue X Dural White Butterfly. Iris Haven 1997/98.

CHARLENE'S DECREE (Tom Burseen, R. 1997). Sdlg. 0-137A. TB, 37" (94 cm), ML. Ruffled and laced cool pink (RHS 65B), F. with lighter wash of pale lavender blue; beards tangerine, white base; musky fragrance. Romantic Mood X Fundango. T.B.'s Place 1997.

CHARLENE STRAWN (Kirk Strawn, R. 1993). Sdlg. 68-1984. LA, 40" (102 cm), M. S. light purple (RHS 76B) veined darker (78B); style arms purple (78B); F. purple (78C fading to 87B), green yellow signal; ruffled. Mrs. Ira Nelson X Kirk Strawn. Bois d'Arc 1996.

CHARLEY O. (Charles Okken, R. 1995). Sdlg. Ab-10-8. TB, 35" (89 cm), M. S. dark purple violet; style arms deep lavender; F. deep violet, edges lighter, with light and dark streaks in throat; beards deep violet, tipped light blue. Magic Man X Dusky Challenger.

CHARLIE'S CLOUD (Joan Roberts, R. 1997). Sdlg. 733-1. TB, 37" (94 cm), ML. S. pale blue;

F. white; beards pale blue; ruffled; slight sweet fragrance. Breakers X Honky Tonk Blues. Friendship 1998.

CHARLOTTE'S CHILD (Chet Tompkins, R. 1998). Sdlg. 94-2C. TB, 37" (94 cm), ML. S. white, stitched blue edge; style arms blue white; F. white, edged and patterned blue black; beards white, tipped blue. ((Good Behavior x Armada) x Charlotte's Web) X (Charlotte's Web x Makebelieve Magic). Fleur de Lis 1998.

CHARLOTTE'S TUTU (Heather Pryor, R. 1994). Sdlg. 57/90-1. LA, 38" (97 cm) EM. Ruffled cerise, all petals with lime green signal lined black; style arms cerise with green rib creating star effect; form slightly reflexed. Desert Jewel X Noble Planet. Rainbow Ridge 1995/96.

CHARM CITY CHOICE (O. D. Niswonger, R. 1992). Sdlg. 39-89. TB, 34" (86 cm), EM. Dark blue, F. darker shading near beard; beards dark blue tipped bronze. Touch of Bronze X Everything Plus. Cape Iris 1992.

CHARMED (Mary Dunn, R. 1993). Sdlg. M84-875X. TB, 38" (97 cm), M. Ruffled creamy ivory orchid, ivory heart and F. center; beards ivory yellow. Pina Colada X Top Gun. M.A.D. Iris 1994.

CHARMING CHICK (Luella Danielson, R. 1990). Sdlg. LD-1-67. AR (OH), 13" (33 cm), EM. S. light orchid pink (RHS 69D), thin light blue mid-line with light blue veining radiating outward; style arms gold, crests light lavender; F. slightly darker light orchid pink, green blue veining radiating from tip of red purple (71A) signal to edge, red purple dotting around signal; beards light violet tipped darker purple. JP-82-3: (*I. samariae* x *I. paradoxa*) X Visiting Queen. Pleasure Iris 1991.

CHARMING IMAGE (Lin Flanagan, AB, R. 1989). Aril Society 1990.

CHAROIT (Adolf Volfovich-Moler, R. 1999). Sdlg. V-176. TB, 41" (105 cm), M. S. purple; style arms purple, edged lighter; F. cardinal red to purple, hafts marked brown; beards yellow, end paler; ruffled; pronounced fragrance. Victoria Falls X Karmen Dance. Volfovich-Moler 1998.

CHARTER MEMBER (Joseph Ghio, R. 1993). Sdlg. PG-172-U2. CA, 11" (28 cm), E. Orchid pink, solid mahogany pink signal. PI-MIX pink, unknown, X Herald. Bay View 1994.

CHARTRES (Jim & Vicki Craig, R. 1997). Sdlg. AH85A8. MTB, 25" (64 cm), E. S. blue, darker midrib; style arms pale purple, darker midrib; F. deep lilac purple paler at edge, velvety finish; beards dark yellow, purple base at end; pronounced sweet fragrance. ((Payoff x 11R4, Reformation sib) x ((En Route x Maroon Caper) x 8L: (Chapeau x (Sacred Mountain x *I. aphylla* "Werckmeister")))) X Bouquet Magic. J. & V. Craig 1997.

CHARTREUSE CIRCUS (Hugh Thurman, R. 1999). Sdlg. 92-10-32. SDB, 10" (25 cm), M. S. cream, tinted chartreuse, darker chartreuse wash; style arms cream, tinted chartreuse, lavender lip; F. cream, tinted chartreuse, faint lavender wash, 1/8" chartreuse rim with lavender inner rim; beards white, end lavender with hairs tipped orange; slight spicy fragrance. Court Magician X Chubby Cheeks.

CHARTREUSE ENCORE (Currier McEwen, R. 1997). Sdlg. T(1)84/80. SIB (tet.), 26" (65 cm), EML & RE. S. white, veined pale chartreuse green (RHS 1C); style arms wide, white, midribs and tufts greenish yellow (1B); F. pale chartreuse green (1C) ground veined deeper (1A), hafts and blaze dresden yellow (5A) with yellow green (154A) veining; ruffled. Butter and Sugar X Ruffled Velvet -- colchicine treated.

CHASING RAINBOWS (Ben Hager, R. 1995). Sdlg. T5516PkBld/OcBld. TB, 32" (81 cm), M. S. peach pink, purple blended up midrib; style arms peach; F. buff, lavender and blue blend; beards tangerine. T4235PkCr/Lv: (Merry Madrigal x Mother Earth) X Sweet Musette. Cooley 1998.

CHASTE (Ben Hager, R. 1996). Sdlg. MD6040ClnWh. MDB, 6" (15 cm), EML. White self; beards white, tipped yellow in throat. MD5152WhChtHft, Nestling sib, X MD4495CrWhT: ((3739: (Pet sib x Tiny Apricot) x ((2562: (Pink Amber x Pink Cushion) x (Frosty Lemonade x Pink Cushion)) x (2562 x Buttercup Charm))) x (3739 x (Pet sib x Tiny Apricot))). Adamgrove 1997.

CHASTE PEARL (George Sutton, R. 1995). Sdlg. G5. BB, 26" (66 cm), ML. Ruffled crystalline pinkish white (paler than RHS 56D); style arms pale orient pink (36C); beards coral. Paradise X Vision in Pink. Sutton 1996.

CHASTE WHITE (Lloyd Zurbrigg, R. 1997). Sdlg. P 33 Chaste. TB, 34" (86 cm) EM & RE. White self; beards white; fragrant. I Do X English Cottage. Viette 1987.

CHAT (Barry Blyth, R. 1999). Sdlg. F102-1. IB, 22" (56 cm), ML. Lemon yellow infused buff, F. with white spot; beards old gold; pronounced sweet fragrance. Touch and Go X C225-2, Gala Greetings sib. Tempo Two 1999/2000.

CHATEAU LAFITE (B.L.C. Dodsworth, R. 1995). Sdlg. EB 91A. TB, 44" (112 cm), L. Ruffled maroon; beards brown. Minisa X Fireball.

CHATTER (Joseph Ghio, R. 1992). Sdlg. 88-11C. TB, 34" (86 cm), EM. S. yellow orange overlaid fuchsia rose; F. yellow orange ground, fuchsia rose sanding at edge; beards burnt tangerine. (Romanticist x 82-113G, Chuckles sib) X Storyline. Bay View 1993.

CHATTER BOX BELLE (Currier McEwen, R. 1990). Sdlg. T(7)83/135(7). SIB (tet.), 32" (80 cm), EM. Blue violet (RHS 83B to 89C) blend, large stippled white signal. T(6)78/57, sdlgs. inv. Blue Brilliant, White Swirl, Violet Flare, Polly Dodge, Pirouette X Windwood Spring. Pope's Perennials, Seaways 1991.

CHAYNAYA ROZA (V. & N. Gordodelovy, R. 1995). Sdlg. 109. TB, 28" (71 cm), M. Pink, tinted orange, F. with brown haft striations; beards red. Parentage unknown. Gordodelovy 1985.

CHEATING HEART (Keith Keppel, R. 1993). Sdlg. 87-21P. TB, 35" (89 cm), EM. S. honeydew (M&P 9-B-8) blended capucine buff (9-E-5) at edge; F. capucine buff, hafts plicata-webbed slate purple (46-I-6); beards golden poppy (9-L-12) to toboggan (1-B-12); ruffled. 82-32A, Rosarita sib, X Daredevil. Keppel 1994.

CHECKERBOARD (Kevin Nilsen, R. 1992). Sdlg. 27-87-1. TB, 34" (87 cm), EM. S. white ground with deep purple plicata edge; F. white ground with slightly paler deep purple edge, stitching and spotting; beards deep blue. Going My Way X Burgundy Brown. Iridescence 1992/93.

CHEERFUL ANGEL (Hooker Nichols, R. 1991). Sdlg. 8740A. SDB, 12" (30 cm), EM. S. pale creamy yellow, darker base; F. pale creamy yellow, darker halo; beards orange and creamy yellow; ruffled. 8259B: (Cotton Blossom x C. Palmer 7259: ((Wilma V. x unknown) x Little Titan)) X 8326A: (Sapphire Jewel x Veiled Sunshine). Hillcrest 1993.

CHEERY LYN (Anna Mae Miller, R. 1990). Sdlg. 85-20-15. SIB, 37" (94 cm), E. S. lilac (RHS 76C) with blue lines; style arms white; F. deep pink (75A to 76A) veined blue (97A), white edge, green eye. Aqua Whispers X Lavender Bounty. Old Douglas Perennials 1991.

CHELSEA FAIR (W. & A. Godfrey, R. 1999). Sdlg. DNDT5. SDB, 11" (28 cm), EM. S. cream, very pale blue veining; style arms cream, pale blue rim; F. deep burgundy rimmed cream; beards cream, deep orange in throat; lightly ruffled. (unknown navy sdlg. x self) X Ditto. Hermit Medlars Walk 1999.

CHELSEA'S DREAM (Keith Fillmore, R. 1990). Sdlg. 8217-BB. BB, 22" (56 cm), L. Light lavender; beards white. 8004-1: (Cup Race x unknown) X Mary Frances. Bar K Iris 1990.

CHELSEA TURNER (Jack Norrick, R. 1997). Sdlg. 92-4. MTB, 18" (46 cm), L. S. bright yellow; F. light yellow, edged darker; beards yellow. Spanish Coins X Topsy Turvy. Miller's Manor 1999.

CHENGDU (Jean Witt, R. 1997). SPEC (evansia), 20-24" (51-61 cm), M. S. and style arms light lavender; F. slightly darker, signal white with medium lavender halo, yellow crest. Collected 1980 by Jeanne Gardiner between Kanding, Tibet, and Yaan, Sichuan, China, ca. 3000' elevation; probably *I. confusa*.

CHER (Roger Nelson, R. 1991). Sdlg. RN 82087J. TB, 30-31" (76-79 cm), M. S. deep orchid violet (RHS 83A/B) with bright purple (77A) highlights; F. same, lighter area near bright orange red (33B) beard; ruffled. Dawn Light X RN 79-3K: (Lady X x Glory Bound). Iris Country 1991.

CHERE MARTINE (J. R. Allen, R. 1994). Sdlg. T 22 A. TB, 32" (81 cm), EM. Medium deep purple self; self beards; ruffled; slight sweet fragrance. R 1 H: (Wedding Vow x Rebecca Anne) X R 3 C: (Sapphire Hills x Rebecca Anne). Allen Iris 1997.

CHERIE HAEGER (Ed Attenberger, R. 1998). Sdlg. 92-01-08. TB, 37" (94 cm), M. S. and style arms medium buff pink; F. light orchid pink; beards red orange; ruffled, lightly laced; slight sweet fragrance. Peach Picotee X Entourage.

CHERI NOBYL (Les Fort, R. 1990). Sdlg. 84-56-A. TB, 36" (91 cm), M. Ruffled smooth satiny pink; beards bright cherry; slight fragrance. Playgirl X (Pink Sleigh x Richardson 75-26-2: (Pink Taffeta x ((Celestial Snow x Blushing Beauty) x Cloud Ruffles))). Fort Iris 1991.

CHERNOMORETS (Irina Driagina, R. 1996). Sdlg. 4-76. TB, 43" (110 cm), M. Dark blue black self; beards black, hairs tipped yellow. Parentage unknown. Driagina 1971.

CHEROKEE DAYBREAK (Bennett Jones, R. 1999). Sdlg. 558-1. SDB, 12" (31 cm), M. S. salmon pink; F. deeper salmon pink, edge matching S.; beards carrot red; lightly ruffled; slight fragrance. Inca Doll X Vintage Rose. Aitken's Salmon Creek 1999.

CHEROKEE HERITAGE (Hooker Nichols, R. 1991). Sdlg. 8861A. TB, 36" (91 cm), EM. S. smooth brown suffused yellow; F. white, red brown hafts, smooth brown edge with inner plicata ring of cinnamon yellow; beards muted orange; ruffled. Dazzling Gold X Beyond. Hillcrest 1992.

CHEROKEE NATION (Jim Hedgecock, R. 1991). Sdlg. 84-100-3. TB, 36" (91 cm), M. S. pale red; F. wine red, edged lighter red, white haft overlay; beards golden yellow; ruffled, laced. Caramba X unknown. Comanche Acres 1992.

CHEROKEE SUNRISE (Bennett Jones, R. 1997). Sdlg. 495-3. SDB, 12" (31 cm), M. S. coral pink, salmon basal flush; style arms coral; F. salmon, pale pink edge; beards coral; lightly fluted; slight fragrance. 448: (412: (Live Jazz x Orange Dazzler) x Pink Caper) X 437-3: (Pink Prevue x Tillie). Aitken's Salmon Creek 1998.

CHEROKEE TEARS (Ben Hager, R. 1990). Sdlg. RE3933Br. TB, 32" (81 cm), M & RE (early Sept.-frost/CA). Silken burnt sienna brown, F. with small orchid blue area at end of yellow beard. Verismo sib. Melrose 1990.

CHERRY BLOSSOM SPECIAL (Jim Hedgecock, R. 1999). Sdlg. H-33-5. TB, 37" (94 cm), EM. Ruffled and laced pale pink, hafts slightly darker; beards bright red orange, long lavender pink upturned horn; pronounced sweet fragrance. Hazel Jean X What's Up Doc.

CHERRYBROOK (Heather Pryor, R. 1995). Sdlg. 57/90-2. LA, 38" (97 cm), M. S. lemon, cherry red marginal wash and line signal; style arms cherry red (RHS 181B), yellow center rib; F. cherry red, yellow dagger signal, paler reverse; ruffled. Desert Jewel X Noble Planet.

CHERRY CERISE (Leslie Donnell, R. 1995). Sdlg. 94-2-14. TB, 37" (94 cm), ML. S. cerise (RHS 74A to 78A); F. cerise, white patch near haft; beards red; sweet fragrance. Bronzed Violet X Olympiad.

CHERRY CHILD (Barry Blyth, R. 1994). Sdlg. A31-5. SDB, 12" (30 cm), EM. S. burgundy purple (cherry black); F. plush black, 1/4" burgundy purple edge, small white area around burnt tangerine beard; slight fragrance. X31-3: (Yipee x Camarilla) X Chanted. Tempo Two 1994/95.

CHERRY CHOCOLATE (Brad Kasperek, R. 1998). Sdlg. 94B-22C. TB, 36" (91 cm), EM. S. cherry chocolate (RHS 187C/D), cream white (155C) streaks; style arms chocolate and gold, crests laced; F. deeper cherry chocolate (187A), cream white streaks; beards dark gold; broken color pattern; ruffled. Gnus Flash X 91P-8A: (89B-42: (Rustic Dance x Maria Tormena) x Tiger Honey).

CHERRY CLASS (Cloyd McCord, R. 1993). Sdlg. 83-45. TB, 36" (91 cm), M. Ruffled and laced white; beards red; sweet fragrance. 73-13: (Angie Quadros x Homecoming Queen) X Homecoming Queen. McCord 1993.

CHERRY CURLS (A. & D. Willott, 1999). Sdlg. W 91-126. SDB, 13" (33 cm), E. S. and style arms deep red violet; F. velvety deep red violet, strongly flared; beards full violet; ruffled. Cherry Festival X W 80-44: (Joyce Terry x Buttons).

CHERRY FROSTING (Connell Marsh, TB, R. 1981). C. Marsh 1990.

CHERRY GLEN (William Maryott, R. 1994). Sdlg. S195A. TB, 38" (97 cm), EM. Ruffled red violet maroon (RHS 74A), F. more velvety; beards orange, prominent; spicy fragrance. Mariachi Music X Twice Told. Maryott 1995.

CHERRY GROVE (Eric Tankesley-Clarke, SDB, R. 1988). Adamgrove 1993.

CHERRY LANE (Glenn Corlew, TB, R. 1986). Cooley 1993.

CHERRY LIME FIZZ (Cloyd McCord, R. 1993). Sdlg. 85-45-1. TB, 37" (93 cm), M. Ruffled and laced mint lime; beards red; sweet fragrance. 73-13: (Angie Quadros x Homecoming Queen) X Homecoming Queen. McCord 1993.

CHERYL ATNIP (Bob Thomason, R. 1991). Sdlg. 8501C. TB, 33" (84 cm), ML. Deep purple; self beards; slight fragrance. Violet Harmony X Lord Jeff.

CHESHIRE CAT (Donald Spoon, R. 1995). Sdlg. 90-45. TB, 34" (86 cm), ML. S. and style arms golden yellow; F. maroon plum, lighter veining and edging, light yellow veined area around beard; beards maroon, hairs tipped mustard; ruffled. Corn Harvest X -- probably Delias's Child. Winterberry 1996.

CHESTNUT AVENUE (Barry Blyth, R. 1994). Sdlg. A63-2. TB, 38" (97 cm), EM. Medium brown, F. with some gold at hafts, lavender blaze below bright mustard beard; pronounced sweet fragrance. Dance Man X Rembrandt Magic. Tempo Two 1994/95.

CHEVALIER DE MALTE (Richard Cayeux, R. 1997). Sdlg. 88212 A. TB, 32" (80 cm), M. S. light pinkish chamois; F. bright pinkish purple, large cream center; beards orange red. Whirl Around X 86167 A: (8461 B, Ruban Bleu sib, x 8459: ((Condottiere x Delphi) x (Condottiere x Metropolitan))). Cayeux 1998.

CHEYENNE DAYS (Chet Tompkins, R. 1996). Sdlg. 93-15. TB, 34-36" (86-91 cm), EML. Cornflower blue self; beards blue, paler at base, changing to lemon white in throat. Sheer Bliss X Honky Tonk Blues. Fleur de Lis 1996.

CHEYENNE SUMMER (Jim Hedgecock, R. 1996). Sdlg. 84-100-5. TB, 33" (84 cm), M. S. medium yellow; F. dark gold yellow, white to pale yellow striations near golden orange beard; ruffled;

lightly (S.) to heavily (F.) laced; slight sweet fragrance. Caramba X unknown. Comanche Acres 1998.

CHEZ MICHELLE (Mary Dunn, R. 1994). Sdlg. L156-8. LA, 36" (91 cm), M. S. light violet; F. light violet with lighter area toward yellow signal, pale violet edge. Easter Tide X Plantation Beau. Bay View 1995.

CHIC (Duane Meek, R. 1993). Sdlg. 395-1-6. TB, 35" (89 cm), EM. Ruffled medium pink; self beards. Anna Belle Babson X Cold Cold Heart sib. D & J Gardens 1993.

CHICA DE SONORA (Floyd Wickenkamp, R. 1994). Sdlg. SP-87-2. SPU, 36" (91 cm), L. S. full blue violet; style arms tipped blue violet; F. large gold blaze shading to brown, 1/4" full blue violet edge. SP-83-2: (Burnished Brass x (Burnished Brass x Proverb)) X SP-83-7: (Highline Honey x Proverb). Shepard Iris 1995.

CHICANERY (David Spence, R. 1996). Sdlg. S83-286-1. TB, 42" (107 cm), L. S. pale lavender veined gold; style arms pale lavender and gold; F. parchment, 1/8" gold edging; beards orange, lavender at end, sometimes with 1/2" hairy lavender horn; ruffled, laced. Chartreuse Ruffles X Lavender Petticoat. Master Creations 1997.

CHIC ATTIRE (James Gibson by Cooley's Gardens, R. 1999). Sdlg. 35-2B. TB, 34" (86 cm), EM. S. cool pink; F. pink, peach wash overlay, small white area around end of red beard; ruffled. Edna's Wish X 125-9A, unknown. Cooley 1999.

CHIC DEBUTANTE (John Wight, R. 1996). Sdlg. J89-11-1. AB (OGB-), 28" (71 cm), M. S. white, very pale greenish yellow veins and midrib; F. medium greenish yellow, slight gold edge, maroon fingerprint signal around beard terminating in faint centerline; beards orange, base white; falls recurved. Ruffled Shamrock X J85-5 yellow amoena: (Irish Valentine x Holk yellow amoena). Aril Society, Wight's Iris 1996.

CHICKA WATCH (Terrell Taylor, R. 1997). Sdlg. 94-17. TB, 30" (75 cm), EM. S. dark wine red (RHS 178A); F. pure white ground trimmed dark wine red; beards bronze; sweet fragrance. Chickasaw Sue X Colorwatch. Bonita Gardens 1997.

CHICORY CHARM (Ben Hager, R. 1991). Sdlg. SD4901FlrBl. SDB, 9-13" (23-33 cm), EML. Light blue with lavender influence; self beards. SD3781: (Just Dandy x (((Hello x (Sunny Heart x ((Evening Storm x Welch H501) x (Sulina x Melodrama)))) x (Blueberry Muffins x Peanuts)) x (Prodigy x ((New Idea x Orchid Elf) x ((Knotty Pine x Grace Note) x Zip))))) X Azure Gem. Adamgrove 1991.

CHICORY DICKORY (Ben Hager, R. 1991). Sdlg. SD4901LaBl. SDB, 13" (33 cm), ML. Medium blue; beards blue white. Sib to Chicory Charm. Adamgrove 1992.

CHIDORI (Shuichi Hirao by Society for Japanese Irises, R. 1993). JI (9 to 12 F.), 39" (100 cm), M. White with light lilac blue central brushing; very drooping foliage. Parentage unknown. Hirao 1956.

CHIDORI-NO-MAI (Toyokazu Ichie/Kamo Nurseries by Currier McEwen, R. 1997). Sdlg. 74-55. JI (6 F.), 30" (75 cm), M. Ruffled white, 1/16" to 1/8" dark violet blue (RHS 89B) edging; style arms white, edges and tufts medium violet blue (89D); signal canary yellow (9B). 0-131: (("Harema-Nishiki" x unknown) x "Ayasegawa") X Hakusan.

CHIEF EXECUTIVE (Abram Feuerstein, R. 1999). Sdlg. 93-100. TB, 32" (81 cm), M. Ruffled medium blue self; beards light blue. Scandia Delight X Tinted Crystal. Stockton 1998.

CHIEF GEORGE (Donald Spoon, R. 1990). Sdlg. 89-3. TB, 32" (81 cm), M. Deep maple red (RHS 183C), beard surrounded by lighter veins and one central vein, orange red at hafts; beards white and yellow. Superstition X Drury Lane.

CHIEF NICHOLAS (Donovan Albers, R. 1994). Sdlg. 8900. SDB, 12" (31 cm), M. Royal purple (HCC 834), darker around bronze beards; slight fragrance. Love Kristin X Michael Paul. Redbud Lane 1995.

CHIEF QUINABY (Schreiner, R. 1991). Sdlg. T 1565-1. TB, 36" (91 cm), EM. Deep red (RHS 61A), ruffled and flared F.; beards old gold. Play With Fire X Deep Fire. Schreiner 1991.

CHIEF RED JACKET (Anna Rettig, R. 1997). Sdlg. AR-014. JI (3 F.), 36" (91 cm), EM. S. reddish magenta (RHS 72A), held at 45° angle; style arms amethyst (79C), reflexed; F. reddish magenta, velvety, small aureolin yellow (12A) signal hidden by style. Numazu X unknown. A & M Perennials 1998.

CHIEF SEQUOIA (John Weiler, R. 1990). Sdlg. CAW-2. CA, 18" (46 cm), EM & RE. Light blue with slight lavender influence, circular white signal. Roving Eye X Claremont Bluebird. Rialto 1991.

CHIFFON RUFFLES (Richard Ernst, R. 1991). Sdlg. F125-32. TB, 40" (102 cm), M. S. very pale lemon; F. cream ground, sanded golden brown and pale blue, lemon edge; beards yellow; heavily ruffled; slight sweet fragrance. Edna's Wish X Wild Jasmine. Cooley 1991.

CHIGO-NO-KANZASHI (Hiroshi Shimizu by Society for Japanese Irises, R. 1999). JI (multipetal), 36" (91 cm), L. White. Sakurajishi X (Oyodo x Renkaku). Introduced in Japan, 1987.

CHIGOSUGATA (Shuichi Hirao by Society for Japanese Irises, R. 1994). JI (6-8 F.), 40" (102 cm), M. Wistaria violet, paling toward edge, prominent white veining and halo, gold signal. Parentage unknown. Hirao 1960.

CHILD BRIDE (Lynda Miller, MDB, R. 1989). Miller's Manor 1990.

CHILDERIC (Jean Peyrard, R. 1992). Sdlg. PN88/10. SDB, 10" (25 cm), E. S. dark red purple; F. satiny dark red purple; beards brown purple; slight fragrance. Lollipop X Eyebright.

CHILE RIVER (Polly Black, R. 1992). Sdlg. ST4-2R. TB, 36" (91 cm), M. S. maroon red; F. deeper, white shoulders lined red; beards bright orange; slight fragrance. Dawn Delight X Apricot Blaze. Polly Black 1992.

CHILI PEPPER (Herbert Holk, R. 1996). Sdlg. 2843. TB, 34" (86 cm) ML & RE. S. oxblood red (RHS 183A/B) plicata markings on white ground; F. white ground, oxblood red 1/4"-3/8" heavily stippled marginal band; beards bronze; heavily ruffled. 2817: (2801: (Grenadine Pacesetter x Cayenne Capers) x Racy Red) X Cayenne Pepper. Cal-Dixie 1997.

CHILL OUT (Tom Burseen, R. 1995). Sdlg. 1-313M. TB, 36" (91 cm), ML. S. and style arms cool icy light lavender; F. pale lavender, slight lavender plicata edging; beards bright tangerine; ruffled, laced; sweet fragrance. Lillypilly Wine X 9-395: (Sterling Stitch x (Trousseau Lace x Wings of Dreams)). T.B.'s Place 1996.

CHIMGAN (Adolf Volfovich-Moler, R. 1995). Sdlg. V-45. TB, 32" (80 cm), E. S. and F. white ground, light purplish brown edge; beards yellow, cream at end; ruffled. Dancers Veil X Rippling Waters. Volfovich-Moler 1992.

CHINA MAGIC (John C. Taylor, R. 1998). Sdlg. UL 13-4. LA, 39" (100 cm), M. S. marbled purple violet; style arms buff, marbled light purple violet; F. dark purple violet, lighter edge, signal yellow with lighter edge. Dancing Vogue X First Favourite.

CHINA MOON (Schreiner, R. 1998). Sdlg. AA 1154-1. TB, 39" (99 cm), M. Lightly ruffled yellow ochre (RHS 22A), F. with yellow area below tangerine beard. S 656-A: (M 437-2: (Pinafore Pink x (Oraglow x unknown)) x M 755-1: (Something Else x (((Golden Ice x Celestial Glory) x Flaming Star) x Gold Trimmings))) X Fireside Glow. Schreiner 1998.

CHINA NIGHTS (Clarence Mahan, R. 1990). Sdlg. 1288-1. TB, 34" (86 cm), EM & occasional RE (late). S. muted red (HCC 178), yellow center and base; style arms yellow, tipped brown; F. deep red (46), yellow haft striations, white blaze below yellow beard; ruffled; slight musky fragrance. Chief Hematite X Red Grapes.

CHINA PEACH (Carol Lankow by J. T. Aitken, R. 1995). Sdlg. 1-D24-3. SDB, 10" (25 cm), ML. S. pale peach; style arms peach; F. white, slight peach rim, peach wash around beard; beards yellow, tipped orange. Pipestone X Broad Grin. Aitken's Salmon Creek 1995.

CHINA PINK (George Sutton, R. 1995). Sdlg. G-4. TB, 37" (94 cm), ML. S. venetian pink (RHS 49C) edged lighter orient pink (36C); style arms venetian pink; F. venetian pink, hafts and edges orient pink; beards shell pink (37D); ruffled. Twice Thrilling X Bubble Up. Sutton 1996.

CHINA SEAS (Nora Scopes, TB, R. 1986). British Iris Society 1989.

CHINA SPRING (Bob Bauer/John Coble, R. 1999). Sdlg. S93B-4. SIB, 40" (102 cm), VE. S. light blue; style arms pallid blue; F. medium blue, darker veins, light blue petal edges, white blaze. Springs Brook X *I. typhifolia*. Ensata Gardens 1999.

CHINA WALK (Barry Blyth, R. 1994). Sdlg. A139-1. TB, 36" (91 cm), ML. S. lemon, veined yellow; F. mustard yellow, veined deeper mustard; beards yellow. W126-A: (((Tranquil Star x Coral Strand) x (Makadola sib x King's Cloak sib)) x Behold a Lady sib) X Curacao. Tempo Two 1994/95.

CHINA WEST LAKE (James Waddick, R. 1996). SPEC (*versicolor*), 40" (107 cm), M. S. medium violet, paler edge; style arms medium violet, edged white; F. medium violet, white rayed pattern on top half, yellow signal. Seed from Hangzhou Botanic Garden, Hangzhou, China. Joe Pye Weed 1996.

CHINESE NEW YEAR (Joseph Ghio, R. 1996). Sdlg. 91-23J. TB, 37" (94 cm), ML. S. buckskin; F. blended rose, fuchsia, wine and tan; beards red. Jungle Princess X Battle Royal. Bay View 1997.

CHINESE SNOW PLUM (James Waddick, R. 1994). Sdlg. HBG-1. JI (3 F.), 28" (71 cm), VE. S.

plum, thin white edge; F. white, pale yellow signal hidden by style arm. Seed from Hangzhou Botanic Garden, China.

CHIP SHOT (Harold Stahly, R. 1995). Sdlg. 1-8. SDB, 12" (31 cm), M. S. medium lavender violet; style arms lavender; F. medium lavender violet, small deep red spot below light violet beard; ruffled. Plum Perfect X Little Annie. Stahly 1995.

CHIRAC IN WHITE (Ladislav Muska, R. 1999). Sdlg. 99-SWWD-02. TB, 35" (89 cm), M. Ruffled and laced white self; beards light yellow, white horn; slight fragrance. ((White Window x Mys Horn) x (Don Epifano x White Crow)) X Soissons.

CHIRICAHUA CANYON (Jim Hedgecock, R. 1997). Sdlg. A-32-7. TB, 32" (81 cm), M. S. white; F. medium purple, dark purple hafts with some white striations near beard; beards yellow, purple at end, with short purple horn; ruffled, laced; slight sweet fragrance. 83-25: (Space Dragon x Tuxedo) X Sophistication. Comanche Acres 1998.

CHITOSE (Toichi Ito by Society for Japanese Irises, R. 1993). JI (3 F.), 27½" (70 cm), EM. S. and style arms red violet, edged white; F. red violet veining and sanding on white ground, ending 1/4" from edge, leaving white rim; yellow signal, red violet halo. Parentage unknown. Introduced in Japan 1953.

CHITOSE HIME (Teikichi Ishiyama by Society for Japanese Irises, R. 1993). JI (3 F.), 23" (60 cm), M. S. dark violet (RHS 86A); style arms dark violet, forming a cup; F. bright violet (83C) with darker halo, yellow signal. Parentage unknown. Ishiyama 1968.

CHIYODAJO (Shuichi Hirao by Society for Japanese Irises, R. 1993). JI (6 F.), 36" (90 cm), L. Deep blue violet, yellow signal; near flat form. Parentage unknown. Hirao 1961.

CHIYO-NO-HARU (Shuichi Hirao by Society for Japanese Irises, R. 1992). JI (3 F.), 39" (100 cm), ML. S. red violet rimmed white; style arms white, veined and blushed red violet; F. white, veined very pale red violet, signal yellow. Parentage unknown. Hirao prior to 1980.

CHOCOLATE CHESS (Walter Moores, R. 1997). Sdlg. 93-29. TB, 34" (86 cm), M. S. and style arms beige brown, aging golden brown; F. darker beige brown, violet flush at end of golden yellow beard; ruffled; slight sweet fragrance. Lemon Chess X Acapulco Sunset.

CHOCOLATE MARMALADE (Les Fort, R. 1989). Fort Iris 1990.

CHOCOLATE MINT (Richard Tasco, R. 1997). Sdlg. 90-30. AB (OGB), 35" (89 cm), ML. S. pale violet, aging white; style arms chartreuse buff; F. light buff yellow, chartreuse cast; beards dark chocolate brown. Apricot Brandy X Bold Sentry. Superstition 1998.

CHOCOLATE SWIRL (Richard Tasco, R. 1998). Sdlg. 94-13-01. SDB, 13" (33 cm), M. S. golden bronze (RHS 163D), greyed burgundy on lower half; style arms golden bronze, greyed burgundy midrib; F. golden bronze (163B), greyed burgundy hafts and upper portion; beards golden bronze, electric blue violet on end; pronounced sweet fragrance. 91-64: (Tender Tears x Bisbee) X Tantara. Superstition 1999.

CHOCOLATE VANILLA (Barry Blyth, R. 1991). Sdlg. X108-1. TB, 34" (86 cm), VE-EM. S. creamy white; F. chocolate to bronze brown; beards deep brown. (Touch of Bronze x Beachgirl) X ((Inca Queen x (Tranquil Star x (Love Chant x Festive Skirt))) x Amber Snow). Tempo Two 1991/92.

CHOCTAW AUTUMN (Henry Rowlan, R. 1991). Sdlg. 87-TB-1. TB, 34" (86 cm), M. S. honey brown; F. honey brown, honey blaze around golden yellow beard; ruffled. Angel's Fire X Wild West. Comanche Acres 1992.

CHOIR ROBE (Ruth Rogers, R. 1998). Sdlg. R 243-A. TB, 32" (81 cm), M. S. beetroot purple (RHS 71A); style arms squirrel brown (166B); F. beetroot purple 3/4" edge on upper fall, violet (87A) flash radiating from beard to bottom; beards gold; slight fragrance. Thriller X Choir Time. Meadowbrook 1999.

CHOIR TIME (Francis Rogers, TB, R. 1989). Meadowbrook 1990.

CHOOSE A JUICE (Tom Burseen, R. 1995). Sdlg. 7-83A. TB, 34" (86 cm), M. S. and style arms tangerine orange (RHS 28B); F. darker tangerine orange (28A), hafts streaked red and with some red spots on F., more prominent at edge; beards orange; ruffled; spicy fragrance. Crowd Pleaser X Lawrence of Arabia. T. B.'s Place 1996.

CHORTLE (Barry Blyth, R. 1992). Sdlg. X2-B. SDB, 10" (25 cm), EM. S. subdued lemon ochre; F. old gold, heavily overlaid red brown; beards lavender. Anjaya X Camarilla. Tempo Two 1992/93.

CHOSIN (Shuichi Hirao by Society for Japanese Irises, R. 1993). JI (3 F.), 31½" (80 cm), M. Very large white, yellow signal; style arms creamy white. Parentage unknown. Hirao 1956.

CHRIS CROSS (Chris Vizvarie, R. 1990). Sdlg. CRV-20-85NB. TB, 33" (84 cm), M. S. yellow, center lighter; F. yellow, cream center; beards orange. Sky Hooks X Twice Thrilling. Last Scent Farm 1990.

CHRISTA N (Manfred Beer, R. 1991). Sdlg. MB 3/80A. TB, 41" (105 cm), M. Salmon pink; beards mandarin. Pink Taffeta X Shepherd's Delight. Gartencenter Kania 1991.

CHRISTIANA BAKER (Frederick Kerr, R. 1999). Sdlg. 890205BEST. BB, 26" (66 cm), M. S. and style arms white; F. white to pale blue violet, 1/4" dark blue edge; beards yellow, tipped white. Classic Treasure X Glistening Icicle. Rainbow Acres 1999.

CHRISTIANE BEYER (Manfred Beer, R. 1991). Sdlg. EWMB 43/81A. TB, 36" (90 cm), M. S. bluish white; F. velvety dark violet; beards yellow. Royal Host X Thunder Bay. Gartencenter Kania 1991.

CHRISTIANE ELIZABETH (Clarence Mahan, R. 1997). Sdlg. IDS-15R. TB, 36" (91 cm), E & RE. Light to medium blue violet, F. with white blaze; beards white, hairs tipped yellow; pronounced spicy fragrance. I Do X Suky.

CHRISTIAN MUSIC (William Grise, R. 1999). Sdlg. AWR. TB, 36" (91 cm), EML. S. white, tinted pallid lavender; style arms pallid lavender; F. light cream, velvet texture; beards medium yellow; ruffled; slight fragrance. St. Petersburg X Persian Gown. Parkwood 1999.

CHRISTINA (R. & F. Walster, R. 1990). Sdlg. 1-1987D. TB, 34" (86 cm), M. S. light lavender; F. dark plum, narrow pale lavender edge; beards bright yellow. Amigo X Latin Lover. Walsterway 1991.

CHRISTINA DIANE (Clyde Hahn, R. 1995). Sdlg. 91-5-C. TB, 35" (89 cm), M. Black self with purplish tint; matching beards; slight sweet fragrance. Black Flag X Midnight Fragrance. Hahn's Rainbow 1995.

CHRISTINE BOEHM (Tomas Tamberg, TB, R. 1986). Schoeppinger 1993.

CHRISTINE'S FANCY (Louise Smith, R. 1991). Sdlg. 83-45. TB, 32" (81 cm), EM. Medium yellow blend; beards yellow, tipped orange; slight sweet fragrance. Parentage unknown.

CHRISTMAS (Joseph Gatty, R. 1990). Sdlg. S31-5. TB, 37" (94 cm), EM. White, F. with faint greenish cast; beards white, lemon in throat. Fine China X Royal Elegance. Keppel 1991.

CHRISTMAS JOY (Howard Shockey, R. 1990). Sdlg. 87-232-B. TB, 35" (89 cm), M. S. white, finely edged gold; F. white, solid yellow shoulders; beards cerise red; sweet-spicy fragrance. 82-235-4A: (80-222-H: ((Carved Cameo x Summer Love) x Flaming Day) x Lunar Flounce) X 82-226-4D: ((On Target x West Coast) x Lunar Flounce).

CHRISTOPHER COLUMBUS (Ben Hager, R. 1992). Sdlg. RE4670Bl. TB, 32" (81 cm), M & RE. Medium blue self; beards blue white. T3532: ((Geometrics sib x Ice Sculpture) x Avalon Bay) X T3961: ((Geometrics sib x Sapphire Hills) x (Ice Sculpture x Geometrics)). Melrose 1992.

CHRONICLES OF CYNTHIANA (George Slade, R. 1995). Sdlg. 90-K-1. TB, 38" (97 cm), M. Dark orange self; beards tangerine; laced. Lois Hill X Memphis Melody. Harrison County Historical Society 1996.

CHUANG-CHE (Ladislav Muska, R. 1996). Sdlg. DELC-05. TB, 38" (97 cm), M. S. lemon yellow; F. white, lemon yellow band; beards gold; lightly ruffled, heavily laced; pronounced fragrance. Don Epifano X Laced Cotton. Muska 1995.

CHUCKATUCK (Sterling Innerst, R. 1996). Sdlg. 3895-3. IB, 18" (46 cm), M. S. medium yellow; F. medium yellow, white wash from beard to tip; beards gold, tipped white; slight musky fragrance. Katy Lynn X 3604-2: (2844-6: (Jared x (Melon Honey x Soft Air)) x 2846-2: ((Melon Honey x Soft Air) x Stockholm)). Innerst 1998.

CHUCK BEGNAUD (Dorman Haymon, R. 1999). Sdlg. 52-92-1. LA, 25-28" (64-71 cm), EM. Rich lavender, edged white; F. velvety; gold ray signal edged white; style arms dark lavender, lighter tip; ruffled, serrate. Kay Nelson X 32-85: (Lafayette Honey sib x Charjoy's Mike).

CHUDNOYE MGNOVENIYE (V. & N. Gordodelovy, R. 1995). Sdlg. 200. TB, 30" (75 cm), ML. Ruffled lilac, tinted pink, F. with brown haft striations; beards white at end, light orange to orange in throat. Parentage unknown. Gordodelovy 1976.

CHUE (Bob Thomason, R. 1993). Sdlg. BT 8641A. TB, 36" (91 cm), EM. S. light lavender; F. deep rose violet, heavily veined white on upper half; beards orange, tipped yellow; ruffled; slight fragrance. Mary Frances X Mary Randall. Okie Iris 1999.

CHUM (Ben Hager, R. 1991). Sdlg. SD4919-4YPcOrBds. SDB, 11-14" (28-36 cm), EML. Bright maize yellow, pale brown plicata edging on F.; beards very bright orange. SD4443YPc: (3255Pc: ((Dainty Royal x Zip) x (Marinka x ((Knotty Pine x Grace Note) x Zip))) x 3844BrtYPc: (Noisemaker x Pepper Mill)) X Toasty. Adamgrove 1991.

CHUSYU-NO-TSUKI (Toyokazu Ichie/Kamo Nurseries by Currier McEwen, R. 1997). Sdlg. C2-52.

JI (3 F.), 28" (70 cm), ML. S. and style arms white, hairline violet (RHS 88B) edging; F. pure white, 1/16"-1/8" dark violet (88A) edging, canary yellow (9B) signal; ruffled; S. small. Tsuki-no-Tamagawa X Yuzen.

CHUTNEY (Joseph Ghio, TB, R. 1989). Roris 1991.

CIAO (Joseph Ghio, R. 1999). Sdlg. PB-266X4. CA, 15" (38 cm), ML. Pure yellow self. PD-204-I2, Big Smile sib, X PD-235 gold, Common Sense sib. Bay View 1999.

CIDAQ (Evelyn Kegerise, TB, R. 1989). Evelyn Kegerise 1991.

CIEL DE NUIT (Jean Peyrard, R. 1990). Sdlg. 150. SDB, 10" (25 cm), M. Medium blue; beards white, tipped blue. Parentage unknown -- seed from British Iris Society.

CIMARRON ROSE (Hooker Nichols, SDB, R. 1988). Hillcrest 1990.

CIN CIN (Sterling Innerst, R. 1998). Sdlg. 4073-5. BB, 25" (64 cm), M. Medium blue self; beards dark blue, dark blue horn; slight fragrance. Deity X Codicil. Innerst 1998.

#CINDERELLA (Kenneth Smith, TB, R. 1945). Not introduced; name released.

CINDERELLA (Bennett Jones, R. 1995). Sdlg. 474-5. SDB, 12" (31 cm), M. Canary yellow self; beards red. 415: ((((Melon Honey x Wright L32) x ((Roberts 65-R-11 x 201) x Melon Honey)) x Pumpkin Center) x Orange Dazzler) X 419: (Straw Hat x Orange Tiger). Aitken's Salmon Creek 1996.

CINDERELLA'S WALTZ (Dudley Carson, R. 1991). Sdlg. APSBE-2. SDB, 10" (25 cm), M. Yellow (RHS 7C) washed greyed orange (166C) on F., giving reddish brown appearance; beards violet blue (97D), yellow in throat; lightly ruffled; slight fragrance. Amazon Princess X (Stockholm x Brighteyes).

CINNABAR SHEIK (Damon Hill, R. 1998). Sdlg. BBXDM. AB (OGB), 18" (46 cm), E. S. white, variable red purple (RHS 58A) streaks, fine spanish orange (26A) veining and midrib, orange red (34B) base; style arms spanish orange; F. light spanish orange (26C) ground, heavily dotted red purple (60A) with variable plum purple (79A) streaks, chrysanthemum crimson (185A) diffuse signal 1" x 3/4"; beards golden brown (164A). Desert Mirage X Bionic Burst.

CINNAMON APPLES (Paul Black, R. 1990). Sdlg. 86262B. MDB, 5" (13 cm), E. S. golden tan; F. smooth chestnut red brown, narrow gold edge; beards red brown, tipped old gold. Beaver Lass X (Pecan Spot x Helter Skelter). Mid-America 1990.

CINNAMON BALL (Cleo Palmer, R. 1992). Sdlg. 89102. SDB, 14½" (37 cm), L. S. light brown, slight violet midrib infusion; F. light brown, large rusty red spot; beards bronze; sweet fragrance. Inscription X unknown. Palmer's Iris 1992.

CINNAMON BLUSH (Duane Meek, R. 1995). Sdlg. 398-4-8. CA, 12" (31 cm), M. S. cinnamon, aging tan; F. yellow gold, widely banded dark cinnamon, aging pale brown, with minute lighter outer rim; ruffled. ((*I. tenax* x *I. innominata*) x Encircle) X Tunitas. D & J Gardens 1995.

CINNAMON CREAM (Stan Dexter by Marie Ingersoll, R. 1992). Sdlg. 6-153-A. TB, 38" (97 cm), M. S. creamy pale peach; F. pale peach overlaid creamy white, dash of cinnamon on either side of rose orange beard. 83-213: ((Beverly Sills x 77-0) x Pink Taffeta) X Cameo Wine. Ingersoll's Iris 1993.

CINNAMON FALLS (Betty Squires, R. 1992). Sdlg. 830PM. TB, 36" (91 cm), M. S. apricot; F. apricot with cinnamon overlay; beards orange; slight fragrance. Orange Plume X Mandolin. Rancho de Los Flores 1994.

CINNAMON FLASH (J. T. Aitken, R. 1999). Sdlg. 94M18-12. IB, 24" (61 cm), ML & RE. S. pale blue fading white, midrib flushed cinnamon; style arms white; F. cinnamon orange blending lighter toward edge; beards yellow to orange. Champagne Elegance X Joe Cool. Aitken's Salmon Creek 1999.

CINNAMON FRINGE (Libby Cross, R. 1993). Sdlg. CD-88-B2. TB, 32" (81 cm), EM. S. pale yellow ground heavily dotted cinnamon tan (RHS 172C); style arms yellow; F. white, yellow hafts tan at base, narrow cinnamon dotted edge fading to white at outer edge; beards yellow; ruffled; pronounced sweet fragrance. Mod Mode X Wild Jasmine. Cross Patch 1994.

CINNAMON GLOW (Richard Ernst, R. 1998). Sdlg. KF125-38. TB, 37" (94 cm), EM. S. cinnamon brown, yellow midrib infusion; style arms cinnamon brown; F. white ground, brown and yellow plicata markings, brown rim and center stripe; beards yellow, hairs tipped brown. F125 series: (Edna's Wish x Wild Jasmine) X sib. Cooley 1998.

CINNAMON SPLASH (Lynda Miller, R. 1996). Sdlg. 592. SDB, 12" (31 cm), EM. S. gold; F. gold, stitched and banded rust; beards orange, light blue base; slight musky fragrance. Toasty X 3987: (Smidget x Baja). Miller's Manor 1996.

CINNAMON SUN (Bernard Hamner by Shepard Iris Garden, R. 1993). Sdlg. 84-44. TB, 38" (97 cm), M. S. lemon yellow; F. dark apricot center, paling to light apricot with dark purple center stripe and purple veining; beards orange. (Hamner 75-11 x Peach Sundae) X amoena sdlgs. Hamner Iris, Shepard Iris 1993.

CINNAMON SWIRL (Sara Doonan, R. 1990). Sdlg. 86-24-12. TB, 38" (97 cm), ML. S. cinnamon copper, blended lavender along veins, giving rosy copper effect; F. blended light yellow and rose brown, darker edge, violet flash, diamond-dusted; beards orange; slight sweet fragrance. Money X Well Endowed. Sunset Iris 1991.

CIRCLE OF FIRE (Keith Fillmore, R. 1993). Sdlg. 8602-21B. IB, 16" (41 cm), L. S. burgundy red; F. same, with darker burgundy red spot, white haft markings; beards yellow. Little Annie X unknown. Bar K Iris 1993.

CIRCUS CIRCUS (George Sutton, R. 1996). Sdlg. C-24-D. TB, 37" (94 cm), EML. S. light lilac (RHS 76C), veined darker; style arms white to light orchid; F. white, heavy violet (83B) veining and edging; beards violet; slight spicy fragrance. Momentum X 4-33: (82-13-D: (Heavenly Harmony x Petite Posy) x French Gown). Sutton 1997.

CIRCUS WORLD (Schreiner, R. 1995). Sdlg. 1985 #41. TB, 39" (99 cm), ML. S. and style arms golden yellow (RHS 15A); F. red brown (181A); beards yellow orange. Parentage unknown. Schreiner 1995.

CIRROCUMULUS CLOUDS (Marie Murdy, R. 1995). Sdlg. D 4-29-95. TB, 28" (71 cm), E. White self, S. finely laced, F. pleated and ruffled; beards golden, white at tip. Horned Lace X Winter Olympics.

CITRON FROMMAGE (Francis Rogers, R. 1993). Sdlg. C-3-A. TB, 36" (91 cm), E. S. white (RHS 157C) with yellow (3D) area radiating up from base; F. yellow (13A), small white area by beard; beards yellow, tipped lighter yellow; lightly ruffled; sweet fragrance. Summer White X Coral Chalice. Meadowbrook 1995.

CITRUS COOLER (Paul Black, R. 1997). Sdlg. A59B. TB, 31" (79 cm), M. S. peach, gilt gold rim; style arms peach; F. butter yellow, hafts blended peach, paler around orange beard; lightly ruffled; slight sweet fragrance. Victorian Frills X Good Show. Mid-America 1997.

CITRUS MISTRESS (Tom Burseen, R. 1995). Sdlg. 0-108A. TB, 30" (76 cm), ML. S. light orange (RHS 28C); style arms slightly darker orange (28B); F. lemon orange (brighter than 24C); beards orange; ruffled; sweet fragrance. Oktoberfest X Burr Scene. T.B.'s Place 1995.

CITY LIGHTS (Mary Dunn, R. 1990). Sdlg. M87-1002-C. TB, 37" (94 cm), M. S. deep violet blue, lighter midrib; F. deep violet blue, large white area surrounding pale yellow beard. Fancy Face X Windsurfer. M.A.D. Iris 1991.

CITY OF PARIS (James McWhirter, R. 1993). Sdlg. J87-110. TB, 38" (97 cm), M. S. white; F. white, gold shoulders; beards blue, tipped white; ruffled; slight fragrance. Ice Castle X Winterscape. Stockton 1994.

CITYSCAPE (Schreiner, R. 1997). Sdlg. AA 938-A. TB, 36" (91 cm), ML. S. and style arms straw yellow (RHS 13C); F. deeper (13B), white in center; beards tangerine; slight fragrance. M 748-O: (K 905-D, Skyfire sib, x J 571-B: (((Golden Ice x Celestial Glory) x Flaming Star) x Gold Trimmings)) X N 720-A: (((Fairy Fable x Christmas Time) x Party Look) x Flaming Light). Schreiner 1997.

CITY TWILIGHT (Janet Hutchinson, R. 1998). Sdlg. GL/B/3. LA, 45" (114 cm), M. S. white, purple veins, heavy centerline, edges washed rosy purple, lightly ruffled; style arms white and rosy violet, green center, violet crest; F. rich velvety violet, strong darker centerline, small light green signal, pale reverse; slight fragrance. Glowlight X unknown.

CLAN MacDOWELL (John Gass, R. 1998). Sdlg. G-90-10. TB, 36" (91 cm), M. S. pale blue; style arms light blue; F. deep blue violet, hafts lighter; beards yellow, white at end; ruffled; pronounced sweet fragrance. Carriage Trade X Scenario. Rainbow Chasers 1999.

CLARA DARRH (Louise Smith, R. 1992). TB, 31" (79 cm), EM. S. pale lavender; F. lavender; beards yellow, tipped lavender; slight sweet fragrance. Parentage unknown.

CLARA ELLEN (B. Charles Jenkins, R. 1993). Sdlg. AA21-OB. SPU, 34-42" (86-107 cm), E. S. and style arms light purple; F. yellow, light edging of purple at crimped margin, intensifying at apex with narrow purple lines. Imperial Bronze X unknown. Shepard Iris 1993.

CLARA GARLAND (Cy Bartlett, R. 1995). Sdlg. C92-103. IB, 20" (51 cm), M. Bright yellow, F. with brown eyelash markings at haft; beards cream yellow; lightly ruffled. Eyebright X Brandy Sipper. Sutton 1996.

CLARENCE (Lloyd Zurbrigg, R. 1990). Sdlg. ZZZ. TB, 35" (89 cm), M & RE (Aug./ NC & VA).

S. white, tinted violet at top; F. light blue violet, white center and hafts; cream beard; sweet fragrance. Parentage unknown. Avonbank 1991.

CLARICE ANNIE (Clarice Pye, R. 1994). SIB, 34" (86 cm), M. S. navy blue; style arms wine, midribs blue; F. dark blue, spoon-shaped gold ray pattern, gold edge. Parentage unknown.

CLARITA K. (George Slade, R. 1991). Sdlg. 86-10-1. TB, 34" (86 cm), M. S. white; F. white center with white stripes radiating into purple violet (RHS 82B) edge; beards yellow, tipped white. Flip Side X In Concert.

CLASSICAL MUSIC (William Maryott, R. 1997). Sdlg. T148A. TB, 38" (97 cm), VE-E. S. velvety deep pansy purple (RHS 83A); style arms deep purple; F. velvety deep purple, center near black; beards old gold, prominent; heavily ruffled; leaf bases purple; sweet fragrance. En Garde X Magician's Apprentice. Maryott 1997.

CLASSICAL NOTE (John C. Taylor, R. 1990). Sdlg. OL 114-1. LA, 43" (110 cm), M. Ruffled and fluted yellow (RHS 8B), yellow green veining intensifying at center. Koorawatha X Helen Naish. Rainbow Ridge 1990/91.

CLASSIC BORDEAUX (Richard Ernst, R. 1996). Sdlg. JF102-4-20. TB, 40" (107 cm), EM. S. dark burgundy red, washed plum, lighter toward base; style arms burgundy red; F. dark burgundy red washed cherry; beards plum at end, burgundy red midsection, orange in throat; ruffled. F102-4: (Danger x Chief Hematite) X Shaniko. Cooley 1996.

CLASSIC ELEGANCE (Sharon McAllister, R. 1996). Sdlg. 86-11-1. AB (OGB+), 24" (61 cm), M. S. iridescent violet (near RHS 84A), finely veined bronze at edge; style arms violet, crest bronze; F. brass (161A), veined bronze inner half, outer half velvety red violet (near 79A) with velvet flush radiating from black signal; beards mustard, diffuse. Ballalaika Music X Sunrise in Glory. McAllister 1996.

CLASSIC GRACE (Elyse Hill, R. 1999). Sdlg. EJ20-10-91. TB, 36" (91 cm), M. Laced medium lavender; style arms medium lavender and gold; beards gold; slight sweet fragrance. Lullaby of Spring X Tequila Sunrise.

CLASSIC HUES (Opal Brown by Margaret McCrae, R. 1998). Sdlg. 91-4C4. TB, 30" (76 cm), M. S. apricot yellow (M&P 9-IJ-5); style arms primrose yellow (10-J-4/5); F. empire yellow (9-K-3), hafts flushed rattan (11-K-6), small 3/4" white center blaze; beards princeton orange (9-K-11); ruffled, laced; slight fragrance. Malaguena X Fun Fest.

CLASSIC IMAGE (Jim & Vicki Craig, R. 1995). Sdlg. C61Y10. BB, 24" (61 cm), E. S. white with wide light blue plicata band; style arms light blue; F. white, blue on hafts, light blue plicata band; beards pale blue; ruffled. 15V26: (10R14: ((Light Fantastic x *I. aphylla* "Van Nes") x ((Enroute x Maroon Caper) x Whole Cloth)) x 1R20: ((Light Fantastic x *I. aphylla* "Van Nes") x (Star Child x (Sacred Mountain x *I. aphylla* "Werckmeister")))) X Bold Crystal. J. & V. Craig 1995.

CLASSIC LOOK (Schreiner, R. 1992). Sdlg. AA 2169-C. TB, 36" (91 cm), EM. Ruffled white (RHS 155D) ground plicata with blue (94A) markings; beards yellow, tipped blue. Go Around X T 1800-1: (C 1080-3: ((Full Circle x Rococo) x (Arpege sib x (Rococo x Emma Cook))) x Spinning Wheel). Schreiner 1992.

CLASSIC NAVY (Carol Lankow by J. T. Aitken, R. 1999). Sdlg. 8K51. BB, 26" (66 cm), ML. Deep navy blue self; beards frost-tipped blue. Dexter 1983-149, Grape Charm sib, X Dress Blues. Aitken's Salmon Creek 1999.

CLASSIC PRIDE (Akihiko Terada, R. 1999). Sdlg. 111-89-5. TB, 34" (86 cm), M. Ruffled deep purple self; beards blue purple. Fresno Frolic X Cherry Smoke. Roris 1999.

CLASSIC SUEDE (Larry Lauer, R. 1999). Sdlg. 91-237-1. TB, 34" (86 cm), EM. S. light sienna brown; F. sienna, patterned burnt sienna; beards gold; ruffled; pronounced sweet fragrance. Busy Signal X Rustler. Lauer's Flowers 1999.

CLASSIC WHITE (Michael Epp, R. 1992). SIB, 22-24" (56-61 cm), M. S. white; F. white, yellow throat. Parentage unknown.

CLASSMATE (Keith Keppel, R. 1990). Sdlg. 84-31A. TB, 36" (91 cm), EM. S. blended creamy peach (M&P 9-D-2 to 9-A-4); F. jonquil (9-J-5) hafts, paling (9-H-4) down edge, paler (9-AB-1 to 9-A-2) center; beards white, tipped forsythia (9-K-6) to chinese orange (9-D-12); slight sweet fragrance. 79-47CC: (Goddess x 77-137F: (Mistress sib x 74-52A: ((Joy Ride x Roundup) x (April Melody x 68-40B: (((Irma Melrose x Tea Apron) x ((Full Circle x Rococo) x Tea Apron)) x April Melody))))) X 80-95C: (Goddess x 77-111KK, Gigolo sib). Keppel 1991.

CLASS MEMORIES (William Plotner, R. 1992). Sdlg. 84-241. TB, 38" (97 cm), ML. S. vatican purple (RHS 89B) flushed white in center; F. white, 1/2" vatican purple edge; beards orchid, yellow in throat; ruffled; slight spicy sweet fragrance. (Going My Way x (Stepping Out x unknown)) X Star Lance sib. Wildwood Gardens 1992.

CLASS OF FORTY-SEVEN (Bob Thomason, R. 1993). Sdlg. BT 8714B. TB, 32" (81 cm), ML. S. lemon yellow; F. gold with brown pattern extending from beards; beards orange, tipped yellow. Lemon Mist X Hold That Tiger.

CLASSY BABE (Lynda Miller, SDB, R. 1989). Miller's Manor 1990.

CLASSY CHASSY (Manley Osborne, R. 1990). Sdlg. 6-9-3. TB, 36" (91 cm), M. Very pale blue (RHS 112D); beards deep blue (100B), usually with short fuzzy horn; slight sweet fragrance. Good Morning America X (Sky Hooks x Jack R. Dee). Melrose 1990.

CLASSY CLOUT (Polly Black, R. 1992). Sdlg. ESA8-7B. TB, 36" (91 cm), M. Ruffled pastel orchid blue; beards orchid; slight fragrance. Parentage unknown. Polly Black 1992.

CLASSY FRIEND (Carl Boswell, R. 1999). Sdlg. 149-85-T. TB, 36" (91 cm), M. S. pale pink, base darker; style arms pink; F. raspberry pink blending to lilac pink edge; beards red orange. (Pink Kitten x (Fair Luzon x Java Dove)) X Under Gleam. Adamgrove 1999.

CLAUDE-LOUIS GAYRARD (Lawrence Ransom, R. 1995). Sdlg. 89/127-2. TB, 42" (107 cm), EM. S. light silvery blue, base flushed violet; style arms lavender blue; F. lighter silvery blue, paling to cream white in center; beards pale yellow, base blue white; ruffled; strong sweet fragrance. Edge of Winter X Mystique. Iris au Trescols 1996.

CLEAN CUT (Jim Hedgecock, R. 1993). Sdlg. 83-20-12. TB, 34" (86 cm), M. Heavily ruffled white ground plicata, wide dark purple stitched border; beards dark purple. Going My Way X Hey Looky. Comanche Acres 1994.

CLEAN SLATE (Carl Boswell, SDB, R. 1989). Adamgrove 1990.

CLEAR CLOUDS (Tom Burseen, R. 1997). Sdlg. 93-384A. TB, 34" (86 cm), EM. S. crystalline white; style arms white; F. white, light lavender blue rim; beards white, hairs tipped tangerine; heavily ruffled. Splish Splash X 8-110: (Edith Wolford x Bubbling Over). T.B.'s Place 1997.

CLEAR CREEK (Bennett Jones, R. 1995). Sdlg. 513-2. TB, 14" (36 cm), M. Medium blue self; beards yellow. Star Date X 472-1: ((((Kentucky Bluegrass x Blithe Blue sib) x (Blithe Blue x ((Meadow Moss x 175) x 218-5)) x (218: (Gingerbread Man x Meadow Moss) x (Meadow Moss x Kentucky Bluegrass))) x Bedford Lilac) x (Bedford Lilac x Pale Star)). Aitken's Salmon Creek 1996.

CLEAR CREEK ROAD (Julius Wadekamper, R. 1999). Sdlg. SIB 88-6. SIB, 26" (66 cm), E. Deep purple; style arms lighter purple; smaller, narrow form, foliage fine, narrow. Parentage unknown. Willowwood 1998.

CLEARLY DEARLY DONE (Tom Burseen, R. 1997). Sdlg. 0-87A. TB, 35" (89 cm), ML. S. flesh pink (lighter, pinker than RHS 179D); style arms light pink; F. flesh pink washed light lavender, hafts touched tan; beards tan pink; ruffled, laced; spicy fragrance. Lacy Adventure X Meeta Areta. T.B.'s Place 1997.

CLEAR MORNING SKY (Richard Ernst, R. 1991). Sdlg. FA103-1. TB, 40" (102 cm), EM. S. light blue, darker at base; F. pale blue; beards blue, yellow in throat; ruffled; slight sweet fragrance. A103-1: (Song of Norway x Inheritance) X sib. Cooley 1991.

CLEARWATER (Vernon Wood, R. 1997). Sdlg. 92-51. TB, 34" (86 cm), M. Light butterfly blue (RHS 106D) self; beards light tangerine, tipped blue to tan brown. 87-33: (85-7: (Cloud Fire x Ron) x Larry Gaulter) X Alexander's Ragtime Band. Stockton 1998.

CLEARWATER RIVER (Richard Ernst, R. 1999). Sdlg. M104-15. TB, 36" (91 cm), M. Pale light blue self; beards light blue; ruffled; slight sweet fragrance. Silverado X Blue It Up. Cooley 1999.

CLEEDOWNTON (Jennifer Hewitt, R. 1998). Sdlg. PT8815/1. SIB (tet.), 34" (86 cm), M. S. light to medium violet blue (RHS 91A/B); style arms same, crest edge darker; F. violet blue (90C), deeper (88A) near hafts, usually with narrow white rim, signal yellow paling to cream at edge, veined dark violet; upright to semi-flared S., semi-flared F. Harpswell Happiness X Dance Ballerina Dance.

CLEETON BUFF (Jennifer Hewitt, SIB (sino-sib), R. 1983). David Austin Roses 1995.

CLEETON DOUBLE CHANCE (Jennifer Hewitt, R. 1995). Sdlg. F812/C8. SIB (sino-sib), 42" (107 cm), ML. S. cream, faint violet speckles; style arms cream, reddish tinge along midrib; F. cream, veined and speckled light violet, signal cream veined dark violet. Cleeton Moon X yellow sdlg.: (possibly -- *I. delavayi* x unknown).

CLEETON WATERCOLOUR (Jennifer Hewitt, R. 1990). Sdlg. F812/B3. SIB (sino-sib), 30" (75 cm), ML. S. pale violet blue (RHS 92C), deeper (92A) edge; F. deep violet blue (93B) around signal, pale violet blue (92C) on lower blade, darker violet central vein and edge, light yellow signal deeper at center, veined and spotted deep violet blue (93B). Cleeton Moon X yellow sdlg.

CLEFT ROSE AMO (Austin Morgan, R. 1990). TB, 36" (91 cm), ML. S. white; F. rose, cleft at lower edge, white rim, brown thumbprints beside brown beard. Parentage unknown. Iris Test Garden 1990.

CLEFT STUNNING (Austin Morgan, R. 1991). TB, 35" (89 cm), EM. S. lilac lavender; F. red, rimmed lilac lavender, white "V" cleft at bottom; beards yellow. Stunning X self. Iris Test Garden 1991.

CLEMENCY (R. E. Nichol, TB, R. 1988). Iris Garden 1993.

CLEVER DEVIL (Joseph Ghio, R. 1993). Sdlg PQ-145Q. CA, 12" (30 cm), EM. S. rusty wine; F. apricot, washed wine. PI-201J, Villa Montalvo sib, X PI-209V2, Santa Clarita sib. Bay View 1993.

CLEVER DISGUISE (Richard Ernst, R. 1999). Sdlg. NJF123-12C. TB, 36" (91 cm) M. Toasted honey gold and amber; style arms with yellow crests; F. with shoulders washed blended violet brown, lighter flush at end of gold beard; ruffled. JF123-1-2: (F123: (Afternoon Delight x Edna's Wish) x F123 sib) X HD175-5: (D175: ((Cheesecake x (Sumptuous x Sandberry)) x Piping Hot) x self). Cooley 1999.

*****CLICK** (Allen Harper, SDB, R. 1985). Harper's Gardens 1986.

CLIP (Pierre Anfosso, R. 1990). Sdlg. P 83 38B. BB, 24" (60 cm), L. Bright orange, light amber around tangerine beards. (Carmen X x Marmalade) X Mulled Wine. Iris en Provence 1990.

CLOSE APPROACH (Sharon McAllister, R. 1992). Sdlg. 85-7-5. AB (OGB), 28" (72 cm) EM. S. pinkish amethyst (near RHS 84C); F. pale buff ground, magenta rose blush intensifying to rose red (186A) around deep burgundy V-shaped signal; beards yellow orange. Esther's Son X Expert Advice. McAllister 1992.

CLOSE SHAVE (Duane Meek, R. 1995). Sdlg. R17-1-8. TB, 34" (86 cm), ML. S. pale pink; F. ivory, edged pink; beard missing, pink ridge; heavily ruffled, laced, styles fringed. Sweet Revenge X Sue Ellen. D & J Gardens 1995.

CLOU (Harald Moos, R. 1992). Sdlg. 88/842B. TB, 36" (90 cm), L. S. pinkish brown; F. light violet, edged pinkish brown, hafts yellow; beards yellow; lightly waved. Gold Galore X (Laced Cotton x Precious Moments). Schoeppinger 1993.

CLOUD BALLET (Lyle Fort, TB, R. 1988). Fort Iris 1990.

CLOUD BANK (Mel Leavitt, R. 1992). Sdlg. H-M-100. TB, 38" (97 cm), M. Light blue, white signal; off-white beards tipped white. H-M-1114: (Skating Party x Song of Norway) X Pledge Allegiance.

CLOUD BERRY (Kerryn Turner, R. 1996). Sdlg. KH91-17-1. TB, 36" (91 cm), ML. S. white, orchid flush; F. white, orchid flush, small gold haft area; beards brilliant red; slight fragrance. Cloud Fire X Holiday Lover. Tempo Two 1996/97.

CLOUDBURST (Kevin Nilsen, R. 1990). Sdlg. 7-83-1. TB, 38" (97 cm), ML. S. heavily ruffled white, slight amethyst tinge in center; F. ruffled white, yellow hafts and green veining; beards orange yellow. Caramba X Splash o' Wine. Iridescence 1990/91.

CLOUDCAPS ON GALILEE (Bernice Miller, R. 1996). TB, 36" (91 cm), E & RE (Oct.-Nov./AL). Ruffled white self, F. with blue veins apparent only in cool weather; beards white, gold in throat. Immortality X Earl Roberts. Garden of the Enchanted Rainbow 1994.

CLOUD COVER (Richard Ernst, R. 1994). Sdlg. HR 8545-9. TB, 38" (97 cm), ML. S. light blue, violet cast (paler than RHS 85D); F. darker violet blue (90D), blended lighter; beards blue, tipped white, yellow in throat; ruffled; slight sweet fragrance. R8545-9, inv. Afternoon Delight, Edith Wolford, X C142-3: (Ringo x (Cranberry Ice x Grand Waltz)). Cooley 1995.

CLOUD DANCING (Daniel Thruman, R. 1997). Sdlg. 97-386. JI (6 F.), 32" (81 cm), M. Violet blue (RHS 93A), white central area, lemon yellow signal; style arms white, tipped violet. Southern Son X Continuing Pleasure.

CLOUDED DREAMS (Graeme Grosvenor, R. 1995). Sdlg. T8-4. TB, 38" (97 cm), EM. S. ice blue; style arms ice blue, flushed violet; F. white, edged blue, darker violet hafts; beards yellow, tipped white; ruffled; slight sweet fragrance. Kiss of Gold X Armada. Rainbow Ridge 1995/96.

CLOUD FAIRY (Nora Scopes, R. 1995). Sdlg. 102PC. CA, 12" (30 cm), M. Pure white self, hint of yellow in heart. From sdlgs., parentage unknown.

CLOUDIA (George Sutton, R. 1995). Sdlg. E-63. TB, 39" (99 cm), M. Ruffled, lightly laced lavender pink (near RHS 69A) self; beards coral, lavender purple (near 76A) flounce. Sky Hooks X Vision in Pink. Sutton 1996.

89

CLOUDING UP (Ed Matheny III, R. 1995). Sdlg. 11-01-91. TB, 39" (99 cm), M. S. and style arms white; F. light violet (RHS 85B) with dark violet (86B) shoulders; beards white, orange in throat; sweet fragrance. Sweet Reflection X Victoria Falls. Ed's Iris 1996.

CLOUD KINGDOM (Chet Tompkins, R. 1992). Sdlg. 84-33. TB, 36" (91 cm), M. Fluted and heavily ruffled white; beards lemon and white. ((Winter Watch x Cynthia Ann) x Frost Alert) X (Skating Party x (Radiant Bride x Wedding Vow)). Fleur de Lis 1992.

CLOUD MISTRESS (Barry Blyth, R. 1995). Sdlg. B89-1. IB, 25" (64 cm), VE-EM. Pure white, F. with small gold haft area; beards white, tipped tangerine; slight sweet fragrance. Esoteric X Electrique. Tempo Two 1995/96.

CLOUD PINNACLE (Cy Bartlett, R. 1998). Sdlg. C 93-109. IB, 20" (51 cm), ML. S. parchment white; F. butter yellow, paler edge; beards blue white, yellow in throat; lightly ruffled; slight fragrance. Pale Shades X Hollywood Blonde.

CLOUDS AND WINE (Carl Boswell, R. 1995). Sdlg. 163-84-1-B. BB, 24" (61 cm), E. S. off-white, pale rose base; F. rosy red, smoky white edge; beards yellow. Marmalade Skies X Lilac Wine. Adamgrove 1995.

CLOUDS OF JOY (Sharon McAllister, R. 1994). Sdlg. 87-6-1. AB (OGB), 29" (74 cm), EM. S. pale ivory, aging white; style arms bright yellow (near RHS 12B); F. yellowish ivory, aging white; beards yellow. Granted Wish X Sunrise in Glory. McAllister 1995.

CLOUDY SKIES (Opal Brown, R. 1993). Sdlg. 17-89. TB, 36-38" (91-97 cm), M. S. mauve buff, violet midrib; F. violet blue, blue blaze below persimmon beard; ruffled. Dualtone sib X unknown. Brown's Sunnyhill 1993.

CLOVER HONEY (B. Charles Jenkins, R. 1994). Sdlg. AY86B. SPU, 35-44" (89-118 cm), M. Amber self. B3-5B: (Crow Wing x Equality) X A15-OE: (Forty Carats x unknown). Shepard Iris 1995.

CLOWN ABOUT (Richard Morgan, R. 1991). Sdlg. L46-A. LA, 28" (71 cm), M. S. light red violet edged yellow; style arms yellow, dusted rose; F. yellow, medium red overlay extending from green yellow line signal. Gypsy Moon X Bayou Comus. Redbud Lane 1993.

CLOYD'S DUTCH GIRL (Cloyd McCord, R. 1994). Sdlg. 85-05-6. TB, 35" (89 cm), M. S. white; F. white, lower portion pale blue; beards light yellow, white at end; ruffled; slight sweet fragrance. Evening Mist X 82-3-A: (Beauty Crown x Homecoming Queen). McCord 1994.

CLOYD'S LOVE (Cloyd McCord, R. 1992). Sdlg. 12. TB, 36" (91 cm), E. Ruffled dark apricot; beards orange; sweet fragrance. Homecoming Queen X 76-13: (Beauty Crown x Homecoming Queen). McCord 1992.

CLUB TROPICANA (Georg Emke, R. 1996). TB, 36" (90 cm), ML. Blackish brown, F. with large blue spot; beards brown. Night Ruler X Santiago.

CLUE (Vernon Wood, R. 1995). Sdlg. 93-8. SDB, 9-10" (23-25 cm), EM. Ruffled yellow (RHS 6C) self, F. slightly lighter in center; beards lavender (92B). Wake Up X Serenity Prayer. Stockton 1995.

CLYDE IKINS (Kirk Strawn, R. 1993). Sdlg. 25-1984. LA, 37" (89 cm), M. S. lilac purple (RHS 70A); F. and style arms beetroot purple (71A); signal yellow orange (14A); ruffled. Merry Whirl X Sun Fury. Bois d'Arc 1996.

COALBROOKDALE (Ed Pickin, R. 1995). Sdlg. 87/CC/3. AR (OH), 15" (38 cm), E. S. and F. grey ground, dark purple veins and spots; beards very dark purple. Royal Affair X Ord Mountain.

COALIGNITION (Tom Burseen, R. 1991). Sdlg. 8-381A. TB, 36" (91 cm), EM. S. dark red maroon (darker than RHS 59A); F. sooty velvety black maroon (much darker than 79A); beards bright gold; ruffled; spicy fragrance. 5-259A: (Fresno Calypso x Lady Friend) X 6-174A: (Lady Friend x (Gondolier x Galen)). T.B.'s Place 1993.

COASTAL GLOW (J. T. Aitken, R. 1992). Sdlg. 82PC14. CA, 16" (41 cm), M. Butter yellow self. From Ghio seed, parentage unknown. Aitken's Salmon Creek 1992.

COASTAL MIST (Schreiner, R. 1998). Sdlg. AA 106-1. TB, 40" (102 cm), L. S. light blue (RHS 97C); style arms blue white; F. icy blue white (155C); beards white, yellow base; pronounced sweet fragrance. T 291-1: (Darkside x L 1242-A, unknown) X Honky Tonk Blues. Schreiner 1998.

COASTAL SAND (Stan Dexter by Marie Ingersoll, R. 1995). Sdlg. 7-148. TB, 38" (97 cm), ML. S. golden yellow; F. yellow, sanded rust red, with purple hash marks near yellow beard; lightly ruffled. Gold Cap X 84-31: (Theatre x (69-26, unknown, x Flamenco)). Ingersoll's Iris 1996.

#COBALT GEM (William Ackerman, JI, R. 1984). Stock destroyed; name released 1996.

COCKALORUM (Ruth Stephenson, SDB, R. 1989). Perennial Gardens 1990.

COCKTAIL PARTY (Nora Scopes, R. 1995). Sdlg. 9S126B. TB, 38" (97 cm), L. S. dusky apricot; F. velvety maroon; beards tangerine; slight sweet fragrance. 6/110: (Rose Opal x unknown) X Magic Man.

COCOA PINK (O. D. Niswonger, R. 1996). Sdlg. SDB 1-95. SDB, 12" (31 cm), EM. S. and style arms pink; F. cocoa pink; beards blue, tangerine in throat. Candy Queen X Chanted. Cape Iris 1997.

COCORICO (Ladislav Muska, R. 1996). Sdlg. GHCM-02/B. TB, 36" (91 cm), ML. S. light maroon; F. light lilac, light maroon rim; beards orange, lavender horn; heavily laced. (Geniality x Sky Hooks) X ("Cipkovana Krinolina": (After All x Grand Waltz) x Mukaddam). Muska 1996.

CODE OF SILENCE (Sharon McAllister, R. 1995). Sdlg. 87-1-3. AB (OGB+), 28" (71 cm), EM. S. very pale pinkish lilac (lighter than RHS 186D); style arms soft yellow; F. soft pinkish yellow blend formed by pale lilac blush over yellow ivory ground; beards wine and honey mead mixture. Wished For Child X *I. kirkwoodii*. McAllister 1995.

CODE TALKER (Sharon McAllister, R. 1994). Sdlg. 85-10-1. AB (OGB+), 22" (56 cm), EM. S. violet ground with wide rosy tan edge; style arms white, midrib violet, crests yellow with green eyelashes; F. iridescent blue violet, 1/2" graham-cracker tan edge, burgundy cherry red signal; beards white, tipped yellow. Hunt sdlg.: ((Wilkes KBKG5: (Kalifa Baltis x Kalifa Gulnare) x Esther the Queen) x Tuesday Song) X Dunshanbe. McAllister 1995.

COFFEE JITTERS (Agnes Frech, R. 1997). Sdlg. 791. TB, 35" (89 cm), ML. S. coffee brown, tinged purple; style arms golden ochre; F. purple center shading to coffee brown, shoulders copper; beards blue and golden ochre; ruffled; slight sweet fragrance. Star Wars X Edna's Wish.

COFFEE WHISPERS (Barry Blyth, R. 1999). Sdlg. E112-3. TB, 38" (97 cm), M. S. white, faint creamy midrib; F. coffee pink, blended light pastel lavender blaze, 1/8" white edge; beards tangerine; sweet fragrance. B178-2: (Wild Vision x Imprimis) X About Town. Tempo Two 1999/2000.

COIRO (Jean Peyrard, R. 1991). Sdlg. 86/B. SDB, 12" (30 cm), E. S. purple violet (RHS 83B); F. violet (80B), slightly veined, dark purple (70B) spot; beards lavender, tipped brown; slight sweet fragrance. Parentage unknown; seed from Franz Kurzmann.

COLBY'S CHOICE (Nancy Burrows, R. 1991). Sdlg. 67-303. TB, 36" (91 cm), EM. Ruffled and laced pale peach; beards orange; slight sweet fragrance. Entourage X Vanity. Stornoway 1992.

COLETTE (Bob Brown, TB, R. 1989). Cottage 1990.

COLETTE THURILLET (Jean Cayeux, R. 1991). Sdlg. 8215 B. TB, 34" (85 cm), ML. S. light tan; F. clear rosy red, narrow tan border; beard tangerine red. Gypsy Caravan X Ringo. Cayeux 1990.

COLLECTOR'S ART (George Shoop, R. 1991). Sdlg. 85-7-1. TB, 36" (91 cm), M. S. purple; F. warm pink; beards tangerine; lightly ruffled. Blushing Duchess X Spring Tidings. Shoop 1991.

COLLEEN'S DREAMSICLE (Donald Spoon, R. 1994). Sdlg. 88-89. TB, 36-38" (91-97 cm), M. S. light pink; F. lighter pink, peach hafts and 1/4" light peach border; beards cherry red, fuzzy lavender horn; ruffled, lightly laced; sweet fragrance. (Bride's Halo x Stately Mansions) X (Christmas Rubies x Battle Star). Winterberry 1995.

COLOCKUM ROAD (Jean Witt, R. 1992). SPEC (*missouriensis*), 29" (74 cm), M. S. and style arms medium blue; F. white, veined blue, raised (2 mm) ruffled median ridge with blue pinpoint dots and yellow lines on either side. Collected northeast of Ellensburg, Kittitas Co., Washington.

COLOMA GOLD (Nancy Bartlett, R. 1995). Sdlg. 89D7. TB, 36" (91 cm), EM. Ruffled yellow self; beards orange to yellow. 82K1: (77J3: ((Doctor K. x Flaming Snow) x (Spooned Lace x New Moon)) x Tawny Wings) X Flaming Victory.

COLONIAL BRIDE (Kevin Nilsen, R. 1992). Sdlg. 23-87-1. TB, 38" (97 cm), EM. S. light yellow tan blend, blushed rose and edged yellow; F. yellow, overlaid rose red, edged yellow tan; beards orange. 42-84-1: (Bride's Halo x Entourage) X 4-84-1: (White Lightning x Goddess).

COLORADO AMBROSIA (Tom Magee, BB, R. 1988). Long 1991.

COLORADOAN (Tom Magee, R. 1995). Sdlg. 8713A. TB, 38" (97 cm), M. S. light tan; style arms darker tan with mulberry strip; F. buff with mulberry plicata halo darker at hafts, white area striped mulberry surrounding beard; beards russet orange; ruffled, laced; slight musky fragrance. Gigolo X Acoma. Long 1996.

COLORADO BONANZA (Tom Magee, R. 1993). Sdlg. 8445. TB, 43" (109 cm), E. Ruffled silver infused gold; style arms silver, veined gold; beards silver, gold at end and in throat; slight sweet fragrance. 8017: (7734: (Colorado Sunshine x White Lightning) x Wedding Cake sib) X New Tomorrow. Long 1996.

COLORADO WINTER MORNING (Roy Krug by Glenn Stoneking-Jones, R. 1998). Sdlg. CIR6-RK78-2. TB, 28" (71 cm), ML. S. white; style arms apricot; F. peach; beards peach to apricot, hairs tipped orange; slight sweet fragrance. Buffy X Symphonette. Orin 1999.

COLOR CURLS (Gene Gaddie, BB, R. 1984). Gaddies' Gardens 1990.

COLOR EXPRESS (Paul Black, R. 1991). Sdlg. 86103C. TB, 34" (86 cm), E. S. and style arms pink; F. deep orchid, pink sanded veins and line down middle, pink spray pattern around orange beard. Sorceress X Planned Treasure. Mid-America 1991.

COLORFLICK (Opal Brown, R. 1991). Sdlg. 82-19A6. BB, 20" (51 cm), M. S. deep apricot pink; F. yellow, edged apricot, deeper apricot shoulders, white area below deep tangerine beard; lightly ruffled. 77-3H6: (Festive Air x Happy Face) X 79-2E10: ((Proclamation x Festive Aire) x Happy Face). Brown's Sunnyhill 1991.

COLOR FOCUS (B. Charles Jenkins, SPU, R. 1989). Shepard Iris 1990.

COLOR GLORY (Paul Black, R. 1999). Sdlg. A10D. TB, 36" (91 cm), L. S. deep rose purple; style arms same, toned amber; F. medium rose purple deeper toward edge; beards burnt orange, wide; ruffled; slight musky fragrance. Enchanting X Ruth Black. Mid-America 1999.

COLOR MAGICIAN (George Shoop, R. 1994). Sdlg. 89-44. TB, 36" (91 cm), M. S. white; F. light cream with fine pink veining; beards tangerine; lightly ruffled. 87-5 pink amoena: ((French Connection x American Beauty) x Snow Crown) X blue amoena sdlg. Keppel 1995.

COLOR ME BLUE (Schreiner, R. 1997). Sdlg. CC 139-B. TB, 36" (91 cm), M. Heavily ruffled light blue (RHS 97B) self; beards white, yellow in throat; pronounced fragrance. Delta Blues X Riverboat Blues. Schreiner 1997.

COLOR ME PINK (Darlene Pinegar, R. 1995). Sdlg. PNS-2-1-1A. TB, 34" (86 cm), M. S. and style arms deep pink; F. peach pink, white area below dark coral red beard; lightly ruffled, laced; slight sweet fragrance. PNS-2-1: (Earlirose x Queen in Calico) X PNS-3-1: (Earlirose x Rancho Rose). Spanish Fork 1996.

COLOR SORCERY (B. Charles Jenkins, R. 1994). Sdlg. BC75E. SPU, 31-50" (79-127 cm), EM. S. deep mahogany purple; F. dark brown ground, yellow veins radiating from yellow signal. SP86B: (Dawn Candle x unknown) X Cinnamon Stick. Shepard Iris 1996.

COLUMBIA SPRINGS (Merle Roberts, R. 1995). Sdlg. D-108F. TB, 36" (91 cm), M. S. white, touched very light blue at base; style arms white, blue and gold; F. blue, paling toward edge, shoulders gold; beards gold, blue at end; ruffled. Edith Wolford X Victoria Falls. Roberts Iris Garden 1996.

COMAL SPRINGS (J. R. Allen, R. 1994). Sdlg. Z 3 A. TB, 42" (107 cm), EM. S. very pale blue, deepening at base; style arms blue; F. very pale blue with chalky white center; beards light yellow, pale blue at end; ruffled; slight sweet fragrance. X-2-A: (Titan's Glory x Adam Conerly) X Miss Carol. Allen Iris 1997.

COMANCHE GOLD (Jim Hedgecock, R. 1992). Sdlg. 83-69-2. TB, 34" (86 cm), M. Laced and ruffled gold self; beards golden orange; pronounced sweet fragrance. Countryman X Miss Illini. Comanche Acres 1993.

COMANCHE TRIBUNAL (Jim Hedgecock, R. 1988). Comanche Acres 1990.

COMANDANTE (Joseph Ghio, R. 1994). Sdlg. 89-78G2. TB, 35" (89 cm), ML. Orange base infused bronze; beards gold. 85-219K3: ((Cinnamon x (((Malaysia x Carolina Honey) x (Hi Top x ((Ponderosa x Travel On) x Peace Offering))) x (Anointed x San Jose))) x Esmeralda sib) X 87-133-Z2: (Esmeralda x Guadalajara). Bay View 1995.

COMBUSTION (Harold Stahly, R. 1995). Sdlg. 90-20. BB, 25" (64 cm), M. S. deep violet; style arms violet; F. deeper violet; beards red orange. Ignition X 84-21: ((71-5-BR: ((Licorice Stick x Black Swan) x Pretty Carol) x Barcelona) x ((((Mary Randall x Edenite) x 71-2-BR: (Orange Chariot x Barcelona)) x (71-2-BR x 71-5-BR)) x (Swahili x 71-2-BR))). Stahly 1995.

COMEBACK TRAIL (Hooker Nichols, R. 1990). Sdlg. 8801A. SDB, 12" (30 cm), EML & RE. S. yellow, creamy undertone; F. cream, yellow edge, gold hafts; beards yellow, tipped orange; ruffled. Fairy Godmother X Dreams Adrift. Hillcrest 1991.

COME CLEAN (Tom Burseen, R. 1995). Sdlg. 1-176B. TB, 36" (91 cm), ML. Ruffled, laced cream self; beards cream, tipped tangerine; sweet fragrance. Pauline Hill X 9-395: (Sterling Stitch x (Trousseau Lace x Wings of Dreams)). T.B.'s Place 1996.

COMEDIAN (Ken Mohr, R. 1992). TB, 39" (97 cm), M. S. medium rose pink; F. medium rose, deeply texture-veined darker rose violet; beards tangerine red. Tropical Tempo X Heather Blush. Pacific Coast Hybridizers 1991.

COME IN SPINNER (Janet Hutchinson, R. 1995). Sdlg. S/lps 1. SPEC (*pseudacorus*), 46" (118 cm), M. S. and F. rich golden yellow, F. with green-tinged yellow signal; style arms paler yellow. Parentage unknown; seed from RHS, U.K. Rainbow Ridge 1998/99.

COME SEE (Allan Ensminger, R. 1990). Sdlg. 84-30. IB, 18" (46 cm), ML. S. white ground, stitched gentian blue (HCC 42/2) on edge; F. white, gentian blue shoulders; beards gentian blue (42). 79-11: ((Miss Region Twenty-One x Charmed Circle) x 73-1, pollen parent of Az Ap) X Charmed Circle. Varigay 1992.

COME TO PARIS (Barry Blyth, R. 1998). Sdlg. D57-1. TB, 36" (91 cm), ML. S. orchid lavender to lilac; F. orchid white; beards tangerine, white at end; ruffled; pronounced sweet fragrance. Hostess Royale X Spring Tidings. Tempo Two 1998/99.

COMET TRAILS (Vernon Wood, R. 1995). Sdlg. 93-72. CA, 14-16" (41-46 cm), ML. S. white lined violet, darker on rim; style arms solid deep violet; F. white, heavily veined medium violet, 1/4" medium violet rim, small yellow arrow in center. Foothill Banner X Fort Point. Stockton 1995.

COME WHAT MAY (Richard Ernst, R. 1994). Sdlg. HR 8545-A. TB, 37" (94 cm), M & RE. S. light creamy apricot, buttery cast; style arms apricot peach; F. bright berry-plum wash on paler background, pale berry-plum rim; beards orange tangerine; light lace. From sdlgs. inv. Edith Wolford, Afternoon Delight. Cooley 1995.

COMING UP ROSES (Joseph Gatty, R. 1991). Sdlg. S5-2. TB, 34" (86 cm), ML. S. near powder pink to miniature pink (M&P 3-EF-7); F. blended peach (9-AB-5) at edge, small pale pink area at tip of beard; beards peachbloom (2-B-9) to melon pink (2-D-10), midnight sun (2-E-12) in throat; slight fragrance. Pink Jade X Pink Swan. Keppel 1992.

COMMITMENT (Joseph Ghio, R. 1998). Sdlg. PC-185G. CA, 14" (36 cm), ML. Wine pink self, F. with deep wine signal. Sib to Bedroom Eyes. Bay View 1998.

COMMON SENSE (Joseph Ghio, R. 1997). Sdlg. PD-235H. CA, 15" (38 cm), EM. Smooth medium red self, faint lighter petal edge. PF-170E2, Battle Alert sib, X PF-155B2: (PI-MIX-S, unknown, x PJ-161B: (Santa Cruz Beach x (Refugio x ((Simply Wild x Camp Capitola sib) x (Big Wheel x California Mystique))))). Bay View 1997.

COMMUNION (Eugene Hunt by Sharon McAllister, R. 1990). Sdlg. ORB 89-1. AB (OGB), 28½" (73 cm), EM. S. amethyst, paling to cream near midrib; style arms barium yellow; F. greyed yellow with pale red overlay, giving flesh-toned effect, blood red signal; beards yellow orange tipped tangerine. Jean Ralls X Hallelujah Chorus. Aril Society 1990.

COMPACT BUDDY (Lynda Miller, R. 1996). Sdlg. 787A. MDB, 4½" (11 cm), E. S. light lemon yellow; style arms cream, base tinted blue; F. cream, sunshine yellow split spot, bottom edged lemon yellow; beards cream, orange in throat; slight spicy fragrance. 784: (What Not x Wee Sooner) X 1184A: (Inca Toy x unknown). Miller's Manor 1997.

COMPADRE (Lynda Miller, R. 1996). Sdlg. 1693A. SDB, 12" (31 cm), ML. S. cream; style arms cream, violet center; F. brown, touched gold; beards blue white, hairs heavily tipped orange; slight sweet fragrance. Late Night X 1790: (2587: (Crispin x (Petite Polka x unknown)) x Maya Midnight). Miller's Manor 1998.

COMPETITION (Raymond Smith, R. 1991). Sdlg. 8609ER. TB, 36" (91 cm), E & RE. Ruffled white; beards orange, tipped white. 7702A: (Cream Taffeta x 7273AR: (6634GR x Winter Olympics)) X Olive Reflection. R. G. Smith 1994.

COMPETITIVE EDGE (Richard Ernst, R. 1991). Sdlg. F169-2. TB, 36" (91 cm), M. S. reddish brown; F. bluish lavender, caramel shoulders, 1/4" reddish brown edge, paler area around yellow beards; ruffled, laced. Afternoon Delight X C142-7: (Ringo x (Cranberry Ice x Grand Waltz)). Cooley 1991.

COMPLIMENTARY (Paul Black, R. 1999). Sdlg. A59C. TB, 34" (86 cm), M. S. buff pink, pale gold rim; style arms and F. buff orange; beards orange; heavily ruffled; pronounced spicy fragrance. Victorian Frills X Good Show. Mid-America 1999.

COMPOSED (Bernard Hamner, R. 1990). Sdlg. 84-338. TB, 34" (86 cm), M. Rose (RHS 55C); beards tangerine; slight fragrance. (Persian Berry x Heather Blush) X (Entourage x Love Magic). Hamner Iris 1990.

COMPOUND (John C. Taylor, R. 1998). Sdlg. UL 14-9. LA, 39" (100 cm), M. Light tan, signals yellow. Dancing Vogue X Watch Out.

#CONCERTINA (Steve Moldovan, TB, R. 1966). Not introduced. Name released.

CONCERTINA (George Sutton, R. 1999). Sdlg. G-86-W. IB, 27" (69 cm), EM & RE. Ruffled amaranth rose (RHS 65), F. with golden tan on hafts; beards orange, dark violet blue at end, dark violet blue horn. Aaron's Dagger X Chanted.

CONCERTO GROSSO (Harald Mathes, R. 1998). AB (OGB), 20" (50 cm), E. Oxblood red, F. with sharp black 2 cm signal; beards uniform dark blue. ((Gelee Royale x sib) x Anacrusis sib) X Invention. Aril Society 1998.

CONCISE (Sterling Innerst, R. 1996). Sdlg. 4060-8. TB, 36" (91 cm), M. Reddish violet purple self; beards white; slight musky fragrance. Silverado X Foreign Statesman. Innerst 1997.

CONCOCTION (Monty Byers, R. 1990). Sdlg. H63-100. IB, 21" (53 cm), EML & RE. S. mauve pink suffused with smoothly blended violet in center; F. mauve pink with suffused violet streak 2/3 way down from beard; beards pale blue base, watermelon red pink tips; slight musky fragrance. Juicy Fruit X My Sheba. Moonshine 1991.

CONCORDE WITH HOOKS (Ladislav Muska, R. 1996). Sdlg. GEDO-04. TB, 38" (97 cm), ML. Cream and lilac, F. deeper; beards orange, lavender horn; spicy fragrance. ((Geniality x Mukaddam) x Sky Hooks) X Don Epifano. Muska 1996.

CONDENSED VERSION (Carol Lankow by J. T. Aitken, R. 1999). Sdlg. 0L-13. SDB, 13½" (34 cm), ML. Creamy yellow, F. with soft apricot flush; beards yellow, hairs tipped orange. (Straw Hat x Orange Tiger) X Aitken 83M15: (M. Wright L56: ((Pink Cushion x Lenna M) x Cotton Blossom) x B Jones 271 pink). Aitken's Salmon Creek 1999.

CONDOR'S SHADOW (Robert Dunn, R. 1999). Sdlg. B2102-X. TB, 36" (91 cm), EM. Deep velvety plum purple self; beards plum purple; heavily ruffled, lightly fluted; slight sweet fragrance. B1056-C: (Star Master x M931, pollen parent of Sorcerer's Stone) X Midnight Madonna.

CONFECTIONERY (Richard Ernst, R. 1991). Sdlg. F108-1. TB, 38" (97 cm), M. S. warm deep pink; F. light cream with pale mint green overlay; beards coral; lightly ruffled and laced; slight sweet fragrance. Afternoon Delight X A114-1: (Pink n' Mint x Gaulter G77-96, inv. Claudia Rene). Cooley 1991.

CONFEDERATE CAVALIER (Jane McKnew, R. 1994). TB, 36" (91 cm), M. Laced and heavily ruffled grey with gold haft markings, faint gold trim on edges; beards gold, tipped grey. Moonlit X Visual Art. Friendship 1999.

CONFEDERATE MUSTER (Walter Moores, R. 1999). Sdlg. 88-13-B. TB, 34" (86 cm), M. S. unmarked grey lavender; style arms dull yellow, streaked lavender; F. white ground with all-over fancy plicata purple to violet dotting; beards bronze; ruffled, flared; slight spicy fragrance. Purple Pepper X Sides 26-E-38-F: (Vanity x Capricious).

CONFEDERATE ROSE (Chet Tompkins, R. 1996). Sdlg. 93-54. TB, 39" (99 cm), EML-VL. Rose cerise, F. with large rayed snow white central area; beards yellowish shrimp pink. (Make Believe Magic x Pat Rollman) X (Total Obsession x Wild Side). Fleur de Lis 1996.

CONFEDERATE ROYALTY (Walter Moores, R. 1994). Sdlg. 88-13. TB, 36" (91 cm), ML. S. greyed lavender; F. white ground, violet purple fancy plicata markings; beards mustard; lightly ruffled; slight sweet fragrance. Purple Pepper X Sides 26-E-38-F: (Vanity x Capricious). Moores 1997.

CONFESSION (Keith Keppel, R. 1991). Sdlg. 85-72B. TB, 36" (91 cm), M. White (M&P 10-A-1), lightly brushed chrome lemon (9-K-2) on hafts; beards capucine red to flame (1-C-12); slight sweet fragrance. Faraway Places X 82-89B: (Orangerie x Precious Moments). Keppel 1992.

CONFETTI DANCER (Lorena Reid, R. 1997). Sdlg. 90J22-2F. JI (6 F.), 36-42" (91-107 cm), M. Light ground marbled violet and purple, light halo and rays around gold signal; style arms violet, light at center; ruffled. Peacock X Harlequinesque. Laurie's Garden 1998.

CON FUOCO (Lawrence Ransom, R. 1993). Sdlg. 87/86-20. TB, 34" (86 cm), M. S. dark salmon to beige pink; F. lilac, blended beige on shoulders; beards glowing deep red; ruffled, lightly laced; musky fragrance. Lady Friend X Opium. Iris au Trescols 1994.

CONFUSED (Lynda Miller, R. 1991). Sdlg. 3587C. SDB, 11" (28 cm), M. S. white veined violet, chartreuse yellow edge; F. same, with white spot; beards orange; slight musky fragrance. Smidget X Sniffs 'n' Sneezes. Miller's Manor 1992.

CONIMBLA (Kevin Nilsen, R. 1992). Sdlg. 5-86-1. TB, 28" (71 cm), ML. S. very dark red with some plicata spotting, lighter (but near full color) edge; F. very dark red, black edge, some yellow on hafts; beards gold. Rustic Dance X Shaft of Gold. Iridescence 1992/93.

CONNECTION (Joseph Ghio, R. 1999). Sdlg. 93-90P2. TB, 36" (91 cm), ML. S. blue white; style arms yellow; F. purple, shoulders blended with red; beards red. Sib to Snowed In.

CONSERVATIVELY CLAD (Paul Black, R . 1990). Sdlg. 84236A. SDB, 14" (36 cm), M. S. violet blue with darker midrib; F. lighter blue, olive spot around blue white beards; pronounced spicy fragrance. 828A: (Tide Pool x (Antique Satin x Encanto)) X Little Louie. Mid-America 1990.

CONSIDER THIS (O. D. Niswonger, R. 1995). Sdlg. SDB 25-93. SDB, 14" (37 cm), M. S. and style arms blue violet; F. buff, pink cast; beards blue. SDB 28-91: (Adoring Glances x (Little Annie x unknown)) X SDB 42-91: (Chubby Cheeks x Goddess). Cape Iris 1996.

CONSISTENT ZEE (David Miller, R. 1992). Sdlg. DM 84-1B. TB, 30" (76 cm), EM. S. crisp white; F. very light blue (RHS 94D) blended with white; beards light orange; distinct zigzag stalk pattern; slight sweet fragrance. Dover Beach X Tipperary.

CONSPIRACY (Virginia Messick, R. 1996). Sdlg. M88-114. TB, 36" (91 cm), M. Vivid red blend of violet brown and cerise; beards red brown; ruffled. Hilow X M84-53: (Ghio sdlg. x Samurai Warrior). Messick 1996.

CONSTANT COMPANION (Connell Marsh, R. 1992). Sdlg. 87-15-10-C. IB, 18" (46 cm), EML & RE. S. velvety intense red violet; F. red violet, intensifying in color depth at end of beards; beards powder blue, orange in throat; ruffled; slight fragrance. Violet Miracle X Third Charm. Iristocrat Acres 1995.

CONSTANTINO (Ladislav Muska, R. 1995). Sdlg. LWLM-05. TB, 38" (97 cm), E. S. light nut-maroon; F. lavender, maroon at haft; beards orange; ruffled, laced; sweet fragrance. (Louise Watts x Lady Madonna) X "Coriolanus Rex". Muska 1995.

CONTENDER (Robert Jeffries, R. 1991). Sdlg. J81-2-B. TB, 38" (97 cm), ML. S. white tinted pale mineral violet at base; F. mineral violet (HCC 635), lighter area around hafts and saturn red (30/1) beard; pleated, laced; slight sweet fragrance. L. Rogers B18 X J79-1: (J70-14-A: ((Lovely Letty x Whole Cloth) x Cloverdale) x Flaming Arrow). Bar K Iris 1993.

CONTINUITY (Sterling Innerst, R. 1993). Sdlg. 3489-5. TB, 36" (91 cm), ML. Light blue; beards blue black; slight fragrance. Codicil X Crystalyn. Innerst 1994.

CONTRIBUTION (Ben Hager, R. 1991). Sdlg. T5018FchPrLc. TB, 38" (97 cm), M. Ruffled and laced fuchsia purple; beards purple, tipped brown. T4093FchPrBld: (Mother Earth sib x (((Merrill K90-RCR, inv. Coffee Royal, x Tucson) x (Tambourine x Gala Madrid)) x Cranberry Ice)) X T4242FchPr: ((((Babson M131-4: (Golden Stairs x (Queen's Lace x (E61-1 x Figurine))) x Rippling Waters) x Warm Laughter) x Paris Opera) x (Silver Flow x Ruffled Ballet)). Melrose 1991.

COOK'S BROTH (Eric & Bob Tankesley-Clarke, R. 1994). SPEC (*variegata*), 15" (38 cm) M & RE (July). S. medium yellow; style arms light yellow; F. white, finely veined maroon, merging to solid maroon at tip, faint yellow edge; beards yellow; slight sweet fragrance. Origin unknown; distributed as *I. variegata* "Cook's Variety" and in commerce prior to 1965.

COOLABAH (Barry Blyth, SIB, R. 1987). Tempo Two 1987/88.

COOLANGATTA (Barry Blyth, R. 1993). Sdlg. ET-1. SPU, 48" (122 cm), ML. S. violet; F. bright gold with very defined 1/8" violet edge, violet filigree veining. Ethic X self. Tempo Two 1993/94.

COOL CHEMISTRY (Tom Burseen, R. 1997). Sdlg. 93-368G. TB, 32" (81 cm), M. Ruffled creamy chartreuse (yellower than RHS 162D); beards white, hairs tipped orange; spicy fragrance. Super Dancer X 8-285: ((Titan's Glory x (Orchidarium x Lacy Snowflake)) x Fluff Stuff). T.B.'s Place 1998.

COOL CONTROVERSY (Tom Burseen, R. 1991). Sdlg. 7-152B. TB, 36" (91 cm), M. S. cool icy violet blue (lighter than RHS 97D), dark center and style arms; F. deep dark velvety violet blue (75A), fine light violet (85A) edge; beards mustard; sweet fragrance. Street Dancer X 3-265: (Congo Song x Stunning). T.B.'s Place 1993.

COOL DRAGON (Leo Barnard, R. 1996). Sdlg. L-88-8B. TB, 40" (107 cm), EM. S. purple, mottled white; style arms purple; F. white ground, 3/8" purple plicata rim, small purple veins across hafts; beards white, tipped gold in throat, white horn with purple-rimmed white flounce; slight sweet fragrance. Angel Bright X Sky Hooks. Paradise Iris 1996.

COOL FANTASY (Luella Danielson, R. 1998). Sdlg. 90-15-R. AR (OH), 14" (36 cm), E. S. porcelain white; style arms long, protruding, dark purple, crests lavender pink; F. white ground densely dotted and veined light lavender pink, purple black signal; beards dark brown; uplifted fall form; slight musky fragrance. (ST 79-406 x Fairy Fantasy) X *I. iberica ssp. elegantissima*. Pleasure Iris 1999.

COOLING TREND (Richard Ernst, R. 1996). Sdlg. HR8545-L. TB, 42" (107 cm), ML. S. pale blue, midrib deeper; style arms pale blue violet; F. dark violet blue, lighter blue flush at end of beard; beards pale blue at end, pale yellow midsection, yellow in throat; lightly ruffled; slight spicy-sweet fragrance. Edith Wolford X R8545: (inv. Afternoon Delight, Edith Wolford, x C142-3: (Ringo x (Cranberry ice x Grand Waltz))). Cooley 1996.

COOL LADY (Leo Barnard, R. 1996). Sdlg. L-91-134E. TB, 40" (107 cm), ML. S. yellow banded edge shading to cream center, mauve midrib; style arms light yellow; F. bright red purple fading to mauve rim, gold outer rim, tan veining on cream shoulders, lighter centerline; beards cream, hairs tipped yellow; ruffled, lightly laced; slight sweet fragrance. Aztec Dance X Ringo. Paradise Iris 1996.

COOL MAID (A. & D. Willott, R. 1996). Sdlg. 90-98. SDB, 13" (33 cm), M. S. and style arms blue white; F. medium blue violet, deeper flush around blue violet beard; lightly ruffled. 83-92: (Gay Parasol x 78-1: (Greenlee GX-2: ((White Mite x self) x *pumila alba* x Hanselmayer)) x Buttons)) X Pilgrims' Choice. Willott 1996.

COOL STEPPER (Barry Blyth, R. 1990). Sdlg. W44-2. IB, 20" (51 cm), EML. S. cream beige to creamy white; F. beige apricot; beards tangerine in throat, outer 1" light lilac. ((Tranquil Star x (Love Chant x Festive Skirt)) x (Persian Smoke x Chimbolam)) X ((Guinea Gold x Pulse Rate) x ((((Serenity x Regards) x Dove Wings) x unknown) x Capricornia)). Tempo Two 1990/91.

COOL TREAT (Carol Lankow by J. T. Aitken, R. 1994). Sdlg. 6 E 25. BB, 26" (66 cm), ML. S. and style arms white; F. blue violet; beards tangerine, white base. Hellcat X (Minute Waltz x Betty Simon). Aitken's Salmon Creek 1994.

COOMANDOOK (Leslie Donnell, R. 1995). Sdlg. 91-12-1. TB, 38" (71 cm), E. Pink self (near RHS 36A); beards red; sweet fragrance. Oasis Broadbeach X 88-15-29: (Hampton Horizon x Flaming Victory).

COONALPYN (Leslie Donnell, R. 1995). Sdlg. 91-12-10. TB, 30" (76 cm), E. Deep orange (RHS 26B) self; beards red. Oasis Broadbeach X 88-15-29: (Hampton Horizon x Flaming Victory).

COONAWARRA (Leslie Donnell, R. 1995). Sdlg. 91-13-1. TB, 31" (79 cm), EM. Yellow self; beards orange. 87-7-5: (Pink Petticoat x Lady Friend) X Tintinara.

COONAWARRA CLARET (Peter Jackson, R. 1999). Sdlg. LGD2. LA, 41" (105 cm), ML. Deep velvety wine red (darker than RHS 71A), deep gold star signal; style arms cream, tipped light wine. Gladiator's Gift X Desert Jewel. Iris Acres 1999/2000.

COORDINATED LADY (Caroline Ryan-Chacon, R. 1999). Sdlg. 1AB92-T-5. AB (OGB-), 30" (76 cm), EM. S. white, base and midrib infused yellow; style arms lemon; F. yellow, rust line signal; beards orange. Syrian Moon X White Lightning. Aril Society 1999.

COOROOLYN (Hilmary Catton, R. 1995). Sdlg. C893-3. SDB, 12-14" (30-36 cm), M. S. bright sky blue; F. bright sky blue, hafts bronze, pink-tinged pale blue signals, deeper sky blue around blue beards; ruffled. Golly Molly X Chubby Cheeks. Richmond Iris 1998.

COPATONIC (Barry Blyth, R. 1994). Sdlg. Z79-1. TB, 32-34" (81-86 cm), EM. S. russet brown; F. plush ruby brown, 1/4" russet brown edge; beards bright mustard yellow; heavily ruffled. Swain X Rustler. Tempo Two 1994/95.

COPE GOODWIN (Sharon McAllister, R. 1995). Sdlg. 89-1-10. AB (OGB-), 28" (71 cm), M. S. very pale blue (near RHS 97D), hint of violet; style arms very pale blue; F. blue violet (near 84A), 3/4" signal of deep purple (darker than 77A); beards yellow, violet base. Sostenique X Tribe of Judah. McAllister 1995.

COPPELIUS (Erhard Woerfel, R. 1990). Sdlg. 7184. TB, 43" (110 cm), M. Melon orange; beards orange red. Papagena X Faninal. Hochheimer 1991.

COPPER AND SNOW (Barry Blyth, R. 1995). Sdlg. A96-1. TB, 32" (81 cm), VE-EM. S. white, faint blue cast when fresh; F. chocolate brown, overlaid blended rosy blue brown in center; beards brown; pronounced sweet fragrance. Y4-3, sib to Breezes, X Chocolate Vanilla. Tempo Two 1995/96.

COPPER BELL (Elvan Roderick, TB, R. 1989). Roderick Iris 1991.

COPPER CYMBAL (Ron Mullin, R. 1996). Sdlg. 84-385A. TB, 36" (91 cm), M. Rosy copper self; beards tangerine. Lady Friend X Copper Classic. M.A.D. Iris 1997.

COPPER GEM (Cleo Palmer, R. 1993). Sdlg. 8916. SDB, 12" (30 cm), E. S. coppery melon orange, violet at base; F. slightly deeper; beards red, tipped light blue. 8613: (8115: (7607: (Dove Wings x ((Wilma V. x unknown) x Little Titan)) x Dove Wings) x unknown) X 8546: (Gigglepot x (7607 x (Dove Wings x 7416: (Baria x -- probably Carpathia)))). Palmer's Iris 1993.

COPPER LADY (Heather Collins, R. 1994). Sdlg. 84-20NC. AR (OH), 19" (49 cm), EM. S. champagne; F. deep champagne, darker veining, lemon signal; beards cinnamon; serrate standard margin, ruffled edge on F.; slight spicy fragrance. From onco sdlgs.

COPPER TIPS (Jean Witt, R. 1990). Sdlg. 85-01-45. MTB, 21" (53 cm), M. S. dark orange yellow

(Munsell 10YR 6/8), inner surface with echo of F. pattern but paler; style arms color of S.; F. medium reddish brown (2.5YR 3/3) at tip, hafts striped same over white ground, yellow reverse; beards yellow orange; slight fragrance. Spanish Coins X -- probably 73-02.

COPPER TRIDENT (Ben Hager, R. 1991). Sdlg. S973SthCp. SPU, 40" (102 cm), M. S. bright copper; style arms creamy copper; F. copper; lightly fluted. S821BzOr: (Forty Carats x S424Or: (S102: ((Elixir x Driftwood) x Driftwood) x Eagle)) X S849SthCp: (S480Br: (S102 x (Archie Owen x Baritone)) x Butter Paddle). Cordon Bleu 1991.

COPY BOY (Joseph Ghio, R. 1999). Sdlg. PB-314B. CA, 10" (25 cm), VE-EM. Creamy apricot, F. with violet haft blush and edges. PD-243-I, Cross Purpose sib, X PD-264-G3, Santa Rosalita sib. Bay View 1999.

COQUETTERIE (Jean Cayeux, R. 1991). Sdlg. 7918 A. TB, 36" (91 cm), ML. S. salmon pink; F. purple pink; beards tangerine, large. Metropolitan X Loudoun Lassie. Cayeux 1986.

COQUETTISH ART (Stan Dexter by Marie Ingersoll, R. 1994). Sdlg. C3-7-79-B. TB, 37" (94 cm), ML. Rose orchid, F. with deeper edge, brown hash marks; beards light red, tipped white; lightly ruffled. 1980-99C: (Coral Magic x 1977-O, unknown) X Sun Dappled. Ingersoll's Iris 1995.

CORAL BRACELET (O. D. Niswonger, R. 1992). Sdlg. 45-89. TB, 33" (84 cm), M. S. light pink; F. white, edged light pink; beards tangerine. 1-76: (Secret Wishes x (May Melody x (Fleeta x Golden Years sib))) X Halo in Yellow. Cape Iris 1992.

CORAL CARPET (Chuck Chapman, R. 1999). Sdlg. 92-60-2. MDB, 8" (20 cm), L. Light orange, beards intense coral tangerine. Pumpkin Center X Chubby Cherub. Chapman Iris 1999.

CORAL DREAMS (Howard Shockey, R. 1995). Sdlg. 89-210-BB. TB, 37" (94 cm), M. S. coral pink; F. white, blending to coral pink; beards white, coral pink in throat; very ruffled; slight sweet fragrance. 86-224-P: ((((Chartreuse Ruffles x Orchid Flash) x (Starfrost Pink x Startler)) x (Mimi x ((Carved Cameo x Summer Love) x (Lilac Mist x Fond Wish)))) x (((Trevi Fountain x (Carved Cameo x Summer Love)) x (Startler x Orchid Flash)) x ((Carved Cameo x Summer Love) x Beige Melody))) X 86-233-A: ((((Starfrost Pink x Startler) x Pink Angel) x Mimi) x (((Pink Angel x Valentina) x (Carved Cameo x Summer Love)) x ((Carved Cameo x Summer Love) x (Pink Angel x Valentina)))). Arilian Acres 1996.

CORAL LACE (Donald Sorensen, R. 1998). Sdlg. S-91-19-7. TB, 34" (86 cm), M. S. and style arms medium orient pink (RHS 36B); F. medium coral pink (38D), blending to cream in center; beards mandarin red (40C); laced; slight sweet fragrance. Belle of Amherst X Christa.

CORALLINE CHARM (Ladislav Muska, R. 1996). Sdlg. QHKD-03. TB, 36" (91 cm), ML. Heavily ruffled and laced pinkish coral self; beards tangerine; sweet fragrance. Queen of Hearts X Kentucky Derby. Muska 1996.

CORAL POINT (George Sutton, R. 1999). Sdlg. G-67. TB, 37" (94 cm), ML. Ruffled and laced pale pink (RHS 56D); beards coral, pink horn; slight musky fragrance. Sky Hooks X F-257: (2-14A: (Pink Ember x Playgirl) x Twice Thrilling).

CORAL SUNSET (Schreiner, R. 1990). Sdlg. S 589-2. TB, 37" (94 cm), ML. Shrimp apricot (RHS 32D); beards tangerine. H 834-5: (((Real Delight x Glittering Amber) x Orange Parade) x (Y 1468-A: ((June Meredith x Lynn Hall) x Fairy Fable) x Esther Fay)) X Piping Hot. Schreiner 1990.

CORBIERES (Jean Segui, R. 1998). TB, 29" (75 cm), E. S. and style arms indian yellow (RHS 17B); F. reddish purple (near 46A); beards golden yellow (24A); slight fragrance. Firecracker X Gala Madrid. Iris de Thau 1982.

CORDOBA (Joseph Ghio, R. 1997). Sdlg. 93-109X. TB, 36" (91 cm), EML. Mango orange, F. with reddish cast; beards red. Dawning X Royal Honey. Bay View 1998.

CORNHUSKER AUTUMN (John Weiler, R. 1995). Sdlg. 87-44. SDB, 10" (25 cm), ML & RE. S. light maize yellow; style arms maize yellow; F. medium maize yellow; beards light lavender blue; slight sweet fragrance. 85-20-1: (81-19-4: (79-36RE: ((Ruby Contrast x Little Blackfoot) x ((70-95: (Brighteyes x Grace Note) x Bronze Babe) x 74-3-1: (Cartwheel x 70-95-6))) x Pink Amber) x 84-46-1: (81-19-8 x 81-19-8)) X 84-50-1RE: (81-19-3 x 82-3-4RE: ((((Yellow Wave x 70-95-2) x 74-3-1) x Chariots) x ((70-95-3 x Gingerbread Man) x Stockholm))). Friendship 1997.

CORNICHE (A. J. Farrington, SDB, R. 1988). British Iris Society 1989.

CORN PUFF (John Marchant, R. 1992). Sdlg. 7487. CA, 12" (30 cm), M. S. almost apricot (HCC 609/3); F. same, overlaid with sandy grey-brown plicata-like markings. Sdlg. X sdlg.

CORONA EL SOL (Ladislav Muska, R. 1996). Sdlg. SKCK-03. TB, 36" (91 cm), ML Ruffled lemon yellow self; beards yellow, long blue horn. Sky Hooks X "Cipkovana Krinolina": (After All x Grand Waltz). Muska 1993.

CORONA GOLD (William Maryott, R. 1997). Sdlg. T128A. TB, 37" (94 cm), M. S. and style arms caramel (RHS 22A); F. caramel, blended light lavender (91D) in center; beards yellow, bushy; heavily ruffled; slight fragrance. Temperence X Juan Valdez. Maryott 1997.

CORONATION ANTHEM (Robert Hollingworth, R. 1990). Sdlg. 87P1B6. SIB (tet.), 32" (81 cm), M. Ruffled medium to deep blue, F. with large creamy yellow blaze aging to white; style arms lighter blue, tinged red. Jewelled Crown X (82J3B1: (Super Ego x Anniversary) x 80U4C6, Windwood Spring sib). Windwood Gardens 1990.

CORPS DE BALLET (Ben Hager, R. 1995). Sdlg. T5507LtPkBlBds. TB, 42½" (107 cm), ML. Pale pink self; beards baby ribbon blue, short horn on early blooms. Sib to Jump For Joy. Cooley 1998.

CORSAIR FIGHTER (Ed Attenberger, R. 1996). Sdlg. 90-02-02. TB, 35" (89 cm), M. Laced orchid blue, white area near beard; beards yellow, white at end; slight sweet fragance. Laced Cotton X Lemon Mist.

CORSO (Ladislav Muska, R. 1997). Sdlg. FGGO-07. TB, 40" (107 cm), M. S. light orchid blue; style arms orchid; F. bluish red, widely banded light orchid blue; beards light orange; ruffled, laced; sweet fragrance. (French Gown x Geniality) X Okavango. Muska 1997.

CORTEGIANNO (Ladislav Muska, R. 1998). Sdlg. 98-BRST-02. TB, 34" (86 cm), L. S. bright blue orchid, style arms lighter; F. deeper blue orchid; beards orange, blue orchid horn; ruffled; slight fragrance. (((Brilantine x Ringo) x (Don Epifano x La Bamba Cara)) x (Silverado x Tide's In)) X Conjuration. Muska 1999.

COSI FAN TUTTE (Laure Anfosso, R. 1991). Sdlg. L 82 4L. LA, 26" (65 cm), L. S. bright fuchsia pink; F. slightly darker, short triangular signal, deep fuchsia centerline. Charlie's Michele X This I Love. Iris en Provence 1991.

COSMIC GLOW (Vernon Wood, R. 1995). Sdlg. 93-90. CA, 14-16" (36-41 cm), ML. S. white, dark violet rib; style arms white, deep violet in heart; F. white base, center near-solid deep violet, 1/4" lines into white area, 1/4" outer unmarked white rim; ruffled. Idylwild X Star Symphony. Stockton 1996.

COSMIC MAGIC (Stan Dexter by Marie Ingersoll, R. 1995). Sdlg. A20-6-86A. TB, 36" (91 cm), M. S. white; F. palest blue, edged silver; beards tangerine, near-white tip. American Beauty X Condottiere. Ingersoll's Iris 1996.

COSMIC WAVE (Frederick Kerr, R. 1995). Sdlg. 88-17-05B. TB, 38" (97 cm), EM. S. medium violet blue, wide white border; F. medium blue violet; beards yellow, white at end; ruffled; pronounced spicy fragrance. Edith Wolford X Lullaby of Spring. Rainbow Acres 1996.

COSTA RICA (Joseph Ghio by Maryott's Gardens, R. 1994). Sdlg. 86-3H. TB, 37" (94 cm), ML. S. very pale lavender (RHS 56C); F. deep red violet (71A); beards tangerine, prominent. Tomorrow's Child X 83-73K: (Success Story x (Fancy Tales x Alpine Castle)). Maryott 1995.

COSTUMED CLOWN (Hooker Nichols, TB, R. 1989). Hillcrest 1995.

COTE D'OR (Schreiner, R. 1990). Sdlg. T 1246-1. TB, 36" (91 cm), L. Ruffled yellow (RHS 9A); beards orange. H 729-E, Gold Galore sib, X M 595-1: ((Royal Gold x Soft Moonbeam) x (C 1506-4, Moon Glimmer sib, x New Moon)). Schreiner 1990.

COTTON CHARMER (Carol Lankow by J. T. Aitken, R. 1998). Sdlg. 7 K. BB, 25" (64 cm), ML-VL. White self; beards white. Parentage unknown. Aitken's Salmon Creek 1998.

COTTON PLANTATION (Mary Dunn, R. 1994). Sdlg. 167-2. LA, 34" (86 cm), M. Pure white, lime yellow line signal. C'est Magnifique X Mary's Charlie. Bay View 1994.

COUNCIL FIRE (Jim Hedgecock, R. 1992). Sdlg. C-83-13-1. TB, 32" (81 cm), M. S. dark red blending to gold at midrib; F. dark red blending to gold at hafts; beards bright gold; lightly ruffled; slight sweet fragrance. Hilow X Lady Friend. Comanche Acres 1993.

COUNCIL MEETING (Chet Tompkins, R. 1995). Sdlg. 91-67B. TB, 39-40" (99-102 cm), ML. S. and style arms ivory cream, touched icy heliotope; F. deeper ivory cream, heavily sanded peppermint and heliotrope, edged glittering smoky amethyst; beards pale lemon, tipped lilac blue. Windwalker X sdlg., F4 from (Tinsel Town x Stepping Out). Fleur de Lis 1995.

COUNT DRACULA (Jim Hedgecock, R. 1999). Sdlg. A-8-1. TB, 36" (91 cm), M. S. dark purple; F. near-black, velvety sheen; beards burnt gold, 1" fuzzy near-black horn; ruffled; slight sweet fragrance. Velvet Eclipse X Battle Star.

COUNTESS CATHLEEN (Marty Schafer/Jan Sacks, R. 1997). Sdlg. S91-9-1. SIB, 30" (76 cm), M. S. very pale blue violet (lighter than RHS 91D), pale blue violet veining; style arms same, with yellow heart, tiny ruffles; F.pale blue violet (91C/D) with darker (93B/C) shoulder edge and veining; signals clean white, light green center, yellow at haft edges, veined blue violet (93B). S89-9-2: (Isabelle x Silver Illusion) X S88-6-2: (Isabelle x Sailor's Fancy). Joe Pye Weed 1997.

COUNTING SHEEP (J. T Aitken, R. 1999). Sdlg. 92M10. SDB, 12" (30 cm), ML. White, F. with soft yellow haft flush; beards violet, hairs tipped white. Pink Blink X sib. Aitken's Salmon Creek 1999.

COUNTRY BUMPKIN (Bob Thomason, SDB, R. 1988). Okie Iris 1999.

COUNTRY CHARM (Schreiner, R. 1998). Sdlg. CC 1324-1. TB, 38" (97 cm), L. S. and style arms empire yellow (RHS 11A); F. maroon purple (187B), 1/8" yellow rim; beards brassy yellow; ruffled. AA 1577-A: (T 543-A: (Sailmaster x M 1098-1: ((E 1054-A: (((Olympic Torch x Allaglow) x Applejack) x (Ruby Mine x Gypsy Jewels)) x (Matinata x (Agatine sdlg. x Edenite))) x (Shoreline sib x Brook Flower))) x S 264-B: (K 866-A x Bristo Magic)) X W 410-A: (S 331-1: (((Breaking Dawn x (Amethyst Flame x ((Lavanesque x Opal Beauty) x Wonderment))) x Navajo Blanket sib) x Distant Chimes sdlg.) x N 502-FF: ((C 973-A: ((Lilac Champagne x (Toll Gate x After Dark)) x ((Alpenrose x Whole Cloth) x Cashmere)) x (C 973-A x ((Broadway Star x Giant Rose) x ((Maytime x Opal Beauty) x Whole Cloth)) x Wine and Roses))) x H 238-A: ((Champagne Music x (R1052-2 x Christmas Time)) x (Orchid Brocade x (Annabel Lee sib x Emma Cook)))). Schreiner 1998.

COUNTRY DANCE (Evelyn Jones, R. 1996). Sdlg. 92-1-2. IB, 24" (61 cm), M. S. rose pink, flushed amber and lilac pink; F. rose pink, flushed lilac pink; beards tangerine, tipped lilac; ruffled; slight fragrance. Champagne Elegance X Chanted. Aitken's Salmon Creek 1997.

COUNTRY DIARY (Frederick Kerr, R. 1996). Sdlg. 89-15-06. TB, 30" (76 cm), EM. S. medium yellow, lighter in center, slight maroon infusion up midrib; F. white ground, heavily marked maroon, darker center stripe, hafts tan; beards tan, tipped brown; heavily ruffled, lightly laced; slight fragrance. Rustic Dance X Polar Seas. Rainbow Acres 1996.

COUNTRY GENTLEMAN (Louise Bellagamba, R. 1993). Sdlg. 491. TB, 34" (86 cm), L. Satiny faded blue denim self; beards brown; slight fragrance. Inv. sdlg. lines. Bella Vista 1993.

COUNTRY LACE (Frederick Kerr, R. 1998). Sdlg. 904704. BB, 27" (69 cm), M. S. reddish brown (RHS 179A); F. reddish brown, yellow with reddish brown veining at haft and throat; beards tangerine orange; ruffled, heavily laced. Fringe Benefits X Guadalajara. Rainbow Acres 1998.

COUNTRY MOON (Joyce Meek, R. 1994). Sdlg. 86-11-1. TB, 36" (91 cm), ML. Ruffled and flared creamy soft yellow with small lighter area around lemon yellow beards; slight sweet fragrance. P. T. Barnum X Brandy. D & J Gardens 1994.

COUNTRY RUFFLES (Frederick Kerr, R. 1995). Sdlg. 90-21-05. TB, 31" (79 cm), EM. S. yellow, shaded tan; F. yellow, shaded tannish green, lighter area around and below yellow beard; laced, heavily ruffled. Black Hills Gold X Magic Raiment sib. Rainbow Acres 1995.

COUNTRY RUSTIC (Ken Mohr by Bryce Williamson, R. 1995). Sdlg. Q32-1. TB, 34" (86 cm), M. S. golden chocolate brown, slight cream yellow area at midrib; F. chocolate brown, bright cream yellow ground in center, white around lemon yellow beard; ruffled. Morocco X Bronco Brown. Bryce Williamson 1995.

COUNTRY SKY (John Weiler, R. 1990). Sdlg. 85-153-1. TB, 37" (94 cm), ML. Lightly ruffled smooth medium blue; beards cream, yellow in throat; pronounced sweet fragrance. 81-97-4: (That Scentsation x Sweetwater) X Azure Luster. Rialto 1991.

COUNT THE KISSES (Barry Blyth, R. 1999). Sdlg. E149-1. TB, 34" (86 cm), EM. S. medium pink; F. light pink blending to pinkish white center; beards bright coral; heavily ruffled, fluted. K. Turner KH90-4-1: (Crystal Glitters x Cloud Fire) X About Town. Tempo Two 1999/2000.

COUNTY CARNIVAL (Ed Attenberger, R. 1999). Sdlg. 90-06-04. TB, 37" (94 cm), ML. Orchid pink self; beards reddish orange; ruffled; slight sweet fragrance. Buffy X Lemon Mist.

COUP DE FOUDRE (Lawrence Ransom, R. 1993). Sdlg. 87/165-10. TB, 36" (92 cm), M. Ruffled and lightly laced salmon pink with orange glow; beards vivid red. Pink Sleigh X Opium. Iris au Trescols 1994.

COUP DE GRACE (Mary Dunn, R. 1990). Sdlg. L158-9. LA, 36" (91 cm), M. S. dark orchid, texture-veined; style arms pale; F. wine orchid, veined, lighter serrate edge, small yellow sunburst signal. C'est Magnifique X Plantation Beau. Bay View 1991.

COUP D'ETAT (Mary Dunn, R. 1990). Sdlg. L120-2. LA, 32" (81 cm), M. S. golden copper orange; style arms greenish copper; F. copper orange, serrate edge of S. color, yellow signal. Gold Reserve X Counterpoise. Bay View 1990.

COUP DE THEATRE (Lawrence Ransom, R. 1999). Sdlg. 90/428-1. TB, 37" (95 cm), EM. S.

naples yellow, lightly peppered pale sienna brown; style arms deep cadmium yellow; F. white ground almost completely peppered and sanded light raspberry red, browner red toward edge, hafts yellow netted red brown; beards light orange. Theatre X Bartlett PS/SP2: ((Patina x Silkirim) x Soul Power).

COUP DE VILLE (Mary Dunn, R. 1990). Sdlg. L117-2. LA, 32" (81 cm), ML. S. and style arms light rose; F. copper rose, large yellow green signal rimmed darker. Ann Chowning X Monument. Bay View 1991.

COURT DANCER (Barry Blyth, R. 1999). Sdlg. D69-1. TB, 38" (97 cm), M. Light pink, F. with light pinkish white center shading; beards tangerine, pink at end. Letter From Paris X Spring Tidings. Tempo Two 1999/2000.

COURTLY AFFAIR (George Shoop, R. 1991). Sdlg. 84-10. BB, 26" (66 cm), M. S. white; F. rose pink; beards tangerine; ruffled. (So Rare x Ringo) X ((Ringo x Color Bash) x pink amoena sdlgs.). Shoop 1991.

COURT MARTIAL (Joseph Ghio by Maryott's Gardens, R. 1991). Sdlg. 82-65Z. TB, 38" (97 cm), M. S. red maroon (RHS 187B); F. slightly darker (187A); beards deep gold; lightly ruffled. (Lady Friend sib x ((Malaysia x Carolina Honey) x (Hi Top x ((Ponderosa x Travel On) x Peace Offering)))) X Marauder. Maryott 1991.

COURTNEY NICOLE (Jim Hedgecock, R. 1995). Sdlg. C-83-12-3. TB, 36" (91 cm), M. Peach pink self, lighter near bright tangerine beard; heavily laced and ruffled. Peach Tree X Entourage. Comanche Acres 1996.

COUSHATTA (Farron Campbell, R. 1998). Sdlg. 95-124-A. LA, 27" (69 cm), EM. S. lavender, veined lavender mauve; style arms yellow green, tips and edges flushed lavender mauve; F. lavender mauve, creamy white spray pattern, soft yellow signal with green crest; ruffled. Dural White Butterfly X Goula sdlg.: (Margaret Hunter x Ann Chowning).

COUTURE STAR (Lawrence Ransom, R. 1996). Sdlg. 90/380-5. SDB, 10" (25 cm), EM. S. white ground, stitched and dotted light lavender blue; style arms light lavender; F. white, very lightly stitched lavender edge, light maroon violet stitched haft; beards bluish white, brushed orange yellow in throat; pronounced sweet fragrance. Pigeon X Trescols. Iris au Trescols 1996.

COVERT ACTION (Harold Stahly, R. 1994). Sdlg. 88-33. TB, 36" (91 cm), M. S. light to medium blue (RHS 91A) deepening (93C) at base; F. light blue (91C), sharply defined center area of medium blue violet (90B); beards light blue, tipped bronze in throat. On the Road X High Five. Stahly 1994.

COVET ME (Barry Blyth, R. 1994). Sdlg. A63-7. TB, 38" (97 cm), EML. Lustrous pure gold; beards mustard gold; pronounced musky fragrance. Dance Man X Rembrandt Magic. Tempo Two 1994/95.

COWABUNGA (Tom Burseen, R. 1995). Sdlg. 1-164M. TB, 36" (91 cm), M. Ruffled metallic blue lilac (near RHS 87B) self; beards golden orange, large; musky fragrance. Where There's Smoke X 8-492A: ((Admiralty x Mandolin) x (Pansy Royale x Lux Aeterna)). T.B.'s Place 1996.

COWRIE SHELL (B.L.C. Dodsworth, R. 1997). Sdlg. EB 141A. TB, 44" (112 cm), M. Ruffled pale pink self; beards red. Vanity X Lovely Kay.

COY (Ben Hager, R. 1991). Sdlg. MD4933TyPkSp. MDB, 6" (15 cm), EML. Light maize yellow, apricot blended on both sides of tangerine beard; style arms yellow. MD4487Ty: (MD3980WY x MD3740PlAprTy: (((Buttercup Charm x 2562B: (Pink Amber x Pink Cushion)) x (2562G x Dache Model)) x ((2562A x Buttercup Charm) x (Buttercup Charm x (Pink Cushion x Roberts 65R28))))) X MD3980Ty: ((Pet sib x Tiny Apricot) x (Pet sib x Tiny Apricot)). Adamgrove 1991.

COZUMEL (Joseph Ghio, R. 1996). Sdlg. PF-188M. CA, 14" (36 cm), EM. Bright ochre gold; F. with maroon signal, veins extending outward. Eagle Eyes X PH-266K: (Las Lomas x Aftershock sib). Bay View 1996.

COZY MOMENT (Richard Morgan, R. 1999). Sdlg. L 607-V. LA, 25" (64 cm), EM. Ruffled medium violet, F. with green yellow lancehead signal; style arms light violet; buds grey blue. L-152-V: (Bayou Waters x (Mac's Blue Heaven x Blue Shield)) X Royal Velour.

CRACKLES (Barry Blyth, R. 1990). Sdlg. W35-1. TB, 18-20" (46-51 cm), EM. S. white ground, heavily veined and edged light violet; F. white, violet edge down sides; beards light tangerine tipped white. (Cupid's Cup x (Sniffs 'n' Sneezes x Hammered Copper)) X Entrancement. Tempo Two 1990/91.

CRAFTY (Carl Boswell, R. 1995). Sdlg. 153-85-2-B. BB, 24" (61 cm), M. S. pale peach; F. pale buff pink, white blaze; beards burnt orange. Frosty Pastel X Autumn Blush. Adamgrove 1995.

CRAFTY LADY (Paul Black, R. 1991). Sdlg. 86103AA. BB, 25" (63 cm), E. S. warm apricot; style arms pink; F. pink ground, bright fuchsia raspberry spot that breaks into pink veining halfway down, white spray pattern around orange beard; ruffled. Sorceress X Planned Treasure. Mid-America 1991.

CRAIG'S CHOICE (Kevin Nilsen, R. 1992). Sdlg. 50-87-1. TB, 31" (79 cm), ML. S. and style arms white; F. blended rose violet, edged white, brownish hafts; beards orange yellow; ruffled. Pass the Wine X unknown. Iridescence 1992/93.

CRANAPPLE (J. T. Aitken, R. 1995). Sdlg. 90M57. BB, 24" (61 cm), EM. S. and style arms cranberry red; F. dark velvety cranberry red; beards russet. (Gyro x Warrior King) X Maid of Orange. Aitken's Salmon Creek 1995.

CRANBERRY COOLER (Robert Dunn, R. 1995). Sdlg. 1034-B. TB, 37" (94 cm), E. S. lustrous cranberry claret; style arms light cranberry; F. cranberry claret, slight blue flash at end of beard; beards coppery, cranberry at end. Skyship X B931-Z: (M747: (((Pagan sib x Royal Heritage) x Manuel) x Plum Dazzle) x M699: (Intuition x Cranberry Ice)). M.A.D. Iris 1996.

CRANBERRY CORDIAL (Walter Moores, R. 1999). Sdlg. 92-16. TB, 34" (86 cm), EM. S. red brown, midrib blended cream; style arms cranberry red; F. cream ground, wide cranberry red plicata band and dotting, red violet centerline; beards bronze; heavily ruffled; slight spicy fragrance. Sterling Prince X Way Out West.

CRANBERRY DELIGHT (J. T. Aitken, R. 1995). Sdlg. 87T7. TB, 40" (107 cm), VL. S. cranberry red; style arms white, edged cranberry red; F. cranberry red, flushed white around red beard. Persian Gown X Lady Friend. Aitken's Salmon Creek 1995.

CRANBERRY FIRE (D. L. Shepard, R. 1994). Sdlg. 91003-8921. BB, 27" (70 cm), M. S. medium cranberry with darker midrib stripe; F. deep rich mulberry; beards bright red; fluted. Cinderella's Coach X Irish Butter. Shepard Iris 1994.

CRANBERRY TEA (Gerald Mapes, TB, R. 1988). Maryott 1989.

CRAQUELURE (Lawrence Ransom, R. 1996). Sdlg. 90/404-4. SDB, 10" (25 cm), EM. S. light silvery blue; F. light blue at edge, remainder flushed darker violet blue, white hafts netted maroon violet; beards white, light blue at end, brushed orange in throat; pronounced sweet fragrance. Sapphire Gem X Trescols. Iris au Trescols 1996.

CRAWFISH PIE (Kevin Vaughn, R. 1996). Sdlg. D-101-1. LA, 34-39" (86-99 cm), ML. S. bright red violet (RHS 72B) edged primrose yellow (4C), signal sometimes present; style arms primrose yellow, center and tips red violet; F. bright red (59B) edged primrose yellow, bright primrose yellow (4A) signal; petals serrate; slight musky fragrance. Cajun Sunrise X Cajun Cookery.

CRAYOLA PINK (O. D. Niswonger, R. 1994). Sdlg. SDB 70-91. SDB, 12" (30 cm), ML. S. pale pink; F. pink; beards white, tipped tangerine. Live Jaz X SDB 16-87: (Peach Bavarian x Peach Eyes). Cape Iris 1994.

CRAZY FOR YOU (Barry Blyth, R. 1998). Sdlg. C208-1. TB, 36" (91 cm), EM. S. oyster grey, pinkish beige midrib flush; F. oyster grey overlaid and heavily veined rose grey, 1/8" oyster grey edge; beards white, hairs tipped bronze tangerine; sweet fragrance. Z51A-1, Wild Vision sib, X Z65-1: (W117-1: ((Alpine Journey x Beachgirl) x (Beachgirl x ((Tranquil Star x Coral Strand) x (Persian Smoke x Chimbolam)))) x X108-2, Chocolate Vanilla sib). Tempo Two 1998/99.

CRAZY HORSE (Jim Hedgecock, R. 1990). Sdlg. 83-20-5. TB, 37" (94 cm), M. S. white ground irregularly stitched and stippled royal blue; F. white ground irregularly stitched and stippled purple; beards purple turning yellow in throat; slight fragrance. Going My Way X Hey Looky. Comanche Acres 1991.

CRAZY IN HORNS (Ladislav Muska, R. 1998). Sdlg. 98-MGSS-08. TB, 34" (86 cm), L. S. and style arms light amethyst; F. deeper amethyst; beards pinkish orange, blue orchid horns; heavily ruffled. Mys Horn X ((Geniality x Sky Hooks) x Lace Jabot). Muska 1999.

CREAM AND PEACHES (O. D. Niswonger, R. 1993). Sdlg. SDB 33-90. SDB, 12" (30 cm), M. S. ivory infused apricot; F. apricot banded ivory; beards white, tipped tangerine. Straw Hat X Ballet Slippers. Cape Iris 1994.

CREAM CAKE (O. D. Niswonger, SDB, R. 1989). Cape Iris 1990.

CREAMCICLE (Joyce Wilcox, R. 1992). Sdlg. 6-J-11B. TB, 32" (81 cm), M. S. yellow orange (RHS 19B); F. cream white, yellow orange area on either side of orange beard, 1/4" yellow orange edge; ruffled; sweet fragrance. Copper Classic X Gold Trimmings. Meadowbrook 1993.

CREAM COCKATOO (A. D. Keith by Robert Strohman, R. 1995). TB, 34" (86 cm), M. Light yellow self; beards full yellow; sweet fragrance; foliage variable, from all green to variegated to white. Probably -- California Gold X Happy Days. Eden Road 1956.

CREAMISH STORM (Ladislav Muska, R. 1999). Sdlg. 98-CSMD-05. TB, 35" (89 cm), M. Ruffled, lightly laced light cream self; beards orange, long lavender horn; slight fragrance. (("Carpathy Styl" x Mys Horn) x Decory Win) X Sky Hooks.

CREAM PIXIE (Chuck Chapman, R. 1996). Sdlg. 89-7-A. SDB, 11" (28 cm), L. S. light creamy yellow; F. deeper, throat yellow; beards very pale blue; slight fragrance. Mary's Lamb X Tender Tears. Chapman Iris 1996.

CREAM SODA (Cy Bartlett, R. 1996). Sdlg. CC-D. TB, 34" (86 cm), M. Lemon cream self; beards white to lemon; slight sweet fragrance. Cannington Creamery X Demelza.

CREAM WITH GOLD (Ladislav Muska, R. 1995). Sdlg. DELM-07. TB, 37" (94 cm), ML. Cream, washed gold; beards orange. Don Epifano X (Lady Madonna x Don Epifano). Muska 1996.

CREAMY CUSTARD (Aaron Logan by Pierce County Iris Society, R. 1995). CA, 10-12" (25-31 cm), M. Creamy light yellow, F. with halo of greyish brown lines and tiny freckles. Parentage unknown.

CREATION TWILIGHT (Bernice Miller, R. 1992). Sdlg. CT93. TB, 34" (86 cm), EM & RE (Oct./AL). S. light lavender; F. light lavender, lighter area under beards, blended pale gold edge; beards coral red, tipped pale lavender; ruffled, laced; pronounced fragrance. (Returning Peace x ((Rippling Waters x (Ola Kala x Mary Randall)) x Pink Fulfillment)) X Jubilant Psalm. Comanche Acres, Garden of the Enchanted Rainbow 1993.

CREATIVE EDGE (Kevin Vaughn, R. 1998). Sdlg. G-93-1. LA, 34" (86 cm), EM. S. light lavender, 1/2" dark lavender border, 1/4" cream halo; style arms light lavender, deeper lavender midrib; F. light lavender, 1/2"-5/8" dark lavender border, 1/4"-3/8" cream halo, cream signal edged lavender. Old South Ball X Marie Dolores.

CREDIBLE JUSTIFICATION (Sterling Innerst, R. 1994). Sdlg. 3642-6. TB, 36" (91 cm), M. Medium yellow ground plicata, F. trimmed brown; beards yellow bronze. Round Table X Progressive Attitude. Innerst 1995.

CREDIT LINE (Joseph Ghio, R. 1995). Sdlg. 91-34-T2. TB, 32" (81 cm), EM. S. white; F. yellow, white marginal band and flash below white beard. 87-135Z: ((Borderline sib x Wedding Candles) x Sunshine Song) X Wings of Gold. Bay View 1996.

CREGRINA (Maureen Foster, R. 1990). Sdlg. 6B3. TB, 35" (89 cm), ML. S. creamy warm yellow orange (RHS 14C), lightening to pale yellow (9D) toward edge, 1/8" orchid laced edge; F. pale red lilac (78D), shoulders brushed tan, reverse primrose yellow (13C); beards orange gold; ruffled. Blorenge X Wild West. V. H. Humphrey 1995.

CREME GLACEE (Richard Cayeux, R. 1995). Sdlg. 8515 A. TB, 30" (75 cm), M. S. pure white; F. bright pink; beards red. Cameo Wine X 75106 A: (Neige de Mai x Gypsy Dream). Cayeux 1994.

CREMONETTE (Ladislav Muska, R. 1997). Sdlg. S-WGLL-05. SDB, 14" (36 cm), E. Ruffled light cream self, F. touched gold in center; beards gold, hairs tipped white; ruffled; sweet fragrance. White Gem X Laced Lemonade. Muska 1992.

CREOLE FANTASY (Marvin Granger, LA, R. 1988). Faggard 1994.

CREOLE RHAPSODY (Joseph Mertzweiller by Farron Campbell, R. 1998). Sdlg. DT 87-34-B. LA, 30-34" (76-86 cm), M. S. creamy white, wine red midrib and veining; style arms green base, yellow green midrib, wine red tips and edges; F. deep wine red to rose red, large yellow signal; lightly ruffled. Colorific X tetraploid sdlg. C-75-26. Lone Star 1998.

CREPE PAPER DOLL (Francis Rogers, R. 1998). Sdlg. C-5-B. TB, 33" (84 cm), M. S. and style arms light lemon yellow; F. violet (RHS 83B), yellow adjacent to and white below beard, violet streaking to border, purple 3/4" edge narrowing to 3/8" at hafts; beards yellow (3D) at end, darkening (3B) toward center; ruffled, crinkled; sweet fragrance. Stella Marie X Edgewater. Meadowbrook 1999.

CRI DE COEUR (Lawrence Ransom, R. 1993). Sdlg. 87/37-3. TB, 33" (85 cm), M. Ruffled and flared rose and deep beige pink blend, cream orange shoulders; beards orange to red; sweet fragrance. Lady Friend X Coup de Coeur. Iris au Trescols 1994.

CRIMPED COPPER (Stan Dexter by Marie Ingersoll, R. 1990). Sdlg. 1980/89A. TB, 36" (91 cm), M. S. copper, edged darker; F. copper with rosy cast, edged darker, bright reddish flash fading to near white in throat; beards deep yellow. Temple Gold X 1977M, unknown. Ingersoll's Iris 1991.

CRIMSON ACCENT (Jean Witt, R. 1998). Sdlg. 98-07-5910. SPEC-X (cal-sib), 20" (51 cm), E. S. ivory, lavender midline, yellow base; style arms paler ivory, faint lavender tint; F. ivory, washed lavender, gold shoulders, diffuse gold signal; spathes crimson, conspicuous; foliage blue green. Snow Queen X yellow *I. innominata.*

CRIMSON FIRE (Schreiner, R. 1990). Sdlg. V 824-1. TB, 32" (81 cm), ML. Red (RHS 178B), beards gold. Distant Fire X R 820-1: (K 699-1: (((Vitafire x (Dazzling Delight sib x Fire Magic)) x (Vitafire x (Forward March x Caldron))) x (Post Time x (Taste of Honey x A 462-15))) x K 1392-A: ((Vitafire x War Lord) x sdlg.)). Schreiner 1990.

CRIMSON TIGER (Gerald Richardson, R. 1996). Sdlg. 88-2-1. TB, 30" (76 cm), M. Buff gold, boldly splashed and streaked red and magenta; beards gold. Broadway X 77-56-1: (74-31-6: ((Celestial Snow x Blushing Beauty) x Campus Flirt) x 74-73-1: ((San Leandro x Mulberry Rose) x Mulberry Rose)). Rainbow's End 1996.

CRIMSON TWIST (Richard Ernst, R. 1996). Sdlg. KF125-1-1. TB, 38" (96 cm), M. S. blended crimson red, gold midrib infusion widening at base; F. blended currant red (RHS 46A) to chrysanthemum crimson (185A) plicata markings, white ground around beard, yellow (14C) ground on shoulders; beards yellow (14B); bloomstalks purple. F125-1: (Edna's Wish x Wild Jasmine) X sib. Cooley 1997.

CRINKLED GLORY (A. Theodore Mueller, R. 1995). Sdlg. 88-35. TB, 36-40" (97-107 cm), ML. S. and style arms bluish lilac, slightly blended; F. same, blended darker lilac toward lower end, lighter in center; beards orange; waved, heavily laced. Minted Halo X (Minted Halo x Capricorn Dancer). Mueller's Garden 1995.

CRINKLETTE (Graeme Grosvenor, R. 1994). Sdlg. T6-1. TB, 34" (85 cm), EM. S. white, suffused and marked pale lilac; F. white, edged and dotted darker lilac mauve, heavier at hafts; beards lilac mauve; heavily ruffled. Foolish Fancy X Snowbrook. Rainbow Ridge 1997/98.

CRITIC'S CHOICE (Lilly Gartman, TB, R. 1988). Roris 1991.

CROFTWAY LEMON (M.J.R. Spencer, R. 1990). TB, 32" (81 cm), EM. Tailored pale lemon yellow; pronounced sweet fragrance. Parentage unknown. Croftway Nursery 1990.

CROSS CURRENT (Keith Keppel, R. 1994). Sdlg. 88-33A. TB, 38" (97 cm), EM. S. and style arms clear light blue (M&P 41-A-6/7); F. violet blue (41-JK-12) paling near beards to blue white with some campanula violet (42-J-10) veining; beards blue white at end, white in midsection, yellow in throat; ruffled; pronounced sweet fragrance. God's Handiwork X Armada. Keppel 1995.

CROSS PURPOSE (Joseph Ghio, R. 1997). Sdlg. PD-243E2. CA, 12" (31 cm), M. S. heliotrope; F. heliotrope, undertoned apricot, large neon violet signal. Local Girl X PF-174H2: ((Las Lomas x Shaker sib) x Villa Montalvo). Bay View 1997.

CROSS YOUR FINGERS (Ada Godfrey, R. 1996). Sdlg. BA87. SDB, 10" (25 cm), EM. S. saturated rich gold; style arms rich gold, crests crossed; F. rich gold; beards golden orange; lightly ruffled. SS1: (unknown deep maroon x self) X Blitz. Hermit Medlars Walk 1996.

CROW (Ken Durio, R. 1992). Sdlg. GR #1. LA, 26" (66 cm), M. S. light red violet; F. very dark red violet. Tokyo Rose X Ann Chowning.

CROWNED HEADS (Keith Keppel, R. 1996). Sdlg. 90-67A. TB, 38" (97 cm), M. S. wistaria violet (M&P 41-E-8/9), slightly deeper (41-HI-10) base; style arms light blue (41-A-5/6); F. light blue (33-A-5) shaded deeper (41-B-8) in heart, aging silvery blue white; beards blue (33-A-7), goldenrod (10-L-5) in throat; slight sweet fragrance. In Reverse X Honky Tonk Blues. Keppel 1997.

CROWNETTE (Barry Blyth, R. 1992). Sdlg. X25-8. SDB, 14" (36 cm), ML. S. creamy apricot, lightly flushed violet on midrib; F. slightly deeper; beards bushy lavender, tangerine in throat. (Oladi x Fifi) X (Peach Eyes x Kandi Moon). Tempo Two 1992/93.

CROWNING MOMENT (Bob Bauer/John Coble, R. 1998). Sdlg. J88H-3. JI (3 F.), 40" (102 cm), E. S. dark violet, white wire rim, base with few white veins; style arms white, light violet crest; F. white, edges sanded and stitched rose violet, signal yellow; flared, arching form. Iapetus X unknown. Ensata Gardens 1997.

CROWN OF ISIS (Darlene Pinegar, R. 1994). Sdlg. CT-1-6. TB, 34" (86 cm), ML. S. and style arms very deep bright golden yellow; F. slightly darker, light honey gold hafts and markings; beards dark yellow orange; ruffled; slight sweet fragrance. Carnival Time X Spiced Custard. Spanish Fork 1995.

CRUISE CONTROL (Larry Lauer, R. 1995). Sdlg. 89-134-6. TB, 37-38" (94-97 cm), EM. S. light blue (near white); style arms blue white, touched violet at top; F. violet blue; beards lavender blue, tipped tangerine in throat. Strictly Ballroom X Alaskan Seas. Stockton 1995.

CRUSHED ICE (Heather Pryor, R. 1995). Sdlg. 44/90-1. LA, 39" (100 cm), EM. Ruffled white, opening pale cream, with yellow to green line signal, veined petals; style arms white, yellow ribs. Dural White Butterfly X Alluvial Gold. Rainbow Ridge 1996/97.

CRYSTAL BLUE HAZE (Donald Sorensen, R. 1999). Sdlg. S-91-6-12. BB, 20" (51 cm), E. S. and style arms light wistaria blue (RHS 92D); F. light wistaria blue, blending to white in center; beards light wistaria blue (92C), hairs tipped white, changing to canary yellow (9C), cadmium orange (23B) in throat; heavily ruffled; pronounced sweet fragrance. Polar Seas X Bridal Fashion.

CRYSTAL FLAIR (J. D. Stadler, R. 1990). Sdlg. L7/77. TB, 36" (91 cm), ML. Heavily ruffled very pale blue, darker F. veining; beards white, yellow in throat; slight sweet fragrance. Ruffled Ballet X Bubbling Over. Celestial Gardens 1991.

CRYSTAL GALAXY (Peter Nilsen, R. 1996). Sdlg. 60-91-1-C. TB, 39" (100 cm), VE-EM. Pale silvery blue, deeper in heart; style arms pale blue, base deeper, crests paler; beards medium blue; foliage based red. Altruist X Crystalyn.

CRYSTAL HONEY (Donald Spoon, R. 1997). Sdlg. 89-116. TB, 34" (86 cm), ML & RE. S. amber gold, finely veined rose; style arms amber gold; F. amber gold, white ray pattern near beard, slight lavender blaze; beards amber gold, darker in throat; ruffled; pronounced sweet fragrance. Summer Olympics X Sheba's Queen. Winterberry 1999.

CRYSTALLINE ENTITY (Perry Dyer, R. 1999). Sdlg. 92-25A. SDB, 12" (30 cm), ML. Satin-finish white self; beards sapphire blue; lightly waved. Serenity Prayer X Star Search.

CRYSTAL MORN (Howard Shockey, R. 1994). Sdlg. 87-258-A. TB, 34" (86 cm), M. S. light pink, edges flushed violet; style arms light pink; F. white, blending to light violet pink edges; beards cerise, blue white at end; slight sweet fragrance. Crystal Dreams X 85-212-P: (((Startler x Starfrost Pink) x Mimi) x (Mimi x ((Carved Cameo x Summer Love) x (Lilac Mist x Fond Wish)))). Arilian Acres 1995.

CRYSTAL PATTERN (Richard Ernst, R. 1996). Sdlg. HA103-2. TB, 40" (107 cm), EM. S. white ground, blue violet plicata markings and midrib stripe; style arms blue violet; F. white ground, edged blue violet, thin blue violet centerline; beards white, yellow in throat; lightly ruffled, laced; slight spicy-sweet fragrance. A103-1: (Song of Norway x Inheritance) X Wings of Doves. Cooley 1996.

CRYSTAL RIBBON (Chet Tompkins, R. 1995). TB, 34" (86 cm), M. S. light cream pink; F. bright dark wine, narrow white edge; beards light tangerine. Sib to Smooth Flow. Roris 1990.

CRYSTAL RING (Akihiko Terada, R. 1997). Sdlg. S 235-89-2. TB, 36" (91 cm), M. S. white; F. purple, white area around yellow beard. Delphi X Dover Beach. Roris 1997.

CRYSTAL SEA (William Plotner, TB, R. 1989). Wildwood Gardens 1990.

CRYSTAL SPRINGS (William Maryott, R. 1991). Sdlg. M147SPR. TB, 35" (89 cm), M. S. medium lavender blue (RHS 97B); F. medium blue with slight silvery rim; beards yellow, tipped white; ruffled. (Scented Nutmeg x ((Prophecy x Gypsy Belle) x Intuition)) X Jean Hoffmeister. Maryott 1991.

CRYSTAL STAR (John Wight, R. 1993). Sdlg. J84-5-1. AB (OGB), 20" (51 cm), M. S. pale yellow aging white, light green midribs; F. light yellow, slight greenish infusion in center, 1/2" maroon line signal below yellow beard. Flanagan 76007-5 X Grecian Form. Wight's Iris 1993.

CRYSTELLA (Alphonse Van Mulders, R. 1990). Sdlg. 50/83. TB, 33" (84 cm), M. Ruffled salmon pink; beards orange. Tahiti Sunrise X Dentelle Rose. Jardinart Van Mulders 1989.

CUBAN RUMBA (John C. Taylor, R. 1993). Sdlg. RL 35-2. LA, 47" (120 cm), M. S. cream, veined purple; F. purple, strong yellow signal. Wine and Dine X Margaret Lee. Rainbow Ridge 1993/94.

CUDDLE ME (Barry Blyth, R. 1994). Sdlg. A44-3. SDB, 10" (25 cm), VE-EM. S. pastel bluish pink over white, deepening in center; F. paler bluish pink, whiter area around beard; beards pale blue, tipped tangerine. V7-5, Gigolette sib, X Chanted. Tempo Two 1994/95.

CUDDLE UP (Ben Hager, R. 1992). Sdlg. MSD5199DpPch. SDB, 12" (30 cm), M. Bright salmon pink; beards flame tangerine; small flowers. SD4978: (Cupid's Cup x ((3393Pk: (2885Y: (Blonde Doll x 2562B: (Pink Amber x Pink Cushion)) x 2888: (2562A x Buttercup Charm)) x ((2563-O: (Pink Cushion x Roberts 65-R-28) x (Frosty Lemonade x Pink Cushion)) x Pet)) x ((3393 x Pet sib) x (((2563-O x (Pink Amber x Pink Cushion)) x 2885Pch) x 3393Pk)))) X 4988: ((Ceremony x Today's Fashion) x My Sheba). Adamgrove 1993.

CULBURRA (Leslie Donnell, R. 1995). Sdlg. 94-5A. TB, 30" (76 cm), ML. Dark violet self (RHS 80A to 81A); beards orange brown tipped blue, bushy; sweet fragrance. Corretto X Hampton Harmony.

CULTURED PEARL (Sharol Longaker, R. 1991). TB, 32" (81 cm), L. S. white with hint of light lavender pink; F. white, veined lavender, light lavender hafts; beards light yellow; laced; sweet fragrance. Priceless Pearl X Laced Cotton. Anderson Iris 1991.

CUMEL (Jiří Dudek, R. 1997). Sdlg. (LCTG)LM. TB, 36" (90 cm), M. S. cream, pale lilac at base; style arms white, edged light yellow; F. cream, hafts light brown, lilac throat; beards white, orange in throat; ruffled, laced; pronounced spicy fragrance. (Laced Cotton x Tut's Gold) X Lady Madonna. Jiří Dudek 1997.

CUPFULL (Barry Blyth, R. 1991). Sdlg. X25-2. SDB, 14" (36 cm), VE. Lemon apricot, F. slightly darker; beards pastel lavender, tangerine in throat. (Oladi x Fifi) X (Peach Eyes x Kandi Moon). Tempo Two 1991/92.

CUPID'S ARROW (Joseph Ghio, TB, R.1989). Roris 1990.

CUPID'S BOW (Joe Saia, R. 1990). Sdlg. 83-5-1. SDB, 13" (33 cm), E. S. bright yellow; F. reddish brown, edged yellow; beards mustard, tipped blue white. Forty Winks X 81-2-1: (Amazon Princess x Gingerbread Man). Saia 1991.

CUPID'S MAGIC (Floyd Dyer, R. 1993). Sdlg. D-141-86-D. SDB, 14" (36 cm), M. White with violet tint and violet veins on F.; beards yellow, tipped white; musky fragrance. D-274-82-D: (D-124-79-D: (((Green Spot x Knotty Pine) x self) x Gingerbread Man) x D-124-79-D) X Ice Chalet. Four Cedars 1993.

CUPID SMILES (Ben Hager, R. 1994). Sdlg. BB5611Pk. BB, 20" (51 cm), EM. Pink self; beards tangerine. Sib to Brain Child. Adamgrove 1997.

CURACAO (Barry Blyth, R. 1990). Sdlg. V114-1. BB, 26" (66 cm), EML. S. pink buff, violet infusion at midrib; F. plum violet, 1/4" light lilac edge; beards light tangerine. (Ambiance x In Smoke) X Moomba. Tempo Two 1990/91.

CURIOUS SPIKE (Ladislav Muska, R. 1998). Sdlg. 98-MCCC-04. TB, 34" (86 cm), L. S. and style arms light lavender orchid; F. deeper lavender orchid; beards tangerine, rosy lavender violet horns; slight fragrance. ((Mys Horn x Calicoball) x Conjuration) X "Cream Secrets". Muska 1999.

CURIOUS TABBY (Donald Spoon, R. 1995). Sdlg. 93-12. TB, 29" (74 cm), M. S. light pink, outer portion blended tan; F. tan, lighter edge, white striations beside tangerine beard; lightly ruffled. Curious Yellow X My Jodie.

CURLY BLUE (D. L. Shepard, R. 1996). Sdlg. 95088-9083. TB, 42" (107 cm), EM. S. and style arms sky blue; F. lighter sky blue, cream white radiating from tip of beard; beards cream white, yellow in throat; heavily ruffled. 88-3: (Prince of Peace x Ruffled Ballet) X Quintessence. Shepard Iris 1996.

CURRENCY (John C. Taylor, R. 1993). Sdlg. RL 9-1. LA, 44" (110 cm), EM. S. cream, veined and flushed pink; style arms yellow; F. buff pink, heavily veined maroon pink, green line signal around yellow center; ruffled, slightly recurved. Green Elf X Margaret Lee. Rainbow Ridge 1993/94.

CURRIERSER AND CURRIERSER (Harry Bishop, R. 1990). Sdlg. SI-B-83-1-B. SPEC-X, 17" (43 cm), ML. S. sky blue; style arms slightly lighter; F. slightly lighter sky blue, blue lines radiating from bright yellow signal, white area extending over 1/3 of F. Stella Main X *I. virginica*, blue.

CURVY COURSE (Tom Burseen, R. 1997). Sdlg. 93-369Y. TB, 35" (89 cm), M. S. majolica yellow (RHS 168D); style arms golden tan (163C); F. tan orange, washed lavender; beards maize yellow; ruffled, heavily laced. Easter Lace X 7-120: (Local Motion x Lace Jabot). T.B.'s Place 1998.

CUSS A'BLUE STREAK (David Miller, R. 1992). Sdlg. DM 85-5A. TB, 32-34" (81-86 cm), EM. S. white with silvery blue green (RHS 157B) cast; F. same, very slight light blue centerline extending from blue beards to edge; slight fragrance. Song of Norway X Lorilee. Long 1993.

CUTE AND SASSY (Larry Lauer, R. 1999). Sdlg. 92-204-1. SDB, 10" (25 cm), E. S. and style arms violet; F. violet, velvety purple wash, shoulders tinted brown; beards violet; slight sweet fragrance. Chubby Cheeks X Bountiful Harvest.

CUTE OR WHAT (O. D. Niswonger, R. 1996). Sdlg. SDB 3-94. SDB, 14" (36 cm), M. S. and style arms apricot; F. white, edged apricot; beards blue, tangerine base. SDB 24-91: (SDB 27-87: (Oriental Blush x unknown) x Tillie) X Chanted. Cape Iris 1997.

CUTE TOT (Ben Hager, R. 1999). Sdlg. AMD 4012GdT. MDB, 5-6" (13-15 cm), EML. S. light yellow; style arms yellow; F. deep gold yellow; beards yellow, tangerine in throat; flared. AMD 3390: ((Libation x 2479: (Idol's Eye x (Scale Model x Brownett))) x 2479) X AMD 3513TyY: (((((Evening Storm x Welch H501) x (Sulina x Melodrama)) x ((Nest Egg x Progenitor) x (Brassie x Brownie))) x 2479) x Buttercup Charm). Adamgrove 1999.

CUTIE EYES (Lawrence Ransom, R. 1994). Sdlg. 90/243-8. SDB, 11" (28 cm), M. Silvery white, light violet eyelash pattern; beards white, blue violet on end, tipped yellow in throat; ruffled. Cindy Mitchell X Peyrard PB 88/1-1: (Planet Iris x *I. pumila*). Iris au Trescols 1995.

105

CUTIE PIE (G. W. Madsen, TB, R. 1956). Correction of spelling in 1959 Check List from CUTE PIE.

CUTTING EDGE (Joseph Ghio, R. 1993). Sdlg. 89-71LL. TB, 33" (84 cm), ML. S. deep coral pink; F. white, edged pink; beards coral, blue base. 86-95B4: (Newlywed x Caption) X (Romantic Mood x 82-156H2, pollen parent of Winning Smile). Bay View 1994.

CYBER NET (W. Terry Varner, R. 1995). Sdlg. V-396-DG. MTB, 19" (48 cm), ML. S. and F. cream 11ground, light to medium purple blotches or patches, broken pattern, variable; style arms cream, light purple edge; beards white, yellow in throat. Here's Lucy X 91-DG-58: (Flashy Flirt x Kaitlin). Ohio Gardens 1996.

CYCLAMINT (Heather Pryor, R. 1995). Sdlg. 53/90-B. LA, 30" (76 cm), M. Ruffled cyclamen purple (RHS 77A); style arms soft mauve, green center; signal on all petals giving star effect, bright green center, yellow edge, ribbed purple. Ann Chowning X Jazz Ballet. Rainbow Ridge 1996/97.

CYRIL FIELD (Cyril Field, R. 1992). Sdlg. CF6. MTB, 16" (41 cm), L. S. lilac blue; style arms paler, reverse with twin yellow ridges with blue triangle at end; F. lilac blue; beards orange, split in two lengthwise, large blue flounces. From sdlgs.: (horned blue x flounced lilac) X flounced.

CY'S CHOICE (Leslie Donnell, R. 1998). Sdlg. 82-5-11. TB, 34" (86 cm), L. S. fawn (RHS 165B); F. purple plicata edge and centerline, large white central patch; beards orange. Kerrie's Kirtle X Hampton Harmony.

CZOCHTAN (Zdeněk Seidl, R. 1997). Sdlg. 88-StX/1. SDB, 10" (25 cm), EM. S. creamy yellow; F. olive green to yellow; beards yellow; ruffled; slight spicy fragrance. Stockholm X unknown. Seidl 1998.

DADDY'S GIRL (Joyce Meek, R. 1997). Sdlg. 102-2-6. TB, 36" (91 cm), ML. S. creamy pink to pinkish ivory; F. creamy pink lightening to pinkish ivory, hafts flushed pink and gold; beards coral, white at end; lightly ruffled. (Candace x Monaco) X (Brandy x Far Corners). D & J Gardens 1997.

DAFFODIL CLOUD (John Weiler, R. 1990). Sdlg. 85-168-1. TB, 34" (86 cm), EML. S. white, slight yellow flush at base of midrib; F. bright full yellow; beards full yellow; lightly ruffled, flared; slight sweet fragrance. Golden Velvet X 81-64-1: (79-121-1: ((White King x Tinsel Town) x ((Minnesota Glitters x Kimberlina) x ((Marquesan Skies x (Rippling Waters x Claudia Rene)) x (Winter Olympics x Georgia Girl)))) x Marmalade Skies). Rialto 1990.

DAINTREE (John C. Taylor, R. 1997). Sdlg. UL 22-5. LA, 35" (90 cm), ML. Yellow, darker around green signal; style arms yellow; lightly ruffled. Gladiator's Gift X Dural Dreamtime. Rainbow Ridge 1999/2000.

DAINTY LACE (Bernard Pryor, R. 1999). Sdlg. 4/92A. LA, 48" (122 cm), M. Small ruffled white, yellow line signal on all petals; style arms white, lemon base. Twirling Ballerina X Obvious Heir.

DAINTY MORSEL (Ben Hager, R. 1993). Sdlg. MD5485TyTPch. MDB, 6" (15 cm), EM. Full apricot pink, deeper around tangerine beards. AMD4965CrY#1: ((Little You x (Inca Toy x (BU67 x Atomic Blue))) x Tiny Cherub) X MD4733PlOrW: (((Tiny Apricot x (((Prodigy x ((Red-Lilli x Pogo) x Regards)) x SD2562: (Pink Amber x Pink Cushion)) x AMD2873: (Buttercup Charm x SD2562))) x (MD2888SmY: (SD2562 x Buttercup Charm) x SD2873LtY)) x (Tiny Apricot x ((SD2562 x (Frosty Lemonade x Pink Cushion)) x MD2888SmY))). Adamgrove 1994.

DAISY JANE (Janet Hutchinson, R. 1998). Sdlg. MS/SL/D51. LA, 33-36" (84-92 cm), M. S. pale yellow; style arms green, pale yellow crests; F. pale yellow, rich yellow star signal over green veining; ruffled; slight fragrance. Marsha Sue X Soft Laughter. Rainbow Ridge 1999/2000.

DAISY'S DAISIES (John Gass, R. 1996). Sdlg. F-84-16. TB, 37" (94 cm), M. Ruffled and laced snow white self; beards yellow orange; slight sweet fragrance. Startler X unknown. Rainbow Chasers 1997.

DAKOTA MOON (Schreiner, R. 1992). Sdlg. S 947-B. TB, 36" (91 cm), EM. Lightly ruffled light yellow (RHS 8A), white in center of F.; beards gold. Moonstruck X Dream Affair. Schreiner 1992.

DAKOTA SHRIMP (C. T. Claussen, R. 1991). Sdlg. 82-70. TB, 33" (84 cm), M. Shrimp pink; beards bright coral. Dakota Treasure X Fashionable Pink. Wagontrail Acres 1992.

DALTON (Ken Durio, R. 1992). Sdlg. ARB-10. LA, 26" (66 cm), ML. S. light yellow, full red violet midrib stripe and veining; F. dark red violet, deeper veining, full gold signal. Ann Chowning X Bellevue's Michelle. Louisiana Nursery 1998.

DA LUS (Ladislav Muska, R. 1995). Sdlg. RTGB-01. TB, 40" (102 cm), ML. Heavily laced white with pinkish tint; beards tangerine; spicy fragrance. (Rapunzel's Tower x Glory Bound) X Beverly Sills. Muska 1994.

DAMFINO (Sharon McAllister, R. 1998). Sdlg. 90-15-1. AB (OGB), 28" (71 cm), M. S. soft greyed rose; style arms yellow, rose midrib and crests; F. blended greyed rose, apricot and rust, small near-black signal in middle of large burgundy spot; beards golden yellow. Hunt 14-4-R-POH-2: (Fourteen for Rachel x Pride of Haifa) X unknown.

DAMNATION (Lawrence Ransom, R. 1996). Sdlg. 90/321-23. SDB, 13" (33 cm), EM. Red purple bitone, blackish F. sheen; beards burnt orange, base lavender. Hushpuppy X Trescols. Iris au Trescols 1996.

DAMOISELLE (Lawrence Ransom, R. 1994). Sdlg. 87/174. TB, 34" (87 cm), M. S. light naples yellow; F. light garnet edged yellow, cream yellow shoulders veined sienna brown; beards light yellow, white base. Dream Lover X 85/13-1: (Vanity x Raspberry Ripples). Iris au Trescols 1997.

DAMON'S DELIGHT (J. Owings Rebert, R. 1999). Sdlg. CB-97-3. SIB, 29" (74 cm), E. Dark purple violet, slight signal. Parentage unknown.

DAMSEL KNIGHT (Hugh Knight by John Wood, R. 1990). Sdlg. K-101-86. JI (6 F.), 38" (96 cm), ML. White ground with 1/2"-3/4" blue violet (RHS 89C) border; white styles edged blue violet, feathered; ruffled. Parentage unknown. John Wood 1991.

DA NARDO (Bob Thomason, SDB, R. 1988). Okie Iris 1999.

DANCE FOR JOY (Monty Byers, R. 1991). Sdlg. E66-1. TB, 30" (76 cm), VE-EM & RE. S. smooth salmon and pearly orchid pink blend, suffusing to pale yellow edge; F. salmon pink overlaid with reddish orchid wash, heavier over hafts, lighter salmon yellow edge; beards bright orange red, with blended salmon and orchid spoon or flounce; heavily ruffled. C37-2: (Sky Hooks x Condottiere) X C6-3: (Spirit of Memphis x (Moon Mistress x D. Meek horned sdlg.)). Moonshine 1992.

DANCE HALL DANDY (William Maryott, R. 1994). Sdlg. T136N. TB, 38" (99 cm), M. S. white, flushed light pink at midrib, hint of cream at tip; F. velvety red maroon, 3/8" near-pink band; beards tangerine. Dance Hall Dolly X Costa Rica. Maryott 1996.

DANCE HALL DOLLY (William Maryott, R. 1991). Sdlg. L226A. TB, 38" (97 cm), M. S. light violet (RHS 84A); F. very deep maroon with bright 1/8" light violet band; beards bright orange; lightly laced. Ringo X Double Agent. Maryott 1993.

DANCE MASTER (Ken Mohr, R. 1992). TB, 34" (86 cm), M. S. blue, strongly flushed blue violet from midrib; F. medium to dark blue violet, paling below beard, texture-veined dark blue violet; beards lemon yellow. (Mystique x (Coolhead x Margarita)) X Mystic Waters sib. Pacific Coast Hybridizers 1992.

DANCE SUZY (Marty Schafer/Jan Sacks, R. 1999). Sdlg. S92-119-18. SIB, 28" (74 cm), EM. S. cream to light canary yellow (RHS 9D); style arms cream, aureolin yellow (12B) crests; F. aureolin yellow (12A/B), deepest in signal area. Careless Sally X S90-48-3: (S86-18-1: (Percheron x Butter and Sugar) x S86-18-2, sib). Joe Pye Weed 1999.

DANCES WITH WOLVES (Joanne Loop, R. 1991). Sdlg. 888-1. TB, 40" (102 cm), ML. S. terracotta maroon; F. velvety maroon with mahogany overlay; beards golden bronze. Speculator X Spectacular Bid. Cottage 1992.

DANCING AGAIN (John C. Taylor, R. 1994). Sdlg. RL 33-X. LA, 52" (103 cm), ML. Pink with greenish yellow line signal. Watch Out X Margaret Lee. Rainbow Ridge 1996/97.

DANCING BRIDESMAID (Lucille Pinkston, R. 1996). Sdlg. 88-2-B. TB, 33-34" (84-86 cm), ML. Ruffled and laced pinkish mauve, F. slightly lighter; style arms creamy mauve; beards white, yellow in throat; slight sweet fragrance. Playgirl X unknown. Sand Hollow 1997.

DANCING DEWDROP (Darrell Weikle, R. 1996). TB, 30" (76 cm), EM. Ruffled rich royal purple self; beards golden orange, tipped dark blue. Bubble Bath X Dark Triumph. Weikle's Wonderland 1996.

DANCING DIVA (Kerryn Turner, R. 1996). Sdlg. KH91-3-4. TB, 36" (91 cm), M. S. rose; F. plush burgundy rose, 1/4" lighter edge; beards tangerine orange. Bama Berry X Holiday Lover. Tempo Two 1996/97.

DANCING DRAGON (Leo Barnard, R. 1996). Sdlg. L 91-76. TB, 36" (91 cm), M. S. and style arms blended buttercream to light yellow; F. yellow overlaid buttercream, lighter cream edge; beards yellow, medium brown horn at tip; ruffled; slight sweet fragrance. Twice Thrilling X Borderline. Paradise Iris 1996.

DANCING FAWN (Francis Rogers, R. 1991). Sdlg. F-717-C. TB, 30" (76 cm), M. S. cream, lavender infusion; F. light yellow, white below beard, maroon plicata markings; beards golden yellow, tipped yellow; heavily ruffled and laced; sweet fragrance. F-120-C: ((Grand Waltz x Princess) x (Grand Waltz x Autumn Leaves)) X Rancho Rose. Meadowbrook 1993.

DANCING FOUNTAIN (Jim & Vicki Craig, R. 1990). Sdlg. 42V13. IB, 24" (61 cm), ML. S. blue white; F. light blue, medium blue spot, white area around beard; beards yellow, tipped white. Payoff X (((Enroute x Maroon Caper) x Whole Cloth) x (Chapeau x (Sacred Mountain x *I. aphylla*))). J. & V. Craig 1990.

DANCING IN PINK (Graeme Grosvenor, R. 1999). Sdlg. U32-1. TB, 35" (89 cm), EM. S. soft pink; F. pale pink; beards red, tipped pink; slight fragrance. Bubble Up X Dance Music.

DANCING SHADOWS (Anna Mae Miller, R. 1994). Sdlg. 80.17.1. SIB, 45" (114 cm), M. S. purple (RHS 93B); F. same, but velvety upper half appears darker, tiny white eye signal. 77.13.35, Dancing Nanou sib, X unknown. Ensata Gardens 1994.

DANCING VOGUE (John C. Taylor, R. 1991). Sdlg. OL 137-3. LA, 43" (110 cm), M. S. pink (RHS 65B); F. pink (65A), signal yellow. Dazzling Star X Helen Naish. Rainbow Ridge 1993/94.

DANDILITE (B. Charles Jenkins, R. 1994). Sdlg. BG34E. SPU, 42-49" (107-124 cm), EM. Ruffled yellow self; style arms aging to white along edge. Lively One X C712A: (Crow Wing x Medallion). Shepard Iris 1994.

DANDY'S HORNPIPE (Marty Schafer/Jan Sacks, R. 1999). Sdlg. S92-119-10. SIB, 29" (74 cm), M & RE. S. pale lavender (RHS 76C/D), some red violet (71A/B, 72A/B) veining; style arms pearly pale lavender blue, large, with aqua midrib; F. pale methyl violet (85C), dappled and veined red violet, undertoned pale yellow, sunset blaze of barium yellow (10B) veined dark red violet, yellow washing out onto F.; slight fragrance. Sib to Dance Suzy. Joe Pye Weed 1999.

DANGEROUS CURVES (Joe Saia, R. 1991). Sdlg. 86-5-7. TB, 36" (91 cm), ML. S. light blue; F. dark blue purple; beards bronze, tipped blue. Blazing Saddles X Bay Fog. Saia 1991.

DANGER ZONE (Calvin Helsley, R. 1990). Sdlg. 86-6. SIB, 30" (76 cm), M. Medium wine red, large white signal. Kismet X Thespian Helsley 1995.

DANIELLE (Marvin Granger, LA, R. 1988). Faggard 1991.

DANIEL THRUMAN (Daniel Thruman, R. 1997). Sdlg. 97-379. TB, 38" (97 cm), EM. S. yellow, tipped honey; style arms yellow; F. fluorescent grape purple, lined darker, purple veining on white shoulders, yellow marginal band; beards yellow gold; sweet fragrance. Afternoon Delight X Spinning Wheel.

DANNY'S SMILE (Connell Marsh, TB, R. 1983. C. Marsh 1990.

DANSELLON (Nora Scopes, TB, R. 1986). British Iris Society 1989.

DANUBE WALTZ (Hooker Nichols, R. 1990). Sdlg. 8856D. TB, 38" (97 cm), ML. S. blue; F. darker blue; beards yellow white; ruffled; pronounced fragrance. Sea of Galilee X Titan's Glory. Hillcrest 1994.

DARING (John C. Taylor, R. 1998). Sdlg. UL17-8. LA, 39" (100 cm), M. S. light pink, some marbling; style arms lemon; F. pink, signal yellow. Dancing Vogue X Dural White Butterfly.

DARINGLY DIFFERENT (Sharon McAllister, R. 1992). Sdlg. 86-11-4. AB (OGB+), 18" (47 cm), EM. S. pale lilac ground, edged tan, fine violet veining; style arms tan; F. white lilac ground washed tan around edge, heavy violet veins radiating from large velvety royal purple signal; beards yellow, tipped lilac. Ballalaika Music X Sunrise in Glory. McAllister 1993.

DARK AURA (Jennifer Hewitt, selector, R. 1996). SPEC-X, 42" (107 cm), ML. S. dark violet (RHS 88A); style arms reddish violet, paler edges; F. velvety dark violet (near 83A), light yellow (153B) signal edged white, dark veins; spring foliage dark red, stems intense black; slight sweet fragrance. Parentage unknown, inv. *I. virginica* and *I. versicolor*. Previously registered as VIRGINICA DE LUXE. Friesland Staudengarten 1986.

DARK ENCHANTMENT (William Ackerman, JI, R. 1984). Nicholls Garden 1988.

DARK FREEZE (Tom Burseen, R. 1997). Sdlg. 92-208A. TB, 35" (89 cm), M. S. red violet (RHS 86D); style arms dark red violet (86B); F. purple black (103A), red violet rim; beards cream, hairs tipped orange; pronounced musky fragrance. Mystic Magic X 8-324: (Bluid x Majestic Beauty). T.B.'s Place 1998.

DARK IDOL (Marvin Granger, LA, R. 1988). Faggard 1992.

DARK LOVER (John C. Taylor, R. 1994). Sdlg. RL 75-1. LA, 35" (88 cm), L. Purple, bright yellow rims and reverse, green line signal surrounded by yellow; style arms yellow, brushed violet. OL 142-A: ((C'est Si Bon x Charles Arny III) x Helen Naish) X Margaret Lee.

DARK MAUL (Glenn Stoneking-Jones, R. 1999). Sdlg. CIR6-54618-09-09-1999). TB, 36" (91 cm), EM. Black; beards orange red, with black horn and spoon; pronounced musky fragrance. ((Dusky Challenger x Art School Angel) x Spitfire) X (Hello Darkness x Art School Angel).

#DARKNESS (J. W. Magruder, TB, R. 1925). Listed as obsolete in 1939 Check List; name released 1992.

DARKNESS (Ben Hager, R. 1992). Sdlg. IB5004Bk. IB, 21" (53 cm), L. Near-black purple; beards bronze. T3923: (Sunday Punch x (Dark Ritual x Cairo Lyric)) X SD4440BkMr: (Combo x Toasty sib). Adamgrove 1993.

DARK OPAL (Hilmary Catton, R. 1978). Change of height and classification: SDB, 9" (22 cm). Wyuna Iris (Catton) 1978/79.

DARK PASSAGE (Darlene Pinegar, R. 1997). Sdlg. HY-1A. TB, 32" (81 cm), EML & RE. S. blackish maroon; style arms brownish maroon; F. near-black maroon, hafts gold, white area with dark maroon markings near beard; beards dark yellow to orange; ruffled; slight sweet fragrance. Harlem Hussy X Witch of Endor. Spanish Fork 1997.

DARK PASSION (Schreiner, R. 1998). Sdlg. CC 270-1. TB, 35" (89 cm), M. Ebony black (RHS 202A to 103A) self; beards black; lightly ruffled; pronounced sweet fragrance. AA 327-B: (Back in Black x Midnight Dancer) X W 484-2: (T 329-A: (((((Broadway Star x Whole Cloth) x Blue Mountains) x (Toll Gate x After Dark)) x ((Dream Time x ((Alpenrose x Anthem) x Gracie Pfost)) x (Skywatch x (Amethyst Flame x Silvertone)))) x (Master Touch x ((((Alpenrose x Anthem) x (Amethyst Flame x Melodrama)) x ((Alpenrose x Brigadoon) x (Amethyst Flame x Melodrama))) x Rondo))) x T 435-C: (Swazi Princess x Darkside sib)). Schreiner 1998.

DARK PAST (Jim Hedgecock, R. 1998). Sdlg. 85-58. TB, 30" (76 cm), ML. Ruffled red black, F. darker, with slight blue striations near beard; beards purple, burnt gold in throat; slight sweet fragrance. Shaft of Gold X Swazi Princess. Comanche Acres 1999.

DARK REFLECTION (Frederick Kerr, R. 1997). Sdlg. 916701A. IB, 24" (61 cm), E. S. white, wide light blue lavender band; style arms blue lavender, lip darker; F. white, narrow dark blue lavender edge, dark brown hafts; beards dark blue lavender, hairs tipped brown; slight sweet fragrance. Snowbrook X Chubby Cheeks. Rainbow Acres 1997.

DARK RINGS (Joseph Gatty by Keith Keppel, R. 1992). Sdlg. W37-8. SDB, 13" (33 cm), EM. S. white ground, 1/2" roslyn blue (M&P 44-I-12) border; beards pale blue at end, white with bronze-tipped hairs changing to sunflower (9-L-4) to deep chrome yellow (9-L-7) in throat; pronounced sweet fragrance. Chubby Cheeks X S48-4, Toy Clown sib. D & J Gardens 1993.

DARKTOWN STRUTTER'S BALL (Darlene Pinegar, R. 1993). Sdlg. AM-1-1-IB. TB, 33" (84 cm), ML. S. and style arms dark violet with taffeta texture; F. velvety darker violet, wine markings on whitish hafts; beards violet, yellow in throat; lightly ruffled; pronounced sweet fragrance. AM-1: (April Melody x Spinning Wheel) X Capricious. Spanish Fork 1994.

DARK TREASURE (Opal Brown, R. 1993). Sdlg. 90-1D5. TB, 36-38" (91-97 cm), M. Ruffled deep red purple, beards tangerine. Persian Gown X Ever After. Brown's Sunnyhill 1993.

DARK TWILIGHT (Ronald Beattie, R. 1992). Sdlg. 84-5. TB, 38" (97 cm), ML. Blend of claret purple, cerise, fuchsia red and violet, faintly touched copper; beards violet brown. (Post Time x Ponderosa) X Cranberry Ice. Fleur de Lis 1992.

DARK WATERS (J. T. Aitken, R. 1992). Sdlg. 86-IB-2-6. IB, 26" (66 cm), ML. Ruffled deep violet; beards light violet, tipped mustard. (Clay's Caper x Stockholm) X Gyro. Aitken's Salmon Creek 1992.

DARLENE JO (Roy Bohrer, R. 1992). Sdlg. 82-30B. TB, 30" (76 cm), M. S. mauve, lavender midrib; F. mauve, yellow hafts and edge; beards orange; slight sweet fragrance. Symphonette X Sheer Poetry. Bohrer's Iris 1992.

DARLEY DALE (B.L.C. Dodsworth, R. 1998). Sdlg. EB 91 U. TB, 42" (107 cm), M. Ruffled white, F. with yellow hafts; beards yellow; ruffled; pronounced fragrance. Early Light X Jill Rosalind.

DARLING DOLLY (Barbara Wight, R. 1996). Sdlg. 91-38. TB, 32" (81 cm), EM. Lavender (RHS 92D), paling with age, sheen on petal edges; beards bright orange tipped lavender, wide; slight sweet fragrance. Marsh Light X Orange Laced Gown. Wight's Iris 1997.

DARLING WHO KNOWS (Luella Danielson, R. 1997). Sdlg. 77-1 L. AB (OGB+), 16" (41 cm), M. S. soft cream ground with dense bright canary yellow veining, bright yellow margin, midrib apple green; style arms bright yellow; F. soft cream, rust brown ray pattern and signal, dense bright canary yellow veining, bright yellow margin; beards bright yellow. Tel Hashi X unknown. Pleasure Iris 1998.

DARNELLA (Jim Hedgecock, R. 1990). Sdlg. 84-55-2. TB, 34" (86 cm), M. S. burnt yellow, chartreuse hint; F. laced and fluted chartreuse, prominent blue blaze; beards gold, 1/2" light purple horn; ruffled; slight spicy fragrance. Sky Hooks X Superstition. Comanche Acres 1991.

DARTS (Monty Byers, IB, R. 1989). Moonshine 1990.

DASHING (Monty Byers, R. 1990). Sdlg. D164-112. TB, 36" (91 cm), EM & RE. S. medium deep purple; F. same, infused reddish violet, lighter area around blue beard; ruffled; slight sweet fragrance. Violet Miracle X B-8-4: (Cease-Fire x Sky Hooks). Moonshine 1991.

DAUBER'S DELIGHT (Manley Osborne by George Sutton, R. 1991). Sdlg. 6-7C3. TB, 36" (91 cm), M. Light blue; beards whitish blue with blue flounce; slight fragrance. Wedding Vow X 1-43: (Rococo x (Miz Lib x Unicorn)). Sutton 1991.

DAUBER'S SURPRISE (George Sutton, R. 1997). Sdlg. A-92 ARISA. TB, 34" (86 cm), EM. S. and style arms pallid lavender; F. violet (RHS 86C); beards antique gold, 2" feathery flounce; ruffled; slight sweet fragrance. Dauber's Delight X Sky Hooks. Sutton 1998.

DAURIYA (Galina Zinoviyeva, R. 1998). Sdlg. 543-2. MTB, 24" (60 cm), M. S. rose, veined darker; style arms pinkish rose; F. brick red, yellow hafts and whitish area veined brown near dark yellow beard; ruffled. Orelio X Maroon Caper. Zabaykalsi 1998.

DAVID CHAPMAN (Cy Bartlett, R. 1990). Sdlg. BE-W1. TB, 36" (91 cm), ML. S. white; F. sky blue, paler by white to cream beard; ruffled. Blue Epaulettes X Wensleydale. V. H. Humphrey 1995.

DAVID KEITH (J. D. Stadler, R. 1990). Sdlg. L14/41. TB, 35" (89 cm), ML. Maroon black; self beards; slight sweet fragrance. Holy Night X Superstition. Celestial Gardens 1991.

DAVID ROY (Janet Bench, R. 1992). Sdlg. 89-U01. TB, 36" (91 cm), VE. S. violet blue (RHS 92C); F. velvety deep violet blue (86A to 89A), slightly lighter toward edge; beards mustard yellow, tipped blue; ruffled; spathes edged and washed red violet; pronounced musky fragrance. Point Made X Honky Tonk Blues.

DAVID'S LAMP (Lois Rich by James Whitely, R. 1994). Sdlg. R80-29D. AR (RC), 6" (15 cm), M. S. white ground veined light orchid; F. cream ground very heavily veined chocolate, dark teardrop signal; dark beards. R69-186B: (Persian Embroidery x (Judean Charmer x Judean Cream)) X R75-245A: ((((K56-4J x *I. lortetii*) x (Kerr "Bronze" x K53-44WF)) x ((Clark-Austin W-159 x 513-OY) x (Judean Cream x OY-164))) x (Ulysses x Clark 63-C20: ((K55-1 x K55-114) x (*I. susiana* x Judean Cream)))). Aril Patch 1994.

DA VINCI (Tony Huber, R. 1992). Sdlg. 1DM-Bar-04. SPEC (*versicolor*), 27½" (70 cm), E. S. violet (RHS 93B); F. deep violet (89A), large white center veined dark violet, bright yellow signal veined violet. Collected in wild, Magdalen Island, Quebec, Canada.

DAVY JONES (Ben Hager, TB, R. 1988). Melrose 1990.

DAWN FAVOUR (Eva Soper, SDB, R. 1960). V. H. Humphrey 1993.

DAWN HAWK (George Sutton, R. 1996). Sdlg. G-80A. SPU, 56" (142 cm), M. S. blended cream and white; style arms white; F. saffron yellow (RHS 19A), edged white; ruffled. Snow Hawk X Dawn Candle. Sutton 1999.

DAWNING (Joseph Ghio, R. 1994). Sdlg. 90-100-J2. TB, 38" (97 cm), EM. S. lemon, blended pink; F. lemon, blending to pink shoulders; beards tangerine. 88-151-A2: ((Esmeralda sib x Montevideo) x Peach Bisque) X 87-43gr: (Mogul sib x Black Hills Gold). Bay View 1995.

DAWNING MOON (Eric & Bob Tankesley-Clarke, R. 1994). Sdlg. 240A-A. SDB, 9" (23 cm), ML. S. and style arms pale cream yellow; F. cream white; beards cream yellow; slight sweet fragrance. Starlight Waltz X Dixie Pixie. Adamgrove 1994.

DAWN LILT (Lin Flanagan, R. 1992). Sdlg. 84007-1. AB (OGB-), 28" (71 cm), M. S. pale violet blended amber; F. dark red with distinct golden yellow rim; beards orange brown; ruffled; slight fragrance. Kilt Lilt X Dawn Victory. Aril Society 1994.

DAWN OF CHANGE (Richard Ernst, R. 1993). Sdlg. G106-1. TB, 38" (97 cm), M. S. light lavender blue, paling to near-white at edge; style arms with yellow highlights; F. white with golden yellow shoulders; beards orange, tipped light yellow; ruffled; slight sweet fragrance. Hula Girl X self. Cooley 1993.

DAWN PRINCESS (David Johnson, R. 1995). Sdlg. DJ-410. SDB, 11½" (29 cm), ML. S. orchid pink, dusted gold near midrib; style arms lavender blue, crests pink; F. orchid pink, faint gold halo around beard, more prominent on shoulders; beards white at end, gold to tangerine in throat; slight sweet fragrance. Kirsten Marie X Flirty Mary. Riverdale 1995.

DAWN SHADOWS (Nora Scopes, R. 1994). Sdlg. 9S143A. TB, 38" (97 cm), ML. S. pale apricot; F. pale pinkish mauve deepening at edge; beards red orange; ruffled; sweet fragrance. China Seas X 3/179, China Seas sib.

DAWN SKY (Keith Keppel, R. 1991). Sdlg. 86-25A. TB, 30" (76 cm), E. S. lavender pink (M&P 51/52-C-1); F. creamy pink to ivory ground (9-AB-1/2), 3/8" hyssop violet (44-G-7) margin; beards flamingo (2-I-11), tipped candy pink (2-H-10). 81-259J: (77-101A: (((Roundup sib x April Melody) x Osage Buff) x ((68-39D: (((Irma Melrose x Tea Apron) x ((Full Circle x Rococo) x Tea Apron)) x April Melody) x 68-40B, sib) x Osage Buff)) x 77-71A: ((Pink Taffeta x (Roundup sib x April Melody)) x Pink Confetti)) X 79-47A: (Goddess x 77-137F: (Mistress sib x ((Joy Ride x Roundup) x (April Melody x 68-40B)))). Keppel 1992.

DAWN SPLENDOUR (Beryl Pederick, R. 1994). Sdlg. 2. TB, 36" (91 cm), E. Dawn pink (HCC 523/3), brown hafts; beards orange; slight fragrance. Pink Angel X Heather Blush.

DAWN WALTZ (Marty Schafer/Jan Sacks, R. 1998). Sdlg. S92-75-2. SIB, 27" (69 cm), EM. S. smooth light pinkish lavender (RHS 85D/C), some darker (86D) veining; style arms pearly white, green midrib in heart, crests curled; F. slightly deeper pinkish lavender (85B), shaded and veined darker (86D), signal apple green on white with lavender veining; ruffled. S89-16-1: (Reprise x Mad Magenta) X S89-9-2: (Isabelle x Silver Illusion). Joe Pye Weed 1998.

DAYETT'S ROYALTY (Louise Smith, R. 1991). Sdlg. 78-14. TB, 32" (81 cm), EM. Deep purple; beards purple, tipped gold; slight sweet fragrance. Parentage unknown.

DAY GLOW (Keith Keppel, R. 1996). Sdlg. 89-110A. TB, 36" (91 cm), EM. S. pinkish apricot (M&P 9-F-6 to 9-D-7); style arms slightly deeper (9-G-7); F. pinkish apricot (9-I-6 to 9-F-5); beards tigerlily (1-F-11) to fire red (1-F-12); slight fragrance. 79-57B: (75-38A: ((((Frances Kent x Mary Randall) x 60-183Q: (Sexton 60: (Gail x Techny Chimes) x Golden Gene) x (Denver Mint x 60-183-O)) x (Radiant Light x (((Golden Gleam x Hallmark) x Sexton 60) x 60-183A)) x Orange Fire) x Orangerie) X Champagne Wishes. Keppel 1997.

DAZZLING DOMINIQUE (A. & D. Willott, R. 1993). Sdlg. 88-35. SDB, 12" (35 cm), EM. Lightly ruffled bright pink, flushed and veined apricot around beard; beards coral, lighter at end. 84-90: (Apricot Elf x Coral Wings) X Ballet Slippers. Willott 1993.

DAZZLING LORA (Donald Spoon, R. 1995). Sdlg. 89-51. TB, 33" (84 cm), ML. Radiant yellow (RHS 8D), F. with white area around darker yellow (8B) beard; style arms radiant yellow (8C); slight spicy fragrance. Lora Kathleen X Dazzling Gold. Winterberry 1995.

DAZZLING WATERS (Albert Faggard, LA, R. 1988). Faggard 1992.

DEAD RINGER (Joseph Ghio, R. 1998). Sdlg. PD-235K2. CA, 15" (38 cm), EM. S. red, gold halo edging; style arms gold; F. red, gold halo edging, black signal. PF-170E2, Battle Alert sib, X PF-155B2: (PI-MIX-S, unknown, x (Santa Cruz Beach x (Refugio x ((Simply Wild x Camp Capitola sib) x (Big Wheel x California Mystique))))). Bay View 1998.

DEANNA FAYE (J. Owings Rebert, R. 1996). Sdlg. UG-2. SIB, 28" (71 cm), M. S. light violet blue, short; F. light violet blue, cream haft markings. Parentage unknown.

DEAR JEAN (Frederick Kerr, R. 1996). Sdlg. 91-11-03. TB, 38" (97 cm), M. S. bright yellow; F. white, extensive golden yellow hafts, wide diffuse red edge; beards dark yellow; ruffled. 88-17-13: (Edith Wolford x Lullaby of Spring) X 88-08-03: (Alpine Castle x Gypsy Woman). Rainbow Acres 1996.

DEARLY BELOVED (A. & D. Willott, R. 1993). Sdlg. 93-85. TB, 35" (89 cm), EM. S. light pink; F. light peach pink, center lighter; beards soft orange; heavily ruffled, lightly laced. Master Gardener X Anna Belle Babson. Willott 1994.

DEAR MIN (Stan Dexter by Marie Ingersoll, R. 1990). Sdlg. 1981/46C. TB, 36" (91 cm), ML. S. pale lemon yellow; F. near cream; beards yellow, tipped white; ruffled; pronounced sweet fragrance. Leda's Lover X Condottiere. Ingersoll's Iris 1991.

DEBBENNIE KAYLYN (Darlene Pinegar, R. 1997). Sdlg. AC-93-232B. TB, 31" (79 cm), ML. S. medium orange, shaded pink; style arms yellow orange; F. medium orange at hafts, blending to yellow orange, with large white center; beards deep orange; ruffled, laced; slight sweet fragrance. Aphrodisiac X Fringe Benefits. Spanish Fork 1998.

DEBBIE REYNOLDS (Oscar Schick, R. 1995). Sdlg. 90-19G02. TB, 34" (86 cm), ML. S. and style arms peach-tinted light pink (RHS 36C); F. peach-tinted light pink edge, lightening toward center; beards light pink; heavily ruffled and laced; slight sweet fragrance. Femme Fatale X Sue Ellen. Stockton 1996.

DEBRENEE (William Maryott, R. 1994). Sdlg. S195C. TB, 36" (91 cm), EM. S. light lavender with hint of pink; F. smooth medium violet maroon; beards tangerine; sweet fragrance. Mariachi Music X Twice Told. Maryott 1995.

DEB'S DELIGHT (David Hall by Philip Edinger, R. 1999). Sdlg. 42-25. TB, 40" (107 cm), M. Light peach pink; beards tangerine. 40-34: (38-26: (36-11: (W. R. Dykes x Dolly Madison) x

Morocco Rose) x 35-40: (Dauntless x Rameses)) X 39-62: (36-01: (W. R. Dykes x Dolly Madison) x Morocco Rose). Topnotch 1946.

DEB SUNSHINE (Everette Lineberger, R. 1999). Sdlg. QHT 135. TB, 33" (84 cm), EM & RE. S. golden yellow; F. cream white, golden shoulders, reverse yellow; beards golden yellow; slight sweet fragrance. Limelighter X Lilac Champagne.

DEBUTANTE BALL (Jim & Vicki Craig, R. 1990). Sdlg. 55T70. TB, 39" (100 cm), L. White ground plicata stitched pale lavender, medium yellow band on serrate edge; style arms yellow; beards light yellow, tipped pale lavender. (Odyssey x (Coral Glow x New Moon)) X Rancho Rose. J. & V. Craig 1990.

DEBUTANTE'S KISS (Barry Blyth, R. 1998). Sdlg. D54-1. TB, 38" (96 cm), ML. White self, buds tinted lilac; beards bright mustard yellow. Silent One X Cafe Risque. Tempo Two 1998/99.

DECIPHER (Joseph Ghio, R. 1995). Sdlg. 90-61H. TB, 32" (81 cm), ML. S. rosy lavender; F. white ground, washed and lined rosy lavender; beards dark tangerine. Storyteller X 87-7K: (((((Handiwork x (Gay Parasol x Mystique)) x Goddess) x (Gem of Sierra x ((((Ponderosa x Honey Rae)) x (((Commentary x Claudia Rene) x Claudia Rene) x (Ponderosa x New Moon))) x Osage Buff) x (Vanity x Anon)))) x Gigolo) x (Desert Fox x Shenanigan)). Bay View 1996.

DECKER (Mitch Jameson, R. 1998). Sdlg. 1-92. TB, 36" (91 cm), EM & RE. S. white ground, heavily marked mulberry; style arms mulberry, gold and white; F. white, heavy mulberry border, edged deeper; beards gold and mulberry. Tennison Ridge X Colorwatch.

DECORATED ARTIFACT (Terrell Taylor, R. 1996). Sdlg. 94-2. TB, 32" (81 cm), E. S. cream ground overlaid ruby red (RHS 59A) plicata infusion; F. ruby red stitching and dotting on cream, yellow to either side of gold beard; lightly ruffled; musky fragrance. Thunder Echo X Jitterbug. Hermosa Gardens 1996.

DECORY WIN (Ladislav Muska, R. 1995). Sdlg. LWLM-03. TB, 38" (97 cm), M. S. light cream-nut; F. light lavender, light nut brown edge; beards tangerine, long lavender spoon; heavily ruffled. Louise Watts X (Sky Hooks x Lady Madonna). Muska 1994.

DEEN DAY SMITH (Michael Moller, R. 1998). Sdlg. 00WOB-1. TB, 36" (91 cm), M. Orange buff (RHS 22B), F. with white flash below bright orange beard. Orange Jewelius X Punkin Patch.

DEEP BLUE SEA (Joseph Ghio, R. 1991). Sdlg. PI-178B3. CA, 20" (51 cm), L. Deep royal blue, small white signal. Miramar X Idylwild. Bay View 1992.

DEEP DARK SECRET (Paul Black, R. 1998). Sdlg. A26C. TB, 34" (86 cm), M. S. dark blue purple, waxy sheen, blending to medium violet blue edge; style arms medium violet blue; F. dark blue purple, pale violet white diffused band, darker plum brown hafts; beards gold; heavily ruffled; pronounced sweet fragrance. In Town X Witches' Sabbath. Mid-America 1998.

DEEP MAGIC (Lois Belardi, R. 1998). Sdlg. DBM-95. CA, 14" (36 cm), M. Ruffled deep royal purple self, metallic sheen, deepening at heart of F. Marine Magic X Deep Blue Sea. Bay View 1998.

DEEP SEA QUEST (Heather Pryor, R. 1998). Sdlg. 25/91-D. LA, 39" (100 cm), M. Violet blue (RHS 93A), petal reverse white, F. with bright yellow signal area, golden steeple signal; style arms white, violet blue tip. Koorawatha X Sea Lord. Lone Star 1998.

DEGAS DANCER (Schreiner, R. 1994). Sdlg. W 515-D. TB, 36" (91 cm), EM. S. white (RHS 155C); F. white ground with 1/2" lavender violet plicata edge; beards yellow; ruffled. R 892-F, On Edge sib, X P 643-B: (Closed Circuit x Focus). Schreiner 1994.

DEIRDRE KAY (Marvin Granger, R. 1990). Sdlg. 82-6. LA, 24" (61 cm), M. S. light lilac lavender with hints of pink on edge; F. lilac lavender with hints of pink, diffused cream sunburst ray pattern spraying out from light greenish yellow signal; ruffled, laced and crimped; slight fragrance. BR77-23: (69-1: ((BQ64-24 x Louisiana Sambo) x King of Clubs) x Charlie's Michele) X 75-15, unknown. Faggard 1991.

DEKAMERON (Sergey Loktev, R. 1999). Sdlg. 94-R14D-L4. TB, 34" (87 cm), EM. S. and style arms cream pink; F. cream rose, small cream pink spot below tangerine beard. (Halo in Pink x Coral Bracelet) X unknown.

DEKHO (Lawrence Ransom, R. 1992). Sdlg. 86/49-2. MDB, 6" (15 cm), M. S. yellow green, greyed purple near base; F. maroon, edged copper brown; beards blue white, hairs tipped mustard. Hocus Pocus X Eyebright. Iris au Trescols 1993.

DELBINO (Lorena Reid, R. 1998). Sdlg. (8S54-1B3)opG92-2G. SIB (sino-sib), 36-40" (91-107cm), L. S. palest ivory, narrow; style arms pale lemon yellow; F. light gold throat (signal) shading gradually to very pale lemon cream edge. 8S54-1B3: (Enbee Deeaych x yellow *delavayi* hybrid #1) X unknown. Laurie's Garden 1998.

DELERAINE (John C. Taylor, R. 1997). Sdlg. SL 76-1. LA, 43" (110 cm), ML. Ruffled white, yellow green veining, green yellow signal on F.; style arms cream. Jazz Ballet X Dural White Butterfly. Rainbow Ridge 1997/98.

DELICATE EMBROIDERY (Sharon McAllister, R. 1992). Sdlg. 87-3-8. AB (OGB+), 28" (72 cm), EM. S. amethyst violet, veined darker, more intense at edge; F. amethyst pink, burgundy dotting and veining more intense in triangular area around beard, signal deep burgundy; beards mustard, tipped burgundy. My Joy X 79-2: (*I. calcarea* x *I. yebrudii v. edgecombii*). McAllister 1993.

DELICATE LADY (Cy Bartlett, R. 1996). Sdlg. C93-8. IB, 20" (51 cm), EM. S. white; F. sky blue, rimmed white; beards white, cream and yellow; lightly ruffled, waved. (Diligence x Eyebright) X Arden sib.

DELICATE TOUCH (Ben Hager, TB, R. 1989). Roris 1991.

DELIGHTFUL STRANGER (Betty Wilkerson, R. 1996). Sdlg. F25-1. TB, 36" (91 cm), L. S. and style arms capri blue (RHS 120C); F. dark royal blue (105A); beards orange. Feedback X Magic Man. Bridge in Time 1996.

DELIGHTSUM (Don Nebeker, R. 1997). Sdlg. 917-4. TB, 40" (107 cm), ML. S. bright white; style arms white, touched violet; F. white, wide washed light veronica violet margin; beards tangerine, white at end; slight fragrance. 683-23: (N 513: (Swan Ballet x Emma Cook) x N 515 T: (((Gold Ruffles x Party Dress) x Clara B.) x Emma Cook)) X Condottiere. Zebra 1997.

DELIRIUM (Marky Smith, R. 1999). Sdlg. 95-27W. IB, 27" (69 cm), EM. S. smoked gold (greyer than RHS 162A); style arms cream rib, gold crests; F. greyed gold rim and veins, dark red violet (greyer than 187A) overlay, hafts gold to smoked salmon around beard; beards greyed orange (170) at end, vermilion (34A) in throat; ruffled, edges crinkled; pronounced sweet fragrance. Flights of Fancy X Brash.

DEL RIO (John Gass, TB, R. 1989). Rainbow Chasers 1997.

DELTA BLUES (Schreiner, R. 1994). Sdlg. Y 952-A. TB, 36" (91 cm), M. Heavily ruffled light blue (RHS 97A); beards yellow, tipped white. Breakers X Tide's In. Schreiner 1994.

DELTAPLANE (Richard Cayeux, R. 1993). Sdlg. 8362 A. TB, 35" (89 cm), ML. S. white; F. bright indigo blue; beards bronze. Night Edition X Condottiere. Cayeux 1991.

DELTA TWILIGHT (Mary Dunn, R. 1995). Sdlg. L174-3. LA, 36" (91 cm), M. Blended lilac, blue, grey and mauve, F. with greenish veins and green signal; style arms green. Fat Tuesday X Cammeray. Bay View 1996.

DEMELZA (R. E. Nichol, TB, R. 1984). British Iris Society 1987.

DEMI ET DEMI (George Sutton, R. 1995). Sdlg. B-498A. TB, 34" (86 cm), ML. Pale blue self; style arms speckled black bronze; beards black bronze to dark blue bronze; ruffled. (Silkwood x Pinch of Spice) X Skating Party. Sutton 1995.

DENALI (Marky Smith, R. 1999). Sdlg. 94-30A. SDB, 11" (28 cm), EML. S. white (RHS 155D), chartreuse green midrib, faint violet veining at tip; style arms cream white (158D); F. white ground, greyed by violet blue (near 93D) veins, small violet (93B) halo below beard, white hafts tinted yellow; beards cream at end changing to yellow, orange in throat; ruffled; pronounced spicy fragrance. 91-30A: (89-52D, white glaciata Ming sib, x Rosie Lulu) X 92-19A: (Muppet Madness x Gemstar).

DENNIS RAYMOND (Clyde & Anna Hahn, R. 1996). Sdlg. 91-12-C. TB, 34" (86 cm), EM. Dark purple self; beards blue, tipped orange; slight sweet fragrance. Midnight Fragrance X (Sailor's Dance x Swazi Princess). Hahn's Rainbow 1996.

DENVER DELIGHT (Frank Foster, R. 1995). Sdlg. 89-30/BLD. TB, 35" (89 cm), M. Ruffled dark blue self; beards cream white; slight musky fragrance. (Valley West x (Millrace x Valley West)) X His Lordship.

DENVER ZEPHYR (Robert Jeffries, TB, R. 1989). Kansas Rainbow 1990.

DENYS HUMPHREY (Cy Bartlett, R. 1992). Sdlg. JP-JT. TB, 34" (86 cm), ML. Light buttery cream, F. paling toward center; beards pale cream; ruffled; slight sweet fragrance. Jeanne Price X Joyce Terry. Sutton, V. H. Humphrey 1995.

DEPARTURE (Jim & Vicki Craig, R. 1994). Sdlg. C63X16. IB, 24" (61 cm), L. Heavily ruffled white self; beards white, light yellow in throat; pronounced sweet fragrance. Hager AMT3798WhSh, sib to Little Me, X 11V3: (2R13, Little Stylist sib, x 11R24, Reformation sib). J. & V. Craig 1996.

DERBY BOY (A. & D. Willott, R. 1995). Sdlg. 91-89. MDB, 7½" (19 cm), ML. Lightly ruffled medium yellow, F. with large red brown spot; beards blue white. Dark Vader X What Not. Willott 1995.

DERIVE (Pierre Anfosso, R. 1991). Sdlg. P 84 A. SDB, 10" (25 cm), E. S. warm white washed mauve in heart; F. tan brown, edged warm white; beards mauve blue. (Petite Fugue x Pulcinella) X Capricornia. Iris en Provence 1991.

DERRY DOWN (Nora Scopes, R. 1979). British Iris Society 1987.

DESCANSO (Glenn Corlew, R. 1995). Sdlg. 1291-A. TB, 36" (91 cm), M. Medium pink self, slightly lighter in center of F.; beards bright tangerine, prominent. Elsiemae Nicholson X Easter Song. Cooley 1996.

DESERT ATTIRE (Howard Shockey by Irene Shockey, R. 1997). Sdlg. 92-112-BB; AB (OGB), 24" (60 cm), M. S. violet, darker small veining, deeper violet basal blush; style arms light yellow tan, midrib violet; F. light tan, shoulders light rose violet, deeper blush on lower half of F., large ruby signal with darker center; beards yellow, hairs tipped lighter. 90-112-BY: (Seraph's Jewel x Queen Sheba) X 89-114-B: ((((79-105H: (Stars Over Chicago x Welcome Reward) x Syrian Moon) x (Heart Stealer x 79-105-C)) x Onlooker) x ((79-105-C x Desert Princess) x (Heart Stealer x (Heart Stealer x Kalifa Gulnare)))). Aril Society 1997.

DESERT CELEBRATION (Lin Flanagan, R. 1994). Sdlg. 90018-1. AB (OGB-), 26" (66 cm), M. S. light violet; style arms golden amber; F. light golden tan, darker streak extending from brown orange beard; ruffled, semi-flared. New Moon X 85035-4: ((((Bethlehem Song x (Dove Song x Kalifa Hirfa)) x Esther's Son) x (Shifting Sands x unknown)) x (Dune Shadows x New Moon)). Aril Society 1996.

DESERT CLOUD (Lois Rich by James Whitely, R. 1991). Sdlg. R66-15C. AB (OGB+), 29" (74 cm), M. S. white veined pale violet; style arms color of F.; F. white with orchid overlay, edged white, widely spaced pale orchid veining, mulberry wine signal; beards brown, wide; diamond- dusted. (Thor x W83-D) X (Wilkes M65 x M624-D). Aril Patch, Aril Society 1991.

DESERT COUNTRY (Barry Blyth, R. 1996). Sdlg. B33-2. SDB, 14" (36 cm), EML. S. tan orange; F. tan orange, slightly deeper near beard, small lavender chevron; beards burnt tangerine, end lavender blue. Z14-1: (X25-4, Impish sib, x V17-8, Camarilla sib) X Z24-1, Volts sib. Tempo Two 1996/97.

DESERT DAYBREAK (David Miller, R. 1998). Sdlg. 93-20C. TB, 33" (84 cm), E. S. bronze yellow (RHS 162A), slight rose brown midrib; style arms bronze; F. rose brown (176B), flushed pale lavender, aging blended golden brown; beards golden bronze; slight musky fragrance. 86-6A: (81-1B: (Dutch Chocolate x Sandberry) x Henna Accent) X Canyon de Chelly. Long 1999.

DESERT DOODLE (Polly Black, R. 1990). Sdlg. GPSBG2. TB, 36" (91 cm), M. Lightly ruffled greenish yellow, F. splashed with maroon stripes; beards yellow; slight fragrance. Striped Butterfly X Green Hat. Polly Black, Pleasure Iris 1991.

DESERT FESTIVAL (Lin Flanagan, R. 1994). Sdlg. 89026-1. AB (OGB-), 26" (66 cm), E. S. pale violet; style arms violet; F. golden tan, blended violet, with darker rays extending from throat; beards pale orange grey; ruffled; F. semi-recurved. Close Contact X New Moon. Aril Society 1996.

DESERT FINERY (Lois Rich by James Whitely, R. 1990). Sdlg. R79-156C. AB (OGB), 23" (58 cm), ML. S. violet, veined dark purple; style arms tan violet; F. rose violet, evenly spaced violet veins from burgundy wine signal to edge; beards light yellow orange; ruffled, fluted. R76-83A: ((R69-203L x Garden Gold) x (Bethlehem Star x aril sdlg.)) X R73-176H (am): ((R69-108A x Welcome Reward) x (Welcome Reward x RR64-23A)). Aril Patch, Aril Society 1990.

DESERT FURY (Howard Shockey, R. 1994). Sdlg. 90-114-A. AB (OGB), 30" (76 cm), M. Dark mulberry red, F. with very broad, diffused red black signal with dark red lower band; beards dark red; slight musky fragrance. Red Sands X 85-104-7B: (Quinta x Heart Stealer). Arilian Acres 1994.

DESERT GALA (Lin Flanagan, R. 1994). Sdlg. 90051-1. AB (OGB-), 24" (61 cm), M. S. golden tan; style arms yellow; F. golden tan, darker red center wash, recurved; beards dark orange; ruffled. 83034: (Distant Mirage x Sky and Earth) X Dazzling Gold. Aril Society 1996.

DESERT JEWEL (John C. Taylor, R. 1991). Sdlg. OL 99-1. LA, 39" (100 cm), M. Brown gold (RHS 167A/168D), S. marbled gold. Edith Fear X Handmaiden. Rainbow Ridge 1992/93.

DESERT JOY (Lin Flanagan, R. 1994). Sdlg. 90013-2. AB (OGB-), 26" (66 cm), E. S. pale violet blended grey; style arms buff grey; F. rosy buff blend; beards dark brown orange; ruffled, semi-flared. 82070-1: ((Distant Mirage x unknown) x (Thunderstorm x Mayfest)) X 85035-4: ((((Bethlehem Song x (Dove Song x Kalifa Hirfa)) x Esther's Son) x (Shifting Sands x unknown)) x (Dune Shadows x New Moon)). Aril Society 1996.

DESERT JUBILEE (Lin Flanagan, R. 1994). Sdlg. 90055-1. AB (OGB-), 24" (61 cm), M. S. and style arms deep golden yellow; F. rich golden yellow, smooth red brown wash over upper third, semi-recurved; beards brown; lightly ruffled. 83040: ((Esther's Son x (Esther the Queen x ((Nomohr x Sundt 5656D) x Dove Song))) x Warrior's Mantle) X Dazzling Gold. Aril Society 1996.

DESERT LULLABY (Frederick Kerr, R. 1995). Sdlg. 90-33-04. TB, 40" (107 cm), ML. S. dusky blue violet, center lighter; F. light dusky blue violet, darker center stripe area, golden brown hafts, wide diffuse honey tan border; beards yellow, blue at end; ruffled. Collage X Kevin's Theme. Rainbow Acres 1995.

DESERT MAJESTY (Lin Flanagan, R. 1997). Sdlg. 97-B. AB (OGB), 26" (66 cm), E. S. light violet; style arms violet; F. rosy tan, smooth dark red brown signal, semi-recurved; beards black. Parentage unknown. Aril Society 1998.

DESERT MELODY (Lin Flanagan, AB, R. 1989). Aril Society 1990.

DESERT MOONLIGHT (Lois Rich by James Whitely, R. 1990). Sdlg. 77-115B. AB (OGB), 25" (64 cm), ML. S. fluted white; style arms bright yellow; F. bright lemon yellow, henna brown signal; beards yellow orange. R73-59: (R69-203L, onco bybrid, x Garden Gold) X R73-176H: ((R69-108A: (onco x TB) x Welcome Reward) x (Welcome Reward x RR64-23A: (onco x AB))). Aril Patch 1990.

DESERT MYSTERY (Darlene Pinegar, R. 1990). Sdlg. KL-2-1. TB, 29" (74 cm), M. Ruffled medium red purple, heavily laced tan edge, yellow haft markings; beards deep yellow. Kilt Lilt X Moon Mistress. Spanish Fork 1992.

DESERT ORANGE (Bennett Jones, R. 1992). Sdlg. 451R. SDB, 12" (30 cm), M. Tailored coral orange; beards red. 415: (378: (352: ((Melon Honey x Wright L32) x ((Roberts 65R11 x 201) x Melon Honey)) x Pumpkin Center) x Orange Dazzler sib) X Orange Dazzler. Bennett Jones 1993.

DESERT PANSY (John Wight, AB, R. 1988). Aril Society 1990.

DESERT PASSION (Larry Lauer, R. 1999). Sdlg. 88-71-2. TB, 34" (86 cm), ML. S. magenta rose; style arms bronze yellow; F. violet purple, golden buff rim; beards saffron yellow; ruffled; pronounced musky fragrance. L85-2-2: (Feminine Wiles x Wedding Party) X Arabian Tapestry. Lauer's Flowers 1999.

DESERT PEACE (James Burch, R. 1994). Sdlg. 48-20. TB, 42" (107 cm), ML. Reddish purple (RHS 59A) self; beards red (42A). Torch Parade X Starstruck. Comanche Acres 1995.

DESERT PLUM (Ben Hager, R. 1991). Sdlg. AR4170LvMvSlk. AB (OGB), 34" (86 cm), ML. Smoky mauve purple, silky texture, black maroon signal; beards bronze black. AR3498: (Syrian Moon x Rich 73-176D: (((Bagdad Beauty x Pink Formal) x Welcome Reward) x (Welcome Reward x ((Bagdad Beauty x Orchid and Flame) x Kalifa Hirfa)))) X AR3379: ((Bethlehem Song x Welcome Reward) x Moon Star). Aril Patch 1992.

DESERT RENEGADE (Richard Ernst, R. 1993). Sdlg. F125-10. TB, 36" (91 cm), EM. S. amber brown, midrib lighter; F. white ground, edge stitched amber brown, thin brown centerline; beards orange amber, tipped yellow; ruffled. Edna's Wish X Wild Jasmine. Cooley 1992.

DESERT ROYALTY (Lin Flanagan, AB, R. 1989). Aril Society 1991.

DESERT SHIELD (W. Terry Varner, R. 1990). Sdlg. 0-355. MTB, 19" (48 cm), ML. S. golden yellow, lightly edged F. color; F. yellow ground, overlaid velvety dark red; beards orange; slight fragrance. Consummation X Marsh Marigold. Ohio Gardens 1991.

DESERT SKETCH (Robert Annand, R. 1993). Sdlg. 85-8A. TB, 37" (94 cm), ML. S. blended grey and yellow tinted blue; style arms straw yellow, blue lip; F. sanded blend of grey, brown and yellow, faint blue midline; beards bronze, tipped white. Desert Echo X Sketch Me. Milwood Nursery 1993.

DESERT SOLITUDE (Lin Flanagan, R. 1992). Sdlg. 88011-1. AB (OGB-), 28" (71 cm), M. S. white blended pale amber; F. pale amber flushed pale violet, slight red violet veining around yellow beard; ruffled; slight fragrance. Silent Dawn X New Moon. Aril Society 1993.

DESERT SPIRIT (Lin Flanagan, R. 1993). Sdlg. 85005-1. AB (OGB-), 20" (51 cm), L. S. pale violet, light violet edge; F. mixture of light violet and light amber with darker violet streak from tip of brown orange beard; slight fragrance. Vanity X Woodsong. Aril Society 1994.

DESERTS RAGE (David Miller, R. 1996). Sdlg. 88-11B. TB, 33" (84 cm), EM. S. sandy grey brown (RHS 199C), very lightly infused violet; style arms blended light brown and yellow; F. hafts yellow, blending to sandy grey brown (161A) margin; beards yellow; slight musky fragrance. 85-4A: (Gold Galore x Copper Classic) X Sunny and Warm. Long 1997.

DESERT SURPRISE (Lin Flanagan, R. 1997). Sdlg. 89037-2. AB (OGB-), 30" (76 cm), E. S. pale cream; style arms pale violet; F. pale yellow; beards grey yellow; ruffled, semi-recurved; slight fragrance. 85006-1: (Charm Ticket x Caravan Trail) X Stepping Proud. Aril Society 1998.

DESERT THUNDER (Lin Flanagan, AB, R. 1989). Aril Society 1991.

DESERT TRIUMPH (James Burch, R. 1991). Sdlg. 44-14. TB, 32" (81 cm), ML. S. greyed orange (RHS 173D); F. greyed purple (187A), 1/2" greyed orange edge; beards yellow orange (23A). Great Divide X Seven Hills. Burch Iris 1992.

DESERT TRUMPET (Lin Flanagan, R. 1990). Sdlg. 82006-1. AB (OGB-), 30" (76 cm), E. S. light violet; F. violet and yellow mixture (not blend); beards dark violet; ruffled, flared. Unknown AB (½-bred) sdlg. X New Moon. Aril Society 1991.

DESERVING TREASURE (Sterling Innerst, R. 1993). Sdlg. 1928-8. TB, 36" (91 cm), ML. S. pastel peach pink; F. pastel lavender blue, edged lighter; beards cream tipped bronze yellow; slight fragrance. Dualtone X Cozy Carol. Innerst 1994.

DESIGNER'S DREAM (John C. Taylor, R. 1991). Sdlg. OL 113-7. LA, 47" (120 cm), ML. Ruffled yellow (RHS 6D), veined darker yellow. Koorawatha X Dazzling Star. Rainbow Ridge 1992/93.

DESIGNER'S RAGE (Paul Black, R. 1991). Sdlg. 8544B. TB, 30" (76 cm), M. Ruffled diamond-dusted rosy mauve; beards burnt orange, purple base. B80-54: (Breath of Morn x Galen) X Spellmaker. Mid-America 1991.

DESIGNING WOMAN (Joseph Gatty, TB, R. 1989). Keppel 1990.

DESIRED ORANGE (Stan Dexter by Marie Ingersoll, R. 1990). Sdlg. 1983/139. TB, 34" (86 cm), ML. Deep orange with F. hash marks; beards near red. Orange Star X 1980/79A: (Maraschino x Pink Taffeta). Ingersoll's Iris 1991.

DESIRIS (Lawrence Ransom, R. 1993). Sdlg. 87/49-4. TB, 30" (76 cm), ML. TB, 30" (76 cm), ML. S. orange pink pastel; F. cream to soft orange, orange on upper shoulders, pinker on lower shoulders and edge; beards light orange, base cream; ruffled, laced; sweet-spicy fragrance. Beverly Sills X Soap Opera. Iris au Trescols 1994.

DESLOGE (Clyde & Anna Hahn, R. 1996). Sdlg. 92-2-C. SIB, 29" (74 cm), EM. S. and F. white, style arms yellow. Parentage unknown. Hahn's Rainbow 1996.

DESLOGE BEAUTY (Clyde & Anna Hahn, R. 1996). Sdlg. 92-3-C. SIB, 29" (74 cm), EM. S. and F. purple; style arms white, veined purple. Parentage unknown. Hahn's Rainbow 1996.

DESLOGE SUNSHINE (Clyde & Anna Hahn, R. 1996). Sdlg. 91-7-C. TB, 38" (97 cm), EM. Light yellow self; beards orange, tipped yellow; slight sweet fragrance. Sunkist Frills X Time Piece. Hahn's Rainbow 1996.

DESPITE ALL (Loleta Powell, R. 1990). TB, 35" (89 cm), ML. S. rose; F. deep rose; beards orange; pronounced sweet fragrance. Two Pinks X Spring Portrait. Powell's Gardens 1991.

DESTINY'S CALL (Mary Dunn by Joseph Ghio, R. 1998). Sdlg. 239-5. LA, 36" (91 cm), EM. Metallic grape, green gold signal. Midnight Drama X self. Bay View 1999.

DESTRY RIDES AGAIN (Richard Gibson, R. 1996). Sdlg. 009-1. TB, 32" (81 cm), EM & RE. S. brown; style arms yellowish brown; F. yellow, tinged brown; beards yellow; ruffled. Buckwheat X Foxy Lady. Stockton 1995.

DETAILS (Paul Black, R. 1998). Sdlg. C114A. SDB, 11" (28 cm), M. S. pearl, pinkish buff central infusion; style arms light turquoise, deeper lip; F. pinkish tan, diffusing to smoky blue band with smoky mauve rim, haft white with olive green veining; beards light blue at end, orange in throat; ruffled; pronounced spicy fragrance. Dorothy Howard X unknown. Mid-America 1998.

DETROIT CITY (Ed Roberts, R. 1995). Sdlg. 9-51-DC. TB, 34" (86 cm), M. S. and style arms white; F. white, cool blue rim; beards white, fuzzy white horn; ruffled. Honky Tonk Blues X Conjuration.

DEVA MARIYA (V. & N. Gordodelovy, R. 1995). Sdlg. 149. TB, 33" (85 cm), E. Ruffled pale pink, tinted orange; beards red. Parentage unknown. Gordodelovy 1986.

DEVIL DANCING (Barry Blyth, R. 1994). Sdlg. A53-1. IB, 22" (56 cm), EM. S. grey lavender; F. deeper, slight reddish violet overlay, deepening toward center, greyed lavender edge; beards navy bronze; slight musky fragrance. X25-5, Impish sib, X Electrique. Tempo Two 1994/95.

DEVILISH NATURE (Carl Boswell, R. 1998). Sdlg. 15-90-2-1. IB, 20" (51 cm), M. S. light chocolate maroon; style arms tan, maroon cast; F. light maroon overlaid violet, chocolate marginal band; beards yellow, violet horn; slight musky fragrance. Chocolate Cupcake X Special Feature. Adamgrove 1998.

DEVIL'S DAWN (William Plotner, R. 1992). Sdlg. 84-564-1. TB, 38" (97 cm), ML. Blended zanzibar and pompeii red, F. center cardinal red; beards dark red tipped bronze violet; slight spicy fragrance. (Spartan x Uproar) X Sultan's Dancer. Wildwood Gardens 1991.

DEVIL'S DREAM (Marty Schafer/Jan Sacks, R. 1990). Sdlg. S 85-13-3. SIB, 33" (84 cm), L. S. wine red (richer, darker than RHS 77A); style arms lighter red (90B); F. velvety red (richer, darker than 72A), purple blaze around signal; ruffled. Percheron X Purple Prose. Joe Pye Weed 1990.

DEVIL'S FORK (D. L. Shepard, R. 1998). Sdlg. 95055-8901. TB, 42" (107 cm), ML. S. sandy red heavily overlaid violet; style arms sandy red violet; F. rich violet, sandy red rim, gold shoulders; beards orange gold with heavily ruffled flounce; ruffled. Battle Star X Howdy Do. Shepard Iris 1998.

DEVIL'S LAKE (Schreiner, R. 1999). Sdlg. BB 598-1. TB, 39" (99 cm), ML. Dark navy blue (RHS 94A) self; beards blue, yellow in throat. W 170-1: (R 256-A: ((Shoreline sib x Brook Flower) x (((Prince Indigo x (Allegiance x (Harbor Blue x (Blue Ensign x Pierre Menard)))) x ((First Violet x Arabi Pasha) x (Salem x Bluebird Blue))) x (Tropical Night x (((Caroline Jane x (Harlequin x Bright Contrast)) x Emma Cook) x (Toll Gate x (Black Taffeta x King's Choice)))))) x Royal Crusader) X T 260-1: (Midnight Express sib x Titan's Glory). Schreiner 1999.

DEVIL'S RIOT (Barry Blyth, R. 1993). Sdlg. Z83-1. TB, 32-34" (81-86 cm), ML. S. apricot with violet midrib flush; F. plush red burgundy; beards orange red tangerine; ruffled, laced; slight fragrance. (Edge of Winter x London Lord) X Curacao. Tempo Two 1993/94.

DEVIL'S SPOON (D. L. Shepard, R. 1998). Sdlg. 95056-8905. TB, 43" (109 cm), M. S. grape burgundy; style arms old gold, midrib burgundy; F. reddish burgundy, hafts heavily veined cream, gold and burgundy; beards rusty gold, large ruffled spooned flounce. Battle Star X Batman. Shepard Iris 1998.

DEVITA MARIE (Jim Hedgecock, R. 1990). Sdlg. C-82-1-H. TB, 30" (76 cm), M. S. pink; F. laced apricot, lighter around bright pink beard; ruffled. Beauty Crown X Homecoming Queen. Comanche Acres 1991.

DEVITSA KRASAVITSA (V. & N. Gordodelovy, R. 1996). Sdlg. 294. TB, 32" (80 cm), EM. S. cream; F. lilac, edged brown; beards light yellow; ruffled. Parentage unknown. Gordodelovy 1993.

#DEVONSHIRE CREAM (Adelaide Williams, TB, R. 1950). Not introduced; name released.

DEVONSHIRE CREAM (George Sutton, R. 1999). Sdlg. H-221. TB, 37" (94 cm), ML-VL. Heavily ruffled cream white, F. with dark lemon hafts; beards yellow, cream at end and cream base; heavily ruffled; slight spicy fragrance. Elizabeth Poldark X Simply Pretty.

DEVOTEE (Ben Hager, R. 1997). Sdlg. AMT5624Ap. MTB, 22" (56 cm), M. S. and F. light apricot; style arms apricot; beards tangerine. Little Who X AMT5206BgPkSh: ((Audacious x (((Flaming Light x (2022: ((666: (Norah x Thisbe) x Glittering Amber) x (983 x Glittering Amber)) x Picture Perfect)) x Fresno Calypso) x ((Louise Hopper x ((New Idea x 2271: (((Seventh Heaven x Jones 157) x 1381: (Frenchi x Pagoda)) x 1242: (666 x 666))) x 2271)) x (((New Idea x 1242) x 2022) x ((666 x 1381) x 1242))))) x Abridged Version). Adamgrove 1997.

DEWA BANRI (Toyokazu Ichie by Currier McEwen, R. 1995). Sdlg. 6A-73. JI (3 F.), 36" (90 cm), M. S. reddish purple (RHS 77A), small; style arms dark violet blue (90A); F. light violet blue (92D) base, pronounced dark violet blue veins and halo around rich yellow signal. Parentage unknown; seed from Nagai Ayame Park, Yamagatu Province. Kamo Nursery 1989.

DEWANA (Graeme Grosvenor, R. 1993). Sdlg. R17-3. TB, 36" (91 cm), EM. S. blue, veined darker; F. blue violet, blending to lighter edge, veined darker; beards white; ruffled; pronounced sweet fragrance. Scented Nutmeg X Tide Crest. Rainbow Ridge 1996/97.

DEWA-NO-AKEBONO (Society for Japanese Irises, R. 1995). JI (3 F.), 33" (85 cm), M. S. very light red violet, darkening toward edge, with narrow white rim; style arms white, light red violet crest; F. red violet, few white veins and narrow rim. Parentage and hybridizer unknown. Introduced in Japan prior to 1940.

DEWBERRY DAWN (Chet Tompkins, R. 1994). Sdlg. 88-58-6. TB, 38" (97 cm), ML. S. pale lilac pink; F. medium dark raspberry pink; beards red. Inv. Camelot Rose, Clarion Call, Blushing Butterfly, Armageddon, Heavenly Body. Fleur de Lis 1994.

DEWBERRY STAINS (Hugh Thurman, R. 1999). Sdlg. 92-15-3. SDB, 12" (31 cm), M. S. white, plum wine overlay and midrib; style arms plum wine; F. white, plum wine edge and centerline; beards pale lavender; slight spicy fragrance. Court Magician X Chubby Cheeks.

DEWDROP WALTZ (Darrell Weikle, R. 1996). TB, 33" (84 cm), EM. S. near-white, faint blue tinge; style arms white; F. blue orchid; beards lavender, golden orange in throat; lightly ruffled. Bubble Bath X Dark Triumph. Weikle's Wonderland 1996.

DEW LINE (Chet Tompkins, R. 1997). Sdlg. 93-46. TB, 39" (99 cm), ML-VL. White, very faint blue green and lilac tints; beards pale lemon, blue green tint. (Intermission x (Hushabye Time x Skating Party)) X ((Ivory Faun x Lace Ballet) x (Hanky Panky x Lace Ballet)). Fleur de Lis 1997.

DIABLOTIN (Pierre Anfosso, R. 1990). Sdlg. P 83 N1. SDB, 10" (25 cm), M. S. white; F. chartreuse, edged white; beards blue. Petite Fugue X Pulcinella. Iris en Provence 1990.

DIABOLIQUE (Schreiner, R. 1997). Sdlg. DD 483-1. TB, 38" (97 cm), ML. Heavily ruffled claret purple (RHS 77A) self; beards blue purple; slight fragrance. T 869-2, Rosette Wine sib, X Y 682-2: (T 453-B, Thriller sib, x T 449-A: ((Master Touch x ((((Alpenrose x Anthem) x (Amethyst Flame x Melodrama)) x ((Alpenrose x Brigadoon) x (Amethyst Flame x Melodrama))) x Rondo)) x (J 411-B, Sailor's Dance sdlg., x ((G 1517-B x Neptune's Pool) x Royal Regency sib)))). Schreiner 1997.

DIAMOND BLUSH (Donald Spoon, R. 1997). Sdlg. 92-192. TB, 28" (71 cm), ML & RE. S. and style arms blended orient pink (RHS 36A) to salmon (27A); F. overlaid brick red (35B), paler pink (36D) to salmon (27D) between prominent haft venation; beards nasturtium red (32B), ruffled, flared; pronounced spicy fragrance. (Cataldo x Infinite Grace) X Pink Attraction. Winterberry 1998.

DIAMOND DOLL (Joyce Meek, R. 1994). Sdlg. 270-1-6. BB, 25" (64 cm), ML. S. rose pink; F. rose pink, paling to ivory area around tip of melon beard, deeper toned hafts; lightly ruffled. Tamara Anne X Paradise. D & J Gardens 1994.

DIAMOND LIL (Larry Lauer, R. 1998). Sdlg. 89-135-2. TB, 35" (89 cm), L. Lightly laced white; beards tangerine, white at end; slight sweet fragrance. Katharine Anne X Silver Fox. Lauer's Flowers 1998.

DIAMONDS AND RUST (Frank Foster, R. 1998). Sdlg. 9204A. SDB, 10½" (27 cm), ML. S. greyed white, tinted cream (RHS 155C); style arms greyed white; F. medium rusty amber (near 168D), 1/8" buff cream edge; beards cream, hairs tipped light blue; lightly ruffled. Flirty Mary X Blood Covenant.

DIANA'S DRESS (Glenn Stoneking-Jones, R. 1999). Sdlg. CIR6-54517-08-31-1999). TB, 36" (91 cm), EM. Lavender; style arms white; beards white, lavender horn and spoon; pronounced sweet fragrance. Mary Frances X Art School Angel.

DICK BUTLER (Tom Dillard, R. 1997). SPEC (*cristata*), 8" (20 cm), M. S. pale lavender; style arms pale purple; F. lavender blue. Collected from wild, Perry County, Arkansas.

DICKY BIRD (Ben Hager, R. 1992). Sdlg. MSD4929WiRdSp. SDB, 12" (30 cm), EM. S. wine red; F. dark red, edged wine red; beards dark red purple. DuBose DU 149 X SD4439Rd: (SD3785BstRd, Small Ritual sib, x Nanny). Adamgrove 1993.

DIDDLER (Hooker Nichols, R. 1991). Sdlg. 83111M. TB, 36" (91 cm), ML. S. creamy ivory to creamy butterscotch, touch of lace; F. maroon, edged S. color, inconspicuous haft marking extending throughout; beards orange; ruffled. Taj Rani X In Tempo. Hillcrest 1992.

DIFFERENT APPROACH (Sterling Innerst, R. 1991). Sdlg. 1928-19. TB, 36" (91 cm), ML. S. dark peach, midrib tinted lavender; F. lavender blue; beards peach orange. Dualtone X Cozy Carol. Innerst 1992.

DIFFERENT DESIGN (George Sutton, R. 1997). Sdlg. D-145HR. TB, 36" (91 cm), ML & RE. S. and style arms golden yellow (near RHS 11A); F. white ground, heavily dotted ruby red (59A), edged translucent naples yellow, white at shoulders; beards bronze yellow (163A); ruffled. C-115: ((Royal Trumpeter x Rancho Rose) x (Mountain Melody x Oh Babe)) X C-116: ((Michigan Pride x Broadway) x (Dazzling Gold x Hindu Magic)). Sutton 1998.

DIFFERENT FLAVORS (Joseph Ghio, R. 1999). Sdlg. 94-118B2. TB, 38" (97 cm), ML. S. tan; F. henna brown, yellow center flash; beards yellow. 92-150U3: (Battle Royal x ((84-133C3: ((Lady Friend x (Flareup x (Capitation x Coffee House))) x Battle Hymn sib) x 84-166J2: (Cafe Society x (Cinnamon x (76-110L: ((Malaysia x Carolina Honey) x (Hi Top x ((Ponderosa x Travel On) x Peace Offering sib))) x (Anointed x San Jose))))) x Heat Pump)) X 92-305L3: (Battle Royal x ((84-133C3 x ((Homecoming Queen x 76-110BB) x Esmeralda sib)) x 88-129Z, sib to pod parent of Star Quality)).

DIFFERENT WORLD (Richard Ernst, R. 1991). Sdlg. F169-11. TB, 34" (86 cm), ML. S. amber brown with lavender infusion; F. pale lavender blue, brown edge, golden brown shoulders; beards yellow; ruffled, lightly laced; slight sweet fragrance. Afternoon Delight X C142-7: (Ringo x (Cranberry Ice x Grand Waltz)). Cooley 1991.

DIGITIZER (Keith Fillmore, R. 1990). Sdlg. 8220-1-BB. BB, 26" (66 cm), ML. S. red brown with red violet (RHS 182B) infusion; F. red brown with red violet blaze, white under yellow beard, yellowish brown haft markings; heavily ruffled, laced. 8009-1: (Post Time x Romanesque) X Post Time. Bar K Iris 1990.

DIGGLES (Sterling Innerst, R. 1999). Sdlg. 4325-3. SDB, 15" (38 cm), ML. White, F. with blue spot; beards gold tipped white. Assignment X Skiddle.

DIJON MOUTARDE (Carl Jorgensen, R. 1994). Sdlg. 84-P-7A. TB, 32" (81 cm), ML. S. olive yellow; style arms long, serrate; F. ecru olive; beards chamois tipped purple; ruffled; slight spicy fragrance. 82-P11-4: (Summit Sweetie x Triple Crown) X Cozy and Warm. Long 1994.

DILLY GREEN (Evelyn Robarts, R. 1996). Sdlg. 819-1. TB, 32-34" (81-86 cm), ML. S. pale blue grey, hint of cream; style arms slightly darker, touched gold; F. blended blue green and pale gold, green gold shoulders and throat; beards gold, base blue green; slight fragrance. Barley Green X Alfresco. Stahly 1997.

DIME A DANCE (Marilyn Boro, R. 1995). Sdlg. SMM 23-89. TB, 35" (89 cm), M. S. white; F. red violet (RHS 80A), 1/4" light red violet (80D) rim, white flash by yellow beard; slight sweet fragrance. Syncopation X Magic Man. Maryott 1996.

DIMITY BUTTERFLY (Lorena Reid, R. 1993). Sdlg. opG88-1G. SIB (sino-sib), 40-48" (102-122 cm), ML. S. white, feathered with light blue lavender lines; style arms white, blue lavender midrib and tip; F. white, light blue lavender line pattern, large dark navy violet butterfly signal centrally marked with yellow rays. Butterfly Mode X unknown. Laurie's Garden 1993.

DINAR MOUNTAINS (Eric & Bob Tankesley-Clarke, R. 1994). SPEC, 18" (46 cm), ML. S. cream; F. pale violet with darker veining, heavy gold brown haft markings; beards yellow orange; slight sweet fragrance. Collected, Dinar Mountains, Bosnia; distributed by Randolph prior to 1970 and in commerce as *I. x-sambucina* 61-34.

DINKY CIRCUS (Paul Black, R. 1998). Sdlg. B247C. MDB, 6" (15 cm), E. S. white ground, wide dark purple band and veins; style arms whitish, purple ridge and crest; F. white, narrow dark purple band, plus veins and lines from beard to edge; beards purple black, base white; pronounced sweet fragrance. Inky Dinky X Flea Circus. Mid-America 1998.

DINNER AT EIGHT (Abram Feuerstein, R. 1999). Sdlg. 93-100-2. TB, 38" (97 cm), M. Ruffled metallic medium blue self; beards medium blue. Scandia Delight X Tinted Crystal. Stockton 1999.

DINNER DATE (Tom Burseen, R. 1990). Sdlg. 5-127B. TB, 35" (89 cm), M. Ruffled reddish violet blue (RHS 92A), F. washed lighter; beards dark yellow; sweet fragrance. Flower Show X Social Register. T.B.'s Place 1990.

DINO (J. T. Aitken, R. 1993). Sdlg. 86-J-15. JI (6 F.), 70" (178 cm), ML. Light lavender overlaid with medium violet veins, violet flush at petal edge and around yellow signal; style arms dark violet. Midnight Stars X 83J6. Aitken's Salmon Creek 1993.

DIOMEDES (Sterling Innerst, R. 1991). Sdlg. 3044-1. JI (6 F.), 40" (102 cm), ML. Light blue, 3/4" dark blue edge, light yellow signal. Center of Interest X Reign of Glory. Iris Pond 1992.

DIPPED IN GOLD (Stephen Stevens, R. 1990). Sdlg. 82-31-3. TB, 34" (86 cm), EM. Ruffled and laced white with 1/4" gold (RHS 16) band; beards yellow; style arms gold, laced; slight spicy fragrance. Lemon Curls X 78-39-3: (Goldie M x Li'l Goldie). Hahn's Rainbow, Roderick 1991.

DIRECT FLIGHT (O. D. Niswonger, R. 1995). Sdlg. 55-92. TB, 34" (86 cm), M. Deep pink self, infused blue; beards tangerine, blue at end. Pink Blue Genes X 58-88: (Matinee Idol x Pink Ballerina). Cape Iris 1995.

DIRIGO AMBER BEAUTY (Edward White, R. 1999). Sdlg. 84-C-1. TB, 36" (91 cm), EM. Amber-scotch blend; style arms light yellow; beards medium yellow; slight sweet fragrance. Scotch Blend X Amber Beauty.

DIRIGO BLACK POINT (John White, R. 1996). SPEC (*versicolor*), 30-36" (76-91 cm), M. Dark blue purple; leaf bases purplish to reddish purple. Collected from cliff above ocean, Black Point, Scarborough, Maine.

DIRIGO BLACK VELVET (John White, R. 1998). Sdlg. 93 B-B4-7. SIB (tet.), 40-44" (107-112 cm), EM. Very dark purple overlaid with velvety black sheen, F. with prominent gold signal; style arms dark purple. Golden Edge X Over in Gloryland. Pope's Perennials 1999.

DIRIGO BLUE PLATE (John White, R. 1998). Sdlg. 93 JB-B6-26. JI (3 F.), 36" (91 cm), EM. S. white, edged blue, upright; style arms white, edged blue violet; F. white, with 1/2"-5/8" blue marginal band, small yellow signal, opening flat. Fuji X McEwen J90-73. Pope's Perennials 1999.

DIRIGO CLOUD NINE (John White, R. 1996). Sdlg. 91E, COL-2 (colchicine treated). JI (6 F.), 36-40" (91-102 cm), ML. Soft blue (near RHS 97B), veined white, signals gold; style arms white, tufted light blue. 89-C8: (86L-7: (Nikko x Continuing Pleasure) x 86L-7) X Southern Son. Pope's Perennials 1998.

DIRIGO DEBUTANTE (John White, R. 1992). Sdlg. 86L-24. JI (3 F.), 41" (104 cm), ML. S. veined violet (RHS 87C); style arms edged and tufted violet (87B), white rib; F. white ground, finely veined and sanded violet (85A), pale yellow signal. Nikko X Continuing Pleasure. Joe Pye Weed 1994.

DIRIGO DELIGHT (John White, R. 1992). Sdlg. 88A-2-22. JI (6 F.), 41" (104 cm), ML. S. white ground with wide multi-colored band shading from dark purple (RHS 77A) to violet blue (93D), red violet wire edge, yellow signal; style arms white, ruffled. Ol' Man River X Continuing Pleasure. Pope's Perennials 1996.

DIRIGO DEVIL (John White, R. 1992). Sdlg. 88A-2-17. JI (6 F.), 40" (102 cm), EM. Red purple (RHS 77A) splashed white, yellow signal; style arms violet (83A), white midrib tufted violet. Ol' Man River X Continuing Pleasure.

DIRIGO FANCY (John White, R. 1992). Sdlg. 88A-2-16. JI (6 F.), 40" (102 cm), L. White with 1/2" to 3/4" blue violet border shading from light violet blue (RHS 95D) to slightly darker (96D); signals bright yellow; style arms white, edged blue violet. Ol' Man River X Continuing Pleasure.

DIRIGO OLD HUNDRED (John White, R. 1999). Sdlg. 91A-15. JI (3 F.), 24" (61 cm), EML. S. red violet paling to near-white at edge; style arms dark red violet, tipped white; F. white ground overlaid dark red violet rays from dark red violet area around yellow signal. 88A-2-10: (Ol' Man River x Continuing Pleasure) X self.

DIRIGO OLD PEWTER (John White, R. 1996). Sdlg. 91E-9. JI (6 F.), 40" (102 cm), ML. Violet blue (RHS 94C), very finely veined slightly darker, thin pale gold signal; style arms tufted and edged violet blue. 89C-8: (86L-7: (Nikko x Continuing Plesure) x self) X Southern Son. Pope's Perennials 1997.

DIRIGO PINK MILESTONE (John White, R. 1999). Sdlg. 95JI-W17-14. JI (3 F.), 34-36" (86-91 cm), EML. S. light pink; style arms edged pink, darker pink tips; F. dark pink lightening to light pink edge, small white blaze around gold signal. 92G-A2-12: (Aitken 86J-1-4: (Ruby Star x Asian Warrior) x Momojido) X Hana-no-Yoi.

DIRIGO PLUM CRAZY (John White, R. 1992). Sdlg. 88A-2-11. JI (6 F.), 43" (109 cm), M. Violet blue (RHS 93B) splashed white, yellow signal; style arms violet blue (93B). Ol' Man River X Continuing Pleasure.

DIRIGO SNOWFLAKE (John White, R. 1992). Sdlg. 88A-2-14. JI (6 F.), 40" (102 cm), M. White, veined light green, greenish yellow signal; style arms white. Ol' Man River X Continuing Pleasure. Pope's Perennials 1998.

DIRIGO STAR (John White, R. 1998). Sdlg. 93-JP-B10-26. JI (6 F.), 40" (102 cm), ML. Deep purple, very small pale yellow signal surrounded by white blaze; style arms white, edged blue violet. Dirigo Snowflake X McEwen J90-73. Pope's Perennials 1999.

DIRTY COWARD (Chet Tompkins, R. 1995). Sdlg. 94-88. TB, 38" (97 cm), ML. S. flame orange, midrib deeper; F. wine rose infused purple and plum; beards blended purple and plum brown. Luxury Lover X Apollodorus. Fleur de Lis 1995.

DIRTY DANCING (Joe Saia, TB, R. 1989). Saia 1990.

DIRTY DEVIL CANYON (John Durrance, R. 1994). Sdlg. JRD 91W-2. TB, 34" (86 cm), ML. S. yellow; F. yellow with red overlay and stripes, edge yellow; beards yellow. Parentage unknown. Long 1994.

DIRTY IS PURDY (Tom Burseen, R. 1991). Sdlg. 7-69D. TB, 29" (74 cm), M. S. greyed orange white, slightly darker edge; F. murky violet (RHS 87C) overlaid orange brown, more concentrated at edge; beards mustard, tipped greyed orange; ruffled; spicy fragrance. Touch of Bronze X 4-199A: (Soap Opera x Satin Glass). T.B.'s Place 1992.

DISCOVERED GOLD (Evelyn Jones, R. 1995). Sdlg. I89-15-1. IB, 22" (56 cm), L. Aureolin self; beards yellow. Shoop orange TB sdlg. X B. Jones 418-2: ((((Melon Honey x Wright L32) x (229: (Roberts 65-R-11 x 201) x Melon Honey)) x Pumpkin Center) x (Wright L85 x ((Solar Flight x (Melon Honey x 229)) x ((Roberts 65-R-10 x Roberts 70-R-32) x 229)))). Aitken's Salmon Creek 1996.

DISTANT NEBULA (Vernon Wood, R. 1995). Sdlg. 90-39. CA, 15" (38 cm), M. Raspberry orchid, F. with cherry red black signal; lightly ruffled. 88-47: (Rincon x Different Drummer) X 88-44: (Roaring Camp x 87-9, unknown parentage sdlgs. from Ghio seed). Stockton 1995.

DISTANT ROADS (Keith Keppel, R. 1990). Sdlg. 84-121B. TB, 38" (97 cm), E. S. olive sheen (M&P 13-K-3) shaded mauve dust (46-C-2); F. white, 1/2"-3/4" huckleberry (47-J-11) to nightshade

(47-H-11) border, burgundy (56-E-8) hafts; beards tan yellow effect; slight sweet fragrance. 80-130P, Armada sib, X Broadway. Keppel 1991.

DIVA DO (Mitch Jameson, R. 1992). Sdlg. 5-88. TB, 30-34" (76-86 cm), M. S. and style arms apricot pink orchid; F. velvety red purple, narrowly edged pink, white and apricot starburst area around orange beard; laced. 1-84: (Cabaret Royale x Son of Star) X Queen in Calico. Knee-Deep in June, 1993.

DIVINE DESIGN (Mary Dunn by Robert Dunn, R. 1998). Sdlg. M1063A. TB, 36" (91 cm), EM. S. cream ground, deep chocolate plicata edging; style arms brown; F. cream, deep cocoa edging and faint midline; beards old gold; heavily ruffled, lightly laced; slight sweet fragrance. Patterns X Change of Heart. M.A.D. Iris 1999.

DIVINE DUCHESS (Barry Blyth, R. 1990). Sdlg. U88-1. TB, 40-42" (102-107 cm), ML. Silvery blue; beards white, tipped cream. Leda's Lover X Morning Shadows. Tempo Two 1990/91.

DIVINE INTERVENTION (Mary Dunn by Robert Dunn, R. 1999). Sdlg. M2148-E. TB, 36" (91 cm), EM. Ruffled plum plicata, small white area in F. center; style arms plum; beards bronze; slight spicy fragrance. Patterns X Power Surge.

DIVINE LIGHT (Richard Ernst, R. 1993). Sdlg. D150-8. TB, 36" (91 cm), M. S. medium cream yellow; F. creamy white, blended yellow rim and yellow shoulders; beards gold; ruffled. Eastertime X A107-1, Panama Fling sib. Cooley 1992.

DIVINE RIGHT (Iris Nelson by Bryce Williamson, R. 1995). TB, 32" (81 cm), EM. S. butterscotch gold; F. cream yellow ground, java brown shoulders, rust brown fancy plicata markings over almost entire petal; beards yellow orange. Caramba X inv. Plum Crazy. Pacific Coast Hybridizers 1990.

DIVNY VALS (V. & N. Gordodelovy, R. 1995). Sdlg. 143. TB, 28" (71 cm), E. S. light blue lilac; F. lilac, tinted pink, light lilac edge, light brown haft striations; beards bright red; ruffled. Parentage unknown. Gordodelovy 1990.

DIXIE COUNTRY (Kirk Strawn, R. 1993). Sdlg. 50-1985. LA, 28" (72 cm), L. S. violet blue (RHS 90); style arms slightly lighter violet blue (90D); F. violet blue (89B), yellow (9A) signal. Lafitte's Retreat X collected *I. hexagona* from Cross City, Florida. Bois d'Arc 1996.

DIXIE CUP (James Burch, R. 1990). Sdlg. 45-8. TB, 32" (81 cm), M. Ruffled yellow (RHS 9C), F. with white center blaze; beards yellow orange (15A). Sophisticated Lady X Ballad of Dixie. Burch Iris 1991.

#DIXIE MOON (E. W. Sheets, TB, R. 1931). Marked as obsolete in 1939 Checklist; name released.

DIXIE MOON (Ben Hager, R. 1995). Sdlg. T5235BgLtY. TB, 35" (89 cm), EML. Luminous medium light yellow self; beards orange yellow; ruffled, faintly laced. T4836CrSh: ((Peach Tree x (Vanity x Pink Persian)) x Silver Flow) X Falling in Love.

DOBERMAN (Viacheslav Gavrilin, R. 1998). Sdlg. 4-18-3-94. TB, 41" (105 cm), M. S. and style arms dark red brown; F. darker, 1/2" rim matching S. color, velvety light rose brown pattern around beard; beards mustard, lighter at end; ruffled. Gypsy Caravan X unknown. Gavrilin 1999.

DOBROYE UTRO (V. & N. Gordodelovy, R. 1995). Sdlg. 129. TB, 37" (95 cm), ML. S. brown, tinted red; style arms yellow; F. dark red brown, brown rim; beards orange. Parentage unknown. Gordodelovy 1991.

DOCHUSUGOROKU (Zensaku Makino by Society for Japanese Irises, R. 1993). JI (6 F.), 32 (81 cm), M. Deep velvety grape purple, fine white veins radiating from large white-sanded halo, yellow signal; style arms white, crests purple. Parentage unknown. Makino 1975.

DOCTOR ALAN (Gary Sides, R. 1996). Sdlg. C4-E19B. TB, 34" (86 cm), M. Lightly ruffled pink self; beards tangerine. AP22-C1Re: (Returning Peace x Vanity) X Lady Friend. Sides 1997.

DOCTOR BEHENNA (R. E. Nichol, R. 1991). Sdlg. J33-1. TB, 35" (89 cm), L. S. tannish gold; F. smooth red brown; beards tan; lightly ruffled. G41-1: (Sketch Me x Show Biz) X G24-2: ((Kilt Lilt x Autumn Leaves) x Show Biz). Iris Garden 1993.

DOCTOR DARK (Tom Burseen, R. 1993). Sdlg. 9-238B. TB, 36" (91 cm), EM. Heavily ruffled, glossy dark grape violet (darker than RHS 89A); beards dark purple; musky fragrance. Dusky Challenger X Royalist. T.B.'s Place 1994.

DOCTOR DAVID (Joseph Shapiro, R. 1999). TB, 32" (81 cm), L. S. light yellow; F. dark yellow to brownish yellow, small lavender blue blaze; beards orange; slight spicy fragrance. Margarita X Gold Galore.

DOCTOR GOLD (Jean Segui, R. 1998). TB, 39" (100 cm), L. Indian yellow (RHS 17A) self; beards saffron yellow (21A); slight fragrance. Royal Gold X Post Time. Iris de Thau 1983.

DOCTOR MOM (Bob Thomason, R. 1991). Sdlg. 8511B. MTB, 12" (30 cm), M. S. lavender, veined deeper on inside; style arms pale lavender, midrib darker; F. violet, white hafts with heavy veining extending to end of beard; beards yellow, white at tip. Soul Searcher X Bellboy.

DOCTOR NO (George Sutton, R. 1999). Sdlg. H-187-B. TB, 37" (94 cm), ML. S. and style arms orient pink (RHS 36A); F. pale orient pink ground, violet purple (77A) sanding, edge and centerline; beards tangerine, violet purple horn. G-7: (Gigolo x Egyptian) X G-7D, sib.

DOC VIC (Dudley Carson, R. 1991). Sdlg. APSBE-3. SDB, 10-11½" (25-29 cm), M. Yellow (RHS 8B) washed greyed orange (164A) on F.; beards violet blue (paler than 97D); slight sweet fragrance. Amazon Princess X (Stockholm x Brighteyes).

#DODGE CITY (Gertrude Hays, TB, R. 1957). Not introduced; name released.

DODGE CITY (Larry Lauer, R. 1995). Sdlg. 89-29-1. TB, 38-40" (97-102 cm), E. S. bronze tan overtoned melon; style arms bronze tan; F. bronze tan, slight blue violet flash around tangerine beard; slight sweet fragrance. Macho Hombre X Role Model. Stockton 1995.

DOEHRENER TURM (Harald Moos, R. 1992). Sdlg. 84/411A. TB, 33½" (85 cm), M. Lightly frilled medium pink; beards orange. Glendale X Vanity. Schoeppinger 1993.

DO IT AGAIN (Herbert Holk, R. 1996). Sdlg. 2810. TB, 34" (86 cm), EM & RE. S. white, light lemon midrib; style arms light lemon; F. white, small light lemon shoulder area; beards lemon yellow, white at end; slight sweet fragrance. 2714: (2625: (Gold Burst x Baroque) x Trousseau Lace) X Sunny Shoulders. Cal-Dixie 1997.

DOKTOR RODIONENKO (Viktor Sheviakov, R. 1998). Sdlg. 1026A. TB, 30" (75 cm), ML. S. and style arms light amethyst violet; F. velvety dark reddish violet, narrow pale yellow violet rim; beards tangerine red, pinkish red at end; ruffled. Latin Lover X Rippling Waters. Sheviakov 1995.

DOLLAR DAYS (John Baldwin, R. 1994). Sdlg. 85-12A. TB, 36" (91 cm), M. S. pale yellow (RHS 8C); F. cream, pale yellow hafts and edge; beards light orange; ruffled. 80-9C: (Silent Serenade x Vanity) X Precious Moments. Tempo Two 1997/98.

DOLL DREAM (Ben Hager, R. 1997). Sdlg. AMT5624-Oc. MTB, 22" (56 cm), M. S. orchid pink; style arms and F. orchid; beards tangerine. Sib to Devotee. Adamgrove 1997.

DOLLY JANE (Polly Black, R. 1995). Sdlg. GR10-4. TB, 34" (86 cm), M. Ruffled very pale pink self, slight green line from orange beard; slight fragrance. Parentage unknown. Polly Black 1995.

DOMINGO (G. F. Wilson, R. 1996). Sdlg. 67-90SMO-0. AB (OGB), 32" (81 cm), E. S. white, veined yellow, bright yellow midrib; F. clear bright yellow, large circular red brown signal; beards yellow. Syrian Moon X Onlooker. Aril Society, Pleasure Iris 1997.

DON (Gerald Richardson, R. 1994). Sdlg. 86-21-1. TB, 40" (102 cm), M. Rosy magenta, lighter area and faint blue cast by beards; beards pale lavender tipped rose red; slight fragrance. Lorilee X 79-59-2: (((Pink Taffeta x (68-2-19 x Cloud Ruffles)) x Dream Fantasy) x ((Esther Fay x Fond Wish) x Pink Taffeta)). Rainbow's End 1994.

DONEGAL (Keith Keppel, R. 1996). Sdlg. 91-41E. IB, 21" (53 cm), M. S. pinkish mauve (M&P 43-D-3), deeper (43-F-6) base; style arms slightly paler (43-CD-2); F. blended pinkish mauve (42-B-2 to 43-C-2); beards lavender blue (43-C-6), white lightly tipped yellow in throat; ruffled; slight sweet fragrance. Gatty T-1-2: ((Nefertiti x Playgirl) x Presence) X Chanted. Keppel 1997.

DON EPIFANO (Ladislav Muska, R. 1995). Sdlg. LCPA-02. TB, 38" (97 cm), M. S. light nut cinnamon; F. lavender rose, brown cinnamon edge; beards gold; heavily laced; spicy fragrance. Laced Cotton X Pink Angel. Muska 1989.

DON HERZBERG (Donald Spoon, R. 1997). Sdlg. 93-16A. BB, 24" (61 cm), M & RE. S. and style arms dresden yellow; F. dresden yellow, darker veining around beard and midrib; beards persimmon orange, wide, ending in 2" upturned yellow flounce; ruffled, lightly laced; flared. Shoot the Moon X Dazzling Lora.

DONNA LOUISE (Francis Rogers, R. 1998). Sdlg. C-308-C. TB, 30" (76 cm), L. Ruffled violet blue (RHS 89C) self; beards darker violet blue (89B); flared; sweet fragrance. Honky Tonk Blues X Kathy's Joy. Meadowbrook 1999.

DONNA'S PEACH TART (Marie Murdy, R. 1995). Sdlg. D-4-30-95. TB, 28" (71 cm), M. S. pale peach; F. peach, hafts slightly deeper; beards orange; finely laced. Parentage unknown.

DONNAY (Allan Ensminger, R. 1999). Sdlg. 96-6. BB, 24" (61 cm), ML. Phlox purple (HCC 632-1), lighter (632-2) streaks; style arms white; beards white; slight fragrance. 192-100: (188-44:

(Painted Plic x 82-27: (Ruffled Surprise x Morning Sunshine)) x Chanted) X 93-18: (91-36 plic: ((Peach Jam x Capricious) x Brindled Beauty) x sib 91-36 variegated).

DON'T BE CRUEL (Sterling Innerst, R. 1994). Sdlg. 1928-11. TB, 36" (91 cm), M. Full lavender self; beards lavender tipped white; slight fragrance. Dualtone X Cozy Carol. Innerst 1995.

DON'T BE SHY (Sharon McAllister, R. 1994). Sdlg. 89-12-6. AB (OGB-), 29" (73 cm), EM. S. greyed greenish yellow (RHS 196D/160D); F. greyed greenish yellow (slightly greener than 160A) with network of burgundy and rust lines radiating from near-black beard, burgundy signal. Casa Vicente X Joint Venture. McAllister 1994.

DON'T LEAVE ME (Barry Blyth, R. 1997). Sdlg. D69-2. TB, 36" (92 cm), M. S. clear medium pink; F. lighter pink, whitish area below pink beard; musky fragrance. A63-D, Stillness sib, X Spring Tidings. Tempo Two 1997/98.

DOO DAH (Mitch Jameson, R. 1990). Sdlg. 3-87. TB, 38" (97 cm), EML. S. and style arms blue white, midrib deeper; F. medium blue, edged lighter; beards cream, heavily tipped yellow orange; pronounced sweet fragrance. Edith Wolford X Song of Spring. Knee-Deep in June 1992.

DOOR PRIZE (Libby Cross, R. 1997). SDB, 9" (23 cm), E & RE. Light yellow self; style arms yellow; beards white; sweet fragrance. Origin unknown, plant given as door prize. Baby Blessed X unknown. Crosspatch 1998.

DOOZEY (Ben Hager, R. 1993). Sdlg. MD5493VAm. MDB, 5" (13 cm), E & RE. S. white; F. medium violet to purple, white rim; beards white. AMD4972TyAm: ((Little You x (Inca Toy x (BU67 x Atomic Blue))) x (Ditto sib x ((((Orange Caper x (Shine Boy x Dark Fairy)) x SD1997D: (Rickshaw x Lilli-Var)) x Wink) x ((SD1997 x Bongo) x (Russet Dot x SD1997))))) X Ditto. Adamgrove 1994.

DORFFEST (Artur Winkelmann, R. 1992). Sdlg. AW 8992. SIB, 31½" (80 cm), EM. Velvety purple, white signal; F. flared. Ruffled Velvet X Fliederfee.

DORIS FLOWERS (Robert Jeffries, R. 1991). Sdlg. J84-3-DD. TB, 36" (91 cm), ML. S. palest mauvette (HCC 537/1), base deeper; F. lighter mauvette violet; beards orange yellow, tipped dark mauvette violet; slight sweet fragrance. Fringed Lace X Song of Norway. Bar K Iris 1992.

DOROTHEA MARQUART (Sterling Innerst, R. 1993). Sdlg. 2953B-51. TB, 36" (91 cm), ML. Medium yellow; beards cream, tipped yellow; slight fragrance. Catalyst X Idol's Dream. Innerst 1994.

DOROTHY DAVIS (Sterling Innerst, R. 1994). Sdlg. 3147-1. TB, 36" (91 cm), M. Medium orange self; beards orange; slight fragrance. Embellishment X Hindenburg. Innerst 1995.

DOROTHY HOWARD (Cleo Palmer, SDB, R. 1986). Correction of parentage. 82-11: ((Dove Wings x 7607: ((Wilma V. x unknown) x Little Titan)) x 7416: ((Baria x Carpathia) x Dove Wings)) X (Daisy x 7525: (Pink Cushion x Dove Wings)).

DOROTHY LEE (Clarence Mahan, R. 1999). Sdlg. MKRB-2. TB, 35" (89 cm), ML. S. light yellow (RHS 160D); style arms light yellow, violet tinge beneath lip; F. light to medium wistaria blue (92C/D), shoulders bright yellow; beards golden yellow; slight musky fragrance. My Katie X Ruffled Ballet.

DOROTHY MARTIN (T. J. Betts, R. 1996). Sdlg. 159A. LA, 35" (89 cm), M. S. pastel lavender (RHS 85D); style arms yellow; F. pastel lavender, pale gold-infused signal and veining. Parentage unknown -- possibly Deeper Echo X Brazen.

DOROTHY PARKER (Tom Burseen, R. 1995). Sdlg. 0-59A. TB, 35" (89 cm), EM. S. creamy apricot, edge washed mulberry rose; style arms darker apricot; F. pale creamy peach ground, mulberry plicata edging, prominent peach outer rim; beards orange; ruffled; sweet fragrance. Too Too Ripe X Choose a Juice. T.B.'s Place 1996.

DOROTHY ROBBINS (Brian Price, R. 1996). Sdlg. BPP 92/C/3. CA, 15" (38 cm), M. S. near-white; F. pale lavender, radiant yellow heart. Sdlg. inv. Ghio line X Little Tilgates.

DOROTHY V (Kathy Millar, R. 1991). CA, 13½" (35 cm), E. Light cream, light purple and yellow veining, F. with pale purple halo around yellow signal. Parentage unknown.

DOSSIER (Mary Dunn by Joseph Ghio, R. 1999). Sdlg. L248-11. LA, 36" (91 cm), ML. Pure yellow; style arms green. ((Charlie's Michele x Rhett) x (Clara Goula x Southerner)) X Rich Tradition.

DOT COM (Bennett Jones, R. 1996). Sdlg. 476-7. SDB, 12" (31 cm), M. S. ethyl blue (HCC 548/3); F. french blue (43/1), wide neat ethyl blue border; beards deep blue; slight fragrance. Bedford Lilac X Tu Tu Turquoise. Aitken's Salmon Creek 1997.

DOT'S NICE (Sharon McAllister, R. 1992). Sdlg. 84-6A-4. AB (OGB), 28" (72 cm), EM. S. white, yellow midrib, yellow veins most concentrated around rim; F. tuscan yellow ground, intensely veined and dotted nutmeg on inner half and lightly marked on outer half; beards nutmeg. Koko Knoll X Promise to Elizabeth. McAllister 1992.

DOTTED COBWEB (Ladislav Muska, R. 1999). Sdlg. 98-DCDQ-01. TB, 36" (91 cm), M. S. light lilac lavender, deep lilac midrib; style arms cream lilac; F. light yellow cream ground widely peppered lilac, lilac centerline; beards yellow mustard; slight fragrance. ((Nejedlo DERRSM-89-2, Spacelight Sketch sib, x Calicoball) x (Spacelight Sketch x Queen in Calico)) X French Gown. Muska 1999.

DOTTED LINE (Lorena Reid, R. 1991). Sdlg. 90-3-6+7. SIB (sino-sib), 24-30" (61-76 cm), EM. S. violet blue (RHS 93D), darker (93B) vertical stitch marks, crinkled white edge; style arms violet blue (93C); F. violet blue (93D), vertically stitched white and violet blue (93B), large white signal, violet blue (93A) edge and lines at center. Butterfly Mode X unknown. Laurie's Garden 1992.

DOTTED MISS (Calvin Helsley, R. 1990). Sdlg. 87-1. SIB, 30" (76 cm), M. Light lavender pink dotted violet pink, gold signal; style arms creamy white. Pink Haze X "Corey's Pink".

DOTTEREL (B.L.C. Dodsworth, R. 1998). Sdlg. EB 94 B. TB, 34" (86 cm), E. S. white; style arms and F. buff; beards yellow; ruffled. Marmalade Skies X Champagne Elegance.

DOTTIE JOY (Jean Witt, MTB, R. 1987). Kirkland Iris 1990.

DOUBLE BOW (Keith Chadwick/Tony DeRose, R. 1999). Sdlg. 99G-8-5-6. TB, 36" (91 cm), EM. S. and style arms white; F. royal blue paling to white at hafts; beards yellow orange, ending with large ruffled blue flounce, white at base; slight musky fragrance. Dauber's Delight X Mesmerizer.

DOUBLE BUBBLE (Joseph Ghio, R. 1997). Sdlg. 91-40K2. TB, 36" (91 cm), EM. Azure blue self; beards white. Water Ballet X Quintessence. Bay View 1998.

DOUBLE BYTE (George Sutton, R. 1996). Sdlg. C-89-B. SDB, 13" (33 cm), VE & RE. S. lemon yellow (RHS 13A); style arms cream yellow; F. lemon yellow edge, almond shell (165) thumbprint; beards white, orange in throat; lightly ruffled; slight sweet fragrance. Manchu Coffee X Amazon Princess. Sutton 1997.

DOUBLE CHARM (George Sutton, R. 1996). Sdlg. D-190. TB, 37" (94 cm), VE-EM & RE. S. amethyst violet (RHS 84C), midrib flushed aster violet (87A), sea lavender (85D) edge; F. aster violet veined darker, edged sea lavender; beards sea lavender, tipped yellow deep in throat; ruffled. Chapeau Blanc X Glory Story. Sutton 1997.

DOUBLE DOSE (Tom Burseen, R. 1995). Sdlg. 1-281A. TB, 37" (94 cm), M. Ruffled red purple (RHS 77A) self; beards cream; pronounced musky fragrance. 8-120: ((Pledge Allegiance x Hypnotic) x (Star Wars x Harlem Hussy)) X Gene Machine. T.B.'s Place 1996.

DOUBLE DRAGON (Leo Barnard, R. 1997). Sdlg. L 91-77 BF. BB, 20" (51 cm), ML. S. and style arms white, tinted blue lavender; F. white, blue lavender wash, gold shoulders; beards white, hairs tipped gold, ending in large lavender blue flounce; heavily ruffled; slight fragrance. Borderline X Twice Thrilling. Paradise Iris 1997.

DOUBLE DRIBBLE (Joseph Ghio, R. 1999). Sdlg. 94-6A3. TB, 36" (91 cm), EM & RE. White ground heavily lined and overstreaked dark blue; beards yellow, tipped white. 92-1: ((Silhouette x ((Go Round x Snowbrook) x Handshake sib)) x (Polar Seas x Handshake)) X Tall Ships.

DOUBLE EDGED (Joseph Ghio, R. 1995). Sdlg. PF-170F2. CA, 15" (38 cm), M. Crimson self, distinct yellow margin on all petals. Mission Santa Clara sib X PI-MIX-S, unknown. Bay View 1995.

DOUBLE ESPOIR (Jean Cayeux by Richard Cayeux, R. 1995). Sdlg. 8488 A. TB, 35" (90 cm), M. S. light salmon pink; F. velvety garnet, edge lighter; beards orange red. 8214 A: (Gypsy Caravan x Embassadora) X 8148 B: (7708 B: ((Gala Madrid x Java Dove) x ((Postscript x Orange Parade) x Grand Chef)) x Color Splash). Cayeux 1994.

DOUBLE OH SEVEN (George Sutton, R. 1998). Sdlg. G-24. TB, 35" (89 cm), ML. Ruffled hyacinth blue (near RHS 91A), F. with white area near beard; beards golden orange, pale violet blue at end extending as tubular white to pale violet petaloid ending in small spoon; slight sweet fragrance. Dauber's Delight X Morwenna. Sutton 1999.

DOUBLE RING CEREMONY (Hugh Thurman, R. 1998). Sdlg. 92-10-40. SDB, 13" (33 cm), M. S. white, 1/4" blue lavender rim and midrib; style arms blue violet, inside off-white with blue violet midrib; F. off-white faintly tinted chartreuse, 1/4" blue violet rim, hafts blue violet with darker veining; beards light lavender, yellow in throat; slight spicy fragrance. Court Magician X Chubby Cheeks.

DOUBLE SHOT (George Sutton, R. 1999). Sdlg. H-51 M. TB, 36" (91 cm), EML & RE. S. white, sanded violet blue; style arms violet blue; F. white, heavily striped violet blue; beards white, hairs tipped yellow; slight sweet fragrance. Point in Time X G-83: (Garden Grace x Bountiful Harvest).

DOUBLE TROUBLE (Jim Hedgecock, R. 1991). Sdlg. 84-25-2. TB, 38" (97 cm), M. Laced and ruffled medium yellow; beards orange, very wide, ending in large yellow flounce. Sunset Sonata X Sky Hooks. Comanche Acres 1992.

DOUBLE VISION (Joseph Ghio, R. 1998). Sdlg. 94-49G. TB, 32" (81 cm), EM & RE. S. gold ground, near-solid red wash; F. gold ground, overall red lining; beards brick. 92-67-I: (((85-25G: (((Handiwork x (Gay Parasol x Mystique)) x Goddess) x (Gem of Sierra x ((((Ponderosa x Honey Rae) x ((((Commentary x Claudia Rene) x Claudia Rene) x Ponderosa) x (Ponderosa x New Moon))) x Osage Buff) x (Vanity x Anon)))) x 85-180: (Indiscreet x Columbia the Gem)) x Filibuster sib) x Epicenter) X 92-159J3: (Spirit World x 90-54-I: (Chatter sib x (85-25pkfancy x (Desert Fox x Shenanigan))))). Bay View 1999.

DOUBLE WEBSITE (George Sutton, R. 1998). Sdlg. H-51-N. TB, 35" (89 cm), EML & RE. S. white ground, edges washed and veined and midib flushed wistaria blue; style arms wistaria blue; F. white washed pale wistaria blue, heavily veined dark wistaria blue, darkest at edge; beards yellow, base white, hairs at end tipped pale wistaria blue; ruffled; slight sweet fragrance. Point in Time X G-83: (Garden Grace x Bountiful Harvest).

DOUBLE WHAMMY (Donald Spoon, R. 1997). Sdlg. 93-49A. TB, 38" (97 cm), ML. S. and style arms yellow; F. white, edged yellow; beards deep yellow, light orange in throat, white 1½" slightly upturned horn at end; ruffled, flared. Triple Whammy X Twice Thrilling.

DOUG GOODNIGHT (Sharon McAllister, R. 1995). Sdlg. 86-9-13. AB (OGB+), 24" (61 cm), EM. Very dark blue violet (between RHS 83A and 103A); style arms with prominent crests; beards black. Persian Pansy X Rose of Sharon. McAllister 1995.

DO WA DIDDY (Tom Burseen, R. 1997). Sdlg. 93-33A. TB, 36" (91 cm), E. S. and style arms chrome yellow (RHS 15C); F. burgundy red (59B) washed purple black, shoulders gold; beards gold; ruffled; pronounced spicy fragrance. 90-27: (((Betty Simon x Generosity) x (Titan's Glory x Harlem Hussy)) x ((Stand and Salute x New Moon) x (Lady Friend x Bordello))) X Tender Tune. T.B.'s Place 1998.

DOWN AND DIRTY (Roy Bohrer, R. 1990). Sdlg. 90-CMSP. SDB, 14" (36 cm), E. S. brown, red violet midrib; F. red violet, veined yellow, edged brown, lavender center stripe; beards lavender tipped yellow; slight fragrance. Chartreuse Mousse X Sugar Please. Bohrer's Iris 1992.

DOWN EAST POSTLUDE (Currier McEwen, R. 1990). Sdlg. T(1)76/66B. JI (6 F.) tet., 32" (80 cm), L-VL. Light blue (RHS 97A) paling to (97C), yellow (8A) signal blended sap green (150B). Jewelled Sea X Returning Tide.

DOWNLAND (Reginald Usher, IB, R. 1969). British Iris Society 1981.

DOWNSIZED (Ben Hager, R. 1998). Sdlg. MD5967Y/LtBr. MDB, 6" (15 cm), ML. Yellow, F. washed light brown; beards white, hairs tipped yellow. MSD5495Var: (Jiffy x Nestling) X Input.

DOWN UNDER (Nora Scopes, R. 1993). Sdlg. 9S126. TB, 36" (91 cm), L. S. pale blue; F. deep rich blue purple, purple-striped shoulders with white area; beards red to tangerine; ruffled. (Rose Opal x unknown) X Magic Man.

DRACULARITY (Deborah Cole, R. 1998). Sdlg. 95-PG-7. CA , 25" (63 cm), ML. S. red, hairline pinkish white rim; style arms light gold, light red crests, pinkish white wire edge; F. dark red with darker veining, near-black signal, irregular 1/8" pinkish white rim; heavily ruffled. Parentage unknown; seed from Joe Ghio.

DRADY (Philip Edinger, R. 1999). BB 24" (61 cm), ML. S. and style arms ice white to pure white, S. with violet wire edge; F. violet, veined white on upper third; beards white at end, yellow in throat. Parentage and hybridizer unknown; in circulation prior to 1960, distributed by Mary Williamson.

DRAGON DRUMS (Barry Blyth, R. 1998). Sdlg. E110-1. TB, 34" (86 cm), EM. S. butterscotch; F. rich velvety burgundy plum to plum brown; beards mustard to old gold; sweet fragrance. B174-1: (Super Dancer x Walking Tall) X Dragon's Fancy. Tempo Two 1998/99.

DRAGONHEART (Oscar Schick, R. 1999). Sdlg. 93-41L03. TB, 38" (97 cm), M. S. dark black cherry; style arms black cherry, center blending to yellow; F. dark black cherry, starburst pattern of 1/2"-3/4" blue white veining radiating from beard; beards black cherry, hairs tipped copper; lightly ruffled; slight musky fragrance. Almaden X Lady Fire.

DRAGONSDAWN (G. F. Wilson, R. 1991). Sdlg. 15-89DVES-B. AB (OGB), 27½" (70 cm), E. S. palest mauve, yellow rib, fine yellow veining; F. pale gold buff and bright rose red blend, deeper toward black brown beard, with brown lines radiating from beard; pronounced fragrance. Dawn Victory X Esther's Son. Pleasure Iris 1993.

DRAGON'S FANCY (Barry Blyth, R. 1996). Sdlg. B217-1. TB, 34" (86 cm), ML. S. cream infused lemon, faint lavender midrib; F. rosy tan, green and violet blend, horizontally flared; beards bright tangerine. What Magic X Electrique. Tempo Two 1996/97.

DRAGON'S TOOTH (Opal Wulf, R. 1995). Sdlg. 92-07. BB, 24-26" (61-66 cm), M. S. warm white; F. burgundy, some cream to yellow shoulder veining; beards yellow gold. Payoff X Obligato. Wulf's Backachers 1999.

DRAGON TEARS (Opal Wulf, R. 1993). Sdlg. 88P-1. BB, 16-17" (41-43 cm), ML. S. red purple (RHS 59A); F. red purple (61A) with red brown (178A) shoulders and veining, violet (80A) blaze below antique gold beards. Glory Bound X Entrepreneur.

DRAKE CARNE (R. E. Nichol by Jean Nichol, R. 1998). Sdlg. S 273-10. TB, 40" (102 cm), M. S. smooth red brown (RHS 178B); style arms pale tan; F. slightly darker red brown (178A); beards soft gold; lightly ruffled; slight fragrance. J 48-1: ((((Kilt Lilt x Autumn Leaves) x Show Biz) x (Kilt Lilt x Autumn Leaves)) x (Port Lisbon x Show Biz)) X Winemaster.

DRAKE'S BAY (Ken Mohr by Bryce Williamson, R. 1995). Sdlg. Q1. TB, 34" (86 cm), M. S. light to medium lavender blue; F. medium dark lavender blue, darker wash, white spray pattern at hafts; beards lemon yellow. Handiwork X Congratulations. Pacific Coast Hybridizers 1991.

DRAMATIC BLUE (Loleta Powell, R. 1998). TB, 38" (97 cm), EML. S. medium blue deepening to violet on lower half, 1¼" light blue edge; F. medium blue, violet center; beards yellow, tipped violet; ruffled; sweet fragrance. (Timescape x Pacific Mist) X unknown. Powell's Gardens 1998.

DRAMATIC PATTERN (Currier McEwen, R. 1994). Sdlg. JT(6)87/14(2). JI (3 F.), tet., 32" (81 cm), EML. S. red purple (RHS 77A), 1/16" white edge; style arms darker purple, with 1/16" white edge and tuft; F. white ground, sanded light purple (78D), veined dark red purple, 1/8" white edge; signals bright yellow (7A), veins radiating from red purple (77A) halo. T(5)83/99(4): (Oriental Royalty sib x Japanese Pinwheel) X Japanese Pinwheel. Eartheart, Seaways 1995.

DRAMATIC PRELUDE (Calvin Helsley, R. 1990). Sdlg. 86-86. SIB, 28" (71 cm), M. S. deep blue violet; style arms blue violet, red violet veining; F. very deep blue violet, reddish infusion on hafts and occasionally on edge, large round gold signal; heavily ruffled. Ruffled Velvet X Halcyon Seas.

DREAM AWHILE (Kirk Strawn, R. 1993). Sdlg. 24-1994. LA, 48" (122 cm), M. S. purple (RHS 78B); style arms greyed purple (186C); F. purple (77A), yellow orange (14A) signal. Mrs. Ira Nelson X Kirk Strawn. Bois d'Arc 1996.

DREAM CATCHER (Sharon McAllister, R. 1993). Sdlg. 85-8-5. AB (OGB-), 30" (75 cm), M. S. ivory; F. yellowish ivory veined mulberry around edge, mulberry line signal; beards rust. Koko Knoll X Asha Michelle. McAllister 1993.

DREAM DESIRE (Kevin Nilsen, R. 1995). Sdlg. 25-89-1. TB, 35" (90 cm), EM. Light yellow, small white area in center of F.; beards deep yellow, base white. Wings of Dreams X White Lightning.

DREAM EXPRESS (Richard Tasco, R. 1998). Sdlg. 92-14-33. TB, 40" (107 cm), M. Heavily ruffled plum purple (RHS 80A), undertoned magenta, F. with thin magenta line from beard to bottom; beards purple with white base, gold in throat; sweet fragrance. Ruffled Goddess X Purple Pirouette. Superstition 1999.

DREAM FEVER (Duane Meek, R. 1993). Sdlg. 216-1-3. TB, 35" (89 cm), ML. S. mauve with pale gold flush; F. white, suggestion of mauve, ruffling and yellow petal reverse giving effect of narrow yellow rim. Chartreuse Ruffles X Trudy. D & J Gardens 1993.

DREAM INDIGO (Cy Bartlett, R. 1994). Sdlg. G-W2. IB, 23" (58 cm), M. S. storm grey; F. violet indigo; beards deep grey; waved, ruffled; moderate sweet fragrance. Gossip X Wensleydale. Sutton 1994.

DREAMING BROWN (Currier McEwen, SIB, R. 1988). Eartheart, Seaways 1994.

DREAMING CLOWN (Ladislav Muska, R. 1999). Sdlg. 98-DZCL-05. TB, 36" (91 cm), M. S. light brown, lilac veining, midrib deep lilac; style arms light brown; F. vanilla yellow ground heavily lined brown maroon, more lightly lined lilac; beards yellow mustard; ruffled, laced; sweet fragrance. Spacelight Sketch X (Zuzana x Calicoball). Muska 1999.

DREAMING LATE (Tomas Tamberg, R. 1997). SIB (tet.), 35" (89 cm), M. Large white, F. flared. SSTT177: (white McEwen tet. sdlg. x white Tamberg tet. sdlg.) X Dreaming Green. Schoeppinger 1997.

DREAMING LILAC (Barry Blyth, R. 1995). Sdlg. A110-2. TB, 36" (91 cm), VE. S. pastel lilac pink;

F. rosy lavender pink, light tan overlay extending from hafts 1/3 way down petal; beards bronze tangerine. Y6-11, Imprimis sib, X Electrique. Tempo Two 1995/96.

DREAMING STAR (Akihiko Terada, R. 1997). Sdlg. S-25-89-1. TB, 35" (89 cm), M. Ruffled pinkish beige, F. slightly deeper; beards dark orange; pronounced sweet fragrance. Sweet Musette X Inga Ivey. Roris 1997.

DREAM LORD (Barry Blyth, R. 1996). Sdlg. C185-1. TB, 38" (97 cm), VE-EM. S. orchid to icy oyster; F. red burgundy, plush finish; beards bright mustard; slight fragrance. A153-3: (And Royal x Electrique) X A80-2: (Y2-1, Royal Honey sib, x Chocolate Vanilla). Tempo Two 1996/97.

DREAM MACHINE (Sid DuBose, TB, R. 1988). Correction of parentage. My Valentine X Condottiere.

DREAM MASTER (Frederick Kerr, R. 1996). Sdlg. 88-05-1. TB, 39" (99 cm), ML. S. blue white, slight blue midrib infusion; F. medium blue, slight violet influence, paler around beard; beards yellow, tipped orange; ruffled; slight fragrance. Mystique X Condottiere. Rainbow Acres 1996.

DREAM OF GOLD (Paul Black, R. 1997). Sdlg. 88105A. TB, 36" (91 cm), S. and style arms brassy gold; F. gold ground sanded rust, brassy gold margin, gold-veined white around orange gold beard; ruffled. 85128A (Love Sonnet x Pencil Sketch) X Wild Jasmine. Mid-America 1997.

DREAM OF YOU (Frederick Kerr, R. 1994). Sdlg. 87-12-02. TB, 39" (99 cm), M. S. pastel dawn blue, blending to wide misty lemondrop yellow edge; F. dark ultraviolet blue, lavender edge tinted yellow, hafts brown; beards orange, tipped blue; ruffled; slight fragrance. Dover Beach X Twist of Fate. Rainbow Acres 1994.

DREAM ON DREAM (Robert Barker, R. 1999). Sdlg. Y2000. SIB, 24" (61 cm), M. S. silver white; style arms translucent white, violet infusion; F. silver white, large yellow haft area, yellow signal; ruffled; flat form. Parentage unknown.

DREAMS (Clarence Mahan, R. 1990). Sdlg. 90901. SIB, 36" (91 cm), EM. Deep red violet, green at hafts changing to gold, large white blaze extending from gold signal. "Kamayama" X unknown.

DREAM SCENE (Duane Meek, R. 1999). Sdlg. 83-1-1. TB, 35" (89 cm), ML. Ruffled and laced deep fluorescent violet, hafts darker; beards fluorescent violet, hairs tipped cinnamon in throat. Awakening X Spring Tidings. D & J Gardens 1999.

DREAMSICLE (Schreiner, R. 1995). Sdlg. BB 1642-1. TB, 36" (91 cm), M. Pink (RHS 49B) self; beards rose pink. Cotton Club X Bright Fire. Schreiner 1995.

DREAMSICLE SODA (Jim Hedgecock, R. 1992). Sdlg. 84-6-X. TB, 34" (86 cm), M. S. pale orange; F. white, orange hafts; beards reddish orange; ruffled, laced; pronounced sweet fragrance. Sun Fire X Mandolin.

DREAMWALKER (Oscar Schick, R. 1996). Sdlg. 92-32A01. TB, 36-38" (91-97 cm), M. Ruffled violet (RHS 88B), F. lightening to white in center; style arms light violet; beards yellow, white at end; slight musky fragrance. Envisioned Dream X Street Walker. Stockton 1997.

DREAM WALTZ (A. & D. Willott, IB, R. 1988). Willott 1990.

DREAM WISH (Richard Morgan, R. 1997). Sdlg. L782-A. LA, 21" (53 cm), L. Small-flowered apricot yellow, small apricot line signal; style arms light rose. LO-A, unknown (possibly inv. Missey Reveley or Gold Reserve) X L64-T, yellow Tomato Bisque sib. Redbud Lane 1999.

DRESDEN CANARY (Joyce Ragle, R. 1995). Sdlg. 87-18CIMR-1. SDB, 9-10" (23-25 cm), EM & RE. S. dresden yellow (HCC 64/2); style arms yellow; F. dresden yellow (64/1); beards pastel lavender (440). Canary Isle X Mister Roberts.

DRESDEN DANCER (John Knaus, TB, R. 1989). Knaus 1990.

DRESS CODE (Bryce Williamson, R. 1996). Sdlg. A-10-B. TB, 34" (86 cm), ML. S. and style arms rose violet; F. rose violet, shoulders blended pink; beards tangerine red; ruffled, lightly laced; slight sweet fragrance. Love Poem X Extravagant.

DRESSED IN BLUE (Duane Meek, R. 1992). Sdlg. 398-4-8. CA, 14" (36 cm), EM. S. white ground, blue plicata markings; F. white, blue plicata markings on border. ((*I. tenax* x *I. innominata*) x Encircle) X Tunitas. D & J Gardens 1992.

DRESS PINKS (Sharon McAllister, R. 1998). Sdlg. 89-15-2. AB (OGB-), 30" (76 cm), ML. S. pinkish tan; style arms and F. slightly darker pinkish tan, F. stippled burgundy around yellow beard. Hunt LBE-1: (Lovely Blanche x Eunice) X Sunrise in Glory. McAllister 1998.

DRESS WHITES (Harry Hite by Jack Norrick, R. 1992). Sdlg. Y212-1. SDB, 9" (23 cm), M. S. white; F. white, faint blue wash; beards yellow, tipped gold; slight sweet fragrance. Parentage unknown. Adamgrove 1992.

DREVNI RIM (Sergey Loktev, R. 1995). TB, 36" (91 cm), E. Lightly ruffled violet, F. with blackish cast; beards yellow. Bang X Stepping Out. Loktev 1995.

DRIFTING TIDE (Henry Danielson by Luella Danielson, R. 1992). Sdlg. HD-11. AB (OGB), 25" (64 cm), M. S. lavender blue, midrib touched green; style arms deeper lavender blue; F. lavender blue, green touch intensifying toward edge; violet signal line markings; beards black. Dee Mouse X Pleasure Ahead. Pleasure Iris 1993.

DROP O' CREAM (Richard Sparling, R. 1991). MDB, 6-7" (15-18 cm), L. Cream; beards cream. Parentage unknown. Green Box Iris 1991.

DROP OF WINE (Floyd Dyer, R. 1991). Sdlg. D-160-85-D. SDB, 13" (33 cm), M. Pale blue; beards dark blue violet; slight sweet fragrance. D-108-81-D: (((Lilli-White x Papoose) x self) x Gingerbread Man) X D-112-81-D: (B. Jones 226-31G x self). Four Cedars 1991.

DROPS OF BRANDY (Marty Schafer/Jan Sacks, R. 1998). Sdlg. S92-67-1. SIB, 27" (69 cm), ML. S. pale blue (RHS 97D), faint darker dappling and veining; style arms semi-upright, pearly blue with some dark blue violet edging, blue green midrib, large light yellow floret crest; F. washed medium blue, paler (97D) 1/2" diffuse edge, darker blue violet (94C) shoulders, small white to yellow signal veined blue violet; ruffled. S89-9-2: (Isabelle x Silver Illusion) X Careless Sally. Joe Pye Weed 1998.

DROP THE HANKY (Tom Burseen, R. 1995). Sdlg. 8-23A. TB, 36" (91 cm), M. S. white, midrib violet (RHS 84B); style arms white, washed violet; F. violet, white wash from beard area; beards white, tipped orange; ruffled; sweet fragrance. Electrabrite X 6-252: (Glory Bound x (Tiburon x Sunny Lilac)). T.B.'s Place 1995.

DRUID'S CHANT (Chet Tompkins, R. 1997). Sdlg. 93-52. TB, 39" (99 cm), ML. S. and style arms apricot, cadmium yellow and chamois buff blend, flushed coppery cocoa; F. smoother red violet blend, lighter near beard, cocoa brown edging; beards reddish blue purple; heavily ruffled. (((Sound and Fury x Dark Twilight) x ((Burgermeister x Adventuress) x inv. Mountain Music)) x (Syncopation x (Jungle Dusk x Syncopation))) X (In Town x Syncopation). Fleur de Lis 1997.

DRUM ROLL (Ben Hager, R. 1992). Sdlg. T5020RfVBl. TB, 34" (86 cm), ML. Heavily ruffled full blue violet, self beards. T4229LaCobBl: (((Geometrics x Ice Sculpture) x Avalon Bay) x Ron) X T4216WLcLv: ((Silver Flow x Ruffled Ballet) x T3703RfV, Mother Earth sib). Melrose 1992.

DRUM SONG (Barry Blyth, R. 1993). Sdlg. Z28-2. IB, 25" (64 cm), EML. S. white; F. butter yellow; beards lemon, outer 1/2" pastel lavender. Gifted X Chocolate Vanilla. Tempo Two 1993/94.

DUANE'S BAD BOY (Duane Meek, R. 1995). Sdlg. 15-1-2. CA, 12" (31 cm), ML. S. deep red black; style arms red black; F. red black, with coal black signal covering most of petal except rim. Stroke of Midnight X Up All Night. D & J Gardens 1995.

DUBLIN (Keith Keppel, R. 1997). Sdlg. 91-41B. IB, 20" (51 cm), M. Clear light pink (M&P 2-C-1), S. with faint orchid flush on inside base, F. with paler and creamier (1-A-7/8) center; beards pale vervain violet (42-B-6) at end, white with light yellow hair tips in center, light yellow faintly tipped orange in heart; sweet fragrance. Sib to Donegal. Keppel 1998.

DUDDY (Sterling Innerst, R. 1999). Sdlg. 4321-5. SDB, 14" (36 cm), M. S. bronze; F. brown bronze, bronze gold feathered trim; beards orange tipped white. Learn X Neon Pixie.

DUDLÍK (Jiří Dudek, R. 1998). Sdlg. SB 1. SIB, 18" (45 cm), M. Light purple blue, F. with white signal veined dark violet. I. sanguinea X unknown. Jiří Dudek 1997.

DUENNA (Nora Scopes, R. 1993). Sdlg. 36A. CA, 15" (38 cm), M. Deep purple, lighter in center of F. Las Olas X unknown.

DUERME (Ben Hager, R. 1992). Sdlg. S897DpV. SPU, 38" (97 cm), M. Deep purple, gold veining from throat to 1/3 down F.; style arms purple, crests deeper. Crow Wing X Far Out. Cordon Bleu 1992.

DUKE OF DUBUQUE (Richard Freund by Joseph Stien, R. 1999). Sdlg. F85N1. TB, 31" (79 cm), ML. Ruffled navy blue self; beards navy blue. Navy Strut X Deep Pacific.

DULAS (Harry Foster, R. 1991). Sdlg. R51/87. SIB (tet.), 37" (94 cm), L. S. rich dark purple blue; F. same, center rose purple, strong silver edge; ruffled. Dear Dianne X Reddy Maid.

DULCET (Ben Hager, R. 1998). Sdlg. MD5152WhChtHftsT. MDB, 6" (15 cm), M. S. white; style arms cream white; F. white, chartreuse haft wash; beards white. Sib to Nestling.

DUMBLEDORE (Sterling Innerst, R. 1999). Sdlg. 4700-1. IB, 19" (48 cm), ML. White, F. with red spot; beards yellow; slight spicy fragrance. Re 3163-5: (1851-1: ((Appalachian Spring x Navy Strut) x (710-1: (Captain Jack x Warm Laughter) x 710-2, sib)) x Twice Delightful) X Smart.

DUNAVERTY (Revie Harvey, R. 1990). Sdlg. 80/R/59. TB, 38" (96 cm), M. S. oxblood red; F.

deeper, distinct brown haft infusion; beards self, tipped blue; slight fragrance. Superstition X Dutch Chocolate. Catton 1991.

DUNE SEA (Donald Spoon, R. 1999). Sdlg. 88-35D. TB, 34" (86 cm), M & RE (Oct/VA). S. and style arms rose; F. plum, prominent white ray pattern; beards yellow; ruffled. Winter Olympics X Spinning Wheel. Winterberry 1999.

DUNKLER WEIN (Tomas Tamberg, R. 1995). Sdlg. SSTT 266. SIB (tet.), 31" (80 cm), M. Deep wine red, F. velvety. Wine red McEwen sdlg. X converted sdlg.: (Apfelblute x Wine Wings). Schoeppinger 1995.

DUNN DEAL (Robert Dunn, R. 1995). Sdlg. B858-1. TB, 38" (97 cm), M. S. champagne cream, style arms deeper cream, slight lilac stain; F. champagne cream, deeper hafts and tiny outer edge, slight opalescent lilac cast toward center; beards golden, end paler, with lilac cast. Pina Colada X Brandy. M.A.D. Iris 1998.

DUNNGAREES (Robert Dunn, R. 1990). Sdlg. B84-882-4A. TB, 34" (86 cm), M. Ruffled smooth pale blue, F. with hints of turquoise; beards pale yellow. Bubbling Over X Blue Maxx. M.A.D. Iris 1990.

DUNSMUIR (Bob Brown, R. 1991). Sdlg. 86-36. TB, 36" (91 cm), ML. Dark red purple (RHS 86A); beards near-white. Titan's Glory X 81-23: (Night Hawk x (His Lordship x (White King x Royal Gold))). Cottage 1992.

DUO DANDY (Ben Hager, R. 1998). Sdlg. RE5319Am#1. TB, 32" (81 cm), E & RE. S. and style arms blue white; F. medium blue; beards white, hairs tipped yellow except at end. RE5071Tn/Lv: (Mother Earth x Feedback) X Christopher Columbus. Cooley 1999.

DURAGLOW (Opal Brown, R. 1991). Sdlg. 82-6B30. TB, 36" (91 cm), M. Ruffled, lightly laced yellow (RHS 12A), white area veined yellow below yellow (12A) beard. Big Dipper X 78-4A20: (Bride's Halo x ((Grandiflora x Arctic Flame) x Buffy)). Brown's Sunnyhill 1991.

DURAL BLUEBIRD (John C. Taylor, R. 1993). Sdlg. RL 8-B. LA, 44" (110 cm), ML. Ruffled blue violet, yellow signal. Dural White Butterfly X Margaret Lee. Rainbow Ridge 1993/94.

DURAL BREAKAWAY (John C. Taylor, R. 1997). Sdlg. RL 56-1. LA, 47" (120 cm), E. S. and F. red purple, light buff edge and reverse, prominent yellow signal with green center; style arms yellow green, edged light purple. OL 107-1: (Gentleman x Limited Edition) X Margaret Lee. Rainbow Ridge 1997/98.

DURAL DREAMTIME (John C. Taylor, R. 1991). Sdlg. OL 118-2. LA, 43" (110 cm), M. White, veined greenish yellow. Jazz Ballet X Dural White Butterfly. Rainbow Ridge 1992/93.

DURAL FANTASY (John C. Taylor, R. 1994). Sdlg. RL 14-2. LA, 48" (120 cm), M. S. white flushed mauve; style arms greenish yellow, tipped mauve and white; F. mauve violet, signal yellow; ruffled. Lavender Ruffles X Margaret Lee. Rainbow Ridge 1994/95.

DURAL LATECOMER (John C. Taylor, R. 1997). Sdlg. OL 137-G. LA, 39" (100 cm), ML. S. blended pink and white, darker centerline; style arms cream, pink edge; F. purple pink, lighter edge, yellow signal. Dazzling Star X Helen Naish. Rainbow Ridge 1997/98.

DURAL PEACOCK (Graeme Grosvenor, R. 1997). Sdlg. JO-1. JI (3 F.), 37" (95 cm), M. S. and F. white, lined and edged dark blue violet, F. with yellow signal; style arms indigo purple; flowers sometimes 6-falled. Jocasta X unknown. Rainbow Ridge 1997/98.

DURAL SNOWFLAKE (Graeme Grosvenor, R. 1999). Sdlg. V71-1. TB, 36" (91 cm), ML. White self; beards white; slight fragrance. Temptone X Think Big. Rainbow Ridge 1999/2000.

DURHAM DREAM (Lloyd Zurbrigg, R. 1999). Sdlg. LL 206-4-1. TB, 40" (107 cm), ML. S. violet, blended yellow and red; style arms violet, heavily blended yellow; F. blended violet, hafts and heart prominently flushed bright yellow; beards yellow, 3/4" blended violet horn. Moonlit X Anew.

DUSKY BILLABONG (Jo Tunney, R. 1998). AB (OGB), 29" (73 cm), M. S. violet (RHS 87B), veined darker, laced; style arms greyed red (181D), large lacy crests; F. beetroot purple (71A), veined and speckled darker, bright purple (80B) center, dark purple black (187A) thumbprint signal; beards violet, tipped ochre; slight sweet fragrance. Cool Oasis X Aril World.

DUSKY DOLL (Beryl Pederick, R. 1994). Sdlg. 1. BB, 27" (69 cm), M. S. chrome yellow, brown infusion; F. brown, 1/2" chrome yellow (RHS 15C) edge; beards orange; slight fragrance. Beachgirl X Spanish Gift.

#DUSKY JEWEL (Bryce Williamson, TB, R. 1975). Name released 1990.

DUSKY JEWEL (Bryce Williamson, R. 1990). TB, 34" (86 cm), M & occasional RE. Ruffled rich raspberry violet, violet blaze on F.; beards tangerine to violet; ruffled, lightly laced; slight fragrance. Lilac Flame X Love Poem. Pacific Coast Hybridizers 1990.

DUSTY FIDDLES (Nora Scopes, R. 1992). Sdlg. PC21. CA, 12" (30 cm), M. S. purple; F. blue purple, edged lighter, yellow signal. Sdlg. X sdlg.

DUSTY RUFFLES (Dorothy Guild, MTB, R. 1989). Ohio Gardens 1991.

DU TOIT (Ladislav Muska, R. 1999). Sdlg. 98-MHVA-08. TB, 34" (86 cm), L. S. medium cream; style arms white, yellow band; F. cream with yellow veining, narrow gold rim; beards light yellow, orchid horn; ruffled, lightly laced; slight fragrance. (((Mys Horn x Visual Arts) x Sky Hooks) x Lady Madonna) X Soissons. Muska 1999.

DVORIANIN (Viacheslav Gavrilin, R. 1999). Sdlg. 6-13-1-94. TB, 32" (82 cm), M. Ruffled warm pink; beards orange. Trevi Fountain X Beverly Sills. Gavrilin 1999.

DWAYNE STONEKING (Glenn Stoneking-Jones, R. 1998). Sdlg. CSIB6-124-07-21-1995. SIB, 26" (66 cm), M. S. white, veined blue; F. bluish white, veined blue. (Caesar's Brother x *I. missouriensis*) X (Snowcrest x *I. missouriensis*). Orin 1999.

DWIGHT ENYS (R. E. Nichol, R. 1995). Sdlg. Q10. TB, 34" (86 cm), EM. S. yellow; F. dark red brown, some haft marking; beards butterscotch; ruffled. From sdlgs. inv. Kilt Lilt, Sketch Me, Show Biz, and Doctor Behenna.

DYNAMIC DUO (Tom Burseen, R. 1995). Sdlg. 8-370A. TB, 36" (91 cm), ML. S. and style arms tannish brown, shaded purple; F. golden brown; beards bright gold; ruffled. My Oh Mio X Norwegian Wood. T.B.'s Place 1996.

DYNAMIC IMPACT (Donald Delmez, R. 1994). Sdlg. WIDR-1. JI (6 F.), 27" (69 cm), E. Dark wine red self, signals yellow; style arms and petaloids darker wine red; ruffled. Yamataikoku X Royal Game. Delmez Gardens 1994.

#DYNAMITE (Robert Schreiner, TB, R. 1950). Not introduced or distributed; name transferred.

DYNAMITE (Schreiner, R. 1997). Sdlg. CC 618-A. TB, 37" (94 cm), M. Cardinal red (RHS 53A) self; beards yellow. War Chief X 1984 #37, unknown. Schreiner 1997.

DYSELBREOK (Siegmar Goerbitz, R. 1991). Sdlg. 8536C1. TB, 39" (100 cm), M. Ruffled medium violet; beards yellow orange, tipped blue. (Cerulean Blue x Stepping Out) X (Powder Snow x Rondo). Schoeppinger 1991.

DYSON MOORE (Tony Huber, R. 1998). Sdlg. 92-143 (sel. 95-183). SPEC-X (reensata), 35" (90 cm), ML. S. violet (RHS 83B); style arms deep lilac (76A), crest aster violet (87B); F. violet, bright yellow signal with yellow line extending outward; slight sweet fragrance. 90-163: (*I. versicolor* Mag-Pk-85 x magenta *I. ensata* sdlg.) X Raspberry Rimmed.

DZHIGIT (Viktor Koroliov, R. 1999). Sdlg. S118-95K. TB, 39" (98 cm), M. S. yellow, tinted tan; style arms yellow, brownish wash; F. wine red, yellow brown haft pattern; beards orange yellow; ruffled, laced; slight spicy fragrance. "Borokko" X Vitafire. Koroliov 1998.

DZVINKA (Oleg Amekhin, R. 1996). Sdlg. SNK-1. TB, 36" (91 cm), M. S. blue white; F. blue violet, narrow whitish edge; beards pale yellow. Helen Collingwood X Superlation. Amekhin 1996.

EAGLE CONTROL (George Sutton, R. 1998). Sdlg. G-65. TB, 36" (91 cm), ML. S. and style arms lobelia blue (RHS 91C); F. pale lobelia blue (91D) to near-white, blending deeper (91C) at centerline; beards pale lobelia blue, some yellow deep in throat, pale lobelia blue horn; ruffled, lightly laced. Dauber's Surprise X Honky Tonk Blues. Sutton 1999.

EAGLE EYES (Joseph Ghio, R. 1992). Sdlg. PH-294V2. CA, 18" (46 cm), EM. S. peach; F. peach, maroon signal, maroon overall veining. (Refugio x PM-210T: (Elberta Peach sib x ((Banbury Candy x Simply Wild) x (San Vicente x Emigrant)))) X PJ-181C2: ((Peanut Gallery x ((Pacific Moon x California Native) x San Vicente sib)) x (Running Wild x (Simply Wild x Camp Capitola sib))). Bay View 1993.

EAGLE LANDING (George Sutton, R. 1999). Sdlg. G-84B. TB, 37" (94 cm), ML. Ruffled white; beards white, hairs tipped pale yellow except at end, white horn; slight sweet fragrance. Mesmerizer X Silverado.

EAGLE'S SONG (Kevin Nilsen, R. 1995). Sdlg. 37-90-1. TB, 36" (91 cm), EM. S. violet purple, base suffused white; style arms violet and white; F. white, stitched and peppered violet purple; beards deep yellow, hairs tipped violet in throat, bushy. Eagle's Flight X Jesse's Song.

EAGLE'S WING (Chun Fan, R. 1990). Sdlg. 86-36. TB, 40" (102 cm), L. Light violet blue; beards deep blue; slight fragrance. Navy Strut X Song of Norway. Fan's Iris 1997.

EARDISLAND (John D. Taylor, IB, R. 1985). V. H. Humphrey 1993.

EARLIGLO (Paul Black, R. 1991). Sdlg. 89229A. SDB, 12" (30 cm), M. S. diamond-dusted pale chartreuse blending to cream edge; F. warm greenish white with lime green veined spot; beards bright yellow orange, end tipped cream; slight spicy fragrance. Toy Boat X 85420B: ((Pulse Rate x Mister Roberts) x (Dove Wings x unknown)). Mid-America 1996.

EARLY AMERICAN (Bennett Jones, TB, R. 1957). Correction of information in 1959 Checklist. (Howard Weed x Susitna Sunset) X Inca Chief.

EARLY LIGHT (Nora Scopes, TB, R. 1983. British Iris Society 1989.

EARLY RISER (Donald Sorensen, R. 1998). Sdlg. S-92-11-1. SDB, 8½" (21 cm), VE. S. light barium yellow (RHS 10C), midrib darker straw yellow (13C); style arms straw yellow (13D), powder blue edge; F. light barium yellow (10B), brown (177A) thumbprint surrounded by bright sulphur yellow (6A), sulphur yellow wire edge; beards powder blue violet (97A); slight musky fragrance. Cincinnati Kid X unknown. Birchwood 1999.

EARTH AND FIRE (Frederick Held, R. 1996). Sdlg. O4. JI (3 F.), 36" (91 cm), M. S. reddish purple; style arms bluish purple; F. medium purple marbled on white, glistening white edge. Parentage unknown; seed from Jelitto Staudensamen, Germany. Nature's Garden 1997.

#EARTHBORN (Ben Hager, SIB, R. 1981). Not introduced or distributed. Name released 1992.

EARTHBORN (Ben Hager, R. 1992). Sdlg. T5292Br/Sal#3W. TB, 33" (84 cm), M. S. brown infused purple; F. salmon bronze edged brown; beards tangerine. T5033: (Fringe Benefits sib x Good Show) X T4595TBrW: (T4291TBr: (3897YTBds: (Golden Brilliance x Glowing Ruffles) x Perfect Accent) x Flaming Victory). Melrose 1993.

EARTHENWARE (William Plotner, TB, R. 1989). Wildwood Gardens 1990.

EARTHQUAKE (Joseph Ghio, R. 1990). Sdlg. PJ-181C2. CA, 15" (38 cm), ML. S. russet; style arms gold; F. red, light gold rim. PL-226A2: (Peanut Gallery x (((Pacific Moon x California Native) x San Vicente sib) x Mission Santa Cruz)) X PL-257C3: (Running Wild x (Simply Wild x Camp Capitola sib)). Bay View 1991.

EARTH'S DARK ANGEL (Gordon Nicholson, R. 1998). Sdlg. G-MT#2. TB, 40" (107 cm), M. Deep purple self, F. shoulders slightly reddish; beards purple, hairs tipped blue; fluted, laced; pronounced spicy fragrance. Master Touch X unknown. Woodland Iris 1998.

EARTH SONG (Evelyn Kegerise, R. 1992). Sdlg. 87-806-1. TB, 35-36" (89-91 cm), ML. S. yellow; F. violet, edge lighter; beards yellow, mustard in throat; ruffled; slight sweet fragrance. Edith Wolford X Helen Wanner. Evelyn Kegerise 1993.

EAST COAST (Maxine McCall, R. 1990). Sdlg. 205. TB, 34" (86 cm), M. Ruffled pink with lavender blush; beards coral, tipped white; slight fragrance. Vanity X Strawberry Sensation. McCall 1991.

EAST COAST BLUES (Maxine McCall, R. 1990). Sdlg. 8601. TB, 34" (86 cm), ML. Ruffled blue; beards blue; slight fragrance. St. Louis Blues X unknown. McCall 1991.

EASTER (Keith Keppel, R. 1995). Sdlg. 91-60A. SDB, 15" (38 cm), EM. S. martius yellow (M&P 9-IJ-1) reverse and 1/8" border, pale lavender blue (33-A-7) washed plicata edge, warm white center; style arms chrome lemon (9-L-2); F. aureolin yellow (10-L-2), 1/8" outer rim, soft lavender blue plic border and faint centerline, white center; beards deep chrome yellow (9-L-7), white base, lavender blue at end; slight sweet fragrance. Le Flirt X Gatty W37-18, sib to Quote. Keppel 1996.

EASTER CLOUDS (Ed Roberts, R. 1994). Sdlg. 899. TB, 32" (81 cm), EM. S. white, midrib touched peach; style arms peach, tipped white; F. peach with thin white rim; beards orange. Love Chant X Peach Spot. Ed Roberts 1995.

EASTER COLORS (Ben Hager, R. 1991). Sdlg. S944Lv/Y. SPU, 39" (99 cm), EM. S. and style crests orchid; F. cream yellow, yellow signal. S690BchB: (S447K, Ila Crawford sib, x (Farolito x Arbitrator)) X S706Bl/Y: ((Marilyn Holloway x S300G: (Port of Call x Farolito)) x (S300G x Blue Spiderweb)). Cordon Bleu 1991.

EASTER DAY (Cloyd McCord, R. 1997). Sdlg. 607. TB, 36" (91 cm), M. Bright yellow self; beards yellow; sweet fragrance. Queen of Love X Lovely Spring. McCord 1997.

EASTER EGG HUNT (Joseph Ghio, R. 1996). Sdlg. PE-187-A3. CA, 13" (33 cm), M. Orchid pink self, F. with yellow line signal. Charter Member X PG-185pink: (PI-MIX-Y, unknown, x PI-MIX-A, unknown). Bay View 1996.

EASTER REMEMBERED (W. H. Clough, R. 1997). Sdlg. W-88. TB, 32" (81 cm), M. Ruffled snow white self; beards white, light yellow in throat; slight sweet fragrance. Parentage unknown.

EASTER TREASURE (A. & D. Willott, R. 1994). Sdlg. 90-47. SDB, 12" (30 cm), M. S. creamy white tinted blue; F. light greenish yellow; beards light blue; lightly ruffled. Nachos X Pilgrims' Choice. Willott 1994.

EASTFIELD KING (C. R. King, R. 1994). Sdlg. 2 CRK 93. TB, 44" (112 cm), E. S. pale yellow; F. burgundy, heavily veined; beards yellow; ruffled; slight fragrance. Parentage unknown.

EAST INDIAMAN (Nora Scopes, R. 1994). Sdlg. 9S143C. TB, 37" (94 cm), ML. S. white; F. pale blue deepening at edges; beards tangerine; ruffled, flared; sweet fragrance. China Seas X 3/179, China Seas sib.

EAST INDIAN SPICE (James Gibson by Cooley's Gardens, R. 1996). Sdlg. 7-5A. TB, 35" (89 cm), EM. S. amber gold (RHS 163A to 17A), brown orange (171A) midrib and flecking; F. gold (near 13B), 1/2" plicata rim and sanded pattern of orange brown (172B); beards orange yellow (23A); ruffled, laced; slight spicy sweet fragrance. Magic Hope X Gigolo. Cooley 1997.

EASY MOOD (Harold Stahly, R. 1996). Sdlg. 89-4. TB, 36" (91 cm), M. S. pale yellow; style arms cream; F. creamy white, pale yellow marginal band, very light brownish violet plicata markings on hafts and around beard; beards bronze, base blue violet; ruffled. Cuddles X Haversham. Stahly 1996.

EASY STYLE (Paul Black, R. 1990). Sdlg. 86356E. SDB, 12" (30 cm), M. S. and style arms violet blue; F. violet blue mostly overlaid maroon, violet blue ray pattern around beard; beards dark violet, tipped pale blue; pronounced fragrance. 83154G: (Cindy Mitchell x Joyous Isle) X 84272B: (Cindy Mitchell x unknown). Mid-America 1990.

EASY TO SEE (O. D. Niswonger, R. 1998). Sdlg. SDB 17-95. SDB, 12" (31 cm), ML. S. and style arms violet; F. violet plicata marking, white central area; beards blue on end and hair tips, marigold orange base and in throat. Plum Ripples X unknown. Cape Iris 1998.

EAU VIVE (Richard Cayeux, R. 1997). Sdlg. 8884 B. TB, 34" (85 cm), M. Medium blue self, lightly tinted lavender; beards orange. 8461, Ruban Bleu sib, X Skyblaze. Cayeux 1998.

EBONY DREAM (Harold Stahly, R. 1993). Sdlg. 86-1. TB, 33" (84 cm), EM. S. deep violet black, F. slightly deeper; beards black; ruffled. Superstition X Black Flag. Stahly 1993.

EBONY EYES (Cleo Palmer, R. 1993). Sdlg. 8321. SDB, 14" (36 cm), E. S. red purple; F. reddish black, near-black spot; beards bronze, tipped light violet; slight sweet fragrance. Tease X 6730: (Bloodspot x Cherry Garden). Palmer's Iris 1993.

EBONY TAN DOUBLE (Austin Morgan, R. 1990). TB, 36" (91 cm), EM. S. dark tan; F. precise tan outer rim on smooth ebony red, tiny red inner rim; beards bronze yellow. Parentage unknown. Iris Test Gardens 1986.

ECHOES (Barry Blyth, R. 1996). Sdlg. C28-2. SDB, 12" (30 cm), VE. S. and F. white, stitched bright lavender blue; beards white, lightly tipped tangerine in throat. A30-4: (Taja x X32-2: (Yipee x sib)) X A14-8, Toff sib. Tempo Two 1996/97.

ECHO THE WIND (Marty Schafer/Jan Sacks, R. 1999). Sdlg. S92-67-5. SIB, 31" (79 cm), EM. S. light blue violet (RHS 97B/C), lighter edge, slightly darker veins; style arms pearly light blue, blue green midrib, yellow tips; F. blue violet over yellow base, large yellow signal with deep blue veins, 1/16"-1/8" canary yellow petal rim. S89-9-2: (Isabelle x Silver Illusion) X Careless Sally. Joe Pye Weed 1999.

ECHUNGA (Ivar Schmidt, R. 1995). Sdlg. PC 89-AE. CA, 14" (36 cm), ML. S. pale mauve, midribs rosy violet; style arms pale mauve; F. bright rosy violet, edged mauve, signals yellow, heavily veined rosy violet. Nayook X unknown. Iris Acres 1995/96.

ECO BLUE BOY (Don Jacobs, R. 1993). SPEC (*verna*), 4" (10 cm), M. Violet blue (RHS 98C), yellow orange (23B) signal fading to ivory (19D) on outer edge; sweet fragrance. Selection of *I. verna smalliana* collected 1982 in Bartow County, Georgia. Eco Gardens 1985.

ECO LITTLE BLUEBIRD (Don Jacobs, R. 1993). SPEC (*cristata*), 3" (7-8 cm), M. Blue (RHS 96C), orange inner signal, ivory outer signal bordered violet (83B). Selection of *I. cristata* collected 1976 in Fannin County, Georgia. Eco Gardens 1979.

ECO ORCHID GIANT (Don Jacobs, R. 1993), SPEC (*cristata*), 4-5" (10-12 cm), M. Purple (RHS 91B), yellow orange (23A) signal bordered dark violet (83B). Selection of *I. cristata* collected 1988 in Murray County, Georgia. Eco Gardens 1992.

ECO PURPLE POMP (Don Jacobs, R. 1993). SPEC (*cristata*), 4" (10 cm), M. Dark violet (RHS 88A), white signal bordered very dark violet (83A) and with three prominent crests, middle crest brushed orange (24A). Selection of *I. cristata* collected 1988 in Murray County, Georgia. Eco Gardens 1992.

ECO ROYAL RUFFLES (Don Jacobs, R. 1993). SPEC (*cristata*), 4" (10 cm), M. Purple (RHS 91A), large white signal bordered dark violet (83A) and with three prominent crests and slight inward orange wash; ruffled. Selection of *I. cristata* collected 1970 in Union County, Georgia. Eco Gardens 1976.

ECO SNOW BUNTING (Don Jacobs, R. 1993). SPEC (*verna*), 4" (10 cm), M. White, yellow orange (RHS 23B) signal; sweet fragrance. Selection of *I. verna smalliana* collected 1985 in Murray County, Georgia. Eco Gardens 1987.

ECO VIOLET (Don Jacobs, R. 1993). SPEC (*verna*), 4" (10 cm), M. Violet (RHS 94B), dark violet (93A) crescent around orange (24A) signal; sweet fragrance. Selection of *I. verna smalliana* collected 1982 in Bartow County, Georgia. Eco Gardens 1985.

ECRU TO YOU (Jerry Hall, R. 1999). Sdlg. 93-02-A. TB, 42" (107 cm), L. S. cream; F. ecru, delicate gold edge; beards yellow, touched blue at end; ruffled; slight sweet fragrance. Chief Hematite X Song of Norway.

EDALE (B.L.C. Dodsworth, TB, R. 1989). Iris Garden 1993.

EDGED DELIGHT (William Ackerman, R. 1990). Sdlg. A4-6-123. JI (3 F.), 34" (86 cm), M. S. white, 1/8" dark purple (RHS 77A) margin; style arms white; F. white, ruffled margin, yellow green (150A) signal. D5-12-115, inv. sdlgs. from Seiko-en Nursery X D5-12-133. Nicholls Gardens 1994.

EDGE OF DARKNESS (Mary Dunn, R. 1996). Sdlg. M940-6. TB, 36" (91 cm), M. S. nearly solid deep plum purple; style arms plum; F. white ground, wide plum purple edge and flecks on haft; beards violet plum, hairs tipped mustard. Patterns X Charmed Life. M.A.D. Iris 1998.

EDITH ANDERSON (Hooker Nichols, R. 1991). Sdlg. 88402. TB, 30" (76 cm), ML. Smooth creamy peach; beards tangerine. Academy Awards X Oklahoma Sunshine. Hillcrest 1995.

EDITH BUBBLES (Monty Byers by Lawrence Ransom, R. 1994). Sdlg. EWxBL-1. TB, 33" (84 cm), M. S. pale creamy yellow, deeper base; F. white, slight yellow shoulder venation, frosty silver edges; beards light yellow, base white; ruffled, lightly laced; pronounced sweet fragrance. Edith Wolford X Bubbling Lace. Iris au Trescols 1995.

EDITH FRANKLIN (Gary Porterfield, R. 1999). Sdlg. 92-513-3. TB, 33-35" (84-89 cm), ML. Ruffled golden yellow, F. with veined white highlights beside orange beard; slight sweet fragrance. Good Show X Yukon Fever.

EDITH P. WHEELER (James McWhirter, R. 1994). Sdlg. J89-89-1. TB, 36" (91 cm), ML. S. ochre gold-honey caramel; style arms gold; F. brown burgundy blend, violet blaze; beards gold; ruffled; pronounced sweet fragrance. Brandy X Enchanting. Stockton 1995.

EDITH'S COLOR (B. Charles Jenkins, SPU, R. 1989). Shepard Iris 1992.

EDONISHIKI (Society for Japanese Irises, R. 1994). JI (3 F.), 31" (80 cm), EM. S. red violet edged white; style arms red violet, crests white; F. pale lavender with bold red violet veining; old Edo type. Parentage unknown. Introduced in Japan prior to 1912.

EDUARDO KAC (George Gessert, R. 1999). Sdlg. 90-36D. CA, 13" (33 cm), M. S. pale lavender, center darker purple; style arms pale lavender, purple rib; F. with white signal brushed yellow and veined dark purple, surrounded by blackish blaze fading to rich purple, veins extending to near thin border of lavender. Rainer von der Schulenburg X Olaf Stapledon: (All Around x collected "Valley Banner type").

EDWARD OF WINDSOR (Cedric Morris, TB, R. 1945). Correction of typographical error (EDWARD WINDSOR) in 1949 Check List.

EFFERVESCENCE (Cayeux, R. 1999). Sdlg. 8680 A. TB, 35" (90 cm), ML. S. pure white; F. clear lilac; beards red; ruffled. 84100 B: (7915: (Casino Queen x (Pink Taffeta x Schiaparelli)) x 8245: (7706 A, Alizes sib, x Love Bandit)) X Colette Thurillet. Cayeux 1995.

EFREETS (Sterling Innerst, R. 1996). Sdlg. 3612-5. SDB, 13" (33 cm), M. S. yellow; F. white; beards yellow, tipped white; slight spicy fragrance. 2846-2: ((Melon Honey x Soft Air) x Stockholm) X 2843-1: (Jared x (Melon Honey x Soft Air)). Innerst 1999.

EGGNOG (Monty Byers, TB, R. 1989). Moonshine 1990.

EGGS OVER EASY (Glenn Stoneking-Jones, R. 1999). Sdlg. CIR6-5346-06-02-1999). TB, 28" (71 cm), M. S. white, slight yellow edge; F. white, chrome yellow blaze; beards golden yellow, hairs tipped golden orange at end. (Blazing Light x Bride's Halo) X (Blazing Light x Gold Trimmings).

EGRET EYES (Elyse Hill, R. 1998). Sdlg EJ 6-21. CA, 9" (23 cm), E. White, F. with 3/4" purple signal, yellow lines; cartwheel form. Pacific High X unknown.

EIDOLIA (Graeme Grosvenor, R. 1993). Sdlg. R4-1. TB, 38" (97 cm), M. Ruffled dark blue violet; beards white. Sea of Joy X Silverado. Rainbow Ridge 1993/94.

EILEEN LOUISE (B.L.C. Dodsworth, R. 1999). Sdlg. EB 93 G. TB, 36" (91 cm), ML. Ruffled pale pink self; beards tangerine; slight fragrance. Early Light X Paradise.

EIRIAN (Maureen Foster, R. 1991). Sdlg. 6W3. TB, 34" (86 cm), EML. S. soft lemon (RHS

4C); F. luminous cream (4D); beards white, tipped gold; lightly ruffled. 2C10: (Laced Cotton x Scintillation) X Demelza. V. H. Humphrey 1995.

EISBLUME (Uwe Knoepnadel, R. 1990). SIB (sino-sib), 39" (100 cm), M. S. white; style arms yellow; F. white, few violet spots, yellow signal. 40 chr. sino-sib sdlg. X unknown. Friesland Staudengarten 1990.

EISMOEWE (Eberhard Fischer, R. 1999). Sdlg. 14. TB, 37" (95 cm), E. Ruffled pure white, F. with small pale yellow haft area; beards wide, near-white at end, changing to pale yellow, medium yellow in throat. Azucena X Leda's Lover.

ELAINEALOPE (Brad Kasperek, R. 1994). Sdlg. 89B-38I. TB, 33" (84 cm), EM & RE. Light lavender (RHS 85D) ground splashed reddish violet (84A); F. slightly flared; beards antique gold, tipped lavender; ruffled; slight sweet fragrance. Maria Tormena X Master Touch. Zebra 1996.

ELAINE'S ANGEL (Greg Schifferli, R. 1991). Sdlg. 2GH12. TB, 32" (81 cm), L. S. shell pink, laced; F. white turning to antique peach at edge, faintly lined S. color, distinctive green reverse; beards tangerine in throat, pink at end; ruffled; slight sweet fragrance. Classico X Extravagant. Willott 1993.

ELAINE'S WEDDING (Bernard Pryor, R. 1996). Sdl. 34/92-B. LA, 30" (76 cm), EM. S. soft lavender, red violet line signal, paler reverse; style arms white, blushed lavender; F. lavender, red violet veining, white rim, raised deep yellow steeple signal edged red violet, F. reverse paler; ruffled. Bayou Short Stuff X Spanish Ballet. Lone Star 1998.

ELBRUS ALMAZNY (V. & N. Gordodelovy, R. 1995). Sdlg. 9. TB, 30" (75 cm), M. White self; beards red, white at end. Parentage unknown. Gordodelovy 1978.

EL CERRITO (William Maryott, R. 1997). Sdlg. U161A. TB, 35" (89 cm), M. S. and style arms light mineral violet (RHS 84D), midrib slightly darker; F. deep velvety beetroot purple (71A), 1/8" lighter maroon rim; beards brick red; ruffled. Cherry Glen X Ghio 88-5: (Costa Rica x 86-29F, Tempting sib). Maryott 1997.

ELDORADO'S GOLD (Labriano Anaya/Julian Wells, R. 1991). Sdlg. 19A-85. TB, 28" (71 cm), M. Heavily ruffled golden yellow, golden brown stripes on either side of golden yellow beard, signal white. Sun Fire X Dazzling Gold. Rancho de la Flor de Lis 1991.

ELEANOR CLARE (Cy Bartlett, R. 1998). Sdlg. C94/3. IB, 22" (56 cm), M. S. pale milky blue lavender; F. pale fawn, greenish overlay; beards white, tipped fawn; lightly waved; slight fragrance. (Mrs. Nate Rudolph x Capricornia) X Echo de France.

ELEANOR JEAN (Lloyd Zurbrigg, R. 1994). Sdlg. HH 18-2-2. TB, 38" (97 cm), M. Light gentian blue self; beards light blue, yellow in throat; slight fragrance. Sapphire Hills X Bethany Claire. Friendship 1995.

ELEANOR KIRKPATRICK (Paul Black, R. 1990). Sdlg. 85165B. TB, 32" (81 cm), L. Heavily ruffled and laced icy blue white; beards powder blue. Venetian Waters X Bubbling Lace. Mid-America 1991.

ELEANOR YATES (B. J. Brown, R. 1992). Sdlg. 0588. TB, 30" (76 cm), EM. S. white; F. white, edged yellow, yellow hafts; beards yellow, tipped white. Starring Role X Light Years. B. J. Brown 1993.

ELECT LADY (Bernice Miller, TB, R. 1989). Garden of the Enchanted Rainbow 1990.

ELECTRIC ELF (Barry Blyth, R. 1998). Sdlg. E45-1. SDB, 12" (30 cm), ML. Pink with bluish cast, F. faintly lighter around beard and with tiny blue chevron; beards navy blue violet, tangerine in throat. Bee's Knees X B25-1: (Z7-2, Toy Kingdom sib, x Z24-1, Volts sib). Tempo Two 1998/99.

ELECTRIC GLOW (J. T. Aitken, R. 1992). Sdlg. 86J3. JI (6 F.), 38" (97 cm), ML. Blue with lighter electric blue rays, violet edge. Electric Rays X Midnight Stars. Aitken's Salmon Creek 1992.

ELECTRIC RAYS (J. T. Aitken, R. 1990). Sdlg. 83J-1-12. JI (6 F.), 40" (102 cm), M. Medium violet, with light blue rays extending from yellow signal to 1/2" from edge; ruffled. Knight in Armor X Reign of Glory. Aitken's Salmon Creek 1990.

ELECTRIC SHOCK (Virginia Messick, R. 1995). Sdlg. M87-37. TB, 34" (86 cm), M. S. white, washed dark blue; F. white, washed blue; beards dark blue; ruffled; sweet fragrance. Olympiad X Cosmic Dance. Messick 1996.

ELECTRIC SURGE (John Weiler, R. 1992). Sdlg. 86-152-6. TB, 37" (94 cm), ML. Lightly ruffled palest blue violet; beards very dark violet; slight sweet fragrance. 84-164-1: (Blackbeard x ((Social Whirl x Bridal Wreath) x (Goodnight Irene x Blue Luster))) X 84-142-1: (82-106-7: (78-32-2B: (((Southern Comfort x White King) x Tinsel Town) x ((Flaming Dragon x New Moon) x (Minnesota Glitters x Kimberlina))) x Bridal Fashion) x (That Scentsation x Swan Dance)). Rialto 1992.

ELECTRIQUE (Barry Blyth, R. 1991). Sdlg. Y7-2. TB, 38" (96 cm), VE-EML. S. pale icy blue; F. slate rose, flaring; beards deep tangerine bronze; spicy fragrance. ((Inca Queen x (Tranquil Star x (Love Chant x Festive Skirt))) x Amber Snow) X (Shine on Wine x sib). Tempo Two 1993/94.

ELEGABALL (Ladislav Muska, R. 1999). Sdlg. 98-MGSS-10. TB, 34" (86 cm), L. Ruffled and laced bright orchid self; beards orange, blue orchid horn; slight fragrance. Mys Horn X ((Geniality x Sky Hooks) x Lace Jabot). Muska 1999.

ELEGANT GIRL (A. & D. Cadd, R. 1999). Sdlg. 28-93-2. TB, 38" (97 cm), M. S. soft pink, shiny gold border; style arms soft pink; F. light peach pink, shoulders tan pink, diamond-dusted; beards deep orange with horn, sometimes spoon; heavily ruffled; slight sweet fragrance. Colette X Pagan Pink.

ELEGANT IMAGE (Duane Meek, R. 1992). Sdlg. 704-1-2. TB, 34" (86 cm), EM. S. sky blue; F. white, veined darker, hint of sky blue around ruffled and pleated rim; beards white, tipped lemon in throat; slight fragrance. Dutch Girl X Winterscape. D & J Gardens 1992.

ELEGANT IMPRESSIONS (Schreiner, R. 1992). Sdlg. Y 566-D. TB, 36" (91 cm), ML. Heavily laced cream yellow (RHS 11C) with white F. center; beards yellow. R 648-A: (L 559-A, Lady Madonna sib, x Chartreuse Ruffles) X Ruffles and Lace. Schreiner 1993.

ELEGIYA (V. & N. Gordodelovy, R. 1995). Sdlg. 87. TB, 28" (71 cm), M. S. dark violet; style arms violet, edged white; F. black violet, white haft striations; beards blue, yellow in throat. Parentage unknown. Gordodelovy 1978.

ELENA LANG (Manfred Beer, R. 1997). Sdlg. MB 17/90 A. TB, 32" (80 cm), E. S. yellow (RHS 7B); style arms yellow (7B and 4C); F. white, yellow (7A) shoulders and edge; beards cadmium orange (23A); pronounced fragrance. Gold Ring X Fringe of Gold. Ortenauer Staudencenter 1997.

ELEPHANT TUSKS (Betty Squires, R. 1992). Sdlg. 87-44-A. TB, 44" (112 cm), ML. Laced white; beards yellow, tipped lavender, 1½" lavender horn; slight fragrance. Happy Bride X Lavender Queen.

ELFENBEINPRINZESSIN (Eberhard Fischer, R. 1995). Sdlg. 7. TB, 51" (130 cm), EM. S. and F. light amber yellow, paling to ivory in center; beards yellow; slight sweet fragrance. Bernsteindom X unknown. Mattuschka 1996.

ELFIN CAPER (A. & D. Willott, R. 1999). Sdlg. W 96-22. MDB, 8" (20 cm), ML. Lightly ruffled light violet blue, F. with full violet blue halo; beards cream. Elfin Magic X unknown.

ELFIN CHARM (Beryl Pederick, R. 1994). Sdlg. 6. BB, 24" (61 cm), ML S. hyacinth blue (HCC 40/3); F. white, dotted and stitched pansy violet (033); beards gold, tipped white; slight fragrance. Splash o' Wine X French Gown.

ELFIN MAGIC (A. & D. Willott, R. 1990). Sdlg. 84-56. MDB, 7" (18 cm), ML. S. pale blue, edge serrate; F. pale blue, yellow green spot; beards light yellow. Amber Blaze X Spring Tracery. Willott 1990.

ELFIN SUNSHINE (B. Charles Jenkins, R. 1998). Sdlg. BJ71B. SPU, 27-33" (69-84 cm), VE & L. Pale yellow self blending to deep yellow at base of petals, style arms; small flowers. *I. halophila* (SIGNA seed 86M163C) X BA24B: (Finally Free x A20-11B: (Ila Crawford x Dawn Candle)). Shepard Iris 1998.

ELF LIGHT (Nora Scopes, R. 1992). Sdlg. PC25. CA, 12-13" (30-32 cm), M. S. yellow; F. lemon yellow, lightly striped pale red. Indian Paint X yellow sdlg.

EL GIGANTE (Sharon McAllister, R. 1996). Sdlg. 92-12-7. AB (OGB-), 32" (81 cm), M. S. and style arms soft gold; F. intense red violet wash on soft gold ground giving reddish brown effect, gold edge, brown veining on gold around beard; beards soft gold, base brownish violet. 84-48-3: (Desert Princess x Rose of Sharon) X Secret Melody. McAllister 1996.

ELINOR HEWITT (Jennifer Hewitt, R. 1992). Sdlg. RD8417/4. SIB (dip.), 30" (75 cm), EML. S. dark wine red (RHS 77A); F. blue violet (88B) at center, changing to red violet (81A) at edge, wine red (77A) at tip, signal white, yellow near hafts. Rejoice Always X Pink Haze. British Iris Society 1995.

ELISABETH McEWEN (John White, R. 1994). Sdlg. JKMxSP-3. SIB, 32" (81 cm), EM. S. pansy (RHS 83A to 83B); style arms slightly bluer (86B) lightening to near white on edge; F. pansy (83A), signal white. Janet K. Merrill X Shirley Pope. Pope's Perennials 1996.

ELIZABETH ANN THOMAS (Ronald Mullin, R. 1994). Sdlg. 84-49Z. TB, 34" (86 cm), EM. S. medium violet; style arms violet; F. violet, some white lines below white beard. Theatre X Galore. M.A.D. Iris 1996.

ELIZABETH GAMBLE (Lois O'Brien, R. 1993). Sdlg. 90-80-A. TB, 38" (97 cm), ML. S. medium blue, lighter midrib; F. marine blue, light spot under beard; beards white, tipped blue; fluted, ruffled; slight sweet fragrance. 7335MG: (Portrait of Larrie x Columbia Blue) X Blues on Parade. O'Brien Iris 1995.

ELIZABETH HESS (Ed Attenberger, R. 1997). Sdlg. 90-05-07. TB, 36" (91 cm), M. S. and style arms light yellow; F. light yellow, hafts and edge darker; beards light orange; ruffled, laced; slight sweet fragrance. Tarlatin X Lemon Mist.

ELIZABETH POLDARK (R. E. Nichol, R. 1987). Sutton 1990.

EL JEFE (Oz Reyna, R. 1996). Sdlg. 92-32B. TB, 30" (76 cm), EM. Ruffled violet blue (near RHS 89C) self; beards gold; slight fragrance. Horatio X Douce France.

ELLA (L. Brummitt, IB, R. 1977). British Iris Society 1997.

ELLA CATHERINE'S FANCY (Louise Smith, R. 1992). TB, 33" (84 cm), EM. S. yellow; F. brown, edged yellow; beards gold; pronounced sweet fragrance. Parentage unknown.

ELLA LeCLAIR (Bryce Williamson, R. 1994). Sdlg. A-11-G. TB, 33" (84 cm), EM. S. soft pink, midrib blended peach; F. deeply ruffled cream pink, haft and edge deeper peach; beards tangerine red, base cream white; slight fragrance. Armistice X Fan Club. Pacific Coast Hybridizers 1994.

ELLEN JOY (D. L. Shepard, R. 1998). Sdlg. 93002-8938. TB, 40" (102 cm), M. Lightly ruffled icy blue white, slight silver edge on all petals, F. with gold shoulders; beards orange gold, ending in purple-tinged white horn; slight fragrance. Howdy Do X Battle Star. Shepard Iris 1998.

ELLEN WARE (Kevin Nilsen, R. 1991). Sdlg. 2-85-2. TB, 38" (96 cm), EM. S. melon apricot flushed pink; F. melon apricot, pink white zone under deep orange beard; ruffled, laced. Loudoun Charmer X Mandolin. Iridescence 1991/92.

ELLIBELLE (Cy Bartlett, R. 1990). Sdlg. WB-C1. TB, 38" (97 cm), ML-VL. S. soft pink plicata flushed mauve; F. pink fading to greenish white, 3/8" pansy purple plicata edge; beards white, tipped bronze orange; ruffled. Wild Berry X Capricious.

ELLIOT GLACIER (Julius Wadekamper, R. 1999). Sdlg. 94-136. SDB, 9" (23 cm), M. Light sky blue self; beards deep blue; slight sweet fragrance. Parentage unknown. Willowwood 1999.

EL MARAN (Mary Ann Heacock, R. 1992). Sdlg. H65-4. SDB, 11" (28 cm), E. S. deep rosy red; F. dark roseine red; beards bronze orange. Sarita X Pink Formal.

EL NAFFASA (Ladislav Muska, R.1997). Sdlg. S-DWHP-01. SDB, 14" (36 cm), E. Ruffled pinkish cream, F. touched light milk chocolate; style arms cream; beards orange; pronounced fragrance. Dove Wings X Hazel's Pink. Muska 1992.

EL NINO (Joseph Ghio, R. 1991). Sdlg. PI-209H3. CA, 10" (25 cm), ML. Peach self, violet to rose signal. Las Lomas X PK-303M2: ((Roaring Camp sib x (San Vicente x Emigrant)) x Wildman). Bay View 1992.

ELSIE RICHARDSON (Gerald Richardson, R. 1992). Sdlg. 85-7-1. TB, 36" (91 cm), M. S. pastel rosy buff beige; F. pastel lavender rose blend, amber hafts; beards pale yellow, tipped gold; ruffled; slight fragrance. Mary Frances X 77-64-1: (75-26-1: (Pink Taffeta x ((Celestial Snow x Blushing Beauty) x Cloud Ruffles)) x Dream Fantasy). Rainbow's End 1993.

EL TORITO (Bennett Jones, R. 1996). Sdlg. 451-12. SDB, 12" (31 cm), M. Deep orange self; beards deep red; slight fragrance. Desert Orange sib. Aitken's Salmon Creek 1997.

ELUSIVE CHARM (William Maryott, R. 1998). Sdlg. S145PKAM. TB, 35" (89 cm), M. S. white, faint pink tinge; style arms pale pink; F. soft medium pink; beards soft pink, hairs tipped orange. L101 yellow amoena, unknown, X Wings of Gold. Maryott 1999.

ELVA MAZE (Louise Smith, R. 1993). Sdlg. 90-101. TB, 39" (99 cm), EM. Lavender self; beards yellow, tipped white; slight sweet fragrance. Parentage unknown.

ELVES GOLD (Barry Blyth, R. 1993). Sdlg. W149-2. SPU, 22" (56 cm), M. Pure rich gold self. Satinwood X self. Tempo Two 1993/94.

ELYSE JUNE (Elyse Hill, R. 1995). Sdlg. EJ 29-8-91. TB, 34" (86 cm), M. S. and style arms yellow, midribs flushed lavender; F. lavender, edged brown; beards orange; ruffled; slight sweet fragrance. Lullaby of Spring X Tequila Sunrise. O'Brien 1998.

EMANATIONS (Mitch Jameson, R. 1995). Sdlg. 1-90. TB, 34" (86 cm), M. S. gold; F. medium violet blue, 1/4"-1/2" laced brown rim; beards violet blue to gold. Edith Wolford X Mary D. Knee-Deep in June 1996.

EMBASSY BALL (George Sutton, R. 1998). Sdlg. E-69. TB, 37" (94 cm), ML. Ruffled dark violet blue (RHS 94A) self; beards bluebird blue. Inaugural Ball X Sky Hooks. Sutton 1999.

EMBLAZONED (Paul Black, R. 1996). Sdlg. A115B. IB, 16" (41 cm), E. S. butter yellow, medium brown plicata band and midrib stripe; style arms brown over yellow; F. yellow, narrow brown band, dark brown plicata haft, dart at end of beard; beards violet to brown, base white; pronounced sweet fragrance. Privileged Character X Hopscotch. Mid-America 1996.

EMBRACEABLE YOU (Harold Stahly, R. 1999). Sdlg. 92-76. TB, 38" (97 cm), ML. S. pale apricot yellow (RHS 16D), pale orient pink (36D) center suffusion; style arms pale apricot yellow (16C); F. ivory white, pale apricot yellow (16D) rim and reverse; beards bright nasturtium red (30B); lightly laced; slight sweet fragrance. Halo in Orange X 87-22: (Sun King x Marmalade). Stahly 1999.

EMERALD DRAGON (Leo Barnard, R. 1996). Sdlg. L-91-130C. TB, 34" (86 cm), EM. S. white, shading to soft yellow gold base; style arms yellow; F. creamy white, yellow gold shoulders, light yellow wash over lower half; beards yellow green, slightly fuzzy matching horn; ruffled, lightly laced; slight sweet fragrance. Startler X Sunset Fires. Paradise Iris 1996.

EMERALD SKIES (Eugene Kalkwarf, R. 1991). Sdlg. 87-1. TB, 34" (86 cm), M. Light blue, lighter spot around yellow beards. Alabama Bound X 82-1: ((White Tutu x Beaux Arts) x Laced Cotton). Newburn's Iris 1991.

EMERALD STAR (A. & D. Willott, R. 1993). Sdlg. 85-28. SDB, 10" (25 cm), M. S. light blue flushed violet at base; F. pale blue, chartreuse spot; beards bright violet blue; lightly ruffled. Jewel Lake X unknown white SDB sdlg. Willott 1993.

EMERALD SUNRISE (Eugene Kalkwarf, R. 1999). Sdlg. EK95-6. TB, 30" (76 cm), M. S. bright clear yellow; F. bright white, edged bright yellow; beards yellow; ruffled, laced; slight fragrance. Joyce Terry X Launching Pad.

EMERGENCY RESPONSE (Berthe Conarty, R. 1999). Sdlg. C-911. BB, 25" (64 cm), M. S. light pink, narrow apricot edge; style arms light pink; F. apricot, center paler, darker hafts with gold veining; beards tangerine; slight sweet fragrance. Lacy Lu X DR/WR 851: (Debby Rairdon x Wine and Roses).

EMIGRE (Mary Dunn, R. 1990). Sdlg. L108-2. LA, 35" (89 cm), M. S. blue with lavender undertone, texture veined; ruffled wide matching styles; F. ruffled, serrate-edged blue with lavender undertones, small yellow spear signal. La Perouse X Monument. Bay View 1990.

EMILE (J. R. Allen, TB, R. 1989). Allen Iris 1992.

EMILIE DOLGE (Donald Spoon, R. 1990). TB, 32" (81 cm), M. Ruffled light yellow, F. with darker edge; beards yellow. Lively Lemon X Mandolin. Winterberry 1995.

EMILY ANNE (Robert Hollingworth, R. 1999). Sdlg. 97C8B15. SIB (tet.), 33" (84 cm), E. S. medium blue violet, speckled cream; style arms medium blue purple, cream edge, blue keel; F. cream shading to yellow at haft, no signal, outer edge dashed medium blue purple; tailored. 92K1A4: (88W8D1: ((Wizardry x Sunburst Blue) x Fourfold Lavender) x 85B4C3: (Jewelled Crown x (Windwood Spring sib x 78N6: (McEwen T(4)72/10 x unknown)))) X Somebody Loves Me.

EMILY ELECT (J. Owings Rebert, R. 1999). Sdlg. CB-97-5. SIB, 29" (74 cm), M. Bluejay blue, touched violet, F. with neat tan signal. Parentage unknown.

EMILY GIANFORTONI (Clarence Mahan, R. 1997). Sdlg. DS-1. TB, 39" (99 cm), EM. S. pallid violet blue (RHS 97C/D), white central zone; style arms light violet blue, darker blue violet on sides and beneath lip; F. red violet (86D), blue violet highlights in center, white pattern around beard; beards white, hairs tipped blue violet, gold in throat; slight spicy fragrance. Divine X Suky.

EMILY STRAWN (Kirk Strawn, R. 1993). Sdlg. K-1985. LA, 37" (93 cm), E. S. mimosa yellow (RHS 8C aging 8D); style arms darker yellow (8B); F. mimosa yellow (8A aging 8C), bright yellow orange signal. King Creole X Just for Joe. Bois d'Arc 1996.

EMMA DOODLE (D. C. Nearpass by Chesapeake & Potomac Iris Society, R. 1999). Sdlg. 94-404. MTB, 20" (51 cm), EML & RE (July-Nov./VA). Ruffled rosy pink, slightly darker venation; beards tangerine; slight sweet fragrance. 91-138: (88-23: (New Idea x ((Baby's Bonnet x Champagne Music) x *I. aphylla* "Coerulea")) x unknown) X 89-21: (Abridged Version x 83-1: (Hager 2542 x L-76-13: (Peach Paisley x April Melody))). Winterberry 1999.

EMMA DORIS (J. Owings Rebert, R. 1996). Sdlg. UG-1. SIB, 30" (76 cm), M. S. light lavender; F. deep blue, signal ivory and tan. Parentage unknown.

EMMA-FAY (T. E. Braybrook, R. 1996). Sdlg. 86/1/A. TB, 28" (72 cm), M. S. light blue; F. blue; beards blue; slight fragrance. Superstition X Mystique. Waimate 1997/98.

EMMA RIPEKA (Frances Love, R. 1990). Sdlg. GW 2/10/59. SIB, 36" (91 cm), M. S. medium blue; style arms sky blue; F. dark blue. Sdlg. X self. Frances Love, Lynette Black 1995/96.

EMORY SMITH (Patrick O'Connor, R. 1999). Sdlg. 95-9. LA, 36" (91 cm), M. S. blue lavender; style arms cream, tipped blue lavender; F. blue lavender, small white thumbprint signal veined blue lavender and small yellow line signal; lightly ruffled, serrate. Noble Moment X Sea Consul. Bois d'Arc 1999.

EMPEROR'S BRIDE (William Ackerman, R. 1994). Sdlg. A4-4-69. JI (3 F.), 25" (64 cm), M. S. near-white along center to dark violet at margins; style arms creamy white, tipped violet; F. mottled violet (RHS 86D), streaked with lighter violet lines, white around signal; signal yellow green (153A), near-white (154C) at margin. "Goshyoasobi", from Kamo Nursery in Japan, X Double Cream. Nicholls Gardens 1995.

EMPEROR'S BUTTERFLY (Daniel Thruman, R. 1997). Sdlg. 97-394. JI (3 F.), 35" (89 cm), M. S. bishops violet (RHS 91B), distinct white marginal line; style arms white and bishops violet; F. bishops violet with outer 1" veined white; signal yellow, yellow green lines. Oriental Classic X Japanese Pinwheel.

EMPEROR'S COMMAND (William Ackerman, R. 1992). Sdlg. A4-5-81. JI (6-10F.), 36" (92 cm), M. Marbled and streaked lavender (RHS 76A) to reddish purple (78B) on near-white ground, yellow green (153A to 154A) signal; style arms white with lavender lip; ruffled. Iso-no-Asakaze X D5-8-112, inv. sdlgs. from Seiko-en Nursery, Japan. Nicholls Gardens 1993.

EMPEROR'S CONCERTO (Vernon Wood, R. 1994). Sdlg. 87-33. TB, 34" (86 cm), EM. Deep violet (darker than RHS 93A); beards light violet, tipped white; heavily ruffled. Titan's Glory X 85-7: (Cloud Fire x Ron). Stockton 1995.

EMPEROR'S DELIGHT (Schreiner, R. 1997). Sdlg. W 61-3. TB, 39" (99 cm), L. Ruffled purple (RHS 86A) self; beards purple, hairs tipped white; slight fragrance. Stormy Night X S 91-1: (K 124-B, Land o' Lakes sib, x Carriage Trade). Schreiner 1997.

EMPEROR'S DRAGON (Daniel Thruman, R. 1997). Sdlg. 97-387. JI (3 F.), 36" (91 cm), M. S. violet blue (RHS 93B), white line edge; style arms violet blue, yellow midrib; F. brushed and splashed bluebird blue (94B). Oriental Classic X Japanese Pinwheel.

EMPRESS JOSEPHINE (Dorman Haymon, LA, R. 1989). Deep South Garden 1990.

EMU ZING (Brad Kasperek, R. 1997). Sdlg. 92B-57T. BB, 23" (58 cm), EM. S. azalea pink (RHS 39D), splashed and blended indian lake (58A) and spinel red (54C/D); style arms azalea pink; F. color of standards, plus pinkish white stripes; beards burnt orange; heavily ruffled, laced. Tiger Honey X Raspberry Fudge. Zebra 1997.

ENCHANTED APRIL (Larry Lauer, R. 1995). Sdlg. 88-104. TB, 36" (91 cm), L. Lavender to orchid blue blend; beards tangerine; pronounced sweet fragrance. McWhirter 81-23-1: (Foolish Pleasure x Love Magic) X Matinee Idol. Stockton 1995.

ENCHANTED HUES (Loleta Powell, R. 1992). Sdlg. 91-3. TB, 35" (89 cm), EML. Rose pink self; beards strawberry coral. Enchanted World X Harmony Hues. Powell's Gardens 1993.

ENCHANTED MESA (Tom Magee, R. 1997). Sdlg. 8815C. TB, 42" (107 cm), M. S. and style arms sky blue; F. ivory, purple plicata edge; beards blue, gold in throat. Mirror Image X Acoma. Long 1999.

ENCHANTED ONE (Richard Ernst, R. 1994). Sdlg. F169-29. TB, 35" (89 cm), ML & RE. S. bright golden yellow, pale violet midrib stripe; F. light orchid lavender veined violet, 3/8" edge and shoulders of amber gold; beards yellow and white; slight sweet fragrance. Afternoon Delight X C142-7: (Ringo x (Cranberry Ice x Grand Waltz)). Cooley 1994.

ENCHANTING TIMES (Terrell Taylor, R. 1994). Sdlg. 93-58. TB, 36" (91 cm), ML. Ruffled purple (RHS 78B) aging paler (78C) except at edge; beards tangerine. Designing Woman X Sweet Musette. Bonita Gardens 1995.

ENCLOSED (Joseph Ghio, CA, R. 1989). Bay View 1990.

ENCRE BLEUE (Richard Cayeux, R. 1995). Sdlg. 8713 B. IB, 22" (55 cm), M. Dark medium blue self; beards white. Open Sky X Swirling Seas. Cayeux 1994.

ENDEARING LASS (Stan Dexter by Marie Ingersoll, R. 1991). Sdlg. 24-84-90A. TB, 29" (74 cm), M. S. ruffled yellow; F. white, edged yellow; beards deep yellow. 80-42-A: (Temple Gold x 1977-F) X Ruffles and Lace. Ingersoll's Iris 1992.

END GAME (Bryce Williamson, R. 1998). Sdlg. D-3-4. TB, 34" (86 cm), EM. S. cool white, faint pale blue marginal marking; style arms medium blue violet; F. cool white, precise 1/2" blue violet plicata edge; beards medium blue violet; ruffled; slight fragrance. Classic Look X Monologue.

ENDURING (Chet Tompkins, R. 1994). Sdlg. 84-29. TB, 39" (99 cm), ML. Carnelian red self. Involved red sdlg. lines. Fleur de Lis 1994.

ENERGIZER (Howard Shockey, R. 1995). Sdlg. 92-119-S. AB (OGB), 28" (71 cm), M. S. medium violet; F. buff ground, lightly overlaid violet, extremely large signal very dark brown purple; beards yellow; slight sweet fragrance. 90-119-B: (((82-113-4A: (79-105-C: (Stars Over Chicago

138

x Welcome Reward) x Desert Princess) x Syrian Moon) x 86-140-T: (((79-105-H x Syrian Moon) x (Heart Stealer x 79-105-C)) x Onlooker)) x Queen Sheba) X 89-114-B: (86-140-T x 86-136-9G: (82-113-4A x (Heart Stealer x (Heart Stealer x Kalifa Gulnare)))). Arilian Acres 1996.

ENFANT PRODIGE (Tony Huber, R. 1993). Sdlg. 90-X-DOM-064. SPEC-X, 43" (110 cm), M. S. lilac (RHS 85A); style arms white; F. violet blue (90D), occasionally marbled with violet marks, deep violet (83A) halo around deep yellow signal. Oriental Touch X -- probably *I. ensata*. Dominion Seed House, Horticlub 1997.

ENGAGING (Joseph Ghio, R. 1996). Sdlg. 91-132H2. TB, 32" (81 cm), ML. Rosy heliotrope, F. aging to silver sheen; beards brick, blue at end. Sib to Star Quality. Bay View 1997.

EN GARDE (William Maryott, R. 1994). Sdlg. M125Q. TB, 37" (94 cm), M. Heavily ruffled velvety purple black; self beards. Majestic Beauty X K90BO: (Titan's Glory x Houdini). Maryott 1994.

ENGELTJE (James Copeland Jr., R. 1990). Sdlg. 80-15-1. JI (3 F.), 32" (81 cm), M. S. white (RHS 155B) fringed violet (87A); style arms white; F. white, yellow (9A) signal. Parentage unknown. Ensata Gardens 1992.

ENGLISH CREAM (O. D. Niswonger, R. 1994). Sdlg. ps 2-93. SPEC (*pseudacorus*), 42" (107 cm), M. Cream, F. with slight maroon eye zone. British Iris Society seed. *I. pseudacorus* "E. Turnipseed" X unknown. Cape Iris 1997.

ENGLISH EYES (G. F. Wilson by Luella Danielson, R. 1995). Sdlg. 29 SMO-8. AB (OGB), 28" (71 cm), M. S. glistening white, bright patent yellow midrib sheen blending to soft yellow veining, form globular; style arms deep yellow, large; F. soft chartreuse yellow, signal red brown, red brown dots sprinkled around yellow beard tipped orange, recurved form; slight sweet fragrance. Syrian Moon X Onlooker. Pleasure Iris 1996.

ENGLISH KNIGHT (George Sutton, R. 1998). Sdlg. G-104. TB, 37" (94 cm), ML & RE. S. and style arms dark pansy (near RHS 83A); F. black, blended pansy, velvety; beards pansy; ruffled. E-242: (Titan's Glory x Watch It) X G-94: (Holy Night x Blue Anew). Sutton 1999.

ENGLISH WHITE (O. D. Niswonger, R. 1994). Sdlg. ps 1-93. SPEC (*pseudacorus*), 40" (102 cm), M. White, F. with slight maroon eye zone. British Iris Society seed. *I. pseudacorus* "E. Turnipseed" X unknown. Cape Iris 1996.

ENGRAVED INVITATION (Sharon McAllister, R. 1992). Sdlg. 87-3-6. AB (OGB+), 28" (72 cm), EM. S. white ground, outer 1/2" edge heavily stitched violet (near RHS 85A); F. creamy golden yellow (near 11C), 1/2" rust veining around edge, clear yellow in center; beards dark mustard. My Joy X 79-2: (*I. calcarea* x *I. yebrudii v. edgecombii*). McAllister 1993.

ENHANCEMENT (Joseph Ghio, R. 1995). Sdlg. 90-101-U2. TB, 36" (91 cm), EML. S. lemon yellow, pink infusion; F. lemon yellow, white blaze; beards yellow. 88-153 pink coral: ((Mogul sib x Guadalajara) x Caracas) X 88-114-R2: ((Montevideo x Guadalajara) x Peach Bisque). Bay View 1996.

ENID BURGOYNE (Enid Burgoyne by Jennifer Hewitt, R. 1997). Sdlg. BUR/1. SIB, 36" (91 cm), M. S. white; style arms pale cream, flecked faint violet; F. naples yellow (RHS 11C), deep yellow hafts veined light violet and turquoise, signal absent; small flowers, S. upright, F. long hafted, blade rounded. Parentage unknown. Joe Pye Weed 1998.

ENJOY THE PARTY (Barry Blyth, R. 1999). Sdlg. E114-3. TB, 35" (89 cm), VE-EM. S. off-white, faint orchid blush, midrib creamier; F. plush red burgundy, 1/4" soft lilac edge; beards bright mustard yellow; musky fragrance. B196-1: (Z75-2: (And Royal x Chocolate Vanilla) x Electrique) X Dream Lord. Tempo Two 1999/2000.

ENKAISHU (Society for Japanese Irises, R. 1999). JI (3 F.), 36" (91 cm), VE. Red violet. Wild form of *I. ensata* collected in Siberia by Sho Sennyo. Introduced in Japan, 1987.

ENLIGHTENMENT (Richard Ernst, R. 1990). Sdlg. 84x23. TB, 36" (91 cm), EM. S. lavender; styles with sky blue accents; F. purple, lavender rim; beards orange. Ringo X unknown. Cooley 1990.

ENNOBLE (Joseph Ghio, R. 1998). Sdlg. 94-179X2. TB, 33" (84 cm), ML. Black cerise self; beards brick red. 91-112Z: (88-90B: ((Battle Hymn sib x (((Ballet in Orange x Coffee House) x Cinnamon sib) x ((Veneer sib x (Capitation x Coffee House)) x Lady Friend sib))) x (((Praline x Lady Friend) x ((((Ponderosa x Honey Rae) x (69-177T x (Ponderosa x New Moon))) x Homecoming Queen) x (Entourage x Homecoming Queen)) x ((Lady Friend sib x 76-110L: ((Malaysia x Carolina Honey) x (Hi Top x ((Ponderosa x Travel On) x Peace Offering sib)))) x ((Entourage x Homecoming Queen) x Mulled Wine)))) x Battle Royal X 92-305T: (Battle Royal x ((((Lady Friend x (Flareup x (Capitation x Coffee House))) x Battle Hymn sib) x ((Homecoming Queen x 76-110B) x Esmeralda sib)) x ((Romantic Mood sib x ((Paris Original sib x ((Princess x (Pink

Sleigh x (Opening Round x Champagne Music))) x (Louise Watts x (Ghost Story x Ponderosa))))
x (((Louise Watts sib x (69-177T: (((Commentary x Claudia Rene) x Claudia Rene) x Ponderosa)
x (Ponderosa x New Moon))) x Crystal Dawn) x (Preface sib x Crystal Dawn)))) x Lightning Bolt))).
Bay View 1999.

EN POINTE (Glenn Corlew, R. 1997). Sdlg. 1296-1A. TB, 30" (76 cm), E. Smooth orchid lavender, F. texture veined, shading to near-white in center and around beard; beards bright tangerine, base white. Stage Door X Ellamae Fehrer. Cooley 1998.

ENSHUNADA (Mototeru Kamo by Society for Japanese Irises, R. 1993). JI (6 F.), 33-36" (85-90 cm), M. Blue violet with white halo and radiating white veining, yellow signal; style arms white, prominent, edged and tipped blue violet. Parentage unknown. Kamo prior to 1980.

#ENSIGN (Grace Sturtevant, TB, R. 1920). Listed as obsolete in 1939 Check List. Name released 1992.

ENSIGN (Eric Tankesley-Clarke, R. 1992). Sdlg. 345C. BB, 25" (64 cm), ML. Dark blue self; beards lemon; slight sweet fragrance. Allegiance X Bubbling Over. Adamgrove 1993.

ENTANGLED (Joseph Ghio, R. 1999). Sdlg. 94-120N. TB, 34" (86 cm), EML. S. pink, violet infusion; style arms pink; F. pink heavily overlaid and lined red purple, pink wire edge and shoulders; beards red. 92-159D3: (Spirit World x 90-54-I: (88-11B, Chatter sib, x 87-7K, pollen parent of Decipher) X Fancy Woman.

ENTERTAINER (George Sutton, R. 1998). Sdlg. E-221. TB, 35" (89 cm), ML & RE. S. shell pink (near RHS 37C); style arms shell pink and violet; F. violet purple (77A) edged pale violet, large shell pink spray pattern; beards indian orange (32A): ruffled, laced; pronounced spicy sweet fragrance. Mother Earth X Double Agent. Sutton 1999.

ENTERTAINMENT (Hooker Nichols, TB, R. 1988). Hillcrest 1993.

ENTICING GEISHA (Currier McEwen, R. 1996). Sdlg. J 89/28. JI (3 F.), 36" (90 cm), ML. S. violet (RHS 87B) with darker (87A) veins; style arms dark violet (86B), edges and tufts very dark (86A); F. lobelia blue (91C) with dark violet blue (90A) halo around rich lemon yellow (13B) signal, dark violet blue veins radiating to edge of F.; ruffled. Ashi-No-Ukifune X Kalamazoo. Eartheart 1997.

ENTITY (Chet Tompkins, R. 1997). Sdlg. 93-43. TB, 39" (99 cm), ML-VL. S. blended empire and baryta yellow, silver cream, giving smoky silver effect; style arms silver smoke shot claret; F. blended claret and russet brown giving smooth brownish black effect; beards dark brown, mustard base. (((Licorice Stick x Tinsel Town) x (Licorice Stick x Ovation)) x (Cimbay x (River Hawk x (Stepping Out x Tinsel Town)))) X (((Silver Peak x Envoy) x (Licorice Stick x Tinsel Town)) x (Cimbay x Bayberry Candle sib)). Fleur de Lis 1997.

ENVISIONED DREAM (Richard Ernst, R. 1990). Sdlg. F120-16. TB, 34" (86 cm), M. S. dark lavender; F. near-white, edged lavender; beards orange. Afternoon Delight X Gaulter 81-17, inv. Irene Nelson. Cooley 1990.

ENVOGUE (Mary Dunn, R. 1991). Sdlg. M84-925A. TB, 36" (91 cm), M. S. white, faint orchid cast when fresh; style arms stained very light orchid; F. ruffled crystal white, violet pencil markings around edge and on hafts; beards orchid white. Momentum X Ghio 77-70: ((Premonition sib x Mystique) x Barletta). M.A.D. Iris 1992.

#ENVY (H. Hill, TB, R. 1930). Not distributed, name released.

ENVY (Richard Ernst, R. 1990). Sdlg. C110-1. TB, 33" (84 cm), EM. Ruffled and laced lime green yellow; beards yellow orange. T611-3X: (Prancing Pony x (Bayberry Candle x Hi Top)) X Dazzling Gold. Cooley 1990.

ENVY IN GOLD (Janet Hutchinson, R. 1995). Sdlg. MSDWB/JH. LA, 43" (110 cm), EM. Rich yellow, edges deeper, strong green signal on all petals; style arms deep green, crests yellow; ruffled; slight sweet fragrance. Marsha Sue X Dural White Butterfly.

EPICENTER (Joseph Ghio, R. 1993). Sdlg. 90-52D. TB, 42" (107 cm), EM. S. solid black cherry; F. orange salmon ground, dotted black cherry edge; beards sienna. Chatter X Power Surge. Bay View 1994.

EPIMETHEUS (Sterling Innerst, R. 1991). Sdlg. 3042-2. JI (6 F.), 40" (102 cm), ML. Wine purple, splashed and speckled white lavender-purple pink. Dark Sea X Japanese Sandman. Iris Pond 1992.

ERAMOSA MISS (Chuck Chapman, R. 1998). Sdlg. 89-278-5. BB, 24" (61 cm), M. Ruffled apricot pink, F. lighter around apricot pink beard. Victorian Frills X Coral Beauty. Chapman Iris 1998.

ERAMOSA SKIES (Chuck Chapman, R. 1996). Sdlg. 91-161-1. SDB, 13" (33 cm), M. Light sky blue self; beards light violet blue. Rain Dance X Chubby Cheeks. Chapman Iris 1996.

ERAMOSA SNOWBALL (Chuck Chapman, R. 1999). Sdlg. 93-121-1. SDB, 11" (28 cm), ML. White glaciata; beards white. Transcribe X 90-190-03: (Chubby Cheeks x Lilac Lulu). Chapman Iris 1999.

ERIN ANNE (James Ennenga, SDB, R. 1989). Ennenga's Iris 1993.

ERIN GO BRAUGH (Jim Hedgecock, R. 1999). Sdlg. 1D-17-4. SDB, 12" (31 cm), M. S. ruffled pale green blending to blue at edge; F. pale green, large medium green thumbprint and striations by beard; beards gold, base blue; heavily ruffled, flared. Royal Magician X Runaway.

ERIN MAY (Isobel Simpson, R. 1991). Sdlg. 81-10-3. SDB, 9½" (24 cm), EML. S. cream, deeper warm cream midrib; F. cream, brown thumbprints, pale area around beard, hafts washed and veined olive; beards white, extending into narrow white blaze. (Moonspinner x Mandarin Jewel) X Blue Pools. Hilmary Catton 1991.

ERIN STROLL (O. D. Niswonger, R. 1995). Sdlg. BB 30-92. BB, 25" (64 cm), M. Ivory, infused green; beards white, base marigold. Nefertiti's Daughter X Coral Light. Cape Iris 1996.

ERLEENA (Polly Black, R. 1992). Sdlg. NH6P. TB, 36" (91 cm), M. Smoky pink, gold on hafts, few gold stripes by coral beards. Erleen Richeson X unknown. Polly Black 1992.

ERMINE DOLL (Stan Dexter by Marie Ingersoll, R. 1992). Sdlg. 109-4-90. TB, 34" (86 cm), ML. Ruffled white, slight orchid hint when fresh; beards yellow orange. 1980-42-A: (Temple Gold x 1977-F) X Ruffles and Lace. Ingersoll's Iris 1993.

EROTIC TOUCH (Sterling Innerst, R. 1998). Sdlg. 4201-2. TB, 37" (94 cm), M. Burnt bittersweet brown, F. with blue purple spot; style arms brown; beards golden orange; slight fragrance. Springhouse X Bogota. Innerst 1998.

ESCALONA (Joseph Ghio, R. 1993). Sdlg. PG-133F2. CA, 12" (30 cm), EM. S. light crimson; F. crimson, gold wire edge, black signal with fingers over F. Bottom Dollar sib X It's Wild. Bay View 1994.

ESCAPE HATCH (Robert Annand, R. 1997). Sdlg. 88-5A. SDB, 11" (28 cm), M. S. and style arms lavender blue; F. light lavender, maroon brown stripes radiating halfway down from beard; beards blue, base yellow, all yellow in throat. Frosted Olive X Escape Artist.

ESK (Michael Wickenden, R. 1998). SPEC (*pseudocorus*), 66" (168 cm), M. Yellow, signal yellow. Parentage and origin unknown; found in abandoned garden. Cally Gardens 1994.

ESKIMO ICE (Jim Hedgecock, R. 1997). Sdlg. 84-85-8. TB, 36" (91 cm), EM. S. blue white, pale blue on inner base; F. blue white; beards white, yellow in throat; heavily laced and ruffled; slight sweet fragrance. Emmanuel X Lacy Snowflake. Comanche Acres 1998.

ESOTERIC (Barry Blyth, R. 1990). Sdlg. X31-5. SDB, 15" (38 cm), VE. S. beige cream, pink cast; F. beige cream, whitish central area; beards tangerine, outer 1/4" light lavender. Yipee X Camarilla. Tempo Two 1991/92.

ESPANCE (Udo & Rudolf Wilkeneit, R. 1996). Sdlg. EW 5/1/94. SDB, 10" (25 cm), M. S. reddish maroon and blue; F. reddish blue, brown border, blue heart; beards blue; slight fragrance. Parentage unknown.

ESSEX MAID (Shirley J. Ryder, R. 1994). Sdlg. LL/SON/M. TB, 37" (94 cm), M. Very pale blue self, base of S. slightly darker; beards pale blue, tipped white; ruffled; sweet fragrance. (Leda's Lover x Song of Norway) X Morwenna.

ESTABLISHED POWERS (Sterling Innerst, R. 1995). Sdlg. 3428-5. TB, 36" (91 cm), M. White ground medium blue plicata; style arms white, tinted blue; beards blue, tipped bronze. Rumbleseat X Sterling Stitch. Innerst 1996.

ESTERBOB'S HONEY (Stan Dexter by Marie Ingersoll, R. 1991). Sdlg. 86-81-24A. TB, 32" (81 cm), M. S. yellow brown; F. yellow overlaid brown, small white line below yellow beard. Paradise X Fashionable Pink. Ingersoll's Iris 1992.

E. T. CETERA (Chet Tompkins, R. 1992). Sdlg. 83-84. TB, 38-40" (99-102 cm), ML. S. milky orchid flushed orchid lilac, F. with slightly deeper tint of lilac and brushing of violet; beards yellow, tipped orange. ((Gentle Shepherd x ((Tinsel Town x Dark Town Strutter) x (Stepping Out x Tinsel Town))) x (Star Trek x (April Lost x Capricious))) X Understudy. Fleur de Lis 1991.

ETERNAL FEMININE (Currier McEwen, JI, R. 1986). Seaways 1986.

ETERNAL FIRE (Cleo Palmer, R. 1994). Sdlg. 89123. IB, 26" (66 cm), L. S. burgundy red; F. dark burgundy red to reddish black; beards bronze; slight fragrance. Glowing Garnet X Sunny Hills. Palmer's Iris 1994.

ETERNAL MORN (Franklin Carr by Margaret Carr, R. 1994). Sdlg. 87-96LB. TB, 37" (94 cm), EM. S. pale blue infused light blue; F. pale blue, darker in throat; beards pale blue, yellow in throat. Edge of Winter X Chico Maid.

ETHEL KENAN (Loleta Powell, R. 1994). Sdlg. 92-16. TB, 35" (89 cm), EML. S. cream; style arms yellow; F. butter yellow; beards yellow; pronounced sweet fragrance. Borderline X Bernice Roe. Powell's Gardens 1996.

ETHEREAL DREAM (Terrell Taylor, R. 1999). Sdlg. 95-3. TB, 33" (84 cm), EM. Light wistaria blue (RHS 92B), F. center aging to near-white; beards white, yellow hair tips in throat; heavily ruffled, flared; slight musky fragrance. Rapture in Blue X Cloud Ballet.

ETTINS (Sterling Innerst, R. 1996). Sdlg. 4322-1. SDB, 12" (31 cm), M. Pink self; beards orange; slight fragrance. Learn X 3526-5: (2875-2: ((Betsey Boo x Cherub Tears) x (Soft Air x Pink Cushion)) x Delicate Pink).

ETTY (Ladislav Muska, R. 1995). Sdlg. INLC-02. TB, 38" (97 cm), ML. Heavily laced rose maroon, F. lightly washed lavender; beards gold; sweet fragrance. Inferno X (Laced Cotton x Don Epifano). Muska 1995.

EUGENIA KING (Elyse Hill, R. 1995). Sdlg. EJ 20-11-91. TB, 34" (86 cm), M. S. and style arms blended buff peach; F. lilac; beards orange; ruffled, laced; slight sweet fragrance. Lullaby of Spring X Tequila Sunrise. O'Brien Iris 1998.

EULENFLUCHT (Harald Moos, R. 1994). Sdlg. 90/75K. TB, 31" (80 cm), M. S. red brown; F. velvety dark red brown, hafts veined around copper beard; heavily ruffled. Baroque Garden X Bischofshol. Moos 1995.

EUPHORIC DREAM (Cleo Palmer, R. 1995). Sdlg. 9365. SDB, 11" (28 cm), L. S. and style arms white; F. light violet blue; beards red. Gypsy Passion X 8947: (8149: ((7259: ((Wilma V. x unknown) x Little Titan) x Bloodspot) x (Dove Wings x 7529)) x 7525 pink sib: (Pink Cusion x Dove Wings)). Palmer's Iris 1995.

EURASIA-BLOOD (Tony Huber, R. 1999). Sdlg. 91-532-02. SPEC-X (pseudata), 30" (75 cm), EM. S. violet (RHS 87B to 86C); style arms violet (87B/D); F. violet (87B to 86C), bright yellow signal on larger creamy base veined purple, surrounded by darker violet (88A) halo. *I. pseudacorus*, white, from SIGNA seed of "Ecru", X *I. ensata* purple sdlg.

EURASIA BRIDE (Tony Huber, R. 1999). Sdlg. 91-532-03. SPEC-X (pseudata), 30" (75 cm), EM. S. base pink, remainder white with fine pinkish veining; style arms cream to white, orange yellow midrib; F. white, shaded pink; signal large, orange yellow on cream to white base, bordered by violet (82B) halo, paler (82B/D) veining. Sib to Eurasia-Blood.

EURASIA-LOVE (Tony Huber, R. 1999). Sdlg. 91-532-04. SPEC-X (pseudata), 33½" (85 cm), EM. S. orchid pink (RHS 62C); style arms orchid pink, midrib orange; F. mallow pink (73B/C), dark lemon (14A) signal on creamy base, small pinkish ruby red (61B) halo, fine radiating veins. Sib to Eurasia-Blood.

EUROPA (John C. Taylor, LA, R. 1989). Rainbow Ridge 1990/91.

EVA LOUISA (Lloyd Zurbrigg, TB, R. 1973). Correction of typographical error (EVA LOUISE) in 1979 Check List.

EVA MARIE (Marge Powell, R. 1993). Sdlg. PIPO601. TB, 33" (84 cm), EM. S. light pink; F. ruffled and laced light pink flushed blue, lighter around tangerine beard. Goddess X Wings of Dreams. Powell's Iris Patch 1993.

EVANDER (Erhard Woerfel, R. 1990). Sdlg. 11/84. TB, 47" (120 cm), M. Amethyst violet; beards orange. Priamos X ((Grilletta x Summer Wine) x Lorna Lee). Hochheimer 1991.

EVELYN HARRIS (James McWhirter, R. 1991). Sdlg. J86-6-1. TB, 36" (91 cm), M. Fluted and heavily ruffled orchid lavender; beards lavender, tipped white; slight fragrance. Winterscape X Hilo Shore. Cottage 1992.

EVELYN HAYES (Ed Matheny III, R. 1998). Sdlg. J:00-02-94. JI (3 F.), 42" (107 cm). M. S. red violet, edged white; style arms light purple, edged white, crest violet, edged white; F. white, veined purple, yellow signal. Returning Tide X unknown. Ed's Iris 1999.

EVELYN KUYKENDALL (Truman Scarborough, R. 1998). Sdlg. 12-93-C12a. TB, 30-36" (76-91 cm), L. S. light lilac; style arms lilac; F. darker lilac, wide lilac rim and hafts, brownish bronze haft veining; beards bright golden yellow; heavily laced; slight musky fragrance. Laced Cotton X Desert Triumph.

EVELYN ROSE (Gerald Richardson, R. 1996). Sdlg. 83-15-1. BB, 27" (69 cm), M. S. pale lemon, infused light pink; F. pale lemon yellow, hafts touched soft apricot; beards tangerine. Old Flame X Paradise. Rainbow's End 1996.

EVELYN WARLICK (Horace Wright by Susan Wright, R. 1992). Sdlg. F-15. TB, 30" (76 cm), E & RE. Pale orange yellow (RHS 18B), F. with white signal; beards yellow; slight fragrance. Parentage unknown. Hall's Flower Garden 1992.

EVEN HANDED (Mary Dunn, R. 1994). Sdlg. 169-1. LA, 37" (94 cm), M. Milky violet, small green spear signal. Plantation Beau X Easter Tide. Bay View 1994.

EVENING CALM (Chet Tompkins, R. 1997). Sdlg. 93-33-I. TB, 38" (97 cm), EML. S. and style arms smooth amber to strontium yellow; F. light wistaria violet blended campanula blue; beards white, hair tips tinted pale blue to cream. (((Burgermeister x Intermission) x Extravaganza) x (Graduation x Syncopation)) X (Megabucks x Up and Coming). Fleur de Lis 1997.

EVENING EPITAPH (Hooker Nichols, R. 1990). Sdlg. 8677-1. IB, 18" (46 cm), EML. S. violet, base deeper; F. violet, deeper hafts with white lines; beards violet, tipped yellow; ruffled. Court Magician X Premonition. Hillcrest 1991.

EVENING LACE (Ruth Goebel, R. 1995). Sdlg. SS-VSP. TB, 38" (97 cm), M. S. violet grape (RHS 84A); F. purple (darker than 78A); beards soft yellow; heavily laced. Sabbath Sunset X VSP: (Georgia Girl x Charcoal).

EVENING MAGIC (Schreiner, R. 1990). Sdlg. V 491-1. TB, 35" (89 cm), ML. Lavender violet (RHS 81B), large white zonal spot below white beard. Lorilee X Raspberry Frills. Schreiner 1990.

EVENING OASIS (Hooker Nichols, TB, R. 1989). Hillcrest 1995.

EVENING SILK (J. T. Aitken, R. 1990). Sdlg. 81-76. TB, 36" (91 cm), M. Deep purple black; beards black. Superstition X Sea Wolf. Aitken's Salmon Creek 1990.

EVENING SONATA (William Ackerman, R. 1999). Sdlg. B3-4. JI (6 F.), 32-36" (81-91 cm), M. Blue violet (RHS 90C/D), long yellow signal highlighted by white and surrounded by deeper blue on opening; petal margins crinkled. Lavender Krinkle X A4-1-119: (A3-6-177 x self).

EVENSONG (Hooker Nichols by Hilmary Catton, SDB, R. 1987). Change of name to WYUNA EVENSONG.

EVENT HORIZON (G. F. Wilson, R. 1991). Sdlg. 10-90SMO-C. AB (OGB), 23½" (60 cm), E. S. light mauve blue veined slightly darker; F. cream, lightly blended grey mauve, slight brown dotting at hafts; signal dark maroon brown, round; beards yellow, wide; slight sweet fragrance. Syrian Moon X Onlooker. Pleasure Iris 1993.

EVENTIDE SUN (Stan Dexter by Marie Ingersoll, R. 1990). Sdlg. 1983/213. TB, 36" (91 cm), M. S. yellow tan; F. same, edged yellow, large purple white flash; beards yellow; pronounced sweet fragrance. 1980/100A: (Beverly Sills x unknown) X Pink Taffeta. Ingersoll's Iris 1991.

EVER AGAIN (Currier McEwen, R. 1991). Sdlg. T(8)86/40(2). SIB (tet.), 34-40" (85-100 cm), E & RE. S. dark violet blue (RHS 89A); style arms violet blue (blended 89A and 83B); F. close to true dark blue (93A), white wire edge, white signal; ruffled. T(5)80/34: (T(4)76/30(1): (Reddy Maid sib x T(1)69/12A) x T(4)76/30(3), sib) X (T(7)83/135(7): ((Dear Dianne x Happy Event sib) x Windwood Spring). Pope's Perennials, Seaways 1992.

EVER ANEW (David Miller, R. 1996). Sdlg. 88-9A. TB, 32" (81 cm), M. Ruffled ruby red self; beards reddish orange; slight musky fragrance. Ever After X Matinee Idol. Long 1998.

EVERGREEN HIDEAWAY (Jack Ames, TB, R. 1988). Ames 1991.

EVER READY (Monty Byers, R. 1990). Sdlg. G9-100. SDB, 11" (28 cm), EML & RE. Medium light yellow, F. with red brown center wash; beards yellow; slight sweet fragrance. Sunstrip X Frankincense. Moonshine 1991.

EVERSON QUEEN (Stan Dexter by Marie Ingersoll, R. 1995). Sdlg. 7-297. TB, 38" (97 cm), ML. S. pink; F. pink, hafts touched orange, paler flash; beards pink. 83-172: (Art Center x Mulled Wine) X 81-13: (unknown x Paradise). Ingersoll's Iris 1996.

EVERYBODY'S DREAM (Graeme Grosvenor, R. 1995). Sdlg. T 1-A. TB, 36" (91 cm), M. S. and style arms apricot; F. blended rosy pink, edges lighter, hafts darker; beards light orange; ruffled. Fortunata X Sweet Musette. Rainbow Ridge 1995/96.

EVERYWHERE (Joseph Ghio, R. 1994). Sdlg. 90-61A. TB, 36" (91 cm), EM. S. solid mulberry; F. white ground, washed and marbled overall with mulberry; beards sienna. Sib to Decipher. Bay View 1995.

EVERY WHICH WAY (Tom Burseen, R. 1995). Sdlg. 9-286C. TB, 34" (86 cm), M. S. orange red (RHS 34B); style arms orange red (33B); F. orange red, washed red brown (183B), white spray pattern by white-tipped yellow beard; ruffled. Chief Hematite X 6-119: ((Theatre x Dazzling Gold) x (Pencil Sketch x Pinwheel)). T.B.'s Place 1995.

EXACTITUDE (Sterling Innerst, TB, R. 1995). Sdlg. 3619-3. TB, 34" (86 cm), M. S. and style arms antique gold; F. full yellow, 1/2" dark blue plicata marking; beards bronze. Point Made X Colorwatch. Innerst 1996.

EXCELLENCY (Barry Blyth, R. 1990). Sdlg. V101-1. TB, 34" (86 cm), M. S. lilac to icy lavender;

F. plush velvety purple, 1/4" lilac edge; beards tangerine orange. Street Dancer X London Lord. Tempo Two 1990/91.

EXCITE ME (Graeme Grosvenor, R. 1994). Sdlg. T 16-7. TB, 36" (90 cm), M. S. light blue, violet at midrib spreading over most of blade; F. white, purple edge, centerline and dotting; beards white, tipped violet; ruffled; slight fragrance. N6-2: (Goddess x (Elsedina x ((Rondo x (Quetta x Ribbon Round)) x Bonifay))) X Seaport. Rainbow Ridge 1995/96.

EXCLUSIVE LABEL (John C. Taylor, R. 1994). Sdlg. RL 58-1. LA, 60" (152 cm), ML. Ruffled burgundy edged yellow; green line signal on F. surrounded by yellow; style arms yellow, brushed burgundy. OL 113-1: (Koorawatha x Dazzling Star) X Margaret Lee. Rainbow Ridge 1996/97.

EXCLUSIVITY (Sterling Innerst, R. 1999). Sdlg. 3966-10. TB, 36" (91 cm), M. S. butterscotch bronze; F. dark brown, 1/2" butterscotch bronze edge; beards orange gold; slight fragrance. Magharee X Fanfaron. Innerst 1999.

EXOTIC CANDY (Lynda Miller, R. 1999). Sdlg. 396A. SDB, 13" (33 cm), ML. Pale pink ground plicata, dotted to solid plum edge, F. edge narrow and more dotted; style arms pale pink, plum midrib; beards white base, hairs tipped blue, tipped orange in throat; slight musky fragrance. Chanted X Sheer Class.

EXOTIC MEMORIES (George Sutton, R. 1996). Sdlg. G-33BRE. BB, 27" (69 cm), EM & RE. S. and style arms canary yellow (RHS 9A); F. banana white, canary yellow hafts and 1/4" edge; beards tangerine (24A); ruffled. Banana Cream X Orange Popsicle.

EXPERIENCIT (Tom Burseen, R. 1997). Sdlg. 93-366E. TB, 35" (89 cm), M. S. light lilac, light magenta rose (RHS 186D) overlay, slight tannish top edge; style arms lilac tan; F. brownish purple (182C), edges browner; beards mustard, purple horn; ruffled, laced; sweet fragrance. 91-124: (Ample Charm x Hello Hobo) X Thornbird. T.B.'s Place 1998.

EXPERTISE (Duane Meek, R. 1999). Sdlg. 74-2-1. TB, 35" (89 cm), M. Ruffled medium dark violet, F. with white ray pattern from beard; beards ivory, lightly tipped lavender. (((Song of Norway x Premonition) x (Apropos x Rococo)) x Blue Luster) X Blues Chaser. D & J Gardens 1999.

EXPO HANNOVER (Harald Moos, R. 1994). Sdlg. 90/77F. TB, 32" (80 cm), M. Ruffled red violet self; beards orange red. 83/350A: (100/79: (Glendale x Vanity) x Lady Friend) X Buchholzer Glut. Moos 1995.

EXPRESSIONS (Eleanor Kegerise, R. 1990). Sdlg. 33-84. TB, 34" (86 cm), EM. Ruffled lavender; beards lavender; slight fragrance. Shipshape X Noble Gentry. Eleanor Kegerise 1991.

EXQUISITE MISS (Kirk Strawn, R. 1993). Sdlg. 1983. LA, 45" (115 cm), M. S. purple (RHS 78C); style arms greenish yellow (1C), yellow (10C) tip; F. purple (78B), yellow (10C) reverse, signal yellow (13A). Marie Caillet X unknown. Bois d'Arc 1996.

EXTRA CHARM (John Weiler, R. 1990). Sdlg. 85-29-7. SDB, 11" (28 cm), EML & RE. Medium blue violet with darker violet spot pattern around blue violet beard; pronounced sweet fragrance. 82-21-4: (Third Charm x Plum-Plum) X 82-30-1: (Watersmeet x Third Charm). Rialto 1990.

EXTRA INNINGS (Darlene Pinegar, R. 1997). Sdlg. WA-1A. TB, 28½" (72 cm), ML & RE. S. and style arms egg yellow, peach center infusion; F. cream white to white, light egg yellow edge, peach hafts; beards white at end, yellow midsection, tangerine in throat; lightly ruffled; slight musky fragrance. Wayward Angel X China Dragon. Spanish Fork 1997.

EXTRAORDINAIRE (Mary Dunn, R. 1990). Sdlg. L122-2. LA, 36" (91 cm), M. Ruffled and serrate metallic purple, lime green signals. L78-1: ((Blue Shield x Black Widow) x Full Eclipse) X Clara Goula. Bay View 1992.

EXTRA STROKES (Daniel Thruman, R. 1997). Sdlg. 97-382. TB, 36" (91 cm), ML. S. white, yellow midrib veining extending outward; style arms white; F. white, yellow hafts, light yellow feathered marginal band and veining; beards yellow, white at end; heavily ruffled. Lady Madonna X (Afternoon Delight x Spinning Wheel).

EXTREME DESIGN (Glenn Bowers, R. 1998). Sdlg. A8-9. TB, 33" (84 cm), ML. S. light yellow (Pantone 3935U); style arms light yellow, lavender midrib; F. light violet (2635C), diffuse buffered gold (110U) edge; beards yellow, light violet at end; ruffled; slight sweet fragrance. Cranberry Tea X Heavenly Body.

EXUBERANT CHANTEY (Currier McEwen, JI, R. 1989). Seaways 1990.

EYE CONTACT (Joseph Ghio, R. 1997). Sdlg. PD-243F3. CA, 14" (36 cm), ML. Rosy lavender, F. with black purple signal. Local Girl X PF-174H2: ((Las Lomas x Shaker sib) x Villa Montalvo). Bay View 1997.

EYED EXCITEMENT (Albert Faggard, R. 1994). Sdlg. FBL-10-88. LA, 37" (93 cm), ML. Ruffled medium blue lavender, rich lime green signal crests; style arms rich lime green, tipped lavender; slight sweet fragrance. Bayou Classic X Gulf Shores. Faggard 1995.

EYE MY EYE (Joseph Ghio, R. 1995). Sdlg. PF-173Y2. CA, 13" (33 cm), E. Golden ochre, F. with maroon black signal edged by red halo. PH-266K: (Las Lomas x Aftershock sib) X PI-201-O, See the Light sib. Bay View 1995.

EYE PATCH (Joseph Ghio, R. 1995). Sdlg. PF-165F2. CA, 14" (36 cm), M. Dusty rose over apricot base, F. with large precise maroon dot signal. PH-236bo: (((Bottom Dollar sib x Something Wild) x Wild Time sib) x ((Roaring Camp sib x (Go Wild x Oval Office sib)) x Native Land sib)) X PH-266R: (Las Lomas x Aftershock sib). Bay View 1995.

EYES FOR YOU (Barry Blyth, R. 1997). Sdlg. D24-2. SDB, 14" (36 cm), EM. Burgundy, faint white around beard; beards white, lavender at end, all hairs tipped tangerine. Flitters X Carats. Tempo Two 1997/98.

EYES RIGHT (Tom Burseen, R. 1991). Sdlg. 7-161D. TB, 36" (91 cm), E. Ruffled and laced orange red (near RHS 47C), lighter at orange red beard. Lady Friend X Copper Lace. T.B.'s Place 1993.

EYE WONDER (Barry Blyth, R. 1998). Sdlg. F76-1. IB, 25" (63 cm), EML. S. buff gold, red violet midrib flush; F. plush deep red burgundy; beards lavender, hairs tipped deep bronze, prominent; slight sweet fragrance. Celsius X Aura Light. Tempo Two 1998/99.

E Z DUZIT (Allen Harper, R. 1991). Sdlg. A6-2. SDB, 14" (36 cm), EM. S. cream (RHS 11D); F. orange (170C); beards yellow, tipped white. A1-3: (Mammy x (It's Tops x Solar Gleam)) X Muchacha.

FABERGE (Duane Meek, R. 1996). Sdlg. 91-2-0. TB, 35" (89 cm), ML. S. greyish tan blended lighter mauve, midribs infused deep mauve; style arms light mauve blend; F. tan with faint mauve, aging to ivory with tan hafts; beards coral; ruffled. Spring Tidings X Glory Be. D & J Gardens 1996.

FABIO (Robert Dunn, R. 1993). Sdlg. B87-1003ZX. TB, 36" (91 cm), L. Blue violet; beards lighter blue violet; F. ruffled. Allstar X Busy Being Blue. M.A.D. Iris 1995.

FACE VALUE (Joseph Ghio, R. 1998). Sdlg. PC-189LST. CA, 12" (31 cm), EM. Smoky orchid, overall deeper veining, F. with deep violet signal. Tulum X PE-189A3: (PG-177G: (PI-MIX-A, unknown, x Valet sib) x PG154, Spanish Don sib). Bay View 1998.

FACSIMILE (Chet Tompkins, R. 1990). Sdlg. 84-55. TB, 39" (99 cm), ML-VL. Very deep pink; beards deep pink. Involved pink crosses. Fleur de Lis 1990.

FADED JEANS (Harry Bishop, R. 1994). Sdlg. SI-B-U-10-F. SPEC (*versicolor*), 15" (38 cm), M. S. purple (RHS 86C) veined darker (86B); style arms pearly white, white purple midrib; F. purple (86B to 89C), paler (90D) at tip, banded much lighter color, signal yellow in center, edged white and veined purple. *I. versicolor* dark purple X unknown. Joe Pye Weed 1994.

FADED LOVE (Joyce Meek, R. 1994). Sdlg. 391-2-3. TB, 28-32" (71-81 cm), M. S. soft pink; F. lavender, white area near beard; beards melon, lavender at end; ruffled and picoteed; slight sweet fragrance. Candace X Janie Meek. D & J Gardens 1994.

FADED MEMORIES (William Plotner, R. 1992). Sdlg. 83-354. TB, 42" (102 cm), ML. S. light pink apricot (RHS 38D); F. china rose, narrowly edged lighter; beards bright orange (33B). ((Camelot Rose x Wine and Roses) x (Camelot Rose x Infinite Grace)) X (Camelot Rose x Stunning). Wildwood Gardens 1990.

FAINT PRAISE (Keith Keppel, R. 1991). Sdlg. 85-33A. TB, 34" (86 cm), E. S. white, pale lilac (M&P 41-C-4/5) allover suffusion; F. white, finely dotted french violet (44-H-7) hafts paling to soft chinese violet (41-I-7) to lilac shaded edge; beards white, tipped indian orange (1-D-12); pronounced sweet fragrance. 80-74A: (Pink Froth x (77-95A: ((Picayune sib x Roundup) x Osage Buff) x ((Barcelona x (Jones 743 x (Marquesan Skies x Babbling Brook))) x ((Roundup sib x April Melody) x Osage Buff)))) X 81-259H: (77-101A: (((Roundup sib x April Melody) x April Melody) x ((68-39D: (((Irma Melrose x Tea Apron) x ((Full Circle x Rococo) x Tea Apron)) x April Melody) x 68-40B, sib) x Osage Buff)) x 77-71A: ((Pink Taffeta x (Roundup sib x April Melody)) x Pink Confetti)). Keppel 1992.

FAIR ALICE (Nancy Burrows, R. 1992). TB, 34" (86 cm), E. S. rich yellow; F. stippled brown on hafts along beards, turning to yellow, large white area below beard, yellow edge; beards orange, tipped yellow; ruffled; pronounced spicy fragrance. Sun Toasted X Broadway.

FAIR CHANCE (J. R. Ellis by Anne Blanco White, R. 1995). SPEC-X, 36" (90 cm), L. S. pale cream buff, small; F. pale cream buff, veined maroon, veins spreading with age. *I. pseudacorus* x *I. ensata.*

FAIRLY DANCING (Opal Wulf, R. 1998). Sdlg. 55-93-9. MTB, 25" (64 cm), EML. S. violet, white area on either side of midrib; style arms violet; F. lighter violet, white area at end of yellow beard. Lisette X Snickerdoodle. Wulf's Backachers 1998.

FAIR MAIDEN (William Maryott, R. 1991). Sdlg. L200E. TB, 35" (89 cm), E. Ruffled flesh pink (RHS 27A), slight yellow tint at shoulders; beards tangerine. J80B: (((Carved Cameo x Songster) x Ghio 76-257: (Entourage x Homecoming Queen)) x (Ghio 76-175, Paris Original sib, x Ghio 76-257X)) X H26A: ((Carved Cameo x Wings of Dreams) x Ghio 76-257X). Maryott 1992.

FAIRMONT (Bob Brown by Stockton Iris Gardens, R. 1995). Sdlg. 91-5. TB, 35-36" (89-91 cm), EM. Light lavender blend; beards tangerine brown, tipped lilac. 85-23: (Collage x 81-41: (((Pink Taffeta x Buffy) x Monaco) x self)) X Silver Flow. Stockton 1995.

FAIRY AIRE (Joyce Meek, R. 1996). Sdlg. 270-3-6. TB, 29" (74 cm), ML. S. soft apricot, midrib deeper pink; style arms apricot; F. ivory, tan hafts, faint apricot rim; beards melon, bushy; lightly ruffled. Tamara Anne X Paradise. D & J Gardens 1996.

FAIRY BERRY (A. & D. Cadd, R. 1999). Sdlg. 79-93-1. SDB, 14" (36 cm), E. S. velvety reddish purple; style arms slightly lighter; F. velvety deep purple, center darker; beards deep blue purple; slight sweet fragrance. Mad Dash X Raspberry Jam.

FAIRY FAVOURS (Barry Blyth. R. 1993). Sdlg. Z15-D. SDB, 12" (31 cm), ML. Pastel apricot to creamy lemon, slight white blaze around beard; beards bright tangerine, outer 1/4" white. Honey Haze X Impish sib. Tempo Two 1993/94.

FAIRY FINGERS (A. & D. Willott, R. 1990). Sdlg. 85-71. SIB, 18" (46 cm), M. S. narrow white, firmly incurved; style arms white, prominent; F. short and narrow white, full yellow signal. Snow Queen X unknown. Willott 1991.

FAIRY FUN (Paul Black, R. 1995). Sdlg. 91269A. MDB, 6" (15 cm), E. S. butter yellow, sparse brown plicata band; style arms butter yellow; F. butter yellow, sparse brown plicata markings on haft and edge, white central patch; beards bright golden yellow; pronounced spicy fragrance. Tender Tears sib X Wake Up sib. Mid-America 1995.

FAIRY LORE (Ben Hager, R. 1993). Sdlg. SD5122PkPc. SDB, 13" (33 cm), ML. S. peach pink, faint lavender plicata edge; F. peach pink, soft purple plicata edge; beards tangerine. SD4908PkPc: (SD4455PkCrPc: (Gigglepot x SD4024PkPc: ((SD3393DpPch: (SD2885Y: (Blonde Doll x SD2862: (Pink Amber x Pink Cushion)) x (SD2562 x Buttercup Charm)) x Pet) x ((((Pink Cushion x Roberts 65-R-28) x (Pink Amber x Pink Cushion)) x SD2885Pch) x SD3393))) x (Catani x SD4024PkPc)) X SD4455Sh. Adamgrove 1994.

FAIRY MEADOW (Opal Brown, R. 1990). Sdlg. 82-20C3. TB, 28" (71 cm), M. White, finely frilled gold (RHS 8C) edge; beards mandarin red (40C). 78-3B5: (Old Flame x ((Grandiflora x Arctic Flame) x Buffy)) X 79-3J1: (Old Flame x (Spring Bride x Royal Coachman)). Brown's Sunnyhill 1990.

FAIRY PATROL (Noel Lapham, R. 1993). Sdlg. 36-4. SDB, 11" (28 cm), ML. S. white; F. white, yellow haft markings; beards blue, tipped yellow; slight fragrance. Fairy Footsteps X Sea Patrol. Mossburn 1994/95.

FAIRY RING (Duane Meek, R. 1998). Sdlg. 197-1-4. SDB, 11" (28 cm), E. S. white, dark blue violet band; style arms blue violet; F. white, deep blue violet haft area, very narrow blue violet rim wider near haft; beards white, some hairs tipped dark violet, giving dotted effect; ruffled. Levity X Chanted. D & J Gardens 1998.

FAIRY TALE PRINCESS (Diana Nicholls, R. 1998). Sdlg. D9017. JI (3 F.), 30" (76 cm), ML-VL & RE. S. purplish pink (RHS 75A), edges lighter (69A); style arms purplish pink; F. purplish pink concentrated around yellow signal, lightening (69A) to edges, veins darker pink. Parentage unknown. Nicholls Gardens 1998.

FAIT ACCOMPLI (Mary Dunn, R. 1990). Sdlg. L107-10. LA, 34" (86 cm), M. Rosy pink with texture veining, yellow green line signals with deep spot at end; style arms green, lacy. Monument X Handmaiden. Bay View 1990.

FAITHFUL AND TRUE (Donald Spoon, R. 1995). Sdlg. 93-33A. TB, 36" (91 cm), EM & RE (Oct./VA). White self; style arms with pale lavender midrib; beards white, light yellow in throat; ruffled; slight sweet fragrance. Lucie Andry X Chaste White. Winterberry 1998.

FAKEL (V. & N. Gordodelovy, R. 1995). Sdlg. 92. TB, 32" (80 cm), E. S. brown red, yellow basal striations; style arms yellow to lettuce green; F. brown red, yellow haft striations; beards brown. Parentage unknown. Gordodelovy 1979.

146

FALCON'S BROTHER (B. Charles Jenkins, R. 1995). Sdlg. C17-7X. SPU, 33-45" (84-114 cm), ML. S. brown; F. yellow, narrowly edged brown, fine brown lines converging toward signal area. Highline Honey X Crow Wing. Shepard Iris 1997.

FALCON'S CREST (B. Charles Jenkins, SPU, R. 1989). Shepard Iris 1995.

FALCONSKEAPE (A. & D. Willott, R. 1992). Sdlg. 84-190. TB, 40" (102 cm), ML. Ruffled light raspberry, lighter F. center, light amber haft wash; beards deep orange. Mandolin X 80-102: (Silver Shower x Far Corners). Willott 1992.

FALKENSTEIN (Lothar Denkewitz, R. 1995). Sdlg. M-86-w-1. IB, 20" (50 cm), M. Cream white self; beards cream white; pronounced spicy fragrance. Baroque Prelude X Sonnentrude. Von Zeppelin 1997.

FALLEN ANGEL (Duane Meek, R. 1995). Sdlg. 92-1-0. TB, 35" (89 cm), ML. S. deep mauve with 2/3" pale lavender border; F. lavender-tinted ivory, slightly darker rim, hafts mauve; beards coral, lavender at end; heavily ruffled. Glory Be X Spring Tidings. D & J Gardens 1995.

FALLEN PLUMS (John Marchant, R. 1990). Sdlg. 3387. CA, 11" (28 cm), M. Beetroot purple (HCC 830/3), dark blue violet blended F. spot. Sdlg. x sdlg. D & J Gardens 1994.

FALL FIESTA (Schreiner, R. 1992). Sdlg. T 1066-B. TB, 36" (91 cm), ML. S. white (RHS 158D); F. ruffled honey tan (164A); beards yellow. H 766-A: (D 1132-D: (Y 1883-BB x Golden Plunder) x Moon River) X K 870-1: (Gold Trimmings x Craig #37). Schreiner 1992.

FALLING IN LOVE (Ben Hager, TB, R. 1988). Roris 1990.

FALL PATTERNS (Opal Wulf, R. 1998). Sdlg. 44-92-3. BB, 26" (66 cm), ML. S. mimosa yellow (RHS 8B); style arms lemon yellow (13B), laced; F. combination of lemon yellow and ruby red (59A), greyed orange (174B) where blended; F. pattern variable, at times half each color, or uniformly colored with contrasting rim; beards golden yellow; slight fragrance. Latin Hideaway X Flaming Sun.

FALL SPOTLIGHT (Walter Moores, R. 1990). Sdlg. 82-20. TB, 36" (91 cm), M & RE (Nov./MS,TX). S. violet purple, white midrib; F. violet purple, large white spot surrounding light yellow beard; ruffled; slight sweet fragrance. Magic Candle X Needlecraft. Moores 1992.

FALL TUCKER (John Durrance, R. 1990). Sdlg. D87-106. AB (OGB), 30" (76 cm), E. S. near-white; F. yellow. Afghanistan X Tabriz.

FALSE RIVER (Patrick O'Connor, R. 1992). Sdlg. 82-9. LA, 36" (91 cm), M. Red with yellow signal lines radiating out irregularly from style arms; style arms yellow green, tinged red. Mockers Song X Harland K. Riley. Bois d'Arc 1994.

FALSTAFF COTTAGE (Brian Price, R. 1994). Sdlg. BPP88/7/C. CA, 13-14" (33-36 cm), M. Deep peach, F. center with radiating strong dark veins. From sdlgs. inv. Ghio line. V. H. Humphrey 1997.

FANCY DRESS (Keith Keppel, R. 1997). Sdlg. 91-152A. TB, 34" (86 cm), E. S. violet (M&P 41-J-9), paler (41-H-8) veining, margin and base; style arms white, flushed violet; F. darker violet (41-L-11), paler veining and margin, white area surrounding beard; beards white, tipped orange in throat; ruffled; slight sweet fragrance. Mind Reader X Fancy Woman. Keppel 1998.

FANCY FAN (Chun Fan, R. 1995). Sdlg. F91-760. TB, 30" (76 cm), M. Violet (RHS 88A) self; beards orange yellow; lightly ruffled; slight sweet fragrance. Up Periscope X Tinted Crystal.

FANCY FILIGREE (John Knaus, R. 1995). Sdlg. 9009. TB, 36" (91 cm), M. S. and style arms white; F. methyl violet (RHS 85B aging 85D), rimmed violet (87A); beards white with gold (24A) tipped hairs, gold in throat; ruffled, laced; slight sweet fragrance. 8190: (Flamingo Blues x Lightning Ridge) X 81-61: (Grand Waltz x Flamingo Blues). John Knaus 1996.

FANCY FILLY (LeRoy Meininger, R. 1998). Sdlg. 91-CC-21. TB, 34" (86 cm), ML. S. lemon yellow, green veining; style arms blended gold and lemon, midrib orange; F. rose, lemon haft marks, veining and narrow rim; beards solid orange. Copper Classic X (Smooth Talk x Party Parfait). Monument, Woodland Iris 1998.

#FANCY STITCHES (James Burch, TB, R. 1981). Not introduced or distributed. Name released.

FANCY STITCHES (James Burch, R. 1992). Sdlg. 46-6. TB, 42" (107 cm), M. S. white ground, dotted and stitched blue violet (RHS 91A) on edge; F. white ground, stitched blue violet (91A) on edge; beards yellow. 39-19: ((Babbling Brook x Kimberly) x Charmed Circle) X Peek-a-Blue. Burch Iris 1991.

FANCY STUFF (Opal Brown by Margaret McCrae, R. 1998). Sdlg. 93-5A6. TB, 30" (76 cm), M. S. lavender blue (M&P 41-B-6); style arms and F. paler lavender blue (41-AB-5); beards bright dandelion yellow (9-L-4), white at extreme end; lightly ruffled, heavily laced; slight sweet fragrance. Kuniko X 90-2H2: (Secret Cove x Laced Cotton).

FANCY WOMAN (Keith Keppel, R. 1994). Sdlg. 87-65A. TB, 38" (97 cm), VE-EM. S. french lilac (M&P 44-H-7) blended light lilac grey (42-B-2) edge and base; F. blended and washed roman purple (44-K-10) to french lilac, paler veining and narrow edge, white area beside beard; beards mikado orange (2-B-12), base white; sweet fragrance. 84-15C: ((((68-39F: (66-35C: ((Irma Melrose x Tea Apron) x ((Full Circle x Rococo) x Tea Apron)) x April Melody) x 68-39D) x 74-52A: ((Joy Ride x Roundup) x (April Melody x (66-35B x April Melody)))) x (Mistress x 75-98B, Peccadillo sib)) x (77-111Q, Gigolo sib, x 78-70A, Rosy Cloud sib)) X 85-15C: ((74-35D, Mistress sib, x Goddess) x (Goddess x (74-35C x 74-52A))). Keppel 1995.

FANCY WRAPPINGS (Chet Tompkins, R. 1995). Sdlg. 91-19. TB, 37" (94 cm), ML. S. mustard gold, heavily striated and sanded ruby red; style arms red; F. mustard gold, heavier ruby red markings on outer edge of hafts, slightly lighter central markings; beards deep oriental orange. (Beguine x Atomic Flame sib) X (Rosy Cloud sib x Wild Side). Fleur de Lis 1995.

FAN FLARE (Larry Lauer, R. 1998). Sdlg. 88-108-3. TB, 36" (91 cm), ML. S. and style arms reddish brown; F. purplish lavender, with reddish brown rim and brown shoulders; beards mustard, tipped purple; ruffled; slight sweet fragrance. Warrior King X L86-19: (Ensemble x Maroon Velvet). Lauer's Flowers 1998.

FANNY HART (Bob Thomason, R. 1993). Sdlg. BT 9035K. TB, 32" (81 cm), EM. S. white, yellow wire rim; F. amber with rose overlay, yellow line from tangerine beard to edge; ruffled; slight fragrance. Boy o' Boy X Skating Party.

FANTAGHIRO (Ladislav Muska, R. 1998). Sdlg. 98-MCCH-03. TB, 35" (89 cm), L. S. pale rosy violet orchid; style arms amethyst orchid; F. deep rosy violet orchid; beards tangerine, rose violet horns; ruffled, laced; sweet fragrance. ((Mys Horn x Calicoball) x Conjuration) X Hellada. Muska 1999.

FANTASM (LeRoy Meininger, R. 1997). Sdlg. T.P.#8. TB, 36" (91 cm), M. Blackish purple, irregular pure white streaks and splashes, velvety texture; beards purple, hairs tipped bronze. Jammy Prints X Maria Tormena. Monument 1997.

FANTASY FLING (A. & D. Willott, R. 1999). Sdlg. W 97-B. SDB, 11" (28 cm), E. S. pale peach, heavily marked purple; style arms light red violet; F. pale peach, edged and striped purple; beards coral; ruffled. Proud Princess X Sabrina's Kiss.

FARA MORGANA (Hyram Ames, R. 1989). Comanche Acres 1990.

FAR AND AWAY (Mary Dunn, R. 1991). Sdlg. L122-1. LA, 35" (89 cm), M. Ruffled deep red purple, yellow signal. L78-1: ((Blue Shield x Black Widow) x Full Eclipse) X Clara Goula. Bay View 1992.

FARAWAY (Nora Scopes, SDB, R. 1982). British Iris Society 1987.

FAR FETCHED (Chet Tompkins, R. 1999). Sdlg. 93-24. TB, 38" (97 cm), ML. S. and style arms bluish white; F. bluish white, tinted brown; beards blue white. (Up and Coming x Smoke Signals) X inv. sdlgs. Fleur de Lis 1999.

FARFUI (Augusto Bianco, R. 1998). Sdlg. 452. SDB, 10" (26 cm), M. S. tobacco caramel, light cocoa plicata marking; style arms tobacco caramel; F. straw ground, lined and dotted brown and cocoa; beards gold, lavender base; pronounced spicy fragrance. Probably -- Carrot Curls X Tender Tears. Iride 1998.

FARLEIGH BEACH (Kevin Nilsen, R. 1992). Sdlg. 27-86-1. TB, 28" (71 cm), EM. S. waved and ruffled cream, flushed pink, edge yellow; F. light rosy tan over yellow ground; beards white, tipped red Beachgirl X unknown. Iridescence 1992/93.

FARRELLOU (C. T . Claussen, R. 1991). Sdlg. 82-76-1. TB, 30" (76 cm), M. Light pink infused lavender; beards coral rust; slight fragrance. Sara Lynn X Blushing Pink. Wagontrail Acres 1992.

FARR'S FORTUNE (Jim Hedgecock, R. 1991). Sdlg. 83-39-1. TB, 36" (91 cm), M. Heavily ruffled medium yellow, small white blaze by bright yellow beard; F. laced; slight sweet fragrance. Fashion Rings X Buttered Popcorn. Comanche Acres 1992.

FASCINATING RHYTHM (William Plotner, R. 1992). Sdlg. 84-401-1. TB, 38" (97 cm), ML. S. white, widely edged orchid purple; F. white ground, stitched dark purple on edge; beards orchid white; slight spicy fragrance. (((Dream Lover x Dualtone) x Dundee) x (Darktown Strutter x On the Go)) X Jigsaw. Wildwood Gardens 1989.

FASCINATION CHILDS (John Lewis Childs by Society for Japanese Irises, R. 1993). JI (6 F.), 36" (90 cm), M. Bright blue violet ground with white central zone, radiating white veins, yellow signal. Parentage unknown. Childs 1926.

FASCINATOR (Ben Hager, TB, R. 1989). Melrose 1990.

FASHIONABLY LATE (Keith Keppel, R. 1997). Sdlg. 90-132A. TB, 36" (91 cm), L. S. blended rose violet (M&P 44-K-6 to 53-B-11); style arms greyed heather (45-I-1); F. blended rose violet (44-K-3/5), old rose (4-I-10) haft suffusion; beards antique red (4-J-11), scarlet vermilion (2-I-12) deep in throat; ruffled, faintly laced; slight sweet fragrance. Newlywed X 86-47A: (Faraway Places x (Veneer x Mulled Wine)). Keppel 1998.

FASHION BUG (George Shoop, R. 1994). Sdlg. 89-59-2. SDB, 9" (23 cm), M. Widely ruffled violet; beards tangerine; slight fragrance. Miss Sunshine X 86-52: (pink IB x Pink Caper). Shoop 1994.

FASHION DESIGNER (Keith Keppel, R. 1994). Sdlg. 89-9A. TB, 40" (102 cm), EM. S. blended warm white, light yellow (M&P 9-C-1) and pale peach (9-B-2); style arms white, edged corn yellow (10-J-5); F. corn yellow (10-I/J-5) hafts and blended edge, lightly flushed apricot (10-F-6) on hafts and along veins in creamy center; beards white at end, dandelion (9-L-4) middle, princeton orange (9-K-1) in throat; ruffled, laced. 85-60C: ((Orangerie x Faraway Places) x Precious Moments) X Inland Princess. Keppel 1995.

FASHION LINE (Lilly Gartman, TB, R. 1989). Roris 1992.

FASHION MARK (Floyd Dyer, R. 1995). Sdlg. D-21-85-B. BB, 25½" (64 cm), M. S. golden yellow; F. blue violet, brown border and hafts; beards yellow; ruffled; slight spicy fragrance. D-34-82-T: (Sister Carrie x Christmas Time) X Gala Madrid. Dyer's Garden 1995.

FASHION PASSION (Tom Burseen, R. 1992). Sdlg. 7-154A. TB, 35" (89 cm), M. S. white, yellow glow at midrib; F. velvety dark red purple (RHS 79B), 1/8" lavender pink edge; beards gold; heavily ruffled; slight fragrance. Street Dancer X Local Motion. T.B.'s Place 1993.

FASHION STATEMENT (Joseph Gatty by Keith Keppel, R. 1996). Sdlg. X45-13. TB, 36" (91 cm), M. S. and style arms lightly greyed rosy lilac (M&P 43-H-6); F. slightly paler and pinker (43-F-4), pallid lilac (43-B-2) in center, hafts shaded sunset (10-C-4); beards flamingo (2-I-11); ruffled. Coming Up Roses X Designing Woman. Keppel 1997.

FASHION VICTIM (John Marchant, R. 1990). Sdlg. 3787. CA, 12" (30 cm), M. Indian yellow (HCC 6/2), red purple halo on F. fading to bluish flush, leaving yellow rim. Sdlg. X sdlg.

FASHION WORLD (John C. Taylor, R. 1994). Sdlg. RL 33-8. LA, 51" (130 cm), ML. Rosy carmine pink, veined darker, white to pale pink rim, yellow signal. Watch Out X Margaret Lee. Rainbow Ridge 1996/97.

FATAL ATTRACTION (Frederick Kerr, R. 1995). Sdlg. 87B-58-01. TB, 36" (91 cm), E. S. medium blue, darker basal infusion; F. velvety blue black, slight blue white whisker markings beside beard; beards blue white, blue at end; heavily ruffled. Twist of Fate X Mystique. Rainbow Acres 1996.

FATHER JOHN (Ed Attenberger, R. 1996). Sdlg. 92-04-07. TB, 38" (97 cm), ML. S. and style arms light caramel yellow; F. white, rusty red edge, hafts and midstripe; beards burnt orange; slight spicy fragrance. Pearl Island X Radiant Apogee.

FATHOM (Marky Smith, R. 1996). Sdlg. 90-28C. IB, 23" (58 cm), ML. S. clear medium violet blue (RHS 97A); style arms lighter (97C), tinted mauve, midrib deeper (97A); F. violet blue (97B to 92B); beards medium grey blue, yellow orange in throat; ruffled; pronounced spicy fragrance. Home Port X Gatty R36-1: (Fly to Vegas x Swirling Seas). Aitken's Salmon Creek 1997.

FATSO (Tom Burseen, R. 1991). Sdlg. 7-266B. TB, 37" (94 cm), EM. S. violet blue (RHS 90D), lighter edge; F. violet blue, lighter center; beards cream; heavily ruffled; spicy fragrance. Local Motion X Ruffled Ballet. T.B.'s Place 1992.

FAULTLESS (Lloyd Zurbrigg, R. 1995). Sdlg. OO 54-2-2. TB, 36" (91 cm), M & RE (Oct./NC). Ruffled, lightly laced yellow, hint of green in S. midrib, F. paling to near-white around beard; beards rich yellow, white base at end. KK 53#1: (((Spirit of Memphis x Double Praise) x Mabel Andrews) x Sunny Disposition) X Northward Ho.

FAULT ZONE (Joseph Ghio, R. 1990). Sdlg. PJ-155L2. CA, 18" (46 cm), L-VL. S. light blue; F. blue violet, edged light blue. Pacific High X Idylwild. Bay View 1991.

FAUX PAS (Keith Keppel, BB, R. 1989). Keppel 1990.

FAVOR (Ben Hager, R. 1991). Sdlg. SD4988WPch. SDB, 10-15" (25-38 cm), EML. Smooth silken peach; beards white, tipped peach. SD4742: (Ceremony x Today's Fashion) X My Sheba. Adamgrove 1991.

FAVORITE ANGEL (Bennett Jones, R. 1990). Sdlg. M405-1. SDB, 12" (30 cm), M. Pure white, lightly ruffled F.; beard silver, large; slight sweet fragrance. Star Dancer X M341-1: ((Pepita x Truce) x (Blueberry Muffins x (Pepita x Truce))). Bennett Jones 1990.

FAVORIT SEZONA (Nina Miroshnichenko, R. 1997). TB, 36" (92 cm), L. S. yellow grey, base pale rose; F. claret beet, hafts cream yellow; beards yellow, pronounced spicy fragrance. Parentage unknown. Miroshnichenko 1995.

FEATHER BOA (Barry Blyth, R. 1995). Sdlg. A164-1. TB, 38" (97 cm), M. S. icy blue to white, midrib flushed orchid; F. icy blue to white, shoulders flushed orchid; beards white, tipped tangerine; ruffled, laced; pronounced sweet fragrance. Tiffany Time X Newlywed. Tempo Two 1995/96.

FEATURE ATTRACTION (Schreiner, R. 1994). Sdlg. AA 2012-A. TB, 37" (94 cm), L. Laced cool lavender-grape (RHS 90D), cool white signal and beards. T 1017-3, Song of Angels sib, X S 454-4: (Visual Arts x M 855-2: (Fabulous Frills sib x (Starina x Grand Waltz))). Schreiner 1994.

FEELING BLUE (Helen Cochran, R. 1996). Sdlg. 83-06-C. TB, 35" (89 cm), M. Ruffled pale blue self; beards blue; slight sweet fragrance. Winterscape X Song of Norway. Stockton 1997.

FELICIANA HILLS (Patrick O'Connor, LA, R. 1987). Bois d'Arc 1992.

FEMININE FIRE (Richard Ernst, R. 1991). Sdlg. F112-2. TB, 35" (89 cm), EM. Ruffled medium pink infused apricot, deeper pink hafts; beards orange red; slight sweet fragrance. Afternoon Delight X Gaulter G80-74, pink sdlg. Cooley 1991.

FERN MAW (Melba Hamblen, R. 1990). Sdlg. H83-08B. TB, 34" (86 cm), ML. Rose pink, F. widely banded deep rose pink; beards cerise pink. H79-02B: (Far Corners x Beauty Is) X Custom Made. Mission Bell 1991.

FERROUS FANTASY (Tom Burseen, R. 1997). Sdlg. 93-305A. TB, 34" (86 cm), EM. S. golden bronze (darker than RHS 164A); style arms golden brown; F. darker, washed beech brown (165A); beards gold; ruffled; musky fragrance. Coalignition X Twilight Blaze. T.B.'s Place 1997.

FESTIVAL CROWN (Maureen Foster, R. 1992). Sdlg. 6K10. TB, 36" (91 cm), ML. Ruffled and flared velvety indigo; beards dark blue. Navy Strut X Song of Norway. V. H. Humphrey 1995.

FESTIVAL PRELUDE (Calvin Helsley, R. 1992). Sdlg. 89-2. SIB, 32" (81 cm), E. S. dark violet (RHS 86A), edged violet (88B); style arms violet (88B) with violet blue (98C) rib; F. violet (88B), lightly veined and edged dark violet (86A), small white signal, gold in throat and under styles; lightly ruffled; slight sweet fragrance. Mabel Coday X D. S. Varner sdlg. Helsley 1992.

FESTIVAL'S ACADIAN (Dorman Haymon, LA, R. 1989). Deep South Garden 1990.

FESTIVE DREAM (Richard Morgan, R. 1991). Sdlg. L203-E. LA, 30" (76 cm), M. S. pale red (RHS 48B); F. slightly darker (48A), narrow buff rim, light yellow signal. Melon Time X Chowning 77-6-C: (Mockers Song x Ann Chowning). Redbud Lane 1992.

FESTIVE FEVER (John C. Taylor, R. 1994). Sdlg. RL 35-F. LA, 48" (120 cm), M. S. violet pink veined darker; F. violet pink, signal yellow; ruffled. Wine and Dine X Margaret Lee. Rainbow Ridge 1994/95.

FESTIVE GLOW (A. & D. Willott, R. 1996). Sdlg. 95-160. MTB, 22" (56 cm), EM. S. bright orange yellow; style arms orange yellow; F. deep brownish red violet, 1/8" orange yellow edge; beards deep orange. 90-137: (Bee's Pride x Bumblebee Deelite) X Desert Shield. Willott 1996.

FESTIVE MOOD (Schreiner, R. 1993). Sdlg. T 778-1. TB, 35" (89 cm), M. S. buff pink (RHS 161C); F. magenta (70A); beards tangerine. Navajo Blanket X I 370-2, Suave sib. Schreiner 1993.

FEU DU CIEL (Richard Cayeux, R. 1993). Sdlg. 8579 A. TB, 35" (89 cm), M. Bright orange self. (Skyfire x China Dragon) X Marcel Turbat. Cayeux 1993.

FEVER PITCH (John Marchant, R. 1990). Sdlg. 5487. CA, 12" (30 cm), M. S. indian yellow (HCC 6/3 to 6/2), chrysanthemum crimson (824/3) wash on midrib; F. indian yellow with allover wash of chrysanthemum crimson, lighter at edge, blue purple halo around darker signal. Sdlg. x sdlg. Portable Acres 1990.

FEY (Ben Hager, R. 1993). Sdlg. MD5490PlGrY. MDB, 4-6" (10-15 cm), E. Clean lemon with hint of green on hafts; beards slightly deeper. AMD5161GrY: (AMD4465TyVar: (Little You x (Inca Toy x (BU67 x Atomic Blue))) x Ditto sib X (AMD4465Var x (Ditto sib x ((((Orange Caper x (Shine Boy x Dark Fairy)) x SD1997D: (Rickshaw x Lilli-Var)) x Wink) x ((SD1997D x Bongo) x (Russet Dot x SD1997))))). Adamgrove 1994.

FIALOVÝ POPRACH (Zdeněk Seidl, R. 1999). Sdlg. 97-PAop/5. JI (3 F.), 24" (60 cm), M. S. purplish blue; style arms lighter; F, white, veined purple, purple dusting and yellow signal. Port Arthur X unknown.

FIBBER (Barry Blyth, R. 1991). Sdlg. X26-1. SDB, 10-12" (25-30 cm), ML. Pale peach apricot, F. with creamy center; beards white, tipped tangerine. (Oladi x Fifi) X Tricks. Tempo Two 1991/92.

FIDDLE-DEE-DEE (Farron Campbell, R. 1998). Sdlg. 95-301-A. LA, 32-35" (81-89 cm), M. S.

medium yellow; style arms medium yellow, orange tips; F. medium yellow, orange veining radiating from orange signal; ruffled. 92-41: (Goula sdlg.: (Ann Chowning x Mrs. Ira Nelson) x C'est Si Bon) X Noble Planet. Lone Star 1998.

FIELD OF DREAMS (Don Denney by James McWhirter, R. 1991). Sdlg. D81-10. TB, 36" (91 cm), M. S. smooth rich deep cherry red; F. slightly darker; beards deep bronze; slight fragrance. Spectacular Bid X (Maroon Velvet x Seeing Red). Cottage 1991.

FIERCE FIRE (Cy Bartlett, R. 1992). Sdlg. D/E-A2. IB, 23" (58 cm), EM. S. bright golden yellow; F. blended red, orange and yellow; beards yellow to orange; lightly ruffled. (Diligence x Eyebright) X A2, Arden sib. David Austin Roses 1997.

FIERY FIGURE (Sterling Innerst, R. 1999). Sdlg. 4039-1. TB, 36" (91 cm), ML. Fiery dark orange; style arms orange; beards orange; slight musky fragrance. Esmeralda X Hindenburg.

FIESTA SONG (Vernon Wood, R. 1990). Sdlg. 87-35. TB, 37" (94 cm), M. Honey gold (RHS 22C) with light violet flush, F. with violet (85C) area in center; beards tangerine. Matinee Idol X Collage. Cottage 1992.

FIGHTING SPIRIT (Heather Pryor, R. 1995). Sdlg. 60/90-3. LA, 47" (120 cm), EM. S. soft rose maroon (RHS 59C), reverse paler; style arms pale green, flushed maroon; F. deep maroon (59B), reverse paler; triangular signal bright yellow, brighter yellow steeple center, on all petals. Gladiator's Gift X Desert Jewel.

FIGHT ON (Robert Annand, R. 1996). Sdlg. 88-33A. TB, 37" (94 cm), M. S. and style arms yellow gold; F. mahogany red maroon, velvety; beards yellow gold, tipped yellow. 82-11: (Siva Siva x (Hindu Wand x Cambodia)) X Brown Lasso. Forest Ranch 1996.

FIGURE HEAD (Chet Tompkins, R. 1996). Sdlg. 93-9C. TB, 38" (97 cm), EML. S. and style arms oxblood; F. ivory cream ground tinted custard in center, broad dotted and washed to solid oxblood border; beards dull yellow; ruffled. (Raspberry Fudge x (Queen in Calico x Paprika Fono's)) X (Raging Tiger x Raspberry Fudge). Fleur de Lis 1996.

FILIBUSTER (Joseph Ghio, R. 1992). Sdlg. 88-138G. TB, 36" (91 cm), ML. S. nearly solid pink wine; F. white ground with pink wine lines and dotting overall, white hairline edge, white sunburst signal around tangerine beard. Cupid's Arrow X 85-25A: ((((Handiwork x (Gay Parasol x Mystique)) x Goddess) x (Gem of Sierra x ((73-31-I: ((Ponderosa x Honey Rae) x (((Commentary x Claudia Rene) x Claudia Rene) x (Ponderosa x New Moon))) x Osage Buff) x (Vanity x Anon)))) x Gigolo). Bay View 1993.

FILIPPIKA (Ladislav Muska, R. 1997). Sdlg. RIGE-02. TB, 36" (91 cm), M. S. and style arms light lavender; F. reddish lilac, rimmed light lavender; beards bright orange; ruffled, laced; slight fragrance. (Ringo x Geniality) X L'Ely. Muska 1997.

FILM FESTIVAL (Keith Keppel, R. 1992). Sdlg. 84-66A. TB, 35" (89 cm), EM. S. rose buff (M&P 4-G-8) ground,blended and suffused dahlia mauve (53-D-9) to bacchus (53-J-4); F. peachy cream (9-B-4/5) ground bordered greyed mauve (46-H-3), darker greyed red purple (55-E-10) hafts; beards navajo (10-C-12) to tomato red (3-I-12); pronounced musky fragrance. Rustler X 81-122K: (Gigolo x Queen in Calico). D & J Gardens 1993.

FILOSOFSKI KAMEN (Nina Miroshnichenko, R. 1996). TB, 41" (103 cm), M. Ruffled bordeaux violet, paler below mustard yellow beard; style arms greenish yellow, violet crests; pronounced spicy fragrance. Parentage unknown. Miroshnichenko 1989.

FIMBRIATED SPACE (George Sutton, R. 1998). Sdlg. G-71-C. TB, 35" (89 cm), ML. Ruffled white, S. very open; style arms with fimbriated crests; beards white, hairs tipped pale yellow in center, orange yellow in throat, extended as white petaloid ending in white flounce; slight spicy fragrance. Skating Party X Twice Thrilling. Sutton 1999.

FINAL DECISION (Elvan Roderick, R. 1991). Sdlg. 8404. TB, 36" (91 cm), ML. Heavily ruffled golden yellow, F. with lighter center area; beards yellow. Parentage unknown. Roderick Iris 1991.

FINAL FRONTIER (Bernard Pryor, R. 1999). Sdlg. 62/96-A. LA, 35" (89 cm), EM. S. spectrum violet (RHS 82B), cream rim and reverse; style arms golden yellow, violet tip; F. lilac purple (70A), golden rim and reverse, yellow thumbprint, golden steeple signal with raised center; ruffled. New Vogue X Our Dorothy.

FINAL INNING (Henry Danielson by Luella Danielson, AB (OGB+), R. 1989). Aril Society, Pleasure Iris 1990.

FINALIST (Joseph Gatty by Keith Keppel, R. 1993). Sdlg. S38-1. TB, 35" (89 cm), L. S. lavender grey (M&P 43-A-2) flushed greenish yellow (11-F-1) to pineapple (11-J-2); F. rubient (55-L-9) to plum (47-J-9) blend, small cotinga purple (43-L-10) blaze, narrow wistaria lavender (41-D-7) edge; beards bronze yellow (11-L-9) tipped lavender; ruffled. Karen X Q39-1: (Tomorrow's Child x K41-1: (Show Biz x Villain)). Keppel 1994.

FINALLY BETTY (Tom Burseen, R. 1999). Sdlg. 93-366B. TB, 35" (89 cm), M. S. white; F. pale lavender; beards white, hairs tipped tangerine, with long fuzzy lavender blue horn; ruffled; slight fragrance. 91-124: (Ample Charm x Hello Hobo) X Thornbird. T.B.'s Place 1999.

FINE BLENDING (Paul Black, R. 1996). Sdlg. 8837A. TB, 35" (89 cm), M. S. and style arms medium yellow; F. pearl white, center blended pale violet, pale yellow border, yellow reverse; beards bright yellow; ruffled; slight sweet fragrance. 8530B: ((Betty Simon x Magic Candle) x (Tequila Sunrise sib x Entourage)) X sib 8530C. Mid-America 1996.

FINE DECOR (Cleo Palmer, R. 1994). Sdlg. 9050. IB, 22" (56 cm), M. S. light yellow; F. light yellow, slightly darker rim and indistinct inner rim; beards yellow, tipped white; slight fragrance. Big Dipper X unknown. Palmer's Iris 1994.

FINE FEATHERED FRIEND (Sharon McAllister, R. 1998). Sdlg. 85-8-7. AB (OGB-), 30" (76 cm), ML. S. white, delicately veined yellow; style arms golden yellow; F. white ground, brownish yellow veins radiating from throat, heavy yellow veining forming plicata-like pattern at edge; beards yellow. Koko Knoll X Asha Michelle.

FINE HARMONY (William Ackerman, R. 1992). Sdlg. A4-4-85. JI (3 F.), 34" (87 cm), M. S. near-white base blending to pale lavender purple (RHS 77C/77A) at edge; F. white around yellow green (154C) signal, blending to mosaic violet (84C to 84A) with white veining, ruffled and crinkled; style arms white, large violet (84B) lips. Gosho-Asobi X D5-12-115, inv. sdlgs. from Seiko-en Nursery, Japan. Nicholls Gardens 1993.

FINE WARRIOR (John C. Taylor, R. 1990). Sdlg. OL 119-1. LA, 43" (110 cm), M. Heavily ruffled greyed orange (RHS 173D), veined deeper (173B), yellow signal on all petals. L93-1: (blue Freddie Boy sdlg. x Grace Scott) X Pintharuka. Rainbow Ridge 1990/91.

FINSTERWALD (Sterling Innerst, R. 1993). Sdlg. 3897-10. IB, 16" (41 cm), M. Medium yellow with brown F. spot; beards orange; slight fragrance. 3277-2: (Glazed Gold x Catalyst) X 3608-1: (Dash sib x Comma). Innerst 1994.

FIODOR SHALIAPIN (V. & N. Gordodelovy, R. 1995). Sdlg. 162. TB, 39" (100 cm), M. S. bright pink, tinted lilac; style arms light yellow, crests pink; F. pink, tinted lilac, white haft striations; beards orange. Parentage unknown. Gordodelovy 1986.

FIOLETOVY NIZKOROSLY (Irina Driagina, R. 1995). Sdlg. 78-01. BB, 24" (60 cm), VE. S. dark cherry violet; F. blackish blue purple; beard blue black; ruffled. Sable X Chernomorets. Driagina 1978.

FIREBREATHER (Schreiner, R. 1992). Sdlg. W 302-4. TB, 37" (94 cm), L. Orange (RHS 23A) self; beards tangerine. Spiced Orange X P 539-A: ((Soft Moonbeam x New Moon) x Fiery Chariot). Schreiner 1992.

FIREBUG (Joseph Gatty by Keith Keppel, R. 1994). Sdlg. W38-2. IB, 26" (66 cm), VL. S. deeper than chrome lemon (M&P 9-L-2); F. blended garnet brown (6-L-9) to algerian red (7-L-5), narrow rim matching S.; beards chrome lemon (9-K-2) based white at tip, bronze yellow (11-L-8) in throat; slight fragrance. Jazzamatazz X Smart Aleck. Keppel 1994.

FIRE DRAGON (Leo Barnard, R. 1997). Sdlg. L 91-77 FD. TB, 38" (97 cm), ML. S. and style arms light yellow; F. golden yellow, light yellow rim, short dark yellow line below beard; beards red orange, yellow end, large and bushy, ending in golden yellow spoon or flounce; heavily ruffled; slight fragrance. Borderline X Twice Thrilling. Paradise Iris 1997.

FIREFLUSH (Hilmary Catton, IB, R. 1986). Wyuna 1987.

FIREMIST (O. D. Niswonger, R. 1991). Sdlg. Sp 2-83. SPU, 40" (102 cm), M. Old rose blend with yellow F. infusion. Sp 5-75: (Transition x Pink Candles) X Pink Candles. Cape Iris 1991.

FIRENZE RED (George Sutton, R. 1993). Sdlg. A-118A. TB, 38" (97 cm), M. Ruffled light burgundy red self; beards burgundy; slight fragrance. 81-7A: (Royal Trumpeter x Rancho Rose) X Florentine Red. Sutton 1993.

FIRE ON ICE (John Weiler, R. 1990). Sdlg. 82-188-4. TB, 36" (91 cm), EML & RE. Ruffled and lightly laced warm white, soft yellow glow on hafts and styles; beards red; slight sweet fragrance. 78-48-13: ((((Glittering Gold x Orange Crush) x (Ballerina x Orange Crush)) x ((Cloth of Gold x Ballerina) x Pompano Peach)) x ((Royal Gold x White King) x ((Marquesan Skies x (Rippling Waters x Claudia Rene)) x self))) X 78-73A: ((((Ballerina x Orange Crush) x Sexton 35-65) x Fresno Calypso) x (Fresno Fiesta x Fresno Calypso)). Rialto 1990.

FIRE PIT (Richard Ernst, R. 1993). Sdlg. F121-4. TB, 34" (86 cm), M. S. warm brick amber with red overlay; F. deep crimson red, slight violet tone near yellow beard; ruffled. Quiet Riot X Mountain Melody. Cooley 1992.

FIREPLACE EMBERS (O. D. Niswonger, R. 1993). Sdlg. SDB 28-90. SDB, 10" (25 cm), M. S. dark yellow; F. dark maroon; beards gold. Jazzamatazz X Slap Bang. Cape Iris 1993.

FIRESIDE CHAT (Cleo Palmer, R. 1995). Sdlg. 9318. SDB, 10" (25 cm), E. Medium yellow, F. with light peach spot; beards orange. 8904, parentage unknown, X 8905: (8539: (Delicate Pink x ((Crescent Moon x Little Titan) x ((Lenna M. x Propecy) x Dove Wings))) x 8531: (((Dove Wings x ((Wilma V. x unknown) x Little Titan)) x ((Baria x Carpathia) x Dove Wings)) x (Daisy x 7525: (Pink Cushion x Dove Wings)))). Palmer's Iris 1995.

FIRESTARTER (A. & D. Willott, R. 1994). Sdlg. 92-97. SDB, 10" (25 cm), M. Lightly ruffled full purple, deeper flush around red orange beards. 84-149A: (Apricot Tart x Coral Wings) X unknown. Willott 1995.

FIRESTORM (Marky Smith, R. 1992). Sdlg. 89-25C. SDB, 13½" (35 cm), E. S. nearly solid burgundy (RHS 183A), fading to buff washed burgundy in center, burgundy midrib; F. aureloin yellow (2A), heavily lined and washed port wine (183C), becoming solid port wine at rim; beards old gold (162A); ruffled. Rusty Dusty X Tender Tears. Aitken's Salmon Creek 1994.

FIRE WITHIN (Monty Byers, TB, R. 1989). Moonshine 1990.

FIRST ALERT (Paul Black, R. 1997). Sdlg. 91389A. SDB, 14" (36 cm), EM. S. and style arms orchid; F. slightly deeper orchid, plum hafts, white rays in heart; beards orange, white at end. Tricks X unknown. Mid-America 1997.

FIRST CHAPTER (G. F. Wilson, R. 1994). Sdlg. 3-89OTW-A. AB (OGB), 33" (84 cm), EM. S. violet purple lightly veined blue; F. cream ground, blended rose red deepening toward edges; signals maroon black, set off by cream area; beards cream, tipped bronze, wide; musky fragrance. Onlooker X Tornado Warning. Pleasure Iris, Potterton & Martin 1995.

FIRST CONTACT (Donald Spoon, R. 1997). Sdlg. 89-62A. BB, 27" (69 cm), M. S. pale lavender, deeper at tip, very lightly peppered; style arms dark purple; F. pale lavender, deeper flush at tip, dark lavender plicata hafts; beards turquoise blue, pale yellow base and in throat; ruffled. (Pledge Allegiance x Pledge Allegiance) X Pledge Allegiance. Winterberry 1999.

FIRST EMBRACE (Donald Spoon, R. 1997). Sdlg. 90-127B. TB, 30" (76 cm), EM. Lightly ruffled peach pink self; beards darker peach pink; flared. My Katie X Pink Pink.

FIRST ENCOUNTER (Frederick Held, R. 1998). JI (6 F.), 28" (71 cm), VE. Orchid pink central flush paling to near-white toward edge, signal yellow; style arms light orchid pink. Parentage unknown; seed from Jelitto Staudensamen, Germany.

FIRST FAVOURITE (John C. Taylor, R. 1991). Sdlg. OL 100-A. LA, 39" (100 cm), M. White, veined yellowish green. Joel Fletcher X Helen Naish. Rainbow Ridge 1992/93.

FIRST FLUSH B.L.C. Dodsworth, TB, R. 1976). British Iris Society 1981.

FIRST FUSS (Tom Burseen, R. 1993). Sdlg. 8-12A. TB, 34" (84 cm), VE-M. S. creamy gold (RHS 19B); F. cream ground washed and veined dark amber gold (26A); beards gold; spicy fragrance; ruffled. 6-217: ((In Tempo x Roundup) x Beyond) X Bridal Fashion. T.B.'s Place 1994.

FIRST INTERSTATE (Schreiner, R. 1990). Sdlg. S 629-1. TB, 36" (91 cm), ML. S. yellow (RHS 12A); F. white, yellow (12A) edge and shoulders; beards yellow. I 1226-16: (Soft Moonbeam x New Moon) X M 591-A: (K 1250-A: ((Lightning Ridge x (Wine and Roses x Gypsy Lullaby)) x (((Imperial Lilac sib x Arctic Flame) x White Taffeta) x Launching Pad)) x Piping Hot). Schreiner 1991.

FIRST MOVEMENT (Graeme Grosvenor, R. 1990). Sdlg. O 22-2. TB, 36" (91 cm), EM. S. apricot, F. slightly lighter; beards red; heavily ruffled. Preface X Words and Music. Rainbow Ridge 1992/93.

FIRST REUNION (Larry Gaulter by Cooley's Gardens, R. 1990). Sdlg. 80-05. TB, 34" (86 cm), ML. S. deep pink with lavender overtone; F. deep pink, paler center, honey shoulders; beards tangerine; lightly ruffled, heavily laced. Inv. sdlgs. from Claudia Rene lines. Cooley 1990.

FIRST ROMANCE (George Shoop, R. 1994). Sdlg. 89-57-1. SDB, 10" (25 cm), M. S. pure pink; F. white; beards tangerine pink; slight fragrance. Spring Dancer X Pink Caper. Shoop 1994.

FISHERMAN'S MORNING (James Copeland Sr., R. 1994). Sdlg. 88-15. SIB, 31" (80 cm), M. S. rosy red violet (RHS 77A); style arms veined and shaded purple (77B), light violet blue (97C) edge, turquoise (107B) midrib; F. rosy red violet (77A) with dark violet blue (95A) central area. 82-20: (Pink Haze x Dear Delight) X 82-06: (Dear Delight x Pink Haze). Ensata Gardens 1994.

FIT THE BILL (Graeme Grosvenor, R. 1998). Sdlg. V19-2. TB, 36" (91 cm), M. S. butterscotch yellow; F. red brown; beards yellow. Guadalajara X First Movement. Rainbow Ridge 1998/99.

FIVE O'CLOCK WORLD (Roger Nelson, R. 1995). Sdlg. RN 89-102DT. TB, 36" (91 cm), ML. S. and style arms rosy orchid violet, F. slightly deeper; beards blue grape; pronounced sweet fragrance. Melancholy Man X Enchanting. Iris Country 1996.

FIVE STAR FINAL (Ed Roberts, R. 1992). Sdlg. RV-3-92. TB, 36" (91 cm), ML. S. deep electric blue, blending to lighter edge; F. light blue white, dark blue violet streak running from dark violet beard to within 1/2" of edge; pronounced sweet fragrance. Olympiad X Honky Tonk Blues. Ed Roberts 1995.

FIXED STAR (Ben Hager, SPU, R. 1989). Melrose 1990.

FIZZGIG (Paul Black, R. 1993). Sdlg. 89221F. SDB, 10" (25 cm), E. S. cream ground with heavy overall ginger brown plicata band and lines up midrib; F. ivory white ground, wide ginger brown plicata band and centerline; beards violet with brown overlay; pronounced spicy fragrance. 84211B: (824A, Chubby Cheeks sib, x 824D, sib) X 86253A: (Auburn Valley x 84211C). Mid-America 1993.

FJORD (Roger Nelson, R. 1995). Sdlg. RN 91-36Z. TB, 37" (94 cm), ML. Blue white self aging white; beards cool white; slight sweet fragrance. Seminole Spring X Silverado. Iris Country 1996.

FLAMBÉ (J. T. Aitken, R. 1999). Sdlg. 94M12-5. IB, 24" (61 cm), ML & RE. S. white, hot yellow midrib flush; style arms hot yellow; F. intense cinnamon orange; beards orange. Champagne Elegance X Joe Cool. Aitken's Salmon Creek 1999.

FLAMBOYANT AFFAIR (Sharon McAllister, R. 1998). Sdlg. 92-11-9. AB (OGB-), 32" (81 cm), ML. S. reddish violet, golden orange basal flush; style arms amber, flushed reddish violet; F. greyed reddish violet, with rust and violet veining on white around bright orange beard, purple dotting in signal area. Unclaimed Treasure X Sterling Mistress.

FLAMBOYANT DANCE (Lynda Miller, R. 1995). Sdlg. 3386B. TB, 32" (81 cm), ML. S. white, narrow light tan stitched edge; style arms white and violet; F. plum, dotted white in center; beards orange, base white. (Odyssey x Petite Posy) X Laced Cotton. Miller's Manor 1996.

FLAMINGO FROLIC (Hugh Knight by John Wood, R. 1992). Sdlg. K-103-84. JI (9 F.), 38" (97 cm), ML. White ground with violet purple veins radiating from yellow (6B) signal, leaving white (155D) margin on edge; style arms white. Parentage unknown. John Wood 1993.

FLAMING RHYTHM (Cleo Palmer, R. 1990). Sdlg. 8819. SDB, 12" (30 cm), E. Light blue violet, very pale red violet halo on F.; beards red orange, tipped cream. 8548: (Delicate Pink x ((Dove Wings x 7259: ((Wilma V. x unknown) x Little Titan)) x Dove Wings)) X 8134: (Show Baby x ((Lenna M. x Prophecy) x Dove Wings)). Palmer's Iris 1990.

FLANDERS LION (Willy Hublau, R. 1996). Sdlg. B7. JI (6-9 F.), 35" (90 cm), ML. Greyed purple (RHS 187D), silver rays and dots, dark yellow signal; style arms greyed purple, stamens forming crest. Sdlg. X Surprise Light. Delmez Gardens 1998.

FLAREOUT (Marvin Granger, LA, R. 1988). Faggard 1992.

FLASHED TIPS (Ladislav Muska, R. 1999). Sdlg. 98-MHVS-03. TB, 34" (86 cm), L. S. medium orchid; style arms orchid; F. claret, narrow orchid rim; beards tangerine, orchid horn; ruffled, laced; sweet fragrance. ((Mys Horn x Visual Arts) x (Sky Hooks x Silverado)) X Concorde With Hooks. Muska 1999.

FLASH OF VIOLET (Sharon McAllister, R. 1998). Sdlg. 90-19-14. AB (OGB+), 24" (61 cm), EM. S. soft blue violet ground veined gold; style arms greenish buff; F. pale greenish buff veined gold and washed red violet; intense iridescent blue violet center wash paling with age; beards golden brown. Werckmeister's Beauty X Whirlwind Tour. McAllister 1998.

FLASHY FANCY (Mary Dunn, R. 1995). Sdlg. M880-2. TB, 38" (97 cm), M. S. grape fuchsia, slightly lighter in center; style arms grape fuchsia, slightly deeper texture veining, light area around beard; beards grape at end, lined deeper at edge, changing to mustard bronze toward throat. Perfecta X Vibrations. M.A.D. Iris 1996.

FLASHY FLIRT (Dorothy Guild, MTB, R. 1989). Guild 1990.

FLAT RATE (Joseph Ghio, R. 1993). Sdlg. 87-53L3. TB, 36" (91 cm), ML. S. none, F. (6) deep purple with metallic sheen, flat; beards purple. (Black Tornado x Witches' Sabbath) X Satin Satan. Bay View 1994.

FLAUNT IT (Sharon McAllister, R. 1996). Sdlg. 91-27-2. AB (OGB-), 30" (76 cm), M. S. iridescent imperial purple (RHS 78A), gold basal infusion and light splashing; style arms golden yellow (13B), red violet midrib, amber (167B) crests; F. purple dotting on white near beard, surrounded by rust stippling on yellow, outer portion blended orange, red, brown and violet; beards mustard to golden amber blend. Goddess X Tribe of Judah. McAllister 1996.

154

FLAVOURS (Barry Blyth, R. 1996). Sdlg. B113-5. BB, 24" (61 cm), ML & RE. S. soft lilac, infused tan; F. silvery lilac, 1/8" gold edge, bright sienna brown signal pattern halfway down petal; beards bronze, lavender base; sweet fragrance. Zing Me X Knight Templar. Tempo Two 1996/97.

FLEDERMAUS (Eberhard Fischer, R. 1999). Sdlg. 11. TB, 29½" (75 cm), M. S. and style arms violet, blended red brown; F. violet, center luminous, edge matching S.; beards dark brown, violet at end, bronze in throat; waved, lightly laced. Royal Tapestry X unknown.

FLEUR COLLETTE LOUISE (A.R.J. Bailey, R. 1992). Sdlg. CBL88-1. LA, 23" (58 cm), E. S. violet; F. violet with white ray pattern, yellow throat, deep yellow signal line; wavy. Cuisine X Bryce Leigh.

FLEUR DELITE (Mary Dunn, R. 1997). Sdlg. M2027-B. TB, 37" (94 cm), M. Yellow self; beards yellow, fuzzy. Gardenlite X Bogota. M.A.D. Iris 1998.

FLEUR JANET COLLETTE (A.R.J. Bailey, R. 1994). Sdlg. M/KM93/8. JI (3 F.), 31" (78 cm), E. S. pure white; style arms pure white, short; F. pure white, signal yellow. Moonlight Waves X Katy Mendez sdlg.

FLEURTATION (Lois O'Brien, R. 1994). Sdlg. 90-88A. TB, 36" (91 cm), EM. S. warm lilac pink (RHS 84A), slightly darker edge; style arms rosy lilac (87D); F. creamy lilac (84D) center, slightly darker edge; beards strawberry cream (62B); ruffled; slight sweet fragrance. 85-308A: (Cheesecake x Frisco Follies) X Vanity. O'Brien Iris 1995.

FLICKERING FIRELIGHT (Chet Tompkins, R. 1993). Sdlg. 86-19A. TB, 39" (99 cm), ML. Deep cream ground flushed greenish lime, edge of F. stitched and dotted dark crushed raspberry and flame red; beards brown, tipped violet. ((Windwalker x Darktown Strutter) x (Ribbon Round x (Stepping Out x Tinsel Town))) X reciprocal crosses. Fleur de Lis 1993.

FLIEDERPRINZESSIN (Eberhard Fischer, R. 1993). Sdlg. 5. TB, 42" (107 cm), ML. Waved light violet self; beards pale yellow; slight sweet fragrance. Parentage unknown. Camehl 1993.

FLIGHT COMMANDER (George Sutton, R. 1998). Sdlg. G-17-B. TB, 34" (86 cm), ML. S. and style arms white, faint blue shading; F. wistaria blue (RHS 92B) blended white; beards pale yellow, white base, 1½" wistaria blue flounce; ruffled, flared. Mystic Lace X Let's Pretend. Sutton 1999.

*FLIGHT OF BUTTERFLIES (Jean Witt, SIB, R. 1972.) White Flower Farm ca. 1975.

FLIGHT PATTERNS (Stephen Stevens, R. 1995). Sdlg. 88-1-5. SDB, 12" (31 cm), EM. S. jasmine yellow (RHS 10B); style arms yellow; F. yellow ground with brown lines radiating from throat, 1/4" yellow border; beards white, tipped orange; ruffled; slight sweet fragrance. Pac Man X Starlight Waltz. Hahn's Rainbow 1995.

FLIGHTS OF FANCY (Keith Keppel, R. 1992). Sdlg. 86-6A. TB, 36" (91 cm), E. S. oyster white (M&P 10-B-1) to cream (9-D-2), flushed soft rosy orchid (43-F-6) in center; F. paler oyster (10-AB-1), rosy orchid wash deepening in center to gloxinia (43-L-10) to grapejuice (44-L-10) with conspicuous paler veining, warm white area by beards, burnous (9-C-4) on inner hafts; beards white to cream, tipped flame (1-C-12); slight sweet fragrance. 82-45A: (77-111Q, Gigolo sib, x 78-70A, Rosy Cloud sib) X 84-15A: (80-98B: (76-137C: ((68-39F: (66-35C: ((Irma Melrose x Tea Apron) x ((Full Circle x Rococo) x Tea Apron)) x April Melody) x 68-39D) x ((Joy Ride x Roundup) x (April Melody x (66-35B x April Melody)))) x (Mistress x 75-98B, Peccadillo sib)) x 82-45A). D & J Gardens 1993.

FLINDER'S DELIGHT (Colin Fidock, R. 1997). Sdlg. F91-4. AB (OGB), 18" (46 cm), E. S. lilac, veined chocolate; style arms tea rose; F. pale burgundy, rich burgundy signal; beards old gold. Heart Stealer X sdlg., parentage unknown.

FLINTRIDGE (Glenn Corlew, R. 1992). Sdlg. SP-11F. SPU, 38-40" (97-102 cm), M. Deep golden yellow. Gilded Chalice X Forty Carats. Bay View 1992.

FLIRTATIOUS (A. & D. Willott, R. 1990). Sdlg. 89-83. IB, 21" (53 cm), M. Ruffled pink, slightly lighter around orange beard. Barney's Delight X Magic. Willott 1992.

FLIRTING (Barry Blyth, R. 1998). Sdlg. E6-3. SDB, 14" (36 cm), EML. Bright flamingo pink, F. slightly deeper, with light tannish haft area; beards burnt tangerine, 1/4" blue lavender end. Little Bev X A44-2, Voyage sib. Tempo Two 1998/99.

FLIRTY WHITE SKIRTS (Opal Wulf, R. 1995). Sdlg. 47-3-92. MTB, 20-22" (51-56 cm), ML. S. white; F. white, faint purple veining around gold beard. Jolly Jim X STGO-B-88: (Striking Gold x unknown). Wulf's Backachers 1997.

FLITTERS (Barry Blyth, R. 1994). Sdlg. A14-5. SDB, 14" (36 cm), VE-EM. S. pink with champagne hue; F. same, brown tan signal area veined white about halfway down; beards white, tipped tangerine; slight fragrance. Smoky Imp X Chanted. Tempo Two 1994/95.

FLOAT (Graeme Grosvenor, R. 1993). Sdlg. O 12-1. TB, 36" (91 cm), ML. Ruffled white self; beards white. Bubbly Mood X Titan's Glory. Rainbow Ridge 1993/94.

FLOATING WORLD (Nora Scopes, R. 1993). Sdlg. PC38A. CA, 15" (38 cm), M. S. purple; F. white, edged and marked violet, round and flat. Seed from SS&J Group (BIS), parentage unknown.

FLOPSY (Philip Loomis by Catherine Gates, R. 1990). TB, 34" (86 cm), M. White with yellow haft veining, drooping S.; beards yellow, tipped white. Parentage unknown.

FLORAL CHIFFON (Joseph Gatty, R. 1989). Keppel 1990.

FLORENCE FISHER (Lynn Markham, R. 1992). Sdlg. 87-4C2. TB, 32" (81 cm), ML. S. cream (RHS 11D); style arms cream, creamy yellow midrib and edge; F. creamy white (155D) in center, shading to cream (11D) at edge, creamy yellow (11) hafts; beards cream white base, tipped bright yellow (14A) in throat, lightening to pure cream white on visible portion; ruffled, satin finish; slight sweet fragrance. 7783-2A: (Angel Feathers x Sheaff 60-3: ((Hall pink sdlg. x Celestial Snow) x Arctic Flame)) X Vanity. Markham 1995.

FLORENTINE FABLE (Margie Robinson, R. 1990). Sdlg. 83-18. BB, 26" (65 cm), M. S. bright apricot (RHS 29C); F. apricot, blending to cream around bright red orange (33B) beard; slight fragrance. 77-40: (Orchid Brocade x unknown) X unknown. M. Robinson 1991.

FLORENTINE RED (George Sutton, R. 1993). Sdlg. 5-118R. TB, 32" (81 cm), EM. Burgundy red; beards dark burgundy; slight fragrance. Fort Apache X Marauder. Sutton 1992.

FLORIMARA (Bruce Clark, R. 1999). Sdlg. 96-210. IB, 24" (60 cm), M. S. white, flushed light pinkish apricot, metallic wire edge; style arms white and pink; F. white, flushed pinkish apricot, some greenish yellow veining; beards orange, end white with hairs tipped orange. Mara X Marmalade Skies.

FLOSSIE BOBBSEY (Elaine Hulbert, R. 1997). SPEC (*sanguinea*), 5" (13 cm), M. Ruffled blue violet, F. with large round white signal with sharp blue veins; flat form. Seed from Florence Stout; parentage unknown.

FLOUNCED BAJAZZO (Ladislav Muska, R. 1998). Sdlg. 98-MCWW-03. TB, 34" (86 cm), L. Lemon yellow; style arms lighter lemon yellow; beards orange, long yellow tan flounce; slight fragrance. ((Mys Horn x Calicoball) x (White Window x Chuang-Che)) X Illulisat. Muska 1999.

FLOW BLUE (Duane Meek, R. 1992). Sdlg. 35-1-2. TB, 36" (91 cm), EM. S. soft blue with darker fleckings; F. light center area, slight blue infusion on ruffled and pleated edge with darker fleckings and veinings; beards soft blue; slight fragrance. Winterscape X 72-1-4: ((Mount Repose x Fanfare Orchid) x Blue Luster). D & J Gardens 1992.

FLOWERFIELD (Opal Brown, R. 1990). Sdlg. 83-5C12. TB, 36-38" (91-97 cm), M. S. orient pink (RHS 36A); F. near-white, laced orient pink edge, pink flush on shoulders; beards mandarin red (40C); ruffled. Glass Slippers X Gold Trimmings. Brown's Sunnyhill 1990.

FLOWER SHOWER (John Weiler, R. 1990). Sdlg. 85-29-9. SDB, 11" (28 cm), EML & RE. Dark red violet; beards violet; pronounced sweet fragrance. 82-21-4: (Third Charm x Plum-Plum) X 82-30-1: (Watersmeet x Third Charm). Rialto 1990.

FLUFFY (Cleo Palmer, R. 1990). Sdlg. 8557. SDB, 11" (28 cm), L. S. white; F. white, hafts veined yellow, ruffled; beards yellow, tipped white. 8236: (Velvet Pride x (Daisy sib x unknown)) X 8225: (Crescent Moon x unknown). Palmer's Iris 1991.

FLUSHED DELIGHT (Chris Vizvarie, R. 1990). Sdlg. CRV-8-85A. TB, 32" (82 cm), M. Lilac lavender, lavender signal; beards pink, pink horn or flounce; pronounced sweet fragrance. Christa X Twice Thrilling. Last Scent Farm 1990.

FLUTE ENCHANTEE (Laure Anfosso, R. 1991). Sdlg. L 83 10 A. TB, 31½" (80 cm), M. Pink, F. with white area in center; beards white to light tangerine, bluish white horn. Beverly Sills X Sky Hooks. Iris en Provence 1991.

FLUTTER BY BUTTERFLY (Robert Hollingworth, R. 1996). Sdlg. 90K1A19. SIB, 32" (81 cm), EM. S. light blue; style arms very light blue, feathered; F. clear medium light blue, small white signal; ruffled. 86K6A1: (83M2A34: (Steve Varner x (Super Ego x Anniversary)) x Kenabee) X 85C3A2: (83M3B8: (Pink Haze x Fairy Dawn) x 80X1C2: (Super Ego x Anniversary)). Windwood Gardens 1996.

FLUTTERING BLUE (Lyle Fort by Dona Fort, R. 1997). Sdlg. 90-520-BL. TB, 40" (107 cm), M. S. light blue, center slightly deeper; style arms blue; F. white, shading to blue around beard; beards blue, base white; heavily ruffled; slight sweet fragrance. Edge of Winter X Wide Hips.

FLYAWAY BLUES (Janet Hutchinson, R. 1998). Sdlg. KW/OM/B2. LA, 33-36" (84-91 cm), M. S. lavender to rosy lavender blend, grey violet influence, pale line edge; style arms rosy lavender over lime, deeper crests; F. rich medium rose violet, grey violet influence, veined, pale line edge, small yellow and green signal; heavily ruffled; slight fragrance. Koorawatha X Our Mister Bailey.

FLYING CARPET (Paul Black, R. 1997). Sdlg. A79C. TB, 38" (97 cm), M. S. medium yellow, edges deeper; style arms medium yellow, violet circular area under crest; F. center fuchsia, blended deep red purple with medium rose margin; beards bright yellow; slight spicy fragrance. 8636A: (Frances Gaulter x Sky Hooks) X Mariachi Music. Mid-America 1997.

FLYING SKIRTS (Tom Burseen, R. 1993). Sdlg. 7-223X. TB, 34" (86 cm), M. Heavily ruffled violet blue (RHS 87A); beards cream, tipped yellow. Superman X Blues Singer. T.B.'s Place 1994.

FLY WITH ME (J. T. Aitken, R. 1990). Sdlg. 85T70. TB, 38" (97 cm), M. Blue violet, self beards; slight fragrance. Memorable X Tide's In. Aitken's Salmon Creek 1990.

FOGBOUND (Keith Keppel, R. 1997). Sdlg. 93-83C. TB, 40" (107 cm), M. S. blue white (M&P 41-A-1/2) shading to soft wistaria blue (41-D-7) in center and base; style arms blue white (41-A-2), lavender lip; F. white, inconspicuous pastel pink (1-B-7) shading on inner haft; beards pinkish orange (9-C-10), white at end; ruffled; pronounced sweet fragrance. Wishful Thinking X Spring Shower. Keppel 1998.

FOLK MUSIC (A. & D. Willott, R. 1994). Sdlg. 91-300. IB, 24" (61 cm), EM. S. light apricot pink, base flushed violet; F. light apricot pink, amber hafts, light violet blaze at tip of violet beard; lightly ruffled. Coral Wings X Magic. Willott 1994.

FOLKSY FUN (Tom Burseen, R. 1997). Sdlg. 94-168A. TB, 34" (86 cm), EM. S. and style arms yellow maize (RHS 22B); F. red purple (77A) texture veined cream, hafts brown; beards maize orange, small lemon horn; pronounced spicy fragrance. Super Dancer X Egyptian. T.B.'s Place 1998.

FOLLOW THE LIGHT (Marie Murdy, R. 1996). Sdlg. 5-29-96. TB, 36" (91 cm), E. Lightly ruffled white self; beards orange, ending with long white horn. Parentage unknown.

FONDATION VAN GOGH (Monique Anfosso, TB, R. 1988). Iris en Provence 1990.

FOND KISS (Marty Schafer/Jan Sacks, R. 1999). Sdlg. S92-70-1. SIB, 33" (84 cm), M. S. warm white, some soft lavender pink basal veining; style arms white, semi-upright; F. white, lavender pink (84C) central flush; pink anthers. S89-9-2: (Isabelle x Silver Illusion) X S89-16-1: (Reprise x Mad Magenta). Joe Pye Weed 1999.

FONDLY (Mary Dunn by Joseph Ghio, R. 1998). Sdlg. 223. LA, 38" (97 cm), EM. Red purple, F. with yellow spear signal. Whistling Dixie X Fine Warrior. Bay View 1999.

FOND REMEMBRANCE (John Weiler, R. 1995). Sdlg. 88-45A. IB, 18" (46 cm), M & RE. Waved dark violet self; beards violet; slight sweet fragrance. 85-29-4RE: ((Third Charm x Plum Wine) x (Watersmeet x Third Charm)) X Raven's Return. Friendship 1997.

FONTAINE (Melba Hamblen, TB, R. 1989). Roris 1996.

FONTANA DI TREVI (Ladislav Muska, R. 1995). Sdlg. LMDE-X. TB, 37" (94 cm), ML. Light rose lavender, nut brown rim; beards orange; heavily ruffled and laced; spicy fragrance. Lady Madonna X Don Epifano. Muska 1995.

FONTANONE (Ladislav Muska, R. 1996). Sdlg. DIFA-05/B. TB, 36" (91 cm), EM. Heavily ruffled plicata, pinkish lilac washed medium amethyst; beards orange, amethyst spoon; slight fragrance. (Discretion x ("Cipkovana Krinolina": (After All x Grand Waltz) x Sky Hooks)) X Sky Falls. Muska 1996.

FOOLED ME (Lynda Miller, R. 1999). Sdlg. 795C. IB, 18" (46 cm), EML. Mottled purple and white, edges stitched purple; style arms purple, edges paler; beards electric blue, hairs lightly tipped bronze; slight sweet fragrance. Cimarron Rose X Melba Hamblen. Miller's Manor 1999.

FOOLING AROUND (Chet Tompkins, R. 1994). Sdlg. 88-33. TB, 38" (97 cm), ML-VL. White ground faintly sanded brown; beards orange brown. Sdlg. lines inv. Starkist x sdlg. lines inv. Foggy Dew. Fleur de Lis 1994.

FOOL NUMBER ONE (Duane Meek, R. 1999). Sdlg. 6-1-1. TB, 34" (86 cm), ML. S. apricot; F. apricot ground, burgundy streaks from beard in ray pattern, dotting between streaks; beards white base, hairs tipped coral; ruffled, picoteed. Gigolo X (Queen in Calico x Mountain Melody). D & J Gardens 1999.

#FOOL'S GOLD (Tell Muhlestein, TB, R. 1945). Not introduced. Name released.

FOOL'S GOLD (Phyllis Dickey, R. 1998). Sdlg. 91P31-1. TB, 29" (74 cm), M. S. medium golden yellow; F. deeper golden yellow with flakes of gold; beards yellow orange; slight sweet fragrance. Skiers' Delight X Voleur de Feu. Misty Hill 1998.

FOOTHILL BANNER (Lewis Lawyer, R. 1990). Sdlg. XP64D. CA, 14" (36 cm), M. S. white, narrow dark violet rib, faintly lined violet at tip; style arms solid dark campanula violet; F. white with cream overlay, heavily veined dark campanula violet, solid violet at tip, faint yellow signal. (Canyon Snow x Sierra Sapphire) X Valley Banner. Lawyer 1990.

FOOTLOOSE (Schreiner, R. 1993). Sdlg. Z 549-D. TB, 36" (91 cm), VE. S. white (RHS 155D) ground stitched violet; F. white ground stitched purple (78A); beards yellow; ruffled. Eagle's Flight X Cinnamon Girl. Schreiner 1993.

FOOTMITTS (Polly Black, R. 1992). Sdlg. SR1-2Y. TB, 34" (86 cm), M. Heavily laced bright yellow, F. with gold shoulders; beards bright orange; slight fragrance. Real Adventure X White Lightning. Polly Black 1992.

FORBIDDEN FRUIT (Lilly Gartman by Roris Gardens, R. 1993). Sdlg. 85-192. TB, 36" (91 cm), ML. Lightly ruffled red coral to persimmon orange; beards red. Skyfire X Status Seeker. Roris 1993.

FOR DAD (Heather Pryor, R. 1996). Sdlg. 55/90-1. LA, 40" (102 cm), M & RE. S. and F. bright yellow, darker veining forming center line, orange line signal changing to lime green near bright yellow style arm; ruffled. Gladiator's Gift X Designer's Dream. Iris Haven 1997/98.

FOREIGN ACCENT (Keith Keppel, R. 1990). Sdlg. 82-43E. TB, 35" (89 cm), M. S. golden apricot (M&P 10-F-5) to peachglow (10-B-5), lightly suffused pale red violet (52-G-2), flecked darker; F. golden apricot solidly washed phlox (54-H-12) to dahlia purple (55-J-12); beards orange rufous (11-L-12) to bittersweet orange (3-B-12); slight sweet fragrance. 78-81J: (Rancho Rose x 75-113B: (Flamenco sib x (Roundup sib x April Melody))) X Rustic Dance. Keppel 1991.

FOREIGN DEVIL (Barry Blyth, R. 1994). Sdlg. A53-6. IB, 22" (56 cm), EM. S. smoky beige pink; F. same, deeper hafts, some white veining, slight lavender midline; beards lavender, tipped burnt tangerine; slight musky fragrance. X25-5, Impish sib, X Electrique. Tempo Two 1994/95.

FOREIGN INTRIGUE (Bob Bauer/John Coble, R. 1995). Sdlg. J85B-13. JI (6 F.), 38" (96 cm), EM. Dark blue purple (darker than RHS 83A or 79B) center, lightening to silvery blue (94D) edge, signals yellow; style arms upright, dark blue purple (86A), crests serrate. Strut and Flourish X Crystal Halo. Ensata Gardens 1995.

FOREIGN KNIGHT (Barry Blyth, R. 1996). Sdlg. B162-2. TB, 38" (97 cm), EM. S. oyster, midrib mushroom; F. reddish rose, faint oyster wire edge; beards bright red tangerine; slight fragrance. Crimson Snow X Electrique. Tempo Two 1996/97.

FOREIGN STATESMAN (Sterling Innerst, R. 1992). Sdlg. 3319-1. TB, 36" (91 cm), M. Full purple; beards purple blue, tipped bronze; slight fragrance. Titan's Glory X Twice Delightful. Innerst 1993.

FOREVER A FAVORITE (Albert Faggard, R. 1994). Sdlg. FLAV-1-89. LA, 38" (97 cm), M. Ruffled dark lavender, pencil line yellow signal; style arms green, veined lavender. Mrs. Ira Nelson X sdlg.

FOREVER BLUE (Chuck Chapman, R. 1996). Sdlg. 92-190-2. SDB, 12" (31 cm), E & RE. Light blue violet self; beards medium violet blue. Shy Violet X 90-45-4: ((Velvet Caper x Michael Paul) x Sigh). Chapman Iris 1997.

FOREVER FRIENDS (William Plotner, R. 1992). Sdlg. 84-401-1. TB, 38" (97 cm) ML. S. white, widely edged minuet blue (RHS 76B/C); F. white, widely edged westminster purple (83C); beards light orchid; slight spicy fragrance. (((Dream Lover x Dualtone) x Dundee) x (Darktown Strutter x On the Go)) X Jigsaw. Wildwood Gardens 1991.

FOREVER GOLD (George Sutton, R. 1996). Sdlg. G-55RE. TB, 35" (89 cm), EM & RE. S. aureolin (RHS 12A); style arms canary yellow (9A); F. darker aureolin (14A), white area veined aureolin around tangerine (23A) beard; ruffled. C-95: (Orange Popsicle x Lemon Custard) X C-101: (4-12: (Hindu Magic x (Crinoline x President Farnsworth)) x 4-178: (Faithfulness x Scented Nutmeg)). Sutton 1997.

FOREVER IN LOVE (Clarence Mahan, R. 1993). Sdlg. BROSU-90R. TB, 36" (91 cm), EML & RE (Oct.-Nov./VA). S. violet (RHS 88C) with prominent white zone; style arms white; F. violet (88C) with prominent white zone around beard; beards white, tipped yellow; pronounced spicy fragrance. Brother Carl X Suky. Iris Pond 1995.

FOREVER NIGHT (Jim Hedgecock, R. 1995). Sdlg. 85-87. TB, 36" (91 cm), M. Blue purple self; beards dark blue, brown in throat, 1" dark blue horn; ruffled, lightly laced; pronounced sweet fragrance. Parentage unknown. Comanche Acres 1996.

FOREVER SNOW (Nadine Yunker, R. 1992). Sdlg. St-1-3. SIB, 36" (91 cm), ML. White with yellow (RHS 7A) throat. Dreaming Yellow X unknown. Yunker 1992.

FOREVER YOURS (Ben Hager, R. 1992). Sdlg. RE5316TIWWh. TB, 36-38" (91-97 cm), M &

158

RE. Clear white; beards white, tipped yellow. RE4839BlWh, Autumn Grandeur sib, X Twice Delightful. Melrose 1993.

FORFUN (Barry Blyth, R. 1993). Sdlg. A14-12. SDB, 14-15" (36-38 cm), M. S. bishops violet, slightly cream base; F. creamy lemon ground, violet stitching at edge, violet spotting and dotting and deeper lines radiating down F.; beards white, tangerine in throat. Smoky Imp X Chanted. Tempo Two 1993/94.

FORGED THUNDER (Glenn Bowers, R. 1998). Sdlg. 89-1. TB, 34" (86 cm), EM & RE. S. and style arms light violet (Pantone 2583C); F. violet (2612C) shaded paler around beard, light violet edge; beards pallid lavender, yellow in throat; ruffled; pronounced sweet fragrance. Mother Earth X Suky.

FORGE FIRE (Richard Ernst, R. 1991). Sdlg. F102-3. TB, 38" (97 cm), ML. S. medium red maroon; F. dark red maroon; beards red, tipped amber; ruffled. Danger X Chief Hematite. Cooley 1991.

FORGIVEN (Richard Ernst, R. 1994). Sdlg. HR8613-2. TB, 35-38" (89-99 cm), EM. S. white, very pale cream pink midrib infusion; F. medium peach pink, near-white blended edge on upper half; beards orange red. R8613-2: ((Pink 'n Mint x Gaulter G77-96, inv. Claudia Rene) x Jelly Roll) X Shoop pink amoena sdlg. Cooley 1994.

FORGOTTEN DREAMS (Nora Scopes, R. 1994). Sdlg. 31PC. CA, 13" (33 cm), M. S. hazed mauve; F. cream, hazed mauve on edge. Canyon Sky X unknown.

FORGOTTEN SECRET (Frederick Kerr, R. 1997). Sdlg. 882901. TB, 28" (71 cm), EM. S. canary yellow; F. smoky lavender; beards orange. Edith Wolford X Betty Simon. Rainbow Acres 1997.

FOR JEANNETTE (Bob Thomason, R. 1993). Sdlg. BT 9075T. TB, 32" (81 cm), ML. S. light red brown; F. dark red brown; beards orange; slight fragrance. Lady Jeannette X Fooled You.

FORMAL OCCASION (Ken Mohr by Bryce Williamson, R. 1995). Sdlg. Q14-147. TB, 36" (91 cm), M. Midnight blue violet self, F. with faint white shoulder penciling; beards cream, hairs tipped soft lemon. Parentage unknown; from mixed seed. Bryce Williamson 1995.

FORNCETT MOON (J. P. Metcalf, R. 1993). Sdlg. FOR/1. SIB, 30" (75 cm), M. White with vivid yellow (RHS 13A) signal. Cambridge X unknown. Four Seasons 1985.

FOR PATSY LOU (Tom Burseen, R. 1991). Sdlg. 7-152X. TB, 37" (94 cm), M. S. bright golden yellow (RHS 15B); F. murky red purple (187A), precise lavender pink (81D) rim; beards bright gold; waved; slight fragrance. Street Dancer X 3-265A: (Congo Song x Stunning). T.B.'s Place 1993.

FORREST WAVES (Reggie Edelman, R. 1999). Sdlg. RKE-1. TB, 36" (91 cm), M. S. lavender orchid veined deeper, golden beige infusion; F. purple violet, blue haze; beards blue. Honky Tonk Blues X Mavis Waves.

FORT REGENT (N. Watkins, TB, R. 1987). V. H. Humphrey 1992.

FORTUNE'S FANCY (Sharon McAllister, R. 1992). Sdlg. 85-3-15. AB (OGB), 28" (72 cm), EM. S. white, veined pinkish lilac around edge; F. soft naples yellow (near RHS 11B), rust purple veining around edge and down midrib; beards orange, tipped tangerine. Boaz X Jean Ralls. McAllister 1993.

FORTY WINKS (Steve Moldovan, SDB, R. 1969). Correction of seedling number and parentage. Sdlg. 18-69A. Blueberry Muffins X Platinum Gold.

FORWARD FLASH (Tom Burseen, R. 1990). Sdlg. 5-86B. TB, 36" (91 cm), E. S. cream, golden orange heart; F. greyed orange (RHS 186C), lighter margin; beards bright orange; serrate, ruffled, lightly laced; slight fragrance. Tropical Tempo X Java Peach. T.B.'s Place 1990.

FOR ZOE (John C. Taylor, R. 1997). Sdlg. UL 28-2. LA, 39" (100 cm), M. S. and F. light purple, purple veining, reverse lighter, signal yellow green; style arms light purple. Lina X Helen Naish. Rainbow Ridge 1997/98.

FOUNDATION (Chet Tompkins, R. 1995). Sdlg. 89-47. TB, 33-34" (84-86 cm), M. Vivid blended red; beards bronze gold to dull mustard. From inv. sdlgs. from reds and pinks. Fleur de Lis 1995.

FOUNTAIN OF YOUTH (Ben Hager, R. 1998). Sdlg. RE5303Am. TB, 36" (91 cm), E & RE. S. and style arms white; F. white around beard, blending to blue, narrow pale blue edge; beards cream white, hairs tipped yellow except at end. Edith Wolford X Mother Earth.

FOURFOLD BLUE (Tomas Tamberg, R. 1997). SPEC-X (tet.), 35" (89 cm), M. Medium blue. Converted sdlg. SSTT381: (Mint Fresh x *I. laevigata alba*) X converted sdlg. SSTT381. Schoeppinger 1997.

FOURFOLD PINK (Currier McEwen, R. 1995). Sdlg. T(6)90/48(ERI). JI (3 F.) tet., 30" (75 cm), EML. S. white, edged phlox purple (RHS 75C); style arms white, edged and tipped lavender pink

(75B); F. lavender pink opening from deeper (75A) buds, white central area crossed by mimosa yellow (8C) veins, signal rich lemon yellow (13B). T(5)88/11(11): (T(4)80/149: (Maine Chance x inv. sdlg. 8 generations from Arlie Payne seed) x Pink Mystery) X Pink Mystery. Eartheart 1996.

FOURSOME (John J. Taylor, R. 1992). SPEC-X, 14-18" (36-46 cm), M. S. bone white, veined lavender blue (RHS 94C); F. same, veined heavier near tips; beards bronze. P-17: (*I. imbricata* x M-3: (*I. timofejewii* x *I. reichenbachii* "Van Nes")) X *I. variegata*.

FOUR WINDS (Harold Stahly, R. 1990). Sdlg. 8-49-A. SIB, 32" (81 cm), M. S. medium blue (RHS 97D); style arms medium blue, deep aqua midrib; F. medium blue (96D), veined slightly darker, yellow green signal blending to short spray pattern and dark blue halo; ruffled, flared and arched. Super Ego X Sally Kerlin. Stahly 1991.

FOXCROFT FULL MOON (Katharine Steele, R. 1997). Sdlg. 12-5-06. SPEC (*pseudacorus*), 40" (107 cm), M. S. and style arms creamy white; F. creamy white ground, deeper cream signal with pronounced maroon eye zone. From unknown yellow *I. pseudacorus*.

FRACTAL BLUE (Lorena Reid, R. 1995). Sdlg. 8J165-G15-2. JI (6 F.), 36-42" (91-108 cm), ML. Dark blue violet ground with white and pale blue lavender sanded and veined pattern; signal greenish yellow with white halo; ruffled. Blue Marlin X "Sakuraku". Laurie's Garden 1995.

FRAGMENT (Ben Hager, R. 1995). Sdlg. MD5496TyVar. MDB, 4" (10 cm), ML. S. white; F. deep violet blue, narrow white border; beards yellow. Nestling X AMD4972YBrSP#1, Jiffy sib. Adamgrove 1995.

FRAGRANTE DELICTO (Philip Edinger, R. 1998). Sdlg. 6-91A. TB, 38" (97 cm), ML & RE. S. and style arms white; F. very pale blue (RHS 108D), narrow darker butterfly blue (106C) line extending from beard tip 2/3 length of petal; beards butterfly blue (106C); pronounced sweet fragrance. 18-57A: (Lady Ilse x (Shining Waters x Great Lakes)) X (133-61E: (18-57A x Arabi Pasha) x Hager sdlg.: (Chivalry x (Sharkskin x *I. balkana*))).

FRAMBOISE (Richard Cayeux, R. 1995). Sdlg. 8374 A. TB, 33" (85 cm), ML. S. bright cyclamen pink; F. cyclamen pink; beards red. Enchanted World X Flaming Light. Cayeux 1994.

FRAMED BEAUTY (Charles Okken, R. 1993). Sdlg. Ig-9. TB, 39" (99 cm), M. S. lavender pink, trace of yellow at base; F. plum red thumbprint in center changing to lavender pink, 1/2" lavender edge, yellow hafts; beards gold. Ringo X Ecstatic Echo. Misty Hill 1995.

FRANAKINS (Peter DeSantis, R. 1995). Sdlg. 82-6A. SPU, 54" (137 cm), M. S. light purple, splashed darker at tips; F. dark purple border, gold brown veined signal. *I. ochroleuca* X Imperial Ruby.

FRANCES IVA (Lloyd Zurbrigg, R. 1990). Sdlg. HH 17-8-2. TB, 37" (94 cm), VE. Creamy yellow, lightly marked brown violet; beards pale yellow. Raspberries and Cream X Spirit of Fiji. Avonbank 1991.

FRANCIS CABOT (Tony Huber, R. 1998). Sdlg. 95-139. SPEC-X (versata), 55-59" (140-150 cm), ML-VL. S. medium violet (RHS 88A); style arms medium violet (88B) bordered lilac; F. deep violet blue (89B), bright yellow signal with central golden line extended outward. China West Lake X Popular Demand.

FRANCOIS PLONKA (Jean-Jacques Francois, R. 1998). Sdlg. 1-8(95). TB, 37" (95 cm), EM. S. light purple; style arms purple; F. velvety dark purple, cream shoulders veined purple; beards dark yellow; pronounced fragrance. Superstition X Champagne Elegance.

FRANK ENSTEIN (Chet Tompkins, R. 1992). Sdlg. 86-9B. TB, 36-37" (91-94 cm), EML. S. coppery orange; F. oxblood red blended brown, edged slightly lighter. Apollodorus sib X ((Royal Gold x Ovation) x (Cosmopolitan x Bayberry Candle)). Fleur de Lis 1991.

FRANK KALICH (O. D. Niswonger, R. 1997). Sdlg. L1-95. SPEC (*lactea*), 20" (51 cm), M. S. blue; style arms and F. white. Seed received by Frank Kalich from Dr. Rodionenko. Cape Iris 1997.

FRANZI (Manfred Beer, R. 1991). Sdlg. MB4/83A. BB, 23½" (60 cm), E. S. white; F. red violet, edged light violet; beards orange. Cloverdale X Camelot Hues. Gartencenter Kania 1991.

FRAPPE (Monty Byers, R. 1990). Sdlg. E66-100. TB, 34" (86 cm), EM & RE. S. varying from very pale strawberry pink to pinkish white; F. slightly deeper pale strawberry pink blended very pale raspberry pink with white striations underlying upper third; beards orange tangerine; lightly ruffled; slight sweet fragrance. C-37-2: (Marmalade Skies x Sky Hooks) X C-6-3: (Spirit of Memphis x Hager horned pink sdlg.: (Moon Mistress x Meek horned sdlg.)). Moonshine 1991.

FRECKLED SUNSHINE (Paul Black, R. 1990). Sdlg. 86142A. TB, 30" (76 cm), M. S. butter yellow, heavily stitched brown; F. bright canary ground with brown plicata sanding, brown centerline, white area around beard with maroon plicata sanding; beards old gold tipped brown; slight musky fragrance. Queen in Calico X Rustic Dance. Mid-America 1990.

#FRECKLE FACE (Roger Nelson, TB, R. 1986). Stock destroyed and name transferred 1991.

FRECKLE FACE (Roger Nelson, R. 1991). Sdlg. 86-86P. TB, 29-30" (74-76 cm), M. S. greyed white with creamy pink influence, greyer near midrib; F. silvery buff pink with white highlights, soft greyed rose at hafts, pink purple dotting at hafts and edge; pronounced sweet fragrance. RN 79-15F: (((Maiden Voyage x Crystal Blaze) x Silver Shower) x Guardian Gate) X sib. Iris Country 1992.

FRECKLETEC (Katharine Steele by John Wood, R. 1992). SPEC (*tectorum*), 12" (30 cm), L. Light lavender (RHS 76A) with pronounced lighter (76C) speckles on hafts and extending over most of F. Selected *I. tectorum* sdlg. of unknown parentage. John Wood 1993.

FRED (Ken Durio, R. 1992). LA, 30-36" (76-91 cm), M. S. light red violet; F. very dark red violet, broad golden yellow signal; pronounced spicy fragrance. Bellevue's Michelle X Charlie's Michele. Louisiana Nursery 1993.

FREDDIE (J. Owings Rebert, R. 1996). Sdlg. UG-6. SIB, 28" (71 cm), L. Deep purple self; F. with cream signal, slight haft venation. Parentage unknown.

FRED'S GAL (Tom Burseen, R. 1999). Sdlg. 95-437A. TB, 36" (91 cm), M. S. light wistaria blue (RHS 92D), midrib violet; style arms light wistaria blue; F. violet blue (97A); beards orange, white in throat, large violet blue flounce; ruffled, flared; slight fragrance. Imagine That X Drop the Hanky.

FREEDOM RIDE (John C. Taylor, R. 1995). Sdlg. RL 9-5. LA, 39" (99 cm), M. S. and F. violet blue (RHS 96A), light rim; style arms white, brushed light violet blue (95D); yellow green dagger signal on F., spray on S. Green Elf X Margaret Lee. Rainbow Ridge 1995/96.

FREEDOM'S BELL (Stan Dexter by Marie Ingersoll, R. 1993). Sdlg. A22-6-86A. TB, 38" (97 cm), ML. S. white; F. white ground heavily lined and overlaid blue; beards red. American Beauty X Condottiere. Ingersoll's Iris 1994.

FREELY GIVEN (Paul Black, R. 1991). Sdlg. 86427A. IB, 24" (61 cm), M. S. full bright yellow; style arms bright gold; F. bright deep yellow gold; beards orange gold; slight musky fragrance. 83135D: (Mister Roberts x Pulse Rate) X Catalyst. Mid-America 1992.

FREE SPACE (George Sutton, R. 1998). Sdlg. G-71-B. TB, 35" (89 cm), ML. Ruffled white self; beards white, hairs tipped yellow in throat, white flounce. Skating Party X Twice Thrilling. Sutton 1999.

FREESTYLE (Mary Dunn, R. 1992). Sdlg. M83-83OC. TB, 36" (91 cm), M. S. white with solid magenta fuchsia band and slight plicata-type markings at edge of band; F. white, narrow magenta fuchsia band and plicata-type lines on hafts and edge of band; beards matching, tipped paler. Galore X Brilliant Excuse. M.A.D. Iris 1993.

FRENCH FASHION (Paul Black, R. 1993). Sdlg. 8826B. TB, 35" (89 cm), M. S. smoky deep violet; style arms blended orchid pink; F. smoky violet blended over orchid pink base; beards burnt orange; ruffled; slight spicy fragrance. 8510C: ((Heather Blush x P. Dyer sdlg.: (Peach Spot x Outer Limits)) x Tropical Tempo) X 86129E: ((Breath of Morn x Galen) x Honey Mocha). Mid-America 1993.

FRENCH FRIEND (Tom Burseen, R. 1997). Sdlg. 93-359A. TB, 36" (91 cm), M. Ruffled metallic bluebird blue (RHS 94B); beards bluebird blue with matching horn. Evelyn Harris X Stingray. T.B.'s Place 1997.

FRENCH HORN (George Sutton, R. 1998). Sdlg. G-19-B. TB, 37" (94 cm), ML. S. phlox pink (RHS 62B), orange at base, edges serrate; style arms phlox pink; F. phlox pink, orange shoulders, white around beard and appendage; beards bright orange, 2" appendage ending in 3/4" phlox pink spoon; ruffled; slight sweet fragrance. Sweet Musette X Twice Thrilling. Sutton 1999.

FRENCH MELODY (Hooker Nichols, R. 1990). Sdlg. 8835Q. TB, 33" (84 cm), ML. S. peach; F. peach ground, banded and dotted violet, darker hafts; beards coral; ruffled; pronounced fragrance. Sorceress X Capricious. Hillcrest 1994.

FRENCH PERFUME (Michael Moller, TB, R. 1989). Long 1990.

FRENCH QUARTER (Mary Dunn, R. 1997). Sdlg. L 216-8. LA, 34" (86 cm), M. Milky chocolate tan, F. ruffled, with large yellow signal; style arms lighter chocolate tan. L 157-3: (Elusive Butterfly x L 95-5: (Ila Nunn x Professor Ike)) X Gladiator's Gift. Bay View 1997.

FRENCH ROSE (George Sutton, R. 1997). Sdlg. F-5. TB, 36" (91 cm), M. Ruffled blended french rose (RHS 49D) and salmon (27A); style arms salmon; beards spanish orange; slight sweet fragrance. Caption X Perils of Pauline. Sutton 1998.

161

FRENCH TOAST (David Sindt by Adamgrove, SDB, R. 1988). Adamgrove 1990.

FRENCH VILLAGE (Ruth Goebel, R. 1995). Sdlg. BSM. TB, 32" (81 cm), M. S. plum purple (RHS 79A); F. violet (84A); beards bright yellow; ruffled; sweet fragrance. Parentage unknown.

FREQUENT FLYER (Richard Gibson, R. 1994). Sdlg. 013-3. TB, 32" (81 cm), E & RE. Ruffled warm white self; beards yellow. Eternal Bliss X White Reprise. Stockton 1994.

FRERE ANDRE (Elaine Bessette, R. 1996). Sdlg. EWMBS-92-11. TB, 33" (84 cm), ML. S. and style arms sea lavender violet (RHS 85D), darker midrib streak; F. medium violet (88B), lightly veined darker blue violet (89D); beards sea lavender violet, lemon yellow (13A) in throat; ruffled; slight sweet fragrance. Edith Wolford X M. Byers "space age" sdlg., parentage unknown.

FRESH AIR (Ben Hager, TB, R. 1989). Roris 1992.

FRESH CREAM (Virgil Bryant by Kevin Morley, R. 1993). SPEC (*pseudacorus*), 27" (69 cm), EML-VL & RE. Pale ivory (RHS 155A) veined chartreuse (150C), pale chartreuse signal veined and stitched red violet (79C). Selection of *I. pseudacorus*. Terra Nova 1997.

FRESH MINT (Mary Dunn, R. 1994). Sdlg. L 125-3. LA, 35" (89 cm), M. S. ivory, faintly shaded lavender; style arms creamy light yellow; F. greenish yellow, fine lime green line signal; wide form. Fantastic X Delta Dawn. Bay View 1995.

FRESH START (Jayne Ritchie, R. 1995). Sdlg. 88-11-9. SDB, 10½" (26 cm), ML. S. white, slight blue tinge; style arms white, tinged blue; F. white undertoned blue green, hafts overlaid chartreuse yellow; beards light blue (RHS 100D); ruffled; slight sweet fragrance. 83-32-5: (Model Child x 79-39-6, Loveshine sib) X Bay Ruffles. Ritchie 1996.

FRIDAY BLUES (Carol Lankow by J. T. Aitken, R. 1997). Sdlg. 6L62. BB, 24" (61 cm), ML. Ruffled soft blue self; beards blue. Friday Harbor X Fly With Me. Aitken's Salmon Creek 1997.

FRIDAY NIGHT (Jim Hedgecock, R. 1994). Sdlg. A-31-1. TB, 30" (76 cm), M. S. indigo blueblack; F. lightly laced blue black; beards blue black, burnt brown in throat, 1" purple horn; ruffled. 83-25: (Space Dragon x Tuxedo) X 84-48: (Sky Hooks x Swazi Princess). Comanche Acres 1995.

FRILLS AND FLOUNCES (Darlene Pinegar, R. 1997). Sdlg. EA-93-172A. TB, 36" (91 cm), ML. S. medium red orchid; style arms blended light gold and mauve; F. medium orchid veined darker, narrow tannish edge, hafts yellow marked medium orchid; beards light yellow, deeper in throat, ending with 1½" smooth lavender horn and big orchid spoon; lightly ruffled. Ever After X Anne Boleyn. Spanish Fork 1998.

FRILLY FANCY (Elyse Hill, R. 1998). Sdlg. EJ 20-23. CA, 8" (20 cm), E. S. cream, lavender midline; style arms cream, yellow midline; F. cream, deep yellow signal 1/2" x 3/4", lavender blaze at end, deep purple lines and stippling, edge cream; ruffled, laced. Pacific High X unknown.

FRIMOUSSE (Cayeux, R. 1999). Sdlg. 91197 A. TB, 33" (85 cm), ML. S. apricot to light pink; F. raspberry; beards tangerine. Sweet Musette X Adobe Rose.

FRINGED APRICOT (Jim Hedgecock, R. 1990). Sdlg. 83-99-1. TB, 35" (89 cm), M. Heavily laced and ruffled apricot pink, large white F. blaze; beards reddish orange. Sunrise Symphony X Flaming Light. Comanche Acres 1993.

FRINGED GOLD (D. L. Shepard, R. 1992). Sdlg. 88013. LA, 30" (76 cm), M. S. brick red; style arms brick red fringed gold; F. brick red, gold 1/4" edge and reverse, rich golden yellow signal spraying out like a star; heavily ruffled. President Hedley X 82U: (Delta King x unknown). Shepard Iris 1992.

FRISCHE BRISE (Uwe Knoepnadel, R. 1990). JI (3 F.), 27½" (70 cm), L. S. violet; style arms dark blue; F. light lavender to white, veined blue violet, signal yellow. Sdlg. X unknown. Friesland Staudengarten 1990.

FRISKY FAWN (A. & D. Willott, R. 1999). Sdlg. W 95-121. SDB, 9" (23 cm), M. Ruffled ecru, F. with large red brown spot; beards light violet, deep yellow in throat. Jade Wizard X Harlem Nocturne.

FRISKY FILLY (A. & D. Willott, R. 1990). Sdlg. 86-51. BB, 22" (56 cm), M. S. light yellow ground washed beige; F. light yellow, brown plicata haft markings, edges washed beige; beards yellow, dotted brown; ruffled. 79-169: (Triple Touch x Gibson TB brown plicata) X Picayune. Willott 1990.

FRISON-ROCHE (Richard Cayeux, R. 1995). Sdlg. 8896 A. TB, 41" (105 cm), EM. Ruffled pure white self; beards ivory. Skating Party X Sapphire Hills. Cayeux 1994.

FRISOUNETTE (Jean Segui, R. 1998). TB, 35" (90 cm), EM. S. greyed yellow (RHS 160C); style arms yellow; F. light violet (85B), ochre rays on shoulders; beards indian yellow (17A); ruffled, laced. Space Blazer X Balançoire. Iris de Thau 1998.

FRITILLARY FLIGHT (Cy Bartlett, R. 1994). Sdlg. MNR-EDF. IB, 26" (66 cm), ML. S. light dove grey; F. greyed ochre yellow; beards cream blue overtoned brown; lightly waved to tailored. Mrs. Nate Rudolph X Echo de France. Sutton 1994.

FRIVOLOUS (Richard Ernst, R. 1991). Sdlg. T606-1. TB, 36" (91 cm), ML. Lemon yellow, white area below yellow beards; slight sweet fragrance. R79-114: (Countryman x Outreach) X Gold Cadillac. Cooley 1991.

FRIZZLE FRACK (D. L. Shepard, R. 1998). Sdlg. 95057-8901. TB, 42" (107 cm), ML. Ruffled violet lavender; beards yellow gold, end lavender white, with violet lavender horn or flounce; ruffled. Battle Star X Howdy Do. Shepard Iris 1998.

FROLICSOME (Paul Black, R. 1999). Sdlg. A119D. IB, 22" (56 cm), E. S. bright yellow gold, edge shaded brown; style arms bright yellow, brownish tip; F. bright yellow ground, 1/2" brown plicata band, yellow outer rim, brown haft veining; beards bright yellow gold; pronounced spicy fragrance. Toasty X 89U10, inv. Glitz 'n Glitter. Mid-America 1999.

FROM A DISTANCE (Richard Ernst, R. 1994). Sdlg. HR8545-15. TB, 38" (97 cm), M. S. light yellow, midrib infused violet; F. light violet, blue cast; beards yellow; ruffled. R8545-1: (Edith Wolford x Merry Madrigal) X (Edith Wolford x self). Cooley 1994.

FRONTIER COWBOY (Hooker Nichols, TB, R. 1986). Hillcrest 1990.

FRONTIER SPIRIT (Lin Flanagan, R. 1993). Sdlg. 85004-1. AB (OGB), 26" (66 cm), M. S. pale violet blended amber; F. rosy buff, dark red brown signal; beards dark brown; ruffled; slight fragrance. Merriglow X High Frontier. Aril Society 1994.

FROSTBITE (Harold Stahly, R. 1997). Sdlg. 91-32. TB, 35" (89 cm), M. S. cool white (lighter than RHS 92D when fresh); style arms cool white; F. cool white, greenish cast (near 155B); beards medium blue; ruffled; slight spicy fragrance. Autograph X High Five. Stahly 1997.

FROST ECHO (J. T. Aitken, R. 1995). Sdlg. 87T19. TB, 34" (86 cm), EM & RE. S. and style arms white; F. very pale lavender with zonal spot, fading to white; beards white; slight spicy fragrance. Immortality X (Seawolf x I Do). Aitken's Salmon Creek 1995.

FROSTED CRANBERRY (Anna Mae Miller, R. 1991). Sdlg. 85.41.4. SIB, 32" (81 cm), ML. S. red violet (RHS 80C), aqua veins; F. darker (78B), veined darker, greenish hafts and signal; spathes red. 80.9.3: ((Pink Haze x 78.5, wine sdlg.) x Pink Haze) X self. Old Douglas Perennials 1991.

FROSTED EMERALD (Harold Stahly, R. 1999). Sdlg. 93-49. SIB, 26-30" (66-76 cm), ML. S. white; style arms white, yellow green midrib, wide and feathered; F. pale green, strong green signal area; ruffled. Snowy Mountain X Bellissima. Stahly 1999.

FROSTED INTRIGUE (Bob Bauer/John Coble, R. 1998). Sdlg. J89T-2. JI (6 F.), 36" (90 cm), M. Dark blue violet center, few light blue rays shading into red violet edge, rim frosty light blue; signals yellow; style arms white, multiple, violet crests feathered. Foreign Intrigue X Frosted Pyramid. Ensata Gardens 1997.

FROSTED LAVENDER (Sharol Longaker, R. 1992). TB, 34" (86 cm), M. Laced light lavender self; beards lavender; sweet fragrance. Lovely Kay X Laced Cotton. Anderson Iris 1992.

FROSTED MOONBEAM (Heather Pryor, R. 1994). Sdlg. 64/90-2. LA, 35" (89 cm), ML. Ruffled soft cream (RHS 4D) veined lime green, lime green yellow signals on all petals; style arms soft lemon. Dural White Butterfly X Designer's Dream. Rainbow Ridge 1996/97.

FROSTED MORN (Rusty Ostheimer, R. 1991). Sdlg. Wh1-85. LA, 38-40" (97-102 cm), VE-EML. White, signal yellow orange. Alston X unknown. Bois d'Arc 1991.

FROSTED PARFAIT (Donald Sorensen, R. 1995). Sdlg. S-91-35-27. TB, 34" (86 cm), M. S. white, midribs light lemon yellow (RHS 8B); style arms creamy lemon (8C); F. white, blending to pale lemon yellow (7D) at margin, hafts yellow gold (8A); beards golden orange (14B); ruffled; pronounced musky fragrance. Easter Finery X Perfect Interlude. Birchwood Gardens 1997.

FROSTED PLUM (Lois Rich by Ensata Gardens, R. 1996). Sdlg. K74-3A. JI (6 F.), 32" (82 cm), M. Near-white ground, blue (95A) halo and veining; style arms multiple, crests and petaloids dark blue purple (89A). Parentage unknown. Ensata Gardens 1996.

FROSTICO (Lilly Gartman, TB, R. 1989). Roris 1992.

FROSTING (Joseph Gatty by Keith Keppel, R. 1992). Sdlg. T23-3A. TB, 36" (91 cm), ML. S. very pastel lilac pink (M&P 49-BC-1) shaded pale lilac (41-C-6); F. shaded pale cool pink (41-AB-1/2) on shoulders and sides, remainder white (9-AB-1); beards soft pinkish orange (9-G-7), white at end; pronounced sweet fragrance. O-19-1: (Pretty Lady x K55-1: (Nefertiti x Playgirl)) X Presence. D & J Gardens 1993.

FROST MAIDEN (Arthur Blodgett, R. 1994). Sdlg. 86-57. TB, 32" (81 cm), M. S. white with greenish cast; F. white, pale yellow edge, greenish cast toward haft; beards light yellow. Eastertime X Chartreuse Ruffles. Blodgett Iris 1994.

FROSTY CLOUDS (Bernard Hamner, R. 1995). TB, 38" (97 cm), E. S. off-white; F. soft violet blue (RHS 93D), white area under beard; beards yellow, white at tip. Frosty Snowball X Ocean Clouds. Hamner Iris 1995.

FROSTY DAWN (Connell Marsh, TB, R. 1983). C. Marsh 1990.

FROSTY ELEGANCE (Cleo Palmer, R. 1994). Sdlg. 9039. IB, 23" (58 cm), E. White self; beards yellow, tipped white. 8711-A: (Lemon Lyric x 76172: ((Esther Fay x Milestone) x (Esther Fay x unknown))) X Fluffy. Palmer's Iris 1994.

FROSTY MITE (A. & D. Willott, R. 1999). Sdlg. W 94-37. MDB, 4" (10 cm), E. White, F. with light blue spot; beards cream. W 91-79, Wee Ghost sib, X unknown.

FROTHINGSLOSH (Sterling Innerst, R. 1992). Sdlg. 3824-2. IB, 20" (51 cm), M. White, trimmed powder blue; beards blue, tipped yellowish; slight fragrance. Point in Time X 3531-5: (Hee Haw x Jeepers). Innerst 1993.

FROZEN BLUE (Richard Ernst, R. 1994). Sdlg. JF167-1A-2. TB, 38" (97 cm), M. S. medium violet blue; F. near-white blending to violet blue edge; beards tangerine orange; ruffled. F167-1: ((Irene Nelson x Honest Pleasure) x Gaulter 81-17, inv. Irene Nelson) X F104-1: ((Irene Nelson x Sun Fire) x Friday Surprise). Cooley 1994.

FROZEN FLAME (Tom Burseen, R. 1994). Sdlg. 8-148A. TB, 44" (112 cm), M. S. light lavender; F. diamond-dusted lavender white; beards bright red; laced. Delirious X 6-174: (Lady Friend x (Gondolier x Galen)). T.B.'s Place 1995.

FRUEHBAROCK (Harald Moos, R. 1990). Sdlg. 86/660A. TB, 31½" (80 cm), M. Light orange; beards tangerine. Fresno Calypso X Herrenhauser Orangerie. Moos 1991.

FRUGAL (Paul Black, R. 1997). Sdlg. B330-C. SDB, 11" (28 cm), E. S. golden yellow; style arms yellow gold; F. slightly darker golden yellow haft and band, paler center, with fine brown plicata dotting and brown dotted line halfway down; beards golden orange, orange in throat; ruffled. Static sib X Wacko. Mid-America 1997.

FRUIT COCKTAIL (Keith Keppel, R. 1996). Sdlg. 92-19A. IB, 23" (58 cm), M. S. marguerite yellow (M&P 10-C-1), flushed vanilla (10-C-3) in center, light primrose yellow (10-J-4) suffusion and veining, darker chinese yellow (10-K-6) base; style arms marguerite yellow flushed primrose yellow; F. yellow ochre (11-L-7) wash over most, remainder marguerite, brushed primrose yellow to light chrome yellow (10-L-4) at edge; beards solid intense fire red (1-F-12); slight sweet fragrance. Florida Orange X Orange Tiger. Keppel 1997.

FRUIT LOOPS (Lynda Miller, R. 1991). Sdlg. 2687B. SDB, 10" (25 cm), M. Light apricot orange, plum spot on F.; beards cream, tipped tangerine; slight musky fragrance. Fruit Salad X Cherub Tears. Miller's Manor 1993.

FRUIT OF MAROON (Richard Ernst, R. 1996). Sdlg. JF162-4-3. TB, 38" (97 cm), ML. S. blended maroon with violet and mauve influence, lighter at center; style arms maroon; F. mulberry maroon, wide deeper rim, violet blue flush at end of beard, hafts yellowish copper; beards mustard, maroon at end; lightly ruffled; moderate sweet fragrance. F 162-4: (Syncopation x (Cranberry Ice x (Sumptuous x Sandberry))) X F106-2: (Syncopation x (Irene Nelson x Honest Pleasure)). Cooley 1996.

FRUIT TINGLES (Beryl Pederick, R. 1994). Sdlg. 3. BB, 27" (69 cm), M. S. orange buff with pink infusion; F. apricot with cream blaze, orange buff (RHS 22D) border; beards orange; slight fragrance. Deft Touch X Lorna Lee.

FUCHSIA DELIGHT (Cleo Palmer, R. 1994). Sdlg. 9379. IB, 26" (66 cm), L. Fuchsia to magenta self; beards red; sweet fragrance. Parentage unknown. Palmer's Iris 1994.

FUCHSIA FANFARE (John Wight, R. 1993). Sdlg. J86-4. AB (OGB), 20" (51 cm), M. S. pale lavender, heavily veined fuchsia; F. fuchsia, slight tan infusion on hafts, purple red signal; beards bronze, tipped purple. Turkish Tracery X New Discovery. Wight's Iris 1993.

FUERSTENTHUM LIPPE (Siegmar Goerbitz, R. 1995). Sdlg. 8936A19. TB, 39" (100 cm), ML. Violet blue self; beards blue, tipped yellow. 8330B5: ((Silver Shower x Rondo) x Condottiere) X St. Louis Blues. Goerbitz 1997.

FUERSTIN PAULINE (Siegmar Goerbitz, R. 1997). Sdlg. 8922 A4. TB, 37" (95 cm), M. Waved deep blue self; beards yellow, blue at end. Augenweide X Dusky Challenger. Goerbitz 1998.

FUGITIVE (John C. Taylor, R. 1998). Sdlg. UL13-4X. LA, 39" (100 cm), M. S. buff, veined light red purple; style arms buff and darker red purple; F. red purple, edge lighter, signal yellow green. Dancing Vogue X First Favourite.

FUJIGAWA (Toichi Ito by Society for Japanese Irises, R. 1995). JI (3 F.), 30" (76 cm), M. S. white; style arms tufted; F. white, signal yellow (RHS 3B), veins fading (3D) halfway to edge. Parentage unknown. Introduced in Japan ca. 1955.

FUJI SKIES (Chet Tompkins, TB, R. 1989). Roris 1990.

FUJI'S SNOWCAP (George Bush, JI, R. 1989). Bush 1990.

FULFILLED PROMISE (Wilford James, R. 1998). Sdlg. 93-50. SIB, 28" (71 cm), M. S. purple; style arms purple, midrib blue; F. deep velvety purple, cream and gold burst signal; ruffled. Mabel Coday X unknown. Cuyahoga Valley 1998.

FULL BLOWN (Tom Burseen, R. 1997). Sdlg. 93-368B. TB, 34" (86 cm), ML. Ruffled metallic orchid grape, washed blue; F. with lighter area near bright carrot red beard. Super Dancer X 8-285: ((Titan's Glory x (Orchidarium x Lacy Snowflake)) x Fluff Stuff). T.B.'s Place 1998.

FULL FASHIONED (Arthur Blodgett, R. 1992). Sdlg. 88-72. TB, 34" (86 cm), M. Ruffled claret rose (HCC 021/3) self; beards tangerine. Coral Satin X 81-15: (Peach Champagne x Shocking Pink). Blodgett Iris 1993.

FULL MOON MAGIC (Chet Tompkins, R. 1997). Sdlg. 93-13C. TB, 39" (99 cm), ML. Ruffled deep cream, pale moonlight yellow and ivory chamois blend, infused gilt; beards pale cream lemon. ((Burgermeister x Smooth Flow) x (Syncopation x Ming Porcelain)) X ((Tinsel Town x Syncopation) x (Hollywood Blonde x Churchill Downs)). Fleur de Lis 1997.

FULL SWING (Tom Burseen, R. 1991). Sdlg. 6-68C. TB, 36" (91 cm), M. S. creamy golden yellow (RHS 164C); F. red purple (70B), lighter area around gold beard; ruffled; slight fragrance. Planned Treasure X 4-161A: (Barletta x Satin Glass). T.B.'s Place 1992.

FULL TIGER STRIPE (Austin Morgan, R. 1990). TB, 34" (86 cm), EML. S. tan; F. tan yellow, full length red stripes; beards yellow. Parentage unknown. Iris Test Garden 1990.

FUNA ASOBI (Mototeru Kamo by Society for Japanese Irises, R. 1995). JI (3 F.), 36" (90 cm), M. S. lavender blue violet, white midrib and veins; style arms white, lavender blue violet crest; F. lavender blue violet, white veins. Parentage unknown. Introduced in Japan, 1976.

FUNDANGO (Tom Burseen, R. 1991). Sdlg. 6-289A. TB, 34" (86 cm), M. S. greyed red purple (RHS 185C); F. light violet blue (85C), rimmed S. color, golden brown shoulders, horizontally flared; beards white, tipped red orange; ruffled; sweet fragrance. Afternoon Delight X 4-184A: (Glory Bound x Latin Lover). T.B.'s Place 1995.

FUNNY BIRD (Ladislav Muska, R. 1996). Sdlg. LORE-01. TB, 34" (86 cm), EM. Amethyst and tan maroon plicata; beards light orange; heavily laced; sweet fragrance. ("Lososova Kader": (Beaux Arts x Miss Dolly Dollars) x "Fialovy Kvet": (Windsor Rose x Laced Cotton)) X Rei Momo. Muska 1996.

FUNNY GIRL (James Gibson by Cooley's Gardens, R. 1994). Sdlg. 39-4A-2. TB, 38" (97 cm), ML. S. deep warm pink, lightly veined cream on midrib; F. deep warm pink with slight cream center wash; beards tangerine red; laced, lightly ruffled. Probably -- Early Wish X 125-9A, unknown. Cooley 1994.

FUNNY VALENTINE (Darlene Pinegar, R. 1995). Sdlg. LT-1-6. TB, 35" (89 cm), EML. S. light pink; style arms apricot; F light pink, apricot hafts, creamy white below beard, slightly deeper pink veining; beards coral orange; lightly ruffled; slight sweet fragrance. Lemon Mist X Moon Mistress. Spanish Fork 1996.

FURIOSO (Barry Blyth, R. 1996). Sdlg. C72-A. IB, 24" (61 cm), EM. S. medium pink; F. orange apricot; beards bright saturn red; sweet fragrance. Mango Kiss X Bogota. Tempo Two 1996/97.

FUTURE CLASSIC (Heather Pryor, R. 1997). Sdlg. 16/93-K. LA, 43" (109 cm), EM. S. salmon red, darker rose veining, lemon rim; style arms yellow, red blush; F. deep red with lemon rib and reverse, bright yellow raised steeple signal; ruffled. Ginger Fudge X Never Say. Iris Haven 1999/2000.

FUTURE PERFECT (Ben Hager, R. 1991). Sdlg. S978BgRfWh. SPU, 37" (94 cm), M. S. and style arms white; F. white, small yellow signal; fluted. S717Wh: (S304Wh: ((Golden Lady x Driftwood) x Windfall) x Ila Crawford) X S795WWh: (Clarke Cosgrove x (Media Luz x Marilyn Holloway)). Cordon Bleu 1993.

FUTURE WATCH (Virginia Messick, R. 1991). Sdlg. M87-42. TB, 36" (91 cm), M. S. light blue; F. white; beards pale blue; heavily ruffled; slight fragrance. Up Periscope X Winterscape. Cottage 1992.

GABRIELENO CHIEFS (Barbara Wight, R. 1996). Sdlg. 90-18. BB, 17" (43 cm), EM. S. bright yellow (RHS 13A); F. greyed red (178C), yellow haft lines; beards bright yellow; slight spicy fragrance. Bright Warrior X IB 86-34: (Banjo Man x Rio Vista). Wight's Iris 1996.

GADABOUT (Marguerite Hagberg, R. 1994). Sdlg. 9-34. SDB, 11" (28 cm), M. S. and style arms light violet blue; F. light beige, edged light violet blue; beards blue; slight sweet fragrance. Flirty Mary X Jade Mist. Hillcrest 1995.

GAELIC JIG (Barry Blyth, R. 1999). Sdlg. F235-2. TB, 34" (86 cm), VE. S. lilac lavender; F. blended rosy brown, deeper toward haft, lavender underlay and fine centerline; beards white, heavily tipped light bronze; sweet fragrance. Cast a Spell X D46-1, Arabian Story sib. Tempo Two 1999/2000.

GAILY FORWARD (Perry Dyer, R. 1998). Sdlg. 91-73A. SDB, 12" (30 cm), M. S. bright yellow, edges blended honey; style arms yellow, edged honey; F. white, edged chrome yellow, honey plicata brushing on shoulders; beards root beer, old gold base. Varmint X Tricks. Contemporary 1999.

GALACTIC DANCER (Colin Hill, R. 1999). Sdlg. CHB-94-D. TB, 32" (81 cm), EM. Orchid self; beards white, fuzzy white horn tipped violet; ruffled, lightly laced. Battle Star X Grand Waltz. l.poppin' Irises 1999.

GALACTIC GOLD (Jim Hedgecock, R. 1999). Sdlg. 85-unk-7. TB, 32" (81 cm), M. Ruffled and laced gold, F. more intense; beards golden orange. Parentage unknown. Comanche Acres 1999.

GALACTIC WARRIOR (Jim Hedgecock, R. 1999). Sdlg. F-17-7. TB, 38" (97 cm), EM. S. dark red; F. darker burgundy red with velour sheen, haft markings yellow and purple; beards burnt gold, dark burgundy spoon or horn; ruffled, lightly laced; slight sweet fragrance. Sangre de Cristo X 84-99-1: (Sky Hooks x black sdlg., unknown).

GALA DESIGN (Floyd Dyer, R. 1993). Sdlg. D-61-88-D. SDB, 13" (33 cm), M. Full yellow, F. stitched red maroon; beards orange; sweet fragrance. D-35-86-D: ((Ohl O-15-74-D x Mini-Spark) x (Elfin Duet x self)) X D-83-86-D: (Fire One x Luxurious). Four Cedars 1993.

GALA GREETINGS (Barry Blyth, R. 1997). Sdlg. C225-5. TB, 36" (92 cm), VE-EM. S. white, slight 1/8" creamy edge at top; F. golden honey apricot blend; beards vivid tangerine; slight fragrance. Z63-3, Aztec Burst sib, X Aztec Burst. Tempo Two 1997/98.

GALA LOUISE (Mark Grumbine, R. 1999). Sdlg. 96-20-5. TB, 31" (79 cm), ML. S. purplish pink, 1/8" golden rim; F. brick red fading to fuchsia edge, hafts yellow with maroon veins; beards red orange; ruffled, lightly laced. St. Helens' Wake X Royal Trumpeter.

GALANTNY SHEYK (Viktor Sheviakov, R. 1996). Sdlg. 22a1a. TB, 30" (75 cm), ML. Dark amethyst violet self; beards pale amethyst violet; slight sweet fragrance. Rippling Waters X Matinata. Sheviakov 1996.

GALATEA MARX (Walter Marx by Society for Japanese Irises, R. 1991). JI (6 F.), 40" (102 cm), M. Ruffled near flax blue with white pencil veining; pure white styles and petaloids. Parentage unknown. Marx 1961.

GALILEE PRINCE (Luella Danielson, R. 1992). Sdlg. BP 82-6. AR (OH), 14" (36 cm), E. S. ruffled deep rose wine, densely veined darker; style arms deep rose wine; F. black rose wine, shading lighter toward hafts with dark (almost black) veining, black signal; beards maroon black. (Charon x L. Clark sdlg.) X (*I. mariae* x *I. atropurpurea*). Pleasure Iris 1993.

GALLANT ROGUE (Barry Blyth, TB, R. 1989). Keppel 1990.

GALLIARD (Maureen Probert, R. 1996). Sdlg. 4E7. TB, 36" (91 cm), M. Ruffled milky blue self; beards milky blue; spicy fragrance. Millrace X Song of Norway.

GALWAY (Keith Keppel, R. 1996). Sdlg. 91-41H. IB, 24" (61 cm), M. S. light pink (M&P 1-D-7 to 43-D-1), base flushed vanda (43-E-4); style arms light pink (1-E-7), pinard yellow (9-J-2) edge, orchid lip; F. peach (9-A-3/4) to light pink (1-C-7/8) blend, paler below beard; beards midnight sun (2-E-12) to mikado (2-B-12), vervain (42-B-6) at end; slight sweet fragrance. Sib to Donegal. Keppel 1997.

GAMAY (J. T. Aitken, R. 1995). CA, 12" (31 cm), ML. S. burgundy red; F. deep velvety burgundy red, lighter rim. Idylwild X unknown. Aitken's Salmon Creek 1995.

GAMLIN BLUE (Bob Gamlin by Marty Schafer/Jan Sacks, R. 1998). SPEC (*ruthenica*),4-6" (10-15 cm), L & RE. Blue violet self, white signal with blue violet veining. Parentage unknown. Joe Pye Weed 1998.

GANNA SHEKERA (Borys Pravdyvy, R. 1999). Sdlg. 5T131-1. TB, 36" (91 cm), M. Ruffled and laced pure white self; beards pinkish red, white base. Silver Shower X Vanity. Pravdyvy 1999.

GARDEN BRIDE (Chuck Chapman, R. 1998). Sdlg. 91-392-2. TB, 37" (94 cm), ML. Heavily ruffled white self; beards white, yellow in throat; slight fragrance. 89-390-2: (Cotton Carnival x Crystal Glitters) X Breakers. Chapman Iris 1998.

GARDEN CLUB DELIGHT (Lloyd Zurbrigg, R. 1997). Sdlg. JJ 93-8-2. TB, 38" (97 cm), EM & RE. S. white, violet plicata marking on edges only; style arms white, violet crest; F. white, violet edge and hafts; beards light yellow. Matrix X Suky. Friendship 1997.

GARDEN ESCORT (Ben Hager, TB, R. 1989). Roris 1991.

GARDEN FESTIVAL (Stan Dexter by Marie Ingersoll, R. 1991). Sdlg. 101-85-37B. TB, 36" (91 cm), M. S. violet white; F. violet, brownish hash marks; beards pale orange tipped white; ruffled. Exotic Flare X Melon Supreme. Ingersoll's Iris 1992.

GARDEN GARNET (Jim & Vicki Craig, R. 1994). Sdlg. C25X2. IB, 22" (56 cm), M. Medium garnet red; beards dark yellow; slight sweet fragrance. Luscious Lass X (((En Route x Maroon Caper) x Maroon Caper) x ((Odyssey x Maroon Caper) x (Chapeau x (Sacred Mountain x *I. aphylla* "Werckmeister")))). J. & V. Craig 1994.

GARDENLITE (Mary Dunn, R. 1990). Sdlg. M84-867-1. TB, 35" (89 cm), M. Ruffled and lightly laced bright golden yellow; beards deep yellow. Catalyst X M77-619-7: (((Kingdom x On Target) x Prosperity) x Sun City). M.A.D. Iris 1991.

GARDEN WHISPERS (O. D. Niswonger, R. 1995). Sdlg. SDB 3-92. SDB, 12" (31 cm), E. S. pale blue; style arms blue; F. yellow, rim white; beards pale blue, frosted white. Little Louie X unknown. Cape Iris 1996.

GARI LYN (Kirk Strawn, R. 1993). Sdlg. 49-1985. LA, 35" (89 cm), L. Dark violet (RHS 86B), yellow green (151A) signal; style arms light violet (88C), darker (86C) tip. Justa Reflection X Lafitte's Retreat.

GARLANDA (R. E. Nichol by Jean Nichol, R. 1998). Sdlg. H 4/6. TB, 40" (102 cm), M. S. shaded biscuit (RHS 164D); style arms yellow; F. shaded biscuit, pale lemon edge, pale gold hafts; beards dull gold; frilled; slight fragrance. C 20: (Cambodia x Liz) X Catalyst.

GARNET AND GOLD (Donald Spoon, R. 1995). Sdlg. 90-204-C. TB, 32" (81 cm), ML. Lightly ruffled brick red; beards golden yellow. Study in Black X Time Lord.

GARNET DREAM (Cy Bartlett, R. 1998). Sdlg. SRT-SPET/4. TB, 38" (97 cm), M. S. garnet red; style arms light greyed red; F. garnet red, slight mauve center haze; beards golden brown; ruffled. ((Superstition x Royal Trumpeter) x (Sultan's Palace x Dodsworth EB 81)) X Tintinara.

GARNET EGG (Carl Boswell, R. 1995). Sdlg. 101-87-S. SDB, 12" (30 cm), M. S. wine purple; F. blackish garnet, wine marginal band; beards brownish purple. U-Turn X (Plum-Plum x Balkana Baby). Adamgrove 1997.

GARNET ETCHING (Walter Moores, R. 1999). Sdlg. 91-11-B. TB, 34" (86 cm), M. S. and style arms golden yellow; F. golden yellow ground with garnet red plicata wash, heavier garnet thumbprints below haft; beards golden yellow; ruffled; slight spicy fragrance. Faux Pas X Waltz Across Texas.

GARNET GLORY (Barry Emmerson, R. 1999). Sdlg. BE 95/4/2. TB, 37" (94 cm), M. S. garnet with brown sheen, slight gold midrib flush; style arms garnet; F. velvety garnet with brown sheen; beards brown; slight fragrance. Red Kite X BE 92/10: (Indian Chief x Ginger Swirl).

GARNET LACE (Hyram Ames, R. 1996). Sdlg. A941. TB, 30" (76 cm), M. Ruffled and laced garnet red, F. darker around maroon black beard; slight spicy fragrance. Quanah Parker X Austrian Garnets.

GARNET MASTER (Stan Dexter by Marie Ingersoll, R. 1994). Sdlg. A-33-86-109 AA. TB, 38" (97 cm), ML. Garnet red, F. velvety; beards yellow brown. 83-226: ((Klondike Kate x Temple Gold) x Hombre) X Lady Friend. Ingersoll's Iris 1995.

GARNET STORM DANCER (Heather Pryor, R. 1994). Sdlg. 55/90-6. LA, 30" (76 cm), ML. Ruffled, slightly reflexed purple black (RHS 187A), green and black midline, gold steeple signal on all petals; style arms purple black, gold centerline, creating star effect. Gladiator's Gift X Designer's Dream. Rainbow Ridge 1996/97.

GARY JOSEPH (Clyde & Anna Hahn, R. 1996). Sdlg. 91-13-C. TB, 38" (97 cm), EM. Reddish purple self; beards yellow, tipped purple; slight sweet fragrance. Midnight Fragrance X Elizabeth Carol. Hahn's Rainbow 1996.

GATE CRASHER (John C. Taylor, R. 1991). Sdlg. OL 137-2. LA, 43" (110 cm), M. S. burgundy (RHS 58B); F. same, edged gold; ruffled; often blooms double with petaloids. Dazzling Star X Helen Naish. Rainbow Ridge 1992/93.

GATEWOOD ROUGETTE (Richard Goula, R. 1992). Sdlg. G-84-R1. LA, 30" (76 cm), EML.

S. medium red; F. velvety bright red, large bright yellow signal; slight spicy fragrance. G. W. Holleyman X Charjoy's Jewel. Gatewood Gardens 1993.

GAWLEE (Tom Burseen, R. 1997). Sdlg. 94-24A. TB, 33" (84 cm), EM. Ruffled light apricot orange; beards orange, creamy horn; spicy fragrance. 9-198: (Hindenburg x (Lavish Lace x Embellishment)) X Stars and Stripes. T.B.'s Place 1998.

GAZA WINDS (Lois Rich by James Whitely, R. 1992). Sdlg. R70-76. AB (OGB+), 22" (56 cm), M. S. off-white ground, heavily veined lavender; style arms cream, peppered henna; F. light cream ground peppered brown henna, wide dark gold brown signal; beards dark brown. Kerr K56-4-0: (*I. lortetii* x *I. auranitica*) X Wilkes sdlg.: (GM 15 x Jebel Jehar). Aril Patch 1992.

GEE BETTY G (Dot Steele, TB, R. 1989). Rancho de la Flor de Lis 1990.

#GEISHA Shown as obsolete in 1939 Check List. Name released.

GEISHA (Marky Smith, R. 1996). Sdlg. 90-26B. IB, 23" (58 cm), EM. S. near-solid dusty violet (RHS 91C), lighter midrib marking, inside center stitched grey to white; style arms dusty violet; F. white (155C) ground, 3/8" outer rim (greyer than 91D), 1/4" clear violet (91A) stitched inner rim; beards grey white at end, merging from gold to gold orange; heavily ruffled; pronounced musky fragrance. Chubby Cheeks X Keppel 83-8A: (Snowbrook x sib 80-131H). Aitken's Salmon Creek 1997.

GEISHA DOLL (Ed Matheny III, R. 1994). Sdlg. J:00-04-93. JI (6 F.), 30" (76 cm), M. Silver white, veined and heavily brushed reddish purple (RHS 77A), yellow signal; style arms violet, edged silver white. Geisha Gown X Glitter and Glamour. Ed's Iris 1995.

GEISHA EYES (Charles Arny, LA, R. 1987). Bois d'Arc 1990.

GEISHUNKA (Yoshio Mitsuda by Society for Japanese Irises, R. 1995). JI (6 F.), 24" (61 cm), M. White, faintly veined light purple (RHS 76C), signal rich yellow (12A); style arms off-white, rich purple (81C) edge. Parentage unknown.

GELBE MOEVE (Tomas Tamberg, SIB, R. 1986). Schoeppinger 1993.

GEMSTAR (Marky Smith, R. 1992). Sdlg. 89-03A. SDB, 12" (31 cm), EM. S. medium dark violet blue (RHS 89C); style arms cream; F. darker violet blue (89A) with pale veining in center, lavender white wire rim and shoulders, white hafts and star tips below beard; beards white, tipped yellow orange in throat; ruffled. Ripple Chip X Coalbucket. Aitken's Salmon Creek 1994.

GEMSTONE (Ben Hager, R. 1998). Sdlg. SD5634PkYBld. SDB, 13" (33 cm), M. S. pink, shaded yellow; style arms pinkish yellow; F. pink, blended yellow areas; beards tangerine. SD4979BrtPkSmFl: (Cupid's Cup x (SD4029: (3393: (2885: (Blond Doll x (Pink Amber x Pink Cushion)) x 2888: ((Pink Amber x Pink Cushion) x Buttercup Charm)) x 3758: (2919: (2563: (Pink Cushion x Roberts 65-R-28) x 2708: (Frosty Lemonade x Pink Cushion)) x Pet sib)) x SD4024: ((3393 x Pet) x (3420: (2920: (2563 x (Pink Amber x Pink Cushion)) x 2885) x 3393)))) X SD5134RndPkPk: ((4029 x (Gigglepot x 4024)) x (((2919 x 2920) x 3420) x My Sheba)). Adamgrove 1998.

GENEFICE (Udo & Rudolf Wilkeneit, R. 1996). Sdlg. EW 91/94. SDB, 10" (25 cm), L. S. yellow, blue flash; F. light creamy brown; beards orange, blue at end; slight fragrance. Parentage unknown.

GENE MACHINE (Tom Burseen, R. 1992). Sdlg. 9-216D. TB, 37" (94 cm), EM. Heavily ruffled dark metallic grape violet (redder than RHS 83B); beards violet, tipped white; musky fragrance. Bluid X Inaugural Ball. T.B.'s Place 1993.

GENE'S GREEN GENES (Eugene Hunt by Sharon McAllister, R. 1992). Sdlg. ORB 92-1. AB (OGB), 28" (72 cm), EM. S. lavender; style arms willow green, midrib lavender, leaf green "eyelashes"; F. willow green, purple dotting and veining around beards, violet wash over center, dark purple signal; beards mustard grey. Esther the Queen X (Esther's Son x Leo's Lort-Chen). Aril Society 1992.

GENE'S GUARDIAN ANGEL (Eugene Hunt by Sharon McAllister, R. 1990). Sdlg. ORB 89-1. AB (OGB+), 28" (72 cm), EM. S. white with delicate lavender veining around edge; F. very pale yellow green (RHS 158C to 157D), violet veins (near 187A) at heart blending to rust at outer edge, clear center; beards mustard. (Lahara x Persian Pansy) X (Clark sdlg.: (*I. lortetii* x Chenik Aga) x Esther's Son). Aril Society, McAllister 1991.

GENIAL GIANT (John C. Taylor, R. 1991). Sdlg. OL 113-2. LA, 47" (120 cm), M. Mauve (RHS 70C). Koorawatha X Dazzling Star. Rainbow Ridge 1992/93.

GENJI BOTARU (Shuichi Hirao by Society for Japanese Irises, R. 1992). JI (3 F.), 31½" (80 cm), M. Red violet ground, veined, sanded and marbled gold-white, light yellow signal; ruffled. Parentage unknown. Hirao 1970.

GENTEEL (Monty Byers, R. 1990). Sdlg. G39-111. TB, 34" (86 cm), EML & RE. Heavily ruffled medium blue lilac; beards pale blue, tipped yellow. Eternal Bliss X Pacific Tide. Moonshine 1991.

GENTIAN ETUDE (Georgia Hinkle, TB, R. 1965). Correction of typographical error (GENTIAL ETUDE) in 1969 Check List.

GENTLE ALICE (Janet Hutchinson, R. 1995). Sdlg. SLTS4. LA, 33" (84 cm), M. S. off-white, green centerline; style arms pale green, crests white; F. off-white, center flushed pale apricot, narrow yellow signal veined green; buds apricot buff; slight sweet fragrance. Soft Laughter X -- probably Our Parris. Iris Haven 1997/98.

GENTLE BLUEBEARD (Barbara Marsh, R. 1992). Sdlg. 87-21-19-B. SDB, 8-12" (20-30 cm), EM. S. creamy white, blue midrib deep in heart; style arms royal blue; F. yellow, 5/8" creamy white edge; beards royal blue, wide; lightly ruffled; slight fragrance. Chubby Cheeks X Jade Mist.

GENTLE FELLOW (Richard Ernst, R. 1996). Sdlg. JF168-2-7. TB, 36" (91 cm), M. S. violet, infused mauve; style arms violet and yellow; F. cream blending to dark butter yellow rim and shoulders; beards bright yellow, orange in throat; lightly ruffled. F168-2: ((Irene Nelson x Honest Pleasure) x Gaulter G81-17, inv. Irene Nelson) X F104-1: ((Irene Nelson x Sun Fire) x Friday Surprise). Cooley 1996.

GENTLE GEORGIA (Lois O'Brien, R. 1994). Sdlg. 90-73A. TB, 34" (87 cm), EM. Ruffled pale amethyst (RHS 76D) self, deepening (76B) in heart and paling to near-white below beards; style arms deep amethyst violet (82B); beards poppy, tipped cream; slight spicy fragrance. Perils of Pauline X 78-22B: (Chartreuse Ruffles x Carriage Trade). O'Brien Iris 1995.

GENTLE KINGDOM (Jean Sanders, R. 1993). BB, 17" (43 cm), ML. Ruffled smoky blue with few brown marks; beards orange, tipped white. I Do X (Soap Opera x White Reprise). Iris Acres 1994.

GENTLEMAN CALLER (Mary Dunn, R. 1994). Sdlg. L 132-1. LA, 35" (89 cm), M. Adobe rose red self, F. slightly deeper, with deep orange line signal; ruffled. L 85-1: (Fantastic x Hager L40 red: (Delta King x Acadian)) X sib. Bay View 1995.

GENTLEMANS CLUB (Kevin Nilsen, R. 1996). Sdlg. 35-90-3. TB, 31½" (80 cm), VE-E. S. and style arms amber gold; F. red black, edged darker, white area under orange beard. 15-84: (Bicentennial x San Jose) X Gigolo.

GENTLE ORCHID (Terrell Taylor, R. 1994). Sdlg. 93-39. TB, 32" (81 cm), ML. Ruffled and laced light lavender orchid (RHS 88D) with F. aging to frosted lavender; beards tangerine, tipped white; sweet fragrance. Designing Woman X Sweet Musette. Bonita Gardens 1995.

GENTLE POET (John Moffitt Jr. by Lloyd Zurbrigg, R. 1993). AB (OGB-), 20" (51 cm), VE. S. near-white; F. light rosy purple; beards light yellow. English Cottage X Rare Form.

GENTLE RIOT (Barry Blyth, R. 1994). Sdlg. A53-7. IB, 24" (61 cm), ML. S. cream with hint of violet at base; F. creamy peach; beards lavender, tangerine in throat. X25-5, Impish sib, X Electrique. Tempo Two 1994/95.

GENTLE WHISPER (Polly Black, R. 1995). Sdlg. GR29-8. TB, 36" (91 cm), M. S. white, orchid cast, green midrib; F. white, orchid cast, green touch near beard; beards bright yellow, end white and yellow; ruffled; slight spicy sweet fragrance. Orchid sdlg. X Mandolin. Polly Black 1995.

GENUINE GEMSTONES (Sharon McAllister, R. 1992). Sdlg. 86-11-6. AB (OGB+), 18" (47 cm) EM. S. pale amethyst, finely veined darker violet; style arms pearl white; F. plush purple, light golden tan edge; beards yellow in throat, blending to violet, white at tip. Ballalaika Music X Sunrise in Glory. Aril Society 1992.

GEOFFREY CHARLES (R. E. Nichol, R. 1990). Sdlg. K83-1. TB, 34" (86 cm), M. S. yellow (RHS 7B); F. white, blending to yellow at edge; beards gold; ruffled. E29: (Luscious Lemon x Starring Role) X Demelza. Sutton 1991.

GEOLYN'S LOYALTY (Stan Dexter by Marie Ingersoll, R. 1991). Sdlg. 107-83-156. TB, 28" (71 cm), EM. Orchid pink; beards hot pink. 80-91A: (1977-F x Beverly Sills) X Vanity. Ingersoll's Iris 1992.

GEORGE RODIONENKO (Tony Huber, R. 1999). Sdlg. 95-214. SPEC-X (versata), 38½" (98 cm), ML. S. purplish violet (RHS 83B/C); style arms violet (84B/C), crests darker (84A); F. plum (79) to purplish violet (83C), large golden yellow signal on cream base. 91-837 biversata: (DOM-033: (Belle Promesse x Nouvel Age) x DOM-033) X Royal Burgundy.

GEORGIAN DANCER (William Plotner, R. 1992). Sdlg. 85-503-4. TB, 36-38" (91-97 cm), ML. S. grape heliotrope (RHS 70A), lightly mottled yellow blend in center and base; F. small cream white spot below beard, then 1/2"-3/4" yellow (2D) band, with wide grape (64B) edge, grape midline;

beards yellow, tipped white; lightly ruffled; slight spicy fragrance. Yellow Splendor X Raspberries and Cream. Wildwood Gardens 1994.

GEORGIAN DELICACY (Marty Schafer/Jan Sacks, R. 1998). Sdlg. SP88-100. SPEC (*spuria*), 30" (76 cm), M. S. light blue (RHS 97B/C), 3/4" gold to yellow haft edge, form upright, quilled; style arms pearl, washed light blue; F. pale blue (97D) veined darker, 2" gold-edged quilled haft, gold signal veined pale blue; lightly ruffled; slight sweet fragrance. *I. spuria ssp. carthaliniae*, seed from SIGNA. Joe Pye Weed 1998.

GEORGIA STREAKER (Harry Turner, R. 1999). Sdlg. 94-88. TB, 28" (71 cm), ML. S. white, infused yellow; style arms white, striped light yellow; F. sulphur yellow veining from haft to tip on white ground; beards full yellow, light yellow at end; slight fragrance. 1192-80-19: (Joyce Terry x Punchline) X Sunshine Song.

GERDA'S GARDEN (Dana Borglum, R. 1995). Sdlg. E29-2. BB, 26" (66 cm), M. Pale blush pink self; beards pinkish white, tangerine red in throat. Anna Belle Babson X self.

GERMANTET ONE (Tomas Tamberg, R. 1993). Sdlg. SSTT166. SIB (tet.), 31½" (80 cm), M. Dark blue self. Laurenbuhl X unknown. Schoeppinger, Tamberg 1993.

GERTIE BUTLER (Charles Arny, LA, R. 1989). Bois d'Arc 1990.

GET A GRIP (Tom Burseen, R. 1997). Sdlg. 93-452A. TB, 36" (91 cm), M. S. and style arms venetian pink (RHS 49B); F. red violet, creamy peach wash; beards orange; ruffled; sweet fragrance. Roar X Fundango. T.B.'s Place 1998.

GETAWAY (John C. Taylor, R. 1996). Sdlg. UL 5-9. LA, 47" (120 cm), ML. Purple self, F. with yellow signal; ruffled; slight fragrance. 'Bout Midnight X Rachel's Request. Rainbow Ridge 1997/98.

GHINGHERI (Hyram Ames, TB, R. 1987). Comanche Acres 1990.

GHOST (Perry Dyer, R. 1999). Sdlg. 92-98A. TB, 30" (76 cm), M. Lightly ruffled pewter grey; style arms flushed violet; beards deep indigo blue violet; foliage purple-based. Touch of Bronze X Traitor.

GHOST DANCER (Sharon McAllister, R. 1992). Sdlg. 85-4-14. AB (OGB), 28" (72 cm), EM. S. wistaria; F. smoky amethyst (greyer than RHS 84A), burgundy black spots on signal area; beards burgundy black. Bold Sentry X Whither Thou Goest. McAllister 1992.

GHOST GOSSIP (Hooker Nichols, R. 1991). Sdlg. 8624A. SDB, 12" (30 cm), EM. S. white ground stitched greyed violet on edge and midrib; F. slightly darker, white center; beards gold and white, tipped violet; ruffled. Court Magician X (Pink Kitten x (Happy Mood x Kiss)). Hillcrest 1994.

GHOST PARTY (Barry Blyth, R. 1994). Sdlg. A44-8. SDB, 12" (30 cm), VE-EM. S. smoky pink with champagne grey overtones; F. pastel lavender, 1/8" edge of S. color, rosy tan brown hafts, violet centerline flash; beards tangerine; slight sweet fragrance. V7-5, Gigolette sib, X Chanted. Tempo Two 1994/95.

GIGANT (Oleg Amekhin, R. 1996). Sdlg. PK-4. SPEC (*pseudacorus*), 71" (180 cm), L. Light yellow, black-shaded signal. "Mtsheta" X *I. pseudacorus*. Amekhin 1996.

GIGOLETTE (Barry Blyth, R. 1990). Sdlg. V7-1. SDB, 10" (25 cm), ML. S. cream overlaid rosy tan; F. apricot cream, rosy tan plicata markings around hafts, some heavier lines below bright tangerine beard. Cupid's Cup X T50-1, Yipee sib. Tempo Two 1990/91.

GILDED CREAM (Betty Wilkerson, R. 1995). Sdlg. C 29-1. TB, 35" (89 cm), EM. S. rich cream (RHS 11C), veined indian yellow (17C); style arms rich cream; F. rich cream, shoulders overlaid indian yellow; ruffled; slight sweet fragrance. Ice Sculpture X Gold Burst. Bridge in Time 1995.

GILDED GOWN (Geraldine Couturier, R. 1995). Sdlg. GC-1-1-93. TB, 33" (84 cm), EM. S. white, gold midrib flush, very slight gold edging and veining; style arms white, flushed gold; F. white, hafts gold; beards golden orange, pale lavender horn; ruffled; slight sweet fragrance. Spooned Blaze X unknown. Sunnyridge 1997.

GILDED MORN (Francis Rogers, R. 1990). Sdlg. F-228-E. TB, 30" (76 cm), L. S. greyed orange (RHS 115C) with lavender infusion; F. greyed orange (164B), greyed lavender under orange beard, greyed yellow at hafts; ruffled; pronounced sweet fragrance. Gold Circle X FR-80-5C: ((Pink Sleigh x Grand Waltz) x Bonbon). Meadowbrook 1991.

GILLA (Manfred Beer, R. 1994). Sdlg. MB 28/84 D. TB, 29" (75 cm), M. S. orange (RHS 27D) blended creamy white and pink; F. orange (27D), brownish-veined shoulders; beards orange red (30C) tipped orange (27D); lightly waved; pronounced sweet fragrance. Lemon Brocade X Beauty Crown. Gartenbau Baensch 1994.

GILSTON GULF (H. Castle Fletcher, TB, R. 1957). British Iris Society 1981.

GIL Y GIL (Ladislav Muska, R. 1999). Sdlg. 99-EWCE-05. TB, 36" (91 cm), L. S. white to light gold;

style arms light gold; F. burgundy red, caramel veined rim; beards yellow; heavily ruffled, laced; slight fragrance. (Edith Wolford x Celebration Song) X (SweeterThan Wine x "Erebuni": (Thriller x ((Vandal Spirit x Okavango) x (Simple Pleasures x Tropicana Doll)))).

GIMLET JEWEL (Donovan Albers, SDB, R. 1986). Albers, Borboleta Gardens 1990.

GIMME A BREAK (Bob Thomason, R. 1993). Sdlg. BT 9031A. SDB, 10" (25 cm), EM. S. white; F. violet, 1/4" white edge; beards white, orange in throat; slight fragrance. Boo X Ja Wohl. Okie Iris 1999.

GIMMICK (Keith Keppel, R. 1998). Sdlg. 91-57P. SDB, 11" (28 cm), EM. S. darker than port (M&P 56-E-12), slightly lighter toward center; style arms darker than port; F. 1/2" lemon yellow (10-K-3) blaze with some port dotting and lining, hafts and margins darker than port; beards mustard brown; pronounced sweet fragrance. Rusty Dusty X Quote. Keppel 1999.

GIMN ZHENSCHINE (Nina Miroshnichenko, R. 1996). TB, 37" (93 cm), M. Ruffled pink self; beards red; slight spicy fragrance. Parentage unknown. Miroshnichenko 1977.

GINA THE GYPSY (Darlene Pinegar, R. 1993). Sdlg. TOF-1-1. TB, 30" (76 cm), EM. S. greenish yellow narrowly edged white; F. velvety deep purple blending outward to light blue purple, narrow brownish edge, brownish red hafts; beards deep yellow; tailored; slight sweet fragrance. Twist of Fate X Rowdy. Spanish Fork 1994.

GIN DELIGHT (Glenn Bowers, R. 1997). Sdlg. B28-2. TB, 36" (91 cm), EM & RE. Ruffled white, hint of pale yellow, F. with yellow green venation below beard; beards yellow, gold in throat; pronounced sweet fragrance. Sunny Shoulders X Blazing Sunrise.

GIN GAME (Calvin Helsley, R. 1999). Sdlg. 93-9. SIB, 38" (97 cm), M. Rose red, white spray pattern over half of F. Mabel Coday X Variation in Blue.

GINGER FUDGE (Heather Pryor, R. 1997). Sdlg. 40/90-10. LA, 40" (102 cm), EM. S. and F. spanish orange (RHS 26B) veined darker, with yellow raised steeple signal; style arms lighter, splashed spanish orange; ruffled. Alluvial Gold X Gladiator's Gift. Lone Star 1998.

GINGER NUTKIN (Heather Pryor, R. 1997). Sdlg. 33/93-A. LA, 35" (89 cm), M. S. ginger apricot, darker apricot line signal; style arms golden apricot, blushed pink; F. ginger apricot, raised orange steeple signal; ruffled. Ginger Fudge X 66/90-29: (Gladiator's Gift x self).

GINGER PUNCH (Richard Morgan, R. 1997). Sdlg. L642-K. LA, 28" (71 cm), EM. Bright orange red, F. with yellow orange signal. Brushed Gold X Little Miss Leighley. Redbud Lane 1999.

GIN-NO-KOTO (Toyokazu Ichie/Kamo Nurseries by Currier McEwen, R. 1997). Sdlg. 91-153. JI (3 F.), 26" (65 cm), ML. S. dark violet (RHS 83A), white hairline edging; style arms violet; F. dark violet (83B), white hairline edging, signal sulphur yellow (6C). 6-99: ("Shu-no-Sode" x 7A-25: ("Maisennyo" x self)) X 9A-23: (Kyomai x 3-48: (Kamiji-no-Homare x "Saicho")).

GINNY G. (Bob Thomason, R. 1998). Sdlg. BT 94-030A. TB, 32" (81 cm), EM. S. pink gold, yellow gold rim; style arms pink, edged gold; F. bright yellow darkening to pink gold toward edge, yellow gold rim; beards orange; ruffled, laced; slight spicy fragrance. Lace Jabot X Mary Frances.

GINNY'S CREAM (Donald Spoon, R. 1995). Sdlg. 89-135. TB, 33" (84 cm), M. S. white, creamy yellow base; style arms creamy yellow; F. white, creamy yellow (RHS 2C/D) hafts and reverse; beards creamy yellow, base and outer end white; ruffled, laced. I Do X Ringo. Winterberry 1996.

GIRAFFE KNEEHIZ (Brad Kasperek, R. 1996). Sdlg. 92B-51S. TB, 40" (107 cm), EM. S. and style arms apricot (RHS 179D) and tan (159B), muted splashing; F. orange (185C) to red (159B), splashed silver; beards tan; lightly ruffled. Hot Streak X Tiger Honey. Zebra 1996.

GIRL CRAZY (Mary Dunn, R. 1993). Sdlg. L142. LA, 30" (76 cm), M. S. deep yellow; style arms green; F. deep golden yellow, deep orange gold line signal. L44-2: (Charlie's Michele x Harland K. Riley) X L44-5, sib. Bay View 1993.

GIRL NEXT DOOR (Paul Black, R. 1990). Sdlg. 851A. TB, 36" (91 cm), EM. S. white, pink lines up midrib; F. pink, hafts toned amber; beards orange; slight musky fragrance. Infinite Grace X Blazing Sunrise. Mid-America 1990.

GIRLS' FAVOURITE (Barry Blyth, R. 1995). Sdlg. A171-1. TB, 34" (86 cm), EML. Medium bright pink self; beards bright coral; pronounced sweet fragrance. Elizabeth Marrison X Presence. Tempo Two 1995/96.

GITTA (Manfred Beer, R. 1991). Sdlg. MB 28/84B. TB, 41" (105 cm), M. Creamy green yellow, F. with large lighter spot. Lemon Brocade X Beauty Crown. Kania Gartencenter, Von Zeppelin 1992.

GIUSEPPE (B. Charles Jenkins, R. 1994). Sdlg. AW82A. SPU, 33-40" (84-102 cm), M. S. creamy white, yellow center; style arms white; F. golden yellow, 1/4" creamy white rim. Janice Chesnik X A8-10H: (Clarke Cosgrove x Crow Wing). Shepard Iris 1994.

GIVE-ME-PATIENCE (Anne Blanco White, selector, R. 1996). JI (3 F.), 36" (91 cm), M. S. vibrant reddish purple, greenish yellow margin; F. reddish purple; ruffled. Parentage and origin unknown.

GIVENDALE (B.L.C. Dodsworth, TB, R. 1989). British Iris Society 1997.

GIZMO THE GREMLIN (Darlene Pinegar, R. 1998). Sdlg. GV-94-27C. SDB, 9" (22 cm), E. S. greyed plum, midrib darker; style arms greyed plum; F. dark greenish gold, brown hafts, darker veining and shading, off-white whisker marking under royal blue beard; slight sweet fragrance. Golden Violet X Jillaroo. Spanish Fork 1999.

GLACIA ISLAND (Akihiko Terada, R. 1995). Sdlg. 214-9. TB, 36" (91 cm), M. Cool white self, S. with lavender cast; beards yellow, tipped white; ruffled. Silverado X Swan Dance. Roris 1997.

GLACIAL BEAUTY (A. & D. Willott, R. 1997). Sdlg. W 80-46. SDB, 11" (28 cm), M. Ruffled blue white self; beards pale blue. Pixie Pinafore X Jack Riley. Willott 1997.

GLACIAL CRYSTALS (Francis Rogers, R. 1998). Sdlg. C-135-A. TB, 40" (107 cm), M. S. and style arms white; F. white, edge pale blue (RHS 97D): beards light yellow, violet blue at end; flared, ruffled; sweet fragrance. Conjuration X F-248-M: (78-FR-26-C: (Martinique x Kathy Rogers 75 K1A: (Pink Sleigh x Grand Waltz)) x Song of Norway). Meadowbrook 1999.

GLACIER KISS (Paul Black, R. 1991). Sdlg. 8519B. TB, 38" (97 cm), L. S. medium yellow; style arms yellow; F. white, slight yellow rim, yellow reverse; beards yellow. Pacific Mist X Love Sonnet. Mid-America 1991.

GLACIER POINT (Richard Tasco, R. 1997). Sdlg. 93-38-08. TB, 38" (97 cm), EM. Lightly ruffled very pale blue self, aging white; beards pale violet at end, white center section, tangerine in throat, with violet horn. Classy Chassy X Art School Angel. Superstition 1998.

GLACIER RIDGE (Stan Dexter by Marie Ingersoll, R. 1992). Sdlg. A32-86-168A. TB, 36" (91 cm), M. S. icy white, finely edged blue; F. purple blue, white flash below yellow beard. American Beauty X Condottiere. Ingersoll's Iris 1993.

GLACIER SPRING (Frederick Kerr, R. 1993). Sdlg. 87-17-3. TB, 35" (89 cm), M. S. blue white; F. medium blue, darker midline from beard to edge; ruffled; slight spicy fragrance. Edith Wolford X Breakers. Rainbow Acres 1993.

GLAD CHOICE (John Pierce by Maryott's Gardens, R. 1995). Sdlg. 84-64. TB, 36" (91 cm), EML. Orchid pink (RHS 56A), lighter in center of F.; beards white, tipped tangerine. Lorilee X Love Magic. Maryott 1995.

GLAD HEART (Ben Hager, R. 1997). Sdlg. T5432#2. TB, 36" (91 cm), EM. S. white, midrib flushed pink; F. deep red purple, lighter edge; beards blue white, hairs tipped tangerine in throat. T4235PkCr/Lv: (Merry Madrigal x Mother Earth) X Street Dancer. Cooley 1998.

GLADIATOR'S GIFT (John C. Taylor, R. 1990). Sdlg. OL 121-1. LA, 39" (100 cm), ML. Ruffled greyed red (RHS 180B), lighter reverse and edge, yellow signal all petals. L94-2: (Edith Fear x Valera) X Limited Edition. Rainbow Ridge 1990/91.

GLAD MEMORY (Ivar Schmidt, R. 1995). Sdlg. EN A 89/3. JI (6 F.), 32" (80 cm), M. Dark beetroot red, daffodil yellow signal surrounded by lilac pink, darker veining. Geisha Gown X My Heavenly Dream. Iris Acres 1995/96.

GLADYS ANNA (Monty Byers by Duane Carey, R. 1993). Sdlg. E16-102. TB, 30" (76 cm), M. White, edged pale purple, F. with yellow haft shading; beards pale purple. Feed Back X Brother Carl.

GLADYS LEE (Donald Spoon, R. 1997). Sdlg. 89-4B. TB, 34" (86 cm), ML. S. peach white, peach pink central area; style arms peach pink; F. cream white, peach pink central area lighter toward margins and below beard; beards tangerine, base and outer end cream; ruffled, flared. Cataldo X Infinite Grace. Winterberry 1997.

GLADYS MY LOVE (Allan Ensminger, R. 1997). Sdlg. 192-63. TB, 40" (102 cm), ML. S. and style arms white; F. orient pink (HCC 416); beards poppy red (16); slight fragrance. Magharee X 89-18: (86-41: (Almost Gladys x Christa) x 85-24: ((Coral Beauty x (Almost Gladys x R. Nelson sdlg.: (((Crystal Blaze x Maiden Voyage) x Silver Showers) x Chartreuse Ruffles))) x Coral Chalice)). Varigay 1998.

GLAIN (Maureen Foster, R. 1993). Sdlg. 4J1. TB, 40" (102 cm), L. Flaring, ruffled and fluted deep red purple self; beards mauve; slight sweet fragrance. Mary Frances X Master Touch. British Iris Society 1999.

GLAM (Barry Blyth, R. 1999). Sdlg. F95-1. IB, 24" (61 cm), ML. Light rosy wine, F. with white spray pattern; beards tangerine, white base; sweet fragrance. D34-15, Proton sib, X C228-A: (Surfie Girl x Legato). Tempo Two 1999/2000.

GLAMOUR PUSS (Sharon McAllister, R. 1994). Sdlg. 84-4B-12. AB (OGB), 28" (72 cm), EM. S. pale primrose yellow, slight pinkish hint; F. primrose yellow, lightly touched pink, arrow-shaped area of nearly solid burgundy veining surrounding tip of burgundy beard. Desert Princess X Rose of Sharon. McAllister 1994.

GLANUSK (Harry Foster, R. 1990). Sdlg. R38/87. SIB (tet.), 38" (97 cm), ML. S. laced bright medium blue; F. ruffled bright medium blue, fine silver edge, gold hafts, discreet white signal. Harpswell Happiness X Dear Dianne.

GLASLYN (Harry Foster, R. 1990). Sdlg. R47/87. SIB (tet.), 38" (97 cm), ML. S. laced cambridge blue; style arms azure; F. rich slate blue, heavily textured, small white, gold and green signal; ruffled. Harpswell Happiness X Dear Dianne. V. H. Humphrey 1995.

GLAS-Y-DORLAN (Harry Foster by Maureen Foster, R. 1993). Sdlg. R82. SIB (tet.), 32" (81 cm), ML-VL. S. dark violet blue (RHS 96A); style arms light blue shading to orchid, heavily feathered; F. dark violet blue edged silver, kingfisher blue flash from signal over most of F., white and gold signal; lightly ruffled. Harpswell Happiness X Dear Dianne.

GLEAM BEAM (Francis Rogers, R. 1992). Sdlg. F-935-A. TB, 30" (76 cm), M. S. greyed yellow (RHS 162); F. yellow (12B), greyed purple (183B) hafts, small white area under beard, lighter purple plicata markings around edge; beards gold; lightly ruffled; slight sweet fragrance. Gigolo X Meadowlark Serenade. Meadowbrook 1994.

GLEBE BROOK (John Burton, R. 1998). Sdlg. 88 H 3. SDB, 11-13" (28-33 cm), E. S. powder blue, midrib shaded green; style arms pale blue, bright blue midrib; F. powder blue, darker blue texture veining heavier near beard, reverse shaded green; beards bright blue, gold in throat. Bibury X unknown. Hermit Medlars Walk 1999.

GLEBE GHOST (Carol Klein by Jennifer Hewitt, R. 1999). JI (3 F.), 18" (45 cm), M. Deep red violet (darker than RHS 77A), F. with bright yellow signal; foliage striped green and white. *I. ensata variegata* X unknown. Glebe Cottage Plants 1994. In commerce in Britain as *I. ensata* "Ghost".

GLENHAVEN (Graeme Grosvenor, R. 1994). Sdlg. T7-1. TB, 40" (100 cm), EM. S. white, heavily edged, dotted and suffused light blue; F. white, edged and dotted blue violet; beards tangerine; heavily ruffled; slight sweet fragrance. Daredevil X Snowbrook. Rainbow Ridge 1997/98.

GLENYS (Maureen Foster, R. 1991). Sdlg. 6D6. TB, 38" (97 cm), L. Heavily ruffled medium blue (RHS 100C) with silvery sheen; beards gold. Mary Frances X Skiers' Delight.

GLISTENING GLEN (Heather Collins, MDB, R. 1984). Wyuna 1987.

GLISTENING GLOW WORM (Marge Powell, R. 1993). Sdlg. PIP1102. TB, 40" (102 cm), EM. S. light lavender, midrib flushed light yellow; F. darker lavender blend, hafts and beard yellow orange; slight fragrance. Hawaiian Surf X Wonder Struck. Powell's Iris Patch 1993.

GLITTER BIT (John Weiler, R. 1995). Sdlg. 90-13-1RE. SDB, 10" (25 cm), EML & RE, Glittering old gold; style arms old gold; beards uniform deep violet; slight sweet fragrance. 88-8-1: (85-47-7RE: (((70-95-3: (Brighteyes x Grace Note) x Gingerbread Man) x Chariots) x (76-1-1: (Ruby Contrast x Little Blackfoot) x (Bloodspot x 70-95-1))) x 84-47-6RE: (81-19-7: ((76-1-15 x ((Ruby Contrast x Little Blackfoot) x 74-3-1: (Cartwheel x 70-95))) x Pink Amber) x 81-42-1RE: ((((Yellow Wave x 70-95) x 74-3-1) x Chariots) x ((70-95-3 x Gingerbread Man) x Stockholm)))) X Little Blue Eyes. Friendship 1997.

GLITTERING PRIZE (John C. Taylor, R. 1991). Sdlg. OL 106-B. LA, 43" (110 cm), EM. S. purple (RHS 87C); F. purple (87A). John's Lucifer X L94-2: (Edith Fear x Valera). Rainbow Ridge 1991/92.

GLITTERING RAYS (Sterling Innerst, R. 1998). Sdlg. 4276-12. JI (6 F.), 36" (91 cm), M. Red purple with shocking blue rays extending from gold signal. Admetus X Diomedes. Draycott 1998.

GLORIA CORTEZ (Neil Bertinot, R. 1997). Sdlg. 92-1. LA, 40" (102 cm), E. S. maroon (Exotica 42-), lightly veined purple; style arms maroon; F. maroon (42), bright gold short steeple signal; ruffled; slight fragrance. 85-83: (Ann Chowning x Charlie's Michele) X 85-86, sib.

GLORIA TORRES (Bob Thomason, R. 1993). Sdlg. BT 91137G. TB, 33" (84 cm), ML. S. light violet; F. deep violet with rose wash, lighter at edge, white haft area around bright orange beard; ruffled; musky fragrance. Painted Plic X Violet Classic. Okie Iris 1999.

GLORIOUS DAY (Hooker Nichols, R. 1991). Sdlg. 8825A-1. IB, 18" (46 cm), ML & RE. S. medium dresden yellow; F. lighter, white blending below gold and white beard. Bridal Ballad X Sky Hooks. Hillcrest 1993.

GLORIOUS MORNING (Schreiner, R. 1999). Sdlg. BB 1993-1. TB, 38" (97 cm), ML. S. and

173

style arms barium yellow (RHS 10A); F. orchid lavender (75D) with barium yellow band and shoulders; beards yellow. S 345-1: (Color Splash x Metropolitan) X V 278-A, Lullaby of Spring sib. Schreiner 1999.

GLORIOUS REIGN (Jerry Hall, R. 1999). Sdlg. 93-01-B. TB, 44" (112 cm), ML. Lightly ruffled violet self, dark F. blush; beards yellow; lightly ruffled; slight sweet fragrance. Song of Norway X Chief Hematite.

GLORIOUS REVIEW (Ed Roberts, R. 1994). Sdlg. B-94-2. TB, 36" (91 cm), M. S. and style arms lemon yellow; F. lemon at haft, blending to soft lavender around light rose orchid marginal band; beards soft yellow; pronounced fragrance. Gypsy Woman X Condottiere. Ed Roberts 1996.

GLORY BALLET (Stephen Stevens, R. 1990). Sdlg. 84-2-30. TB, 34" (86 cm), E. Ruffled violet blue (RHS 92); beards violet blue, tipped yellow; pronounced fragrance. Titan's Glory X Ruffled Ballet. Hahn's Rainbow, Roderick Iris 1991.

#GLORY BE (Fran Smith, TB, R. 1954). Not introduced; name released.

GLORY BE (Melba Hamblen by Duane Meek, selector, R. 1995). Sdlg. H85-02B. TB, 34" (86 cm), ML. S. soft tan, faint mauve shading; style arms deep yellow; F. creamy yellow, deeper hafts; beards brick; ruffled. Glorious Sunshine X (Sophistication x Henna Accent). D & J Gardens 1995.

GLORY GLORY GLORY (Joe Saia, R. 1993). Sdlg. 88-16-22. TB, 36" (91 cm), ML. S. raspberry orchid, midrib darker; F. same, lighter around deep tangerine beard; pronounced sweet fragrance. Wet on Wet X Matinee Idol.

GLORY IN SNOW (Graeme Grosvenor, R. 1996). Sdlg. R2-W. TB, 36" (92 cm), M. White self; beards golden yellow; slight sweet fragrance. Silverado X Skyblaze. Rainbow Ridge 1996/97.

GLOWING CLOUDS (Darlene Pinegar, R. 1992). Sdlg. V-3-3. TB, 33" (84 cm), M. S. off-white; F. off-white with light greenish gold shoulders, light blue grey area by beard, blue line under old gold beard; lightly ruffled and laced; slight musky fragrance. Vanity X Song of Norway. Spanish Fork 1993.

GLOWING EYES (A. & D. Willott, R. 1993). Sdlg. 91-133. SDB, 12" (30 cm), M. S. full red violet; F. light red violet, deeper around beard, hafts amber brown; beards white to yellow in throat; lightly ruffled. Raspberry Whip X 84-35: ((Mister Roberts x Fresh Face) x Coral Wings). Willott 1993.

GLOWINGLY (Barry Blyth, R. 1996). Sdlg. D8-2. SDB, 12" (30 cm), VE-EM. Light to medium pure pink, F. with small white area around beard; beards white, tipped tangerine in throat. Smoky Trail X A44-2, Razoo sib. Tempo Two 1997/98.

GLOWING RUBIES (Opal Brown, R. 1996). Sdlg. 91-8E7. TB, 32" (81 cm), M. S. and style arms medium bronze red; F. medium reddish bronze, small blue area below bronze beard. Caliph X Indian Caper. Brown's Sunnyhill 1997.

GLOW OF HAPPINESS (Anna Mae Miller, R. 1994). Sdlg. 85.17.18. SIB, 30" (76 cm), M & RE. S. white with light yellow lines; style arms white, cream cast; F. light yellow (RHS 9C) with darker yellow lines, darkest in center and haft area. 79.16.1: (75.24.26: (67.8U: (Mountain Lake x unknown) x Jimmy's Gem) x Wing on Wing) X Butter and Sugar. Ensata Gardens 1994.

GNOM YELLOW (Udo & Rudolf Wilkeneit, R. 1996). Sdlg. EW 6/1/94. MDB, 7" (18 cm), M. Bright yellow; beards blue; slight fragrance. Parentage unknown.

GNU (Brad Kasperek, R. 1993). Sdlg. 89-40F. TB, 32" (81 cm), M. S. light lavender (RHS 76B) ground washed medium lavender (76A) and off-white (155C) with medium violet (83B) splashes; F. same, heavier medium violet purple on shoulders; beards burnt orange tipped medium violet; ruffled; slight fragrance. Maria Tormena X Eagle's Flight. Zebra 1994.

GNU AGAIN (Brad Kasperek, R. 1993). Sdlg. 89-40F (SPORT). TB, 32" (81 cm), M. S. medium violet (RHS 83B) with random off-white (155C) splashes; F. dark violet (83A) with random breaks and splashes of off-white; beards burnt orange tipped medium violet; ruffled; slight fragrance. Maria Tormena X Eagle's Flight. Zebra 1994.

GNU BLUES (Brad Kasperek, R. 1993). Sdlg. 89-56B. TB, 36" (91 cm), M. Lightly ruffled medium violet blue (97C) with random blotches of medium (93C) to dark (93B) blue violet; beards orange, tipped medium blue violet; pronounced fragrance. Painted Plic X Babbling Brook. Zebra 1994.

GNU GENERATION (Brad Kasperek, R. 1998). Sdlg. 95NB-85A. SDB, 10" (25 cm), ML. Clean light barium yellow (RHS 10A), streaked white (155A); beards lemon yellow; broken color pattern; lightly ruffled. Saharan Sun X 93ICE-19M: (Snow Cub x Invisible Ink).

GNU RAYZ (Brad Kasperek, R. 1996). Sdlg. 92B-N44S. IB, 26" (66 cm), EM. S. and style arms violet (RHS 83B); F. greenish yellow (1C) ground, veined and edged violet; beards lavender, hairs tipped orange tan; ruffled; slight fragrance. Tiger Honey X Flea Circus. Zebra 1997.

GNUS FLASH (Brad Kasperek, R. 1994). Sdlg. 91B-3A. TB, 38" (97 cm), E. S. light tan fading to grey (RHS 160C), slight violet on midribs streaked silver white (155C); style arms tan, violet lip; F. dark to medium violet (83A/C) highlighted with creamy white (155D) streaking; beards yellow, tipped violet; lightly ruffled; slight sweet fragrance. Glitz 'n Glitter X Tiger Honey. Zebra 1996.

GNUZ SPREAD (Brad Kasperek, R. 1996). Sdlg. 92R-29S. MDB, 7" (18 cm), M & RE. S. creamy butter yellow (RHS 13D); F. white (155A) overlaid butter yellow (14D) in center, edges paling to match S.; beards light orange, white at end, white ridge flattening into F. Baby Boom X Footlights. Zebra 1996.

GO (Barry Blyth, R. 1995). Sdlg. A6-2. SDB, 12-14" (30-36 cm), VE. S. mushroom pink; F. slightly deeper mushroom pink, rosy tan haft shading, small bright violet chevron below beard; beards bright violet, tangerine in throat. Merry Dance X Cupfull. Tempo Two 1995/96.

GOBBLE GOBBLE (Jack Worel, R. 1999). Sdlg. DDP. SPEC-X, 20" (51 cm), M. S. absent; F. (6) pinkish amethyst (pinker than RHS 84C), signal yellow, outer edge white veined amethyst violet; style arms (3) lighter pinkish amethyst violet; flat form, hollow stems. Dottie's Double X unknown siberian. Holly Lane 1999.

GO BETWEEN (Graeme Grosvenor, R. 1998). Sdlg. U87-1. TB, 35" (89 cm), M. Heavily ruffled white self; beards white, some yellow in throat; slight fragrance. Kuniko X Silverado. Rainbow Ridge 1998/99.

GOBLIN AUTUMN (Cloyd McCord, R. 1991). Sdlg. 82-66. TB, 38" (97 cm), L. Dark orange, dark reddish veining radiating from midline of F.; beards orange; spicy fragrance. 73-13: (Angie Quadros x Homecoming Queen) X Entourage. McCord 1991.

GOBLIN CITY (Suz Winspear, R. 1997). Sdlg. 90C2. SDB, 8½" (22 cm), M. Cream, F. veined and shaded olive green; beards yellow and white; spicy fragrance. Jeremy Brian X Fantasy Isle.

GOBLIN DANCER (Cloyd McCord, R. 1993). Sdlg. 85-33-3. TB, 36" (91 cm), M. S. orange; F. orange veined dark red; beards dark orange; sweet fragrance. Homecoming Queen X 73-13: (Angie Quadros x Homecoming Queen). McCord 1993.

GOBLIN'S SONG (Barry Blyth, R. 1993). Sdlg. W149-4. SPU, 30" (76 cm), M. Golden yellow self. Satinwood X self. Tempo Two 1993/94.

GODDESS OF BLUE (O. D. Niswonger, R. 1995). Sdlg. IB 57-91. IB, 25" (64 cm), M. S. deep blue, midrib white; style arms deep blue; F. deep blue plicata markings on white; beards tangerine, tipped white. Chubby Cheeks X Goddess. Cape Iris 1996.

GODDESS OF GREEN (O. D. Niswonger, R. 1995). Sdlg. IB 64-91. IB, 26" (66 cm), M. S. and F. chartreuse plicata markings on white ground; style arms chartreuse, beards pale blue, white base. Goddess X Chubby Cheeks. Cape Iris 1996.

GODDESS OF LUCK (O. D. Niswonger, R. 1995). Sdlg. IB 23-92. IB, 25" (64 cm), M. S. blue and yellow blend; style arms buff; F. with blue plicata markings, yellow outer rim, white central area; beards blue, hairs tipped bronze. Chubby Cheeks X --- probably Goddess. Cape Iris 1996.

GODDESS OF PINK (O. D. Niswonger, R. 1996). Sdlg. IB 16-94. IB, 20" (51 cm), M. S. pink, midrib flushed blue; style arms and F. pink; beards blue with tangerine base at end, remainder tangerine. Sky Blue Pink X Chanted. Cape Iris 1997.

GODFREY OWEN (Margaret Owen, TB, R. 1986). British Iris Society 1989.

GOD'S HANDIWORK (Joseph Ghio, R. 1990). Sdlg. 80-168-G5. TB, 34" (86 cm), M. S. white ground marbled medium blue; F. white ground with more pronounced medium blue marbling, white zonal area at hafts and around white beard; ruffled. Handiwork X Victoria Falls. Maryott 1990.

GODSPELL (George Sutton, R. 1999). Sdlg. H-336. TB, 37" (94 cm), ML. S. white, midrib shaded lavender; style arms lavender white; F. white; beards white, hairs tipped pale yellow; ruffled; slight sweet fragrance. Silverado X Winterscape.

GOGO BOY (Monique Dumas-Quesnel, R. 1992). Sdlg. 90-X-versata-1. SPEC-X (versata), 40½" (105 cm), M. S. light violet (RHS 94C), veined white; F. light violet (90D), veined, white lines near center, darker violet halo around dull yellow signal. VF-400, *versicolor* sdlg. X white *ensata* sdlg. Dominion Seed House, Horticlub 1998.

GOING BAROQUE (Peter Jackson, R. 1999). Sdlg. LAW4. LA, 45" (115 cm), EM. Smoky amethyst (RHS 86C), gold star signal on all petals; style arms buff, washed soft amethyst; lightly ruffled. All Agaze X Watch Out. Iris Acres 1999/2000.

GOING BONKERS (David Shannon, R. 1999). SDB, 11" (28 cm), EM. S. bright cherry orchid; style arms lemon cream; F. cherry orchid with large fuchsia ruby spot aging paler, leaving network of dark red lines; beards lilac blue. Forte X Peach Eyes. Shannon Gardens 1997.

GOING FOR GOLD (Peter Jackson, R. 1999). Sdlg. LDV1. LA, 41" (105 cm), M. Ruffled light gold, raised dark gold signal on all petals; style arms light gold, deeper gold center. Dancing Vogue X Valera. Iris Acres 1999/2000.

GOING HOME (Barry Blyth, R. 1997). Sdlg. D53-1. TB, 36" (92 cm), M. S. cream white, pink midrib infusion; F. cream white, light pink overlay, deeper pastel pink hafts and texture veining; beards bright tangerine; slight fragrance. Dragon's Fancy X Hostess Royale. Tempo Two 1997/98.

GOING SHOPPING (Graeme Grosvenor, R. 1999). Sdlg. U35-1. TB, 30" (76 cm), ML. Pink, F. with mauve pink hafts; beards red; slight fragrance. Bubble Up X Shopper's Holiday.

GOING SOUTH (John C. Taylor, R. 1993). Sdlg. RL 28-1. LA, 44" (110 cm), EM. S. cream flushed pink, veined mustard; F. darker cream flushed pink, heavily veined mustard, greenish line signal. Our Parris X Margaret Lee. Rainbow Ridge 1993/94.

GOLD AND WINE (Leo Barnard, R. 1995). Sdlg. 91L-14A. SDB, 10-12" (25-31 cm), EM. S. pure yellow (RHS 12B); style arms gold; F. burgundy, pure yellow rim, gold at hafts, slight veining on hafts near beard; beards gold, bushy; slight sweet fragrance. Little Buccaneer X Ritz. Paradise Iris 1995.

GOLD BAR (Stan Dexter by Marie Ingersoll, R. 1992). Sdlg. 9-85-46. TB, 30" (76 cm), M. Dark reddish purple, F. with brown spot near throat; beards orange. Garnet Sport X Maraschino. Ingersoll's Iris 1993.

GOLD BEACH (Vernon Wood, R. 1997). Sdlg. 93-106. TB, 34" (86 cm), ML. Deep yellow self with slight mustard tone (near RHS 7A); beards orange tangerine. Fiesta Song X Stratagem. Stockton 1998.

GOLD CAP (Stan Dexter by Marie Ingersoll, R. 1991). Sdlg. 16-84-10-3. TB, 34" (86 cm), EM. S. deep gold; F. deep red maroon, white hafts with gold and maroon hash marks; beards gold. Caramba X 81-23A: (69-26 x Flamenco). Ingersoll's Iris 1992.

GOLDCINDA (Barry Blyth, R. 1995). Sdlg. A70-5. TB, 36-38" (91-97 cm), ML. Vibrant lemon yellow, large white outpouring in F.; beards bright lemon yellow; ruffled; foliage very dark-based; slight spicy fragrance. Liqueur Creme X Taffeta Bow. Tempo Two 1995/96.

GOLD CLASS (Cloyd McCord, R. 1992). Sdlg. 66-2. TB, 40" (102 cm), M. Ruffled and laced pale yellow, light yellow area around light orange beards. Homecoming Queen X 73-13: (Angie Quadros x Homecoming Queen).

GOLD COPPER CURLS (Barbara Wight, R. 1996). Sdlg. 93-9. IB, 17" (43 cm), EM. S. spanish orange (RHS 26C); style arms bright orange; F. spanish orange, dark tan hafts; beards tangerine; ruffled; pronounced spicy fragrance. Chickasaw Sue X Mandarin Jewel. Wight's Iris 1997.

GOLD DOUBLOONS (Donna Aldridge, R. 1998). SPEC (*pseudacorus*), 36-40" (90-101 cm), EML. Deep clear yellow (RHS 6A) self, little or no signal marking; F. large, round. Parentage and origin unknown.

GOLD DRAGON (Leo Barnard, R. 1996). Sdlg. L-91-77-B-1. TB, 38" (97 cm), ML. Ruffled golden yellow with lighter wash; beards white, tipped dark gold in throat, ending in prominent long light brown horn; slight sweet fragrance. Borderline X Twice Thrilling. Paradise Iris 1996.

GOLD DUSTED (B. Charles Jenkins, R. 1990). Sdlg. B11-4D. CA, 14" (36 cm), M. Purple ground speckled gold. San Gregorio sib X Californian. Shepard Iris 1990.

GOLDEN ALIEN (Geraldine Couturier, R. 1995). Sdlg. GC-1-6-93. TB, 31" (79 cm), ML. Gold self, small lighter spot at end of beard; beards golden orange, with large ruffled gold flounce (sometimes spoon or white horn); ruffled; slight sweet fragrance. Spooned Blaze X unknown. Sunnyridge 1996.

GOLDEN ANGEL (Donald Spoon, R. 1996). Sdlg. 93-20. TB, 32" (81 cm), E. Brilliant yellow gold, F. with lighter center; beards deep yellow gold, yellow horn; ruffled, laced; slight fragrance. Dazzling Lora X Jester.

GOLDEN BLOOM (Cloyd McCord, R. 1996). Sdlg. 66-94. TB, 36" (91 cm), M. Rich gold self; beards pale yellow; sweet fragrance. Orange Fall X McCord's Gold. McCord 1996.

GOLDEN EDGE (Currier McEwen, R. 1991). Sdlg. T(7)83/107(3). SIB (tet.), 30" (75 cm), EM. S. medium violet blue (RHS 89C); style arms violet blue (blended 86B and 89A); F. darker velvety violet blue, veining (9C) wire edge, rich yellow (9B) signal shading lighter (9D) at edge; ruffled. T(2)80/260(2): ((Ruffled Velvet x Tealwood) x unknown) X T(6)78/47(W-1): (Dear Dianne x Happy Event sib). Pope's Perennials, Seaways 1992.

GOLDENE HOCHZEIT (Frank Kathe, R. 1998). Sdlg. 114/1-91. IB, 18" (46 cm), M. S. and style arms golden yellow; F. golden yellow, brown haft veining, small white center stripe; beards golden yellow. Little Amigo X Cimarron Strip. Kathe 1999.

GOLDENES TOR (Harald Moos, R. 1991). Sdlg. 84/459C. TB, 31½" (80 cm), M. Orange yellow; beards orange. Flaming Day X (Flaming Light x Fresno Calypso). Schoeppinger 1993.

GOLDEN FASAN (Ladislav Muska, R. 1999). Sdlg. 99-KMHS-05. TB, 35" (89 cm), M. S. deep cream, tinted gold; style arms cream and gold; F. cream white, wide gold rim; beards light yellow, long bristly gold flounce; ruffled, laced; sweet fragrance. ((Krimhilde x Mys Horn) x Sky Hooks) X Decory Win.

GOLDEN FROLIC (Opal Brown, R. 1990). Sdlg. 82-18A. TB, 28-30" (71-76 cm), ML. S. canary yellow (RHS 9B); F. white, canary yellow hafts and edge; beards orange, wide; frilled, laced. Cascade Morn X 78-3B5: (Old Flame x ((Grandiflora x Arctic Flame) x Buffy)). Brown's Sunnyhill 1990.

GOLDEN GLOBE (George Sutton, R. 1998). Sdlg. F-232. SDB, 12" (31 cm), VE-E & RE. S. near indian yellow (RHS 17C) dotted pale purple; style arms indian yellow; F. white, 1" indian yellow border; beards white, hairs tipped indian yellow; ruffled; slight sweet fragrance. Le Flirt X Auroralita. Sutton 1999.

GOLDEN GLOVES (Perry Dyer, R. 1999). Sdlg. 94-35A. SDB, 11" (28 cm), L-VL & RE. Full golden yellow self; beards deep golden orange, bushy. Lemon Rings X Bright Chic.

GOLDEN GUSTO (Gene Gaddie, IB, R. 1989). Gaddies' Gardens 1990.

GOLDEN ICON (Franklin Carr, TB, R. 1986). Carr 1990.

GOLDEN IDOL (Francis Rogers, TB, R. 1989). Meadowbrook 1991.

GOLDEN IMMORTAL (George Sutton, R. 1996). Sdlg. G-63-RE. TB, 37" (94 cm), EML & RE. S. and style arms barium yellow (RHS 10A); F. naples yellow (11A), white area near beard, 1/4" bronze gold centerline; beards cadmium orange (23A), white base; ruffled, edges serrate; pronounced musky fragrance. Orange Popsicle X Zurich. Sutton 1997.

GOLDEN KITTY (Floyd Dyer, R. 1996). Sdlg. D-54-90-B. BB, 26" (66 cm), M. S. yellow; F. yellow with white blended overlay; beards dark yellow. D-81-87-B: (D87-71-T: (((Riptide x Gypsy Baron) x Dotted Swiss) x (Helen Louise x W. F. Brown 59-3)) x Orange Icing) X D-36-87-B: (Gala Madrid x Friedline 72-100). Dyer's Garden 1996.

GOLDEN LOCKS (Lynda Miller, R. 1993). Sdlg. 1188D. TB, 29" (84 cm), EM. S. deep canary yellow; F. deep canary yellow at hafts and signal, blending to cream toward yellow edge; beards yellow orange; slight musky fragrance. At Dawn X Blazing Light. Miller's Manor 1994.

GOLDEN LOVE (Cloyd McCord, R. 1997). Sdlg. 702-6. TB, 36" (91 cm), M. S. and style arms gold; F. gold, lower portion trimmed tan; beards yellow; sweet fragrance. McCord's Gold X Tannish Anna. McCord 1997.

GOLDEN MISTRESS (Darlene Pinegar, R. 1990). Sdlg. TG-1-1. TB, 31" (79 cm), M. S. bright yellow; F. yellow gold with darker gold sheen; beards orange, 3/4" smooth horn; lightly ruffled, crinkled; slight sweet fragrance. Tut's Gold X Moon Mistress. Spanish Fork 1991.

GOLDEN OLDIE (Mary Dunn, R. 1994). Sdlg. 161-1. LA, 35" (89 cm), M. S. light yellow with texture veining and slight mauve stain; F. ruffled light yellow, texture veined, deeper yellow signal area. Sun Fury X L85-2: (Fantastic x Hager L40: (Delta King x Acadian)). Bay View 1994.

GOLDEN PONDS (Janet Hutchinson, R. 1995). Sdlg. (BxVaLa1)Dz. LA, 41" (105 cm), ML. S. pale yellow, deeper edge, irregular lemon tip blotching, yellow veining and centerline; style arms yellow; F. rich lemon yellow, paler linear edge, heavy green and yellow veining, signal small, strong green over yellow, yellow centerline to fall tip; edges serrate; ruffled; slight sweet fragrance. (Buxom x Valera) X Danza.

GOLDEN RIAL (Allan Ensminger, R. 1998). Sdlg. 92-42. TB, 31" (79 cm), ML. Saffron yellow (HCC 7/2) self; beards saffron yellow. Bronzette Star X 89-21: (87-40: (182-29: (Striped Britches x (((64-12 x Stepping Out) x (68-21 x sib)) x Painted Plic)) x Loop the Loop) x 86-26: (Michel C-120-2: (Bride's Halo x Joyce Terry) x (Ruffled Surprise x Morning Sunshine))). Varigay 1998.

GOLDEN ROAD (George Sutton, R. 1996). Sdlg. C-95. TB, 36" (91 cm), VE-EM & RE. S. blended lemon yellow (RHS 13A) to aureolin (12B); style arms lemon yellow; F. aureolin, gold veining and 1/4" center band; beards gold; ruffled. Orange Popsicle X Lemon Custard. Sutton 1997.

GOLDEN SCISSORTAILS (Robert Annand, R. 1997). Sdlg. 91-100APCl. CA, 15" (38 cm), ML. Golden yellow, F. with brown veined wash, yellow gold signal; S. tips cut to form thin central segment. CA hybrid, parentage unknown, X *I. hartwegii*.

GOLDEN SCROLL (Chet Tompkins, R. 1994). Sdlg. 85-7. TB, 39" (99 cm), EM. Ruffled and laced golden yellow self. ((Truly Blessed x Genesis) x Stately Mansions) X Genesis. Fleur de Lis 1994.

GOLDEN SCULPTURE (Lois Rich, R. 1990). Sdlg. R77-112C. AB (OGB), 36" (91 cm), E. Light yellow, F. with gilt film, sketchy signal; beards deep orange yellow. Yellow aril sdlg. R71-117G X White Lightning. Aril Society, Melrose 1990.

GOLDEN SLUMBERS (Leslie Donnell, R. 1998). Sdlg. 96-5-2. TB, 37" (94 cm), E. Buttercup yellow (RHS 15A) self; beards buttercup yellow. Hampton Gold X Cherry Cerise.

GOLDEN TIGER (John Wight, R. 1990). Sdlg. 79-1B. SPU, 42" (107 cm), M. Golden green with prominent light maroon veining. Char-True X Forty Carats. Wight's Iris 1991.

GOLDEN VIOLET (John Weiler, R. 1993). Sdlg. 87-48-1RE. SDB, 9" (23 cm), ML & RE. S. golden bronze, F. slightly darker; beards dark violet. Sib to Mini Might. Rialto 1993.

GOLDEN WEDDING LACE (Donald Sorensen, R. 1995). Sdlg. S-84-10-9. TB, 32" (81 cm), M. S. yellow gold (RHS 13B); style arms lighter (13C): F. yellow gold with 1" diameter white area below darker yellow gold (13A) beard; heavily ruffled and laced; slight musky fragrance. Burning Desire X Laced Cotton. Birchwood 1997.

GOLDFINGER (George Sutton, R. 1996). Sdlg. F-49. TB, 35" (89 cm), EML. S. mimosa yellow (RHS 8B) edged dark lemon (13A); style arms golden yellow (14A); F. white, edged dark lemon, golden yellow hafts; beards bright spectrum orange, with mimosa yellow to dark lemon flounce; ruffled, lightly laced; slight spicy fragrance. Candlegleam X Sky Hooks. Sutton 1997.

GOLD FROSTING (O. D. Niswonger, R. 1992). Sdlg. 39-85. TB, 33" (84 cm), M. S. white with some yellow infusion; F. gold; beards yellow. 27-82: (Misty Moonscape x Sun Dappled) X Sunshine Song. Cape Iris 1992.

GOLDIE'S GLOW (Polly Black, R. 1995). Sdlg. WG7-9-GR10. TB, 34" (86 cm), E. Ruffled deep gold, F. with few brown veins and white lines near deep orange beard. Joyce Terry X Plum Gleam. Polly Black 1995.

GOLDIE THE PIRATE (Barry Blyth, R. 1996). Sdlg. A63-A. TB, 36" (91 cm), EM. Pure gold self; beards slightly deeper pure gold. Dance Man X Rembrandt Magic. Tempo Two 1996/97.

GOLDKIST (Paul Black, R. 1993). Sdlg. 89162A. TB, 36" (91 cm), M. S. white; style arms white with slight gold tips; F. white, 3/4" wide yellow gold hafts, purple striations between haft edge and bright yellow gold beard; ruffled. 85150A: ((Coffee House x Hombre) x (Old Flame x Instant Charm)) X 8774A: (Porcelain Ballet x (Tequila Sunrise sib x Entourage)). Mid-America 1993.

GOLD MARGARITA (Gustav Seligmann by Sharon McAllister, R. 1992). Sdlg. 84-22-14. AB (OGB), 28" (72 cm), EM. S. icy blue white; F. creamy golden yellow (near RHS 161C), signal area dotted and veined rust; beards mustard, tipped rust. Martha Mia X Moon Dust. McAllister 1992.

GOLDMARIE (Siegmar Goerbitz, R. 1990). Sdlg. 8327B9. TB, 41" (105 cm), M. Golden yellow, F. with lighter center; lightly waved to ruffled. (Joyce Terry x Ming Dynasty) X Gold Galore. Schoeppinger 1990.

GOLD NIMBUS (Eleanor Zimmerly, R. 1993). CA, 15" (38 cm), M. Ruffled yellow self; slight spicy fragrance. *I. douglasiana*, open pollination.

GOLD 'N ROSE (Joseph Hoage, R. 1993). Sdlg. H86-15. TB, 34" (86 cm), ML. Deep rose with gold area around orange beards. Mulled Wine X Silver Flow. Long 1994.

GOLD NUGGET TREE (Henry Danielson by Luella Danielson, R. 1990). Sdlg. HD-8. IB, 16" (41 cm), M. S. white, prominent bright gold veining, gold midrib; style arms gold; F. bright gold veined darker, soft cream white lines around beard; beards white, tipped bright gold. Heart Thumper X Sunshine Boy. Pleasure Iris 1991.

GOLD RETRIEVER (Raymond Smith, R. 1992). Sdlg. 7711GR. TB, 28" (71 cm), M. S. yellow (Munsell 2.5Y 7/10); F. vivid yellow (2.5Y 8/12), edged strong yellow (2.5Y 7/10); beards orange. 7316B: ((6629G x Laced Duet) x (D19AF x Memphis Lass)) X 2571DR: (Leora Kate x (Pin Up Girl x Gibson Girl sdlg.)).

GOLD SPECULATOR (Bryce Williamson, R. 1993). Sdlg. A-18-A. TB, 34" (86 cm), EM. Dark sunfast yellow gold, self beards; slight fragrance. Gold Galore X Speculator. Pacific Coast Hybridizers 1993.

GOLD VELOCITY (Bernard Hamner by Shepard Iris Garden, R. 1994). Sdlg. 89-15. BB, 24" (61 cm), M. S. rich mustard gold; F. darker mustard gold overlaid cinnamon, darker veining extending to edge, light area veined dark cinnamon around gold beard; ruffled. Wild Jasmine X (Baja Bandit x Bronco Brown). Hamner Iris, Shepard Iris 1994.

GOLUB MIRA (V. & N. Gordodelovy, R. 1995). Sdlg. 22. TB, 32" (80 cm), E. White self; beards yellow. Parentage unknown. Gordodelovy 1995.

GOLUBOGLAZAYA BLONDINKA (Nataliya Khimina, R. 1997). Sdlg. 7. SDB, 14" (35 cm), EM.

S. yellow; F. yellow, large blue spot; beards blue; slight fragrance. Chanted X Chubby Cheeks. Khimina 1998.

GOLUBOY BLIUZ (Viktor Sheviakov, R. 1995). Sdlg. 22S 15B. BB, 24" (60 cm), ML. Heavily ruffled blue self, light violet cast; beards white. Matinata X Rippling Waters. Sheviakov 1997.

GOLUBOY CHARODEY (Piotr Hattenberger, R. 1996). SDB, 13" (32 cm), E. Vivid sky blue self; beards blue, slight fragrance. Chemically induced sport of unknown blue tall bearded. Hattenberger 1993.

GONE FISSION (Barry Blyth, R. 1995). Sdlg. A166-5. TB, 36" (91 cm), ML. S. light burgundy; F. plush deep burgundy, 1/8" light burgundy margin; beards mustard gold; slight sweet fragrance. Town Gossip X Supreme Sultan. Tempo Two 1995/96

GOOD BEHAVIOR (Chet Tompkins, R. 1993). Sdlg. 89-36. TB, 38" (97 cm), ML. S. ivory white; F. ivory white ground with precise edge of blended fuchsia and strawberry rose; beards mustard, tipped lilac tan. Added Elegance X (Heather Diane x Hawaiian Halo). Fleur de Lis 1993.

GOODBYE GIRL (Schreiner, R. 1995). Sdlg. AA 1710-1. TB, 36" (91 cm), M. Pink (RHS 49C) self; beards tangerine. My Girl X V 476-1: (Carved Angel x Paradise). Schreiner 1995.

GOOD DAY (Kirk Strawn, R. 1993). Sdlg. B-1985. LA, 32" (81 cm), ML. S. yellow (RHS 7B); style arms yellow (8A); F. slightly darker yellow (9A), orange (17B) signal. Mighty Rich X President Hedley. Bois d'Arc 1996.

GOOD DAY SUNSHINE (Larry Lauer, R. 1998). Sdlg. 92-212. IB, 16" (41 cm), E & RE. S. and style arms yellow; F. white, yellow edge and darker yellow haft markings; beard white, tipped yellow; pronounced sweet fragrance. Eggnog X Rabbit's Foot. Lauer's Flowers 1998.

GOOD DOCTOR (Joseph Mertzweiller, R. 1990). Sdlg. 78-89. LA, 38-40" (97-102 cm), E. S. pure white; style arms green; F. pure white, strong green brown veining, green signal; musky fragrance. Ashley Michelle X Clara Goula. Cordon Bleu 1993.

GOOD HEAVENS (Mary Dunn, R. 1997). Sdlg. L 228-2. LA, 36" (91 cm), M. Smooth lavender blue, small yellow signal; style arms greenish white. Parentage unknown. Bay View 1997.

GOOD HUMOR (George Shoop by Keith Keppel, R. 1998). Sdlg. 91-27. TB, 38" (97 cm), ML. S. corinth purple (M&P 46-J-2) blended onionskin (11-A-7); style arms golden apricot tan (11-H-7), slight corinth purple flush; F. light apricot (10-F-7), flushed and overlaid greyed rose (45-G-1); beards solid mandarin red (2-F-12); ruffled; slight musky sweet fragrance. 87-26: (84-19: ((Orange Burst x Orange Surprise) x (Dream Affair x Blazing Light)) x 85-25: ((Playgirl x 76-17 fuchsia rose: ((Dutch Magic x ((Ole x Gypsy Rings sib) x unknown)) x pink sdlg.)) x Blushing Duchess)) X sib. Keppel 1999.

GOOD LOOKING (Schreiner, R. 1995). Sdlg. CC 411-A. TB, 37" (94 cm), EM. Dusky lavender (RHS 86C) self; beards dusky lavender. Sultry Mood X V 495-A: (Visual Arts x (G 525-6: (((Crinkled Beauty x P 309-1) x Lilac Supreme) x ((Amethyst Flame x Silvertone) x Lilac Supreme)) x Fond Wish)). Schreiner 1995.

GOOD LUCK CHARM (Lilly Gartman by Joseph Ghio, R. 1999). Sdlg. 89-1T. TB, 36" (91 cm), M. S. pale yellow, violet midrib flush; F. violet, thin yellow halo; beards bronze. Edith Wolford X Critic's Choice. Roris 1999.

GOODNIGHT MOON (Schreiner, R. 1995). Sdlg. BB 1055-1. TB, 39" (99 cm), M. Lemon yellow (RHS 7C) self; beards golden yellow. Idol's Dream X Precious Moments. Schreiner 1995.

GOOD SHIP LOLLIPOP (James McWhirter by Abram Feuerstein, R. 1999). TB, 34" (86 cm), EM. S. orange beige; F. beige orange, raspberry tan rim; beards tangerine; lightly ruffled; slight sweet fragrance. Citoyen X Life of Riley. Stockton 1998.

GOOD VIBES (John C. Taylor, R. 1990). Sdlg. OL 108-1. LA, 51" (130 cm), M. Fluted violet (RHS 88C), yellow signal on all petals; cartwheel form. Lucile Holley X Dazzling Star. Rainbow Ridge 1990/91.

GOOD VIBRATIONS (Schreiner, R. 1997). Sdlg. DD 753-A. TB, 37" (94 cm), ML. S. and style arms tangerine orange (RHS 24B); F. white (155D), 1/2" tangerine orange marginal band; beards tangerine, white at end; ruffled; slight fragrance. W 752-2: (S 656-1: ((Pinafore Pink x (Oraglow x unknown)) x (Something Else x (((R 16-2 x Celestial Glory) x Flaming Star) x Gold Trimmings))) x N 720-1: (((Fairy Fable x Christmas Time) x Party Look) x Flaming Light) X Y 716-A: (R 513-7: (Fiery Chariot x (((((June Meredith x Lynn Hall) x Fairy Fable) x Esther Fay) x Bright Butterfly) x Flaming Day)) x S 656-1). Schreiner 1997.

GOODWILL MESSENGER (Richard Ernst, R. 1990). Sdlg. 84x17. TB, 35" (89 cm), ML. S. yellow, edged cream; F. creamy white, yellow reverse; beards orange, yellow in throat; lightly ruffled. Tulip Festival X unknown. Cooley 1990.

GORBY'S RED (John Durrance, R. 1992). Sdlg. D90-1. TB, 35" (89 cm), EM. Mahogany red self; beards rust gold. Probably -- Garnet Velvet X Mulled Wine. Long 1992.

GORDOLA (Joseph Ghio, R. 1996). Sdlg. PE-172-J2. CA, 13" (33 cm), L. Pure gold self. PG-153G: (PI-211J: (Black Eye sib x (Los Padres x (Elberta Peach sib x San Tomas sib))) x PI-205-M2: ((Ignacio sib x (Rincon sib x Reflecting Pool)) x (((Big Wheel x (Pacific Moon x California Native)) x Montara sib) x San Gregorio))) X Spanish Don. Bay View 1996.

GORDONVILLE CREAM (O. D. Niswonger, R. 1994). Sdlg. ps 1-87. SPEC (*pseudacorus*), 42" (107 cm), M. Light chartreuse, F. with slight burgundy eye-zone. *I. pseudacorus* chartreuse X unknown. Cape Iris 1995.

GORDONVILLE WHITE (O. D. Niswonger, R. 1994). Sdlg. ps 1-91. SPEC (*pseudacorus*), 40" (102 cm), M. White, F. with slight maroon eye-zone. Horinaka white *I. pseudacorus* sdlg. X unknown. Cape Iris 1995.

GORE MOYO (Piotr Hattenberger, R. 1996). SDB, 9" (23 cm), VE. Black self; beards black; slight fragrance. Chemically induced sport of Captain Gallant. Hattenberger 1994.

GORING ACE (Peter Maynard, R. 1990). Sdlg. PM/3. CA, 10" (25 cm), M. Gold ground with crimson veining and solid crimson edge. Parentage unknown. V. H. Humphrey 1993.

GORING SUNRISE (Peter Maynard, R. 1999). Sdlg. GBS 5/97. CA, 18" (45 cm), M. S. light amber yellow (RHS 18A/B); style arms amber yellow (18B); F. orange, veined, light amber yellow edge and signal. Colchicine treated sdlg. Goring Ace X self.

GORNAYA VERSHINA (V. & N. Gordodelovy, R. 1995). Sdlg. 82. TB, 30" (75 cm), E. S. white, tinted pink, violet basal dotting; F. white, tinted pink, brown haft striations; beards red. Parentage unknown. Gordodelovy 1988.

GOSAN-NO-TAKARA (Society for Japanese Irises, R. 1992). JI, 18" (46 cm), ML. White, edged red purple, yellow gold signal; style arms white with some red purple marking; blooms with 3, 4, 5 or 6 petals. Parentage and hybridizer unknown; introduced in Japan prior to 1940.

GOSH (Barry Blyth, R. 1993). Sdlg. A44-9. SDB, 14" (36 cm), EM. Pink with bluish cast, F. with few brown lines at hafts and bluish area around beard; beards tangerine tipped lavender on outer 1/4"; slight sweet fragrance. (Cupid's Cup x Yipee sib) X Chanted. Tempo Two 1993/94.

GOSHO ASOBI (Yoshino-En by Society for Japanese Irises, R. 1993). JI (3 F.), 36" (91 cm), M. S. white with heavy pinkish lilac infusion toward edge; style arms white, feathered crests pinkish lilac; F. white center and veins, with heavy pinkish sanding around border, yellow signal. Parentage unknown. Yoshino-En prior to 1930.

GOSPEL LIGHT (Eugene Hunt by Sharon McAllister, R. 1992). Sdlg. JR-HC-3. AB (OGB), 28" (72 cm), EM. S. naples yellow (near RHS 11B); F. slightly darker (near 11A), grey purple signal; beards gold, tipped tangerine in throat. Jean Ralls X Hallelujah Chorus. McAllister 1992.

GOSSAMER GOWN (Chet Tompkins, R. 1996). Sdlg. 93-44A. TB, 37" (94 cm), ML. S. and style arms flesh overtoned orchid, pink and copper; F. deep colonial ivory blended flesh and pallid orchid pink, 1/2" flesh-tinted copper border; beards flesh-tinted white. ((Summer Serenade x Lovely Jan) x ((Summer Serenade x (Ming Porcelain sib x Summer Serenade)) x Summer Serenade)) X ((Royal Gold x Tinsel Town) x Ovation). Fleur de Lis 1997.

GOSTINETS (Viacheslav Gavrilin, R. 1998). Sdlg. 7-3-2-94. TB, 33" (85 cm), M. Ruffled and laced pinkish lavender, S. yellowish at base, F. lighter, hafts yellow, narrow indistinct light yellow edge; beards lavender, light lilac at end, hairs tipped yellow; slight fragrance. Pearl Chiffon X Rustic Cedar. Gavrilin 1999.

GOTHAM CITY (Larry Lauer, R. 1994). Sdlg. 87-7-1. TB, 34" (86 cm), M. Smoky garnet self; beards garnet; slight fragrance. Chocolate Shake X Cinnamon. Stockton 1994.

GOTHIC (Monty Byers, R. 1990). Sdlg. E49-1. TB, 36" (91 cm), L. S. tan; F. pale orchid grey, tan hafts and blended tannish edge; beards light violet base tipped bright yellow, violet horn; ruffled, sometimes lightly laced; pronounced sweet fragrance. Moonlit X Visual Arts. Moonshine 1991.

GOTHIC CATHEDRAL (A. & D. Cadd, R. 1999). Sdlg. 3-91-4. TB, 36-38" (91-97 cm), L. S. golden brown, darker center with yellow green midrib, tiny golden border; style arms golden yellow; F. golden brown, shoulders and edges darker, tiny golden border, neon violet center wash, small white dart at end of deep yellow beard; pronounced sweet fragrance. Baja Bandit X Spanish Tile.

GOTTA LOTTA BODDA (Tom Burseen, TB, R. 1989). T.B.'s Place 1990.

GOT THE BLUES (Barry Blyth, R. 1996). Sdlg. A77-2. TB, 35" (89 cm), ML. S. silvery pastel blue, midrib slightly deeper; F. violet to red violet, paling slightly toward edge; beards blue, hairs tipped lemon in throat. Silverado X Blues Brothers. Tempo Two 1996/97.

GOURMET (Mary Dunn, LA, R. 1989). Bay View 1990.

GOWNED IN VELVET (Beryl Pederick, R. 1994). Sdlg. 12. TB, 34" (86 cm), E. Pansy violet (HCC 033/1) veined darker, F. with brown hafts; beards deep gold to orange; slight fragrance. Lady Vera X Bluebird Wine.

GOYA (Monique Dumas-Quesnel, R. 1992). Sdlg. 89-PV-WY-SLO-0. SPEC (*versicolor*), 27½" (70 cm), M. S. lilac (RHS 85A); F. violet (88A), large white central area and violet veining, yellow signal; slight spicy fragrance. 87-SLO-VG-046, *versicolor* sdlg., X unknown.

GRACEFUL DANCER (Donald Delmez, R. 1995). Sdlg. DTBVO-WRA-SA-WVO. JI (6 F.), 38" (97 cm), M. Violet with blue undertone; yellow green signals surrounded by white halo and rays extending to wide darker violet rim; style arms white, tipped violet; ruffled. Parentage unknown. Delmez Gardens 1995.

GRACEFUL GOLD (Graeme Grosvenor, R. 1993). Sdlg. R27-2. TB, 38" (97 cm), EM. Ruffled yellow self; beards orange red. Snow Cream X First Movement. Rainbow Ridge 1993/94.

GRACE WHITTEMORE (Gerald Richardson, R. 1997). Sdlg. 91-70-1. TB, 32" (81 cm), L. S. light golden yellow, cream white reverse; style arms cream, edged yellow; F. cream white, 3/16" yellow edge, yellow reverse; beards gold to orange; heavily ruffled; slight fragrance. Irene Frances X Wide Hips. Rainbow's End 1998.

GRAF (Sergey Loktev, R. 1999). Sdlg. 93-R13-9D. TB, 32" (80 cm), ML. S. blended grey lilac; style arms yellow, midrib lilac, crests grey lilac; F. lilac, dark lilac claret spots below white to cream yellow hafts marked wine brown; beards dark yellow, end light yellow with white base. Arc Above X Siva Siva. Loktev 1999.

GRAFFITI (Ladislav Muska, R. 1996). Sdlg. QCCA-08A. TB, 36" (91 cm), ML. Tannish maroon plicata; beards orange; heavily ruffled, laced, sweet fragrance. Queen in Calico X (Calicoball x Queen in Calico). Muska 1996.

GRAFINIA UVAROVA (Olga Drobnich, R. 1996). TB, 32" (80 cm), M. S. light lilac, deeper shading; F. dark lilac, shaded violet, yellowish edge; beards dark yellow; pronounced fragrance. Rippling Waters X unknown.

GRAFT (Harald Moos, R. 1990). Sdlg. 86/6012A. TB, 35" (90 cm), M. Heavily ruffled light violet; beards white yellow. Pretty Lady X Laced Cotton. Moos 1991.

GRAF TOLSTOY (V. &. N. Gordodelovy, R. 1995). Sdlg. 11. TB, 35" (90 cm), M. S. brown, tinted rose; style arms yellow; F. brown edges, lavender center, white haft striations; beards light brown. Parentage unknown. Gordodelovy 1976.

GRANATOVOYE OZHERELIYE (Nina Miroshnichenko, R. 1996). TB, 33" (85 cm), M. Garnet red violet, hafts brownish; style arms greenish yellow, crests violet; beards lilac, bronze yellow at end; slight sweet fragrance. Parentage unknown. Miroshnichenko 1989.

GRAND AMIRAL (Cayeux, R. 1999). Sdlg. 89212 B. TB, 35" (90 cm), ML. Medium blue violet, F. with white centerline; beards sky blue. Memphis Blues X Sapphire Hills.

GRAND BIJOU (John Gass, R. 1996). Sdlg. G-60-83. TB, 38" (97 cm), M. S. and style arms tan yellow; F. reddish rose; beards tan yellow; slight fragrance. Song of Shalimar X Fiction. Rainbow Chasers 1997.

GRAND ISLAND (Anna Rettig, R. 1995). Sdlg. AR-099. JI (3 F.), 35" (89 cm), M. Slightly ruffled pure white, F. with deep yellow signal radiating into five central veins. Gift of Heaven X unknown. A & M Perennials 1995.

GRANDMA AMANDA (Maj Ohrstrom, R. 1999). SDB, 13" (33 cm), E & RE. Purple, F. with white stripes and dark veins inside; beards white, tipped blue. Origin unknown; found on stone wall in Ostergotland, Sweden, 1960.

GRANDMA APPLE PIE (Sandra Underwood by Louise Smith, R. 1991). Sdlg. 86-100. TB, 33" (84 cm), EM. Very pale yellow; beards dark yellow; slight sweet fragrance. Parentage unknown.

GRANDMA'S BLOOMERS (Darlene Pinegar, R. 1993). Sdlg. SKK-1. TB, 28" (71 cm), EM. S. apricot ground almost solidly overlaid greyed medium red purple; style arms medium greyed red purple; F. medium apricot ground, shoulders and edge greyed medium red purple, white area around beards, red purple line at base of beard; beards burnt orange, tipped white; ruffled; pronounced sweet fragrance. Skookumchuck X Daredevil. Spanish Fork 1994.

GRANDMA'S BONNET (Eric & Bob Tankesley-Clarke, R. 1999). Sdlg. 393A. SDB, 11" (28 cm), M. Ruffled medium blue self; beards blue white; slight sweet fragrance. Frosty Atom X Sky Drops. Adamgrove 1997.

GRANDMA'S LOVE (Shannon Melliere, R. 1999). Sdlg. 96-2-1. TB, 29" (74 cm), L. Deep purple self; beards orange; ruffled, flared. Senior Prom X Navy Strut.

GRAND PRAISE (H. C. Mohr, R. 1992). Sdlg. M-4-1. TB, 36" (91 cm), M. S. apricot orange flushed peach pink; F. cream white, edged apricot orange, hafts flushed peach; beards tangerine red; slight musky fragrance. Orange Float X Orange Wave. Pacific Coast Hybridizers 1992.

GRAND RESERVE (Chet Tompkins, R. 1997). Sdlg. 93-33. TB, 39" (99 cm), EML. Ruffled royal violet; beards pale to medium violet. ((inv. Untamed x (Pizzazz x Rumbling Thunder)) x ((Matinee Idol x Masada) x (Syncopation x Masada))) X (Night Lightning x Thriller). Fleur de Lis 1997.

GRAND STYLE (Monty Byers by Phyllis Dickey, R. 1996). Sdlg. G59-5. TB, 29" (74 cm), M. S. medium dark purple, veined white; F. white ground, medium dark purple edging, dotting and median line; beards mustard, large purple horn; ruffled. Everything Plus X Egyptian. Misty Hill 1996.

GRANNY'S GRANITE POT (Sharon McAllister, R. 1995). Sdlg. 90-29-18. AB (OGB-), 28" (71 cm), M. S. purple violet (near RHS 80A) with splashed white variegation; style arms purple violet; F. matching S. on outer half, inner half heavily dotted violet on white; beards violet, based mustard, giving brownish effect. Unknown blue violet and white TB plicata X Whither Thou Goest. McAllister 1995.

GRAPE CHAMPAGNE (D. L. Shepard, R. 1996). Sdlg. 91010-8912. TB, 38" (97 cm), EM. S. and style arms lavender; F. white ground, 1/2" violet purple rim and freckling; beards mustard gold, tipped orange. Dotted Dove X Carnival Magic. Shepard Iris 1997.

GRAPE CHARM (Stan Dexter by Marie Ingersoll, R. 1990). Sdlg. 83-149A. TB, 36" (91 cm), M. Ruffled grape blue, slightly silver on hafts; self beards; pronounced fragrance. 80-127B: (Dream Lover x Pacific Shores) X Ritchie 75-18-2. Ingersoll's Iris 1990.

GRAPE CRUSH (Donald Sorensen, R. 1999). Sdlg. S-91-4-1. IB, 20" (51 cm), M. S. bishops violet (RHS 81A to 82A); style arms spectrum violet (82B); F. bishops violet; beards violet blue (90C); lightly ruffled; slight sweet fragrance. Rare Edition X Perfect Couple.

GRAPE EXPECTATIONS (William Maryott, R. 1998). Sdlg. X144BST. TB, 37" (94 cm), M. S. and style arms smooth dark wine (RHS 79B); F. metallic deep wine, center crushed grape, slightly darker brown hafts and band; beards deep bronze. K11B: (F7A: (Brandy x Coffee House) x F89B: (Seeing Red x Maroon Bells)) X U114A: (Houdini sib x S112A: (Danger x Austrian Garnets)).

GRAPE ICE (Schreiner, R. 1997). Sdlg. T 565-C. TB, 37" (94 cm), L. Laced warm lavender (RHS 76A), white signal; beards white, tipped yellow. K 366-2: (Silver Shower x Fabulous Frills) X R 297-B: ((Craig #41 x Breaking Dawn) x (C 973-A x ((Alpenrose x Whole Cloth) x Cashmere)) x Breaking Dawn)). Wayside Gardens 1997.

GRAPE REPRISE (Walter Moores, R. 1994). Sdlg. 86-30-B. TB, 34" (86 cm), EM & RE (Sept./MS). Lightly ruffled dark red violet; beards lighter violet; pronounced sweet fragrance. Earl of Essex X Feed Back. Moores 1994.

GRAPE ROYALE (Leo Barnard, R. 1997). Sdlg. L 91-140. TB, 38" (97 cm), ML. S. red purple, darker veining; style arms red purple; F. red purple, white shoulders and area below beard, brown haft veining; beards gold, bushy; heavily ruffled, flared; slight fragrance. Master Touch X Renaissance Faire. Paradise Iris 1997.

GRAPE RUFFLES (Dana Borglum, R. 1999). Sdlg. LKNS 2. SIB, 29" (74 cm), M. S. grape-toned violet blue (RHS 93B); style arms multicolored; F. darker violet blue (93A), slight white spray signal; ruffled. Lake Keuka X Seneca Night Sky.

GRAPE SITUATION (David Miller, R. 1990). Sdlg. DM85-5B. TB, 36-38" (91-97 cm), EM. Grape purple; self beards; slight fragrance. Lorilee X Song of Norway. Long 1991.

GRAPE SNAKEZ (Brad Kasperek, R. 1998). Sdlg. 94B-34D. TB, 37" (94 cm), M. S. toffee (RHS 164C), light silver white (155C) streaking with purple (186A) flecking; style arms toffee and grape; F. purple (187A), streaked toffee and cream white (155B/C); beards dark gold; broken color pattern; ruffled; slight fragrance. Bewilderbeast X Gnus Flash. Zebra 1999.

#GRAPHIQUE (Mary Dunn, TB, R. 1982). Stock destroyed, name released.

GRAPHIQUE (Mary Dunn, R. 1993). Sdlg. M84-885T. TB, 36" (91 cm), M. S. white ground, wide deep violet band, tiny plicata markings in center, violet midrib; F. white, narrow deep violet edge; beards violet, tipped light yellow. M75-531: (Going My Way x Midway) X Momentum. M.A.D. Iris 1994.

GRASS IS GREENER (Lynn Bausch, SDB, R. 1989). Garden of the East Wind 1992.

GRATEFUL CITIZEN (Sterling Innerst, R. 1992). Sdlg. 1013-10. TB, 36" (91 cm), M. Light pink; beards whitish pink tipped bluish; slight fragrance. Sterling Blush X 331-2: (Point Clear x Pink Taffeta). Cooley 1994.

GRATSIYA (Oleg Amekhin, R. 1996). Sdlg. SPG-2. SPEC-X, 32" (80 cm), VE. Light purple self; style arms cream, shaded purple. *I. klattii* X *I. sogdiana*. Amekhin 1996.

GRATUITY (Ben Hager, TB, R. 1989). Melrose 1990.

GREAT AMERICA (William Maryott, R. 1995). Sdlg. S104F. TB, 37" (94 cm), M. Heavily ruffled blue violet (RHS 92B) self; beards blue violet; slight sweet fragrance. Altruist X Breakers. Maryott 1997.

GREAT GATSBY (James McWhirter, R. 1993). Sdlg. J89-125. TB, 38" (97 cm), M. S. greyed blue purple; F. rich velvety maroon; beards white, tipped blue; heavily ruffled; slight fragrance. (Winterscape x (Larry Gaulter x Bridal Fashion)) X Hilo Shore. Stockton 1995.

GREAT SWAN RIVER (Frederick Kerr, R. 1995). Sdlg. 89-29-04. TB, 32" (81 cm). M. Ruffled white self; beards white at end, changing to yellow, deep gold in throat; slight sweet fragrance. Leda's Lover X Jean Hoffmeister. Rainbow Acres 1996.

GREAT WHITE HOPE (Dorman Haymon, R. 1999). Sdlg. 28-92-1. LA, 51" (130 cm), M. S. dark blue violet; style arms near black, edged cream; F. very dark purplish violet; ruffled, flared. Jerri X Easter Tide.

GRECIAN GODDESS (Maryott's Gardens, TB, R. 1986). Maryott 1989.

GREEK WHITE (Aaron Davis, R. 1991). Sdlg. ELLJ 8269. SPEC (*unguicularis*), 7½" (15 cm), winter. S. white; F. white, edged medium orange yellow; slight fragrance. Collected in Greece by Dr. Jack Elliot.

GREENAN GOLD (Duane Meek, R. 1992). Sdlg. 398-1-8. CA, 14" (38 cm), EM. Citron yellow to gold, F. with brown plicata markings. ((*I. tenax* x *I. innominata*) x Encircle) X Tunitas. D & J Gardens 1992.

GREEN EYED QUEEN (Steve Varner, R. 1990). Sdlg. 7083. SIB, 28" (71 cm), EM. S. light grape veined deep purple, deep purple bar near base; styles ruffled, aqua midrib; F. light grape with deeper purple veining and wash in center, light green bar on shaft; heavily ruffled. Temper Tantrum X 3133: (Ruffled Velvet x Dutch). Illini Iris 1991.

GREEN-EYED SURFIE (T. J. Betts, R. 1997). Sdlg. 005C. LA, 36" (91 cm), E. S. pale yellow (RHS 11C); style arms yellow; F. pale yellow, veined green, long green streak signal; ruffled. Lime Dash X Joy Flight.

GREEN GIZMO (Chris Vizvarie, R. 1992). Sdlg. GR-1. SDB, 9½" (24 cm), M. S. cream white; F. green, edged cream; beards grey blue; pronounced sweet fragrance. Starlight Waltz X Joyous Isle. Last Scent Farm 1992.

GREEN PROPHECY (Duane Meek, R. 1991). Sdlg. 804-1-2. TB, 30" (81 cm), EM. Lightly ruffled citrine green; beards mustard. (Solano x Song of Norway) X Blue Moustache. D & J Gardens 1991.

GREEN STREAK (Tom Burseen, R. 1997). Sdlg. 93-366C. TB, 36" (91 cm), EM. S. light lemon green; style arms brown green; F. yellow green (RHS 153D), center lighter, hafts brown green; beards mustard, ending in purple horn; ruffled; spicy fragrance. 1-124: (Ample Charm x Hello Hobo) X Thornbird. T.B.'s Place 1997.

GREENSTUFF (A. J. Farrington, SDB, R. 1986). British Iris Society 1987.

GREEN THUMBS (Dudley Carson, R. 1991). Sdlg. APSBE-1. MDB, 6" (15 cm), M. S. yellow green (RHS 145C) paling (145D) at edge; style arms blue green (112D), violet blue (94B) stigmatic lip; F. blue green (112D), yellow green (152D) thumbprint on either side of violet blue (94C) beard; slight sweet fragrance. Amazon Princess X (Stockholm x Brighteyes).

GREEN WAVES (Donovan Albers, R. 1994). Sdlg. 8911. SDB, 11" (28 cm), M. S. chartreuse; F. lighter chartreuse, green area around light lemon beard; slight fragrance. Parentage unknown. Redbud Lane 1995.

GREEN WITH ENVY (Jim Hedgecock, SDB, R. 1987). Comanche Acres 1990.

GREETING CARD (Joseph Ghio, R. 1993). Sdlg. PG-176-I2. CA, 14" (36 cm), ML. S. blue orchid pink; F. apricot with blue pink overlay, neon violet signal. PI-MIX-A, unknown, X PI-209V, Santa Clarita sib. Bay View 1996.

GREG GARIOUS (Chet Tompkins, R. 1990). Sdlg. 83-101A. TB, 38" (97 cm), ML. Red; beards rich chocolate red. Camelot Rose lines X pink and red sdlgs. inv. (Twilight Sky x Defiance). Fleur de Lis 1990.

GREYWOODS FLOWING WATERS (Darlyn Wilkinson, R. 1999). Sdlg. 92-2A. JI (6 F.), 35" (89 cm), EM. White ground overlaid medium violet blue, variable white lines and thin lavender veins giving overall blue effect, vivid gold spear signals lined darker; style arms white center, lavender blue edge. Falling Star X McEwen light blue sdlg.

183

GREYWOODS LADY LUCK (Darlyn Wilkinson, R. 1999). Sdlg. 92-32B. JI (6 F.), 34" (86 cm), M. Clear white boldly lined purple blue blending to violet purple, yellow spear signals lined violet; style arms dark violet purple, sometimes tipped white. Crystal Halo X Lavender Hint.

GREYWOODS MORNING DEW (Darlyn Wilkinson, R. 1999). Sdlg. 92-30A. JI (6 F.), 36" (91 cm), EM. Waved violet, slight blue violet central wash when fresh, white lines radiating to pastel white violet edge, lined deep yellow spear signal; style arms medium violet fading to lighter tips, some lavender lines. Ike-no-Sazanami X Eternal Feminine.

GREYWOODS MULBERRY CASCADE (Darlyn Wilkinson, R. 1999). Sdlg. 92-15. JI (6 F.), 36" (91 cm), EM. Mauve violet fading to violet white edge, occasional flecked violet white lines, blue center wash, bright golden yellow spear signals; style arms white, edged pastel lavender violet. Caprician Butterfly X Pink Dimity.

GRIFEL (Viacheslav Gavrilin, R. 1999). Sdlg. 6-12-1-94. TB, 37" (94 cm), EM. Ruffled violet blue, F. with white washed spot from light blue beard halfway to edge. Darkside X Silver Shower. Gavrilin 1999.

GRINDELWALD (Sterling Innerst, R. 1999). Sdlg. 4698-1. IB, 19" (48 cm), ML. White, F. with blue spot; beards gold; slight sweet fragrance. Night Fires X Smart.

GRIZZLED OLD WARRIOR (Sharon McAllister, R. 1998). Sdlg. 85-3-21. AB (OGB), 28" (71 cm), M. S. near-white ground, veined blue violet; style arms yellowish ivory; F. yellowish ivory ground, dotted and veined red violet; beards near-black. Boaz X Jean Ralls. McAllister 1998.

GROBSWITCHER (Sterling Innerst, R. 1994). Sdlg. 3267-1. BB, 26" (66 cm), M. Full peach orange self; beards orange; slight fragrance. 1827-1: (Hayride x (Golden Brilliance x (Gypsy Rings x Candy Counter))) X Hindenburg. Innerst 1995.

GROOVY GRUBWORM (Paul Black, R. 1995). Sdlg. 89231B. SDB, 10" (25 cm), M. S. greyed lime yellow; style arms lime yellow; F. dark olive green; beards violet, tipped old gold; pronounced sweet fragrance. Bunny Hop X Fuzzy Face. Mid-America 1995.

GROSSER GARTEN (Harald Moos, R. 1991). Sdlg. 85/571A. TB, 36" (90 cm), M. Dark violet; beards white yellow. Jean Hoffmeister X God Bless. Schoeppinger 1993.

GROUND ZERO (Chet Tompkins, R. 1998). Sdlg. 95-52C. TB, 30" (76 cm), ML-VL. S. bright lavender orchid; style arms orchid, lavender stripes; F. blended reddish blue and sooty tan; beards bronze, hairs tipped blue. From involved sdlg. lines. Fleur de Lis 1998.

GRUENFINK (Lothar Denkewitz, R. 1995). Sdlg. N-86-gr. am 1. SDB, 14" (35 cm), ML. S. white, shading to pale blue edge, yellow green midrib; style arms white; F. intense olive green; beards strong blue; slight sweet fragrance. ((Adrienne Taylor x Snow Elf) x (Blueberry Muffins x (Toskanerprinz x Scot Cream))) X Irish Lilt. Von Zeppelin 1997.

GRUST (Nataliya Khimina, R. 1998). Sdlg. 96-18. SDB, 15" (38 cm), M. S. blue lilac; style arms light blue; F. dark purple; beards blue. Tarheel Elf X Yat Rock.

GUADALUPE (William Maryott, R. 1994). Sdlg. P120C. TB, 34" (86 cm), M. S. light pink (RHS 56A) ground with violet plicata infusion; F. pink ground with heavier violet (72B) plicata markings on shoulders; beards tipped tangerine. M106A: (Colortart x ((Roundup x Porta Villa) x (Orange Plush x Anon))) X Highland Haze. Maryott 1994.

GUARDIAN GATE (Steve Moldovan, TB, R. 1978). Correction of parentage. 69-3: (Pink Taffeta x Wide Acclaim) X 69-4: (Irish Lullaby x Pink Taffeta).

GUBIJIN (Hiroshi Shimizu, R. 1999). SPEC (*pseudacorus*), 43" (110 cm), M. Yellow. Seed from British Iris Society seed exchange. Parentage unknown; chromosome count 2n = 35.

GUESSING GAME (John C. Taylor, R. 1994). Sdlg. RL 66-2. LA, 58" (145 cm), ML. Ruffled pale mauve, veined and dotted blue violet, green line signal surrounded by pale cream. OL 133-1: (Flight of Fantasy x Helen Naish) X Margaret Lee. Rainbow Ridge 1994/95.

GUESS WHO (Sharon McAllister, R. 1998). Sdlg. 91-41-2. AB, (OGB-), 32" (81 cm), ML. S. silver ground brushed yellow; style arms lemon yellow; F. blended golden to pinkish tan, near-solid dotting of deep chocolate framing beard; beards yellow, hairs tipped orange. Sostenique X Keep 'em Guessing.

GUIDEWORD (Sterling Innerst, R. 1995). Sdlg. 3613-6. SDB, 14" (36 cm), M. S. medium brown; style arms brown; F. medium brown, very large red spot; beards brown. 2825-1: (Pippi Longstockings x Do-Si-Do) X 2815-3: (Little Episode x Pippi Longstockings). Innerst 1996.

GULF MOON GLOW (Albert Faggard, R. 1994). Sdlg. FBT-31-91. LA, 40" (102 cm), EM. S. light lavender blue, edged yellow; style arms green, yellow edge and claws; F. yellow green, heavily veined green, hint of lavender around edge, darkening toward center, long yellow green signal; slight spicy fragrance. Easter Tide X Old South.

GULMIRA (Viacheslav Gavrilin, R. 1999). Sdlg. 96-232-2. TB, 34" (87 cm), E. S. and style arms light violet rose; F. rose violet with indistinct lighter rim, light rose violet patterning around beard; beards tangerine red, light rose violet at end. Vanity X Latin Lover.

GULPHA GORGE (Richard Morgan, R. 1991). Sdlg. 203-C. LA, 26" (66 cm), M. Serrate bright red, signal yellow. Melon Time X Chowning 77-6-C: (Mockers Song x Ann Chowning).

GUNNER (John C. Taylor, R. 1998). Sdlg. UL 29-1. LA, 43" (110 cm), M. Fluted violet; signals yellow. Louie X Rachel's Request.

GUNSLINGER (Chet Tompkins, R. 1995). Sdlg. 89-23. TB, 37" (94 cm), EML. S. sunflower yellow; style arms vinaceous yellow; F. dark valencia orange overtoned mahogany red, edged vivid sunflower gold; beards orange. (Apollodorus x Dance Fever) X Smart Aleck. Fleur de Lis 1995.

GURU (Keith Keppel, R. 1994). Sdlg. 90-13B. IB, 22" (56 cm), ML. S. near royal purple (M&P 43-K-10), faint white center infusion; style arms royal purple; F. 1/4" matching edge, slightly redder (43-K-10) shoulders; white blaze; beards chrome orange (10-K-12), blue white at end; pronounced sweet fragrance. 84-101B: (((74-48G: ((April Melody x 68-40B: (66-35B: ((Irma Melrose x Tea Apron) x ((Full Circle x Rococo) x Tea Apron)) x April Melody)) x (Roundup x 69-30D, Artwork sib)) x (((66-35C x April Melody) x 68-40B) x Osage Buff)) x (Firewater x 74-48A)) x Daredevil) X Nimble Toes. Keppel 1995.

GUSARSKAYA BALLADA (Sergey Loktev, R. 1998). Sdlg. 94-R14-1H. TB, 33" (83 cm), ML. S. pink, veined darker; style arms pink, salmon crests; F. pink, slightly darker spot below beard, hafts yellowish cream, edges pinkish salmon; beards tangerine, brownish at end. Pink Blue Genes X unknown. Loktev 1998.

GUS' STYLISH LADY (Gustav Seligmann by Sharon McAllister, R. 1992). AB (OGB), 28" (72 cm), EM. S. white; F. butter yellow, rust signal; beards yellow. Kalifa Gulnare X unknown C.G. White sdlg. Aril Society 1992.

GVARDEYSKI (Irina Driagina, R. 1996) Sdlg. 6-42. TB, 49" (125 cm), EM. Sunlight yellow self; beards yellow; pronounced sweet fragrance. Parentage unknown. Driagina 1971.

GWENNETH ANN (Les Donnell, TB, R. 1989). Tempo Two 1994/95.

GWYDION (Maureen Foster, R. 1992). Sdlg. 6T12. TB, 36" (91 cm), ML-VL. S. yellow ground speckled delicate tan overall; F. yellow, 1/3" clean oxblood rim, cream area below light tan beard; heavily ruffled. Showcase X Wild Berry. British Iris Society 1999.

GWYNETH EVANS (Cy Bartlett, R. 1998). Sdlg. CTS-SB. BB, 20" (51 cm), ML. S. white ground, blue purple plicata markings; style arms purple; F. white, blue purple markings at haft; beards blue purple; ruffled. (Concord Touch x Orinoco Flow) X Snowbrook.

GYPSY BRIDE (Lynda Miller, TB, R. 1988). Miller's Manor 1990.

GYPSY MYSTIC (Chet Tompkins, R. 1993). Sdlg. 88-88A. TB, 36" (91 cm), M. S. silvery chamois with greenish gold cast at base; F. bright copper toned fuchsia; beards mustard. (Comanche Drums x Infinite Grace) X (Comanche Drums x Up and Coming). Fleur de Lis 1993.

GYPSY PASSION (Cleo Palmer, R. 1990). Sdlg. 8943. SDB, 12" (30 cm), M. S. pale pink infused palest yellow; F. light pink overlaid palest lavender, light orange shoulders; beards red. Parentage unknown. Palmer's Iris 1990.

GYPSY ROMANCE (Schreiner, R. 1994). Sdlg. W 603-1. TB, 37" (94 cm), ML. Ruffled violet raspberry (RHS 77A), hafts washed bronze; beards blue purple. R 720-D: (Louisiana Lace x Entourage) X T 879-B: (L556-1: (G 510-A x Fabulous Frills) x Starcrest). Schreiner 1994.

GYPSY STAR (Floyd Dyer, R. 1990). Sdlg. D-275-86D. SDB, 12" (30 cm), M. S. light yellow violet blend; F. flaring, ruffled yellow green blend; beards dark violet. D-301-82-D: ((Knotty Pine x self) x Gingerbread Man) X Ice Chalet. Four Cedars 1990.

HABIT (Paul Black, R. 1999). Sdlg. B61A. TB, 34" (86 cm), M. S. palest violet white, darker violet lines around edge; style arms palest violet white, darker violet lines at top; F. dark purple black; beards old gold; pronounced sweet fragrance. In Town X Oklahoma Crude. Mid-America 1999.

HACKMATACK (Sterling Innerst, R. 1996). Sdlg. 4156-1. IB, 18" (46 cm), M. S. mauve; F. cream, trimmed mauve; beards cerise; slight sweet fragrance. Sterling Mistress X Heepers. Innerst 1998.

HAFINA (Maureen Foster, R. 1991). Sdlg. 4H1. TB, 40" (102 cm), ML-VL. Ruffled violet (RHS 88B), silky sheen; self beards; pronounced fragrance. Dream Lover X Heather Blush.

HAGOROMO (Society for Japanese Irises, R. 1992). JI (9 F.), 36" (90 cm), M. White with lavender pattern, yellow signal. Parentage and hybridizer unknown. Introduced in Japan prior to 1940.

HAI (Ed Matheny III, R. 1997). Sdlg. J:01-02-93. JI (6 F.), 39" (99 cm), EM. White, brushed lavender silk (RHS 88D) and veined red violet, signal zinnia yellow (14A); style arms lavender silk, violet crest. Rose World X Midsummer Reverie. Ed's Iris 1998.

HAIL MARY (Mary Dunn by Joseph Ghio, R. 1999). Sdlg. L231. LA, 28" (71 cm), M. Terracotta red self, yellow steeple signal. L170-2: (L70-4: (Mary's Charlie x Ann Chowning) x sib) X Gladiator's Gift.

HAIL THE CHIEF (Lilly Gartman by Joseph Ghio, R. 1994). Sdlg. G89-14P. TB, 36" (91 cm), EM. Deep purple self; beards purple. 87-11P: ((((Dignitary x Superstition) x Titan's Glory) x Bubbling Over) x Orbiter) X Silk Silhouette. Roris 1995.

HAKAN (Jean Peyrard, R. 1996). Sdlg. J302. SPEC (*albertii*), 20" (50 cm), E. S. grey green; F. grey green, brown veins from haft to end of beard; beards yellow, narrow. Seed from SIGNA (86B016, B. Richardson). Ohio Gardens 1999.

HAKUGYOKURO (Shuichi Hirao by Society for Japanese Irises, R. 1992). JI (6 F.), 36" (90 cm), M. White, signals yellow. Parentage unknown. Hirao 1965.

HAKUNA MATATA (A. & D. Cadd, R. 1999). Sdlg. 12-92-1. AB (OGB-), 24-28" (61-71 cm), VE & RE. S. straw yellow, brown infusion; style arms slightly darker yellow; F. straw yellow, maroon brown area around beard with radiating darker maroon brown lines; beards brown, tipped yellow; lightly ruffled; slight musky fragrance. Jolt X Dawn Victory.

HAKUROKU-TEN (Yoshio Mitsuda by Society for Japanese Irises, R. 1993). JI (6 F.), 32" (81 cm), M. Fluted white, signal yellow. Parentage unknown. Mitsuda prior to 1980.

HAL (J. Owings Rebert, R. 1996). Sdlg. UG-5. SIB, 29" (74 cm), M. Pansy violet self, minimal F. signal with few tan hafts markings. Parentage unknown.

HALFPENNY GREEN (Barry Blyth, R. 1994). Sdlg. A49-6. IB, 25" (63 cm), EM. S. peachy apricot cream, creamy lemon midrib and light creamy blended edge; F. similar but more creamy outpouring, greenish hafts; beards light tangerine. Chanted X Electrique. Tempo Two 1994/95.

HALFWAY TO HEAVEN (O. D. Niswonger, R. 1995). Sdlg. 45-92. TB, 34" (86 cm), M. Blue pink self; beards tangerine, tipped blue. Pink Blue Genes X Fontaine. Cape Iris 1996.

HALLOWEEN HALO (John Weiler, R. 1990). Sdlg. 82-178-3-RE. TB, 35" (89 cm), EML & RE. S. white, very pale yellow rim; F. white, bordered soft amber yellow; beards orange red; slight sweet fragrance. 79-133-2: (76-19-2: (((Ultrapoise x Travel On) x Orange Chiffon) x ((Moon River x Orange Crush) x Ole)) x 75-4: (Fresno Fiesta x Fresno Calypso)) X Peach Sundae. Rialto 1991.

HALLOWEEN RAINBOW (John Weiler, R. 1995). Sdlg. 89-4-1RE. IB, 20" (51 cm), EML & RE. S. and F. opalescent white, palest blue violet and cream undertones in cool weather; style arms white, suffused cream; beards orange red; slight sweet fragrance. Rainbow Sherbet X Halloween Halo. Friendship 1997.

HALLS OF IVY (Mary Dunn by Joseph Ghio, R. 1999). Sdlg. L232. LA, 36" (91 cm), M. Greenish yellow, green line signal; style arms green. Gladiator's Gift X L165: (Joel Fletcher x self).

HALO DOLLY (Bernard Pryor, R. 1997). Sdlg. 43/92-C. LA, 36" (91 cm), E. S. lilac (RHS 87D), white rim and cream reverse; style arms creamy lemon blushed lilac; F. darker violet (87B), white rim and cream reverse, highly raised steeple signal surrounded by lime and yellow; heavily ruffled. Little Nutkin X Magic Style.

HALO EVERYBODY (Francis Rogers, R. 1997). Sdlg. C-106-C. TB, 32" (81 cm), M. S. and style arms greyed yellow (RHS 162B); F. greyed purple (187), 1/8" greyed yellow (162A) edge; beards saffron yellow (21A); slight spicy fragrance. Chippewa Brave X Gallant Rogue. Meadowbrook 1998.

HALOGRAM (Tom Burseen, R. 1997). Sdlg. 92-495B. TB, 35" (89 cm), ML. Ruffled dark red violet (RHS 83C), black burgundy overlay; beards bronze brown; ruffled; pronounced musky fragrance. 8-492: ((Admiralty x Mandolin) x (Pansy Royale x Lux Aeterna)) X Magician's Apprentice. T.B.'s Place 1998.

HALO IN BURGUNDY (O. D. Niswonger, R. 1998). Sdlg. 39-95. TB, 34" (86 cm), M. S. and style arms light old rose, pinkish cast; F. light lavender, old rose marginal band; beards tangerine. Halo in Cream X 52-92: (Coral Bracelet x Peach Band). Cape Iris 1998.

HALO IN CREAM (O. D. Niswonger, R. 1992). Sdlg. 48-89. TB, 36" (91 cm), M. S. pale yellow; F. white, edged pale yellow; beards light yellow; ruffled. Halo in Yellow X Peach Band. Cape Iris 1992.

HALO IN GOLD (O. D. Niswonger, R. 1992). Sdlg. 70-89. TB, 36" (91 cm), M. S. gold; F. white, edged gold; beards gold. Halo in Yellow X Peach Band. Cape Iris 1993.

HALO IN PEACH (O. D. Niswonger, R. 1998). Sdlg. 20-95. TB, 32" (81 cm), M. S. and style arms peach; F. white, peach marginal band; beards tangerine. Halo in Rosewood X 35-92: (Nefertiti's Daughter x 39-88: (Halo in Yellow x Peach Band)). Cape Iris 1998.

HALO IN PEARL (O. D. Niswonger, R. 1998). Sdlg. 30-95. TB, 32" (81 cm), EM. S. and style arms pinkish mauve; F. light pearl, pinkish mauve marginal band; beards tangerine. Halo in Cream X 52-92: (Coral Bracelet x Peach Band). Cape Iris 1998.

HALO IN ROSEWOOD (O. D. Niswonger, R. 1993). Sdlg. 51-89. TB, 33" (84 cm), M. S. old rose; F. pale lilac with old rose band; beards white base, tipped tangerine. Minted Halo X Kabaka. Cape Iris 1993.

HALSTEAD'S PRIDE (A. Theodore Mueller, R. 1994). Sdlg. 84-58W. TB, 30-32" (76-81 cm), EM. White, very light tint of lilac blue when fresh; style arms white; beards light, tipped red. Pink Angel X Vanity. Mueller's Garden 1994.

HALSTON (Eric Tankesley-Clarke, R. 1995). Sdlg. 912A. IB, 18-22" (46-56 cm), ML. S. silky deep mineral violet; style arms deep violet, blue white flanges; F. velvety deep mineral violet; pronounced sweet fragrance. 264A: (Nearpass U-80-10: ((Mod Mode x Pink Picotee) x (4-66-36 sib x (4-66-36: (*I. aphylla* "Hungary" x Captain's Lady) x (Harlequin x Yucca)))) x Spinning Wheel) X Sindt 651: (Svelte x (254 sib x (New Idea x 254: (Annikins x (Kiss Me Kate x ((Emma Cook x Dotted Swiss) x *I. balkana* "Darby"))))))). Adamgrove 1995.

HAMBURG BARONESSE (Lothar Denkewitz, R. 1995). Sdlg. N-88-Pl. 2. SDB, 14" (35 cm), E. S. cream ground, light lavender plicata markings; style arms cream; F. cream, light lavender plicata haft markings; beards lavender, tipped yellow; slight spicy fragrance. Wire Rim X Bodderlecker. Von Zeppelin 1997.

HAMBURG BRISE (Lothar Denkewitz, R. 1995). Sdlg. N-88-pl 3. SDB, 12" (30 cm), VE. S. white ground, broad nearly uniform light lobelia blue plicata markings; style arms white; F. white, tinged green, few light lobelia blue dots and stripes; beards white, tipped yellow in throat. Bodderlecker sdlg. X Wire Rim. Von Zeppelin 1997.

HAMBURGER HAFENKONZERT (Lothar Denkewitz, R. 1995). Sdlg. N-88-bic 2. SDB, 11" (28 cm), L. S. light violet, ochre at top; style arms pale violet; F. olive brown, brown red hafts with pale violet lines; beards pale blue, tipped yellow. ((Adrienne Taylor x Snow Elf) x (Toskanerprinz x Scot Cream)) X (sdlg. x Gingerbread Man). Von Zeppelin 1997.

HAMPTON FROST (Leslie Donnell, R. 1990). Sdlg. 81-8-8. IB, 24" (61 cm), M. White, yellow infusion on reverse; beards cream. Lilac Lustre X 76-27-16: (Lemon Soda x Commentary).

HAMPTON GLORY (Leslie Donnell, R. 1990). Sdlg. 88-15-20. TB, 33-34" (84-86 cm), E. Apricot (RHS 24D); beards red. Hampton Horizon X Flaming Victory. Iris Acres 1993/94.

HAMPTON GOLD (Leslie Donnell, R. 1993). Sdlg. 88-5-12. TB, 32" (82 cm), ML. Golden yellow; beards deep yellow. 83-15-6: (((Dingley Dawn x Latin Tempo) x End Play) x Sugarplum Fairy) X Sugarplum Fairy. Tempo Two 1995/96.

HAMPTON HORIZON (Leslie Donnell, R. 1990). Sdlg. 86-13-1. TB, 30-32" (76-81 cm), M. Medium pink; beards light red. 83-20-15, Helen Allen sib, X Pink Petticoat. Tempo Two 1992/93.

HANADAYU (Shuichi Hirao by Society for Japanese Irises, R. 1993). JI (3 F.), 47" (120 cm), M. Deep red violet, F. with prominent white halo and veins, yellow signal. Parentage unknown. Hirao 1976. Also incorrectly in commerce as "Hanadaya".

HANAMARA (Ivar Schmidt, R. 1995). Sdlg. EN A 89/1. JI (6 F.), 29" (74 cm), ML. Soft lilac pink, heavy carmine veining radiating from daffodil yellow signal; style arms carmine. Geisha Gown X My Heavenly Dream. Iris Acres 1995/96.

HANA-NO-YOI (Hiroshi Shimizu by John White, R. 1999). JI (3 F.), 26" (66 cm), M. S. and style arms white, edged pink; F. pink, veined white, medium-size pale yellow signal. Sen Hime X Sakura Komachi.

HANARAVI (Ivar Schmidt, R. 1995). Sdlg. EN A 89/4. JI (6 F.), 32" (81 cm), EM. Rich velvety mulberry red self, near-black effect around daffodil yellow signal, thin lilac pink edge around F.; style arms mulberry red. Geisha Gown X My Heavenly Dream. Iris Acres 1995/96.

HANAZUKIYO (Kamo Nursery by Society for Japanese Irises, R. 1999). SPEC-X, 30" (76 cm), M. Creamy yellow, F. with red violet veins extending from edge of very large deep yellow signal. *I. ensata* X *I. pseudacorus*. Kamo Nursery 1988.

HAND IN HAND (Mary Dunn by Joseph Ghio, R. 1998). Sdlg. 228-4. LA, 36" (91 cm), M. Rosy fuchsia with yellow reverse, F. with yellow dart signal; style arms green. Parentage unknown. Bay View 1998.

HAND PAINTED (Monty Byers, R. 1990). Sdlg. D80-100. TB, 35" (89 cm), M & RE. S. medium beetroot; F. blend of dark beetroot, ruby red and wine red, centerline and suffused underlay of electric violet down middle, dark brownish red shading at hafts overlaid with spray of white stripes, diffusing into tiny pin points of violet white below beard; beards electric violet blue, brushed chestnut brown in throat; ruffled; sweet spicy fragrance. Well Endowed X Violet Miracle. Moonshine 1990.

HANDSEL (Jayne Ritchie, R. 1995). Sdlg. 88-11-4. MDB, 5½" (14 cm), EML. S. and style arms lavender blue (near RHS 98D); F. lavender blue with greenish undertone; beards lavender blue; ruffled; slight sweet fragrance. 83-32-5: (Model Child x 79-39-6, Loveshine sib) X Bay Ruffles. Ritchie 1996.

HANDSHAKE (Joseph Ghio, R. 1991). Sdlg. 86-86D. TB, 34" (86 cm), VE-E. White ground plicata stitched blue, deeper shoulders; beards yellow. God's Handiwork X Snowbrook. Bay View 1992.

HANDSOME IS (Ben Hager, R. 1993). Sdlg. S969Pr/Br. SPU, 44" (112 cm), ML. S. purple brown; F. brown, deep yellow signal; fluted. S731DkBr: (Crow Wing x Forty Carats) X Walker Ferguson. Cordon Bleu 1994.

HANDS ON (Joseph Ghio, R. 1993). Sdlg. PG-144B. CA, 13" (33 cm), EM. Rust with slight black signal; style arms yellow. Villa Montalvo X PI-MIX-D, unknown. Bay View 1994.

HANDYMAN (Frederick Kerr, R. 1995). Sdlg. 89-9B-01. TB, 30" (76 cm), M. Medium blue, F. with darker blue stripes extending down from beard area; beards yellow, white at end; ruffled; slight musky fragrance. Fancy Fellow X Breakers. Rainbow Acres 1995.

HANIT (David Shahak, R. 1992). Sdlg. S-T-85-93B. AR, 20" (50 cm), M. S. purple (RHS 78B) veined darker; F. greyed purple (186A), dark purple signal; beards greyed purple. *I. samariae* X (*I. samariae* x Judean Charmer). Aril Society 1995.

HANNAH DENETTE (Truman Scarborough, R. 1998). Sdlg. 14-93-14a. TB, 30-32" (76-81 cm), M. Lightly ruffled near-white, S. with light blue cast, F. with dark blue haft veining; style arms blue; beards white, base yellow; slight musky fragrance. 5-90-C5c: (Gala Madrid x unknown purple) X Laced Cotton.

HANNI (Thomas Burge, R. 1990). Sdlg. T101/86. SIB, 27½" (70 cm), M. S. medium blue; style arms and crests fimbriated; F. medium blue (aging lighter), small white arrow signal, yellow in throat. T31/84: (Dear Dianne x Happy Event) X McEwen T5 75/83/1.

HANNIBI (Manfred Beer, R. 1997). Sdlg. MB 6/87 B. TB, 40" (100 cm), M. S. canary yellow (RHS 9A); style arms and F. aureolin yellow (12A); beards tangerine orange (24A) to cadmium orange (23A), maize yellow (21B) at end; pronounced fragrance. Gold Galore X Tut's Gold. Ortenauer Staudencenter 1997.

HANNOVER EXPRESS (Harald Moos, R. 1996). Sdlg. 88/853A. TB, 32" (80 cm), M. Wavy red brown self; beards copper. Post Time X Spartan. Moos 1997.

HANNOVER GLORY (Harald Moos, R. 1995). Sdlg. 90/120L. TB, 36" (91 cm), M. Violet, F. with white area around beard; beards yellow, white at end; ruffled. Graft X Oedipussi. Schoeppinger 1996.

HANNOVER GOLD (Harald Moos, R. 1992). Sdlg. 87/732C. TB, 33½" (85 cm), M. Heavily frilled gold yellow; beards dark yellow. Sommernachtstraum X Aztec Sun. Schoeppinger 1993.

HANNOVER RED (Harald Moos, R. 1992). Sdlg. 88/861A. TB, 31½" (80 cm), M. S. light red brown; F. red brown; beards yellow; heavily frilled. Warrior King X Niedersachsenross. Schoeppinger 1993.

HANS BRINKER (C. T. Claussen, R. 1991). Sdlg. 82-17. TB, 34" (86 cm), M. Very pale blue (near-white); beards pale blue, tipped white; slight fragrance. Song of Norway X Mirrored Sky. Wagontrail Acres 1992.

HANSELMAYER'S DWARF BLUE (Eric & Bob Tankesley-Clarke, R. 1994). SPEC, 6-12" (15-30 cm), ML. S. light violet; F. violet; beards white, tipped orange in throat; slight sweet fragrance. Collected; distributed by Hanselmayer and in commerce prior to 1985 as *I. pallida* H5.

HAPPY AIRE (Loleta Powell, R. 1994). Sdlg. 92-15. TB, 32" (81 cm), EML. Yellow self; beards yellow; pronounced sweet fragrance. Borderline X Wedding Candles. Powell's Gardens 1996.

HAPPY CAMPER (Lynn Bausch, R. 1991). Sdlg. L-60-5. SDB, 9" (23 cm), M. S. white ground, full red violet rib and hash marks; style arms pale blue; F. white ground, wide border of full red violet hash marks; beards full gold, tipped white; lightly ruffled; slight sweet fragrance. Bashful Bunny X Prisoner. Garden of the East Wind 1996.

HAPPY CARVER (Tom Burseen, R. 1995). Sdlg. 0-64A. TB, 36" (91 cm), EM. S. golden yellow; style arms slightly darker; F. lemon yellow ground, edged red; beards tangerine, white base; ruffled; spicy fragrance. 7-101: (Gigolo x (Sun Toasted x Joy Ride)) X 7-66: ((Silver Shower x Rancho Rose) x Villa Splendor). T.B.'s Place 1996.

HAPPY CHILDHOOD (Adolf Volfovich-Moler, R. 1997). Sdlg. V-153. TB, 47" (120 cm), EM. S. light yellow; style arms cream, edged greenish yellow; F. cream white, yellow edge; beards yellow, paler at end; ruffled, laced; slight musky fragrance. Pink Sleigh X Chartreuse Ruffles. Volfovich-Moler 1998.

HAPPY-HAPPY (Kirk Strawn, R. 1993). Sdlg. 26B-1985. LA, 41" (104 cm), M. S. yellow orange (RHS 16C); styles yellow orange (15D); F. greyed orange (164C), yellow orange (17A) signal. Freddie Boy X President Hedley.

HAPPY MARRIAGE (Joseph Ghio, R. 1996). Sdlg. 87-115H. TB, 34" (86 cm), EM. S. pink, slight orchid cast; F. light pink deepening at edge, amber haft wash; beards red. 84-85F2: (Romantic Mood x ((Blushing Pink x (((Ponderosa x Debby Rairdon) x (Show Time x San Leandro)) x ((New Moon x ((Gracie Pfost x Ponderosa) x Ponderosa)) x Valentina))) x Exhilaration)) X 84-173L2: (Designer Gown x (((Artiste x Tupelo Honey) x ((Malaysia x Carolina Honey) x (Hi Top x ((Ponderosa x Travel On) x Peace Offering sib)))) x Praline)). Roris 1997.

HAPPY NEW YEAR (Monty Byers, TB, R. 1989). Moonshine 1990.

HAPPY PRINCE (Beryl Pederick, R. 1994). Sdlg. 3. BB, 21" (53 cm), L. Vivid white, precise narrow royal purple border; beards gold, tipped white; slight fragrance. Splash o' Wine X French Gown.

HARBOR HIGH (Joseph Ghio, R. 1997). Sdlg. PD-273M5. CA, 12" (31 cm), L. Marine blue, streaked silver when mature. PF-191S3: ((Los Californio x San Andreas) x Sierra Dell) X Seabright Cove. Bay View 1997.

HARBOR MASTER (Howard Shockey, R. 1993). Sdlg. 88-235-B. TB, 37" (94 cm), M. Violet (near 88A) self; beards blue violet; slight sweet fragrance. Ron X 85-220-7B: (El Morado x High Flight). Arilian Acres 1995.

HARD ROCK (Sergey Loktev, R. 1998). Sdlg. 94-1-10E. SDB, 8½" (21 cm), M. S. and style arms violet; F. dark red brown, blackish sheen, wide violet rim; beards yellow, lilac base. Nut Ruffles X unknown. Loktev 1998.

HAREM PEARLS (Jane Barry, TB, R. 1988). Wild Mountain Thyme 1990.

HARE SUGATA (Toyokazu Ichie by Society for Japanese Irises, R. 1995). JI (6 F.), 35" (90 cm), M. Red violet, very large white center with radiating white veins; style arms white, red violet crests. Parentage unknown. Introduced in Japan, 1981.

HARK (Barry Blyth, SDB, R. 1987). Correction of parentage. (Cupid's Cup x Tiger Rouge) X Capricornia.

HARLAND HAND (Harland Hand by David Lennette, CA, R. 1989). Portable Acres 1990.

HARLEM NOCTURNE (A. & D. Willott, R. 1993). Sdlg. 88-138. SDB, 14" (36 cm), ML & RE. S. dark violet; F. velvety darker violet; beards light blue violet, full yellow in throat; ruffled; foliage purple-based. Nachos X Pilgrims' Choice. Willott 1993.

HARMONICS (Barry Blyth, R. 1994). Sdlg. Z62-1. TB, 38" (97 cm), ML. S. white, heavily overlaid and stitched light blue; F. white, 1/2" stitched and stippled deep blue edge, deeper hafts with violet tone, flared and ruffled; beards whitish, lemon in throat. W56-1: (Lipstick Lies x Light Beam) X Snowbrook. Tempo Two 1994/95.

HARPSWELL CHANTEUSE (Currier McEwen, R. 1991). Sdlg. T(7)83/171. SIB (tet.), 36" (91 cm), M. S. white; F. creamy white, light greenish yellow signal; heavily ruffled. T(5)79/174(4): (Lady of Quality sib x Dear Dianne) X Ivory Cream. Pope's Perennials, Seaways 1992.

HARPSWELL LOVE (Currier McEwen, R. 1995). Sdlg. T(6)83/206. SIB (tet.), 29" (73 cm), ML. S. and style arms pale greenish yellow (RHS 1D), aging white; style arms with white tufts; F. white, greenish yellow veining to tips, crimped yellow (7D) edging aging cream, signals bright yellow (7A); ruffled. Ivory Cream X T(5)79/174(3): (Lady of Quality x Dear Dianne). Eartheart 1998.

HARPSWELL MOONLIGHT (Currier McEwen, R. 1993). Sdlg. T(6) 84/103A. SIB (tet.), 28" (70 cm), EM. S. white; style arms 1½" tufted white, pale yellow (RHS 4D) midrib; F. creamy yellow (4C) edged deeper (4A), greenish yellow (154C) veins, rich yellow (12A) signal. T(5) 79/174(4): ((Harpswell Hallelujah x sib) x Dear Dianne) X Ivory Cream. Eartheart, Seaways 1993.

HARPSWELL PRELUDE (Currier McEwen, R. 1994). Sdlg. T(8)88/1(2). SIB (tet.), 20" (51 cm), VE & RE. S. medium violet blue (RHS 90C); F. darker (93B), brown gold signal. White Prelude X Lucky Lilac. Eartheart, Seaways 1994.

HARPSWELL SNOW (Currier McEwen, R. 1995). Sdlg. T(8)84/54. SIB (tet.), 34" (85 cm), M. S. white; style arms white, crests feathered; F. white, small greenish yellow (RHS 2C) signal hidden under styles. T(7)81/99(10): (Variation in Blue sdlg. x Marshmallow Frosting) X T(5)79/221(1): ((Cambridge x Wing on Wing) x T(4)76/25, inv. Fourfold White, Pirouette). Eartheart 1996.

HARPSWELL SNOWBURST (Currier McEwen, R. 1990). Sdlg. T(6)83/37(3). SIB (tet.), 36" (90 cm), EM. S. blue violet (RHS 94C) veined darker (95B); F. same, edged silver, large stippled white signal. T(5)75/83(1): (T(4)72/10(1), inv. White Swirl, Snowy Egret, Pirouette, Morning Magic, Fairy Dawn, McGarvey pink sdlg. x (Sally Kerlin x Cambridge)) X Windwood Spring. Pope's Perennials, Seaways 1991.

HARPSWELL'S PRINCESS KAREN (Currier McEwen, R. 1996). Sdlg. T(7)85/97(4). SIB (tet.), 36" (90 cm), ML. S. gentian blue (RHS 94D) ground veined deeper (94A) giving overall effect of bluebird blue (94B); style arms bluebird blue aging lighter (94C); F. very dark blue (darker than 94A, aging to 94A), green (148D) signal. Regency Buck X T(8)82/114: (Adj x Dear Dianne). Eartheart 1997.

HARPSWELL VALOR (Currier McEwen, R. 1994). Sdlg. T(7)85/97(6). SIB (tet.), 30" (75 cm), ML-VL. S. dark violet blue (RHS 90B), veined darker (90A); style arms violet (86B), tufted, infused red violet (83D); F. velvety dark violet blue (90A) veined darker (95A), white signal; ruffled. Regency Buck X T(6)82/114: (Adj sib x Dear Dianne). Eartheart, Seaways 1994.

HARPSWELL VELVET (Currier McEwen, R. 1990). Sdlg. T(3)83/107(6). SIB (tet.), 32" (80 cm), EM. S. dark blue purple (RHS 89A to 86A); styles 1"; F. darker velvety blue purple, white signal. T(2)80/260(2) X T(6)78/57 -- both inv. sdlgs. going back to Blue Brilliant, White Swirl, Violet Flare, Pirouette, Polly Dodge and Tealwood. Pope's Perennials, Seaways 1991.

HARRIGAN (O. D. Niswonger, R. 1992). Sdlg. SDB 9-88. SDB, 12" (30 cm), M. Light blue, F. with deep chartreuse spot; beards blue. Hooligan X unknown. Cape Iris 1992.

HARRY'S GOLD (Indra Belford, R. 1997). Sdlg. 89-A-6-9124. TB, 38" (97 cm), VE-E. Golden yellow, F. washed butterscotch; beards golden orange. Camelot Rose X Horned Tantalizer.

HARU-NO-UMI (Shuichi Hirao by Society for Japanese Irises, R. 1993). JI (3 F.), 32" (81 cm), VE. S. and style arms red violet, edged lighter; F. bright red violet center and veining radiating out over light violet ground, signal light yellow. Parentage unknown. Hirao prior to 1985.

HARVEST BLESSING (Hooker Nichols, R. 1991). Sdlg. 8733B. TB, 38" (97 cm), ML. S. yellow brown, base darker; F. white yellow; beards gold; ruffled. Eastertime X Glory Days.

HARVEST FAIRE (Schreiner, R. 1997). Sdlg. CC 1325-C. TB, 36" (91 cm), L. S. and style arms light yellow (RHS 162B); F. amethyst violet (81C), tan (176D) shoulders and 1/2" rim; beards yellow, lavender blue at end; slight fragrance. Adventuress X Jazz Festival. Schreiner 1997.

HARVEST HUES (Lynda Miller, R. 1994). Sdlg. 5181. BB, 27" (69 cm), L. S. bright yellow gold; style arms yellow gold; F. gold, washed and rayed rust brown; beards yellow orange; slight musky fragrance. Brown Lasso X Anon. Miller's Manor 1995.

HARVEST KING (Schreiner, R. 1990). Sdlg. T 1144-1. TB, 38" (97 cm), ML. S. laced tan (RHS 165C); F. flaring, ruffled golden tan; beards yellow. M 629-A: (1974 #16, unknown, x K 872-A: (C 1365-2 x Craig #37)) X R 589-A: ((C 738-A: (Burnished Gold x Bayadere) x E 1068-A: (Calypso Bay sib x ((Olympic Torch x Brass Accents sib) x ((Casa Morena sdlg. x Inca Chief) x Dutch Chocolate)))) x (Gold Trimmings x Craig #36)). Schreiner 1990.

HASARYA (Peter DeSantis, R. 1999). Sdlg. 84-40C. SPU, 56" (142 cm), EM. S. light violet (RHS 88D) with darker (88A) streaks, golden yellow veining; style arms off-white, light violet (88D) tip, golden yellow midrib; F. wide violet (88A) rim around large golden yellow (163B) veined center. Vintage Years X Imperial Sun.

HATSUHIME (Kamo Nursery by Society for Japanese Irises, R. 1999). Sdlg. Ichie 6A-67. JI (6 F.), 35" (90 cm), E. Pale to light lavender pink (RHS 75C/D), darker (75B) veins, signals buttercup yellow (15B). (Miyoshino x (Miyoshino x "Kyokusui-no-Uta")) X Miyoshino. Kamo Nursery 1989.

HATSUHO (Kamo Nursery by Society for Japanese Irises, R. 1999). SPEC-X, 30" (76 cm), M. S. creamy then yellow; style arms yellow; F. brownish yellow, veined brown. *I. pseudacorus* X *I. ensata* "Sakigake". Kamo Nursery 1989.

HATSU KAGAMI (Shuichi Hirao by Society for Japanese Irises, R. 1992). JI (3 F.), 36" (91 cm), E. S. pink; F. pink, veined darker, yellow signal. Parentage unknown. Hirao 1966.

HATSUKURENAI (Seiro Yoshie by Society for Japanese Irises, R. 1993). JI (3 F.), 26" (65 cm), VE-E. S. white, edged red violet; style arms white, barely brushed maroon; F. large white center and veins radiating outward into red violet edge, signal yellow. Parentage unknown. Yoshie prior to 1980.

HATSUYUME (Toyokazu Ichie by Society for Japanese Irises, R. 1995). JI (3 F.), 30" (76 cm), M. S. campanula violet (RHS 82C); style arms near-white, edged and tufted campanula violet; F. campanula violet outer quarter and haft area, center paler (lighter than 82D), signal rich yellow (12A). Parentage unknown. Introduced in Japan, 1984.

HAUNTING REFRAIN (Connell Marsh, BB, R. 1981). C. Marsh 1990.

HAUNTS ME (Barry Blyth, R. 1997) Sdlg. D22-2. SDB, 15" (38 cm), EM. S. lavender, grey sheen; F. plum burgundy, 1/4" soft lavender edge; beards purple, tipped bronze; pronounced sweet fragrance. A5-1: (Scat x X32-B: (Yipee x sib) X Celsius. Tempo Two 1997/98.

HAUTE COUTURE (Joseph Gatty by Keith Keppel, R. 1995). Sdlg. X63-5. TB, 34" (86 cm), ML. S. light peach-toned pink (M&P 9-AB-3); style arms slightly more peach (9-B-3); F. creamier peach pink (9-A-2) edges and (9-A-1) center, maize (10-G-5) hafts; beards capucine red (9-E-11), base pinkish cream (9-B-4); heavily ruffled and crimped. T-1-2: ((Nefertiti x Playgirl) x Presence) X Rare Occasion. Keppel 1996.

HAUT LES VOILES (Cayeux, R. 1999). Sdlg. 9392 C. TB, 33" (85 cm), ML. S. light butter yellow; F. light blue lavender; beards yellow, blue lavender at end, inconspicuous. Edith Wolford X Honky Tonk Blues.

HAVANA REVELS (Darlene Pinegar, R. 1990). Sdlg. P-1-1. TB, 28" (71 cm), M. S. bright yellow; F. dark velvety fuchsia at shoulders to lighter red purple with blue tints, yellow haft markings, dull gold edge; beards yellow orange; ruffled; slight sweet fragrance. Palladium X Spinning Wheel. Spanish Fork 1991.

HAVE A HEART (Evelyn Kegerise, R. 1991). Sdlg. 86-738-1. TB, 36" (91 cm), ML. Light salmon, F. with deeper hafts; beards burnt orange; deeply ruffled; slight sweet fragrance. Iris Irene X Jewel of Spring. Evelyn Kegerise 1992.

HAVEN (Monty Byers, R. 1990). Sdlg. G8-102. SDB, 11" (28 cm), M & RE. S. medium blue; F. medium green, edged lighter blue; beards blue. Willowmist X Twinkle Twinkle. Moonshine 1991.

HAVENDANCE (Ken Mohr by Bryce Williamson, R. 1994). Sdlg. Q-61. TB, 36" (91 cm), EM. S. light to medium lobelia blue tinted lavender; F. ruffled medium lobelia blue, deeper lavender violet wash intensifying to distinct center stripe; beards cream yellow, tipped white; slight fragrance. J-172-1 X 69-1. Pacific Coast Hybridizers 1994.

HAVERSHAM (Harold Stahly, R. 1990). Sdlg. 86-3. TB, 33" (84 cm), M. S. pale yellow; F. cream, hafts yellow, lightly stippled violet to brown plicata markings around yellow beard and exending halfway down edge; ruffled. 81-28: (Frills x (High Life x Joy Ride)) X Shah's Court. Stahly 1990.

HAWAIIAN HALO (Chet Tompkins, R. 1990). Sdlg. 84-88A. TB, 38" (97 cm), ML-VL. S. lemon ivory ground lightly flushed and edged lilac rose; F. deeper ivory lemon, widely edged lilac rose; beards amber, tipped lilac; ruffled; musky fragrance. Inv. sdlgs. X ((April Lost x (Rippling Rose x Tinsel Town)) x Capricious). Fleur de Lis 1990.

HAWAIIAN MOONLIGHT (Darlene Pinegar, R. 1995). Sdlg. TS-3-2. TB, 36" (91 cm), M. Heavily ruffled and laced white, F. with yellow shoulders; beards yellow, white at end; slight sweet fragrance. Timpanogas Snows X Speculator. Spanish Fork 1996.

HAWAIIAN SERENADE (Schreiner, R. 1991). Sdlg. S 295-A. TB, 36" (91 cm), ML. S. peach pink (RHS 29D); F. rose pink (50C); beards tangerine. H 244-C: ((Rippling Waters x B 715-1: (Lilac Supreme x Christmas Time)) x (Dream Time x A 973-1: ((Alpenrose x Anthem) x Gracie Pfost))) X M 851-1: ((Rippling Waters x (Annabel Lee sib x Claudia Rene)) x J 215-A: ((Annabel Lee x Gracie Pfost sdlg) x (((Amethyst Flame x (Amethyst Flame x Alpenrose)) x Lilac Supreme) x Warm Laughter sib))). Park Seed Company 1991.

HAZEL JEAN (Jim Hedgecock, R. 1992). Sdlg. 84-71-6. TB, 33" (84 cm), ML. S. pink, touched apricot at edge; F. pink, apricot edge and hafts; beards reddish orange; heavily laced and ruffled; pronounced sweet fragrance. Carved Cameo X Sunset Sonata. Comanche Acres 1994.

HAZY JAYNE (Barry Emmerson, R. 1998). Sdlg. BE 94/2/A. TB, 38" (97 cm), M. S. and style arms deep lavender blue; F. pale sky blue, greenish white area below beard; beards near white, tipped orange in throat; lightly ruffled; pronounced musky fragrance. Lamorna X Sullom Voe.

HEAD HONCHO (Chet Tompkins, R. 1995). Sdlg. 92-41N. TB, 39" (99 cm), ML. S. white, blushed rosy orchid; style arms lilac; F. white ground, stitched cerise red border; beards bronze, tipped blue; ruffled. Wheeler Dealer X Playing Around. Fleur de Lis 1995.

HEADLANDS BEACH (A. & D. Willott, R. 1995). Sdlg. 92-171. IB, 27" (69 cm), EM. S. white ground, heavily stippled with blended light brown; F. white ground, edged blended brown, brown line extending from end of deep orange beard; ruffled. North Coast X Chubby Cheeks. Willott 1995.

HEADLINE BANNER (George Sutton, R. 1998). Sdlg. B-167-ER. BB, 26" (66 cm), ML & RE. S. white, mottled lavender blue darkest at midrib, 1/8" gilt edge at top; style arms white to lavender blue; F. white, 1/8" gilt edge, 1¼" lavender blue dotted and stitched border, darker centerline; beards yellow, base white; ruffled; slight sweet fragrance. Sterling Prince X Aztec Affluence. Sutton 1999.

HEADY PERFUME (John Weiler, R. 1990). Sdlg. 82-130-2. TB, 36" (91 cm), EM. Tailored white; beards deep golden yellow; pronounced sweet fragrance. Sunrise Sunset X Thick and Creamy. Rialto 1991.

HEALING HOPE (Terrell Taylor, R. 1998). Sdlg. 96-24. TB, 38" (97 cm), EM. Lightly ruffled light blue (RHS 93C) self; beards orange. Skyblaze X (Daredevil x Allstar). Bonita Gardens 1998.

HEAPER (Barbara Berg, R. 1993). Sdlg. BB-1. TB, 42" (107 cm), M. S. white; F. white, slight yellow green haft markings, greenish cast on midrib and reverse; beards yellow, tipped white; pronounced sweet fragrance. Victoria Falls X Heavenly Angels. Phoenix Flower Farm 1998.

HEARTBREAK HOTEL (George Sutton, R. 1997). Sdlg. G-19-ARSA. TB, 37" (94 cm), ML. S. and style arms salmon (RHS 27A); F. imperial purple (78A); beards nasturtium red (32B), 1¼" salmon and violet purple horn; ruffled, laced; slight sweet fragrance. Sweet Musette X Twice Thrilling. Sutton 1998.

HEARTFELT LOVE (David Shahak by Arnold Ferguson, selector, R. 1997). Sdlg. RxPM#2. AR (OH), 19" (48 cm), E. S. pale blue, slightly darker veining; style arms yellow green; F. lemon yellow, small burgundy red streaks, orange signal overlaid burnt orange red; beards yellow, split around signal; slight sweet fragrance. Ravid X Princess Maya. Grandview Iris Patch 1997.

HEARTHSTONE (Richard Ernst, R. 1993). Sdlg. F125-27. TB, 37" (94 cm), EM. Ruffled amber and brick-red plicata with white zone at end of gold beards; F. reverse amber gold. Edna's Wish X Wild Jasmine. Cooley 1993.

HEARTLAND (Frederick Kerr, R. 1995). Sdlg. 90-28-02. TB, 32" (81 cm), M. Smooth light pinkish tan, F. with golden haft infusion; beards tangerine, yellow at end; ruffled. Chief Redskin X Role Model. Rainbow Acres 1995.

HEART OF AFRICA (Brad Kasperek, R. 1999). Sdlg. 94B-43C. BB, 26" (66 cm), M. S. light dawn pink (RHS 49A); F. dawn pink, haft heavily dotted greyed magenta rose (186B); beards cadmium orange; ruffled, style crests laced; slight fragrance. 92B-56R: (Baboon Bottom x 89B-42E: (Rustic Dance x Maria Tormena)) X Tanzanian Tangerine.

HEART REJOICE (Frederick Kerr, R. 1998). Sdlg. 905303. TB, 38" (97 cm), M. S. light pinkish ivory, center more yellow; style arms pinkish ivory to pinkish violet at lip; F. dark pinkish red violet; beards yellow gold, light red violet at end; ruffled. Gypsy Woman X Silverado. Rainbow Acres 1998.

HEART'S AFFAIR (Barry Blyth, R. 1992). Sdlg. X107-A. TB, 36" (91 cm), EM. Metallic smoky lilac self; beards bright mustard. (Flower Show x Dutch Girl) X Street Dancer. Tempo Two 1992/93.

HEARTSTRING STRUMMER (Ben Johnson, R. 1997). Sdlg. A49-A. TB, 40" (107 cm), ML. S. white, edges flushed pale violet blue; style arms pale violet blue; F. medium violet blue, edges deeper, paling to near-white by beard; beards pale violet blue, yellow in throat; heavily ruffled; slight sweet fragrance. Rapture in Blue X Conjuration.

HEART WARMER (Les Peterson by Ardy Kary, R. 1991). Sdlg. LP-79-13. TB, 30" (76 cm), L. Ruffled and laced chrysanthemum crimson (HCC 824/1); beards burnt orange (14). Bride's Halo X Le Sedna. Kary Iris 1991.

HEATH (Heather Collins, R. 1994). Sdlg. 84-10NC. AR (OH), 17" (42 cm), EM. S. pale lavender; F. cherry, lower portion pale pink, frilled champagne edge; beards orange; musky fragrance. Parentage unknown.

HEATHER CARPET (Chuck Chapman, R. 1999). Sdlg. 89-05-G. SDB, 12" (31 cm), M. S. light rosy purple, darker veins; F. light rosy purple, darker center and lines radiating from beard; beards pastel lilac, wide. Royal Silk X Raspberry Jam. Chapman Iris 1999.

HEATHER DIANE (Chet Tompkins, R. 1992). Sdlg. 86-121A. TB, 38-40" (99-102 cm), ML. S. icy white, flushed and border vervain violet; F. icy white, 1/2" rich violet blue edge; beards lemon white. 80-13C: ((Bandera Waltz x Rippling Rose) x Calliope Tune) X inv. plicata lines. Fleur de Lis 1991.

HEATHER JOEL (Clyde Hahn, R. 1995). Sdlg. 91-10-C. TB, 28" (71 cm), M. S. chinese yellow; F. white, 1/2" chinese yellow rim; beards red, tipped yellow; slight sweet fragrance. Sunkist Frills X Piping Hot. Hahn's Rainbow 1995.

HEATHER PRYOR (John C. Taylor, R. 1993). Sdlg. RL 67-1. LA, 51" (130 cm), ML. S. cream, veined and flushed pink, rimmed paler, green yellow signal; F. cream ground, veined and heavily flushed pink toward paler rim, green line signal surrounded by yellow center area; heavily ruffled. OL 136-1: ((C'est Si Bon x Koorawatha) x Helen Naish) X Margaret Lee. Rainbow Ridge 1993/94.

HEATHER'S GEM (Elsie Lucas, R. 1994). Sdlg. A89/3x181. SIB, 36" (90 cm), ML. S. medium blue; style arms pale blue; F. medium blue shaded deeper, fine white edge, yellow green hafts blending with burgundy veining at edge; flared, lightly ruffled; slight fragrance. Parentage unknown.

HEATHER SKY (George Sutton, R. 1999). Sdlg. H-159. TB, 34" (86 cm), ML. Ruffled pale orient pink (36D) self; beards tangerine, orient pink horn; edges serrate; pronounced spicy fragrance. Custom Made X Mesmerizer.

HEATHER'S SONG (Joyce Meek, R. 1993). Sdlg. 391-1-3. TB, 31" (79 cm), ML. S. light pink orchid with darker midrib infusion; F. deep orchid, light area around coral beard; ruffled. Candace X Janie Meek. D & J Gardens 1993.

HEATHER SUZANNE (Carl Jorgensen, R. 1994). Sdlg. 85-P-1C. BB, 26" (66 cm), ML-VL. S. shell pink (HCC 516/2); style arms pink, lacy; F. geranium lake (20/3) blending to magenta rose (027/3) at rim; beards mandarin red (17) tipped lighter (17/2); ruffled; slight sweet fragrance. 83-P-1: (Beverly Sills x Summit Sweetie) X Custom Made. Long 1994.

HEAVEN (Joseph Ghio, R. 1997). Sdlg. 91-123Q2. TB, 38" (97 cm), ML. White with blue cast, F. with coral red shoulders; beards coral red. 88-105X: ((Wedding Band x (((Cream Taffeta x (Show Time x (Ponderosa x New Moon))) x (Ballet in Orange x (Hi Top x ((Ponderosa x Travel On) x Peace Offering)))) x Caption)) x (Fortunata x ((Act of Love x Lady Friend) x Caption))) X 89-69N2: ((Stratagem x ((Fortunata x Caption) x Marriage Vows)) x (Stratagem x (Romantic Mood x ((Blushing Pink x (((Ponderosa x Debby Rairdon) x (Show Time x San Leandro)) x ((New Moon x ((Gracie Pfost x Ponderosa) x Ponderosa)) x Valentina))) x Exhilaration)))). Bay View 1998.

HEAVEN AND EARTH (Larry Lauer, R. 1999). Sdlg. 448-1. TB, 33" (84 cm), ML. S. aureolin yellow, edge darker; style arms aureolin yellow, hyacinth blue crest; F. blue violet blend rimmed barium yellow, shoulders brownish yellow; beards hyacinth blue at end, changing to saffron yellow, cadmium orange in throat; pronounced sweet fragrance. 91-186-2: (Blue Ballet x God's Handiwork) X Special Feature.

HEAVEN KNOWS (Joseph Ghio, R. 1991). Sdlg. PI-MIX-R2. CA, 14" (36 cm), EML. Solid crimson self, black signal. Parentage unknown. Bay View 1992.

HEAVENLY BODY (Chet Tompkins, R. 1992). Sdlg. 85-58B. TB, 39" (99 cm), ML. S. creamy white, faintly tinted pink; F. creamy white overlaid watermelon pink with faint blue cast, wide ruffled cream border; beards red. Sdlgs. inv. Clarion Call, Kin-na-Zin, Camelot Rose, Whole Cloth. Fleur de Lis 1991.

HEAVENLY DAYS (Paul Wickersham by Roger Nelson, R. 1999). TB, 36" (91 cm), M. Ruffled sky blue to flax blue self; beards warm white. Parentage unknown. Cooley 1963.

HEAVENLY HALO (Lilly Gartman, TB, R. 1988). Roris 1990.

HEAVENLY HORNS (Jim Hedgecock, R. 1995). Sdlg. 84-25-4. TB, 36" (91 cm), M. Medium yellow, F. with small white blaze; beards golden orange, 1½" upturned white horn; ruffled, laced; slight sweet fragrance. Sunset Sonata X Sky Hooks. Comanche Acres 1995.

HEAVENLY LARK (Ken Mohr by Bryce Williamson, R. 1995). TB, 34" (86 cm), M. Light to medium azure blue self; beards blue white; ruffled. Parentage unknown. Pacific Coast Hybridizers 1991.

HEAVENLY POND (Daniel Thruman, R. 1997). Sdlg. 97-384. SIB, 37" (94 cm), M. S. violet blue (RHS 94A), darker veining; style arms hyacinth to wistaria blue (91B to 92B), turquoise midrib; F. cornflower blue (95A), brownish on outer haft, white signal speckled and veined violet blue. Halcyon Skies X Swank.

HEAVENLY REFLECTION (Donald Delmez, R. 1999). Sdlg. SBWST. JI (3 F.), 33" (84 cm), M. S. white, splashed and tipped blue violet, upright; style arms white, tipped blue violet; F. deep blue violet, white lines radiating from yellow green signal; ruffled. Funa Asobi X SLBWST-1: (Funa Asobi x self). Delmez Gardens 1999.

HEAVENLY SUNLIGHT (Eugene Hunt by Sharon McAllister, R. 1990). Sdlg. ORB 89-2. AB (OGB), 28½" (73 cm), EM. S. very pale flesh tones (near RHS 27D) with slight lavender overlay around edge; style arms yellow; F. greyed yellow gold (near 162B), signal veined burgundy on cream ground; beards mustard, tipped burgundy; slightly ruffled. Jean Ralls X Hallelujah Chorus. Aril Society 1990.

HEAVENLY VISION (Schreiner, R. 1996). Sdlg. W 549-A. TB, 36" (91 cm), ML. S. coral pink (RHS 38D); style arms light pink; F. coral pink, center fading to white; beards tangerine; ruffled. Custom Made X Paradise. Schreiner 1996.

HEAVEN'S EDGE (Chet Tompkins, R. 1995). Sdlg. 93-6. TB, 36" (91 cm), EML. S. white, faint blue flush; style arms pale blue white; F. snow white, narrow blackish indigo blue edge; beards white. (((Full Circle x Crown Point) x reverse sib) x ((Radiant Bride x Stepping Out) x (Radiant Bride x Full Circle))) X (((Calliope Tune x Winter Watch) x Jigsaw) x Armada). Fleur de Lis 1996.

HECITU WELO (L. J. Duffy, R. 1999). Sdlg. WI-85-95. SPEC (*setosa*), 24-30" (61-76 cm), M. Lavender (RHS 69D); style arms pale yellow, purple pencil-line midstripe, lavender crests; flat form; purple-overtoned 2- to 3-branched stalks. Collected from wild 6½ miles SE of Fairbanks, Alaska, Nordale Road area, 1995.

HEEPERS (Sterling Innerst, R. 1991). Sdlg. 3531-3. SDB, 14" (36 cm), ML. White, narrowly edged light blue; slight sweet fragrance. Hee Haw X Jeepers. Innerst 1992.

HEHAK SAPA (L. J. Duffy, R. 1992). Sdlg. WI-17-72. SPEC (*setosa*), 30-36" (76-91 cm), E. Purple blue (may vary from navy blue to purple blue shades) with yellow and white streaking at base of F.; style arms rose, purple mid-streak, purple crest area; buds deep blue. Selection of *I. setosa interior* collected 1972, near Fairbanks, Alaska.

HEIDI CHRISTOPH (Manfred Beer, R. 1992). Sdlg. MB 14/79 C. TB, 36" (90 cm), EM. Wavy and lightly frilled white, touched pinkish violet; beards orange red; sweet fragrance. Pink Fringe X Pink Taffeta. Beer 1994.

HEIDI'S DREAM (Sharol Longaker, R. 1993). TB, 38" (97 cm), M. Lightly laced white self; beards bright gold, tipped white. Mary Frances X Pink Taffeta. Anderson Iris 1993.

HEIKE HELD (Frederick Held, R. 1996). Sdlg. 09. JI (3 F.), 42" (107 cm), L. S. medium purple; style arms dark purple; F. dark purple, dark blue surrounding signal aging to purple. Parentage unknown; seed from Jelitto Staudensamen, Germany. Nature's Garden 1997.

HEIMDALL (Harald Mathes, R. 1994). AB (OGB), 32" (80 cm), E. Medium to dark blue violet, black F. signal; beards blue violet, tipped mustard. Mondsee X Moon Dust. Aril Society 1995.

HEIRLOOM AMETHYST (Bernard Pryor, R. 1997). Sdlg. 43/92-D. LA, 36" (90 cm), E. S. violet (lighter than RHS 84A), lilac rim and pale reverse; style arms lilac; F. violet (84A), lilac rim and pale reverse, highly raised steeple signal surrounded by yellow; heavily ruffled. Little Nutkin X Magic Style.

HEKIKAI (Mototeru Kamo by Society for Japanese Irises, R. 1995). JI (6 F.), 28" (71 cm), M. F. dark violet blue (RHS 90A), widely veined white, with medium light yellow (7B) signals; style arms white, tufts edged violet blue (90A). Parentage unknown. Introduced in Japan, 1975.

HEKITO (Shuichi Hirao by Society for Japanese Irises, R. 1992). JI (6 F.), 31½" (80 cm), L. Cobalt blue, signal yellow; style arms white, tipped blue. Parentage unknown. Hirao 1958.

HEKIUN (Toyokazu Ichie by Society for Japanese Irises, R. 1992). Sdlg. N-7A. JI (3 F.), 30" (75 cm), M. S. blue (RHS 89B) shading to white at center; style arms blue (89B); F. blue (96A), sharp white lines often forked at endings about 1.25 cm from blue (89B) edge, signal yellow. "Mezame" X "Hekihou". Kamo Nursery, Japan, 1989.

HELEN ALLEN (Leslie Donnell, TB, R. 1986). Iris Acres 1993/94.

HELEN BONFILS (Joseph Hoage, TB, R. 1988). Long 1990.

HELEN COCHRAN (James McWhirter by Abram Feuerstein, R. 1996). Sdlg. J89-83-1. TB, 35" (89 cm), EM. Ruffled white self; beards white, slight yellow in throat; pronounced spicy fragrance. Denney 79-174: (Regents' Row sib x Winterscape) X Navajo Jewel. Stockton 1996.

HELEN DAWN (Graeme Grosvenor, R. 1998). Sdlg. U163-1. TB, 35" (90 cm), M. White self; beards white; slight fragrance. Skating Party X Scandia Delight. Rainbow Ridge 1999/2000.

HELENE C. (Jean Cayeux by Richard Cayeux, R. 1995). Sdlg. 8372 A. TB, 37" (95 cm), EM. Ruffled pure cyclamen pink self, paling with age; beards orange red. Rosé X Enchanted World. Cayeux 1994.

HELEN K. ARMSTRONG (Sterling Innerst, R. 1993). Sdlg. 4077-1. TB, 36" (91 cm), ML. S. light blue; F. dark blue; beards dark blue. Thunder Mountain X Codicil. Innerst 1994.

HELEN LEADER (Sterling Innerst, R. 1996). Sdlg. 3953-5. TB, 36" (91 cm), M. S. dark pink; style arms pink; F. dark pink, overlaid light lavender fancy pattern; beards pink, tipped white; slight spicy fragrance. Deserving Treasure X Goodbye Heart. Innerst 1997.

HELEN NELSON (Wayne Barry, R. 1999). Sdlg. WB 91-9-2. AB (OGB-), 28" (71 cm), E. S. violet, purple stripes; style arms tan; F. tan, brown hafts, stripes and rim, purple spot; beards brown. Galleon Gold X Judean Jewel.

HELEN NIA (Frances Love, R. 1998). JI (6 F.), 24" (61 cm), L. White self. Parentage unknown; seed from America.

HELEN RUSK (Abram Feuerstein, R. 1999). Sdlg. 94-112. TB, 34" (86 cm), ML. S. orchid; style arms copper; F. orchid, lemon at shoulders; beards yellow; lightly laced, ruffled. April in Paris X Rosette Wine. Stockton 1998.

HELEN'S HONEY (Caroline Ryan-Chacon, R. 1999). Sdlg. SGR(VG)#1. TB, 34" (86 cm), ML. Honey tan, overlaid pink; style arms honey tan; beards violet, hairs tipped tangerine; slight sweet fragrance. Schortman's Garnet Ruffles X Varga Girl. I.poppin' Irises 1999.

HELGA'S HAT (Hooker Nichols, IB, R. 1989). Hillcrest 1990.

HELIACAL CARNELIA (Sterling Innerst, R. 1990). Sdlg. 2149-14. TB, 36" (91 cm), ML. S. clear full yellow; F. clear red; beards bronze. Show Biz X Gypsy Caravan. Innerst 1990.

HELIOSGOLD (Alphonse Van Mulders, R. 1991). Sdlg. 91/5. TB, 28" (71 cm), M. S. canary yellow; F. creamy white with golden tones; beards deep yellow. Vanity X Ultrapoise. Jardinart-Van Mulders 1992.

HELIOSTAT (John C. Taylor, LA, R. 1989). Rainbow Ridge 1990/91.

HELLADA (Ladislav Muska, R. 1996). Sdlg. DISK-12. TB, 34" (86 cm), EM. Ruffled deep amethyst self; beards tangerine; ruffled; slight fragrance. (Discretion x ("Cipkovana Krinolina": (After All x Grand Waltz) x Sky Hooks)) X Decory Win. Muska 1996.

HELLBLAUER RIESE (Tomas Tamberg, R. 1997). SIB (tet.), 40" (102 cm), M. Large light blue. Light blue sdlg. X medium blue sdlg. Schoeppinger 1997.

HELLO DARKNESS (Schreiner, R. 1992). Sdlg. Y 882-1. TB, 37" (94 cm), EM. Ruffled purple black (RHS 202A) self; beards black. R 124-4: (M 229-C: ((((Allegiance x ((Envoy sdlg. x Black Castle) x L 474-J: ((Blue Glow x Black Belle) x Storm Warning))) x Black Swan sdlg.) x Navy Strut) x (((((Black Mischief x (Black Forest x Starless Night)) x L 474-J) x Black Swan) x Matinata) x Navy Strut)) x Titan's Glory) X Midnight Dancer. Schreiner 1992.

HELLO-GOODBYE (Roger Nelson, R. 1991). Sdlg. RN 84-32L. TB, 40" (102 cm), ML. S. soft lavender blue (RHS 152C) shot green gold, lightening (153D) near midrib and edge; F. lavender blue, yellow green (152D) edge and reverse, yellow green (152C) hafts; beards blue white, tipped orange deep in throat; musky fragrance. Pieces of Ice X Art Center. Iris Country 1992.

HELLO YELLOW (Robert Hollingworth, R. 1999). Sdlg. 91A2B13. SIB, 37" (94 cm), M. S. cream; style arms cream, keel yellow; F. yellow, no signal. 88V7C18: (85E4A1: (83N3B17: (Butter and Sugar x (Shadow Lake x (Polly Dodge x Anniversary))) x Pas-de-Deux) x Ruffled Velvet) X 88V8C6: (85H4B3: (Pas-de-Deux x 82G5C2: (Butter and Sugar x (Super Ego x Anniversary))) x 85E1A6: (Lady Vanessa sib x (Forrest McCord x sib))). Windwood Gardens 1999.

HELMY MILDENBERGER (Lothar Denkewitz, R. 1990). Sdlg. N-80-bic-4. SDB, 10½-12" (26-30 cm), L. S. intense bright violet, gleaming pale yellow top; F. soft ochre, washed pale violet toward edge; beards bright clear blue. ((unknown x Gingerbread Man) x Alsterquelle) X ((Gingerbread Man x Alsterquelle) x self). Von Zeppelin 1992.

HE-MAN BLUES (Gerald Richardson, R. 1992). Sdlg. 84-63-1. TB, 42" (107 cm), M. Heavily ruffled medium to light blue with faint lavender cast, silvery blue accents; beards cream, tipped gold; slight sweet fragrance. 81-22-1: (Victoria Falls x 77-17-5: (Mystique x Ermine Robe)) X Added Praise. Rainbow's End 1993.

HEMSTITCHED (Ben Hager, TB, R. 1989). Melrose 1990

HENNA RUSH (Barry Blyth, R. 1993). Sdlg. BK-1. SPU, 48" (122 cm), ML. Parchment brown self. Barbara's Kiss X self. Tempo Two 1993/94.

HERALD (Joseph Ghio, CA, 1989). Bay View 1990.

HERB McKUSICK (Sharon McAllister, R. 1992). Sdlg. 84-1-2. AB (OGB), 28" (72 cm), EM. S. iridescent violet (near RHS 84A); F. deep plum purple (near 79D) ground, large signal area marked by separation of pigments into burgundy veining on ivory ground; beards orange in throat, brownish violet at tip. Bangladesh X Martha Mia. McAllister 1993.

HERE'S HEAVEN (Duane Meek, R. 1992). Sdlg. 35-2-2. TB, 35" (89 cm), EM. Pleated, heavily ruffled and slightly picoteed pure white; beards white; slight fragrance. Winterscape X 72-1-4: ((Mount Repose x Fanfare Orchid) x Blue Luster). D & J Gardens 1992.

HER KINGDOM (Larry Johnson, R. 1994). Sdlg. JO88-31-2. TB, 38" (97 cm), M. S. cool medium pink; F. same, darker shoulders with some lavender tones, slight white flush; beards orange red; ruffled. Pink Swan X Endless Love. Cooley 1994.

HER PINKNESS (Oscar Schick, R. 1999). Sdlg. 92-19C02. TB, 36-38" (91-97 cm), M. S. and style arms light pink (RHS 55D); F. light pink (56A); beards pinkish orange; ruffled; slight musky fragrance. Alice Goodman X Vision in Pink. Stockton 1999.

HERS (Allan Ensminger, IB, R. 1989). Varigay 1990.

HE'S A PIRATE (Barry Blyth, R. 1994). Sdlg. A49-2. IB, 25" (63 cm), ML. S. burgundy wine; F. cherry black; beards lavender overlaid cherry bronze; pronounced sweet fragrance. Chanted X Electrique. Tempo Two 1994/95.

HEY DREAMER (Barry Blyth, R. 1994). Sdlg. Z39-2. TB, 35" (89 cm), ML. S. white washed blue lilac, midrib slightly deeper; F. white, 1" bishops violet plicata edge deepening at hafts, deeper line below insignificant lemon and white beard; slight sweet fragrance. He Man X Snowbrook. Tempo Two 1994/95.

HEY HEY (Barry Blyth, R. 1997). Sdlg. D35-1. SDB, 10" (25 cm), EM. S. white, pastel lavender veining, open form; style arms bright pink; F. white, less lavender veining; beards white, tangerine in throat; slight sweet fragrance. Bee's Knees X Z10-3, Rockabye sib. Tempo Two 1997/98.

HEY THERE (Carol Lankow by J. T. Aitken, R. 1992). Sdlg. 0-H-1-1. MDB, 5" (13 cm), E. S. smooth medium yellow; F. pale powder blue; beards frosty pale violet; slight fragrance. Rain Dance X Funny Face. Aitken's Salmon Creek 1992.

HI (Monty Byers, IB, R. 1989). Moonshine 1990.

HI CALYPSO (Joseph Hoage, R. 1998). Sdlg. H 89-63-2. TB, 40" (101 cm), M. S. gold; F. blended violet, shoulders and rim burnished gold; beards burnt gold. Syncopation X Enchanting. Long 1998.

HICKEY (C. R. King, R. 1994). Sdlg. 4 CRK 93. TB, 52" (132 cm), M. S. light purple; F. dark purple; beards yellow; sweet fragrance. Parentage unknown.

HICKORY LEAVES (O. D. Niswonger, R. 1998). Sdlg. Sp 7-93. SPU, 42" (107 cm), M. Yellow gold, F. with slightly deeper gold signal. Goldmania X Destination. Cape Iris 1998.

HIDDEN GLOW (Duane Meek, R. 1996). Sdlg. 05-1-8. TB, 36" (91 cm), EM. Slightly ruffled blue white, deeper on midrib and below white beard; style arms deeper blue white. Laced Cotton X Breakers. D & J Gardens 1996.

HIDDEN OASIS (Lois Rich by James Whitely, R. 1991). Sdlg. R80-14. AR (RC), 14-16" (36-41 cm), EM. S. cream boldly veined violet, bright blue violet midrib; style arms honey brown, blue violet at throat; F. cream covered with brown violet veining at shoulders and around large black signal to edge, medium brown covering veining below signal to edge; beards white base, brown top. R75-184B: ((((Persian Bronze x (Kerr 55-1 x 55-14)) x ((Bagdad Beauty x *I. gatesii*) x *I. hermona*))) x *I. stolonifera* USSR 163) X Persian Pansy. Aril Patch, Aril Society 1991.

HIDDEN PINK (Harald Mathes, R. 1998). Sdlg. T-12-V-95-1. AB (OGB), 31" (80 cm), E. Light orange brown, veined darker, F. with large black brown signal; style arms light orange brown; beards orange; slight fragrance. Tetraploid OG sdlg. X Vanity. Aril Society 1998.

HIDDEN RICHES (Duane Meek, R. 1999). Sdlg. 181-1-5. TB, 33" (84 cm), M. S. pale blue white, deeper blue on lower quarter; style arms blue, crests tipped blue white; F. blue white, soft blue on upper edges; beards soft blue, hairs tipped pale cream yellow; ruffled, picoteed. Honky Tonk Blues X Carriage Trade. D & J Gardens 1999.

HIDDEN TALENTS (Sharon McAllister, R. 1990). Sdlg. 77-22-2. AB (OGB), 28½" (73 cm), EM. S. very pale lavender, aging creamy white; style arms buff; F. buff, faint blush of pinkish lavender when fresh, aging pale buff, signal burgundy; beards dark burgundy. Esther the Queen X Sheik. Aril Society 1990.

HIDDEN WORLD (Richard Ernst, R. 1990). Sdlg. F119-2. TB, 34" (86 cm), M. Ruffled and laced lavender pink, F. lighter in center; beards orange. Afternoon Delight X Gaulter 81-099, pink inv. Claudia Rene. Cooley 1990.

HIDENISHIKI (Society for Japanese Irises, R. 1992). JI (6 F.), 36" (91 cm), VE-E. Ruffled deep red purple splashed white, signal yellow. Parentage unknown. Mototeru Kamo prior to 1980.

HIGGLEDY-PIGGLEDY (Sterling Innerst, R. 1990). Sdlg. 3379-2. IB, 20" (51 cm), ML. S. white;

F. white, faintly blushed ice blue; beards white, tipped yellow; slight sweet fragrance. Scented Nutmeg X 2815-1: (Little Episode x Pippi Longstockings). Innerst 1990.

HIGH AZURE (Roy Fielding by Philip Edinger, R. 1999). TB, 38" (97 cm), M. Ruffled pale azure blue, shaded darker at base of S. and around beards; beards bluish white at end, lemon midsection, yellow in throat. Snow Flurry X Azure Skies. Melrose 1957.

HIGH BLUE SKY (Richard Ernst, R. 1998). Sdlg. M100. TB, 35" (89 cm), M. S. light blue, slight pale violet cast; style arms light blue; F. light blue darker than S., deeper veining; beards light blue, yellow in throat. Proud Tradition X Blue It Up. Cooley 1998.

HIGH CALIBER (George Sutton, R. 1999). Sdlg. H-149. TB, 39" (99 cm), ML-VL. Fluted dark wistaria blue, F. with lighter hafts; beards orange, medium wistaria horn; slight musky fragrance. Lurid X Aaron's Dagger.

HIGH-CLASS GIRL (Hooker Nichols, TB, R. 1988). Hillcrest 1996.

HIGH DI (J. T. Aitken, R. 1995). Sdlg. 88 S-1-D. SIB (tet.), 48" (122 cm), ML-VL. Dark blue purple, F. with small white signal and faint white rim. High Standards X Dear Dianne. Aitken's Salmon Creek 1995.

HIGH DRAMA (Joseph Gatty, R. 1990). Sdlg. Q10-1. TB, 36" (91 cm), ML. S. colonial yellow (M&P 11-K-3) to chamois (11-I-5) with slight rosy (7-A-4) flush at base; F. dark burgundy (56-L-10) paling to carbuncle (8-L-7) toward edge; beards mustard yellow; slight sweet fragrance. K84-2, Syncopation sib, X K41-1: (Show Biz x Villain). Keppel 1991.

HIGH ENERGY (Mary Dunn, R. 1995). Sdlg. M1062-E. TB, 36" (91 cm), M. S. light yellow; style arms golden yellow; F. ivory, cinnamon marginal plicata marking; beards yellow, deeper in throat. Freestyle X Hamblen 82-42B. M.A.D. Iris 1996.

HIGH FLYING (Mary Dunn, R. 1995). Sdlg. L209-4. LA, 37" (94 cm), M. S. medium blue; style arms pale blue, edge and tip darker; F. medium blue, texture veined, small light yellow signal. Plantation Beau X Wine Country. Bay View 1996.

HIGH GRADE (John C. Taylor, R. 1998). Sdlg. UL 34-5. LA, 43" (110 cm), ML. S. lemon, veined; style arms lemon, flushed green; F. lemon, veined, with veined yellow green signal; slightly recurved form. Poseidon's Pool X Helen Naish. Rainbow Ridge 1998/99.

HIGH IMPACT (George Sutton, R. 1997). Sdlg. G-19 BRSA. TB, 39" (99 cm), ML & RE. Ruffled white, infused pale pink, F. with brown shoulders; beards golden orange, extension curved upward 3½" ending in small upside-down spoon; slight sweet fragrance. Sweet Musette X Twice Thrilling. Sutton 1998.

HIGHLINE SNOWFLAKE (Eleanor McCown, R. 1991). Sdlg. 88-3. SPU, 31" (79 cm), M. S. white; F. white, bright yellow signal, heavily ruffled. *I. halophila* sdlg. X Ruffled Canary. Cordon Bleu 1991.

HIGHLINE TOPAZ (Eleanor McCown, R. 1994). Sdlg. 88-22. SPU, 48" (122 cm), L. S. topaz; style arms golden yellow; F. golden orange, edged topaz. Mariposa Tarde X 83-3: (79-16 x Highline Amethyst). Cordon Bleu 1995.

HIGH LONESOME (Sterling Innerst, R. 1990). Sdlg. 2370-10. TB, 34" (86 cm), EML. S. medium blue; F. dark blue; beards dark blue, tipped bronze; slight fragrance. 1856-1: (Sapphire Hills x (San Leandro x Shipshape)) X 1329-9: (Mary Frances x Starina). Innerst 1991.

HIGH PEAK (B.L.C. Dodsworth, TB, R. 1987). British Iris Society 1989.

HIGH PITCH (Mary Dunn, R. 1991). Sdlg. L139-2. LA, 36" (91 cm), M. Velvety deep red wine purple, bright orange yellow signal. Full Eclipse X Gold Reserve. Bay View 1992.

HIGH POINT (George Sutton, R. 1998). Sdlg. H-206-F. TB, 38" (97 cm), ML & RE. S. and style arms white, tinted pink; F. plum purple (RHS 79A), white and pale violet 3/8" blended edge; beards yellow orange, short red violet horn; ruffled; slight sweet fragrance. F-68: (Thornbird x Platform) X Sweet Reflection. Sutton 1999.

HIGH POWERED (John C. Taylor, R. 1998). Sdlg. UL 8-X. LA, 51" (130 cm), ML. S. blue; style arms white, edged violet; F. blue, yellow signal surrounded by white spray pattern. C'est La Mote X First Favourite.

HIGH RANK (Mary Dunn, R. 1990). Sdlg. L155-3. LA, 36" (91 cm), M. S. henna red infusion over gold ground, light edge; style arms lime green; F. deeper henna red infusion over gold base, light serrated edge, yellow green signal. Southerner X L96-15: (Charlie's Michele x Rhett). Bay View 1991.

HIGH ROLLER (Graeme Grosvenor, R. 1996). Sdlg. T2-K. TB, 37" (95 cm), M. Light rosewood tan, F. with orange yellow hafts; beards orange yellow; slight fragrance. Rancho Grande X Sweet Musette. Rainbow Ridge 1997/98.

HIGH SONG (D. C. Anderson, TB, R. 1988). Brown's Iris Garden 1990.

HIGH SPLENDOR (Vernon Wood, R. 1994). Sdlg. 93-82. CA, 10-12" (25-30 cm), ML. S. white with medium violet (RHS 93B) line down center; style arms medium violet (93B); F. white, small yellow signal with medium violet rays radiating out to near edge; lightly ruffled. Foothill Banner X Fort Point.

HIGH STAKES (Schreiner, R. 1999). Sdlg. DD 456-1. TB, 36" (91 cm), M. Deep royal purple (RHS 89C) self; beards dark purple; ruffled. W 83-1: (Stormy Night x Silverado sib) X Royal Intrigue. Schreiner 1999.

HIGH TECH (Ben Hager by Roris Gardens, R. 1993). Sdlg. T4840. TB, 38" (97 cm), M. S. light lavender blue; F. blue white; beards white, tipped yellow; lightly ruffled. Tinted Crystal X T3702Sh: (Silver Flow x Ruffled Ballet). Roris 1993.

HIGH WINDS (Joseph Ghio, R. 1996). Sdlg. PE-212-P2. CA, 14" (36 cm), L. S. white; F. white, lined and dotted light blue, yellow dime signal. PG-204-R2: (Sierra Dell x Age of Chivalry) X PG-132-N2: (Westerlies x Sierra Stars). Bay View 1996.

HIKURANGI (Revie Harvey by Marion Ball, R. 1999). Sdlg. 78/1/1. TB, 39" (100 cm), ML. S. deep golden yellow; F. deep gold, slightly deeper gold infusion; beards gold, heavy; musky fragrance. (Saffron Robe x Angel Unawares) X Catalyst.

HILLS AND DALES (Graeme Grosvenor, R. 1996). Sdlg. R6-9. TB, 37" (94 cm), M. S. white; F. blue violet; beards yellow, hairs tipped white. Silverado X Snowbrook. Rainbow Ridge 1996/97.

HILLS DISTRICT (Graeme Grosvenor, R. 1994). Sdlg. S83-1. TB, 38" (97 cm), M. S. orange; F. lighter orange, darkening at edge; beards red; ruffled; slight sweet fragrance. Samurai Silk X Esmeralda. Rainbow Ridge 1994/95.

HILLS OF SARANAP (Carl Boswell, R. 1994). Sdlg. 60-86-1-S. SDB, 10" (25 cm), M. S. warm white, yellow midrib; F. warm white, heavily washed yellow; beards white; slight fragrance. Jewel Baby X ((Copy Cat x (Tea Apron x April Melody)) x Marmalade Skies). Adamgrove 1994.

HILLTOP VIEW (Larry Gaulter, R. 1990). Sdlg. L82-4. TB, 38" (97 cm), M. Clear blue; beard near-white, tipped blue, yellow in throat. Inv. sdlgs. from Portrait of Larrie. Cooley 1990.

HILLVIEW DAZZLER (Graeme Grosvenor, R. 1998). Sdlg. U129-2. TB, 35" (90 cm), EM. S. yellow; F. creamy white, edged red; beards yellow; slight fragrance. Point in Time X Glitz 'n Glitter. Rainbow Ridge 1999/2000.

HILLVIEW INDIGO (Graeme Grosvenor, R. 1998). Sdlg. U31-1. TB, 39" (100 cm), ML. Dark violet self; beards yellow, tipped blue; slight fragrance. Breakers X Lord Olivier.

HILO SURF (John Durrance, R. 1990). Sdlg. D83-19. TB, 36" (91 cm), ML. Ruffled white; beards yellow in throat. Prince of Peace X Ice Sculpture. Long 1990.

HIME KAGAMI (Shuichi Hirao by Society for Japanese Irises, R. 1993). JI (6 F.), 36" (90 cm), EM. Ruffled pink with darker pink veins, signal yellow; style arms pink, crests dark pink. Parentage unknown. Hirao 1976.

HIME KOMACHI (Kamo Nursery by Society for Japanese Irises, R. 1999). JI (6 F.), 35" (90 cm), EM. Pink veined darker pink; style arms pink. Parentage unknown. Kamo Nursery 1987.

HINEBLUE (Heather Collins, SDB, R. 1984). Wyuna 1987.

HINEMOA (Heather Collins, R. 1993). Sdlg. 1/3/81. CA, 20" (50 cm), EML. S. pale lavender, purple midrib, laced; F. pale lavender, pale blue stripe at end of deep yellow signal surrounded by white veining. Parentage unknown.

HINT (Ben Hager, R. 1993). Sdlg. MD5497PlBlAmW. MDB, 4" (10 cm), EM. S. white; F. white with very pale blue flush that fades; beards white. Nestling X unknown. Adamgrove 1995.

HINT OF YELLOW (Currier McEwen, R. 1990). Sdlg. 85/95C. JI (6 F.), 36" (90 cm), ML. Creamy white with light yellow (RHS 12A) signal and veins at inner half; style arms light yellow. White Parachute X Continuing Pleasure.

HIP-HOP (Barry Blyth, R. 1999). Sdlg. E12-1. SDB, 12" (30 cm), ML. Bright golden yellow, F. with tiny white chevron below beard; beards gold, white at end, orange in throat; slight fragrance. Moustache X Little Bev. Tempo Two 1999/2000.

HIPPIE (Paul Black, R. 1998). Sdlg. B305G. SDB, 11" (28 cm), E. S. and style arms peach; F. blended coppery violet, lime gold haft and diffuse edge; beards orange; pronounced spicy fragrance. 86276A: (Marvelous Magic x Joyce McBride) X 91213D: (Oh Jay x Patacake). Mid-America 1998.

HIPPO'Z TUTU (Brad Kasperek, R. 1996). Sdlg. 92P-55V. TB, 32" (81 cm), EM. S. cyclamen purple (RHS 74A/B), lighter around midrib; style arms cyclamen purple, laced; F. white ground

(155C), 1/2" cyclamen purple edge, inner side stippling, center stripe; beards burnt orange; moderately ruffled and laced. Baboon Bottom X Raspberry Fudge. Zebra 1996.

HIS (Allan Ensminger, IB, R. 1989). Varigay 1990.

HIS AND HERS (Richard Ernst, R. 1996). Sdlg. KF125-32E. TB, 38" (97 cm), M. S. white, infused violet blue (near RHS 94C) deeper on midrib, pale yellow partial rim at top; style arms pale violet blue, crests pale yellow; F. white tinted violet blue, pale yellow (9D) rim; beards yellow (14B); purple foliage base and bloomstalks. Chiffon Ruffles X sib. Cooley 1997.

HIS HONOR (Duane Meek, R. 1992). Sdlg. 268-1-3. BB, 27" (70 cm), M. Fluted and heavily ruffled gold with large white area around deeper gold beards. Dazzling Gold X 166-5-7: (Kilt Lilt x Seven Hills). D & J Gardens 1992.

HIT AND MISS (Robert Annand, R. 1999). Sdlg. 88-48A. TB, 35" (89 cm), ML. White, irregularly blotched, striped and dotted purple; beards orange, end and hair tips yellow; broken color pattern. 83-3A: (Doodle Strudel x Tye-Dye) X Iris Bohnsack. Stockton 1999.

HOAR EDGE (Jennifer Hewitt, R. 1990). Sdlg. T782/1. SIB (tet.), 30" (75 cm), EM. S. dark violet blue (RHS 89B); F. velvety dark violet blue (89B), fine white edge, small creamy white signal with diffused edge. Laurenbuhl X McEwen T(2)66/38LB. British Iris Society 1993.

HOBO HEAVEN (William Maryott, R. 1994). Sdlg. S130C. TB, 36" (91 cm), M. S. spectrum grey (RHS 197B) with slight hint of green; F. spectrum grey, yellow shoulders; beards yellow; sweet fragrance. H113A: (Honey Mocha x Coffee House) X Norwegian Wood. Maryott 1998.

HOCKA HOONA (Peter DeSantis, R. 1999). Sdlg. 82-6C. SPU, 49" (124 cm), EM. S. blue (RHS 89C), golden yellow (163B) veining; style arms off-white tinged blue, light blue (89C) tip; F. wide blue (89C) rim shading to brown (177A), golden yellow (163B) signal and veining. *I. ochroleuca* X Imperial Ruby.

HOGGAR (Vivette Sazio, R. 1990). Sdlg. V 81 17B. BB, 23½" (60 cm), M. Ruffled bright light pink; beards tangerine. Vanity X Venetian Dancer. Iris en Provence 1990.

HOKKAIDO (Perry's Plant Farm by John Carter, R. 1999). JI (3 F.), 36" (91 cm), M. S. violet; style arms pale violet, darkening toward edge; F. very pale violet, darker violet veins, yellow signal. Parentage unknown. Perry's Hardy Plant Farm prior to 1960.

HOLDEN'S CHILD (Sarah Tiffney, SPEC-X, R. 1988). Pope's Perennials 1991.

HOLD ME (Barry Blyth, R. 1995). Sdlg. A44-21. SDB, 14" (36 cm), VE-EM. S. cream heavily overlaid mauve pink; F. creamy white with pink glow, 1/8"-1/4" mauve pink plicata edge; beards white, tipped tangerine bronze; slight sweet fragrance. V7-5, Gigolette sib, X Chanted. Tempo Two 1995/96.

HOLIDAY LOVER (Barry Blyth, R. 1991). Sdlg. W131A. TB, 38-40" (96-102 cm), ML. Rose pink to rose wine pink; beards deep orange, fuzzy. Dance Man X Mulled Wine. Tempo Two 1991/92.

HOLLIS BLUE EYES (Everette Lineberger, R. 1999). Sdlg. QHT 136. TB, 34" (86 cm), ML. Pale blue self; beards mustard gold. Parentage unknown.

HOLLY GOLIGHTLY (James McWhirter by Abram Feuerstein, R. 1997). Sdlg. J89-104-3. TB, 33" (84 cm), ML. Heavily ruffled blue violet self, metallic sheen; beards blue violet; pronounced sweet fragrance. Winterscape X Honky Tonk Blues. Stockton 1997.

HOLLYWOOD AND VINE (James McWhirter, R. 1991). Sdlg. J85-30-2. TB, 36" (91 cm), M. S. light magenta grape; F. darker magenta grape; beards blue violet; ruffled; slight fragrance. Ensemble X Noble House. Cottage 1992.

HOLSTEIN GRAF (Lothar Denkewitz, R. 1995). Sdlg. N-88-pl. 1. SDB, 13" (33 cm), E. S. white, light purple plicata edge; style arms white; F. white, purple plicata hafts, narrow edging; beards lavender, tipped yellow; pronounced spicy fragrance. Wire Rim X Bodderlecker. Von Zeppelin 1997.

HOLY COW (Tom Burseen, R. 1997). Sdlg. 93-305B. TB, 33" (84 cm), EM. S. and style arms dark cherry wine (redder than RHS 79C); F. black burgundy (darker than 79A); beards bright carrot red; heavily ruffled; musky fragrance. Coalignition X Twilight Blaze. T.B.'s Place 1998.

HOLY FIRE (George Sutton, R. 1999). Sdlg. H-133. TB, 35" (89 cm), ML. S. white, thin yellow midline; style arms white; F. white, hafts touched yellow; beards fiery red orange, white base at end, white horn. Mesmerizer X Filoli.

HOLY HEART (Donald Spoon, R. 1995). Sdlg. 90-44. TB, 31" (79 cm), ML. S. blended lavender rose, peach tan central infusion; style arms rose and mauve; F. rose edge, lighter blended mauve and tan center; beards bright tangerine orange; ruffled. Copper Classic X Olympic Challenge. Winterberry 1999.

HOLY TOLEDO (Chet Tompkins, R. 1992). Sdlg. 85-112. TB, 38-40" (97-102 cm), ML-VL. Ruffled apricot pink; beards brilliant red. Pink and apricot sdlgs. inv. Ovation, High Esteem, Cameo Coral, Cloud Cap. Fleur de Lis 1991.

HOLY TRINITY (Donald Sorensen, R. 1999). Sdlg. S-96-18-14. TB, 35" (90 cm), M. Pure white (RHS 155D), slight greenish S. midrib and central F. flush; beards white, light yellow (7D) in throat; heavily ruffled; slight musky fragrance. S-92-2-9: (Cloudless Sunrise x Amber Snow) X Champagne Elegance.

HOME BEFORE DARK (Gerald Moorhead, R. 1997). Sdlg. 91-35-6. TB, 36" (91 cm), M. Medium to dark reddish maroon, F. with deeper saturation in center; beards orange red, wide; ruffled; slight sweet fragrance. Magician's Apprentice X Guadalajara.

HOMER UNN (Chet Tompkins, R. 1992). Sdlg. 88-15. TB, 38" (97 cm), ML. Bright scarlet blended brown red; beards brown. Inv. red lines. Fleur de Lis 1991.

HOMESTEADER'S DAUGHTER (Ruby Short, R. 1991). Sdlg. 1639a. TB, 38" (97 cm), M. Near-white; beards light blue. ((Inverness x Mary McClellan) x Jack R. Dee) X Song of Norway. Short 1994.

HOME STYLE (Frederick Kerr, R. 1998). Sdlg. 915403. TB, 36" (91 cm), EML. S. white ground, wide medium blue violet edge and center stripe; style arms medium blue violet; F. white, 1/4" to 1/2" dark blue violet plicata edge, dark blue violet veins beside beard; beards yellow, blue violet at end; ruffled. Momentum X 892003: (Polar Seas x self). Rainbow Acres 1998.

HOME TOWN HERO (George Slade, TB, R. 1988). Wyle Wynde 1990.

HONEST ILLUSION (Duane Meek, R. 1999). Sdlg. 116-1-1. TB, 32" (81 cm), M. Ruffled mauve, flushed rose, F. with ivory area below beard; beards melon, rosy mauve at end. Delirious X Chapel Bells. D & J Gardens 1999.

HONEY APRICOT (Francis Rogers, R. 1993). Sdlg. F-613-A. BB, 26" (66 cm), M. S. yellow orange (RHS 22C); F. greyed orange (164C); beards red orange; lightly ruffled; sweet fragrance. Love Chant X Marmalade Skies. Meadowbrook 1994.

HONEYBUN'S LOVE (Tom Burseen, R. 1999). Sdlg. 95-307A. TB, 35" (89 cm), M. S. white, lavender blue midrib infusion; F. lavender blue; beards blue, with long uplifted lavender blue flounce; heavily ruffled. 93-299: (Birdbath x Beat the Heat) X 92-351: (Splish Splash x Imagine That). T.B.'s Place 1999.

HONEY BUTTER (Bernard Hamner, R. 1991). Sdlg. 84-108. TB, 32" (81 cm), M. S. pale orange (RHS 27B) at base shading to very pale orange (27D) at edge; F. light orange (26D), edged yellow orange (20D); beards tangerine. Peach Sundae X (Party Parfait x Beauty Crown). Shepard Iris 1991.

HONEY CREME KISSES (Dagon Gillespy, R. 1991). Sdlg. 86-11-13-46. TB, 34" (86 cm), EML & RE. S. light honey yellow; F. cream, light honey yellow edge; beards yellow; slight spicy fragrance. Summer Olympics X Double Time.

HONEY CUB (Brad Kasperek, R. 1996). Sdlg. 93B-69H. BB, 22" (56 cm), EM. S. and style arms lemon yellow (RHS 13B) ground, lightly streaked primrose yellow (4D); F. lemon yellow ground, splashed primrose yellow and golden brown (164A); beards burnt amber; ruffled; slight fragrance. Tiger Honey X Tennessee Woman. Superstition 1998.

HONEY GALORE (Ron Betzer, R. 1999). Sdlg. 94-1-1. LA, 32" (81 cm), M. S. orange buff (RHS 22C); style arms orange buff, infused black and green toward base; F. dark honey, veined and overlaid bright amber, orange buff edge, lime green steeple signal; ruffled, waved. Louisiana Teddy Bear X Gladiator's Gift.

HONEY GEM (Ladislav Muska, R. 1997). Sdlg. IB-HOLE-07. IB, 24" (61 cm), M. S. light golden honey; style arms deeper gold; F. light brown, banded light gold; beards orange; heavily laced; slight fragrance. (Honey Lace x White Gem) X "Lemonette". Muska 1996.

HONEY HAZE (Barry Blyth, R. 1992). Sdlg. X25-6. SDB, 13" (33 cm), ML. Creamy pastel lemon, F. with slightly deeper hafts; beards bright tangerine, white on outer 1/4". (Oladi x Fifi) X (Peach Eyes x Kandi Moon). Tempo Two 1992/93.

HONEY HUSH (Marvin Davis, R. 1995). Sdlg. 87-096-2. TB, 34" (86 cm), M. S. and style arms medium yellow; F. white, deep yellow hafts, cream yellow edge; beards white with hairs tipped yellow, lavender extension with white flounce; ruffled; slight sweet fragrance. Be Mine X Howdy Do. Miller's Manor 1996.

HONEY JUMBLE (Heather Pryor, R. 1998). Sdlg. 56/93-B. LA, 39" (100 cm), ML. Majolica yellow (RHS 168D), overall brown veining, yellow rim, F. with yellow and lime line signal changing to brown at petal edge; style arms lighter majolica yellow, deeper crests; ruffled. Monet's Magic X unknown. Iris Haven 1999/2000.

HONEYMOON DANCE (Hooker Nichols, R. 1990). Sdlg. 8829A. TB, 36" (91 cm), E. S. pinkish red violet; F. pale peach, edged raspberry, hafts darker; beards rusty orange; ruffled. Beyond X Pink Confetti. Hillcrest 1991.

HONEYMOON SUITE (Joseph Ghio, R. 1990). Sdlg. 86-98R2. TB, 36" (91 cm), ML. S. pastel pink; F. light orchid pink; beards tangerine. Newlywed X (Caption x (Dream Affair x (Artiste x Tupelo Honey))). Bay View 1991.

HONEY MUSTARD (J. T. Aitken, R. 1998). Sdlg. 87 T 106. TB, 32" (81 cm), ML. S. honey tan, yellow laced edge; style arms yellow; F. white, blending to yellow at rim; beards ochre orange. 84 T 65: ((Sunshine Express x Brown Lasso) x (Peach Float x Irene Nelson)) X 82 T 104: (Irene Nelson x Playgirl). Aitken's Salmon Creek 1998.

HONEY SCOOP (George Sutton, R. 1996). Sdlg. G-14-A. TB, 35" (89 cm), EM. S. chrome yellow (RHS 158A) edged sulphur yellow (6A); style arms sulphur yellow; F. white, veined and edged sulphur yellow; beards bright tangerine, cream to chrome yellow spoon at end; ruffled, laced. Contrite X Sky Hooks. Sutton 1997.

HONEY STAR (Janet Hutchinson, R. 1991). Sdlg. 89-MHB21. LA, 34" (87 cm), M. S. cream, veined buff wine, giving pale apricot effect; F. cream, blushed and veined buff wine, rich yellow signal. Margaret Hunter X unknown. Rainbow Ridge 1991/92.

HONEY WIND (Barry Blyth, R. 1990). Sdlg. X28-3. SDB, 10" (25 cm), VE-E. S. antique to buff gold with tannish influence; F. similar, with creamy center area around beard, deeper tannish stippled and stitched area around cream; beards lavender, tipped mustard gold. Yipee X Royal Magician. Tempo Two 1990/91.

HONKY TONK HUSSY (Duane Meek, R. 1991). Sdlg. 261-1-2. BB, 26" (66 cm), EM. Ruffled deep maroon; self beards. Honky Tonk X Harlem Hussy. D & J Gardens 1991.

HONORARIUM (Robert Dunn, R. 1993). Sdlg. B66-1065A. TB, 37" (93 cm), M. S. lilac; F. white tinted very light lilac; beards light yellow. B83-809: (Trident x High Falutin) X Cruzin. M.A.D. Iris 1994.

HONOURED GUEST (John C. Taylor, R. 1991). Sdlg. OL 142-A. LA, 39" (100 cm), M. Ruffled purple (RHS 90A), yellow signal, white center on sepal; style arms ivory, brushed mauve. M24-4: (C'est Si Bon x Charles Arny III) X Helen Naish. Rainbow Ridge 1991/92.

HONOURED QUEEN (Chuck Chapman, R. 1997). Sdlg. 92-635-D. TB, 35" (89 cm), L. S. white, 1/4" light yellow gold laced edge; style arms white, yellow gold edge; F. violet, white centerline and area around beard, 1/8" golden yellow laced edge; beards yellow; ruffled, lightly laced. Bride's Halo X Spring Satin.

HOODLUM (Keith Keppel, R. 1996). Sdlg. 91-63B. SDB, 15" (38 cm), EM. S. port (M&P 56-E-12) paling toward center; style arms dark reddish violet, paler margin, port crests; F. port, velvety sheen on lower edge, paler and speckled white near beard; beards bronze, lavender blue at end, yellow base in throat; ruffled; slight sweet fragrance. Privileged Character X Gatty W37-19, Quote sib. Keppel 1997.

HOODSPORT (Jim & Vicki Craig, R. 1999). Sdlg. AH10C14. MTB, 22" (56 cm), M. Smooth medium lavender self; beards coral; ruffled, flared. 17W3, Rave Review sib, X Rave Review. J. & V. Craig 1999.

HOOKEM HORNS (George Sutton, R. 1996). Sdlg. F-66. TB, 38" (97 cm), EM. S. lilac purple (RHS 70A), paler midrib; F. ruby red, white spray pattern at haft, edges darker; beards white, yellow in throat, 1½" hairless ruby red horn at end; ruffled; slight spicy fragrance. Bubble Up X Sky Hooks. Sutton 1997.

HOOSEGOW (Lynda Miller, R. 1996). Sdlg. 1093. SDB, 11" (28 cm), EM. S. and F. white ground, edged and veined bishops purple; style arms dark bishops purple; beards white, hairs tipped brown; slight sweet fragrance. 12586C: ((Petite Polka x unknown) x unknown) X 2889, unknown. Miller's Manor 1997.

HOOSIER GOLD (Lucille Robinson, R. 1992). Sdlg. 6N4. TB, 34" (86 cm), ML. Dark gold self; beards gold. On Target X Gold Galore. Iris Acres 1993.

HOOTER (Hooker Nichols, R. 1991). Sdlg. 8655C. SDB, 12" (30 cm), EM. S. gentian blue flushed red violet; F. same, chartreuse halo; beards powder blue; ruffled. Evening Event X Dixieland Delight.

HOPI BRAVE (Jim Hedgecock, R. 1997). Sdlg. 84-72-7. TB, 28" (71 cm), M. S. pale smoky purple, white rays at midrib; F. white ground, wide pale smoky purple band; beards white, yellow in throat; ruffled; slight sweet fragrance. Roundup X Smoke Rings. Comanche Acres 1998.

HORATIO (Ben Hager, R. 1991). Sdlg. T5057TPrSh. TB, 35" (89 cm), ML. S. royal violet purple;

F. violet purple maturing to blue over silver with violet purple edge; beards tangerine, last 1/4" bluish. T4392TPr: (((((Babson M131-4: (Golden Stairs x (Queen's Lace x (E61-1 x Figurine))) x Morning Breeze) x Dream Time) x Grand Waltz) x Irene Nelson) x (Silver Flow x Irene Nelson)) X T4244FchPr: (((((Gay Adventure x Sass 55-349) x Keppel 68-52: (Jones 743: (sdlg. x Crystal Flame) x Keppel 65-32A: (Marquesan Skies x Babbling Brook))) x Caro Nome) x Royalace) x Matinee Idol). Melrose 1991.

HORDERN'S HENRY (Heather Pryor, R. 1994). Sdlg. 20/90-1. LA, 43" (108 cm), E. Lightly ruffled soft brandy (RHS 163B), washed and veined slightly darker, yellow green steeple signal on all petals; honey reverse; style arms yellow. Southerner X Fine Warrior. Iris Haven 1996/97.

HORIHORA (Ladislav Muska, R. 1997). Sdlg. RGTP-08. TB, 39" (99 cm), M. S. bright pinkish peach; style arms pinkish caramel; F. burgundy red flushed lilac, wide smoky pink edge; beards light orange; sweet fragrance. ((Ringo x Geniality) x Tomorrow's Child) X Pu Abi. Muska 1997.

HORNED HONEY (Lola Quinn, R. 1998). Sdlg. L4-8. TB, 34" (86 cm), M. S. honey yellow; style arms light brown; F. honey yellow, light brown and white; beards light yellow to deep golden honey in throat and on hair tips, 1½"-2" straight purplish brown horn; slight fragrance. Horned Mystery X Summit Snow.

HORNS AND BLUES (Jim Hedgecock, R. 1991). Sdlg. 84-1-1. TB, 38" (97 cm), M. Ruffled pale blue; beards yellow, fuzzy pale blue horn; slight sweet fragrance. Sky Hooks X Soul Music. Comanche Acres 1996.

HORSE (Joseph Griffith, R. 1990). Sdlg. B-8387. TB, 28" (71 cm), M. S. dark brown overlaid purple; F. slightly lighter, white shading to reddish purple around beard; beards purple tipped yellow, yellow in throat; slight spicy fragrance. Superstition X Spartan.

#HORTENSE (Gillot, TB, R. 1928). Marked as obsolete in 1939 Checklist; name released.

HORTENSE (Jean Cayeux by Richard Cayeux, R. 1995). Sdlg. 8461 E. TB, 37" (95 cm), ML. S. pinkish white; F. pansy violet; beards red. 8245 A: (7706 A, Alizes sib, x Love Bandit) X 8109 A: (Condottiere x Delphi). Cayeux 1993.

HOSTESS ROYALE (Barry Blyth, R. 1994). Sdlg. A61-2. TB, 42" (107 cm), ML. Peach with creamy white area around apricot tangerine beards; pronounced sweet fragrance. Dance Man X Pink Swan. Tempo Two 1994/95

HOT (Monty Byers, SDB, R. 1989). Moonshine 1991.

HOT AND SPICY (Heather Pryor, R. 1995). Sdlg. 60/90-64. LA, 35" (89 cm), M. Lightly ruffled tomato red (RHS 34B) with fine yellow rim, lemon reverse; raised yellow steeple signal surrounded by yellow dagger signal; style arms bright green, tipped yellow. Gladiator's Gift X Desert Jewel. Lone Star 1997, Iris Haven 1997/98.

HOT BLOODED (Joseph Ghio, CA, R. 1989). Bay View 1990.

HOT BUTTONS (J. T. Aitken, R. 1996). Sdlg. 91M86. MDB, 6" (15 cm), ML. S. and style arms orange; F. orange, narrow yellow rim, edge serrate; beards deep orange. Pele X 87M4"Spot": ((Pumpkin Center x Jones 304: ((Roberts 65-R-11 x 201) x Melon Honey)) x ((Lemon Rings x Jones 304) x Lucky Duck)). Aitken's Salmon Creek 1996.

HOT CHOCOLATE (Joseph Ghio, R. 1994). Sdlg. 90-42C. TB, 36" (91 cm), EM. S. solid chocolate; F. bright yellow, speckled chocolate band; beards brass. 87-85H: ((82-113br, Chuckles sib, x (Thistle Belle x ((Flareup x Osage Buff) x (Vanity x Anon)))) x (Chuckles x Broadway)) X 87-21B: ((82-113N x Chickasaw Sue) x Chutney). Bay View 1995.

HOTDOGS AND MUSTARD (Kathie Kasperek, R. 1995). Sdlg. 89-39N. TB, 36" (91 cm), M. S. deep mustard (RHS 85B) lightly streaked wine purple (7A); F. deep mustard heavily streaked and splashed wine purple, with colors blending at edge of markings; beards grey yellow; ruffled. Maria Tormena X Winemaster. Zebra 1995.

HOTEL CALIFORNIA (Augusto Bianco, R. 1999). Sdlg. 768. BB, 26" (65 cm), EM. S. and style arms yellow; F. wine, center touched lavender; beards yellow orange; slight musky fragrance. ((Lovely Glow x Planned Treasure) x Ensminger 83-79: (Maria Tormena x (75-18 x Rancho Rose))) X (Queen in Calico x (Betty Simon x Shenanigan)).

HOT GINGER (Jim Hedgecock, R. 1992). Sdlg. 84-68-1. TB, 32" (81 cm), M. S. ginger brown; F. yellow, white area at hafts, heavy cinnamon red plicata band; beards burnt gold; heavily ruffled and laced; pronounced sweet fragrance. Kilt Lilt X Rustic Dance. Comanche Acres 1993.

HOT GOSSIP (Barry Blyth, R. 1992). Sdlg. X85-A. TB, 34" (86 cm), EM. S. buff pink; F. lavender pink; beards saturn red. Street Dancer X Mulled Wine. Tempo Two 1992/93.

HOT ICE (Lois Rich by James Whitely, R. 1994). Sdlg. R88-20. AB (OGB), 27" (70 cm), ML. Fuchsia pink, small mahogany chevron signal; beards orange, tipped pink; slight fragrance.

(((((K55-9A x (*I. atropurpurea* x K53-44DF)) x 633A, yellow TB) x (62-OB-1D x ((Chenik Aga x *I. lortetii*) x RR64-23A))) x ((63-C-16: ((((*I. helenae* x (*I. auraniticax* Charon)) x 53-44LF) x Kerr 55-9A) x sib) x (Persian Bronze x (K55-1 x K55-14)))) x (((R66-38J: (inv. K55-9A, *I. lortetii*, *I. auranitica*, W83-O, *I. barnumae*) x Campus Flirt) x (R65-17E: (K56-4 x (*I. susiana* x OY-640)) x Snoqualmie)) x (((Kelita Adah x V.G.A. AM) x (Welcome Reward x (*I. susiana* x *I. samariae*))) x sib))) X R77-96: ((KOM 265 x *I. lortetii*) x Esther Fay). Aril Patch 1994.

HOT JAZZ (Paul Black, R. 1998). Sdlg. B265A. SDB, 12" (30 cm), E. S. and style arms medium orchid; F. brighter orchid, short white rays around beard, crystalline haft rim; beards orange, red orange in throat and violet at outer end; ruffled; slight sweet fragrance. Sheer Class X First Alert sib. Mid-America 1998.

HOT NIGHT (Chet Tompkins, R. 1993). Sdlg. 7A-EON. BB, 20" (51 cm), EML. Glowing black red; beards rich black red. Red sdlgs. inv. Ebony Echo, Uproar, Catawba Ruby, etc. Fleur de Lis 1993.

HOT NUMBER (Joseph Ghio, R. 1993). Sdlg. PG-166L. CA, 11" (28 cm), ML. Bronzed orange self. PI-MIX-U, unknown, X PJ-178D: ((Peanut Gallery x Villa Branciforte sib) x PL-230E: (San Gregorio x (Montara sib x Mission Santa Cruz sib))). Bay View 1994.

HOT PINATA (Chet Tompkins, R. 1992). Sdlg. 86-11. TB, 37" (94 cm), ML. Blend of brilliant blue, copper, brass, lilac, pink and rose, 1/2" band of brilliant copper with gilt yellow on rim. ((Olympic Torch x Allaglow) x Masada) X (((Prancing Pony x Elegant Era) x (Stormy Weather x Rowdy)) x Masada). Fleur de Lis 1991.

HOT PINK (John Weiler, R. 1990). Sdlg. 85-160-1. TB, 35" (89 cm), EML. Hot pink with orange glow in center; beards red. Golden Galaxy X 81-106A-21: (78-19-6, Flaming Victory sib, x Catalyst). Rialto 1990.

HOT RHYTHM (Riley Probst, R. 1990). Sdlg. 87CX5S2. TB, 29" (74 cm), ML. S. orange (RHS 163B) with purple midrib; F. purple (187A); beards dark gold. Caliente X Syncopation. Manchester Garden 1993.

HOTSEAT (Barry Blyth, R. 1996). Sdlg. C27-1. SDB, 14" (36 cm), EML. S. solid apricot orange; F. creamy white, 3/8" orange apricot plicata edge; beards pastel lavender, tangerine in throat. Scion X Carats. Tempo Two 1996/97.

HOT SUMMER NIGHT (Opal Brown, R. 1992). Sdlg. 84-1A3. TB, 38½" (98 cm), ML. S. cadmium orange (RHS 23B); F. ruffled, lightly laced tangerine orange (24B); beards orange red (33A). 78-1F1: (Satin Bow x Symphonette) X Orange Star. Brown's Sunnyhill 1992.

HOTTENTOT (Marky Smith, R. 1993). Sdlg. 90-05N. SDB, 10" (25 cm), EM. S. silky dark bramble violet (RHS 86B); F. velvety dark fluorite violet (79A), darker in center; beards pale lavender blue (94D), yellow in throat; lightly ruffled. Coalbucket X Dark Vader. Aitken's Salmon Creek 1995.

HOT TO TROT (James McWhirter, R. 1991). Sdlg. J85-8-2. TB, 38" (97 cm), EM. S. deep golden yellow; F. red burgundy mahogany over white ground; beards gold, tipped yellow; slight fragrance. Gigolo X Captured Beauty. Cottage 1991.

HOT WHEELS (Paul Black, R. 1990). Sdlg. 86432B. IB, 22" (56 cm), M. S. warm white ground with orchid tan plicata markings blending to wide buff band; F. white ground with red purple plicata markings inside red purple band, dark purple spear at end of beard; beards white, tipped pale orchid; slight fragrance. Prediction X Chubby Cheeks sib. Mid-America 1990.

HOT ZIGGEDY (Frederick Kerr, R. 1999). Sdlg. 9340A. TB, 38" (97 cm), M. S. cantaloupe, tinted terracotta pink; style arms cantaloupe; F. dark terracotta wine, lighter under tangerine orange beard; lightly laced; slight sweet fragrance. 904301: (Ever After x Punkin Patch) X Prestige Item. Rainbow Acres 1999.

HOUSE OF ORANGE (Frank Foster, R. 1995). Sdlg. 90-199 OR. TB, 33-34" (84-86 cm), M. S. medium apricot orange, slight yellow undertoning at base; F. medium apricot orange; beards tangerine red; ruffled; slight sweet fragrance. Fresno Calypso X (J. Arthur Nelson x (Fresno Calypso x Flaming Light)).

HOWARD D. BROOKS (Currier McEwen, R. 1993). Sdlg. 85/109B. JI (6 F.), 36" (90 cm), EM. Rich violet (RHS 88A) with delicate white lines to edge, yellow signal; style arms white, lighter violet tufts. Purple Parasol X Continuing Pleasure. Eartheart, Seaways 1993.

HOZAN (Society for Japanese Irises, R. 1994). JI (6 F.), 40" (102 cm), M. Opaline pinkish lavender, yellow signal. Parentage and hybridizer unknown. Introduced in Japan prior to 1980.

HUASCARAN (Ladislav Muska, R. 1996). Sdlg. QKKA-03/D. TB, 38" (97 cm), ML. S. light cocoa brown; F. brownish red, light cocoa brown rim; beards orange; heavily ruffled, laced; spicy fragrance. (Queen in Calico x Krimhilde) X "Kakaova Kader": (Kilt Lilt x Laced Cotton). Muska 1996.

HUBBA HUBBA HUBBA (Tom Burseen, R. 1991). Sdlg. 7-103B. TB, 36" (91 cm), EM. S. blend of tan, pink and red (near RHS 39C) washed darker; F. red purple (61A) overlaid maroon, edged S. color; beards tangerine; heavily waved, ruffled and laced; sweet fragrance. Lavish Lace X Villa Splendor. T.B.'s Place 1992.

HUBBLE SPACE TELESCOPE (Barbara Wight, R. 1990). Sdlg. 86-7. TB, 29" (74 cm), EM. S. ivory white; style arms white; F. ivory white, purple lines and dotting halfway down; beards yellow, tipped purple, sometimes with thin purple and white horn; slight sweet fragrance. 80-130: (sdlg. x Dresden Gold) X Abu Zabad. Wight's Iris 1991.

HUCK FINN (Virginia Messick, R. 1991). Sdlg. M86-53. IB, 17" (43 cm), EM. S. rosy brown blend; F. chocolate brown; beards brick bronze, tipped bronze; slight fragrance. Hilow X Oklahoma Bandit. Cottage 1991.

HUCKLEBERRY FUDGE (James Gibson by Cooley's Gardens, R. 1996). Sdlg. 24-0A. TB, 35" (89 cm), M. S. warm chocolate brown (RHS 183B); F. white ground, plicata markings of chocolate brown and violet blue (near 94C); beards mustard (near 163B); ruffled. 12-8B: (28-4I, Inspiration Point sib, x Burgundy Brown) X 18-6A: (104-4A, Chestnut Beauty sib, x Gingerbread Girl). Cooley 1997.

HUE HEAVEN (Tom Burseen, R. 1997). Sdlg. 1-296A. TB, 36" (91 cm), M. S. greyed oxblood red (RHS 183C); style arms tannish red brown; F. oxblood red washed gold, violet flash at end of golden tan beard. 7-210: (Lady Friend x Exhilaration) X 9-220: (Bluid x Quite Quaint). T.B.'s Place 1997.

HUIA (Frances Love, R. 1991). SIB, 6½" (15 cm), M. Blue purple. Parentage unknown. Seed from Currier McEwen.

HULA FLIRT (Luella Danielson, AB (OG), R. 1989). Pleasure Iris 1990.

HULA HOOP (George Shoop, R. 1994). Sdlg. 85-34. BB, 26" (66 cm), M. S. lavender; F. white with yellow marginal band; beards tangerine. 79-14: (Hula Girl x 76-5: (Hula Girl x Dutch Magic)) X 82-32: (79-14 x ((74-3 x (Blond Goddess x Buffy)) x 76-5)). Keppel 1995.

HUM (Barry Blyth, R. 1999). Sdlg. F112-1. IB, 24" (61 cm), VE-E. S. old gold; F. bronze gold, slightly deeper toward haft; beards purple, small bronze tip; faint sweet fragrance. Aura Light X Celsius. Tempo Two 1999/2000.

HUMILITY (Larry Harder, R. 1992). Sdlg. 87-1. IB, 19" (48 cm), M. Light blue; beards white, tipped very pale yellow. Love X Am I Blue. Stockton 1994.

HUMPTY DUMPTY (Barbara Wight, R. 1998). Sdlg. 94-2. BB, 26" (66 cm), M. S. light yellow; style arms lemon; F. lemon, lined tan; beards dark yellow with long curled spoon lined maroon; slight musky fragrance. Star Trip X 85-11, horned dark rose. Wight's Iris 1998.

HUNK (Tom Burseen, R. 1995). Sdlg. 9-238A. TB, 37" (94 cm), M. S. white, slight purple (RHS 78B) wash; style arms white, washed purple; F. dark purple (bluer than 79C), lighter at beard and edges; beards mustard, tipped purple; ruffled; musky fragrance. Dusky Challenger X Royalist. T.B.'s Place 1995.

HURRICANE COLIN (Patrick O'Connor, R. 1992). Sdlg. 80-3. LA, 37" (94 cm), M. Rose orange, yellow crown-shaped signal ending in deep rose line extending short distance down F. Parentage unknown. Bois d'Arc 1993.

#HURRICANE SEASON (Chris Vizvarie, TB, R. 1985). Name released.

HURRICANE SEASON (Chris Vizvarie, R. 1990). Sdlg. CRV-47-85A. TB, 32½" (83 cm), E. Greyed lavender with yellow haft area; beards yellow; slight sweet fragrance. CRV-9-82A: (Beverly Sills x Marie Phillips) X CRV-7-82B: (Trill x Actress). Last Scent Farm 1990.

HURRIN' HOOSIER (Lynda Miller, R. 1993). Sdlg. 12387B. TB, 33" (86 cm), M. Maroon red self; beards old gold; slight sweet fragrance. 5384: (Spartan x unknown) X Lady Friend. Miller's Manor 1994.

HUSH DIANA (Tom Burseen, R. 1995). Sdlg. 0-86A. TB, 38" (97 cm), M. S. cranberry red (near RHS 185A); style arms slightly lighter; F. lighter cranberry red (185B), some orange (179B) influence; beards orange; ruffled; pronounced spicy fragrance. 6-54: (Lady Friend x Harlem Hussy) X Along the Way. T.B.'s Place 1996.

HUSH MONEY (Mary Dunn by Joseph Ghio, R. 1998). Sdlg. 224-2. LA, 36" (91 cm), M. S. cream with blue cast; F. cream, raised gold line signal. L164-2: (Clara Goula x self) X 107-12: (Monument x Handmaiden). Bay View 1998.

HUSKY HERO (William Ackerman, R. 1990). Sdlg. A3-5-90. JI (3 F.), 46" (117 cm), ML. S.

violet (RHS 83A); style arms violet, large; F. violet (83A) veined darker; signal yellow (7A). Yamataikoku X D5-6 double cream, inv. sdlgs. from Seiko-en Nursery, Japan.

HUSTLE (Barry Blyth, R. 1996). Sdlg. C30-2. SDB, 10-12" (26-30 cm), VE. S. burgundy brown; F. cream ground, deeper burgundy 3/8" plicata edge; beards white, hairs tipped mustard. A30-5, Imbue sib, X A21-20: (X20-A: (Camarilla x Yipee) x Chanted). Tempo Two 1996/97.

HYAPATHIA (Bob Thomason, R. 1992). Sdlg. BT 8910B. SDB, 8¼" (21 cm), EM. S. bluebird blue with darker blue basal infusion; F. same, white pattern on hafts, light violet area around beard; beards yellow, tipped white; slight musky fragrance. Sapphire Jewel X Truly.

HYENASICLE (Kathie Kasperek, R. 1996). Sdlg. 92B-55R. TB, 31" (79 cm), EM. S. and style arms spanish orange (RHS 26D); F. blended spanish orange and greyed red (180C/D); beards dark orange; lightly ruffled; slight fragrance. Baboon Bottom X Raspberry Fudge. Superstition 1998.

HY KLASS (Chet Tompkins, R. 1990). Sdlg. 83-64. TB, 37" (94 cm), EML. Medium blue; beards pale blue. (Winter Watch sib x Bubbling Over) X Chico Maid. Fleur de Lis 1990.

HYPNOSIS (Graeme Grosvenor, R. 1998). Sdlg. V69-4. TB, 36" (91 cm), M. Pink, F. lighter around red beard; slight fragrance. Spring Tidings X First Movement. Rainbow Ridge 1999/2000.

IAN (Thomas Burge, R. 1990). Sdlg. T21/86. SIB, 29½" (75 cm), M. S. ruffled medium light blue with trace of mauve; style arms prominent; F. medium blue with trace of violet, white signal veined blue, yellow in throat. T31/84: (Dear Dianne x Happy Event) X sib.

IATAN TITAN (Kevin Morley, R. 1993). SPEC (*virginica*), 40" (102 cm), E. S. light blue (RHS 93C) veined darker blue (90A), white base veined brown; style arms white, blending to light blue at crests; F. light blue (93B) veined darker (90A), white halo in center, yellow (2B) signal veined dark blue (90A). Selection of *I. virginica shrevei* collected near Iatan, Missouri. Terra Nova 1997.

I BE PINK (Les Fort, R. 1994). Sdlg. 88-369. IB, 25" (64 cm), M. S. taffeta pink; F. old rose fading to taffeta pink at edge; beards melon rose; ruffled. Frisco Follies X Tillie. Fort Iris 1994.

IBIZA (Kevin Nilsen, R. 1995). Sdlg. 64-87-1. TB, 35" (90 cm), EM. S. light reddish tan, deeper rose red blush; F. deeper raspberry red, edges paler; beards light red. 59-84: ((Golden Brilliance x Lisa Ann) x Entourage) X Chief Hematite. Iridescence 1995/96.

#ICARUS (Van Houtte, TB, 1854). Marked as obsolete in 1939 Checklist. Name released.

ICARUS (John C. Taylor, R. 1995). Sdlg. RL 9-Y. LA, 35" (89 cm), M. Primrose yellow (RHS 4C) occasionally infused white; green signals surrounded by yellow. Green Elf X Margaret Lee. Rainbow Ridge 1995/96.

ICE AND INDIGO (A. & D. Willott, R. 1990). Sdlg. 88-2. SDB, 10" (25 cm), E. S. pale blue; F. pale blue with large deep blue violet spot; beards white. Do-Si-Do X 84-92: (Tortuga x unknown). Willott 1991.

ICE ANGEL (Albert Faggard, LA, R. 1988). Faggard 1991.

ICE BLUE (Alphonse Van Mulders, R. 1990). Sdlg. 550/83. TB, 38" (97 cm), M. S. white; F. blue lavender; ruffled. Grand Waltz X Victoria Falls. Jardinart-Van Mulders 1989.

ICE BLUE PEARL (Donald Spoon, R. 1999). Sdlg. 93-1C. IB, 27" (69 cm), E. Ruffled light blue lavender; beards darker blue lavender, yellow in throat; horizontally flared. Busy Being Blue X Little Showoff. Winterberry 1999.

ICE BONBON (Lothar Denkewitz, R. 1990). Sdlg. N-80-hbl-2. SDB, 8½" (22 cm), E. S. white, white blue toward edge; F. white; beards pale lavender. (Sky and Snow x Bodderlecker) X sib. Von Zeppelin 1992.·

ICE CHERUB (A. & D. Willott, R. 1999). Sdlg. W 91-116. MDB, 5" (13 cm), ML. Blue white; beards light blue. Daisy Fresh X W 79-13: (Greenlee GX-2 x Buttons).

ICE CREAM TREAT (Richard Ernst, R. 1996). Sdlg. JF169-11-3. TB, 35" (89 cm), ML. S. peach pink, highlighted yellow; F. near-white, rim and veining peach, deeper peach shoulders, yellow rim highlights; beards tangerine orange; ruffled. Different World X F123-2: (Afternoon Delight x Edna's Wish). Cooley 1997.

ICE DANCER (Cy Bartlett, R. 1993). Sdlg. BR.MT.M. TB, 38" (97 cm), M. Ruffled white self; beards white, yellow in throat; pronounced sweet fragrance. (Blue Reflection x Misty Tide) X Morwenna. British Iris Society 1999.

ICED SUNSHINE (Chet Tompkins, R. 1997). Sdlg. 93-78. TB, 39" (99 cm), ML. S. white, flushed and edged lemon; style arms white, tinted lemon; F. white, deep lemon gold haft and edge, petal reverse chrome yellow; beards deep chrome; ruffled. (Majestic Moonlight x ((Royal Gold x Tinsel Town) x Ovation)) X (Elegant Era x Majestic Moonlight). Fleur de Lis 1997.

ICED TEA (Larry Lauer, R. 1994). Sdlg. 86-25-1. TB, 36" (91 cm), M. S. bronzed tan; F. violet, with veining, shaded bronzed tan on shoulders; beards gold, tipped bronze; slight fragrance. Captured Beauty X Hilow. Stockton 1994.

ICED VANILLA (Cy Bartlett, R. 1995). Sdlg. C91-30. IB, 25" (63 cm), ML. Ruffled pale cream self; beards cream; slight sweet fragrance. Mrs. Nate Rudolph X Sunny and Warm. Kelways 1999.

ICED WINE (Chuck Chapman, R. 1999). Sdlg. 93-91-3. SDB, 11" (28 cm), M. Rosy violet luminata wash on white, white edge and center; style arms white; beards white, yellow in throat. 90-190-2: (Chubby Cheeks x Lilac Lulu) X Rosie Lulu. Chapman Iris 1999.

ICE ETCHING (Paul Black, R. 1998). Sdlg. B324A. SDB, 14" (36 cm), M. S. dark violet blue midrib blending over white ground to pure white edge; style arms white; F. white ground, medium violet blue wash leaving edge unmarked, luminata patch and dart below beard; beards white at end, changing to yellow orange and gold; ruffled; pronounced spicy fragrance. 91242A: (Wire Rim x (85-360D, Tender Tears sib, x 86286A, Inky Dinky sib)) X 91243B: (Yipee x 89217A: ((Gigglepot x Oriental Blush) x (Apricot Elf x (Melon Honey x unknown)))). Mid-America 1998.

ICE GODDESS (A. & D. Willott, R. 1994). Sdlg. 92-217. TB, 34" (87 cm), ML. S. palest violet; F. white, flushed violet at edge; beards bright red orange; ruffled, laced. Beverly Sills X Master Gardener. Willott 1994.

ICELAND (Monty Byers, R. 1990). Sdlg. E76-100. TB, 35" (89 cm), EM & RE. S. snow white; F. very pale glacial blue; beards blue white, tipped yellow; lightly ruffled. Latest Style X C-22-6: (Hallowed Thought x Glistening Icicle). Moonshine 1991.

ICELANDIC MOON (Nora Scopes, R. 1991). Sdlg. 5/68E. TB, 37" (94 cm), M. S. pale milky blue, deeper at heart; F. same, green reverse; beards lavender; sweet fragrance. Song of Norway X Cobweb Morning.

ICELANDIC SUMMER (Georg Emke, R. 1996). TB, 34" (86 cm), M. S. white; F. light blue; beards whitish; ruffled. Rapture in Blue X Winterscape.

ICE MAGIC (John C. Taylor, R. 1991). Sdlg. OL 128-1. LA, 43" (110 cm), M. Creamy white, veined darker, orange line signal. Warramunda X Helen Naish. Rainbow Ridge 1991/92.

ICE PINNACLE (B.L.C. Dodsworth, R. 1997). Sdlg. EB 94 MM. TB, 44" (112 cm), M. S. white; F. lavender; beards white; ruffled. Amadora X Annabel Jane.

ICE STORM (Graeme Grosvenor, R. 1998). Sdlg. U125-4. TB, 36" (91 cm), ML. Laced white self; beards red, tipped blue; pronounced sweet fragrance. Perils of Pauline X Sweet Musette. Rainbow Ridge 1998/99.

ICY RUFFLES (James Burch, R. 1993). Sdlg. 44-7. TB, 32" (81 cm), ML. S. white (RHS 155C); F. greenish white (157D); beards yellow orange (21A); ruffled. Bledsoe 81-8 X Ocean Swells. Burch Iris 1993.

ICY STRAITS (Vernon Wood, R. 1998). Sdlg. 93-27. TB, 36" (91 cm), EM. Icy blue white self; beards white. 90-72: (Skating Party x 87-32: (Titan's Glory x (Cloud Fire x Ron))) X Silverado. Stockton 1999.

IDA EMILY (Ed Attenberger, R. 1996). Sdlg. 90-05-08. TB, 36" (91 cm), M. S. and style arms medium shell pink; F. peach to buff pink, deeper at hafts; beards red; ruffled, laced; slight sweet fragrance. Tarlatin X Lemon Mist.

IDAHO BLIZZARD (Lucille Pinkston, R. 1996). Sdlg. 87-1-A. TB, 48" (122 cm), EM. Pure white self; beards white, yellow in throat; slight fragrance. Silver Shower X unknown.

IDEA (Sterling Innerst, R. 1991). Sdlg. 2846-6. SDB, 12" (30 cm), EM. S. medium yellow; F. white, edged medium yellow; beards white, tipped cream. 1559-1: (Melon Honey x Soft Air) X Stockholm. Innerst 1992.

IDEAL ROMANCE (Graeme Grosvenor, R. 1999). Sdlg. V7-8. TB, 36" (91 cm), M. S. yellow ochre; F. brown, violet influence below yellow area around butterscotch beard; slight fragrance. Composed X Romantic Mood.

IDIDIT (Oscar Schick, R. 1996). Sdlg. 91-27B07. TB, 36-38" (91-97 cm), M. S. dark lavender (RHS 83C), lightly blended rusty lavender at edge; style arms light rusty lavender; F. dark lavender edged rusty lavender, shoulders rusty brown (178B); beards mustard yellow; lightly ruffled; slight musky fragrance. Bateau Ivre X Collage. Stockton 1997.

IDITAROD (Larry Johnson, R. 1998). Sdlg. J087-8A-5. TB, 42" (107 cm), EM. White self; beards light yellow. Titan's Glory X Song of Norway. Cooley 1998.

IDLE DREAMS (Bryce Williamson, R. 1993). Sdlg. 889-C. TB, 38" (97 cm), EM. S. salmon pink with heavy plicata markings of medium to dark raspberry pink; F. creamy salmon pink ground with wide plicata edge of medium to dark raspberry pink; beards orange red; ruffled. Pretty in Pink X Anon. Pacific Coast Hybridizers 1993.

IDOL (Joseph Ghio, R. 1998). Sdlg. 93-2G2. TB, 38" (97 cm), EML. S. golden apricot orange; F. solid claret red; beards red. Chinese New Year X Romantic Evening. Bay View 1999.

IDRIS DOT (Dora Sparrow, R. 1991). Sdlg. 87/3. CA, 16" (41 cm), ML. Peachy cream shaded brown yellow with light turquoise blush and dots. Third generation sdlg. of Soquel Cove.

IKAR (Adolf Volfovich-Moler, R. 1995). Sdlg. V-24. TB, 41" (105 cm), L. S. white, tinted soft lilac; F. light lilac, pale lilac rim; beards orange; ruffled. Rippling Waters X Pipes of Pan. Volfovich-Moler 1992.

IKEBANA (Ed Matheny III, R. 1995). Sdlg. J:00-02-92. JI (6 F.), 42" (107 cm), EM. White, heavily brushed pinkish violet, signals yellow (RHS 9A); style arms cream, sanded pinkish violet. Snowy Hills X Flashing Koi. Ed's Iris 1996.

IKE-NO-SAZANAMI (Shuichi Hirao by Society for Japanese Irises, R. 1992). JI (6 F.), 36" (90 cm), EM. Lilac-blue brushed on white, yellow signal. Parentage unknown. Hirao 1956.

IKTOMI (L. J. Duffy, R. 1992). Sdlg. WI-7-72. SPEC (*setosa*), 36-41" (91-104 cm), E. Lavender blue with large white blotch on F.; style arms tinted rose with dark purple mid-streak, dark blue stigma and crest area; base of bud and perianth tube almost black, with some blue and white marbling on balance of bud. Selection of *I. setosa interior* collected 1972 near Fairbanks, Alaska.

ILA NUNN (Charles Arny, LA, R. 1967). Correction of parentage: Dora Dey X Tressie Cook. Correction of typographical error in 1969 Checklist (listed as ILN NUNN).

ILA REMEMBERED (Ben Hager, R. 1992). Sdlg. S952-BRfWh. SPU, 38" (97 cm), M. S. white; F. deep yellow, edged white; ruffled. Ila Crawford X Elan Vital. Cordon Bleu 1992.

ILIYA PROROK (Viacheslav Gavrilin, R. 1999). Sdlg. 2-8-3-94. TB, 33" (84 cm), ML. S. and style arms light red violet; F. lilac, dark lilac blue spot around red beard; ruffled; slight fragrance. Taj Regis X In Town. Gavrilin 1999.

I'LL FLY AWAY (Leonard Michel, R. 1994). Sdlg. C 163-1. TB, 34" (86 cm), M. White (RHS 155C), blue cast in heart and beside white beards; deeply fluted. Tide's In X Silver Years. Michel 1995.

ILLINI FANTASY (D. Steve Varner, R. 1991). Sdlg. 91111. SIB, 26" (56 cm), ML. True lavender, F. heavily ruffled; style arms icy, green midrib. Silver Illusion X Illini Rose.

ILLINI FOUNTAIN (D. Steve Varner, R. 1993). Sdlg. V1014. SPEC (*lactea*), 14" (36 cm), VE. S. light lavender blue; F. very light blue, veining light lavender blue. Selection of *I. lactea* from seed collected near Budapest, Hungary. Illini Iris 1994.

ILLINI ROSE (D. Steve Varner, R. 1996). Sdlg. 7120. SIB, 28" (71 cm), ML. S. short, deep grape rose; style arms with aqua midrib; F. deep grape rose, no visible signal. King of Kings X Limeheart.

ILLINI RUBY (D. Steve Varner, SIB, R. 1987). Illini Iris 1990.

ILLINI VALOR (D. Steve Varner, R. 1992). Sdlg. 3133. SIB, 31" (79 cm), EM. S. deep burgundy wine; F. same, veined blue purple overall, blue purple center wash; ruffled; slight fragrance. Ruffled Velvet X Dutch. Illini Iris 1992.

ILLULISAT (Ladislav Muska, R. 1995). Sdlg. SKCK-01/A. TB, 37" (94 cm), M. Ruffled and laced white to light blue; beards tangerine, long blue horn. (Sky Hooks x "Cipkovana Krinolina": (After All x Grand Waltz)) X Sky Hooks. Muska 1995.

ILONA KUHLEMANN (Manfred Beer, R. 1995). Sdlg. MB 17/87 A. TB, 33" (84 cm), E. S. blended burgundy (RHS 187A/B) and garnet red (183A/B); style arms orange brown (172A); F. garnet red (183A); beards bronze yellow (163A), garnet at base; spicy fragrance. Samurai Warrior X Gallant Moment. Beer 1996.

ILONA LYLE (Harry Foster, R. 1991). Sdlg. R57/87. SIB (tet.), 30" (76 cm), ML. S. pale violet blue (RHS 93C); style arms silver blue; F. rich ocean blue (95A), fine silver edge, golden green signal; ruffled. Harpswell Happiness X Dear Dianne.

I LOVE YOU (Lilly Gartman by Roris Gardens, R. 1993). Sdlg. 86-9L. TB, 34" (86 cm), M. S. orange tan flushed lavender on edge; F. pale lavender with orange tan edge and shoulders; beards orange; ruffled. 83-34B: (Piping Hot x 180-10B: (Soap Opera x (Joyce Terry x Entourage))) X Alluring. Roris 1993.

IMAGE (Mary Dunn by Joseph Ghio, R. 1998). Sdlg. 240-6. LA, 33" (84 cm), EM. Blue lilac; style arms cream. Lina X Makebelieve World. Bay View 1999.

IMAGINARIUM (Duane Meek by Roris Gardens, R. 1993). Sdlg. 147-9-9. TB, 38" (97 cm), ML.

S. clear light pink; F. white with coral pink shoulders, and medium pink edge suffusing into petal; beards tangerine red; ruffled, laced. 262-8-7: (Blond Goddess x Chanteuse) X Highness. Roris 1993.

IMAGINE THAT (Monty Byers, TB, R. 1989). Moonshine 1990.

IMA KINDA LIMA (Tom Burseen, R. 1990). Sdlg. 4-172A. TB, 37" (94 cm), EM. S. greenish yellow blended blue violet; F. greenish brown, center washed light violet, greenish tan edge; beards yellow; ruffled; musky fragrance. Seven Hills X Satin Glass. T.B.'s Place 1991.

IMBUE (Barry Blyth, R. 1996). Sdlg. A30-B. SDB, 12-14" (30-36 cm), ML. S. gold to mustard gold, few plicata marks; F. white, 1/8" gold to mustard gold edge, softer toward haft; beards lavender, old gold base and in throat; ruffled. Taja X X32-2: (Yipee x sib). Tempo Two 1996/97.

IMMORTAL LIGHT (Hooker Nichols, R. 1991). Sdlg. 8857A. TB, 36" (91 cm), ML. S. white, suffused yellow; F. white edged gold, deeper gold hafts; beards gold; ruffled. 8368K: (Pagan x Lunar Child) X Oklahoma Sunshine.

IMPASSIONED (John C. Taylor, R. 1995). LA, 35" (89 cm), M. White (RHS 155D) with heavy green veining; green signals surrounded by yellow; style arms green. Parentage unknown. Rainbow Ridge 1995/96.

IMPERATIVE (Paul Black, R. 1997). Sdlg. C108G. IB, 20" (51 cm), ML. S. and style arms dark purple; F. black purple, few short white rays around beard; beards orange, white at end; slight spicy fragrance. 91260A: (85319B: (Gentle Air x Chubby Cheeks sib) x 88267A: ((Caesura x (Betsey Boo x (Antique Satin x Encanto))) x (Gigglepot x Oriental Blush))) X Tom Johnson. Mid-America 1997.

IMPERIAL KIMONO (George Bush, JI, R. 1986). Bush 1990.

IMPERIAL MAGICIAN (John C. Taylor, R. 1990). Sdlg. OL 138-A. LA, 47" (120 cm), M. S. marbled light purple (RHS 75D) with purple (75A) veining, reverse and edge lighter; F. medium purple (75A); ruffled. Dazzling Star X Watch Out. Rainbow Ridge 1990/91.

IMPERIAL PRESENCE (Lois Rich by Ensata Gardens, R. 1995). Sdlg. K79-7A. JI (3 F.), 38" (96 cm), M. S. and style arms white, held at 45° angle; F. white, signal yellow; ruffled. Parentage unknown. Ensata Gardens 1996.

IMPERIAL SEAS (Eleanor McCown, R. 1994). Sdlg. 87-8. SPU, 49" (124 cm), ML. S. and style arms blue lavender; F. blue lavender, antique bronze signal; slight fragrance. 78-22: (Proverb x Ripe Wheat) X Crow Wing. Cordon Bleu 1994.

IMPERIAL VEIL (Eleanor McCown, R. 1994). Sdlg. 88-15. SPU, 48" (122 cm), EM. S. creamy mauve veined allover except at solid mauve tip; style arms cream; F. creamy mauve veined allover except at solid mauve edge; slight fragrance. Highline Coral X 84-8, unknown. Cordon Bleu 1994.

IMPERIAL YELLOW (Richard Sloan by John Wight, R. 1990). Sdlg. 79-4-A. SPU, 40" (102 cm), M. Full yellow (RHS 13A). Far Out X Archie Owen. Wight's Iris 1991.

IMPISH (Barry Blyth, R. 1991). Sdlg. X25-10. SDB, 12-14" (30-36 cm), ML-VL. Creamy smoky pastel salmon, fine blue lavender line 3/4" below very bright blue lavender beard. (Oladi x Fifi) X (Peach Eyes x Kandi Moon). Tempo Two 1991/92.

IMPOSTOR IN PURPLES (Eric & Bob Tankesley-Clarke, R. 1994). SPEC, 18-20" (46-51 cm), E. S. blue violet; F. deep wine red, edged blue violet; beards white; pronounced sweet fragrance. Collected; distributed prior to 1980 and in commerce as *I. lutescens* U46.

IMPRESSIONISTIC GAL (Clarence Protzmann, TB, R. 1989). Protzmann 1990.

IMPRESSIVE COMBINATION (James Gibson by Cooley's Gardens, R. 1996). Sdlg. 9-5F-1. TB, 35" (89 cm), EM. S. and style arms tan cream overlaid imperial purple (near RHS 78A/D); F. salmon (27C) ground with imperial purple (78B) and violet purple (77A) plicata markings; beards light orange (30D); lightly ruffled. Parentage unknown. Cooley 1997.

I'M PRETTY (Ben Hager, R. 1997). Sdlg. T5767RfPkPk. TB, 37" (94 cm), M. Laced full-toned pink self; beards tangerine. T5237PkPkLc: (Falling in Love x Presence) X T5293RfPk: (Glorious Sunshine x T4589Pk/Ap, Fascinator sib). Cooley 1999.

IMPRIMIS (Barry Blyth, R. 1991). Sdlg. Y6-6. TB, 40" (102 cm), EM. S. icy oyster; F. smoky rose; beards bronze tangerine; slight fragrance. ((Inca Queen x (Tranquil Star x (Love Chant x Festive Skirt))) x Amber Snow) X ((Alpine Journey x Beachgirl) x ((Beachgirl (Tranquil Star x Coral Strand)) x (Persian Smoke x Chimbolam))). Tempo Two 1992/93.

I'M PROUD (Carl Boswell, R. 1999). Sdlg. 47-84-T. TB, 36" (91 cm), M. White self; beards dark yellow. Dutch Girl X Mais Oui. Adamgrove 1999.

IMPROVISATION (Ben Hager, R. 1991). Sdlg. IB5005BgPkPrBds. IB, 20" (51 cm), M. Beige pink; beards purple. Magic X Coral Wings. Adamgrove 1992.

IMPUDENT ELF (Sharon McAllister, R. 1993). Sdlg. 86-8-2. AB (OGB), 16" (42 cm), E. S. soft pinkish lilac; F. soft honeysuckle yellow with large red violet spot almost covering inner half; beards violet. Gene's Little Secret X Rose of Sharon. McAllister 1993.

I'M YOUR LADY (Barry Blyth, R. 1999). Sdlg. E102-6. TB, 38" (97 cm), ML. S. peach to pastel apricot; F. coral pastel peach; beards tangerine base, white hair tips; ruffled, laced; pronounced sweet fragrance. It's Delicious X Lavish Lover. Tempo Two 1999/2000.

I'M YOURS (Barry Blyth, R. 1995). Sdlg. A113-5. TB, 34" (86 cm), VE-EM. S. pastel lilac; F. rosy cocoa over tan, deepening toward hafts; beards bright tangerine, white base; pronounced sweet fragrance. Electrique X Imprimis. Tempo Two 1995/96.

INCA DOLL (Bennett Jones, R. 1994). Sdlg. 451-OO. SDB, 12" (30 cm), M. S. blended nasturtium orange (HCC 610/3) and orient pink (416/2); F. orpiment orange (10/2); beards bright red; slight fragrance. Sib to Desert Orange. Aitken's Salmon Creek 1995.

INCAN LEGACY (Les Fort, R. 1990). Sdlg. 86-122-D. TB, 32" (81 cm), M. Ruffled rich warm bronze copper mellowing to bright old gold, bronze shoulders; beards gold; slight fragrance. Gold Galore X Flaming Victory. Fort Iris 1991.

INCENDIARY (Marky Smith, R. 1996). Sdlg. 92-20A. SDB, 14" (36 cm), EM. S. blackened burgundy (darker than RHS 187A), few lavender grey marks near midrib; style arms mauve-tipped burgundy, midribs deep blue violet; F. small yellow (2A) center, black red 1/4" solid outer rim, 3/8" inner rim almost solidly stitched darkest scarlet (blacker than 187A); beards bronze end, gold midsection, yellow orange in throat; ruffled; pronounced spicy fragrance. Firestorm X Byers H39-1: (Chubby Cheeks x Mini Busy). Aitken's Salmon Creek 1997.

IN CHA (Udo & Rudolf Wilkeneit, R. 1996). SDB, 12" (30 cm), M. White, petals edged light blue; beards white; slight fragrance. Parentage unknown.

INCOGNITO TOO (Ken Mohr by Bryce Williamson, R. 1995). Sdlg. L159. TB, 36" (91 cm), ML. S. normally missing; flowers opening flat with F. medium blue violet; beards cream white; lightly ruffled. J96-1: ((Cup Race x Babbling Brook) x Five Star Admiral) X K97-2: (Celestial Ballet x (Shipshape x (Matinata x Grand Alliance))). Introduced under invalid name "Incognito". Pacific Coast Hybridizers 1991.

IN DEMAND (Graeme Grosvenor, R. 1994). Sdlg. L 73-20. JI (6 F.), 48" (120 cm), M. Red violet with white spray pattern, yellow signal; style arms white, tipped red violet. Rose Tower X Frilled Enchantment.

INDEX (Sterling Innerst, R. 1995). Sdlg. 3611-5. SDB, 14" (36 cm), M. S. yellow gold; style arms yellow; F. yellow, brown spot; beards orange, tipped white. Comma X Dash. Innerst 1996.

INDIAN BEAUTY (John Weiler, R. 1990). Sdlg. 84-55-2-RE. SDB, 8½" (21 cm), EM & RE. Yellow brown with heavy violet infusion; beards bright blue; slight sweet fragrance. 79-38-1: (76-3 RE: (74-5-1: (70-95-5: (Brighteyes x Grace Note) x Bronze Babe) x 74-3-1: (Cartwheel x 70-95-6)) x 75-101-16 RE: (70-95-3 x Gingerbread Man) X 82-16-1: (79-38-4: (76-3 RE x 75-101-16 RE) x 79-36-1 RE: ((Ruby Contrast x Little Blackfoot) x 76-3 RE)). Rialto 1991.

INDIAN CANYON (Darlene Pinegar, R. 1992). Sdlg. FU-1-1. TB, 36" (91 cm), EML. S. medium copper brown, yellowish midrib; style arms medium brown; F. honey brown, yellow shoulders; beards orange gold; lightly ruffled; slight sweet fragrance. Flareup X Rusticana. Spanish Fork 1993.

INDIAN FOOTPRINT (David Sindt by Adamgrove, R. 1992). Sdlg. 752. SDB, 12" (30 cm), M. S. yellow gold, heavily dotted cinnamon; F. gold with thick cinnamon band at sides, narrowing at tip; beards white, tipped yellow. (Ginger Tart x Quip) X Pepper Mill. Adamgrove 1992.

INDIAN IDYLL (Barry Blyth, R. 1993). Sdlg. Z33-2. IB, 24" (61 cm), EM. S. red tan; F. burgundy, slightly lighter edge; beards mustard; slight fragrance. Swain X Gigolette. Tempo Two 1993/94.

INDIAN MAIZE (Jim Hedgecock, R. 1999). Sdlg. F-48-10. TB, 31" (79 cm), M. S. white, yellow midrib infusion; F. straw yellow, dark yellow hafts, white area by golden yellow beard; lightly laced, ruffled; pronounced sweet fragrance. Sun Dappled X unknown.

INDIAN MYTH (Franklin Carr, R. 1990). Sdlg. 84-42. TB, 35" (89 cm), M. S. light brown infused reddish brown; F. light brown, red halo, yellow haft markings; beards yellow; slight sweet fragrance. Gold Galore X Dazzling Gold.

INDIAN PAINTBRUSH (Vernon Wood, R. 1990). Sdlg. 90-14. CA, 10" (25 cm), EM. Dark red violet in center 1/4, lightening to light red violet, some pale red areas near rippled edge, dark red violet lines radiating from center. 88-47: (Rincon x Different Drummer) X 88-44: (Roaring Camp x (Three Cornered Hat x 84-6, inv. Ghio sdlgs.)). Portable Acres 1992.

INDIAN SANDSTONE (Richard Ernst, R. 1996). Sdlg. KF125-L. TB, 35" (89 cm), M. S. cinnamon brown blended amber from base up midrib; style arms cinnamon brown, yellow highlights; F. white ground, sanded cinnamon brown plicata markings, midstripe; beards orange; ruffled. (Edna's Wish x Wild Jasmine) X sib. Cooley 1996.

INDIGO DELIGHT (J. T. Aitken, R. 1997). Sdlg. 88J31. JI (3 F.), 32" (81 cm), M. S. wine red, short; style arms dark gunmetal blue; F. medium blue, small yellow signal surrounded by white. Parentage unknown. Aitken's Salmon Creek 1997.

INDIGO DOLL (Carol Lankow by J. T. Aitken, R. 1997). Sdlg. 7L75. BB, 26" (66 cm), ML. S. light blue, midrib deeper; F. dark blue; beards red, bushy. American Beauty X Cool Treat. Aitken's Salmon Creek 1997.

INDIGO FLIGHT (Thelma Naylor, IB, R. 1988). V. H. Humphrey 1993.

INDIGO MAGIC (Lois Rich by Ensata Gardens, R. 1995). Sdlg. K82-1K. JI, (6 F.), 36" (92 cm), M. Blue violet (RHS 93A) with dark blue halo and veins, yellow signal; style arms multiple, deep indigo blue (89A). Parentage unknown. Ensata Gardens 1996.

INDIGO MOOD (Frank Foster, R. 1990). Sdlg. 75415A. TB, 34" (86 cm), M. S. light lavender toned blue; F. lightly ruffled deep indigo blue, edged S. color, blue white haft lines around beard; beards golden yellow, tipped cream; slight musky fragrance. (Silver Peak x Age of Aquarius) X (Mystique x Rocky Mountain High). Vagabond Gardens 1992.

INDIGO PRINCESS (Schreiner, R. 1992). Sdlg. V 51-A. TB, 39" (99 cm), ML. Ruffled deep violet (RHS 89C); beards yellow, tipped blue. Breakers X P 81-A: (L 37-4 : (G 11-1, St. Louis Blues sib, x I 144-18: (G 1517-B x Neptune's Pool)) x L 93-5: ((Navy Strut x E 1313-A) x (Fuji's Mantle x Matinata))). Schreiner 1992.

IN DISGUISE (Louise Bellagamba, R. 1995). Sdlg. D-191. SDB, 9" (23 cm), EM. S. clear lavender; style arms lavender; F. olive green gold; beards lavender. Hocus Pocus X unknown. Bella Vista Gardens 1996.

INDULGE (Roger Nelson, R. 1992). Sdlg. RN 85-115AG. TB, 32-33" (81-84 cm), EM. S. medium orchid (RHS 80C), deeper (near 80A) veins and midrib; F. deeper rose orchid (79C) at edge to orchid (80B) near center, medium violet blue (87C) area at end of beard, yellow-infused wine brown thumbprint at hafts; beards gold orange (23A), tipped bright gold orange (17B); ruffled, laced; sweet fragrance. High Falutin X RN 83-85F: (Warm Embrace x (Blushing Pink x Glory Bound)). Iris Country 1993.

IN FASHION (Kenneth Fisher, R. 1994). Sdlg. 91-3. MTB, 23" (58 cm), E. Purple self; beards white. TC5: (Ting-a-Ling x (Pink Kewpie x Puppy Love)) X EE4: ((Blue Bisque x (Sherwin-Wright x Baby Lace)) x (79-3 x Consummation)). Aitken's Salmon Creek 1995.

INFERNAL FIRE (Gerald Richardson, R. 1994). Sdlg. 89-61-1. TB, 32" (81 cm), EM. Buff gold, heavily striped and splotched magenta; beards golden orange; slight fragrance. 77-56-1: (((Celestial Snow x Blushing Beauty) x Campus Flirt) x ((San Leandro x Mulberry Rose) x Mulberry Rose)) X Broadway. Rainbow's End 1994.

#INFINI (Glenn Corlew, TB, R. 1986). Not introduced or distributed. Name released.

INFINI (Glenn Corlew, R. 1992). Sdlg. SP12-6A. SPU, 40" (102 cm), ML. S. white; F. bright yellow, edged white, finely ruffled. Ila Crawford X Social Circle. Bay View 1993.

IN FLIGHT (Jim & Vicki Craig, R. 1995). Sdlg. C63X39. TB, 31" (79 cm), E. Ruffled warm white self; beards pale yellow; slight sweet fragrance. Sib to Departure. J. & V. Craig 1995.

IN FULL SAIL (Marty Schafer/Jan Sacks, R. 1999). Sdlg. S92-82-24. SIB, 27" (69 cm), L. S. white to cream; style arms cream shaded yellow, large and upright, petaloid crest curls; F. creamy canary yellow (9D), deeper (9B) signal with green veins. S89-23-1: (S85-6-6: (Star Cluster x Ruffled Velvet) x Isabelle) X Careless Sally. Joe Pye Weed 1999.

INGENIOUS (Barry Blyth, R. 1995). Sdlg. B111-1. BB, 20-22" (51-56 cm), ML. S. light rosy violet; F. ruby to ruby black with 1/2" rosy violet band; beards violet, heavily tipped bronze black; slight sweet fragrance. Zing Me X Y6-1, Imprimis sib. Tempo Two 1995/96.

INGLESIDE (Revie Harvey, R. 1990). Sdlg. 80/R/31. TB, 30" (76 cm), ML. S. garnet red; style arms gold, purple midrib; F. garnet red, faint purple flecks under dark bronze beard. Credo X Frontier Marshall. Hilmary Catton 1991.

IN HEAVEN (Barry Blyth, R. 1992). Sdlg. X31-7. SDB, 12" (31 cm), VE. S. rich apricot; F. slightly lighter, broad cinnamon area spreading out over all, lightly ruffled orange edge; beards tangerine, outer 1/4" pastel lavender. Yipee X Camarilla. Tempo Two 1992/93.

IN HER GLORY (David Silverberg, R. 1995). Sdlg. 89-43F. SIB, 31-33" (79-84 cm), M. Cream, aging white, F. with sunny yellow throat and veining; style arms feathered. Percheron X Creme Chantilly. Abbey Gardens 1995.

INITIATION (Helen Reid, R. 1995). Sdlg. 90-23. LA, 34" (86 cm), ML. Orchid pink self, faint chartreuse line signal on F. (Ann Chowning x Full Eclipse) X unknown.

IN JEST (Barry Blyth, R. 1994). Sdlg. A4-1. SDB, 14" (36 cm), VE-EM. Creamy lemon with white area in center of F.; beards lavender blue, tangerine in throat. Merry Dance X Melodic. Tempo Two 1994/95.

INKLING (Monty Byers by Phyllis Dickey, R. 1995). Sdlg. G 18-100. SDB, 14" (36 cm), M & RE. White ground plicata, S. marked medium blue purple, F. marked deep blue purple; beards yellow. Muchacha X Egyptian. Misty Hill 1995.

INK ON ICE (J. T. Aitken, R. 1994). Sdlg. 88J23. JI (6 F.), 33" (84 cm), EM. S. white with irregular blotches of purple; style arms cream, edged light violet; F. white, flushed light violet near edge. (T. Hill 81-J-10 x Izu-no-Umi) X sib. Aitken's Salmon Creek 1994.

INKY DINKY (Paul Black, R. 1991). Sdlg. 86286C. SDB, 11" (28 cm), L. S. stark white, wide inky blue black plicata band and line up midrib; F. stark white, inky blue black stitching around edge and random veining over remainder; beards white, tipped blue black. Twink X Chubby Cheeks. Mid-America 1991.

INKY ELF (A. & D. Willott, R. 1996). Sdlg. 91-158. MDB, 5" (13 cm), ML. Deep violet, F. with deeper rayed spot; beards light blue violet. Dark Vader X What Not. Willott 1996.

IN LIMBO (Joseph Gatty by Keith Keppel, R. 1995). Sdlg. W37-22. IB, 20" (51 cm), EM. S. white ground, violet blue (M&P 43-I-9) band and midrib; style arms violet blue; F. violet blue (43-H-9) haft veining, shaded edge and faint overlay on white ground; beards blue white, hairs tipped bronze. Chubby Cheeks X S48-4, Toy Clown sib. Keppel 1996.

INNER BEAUTY (Mary Dunn, R. 1990). Sdlg. L110-3. LA, 34" (86 cm), M. Violet with deeper veining, yellow spear signal; style arms light. C'est Chic X Easter Tide. Bay View 1991.

INNER DELIGHT (Elyse Hill, R. 1999). Sdlg. EJ 19-16-91. TB, 30" (76 cm), M. S. icy light blue blend; style arms blended light blue and white; F. white, edges blended lavender; beards gold; slight sweet fragrance; heavily laced. Lullaby of Spring X Silver Shower.

INNER GLEAM (Jim & Vicki Craig, R. 1995). Sdlg. C37X7. IB, 27" (68 cm), M. S. creamy white, blending to pale yellow center; style arms medium yellow; F. medium fuchsia, slightly bluer near medium yellow beard, hafts marked light yellow; slight sweet fragrance. Payoff X 31T4, Takeoff sib. J. & V. Craig 1995.

INNER JOURNEY (Barry Blyth, R. 1995). Sdlg. A63-E. TB, 40" (102 cm), ML. S. brown, faint violet infusion; F. brown, overlaid violet, deepening toward light mustard beard, hafts golden tan; slight sweet fragrance. Dance Man X Rembrandt Magic. Tempo Two 1995/96.

INNER PEACE (A. & D. Willott, R. 1990). Sdlg. 88-6. SDB, 14" (35 cm), E. Light blue, slight white halo around light blue beards. Sapphire Gem X Pilgrims' Choice. Willott 1991.

INN-KEEPER (John C. Taylor, R. 1997) Sdlg. UL 29-4. LA, 47" (120 cm), ML. S. and F. violet blue, yellow gold signal; style arms violet, edged lighter. Louie X Rachel's Request. Rainbow Ridge 1997/98.

INNOCENT BLUSH (Schreiner, R. 1993). Sdlg. W 611-1. TB, 38" (97 cm), L. Ruffled and laced dusty rose pink (RHS 65B), F. with white blaze; beards yellow, tipped white. S 435-4: (Fabulous Frills x Lorilee) X T 879-A: (L 556-1: (G 510-A x Fabulous Frills) x Starcrest). Schreiner 1993.

INNOCENT STAR (George Sutton, R. 1998). Sdlg. H-145. TB, 35" (89 cm), EM & RE. S. white, washed dark beetroot (RHS 71); style arms dark beetroot and cream; F. yellow and white ground, edged, veined and dotted dark beetroot; beards cream, hairs tipped beetroot; ruffled; slight sweet fragrance. Innocence Abroad X Rock Star. Sutton 1999.

INNOVATOR (Ben Hager, R. 1991). Sdlg. S919LvVRdSg. SPU, 39" (99 cm), M. S. deep lavender; style arms cream yellow, prominent; F. reddish mauve blend, edged lavender, signal yellow. First Fruits X Perfect Spring. Cordon Bleu 1991.

INNU SPRING (Tony Huber, R. 1999). Sdlg. 94-03. SPEC-X, 11" (28 cm), E. S. small, blue and white; style arms violet blue (RHS 90A), edged white; F. violet blue (90A/B), hafts brown and yellow; white signal line extending into blade, bordered by five white spots on either side. Point Riche X *I. setosa interior*, wine red, from NARGS seed, "Farm Park", from Fairbanks, AK.

IN PERSON (Ben Hager, R. 1990). Sdlg. T5049Pk8. TB, 35" (89 cm), ML. Lightly laced light pink; beards soft tangerine. T4127ClrPk: (Paradise x (Carved Cameo x Vanity)) X T4322SfPk: (Anna Belle Babson sib x Muchas Gracias). Melrose 1991.

INPUT (Ben Hager, SDB, R. 1989). Melrose 1990.

IN RETROSPECT (Raymond Smith, R. 1991). Sdlg. 0172BR. TB, 32" (81 cm), EM & RE. S. lavender purple (Nickerson 5P 5/9); F. white ground lightly stitched lavender purple on edge, darker lavender purple signal; beards yellow. 69260R: ((Sass F53-1 x Rundlett sdlg.) x ((Rundlett sdlg. x Gibson Girl) x D103, inv. Gibson Girl)) X 6913R: ((Memphis Lass x D19AF) x (D64AR, inv. Gibson Girl, x (Snow Flurry x Autumn Snowdrift))). R. G. Smith 1992.

IN REVERSE (Joseph Gatty by Keith Keppel, R. 1992). Sdlg. S29-1. TB, 36" (91 cm), EM. S. bluer than columbine blue (M&P 41-E-9/10); F. palest blue (41-A-4) aging to white; beards white to blue white, cadmium yellow (9-L-8) deep in throat; slight sweet fragrance. Edge of Winter X Swirling Seas. D & J Gardens 1993.

INSCRUTABLE (Sharon McAllister, R. 1992). Sdlg. 86-10-6. AB (OGB+), 24" (60 cm), EM. S. smoky blue violet; F. pale violet ground showing only at edge, heavily veined and dotted deep smoky violet (appearing almost solid), violet black signal; beards yellow. Persian Pansy X Koko Knoll. Aril Society 1992.

INSIDER (John C. Taylor, R. 1996). Sdlg. UL 20-2. LA, 43" (110 cm), ML. S. yellow, edged red brown; style arms red brown; F. yellow spray pattern, red brown border; triangular form; slight fragrance. Desert Jewel X Margaret Lee. Rainbow Ridge 1998/99.

INSPIRING (John C. Taylor, R. 1998). Sdlg. UL 34-1. LA, 39" (100 cm), M. Purple violet, yellow signal on all petals. Poseidon's Pool X Helen Naish. Rainbow Ridge 1999/2000.

INSTANT SMILES (Tom Burseen, R. 1997). Sdlg. 93-60B. TB, 34" (86 cm), M. S. golden bronze (RHS 168C), darker edge, midrib golden; style arms bronze (168B); F. saffron yellow (21C), darker bronze edge; beards bright gold; heavily ruffled. Bronzette Star X 9-137: (Homecoming Queen x Role Model). T.B.'s Place 1998.

INSURRECTION (Mitch Jameson, R. 1991). Sdlg. 5-87-A. TB, 36" (91 cm), M. S. apricot orange, slight orchid flush; F. red maroon, edged S. color; beards orange; laced; slight fragrance. 1-84: (Cabaret Royale x Son of Star) X Song of Spring.

IN SUSPENSE (Graeme Grosvenor, R. 1994). Sdlg. L 71-18. JI (6 F.), 60" (152 cm), ML. White, heavily edged blue violet, signal yellow. Frilled Enchantment X Chigokesho.

INTARZIS (Ladislav Muska, R. 1998). Sdlg. GZQM-01. TB, 36" (91 cm), M. S. medium cream, veined lilac; style arms mustard; F. light cream ground, 2" cinnamon brown peppering darkest at edge; beards gold; heavily ruffled, laced; slight fragrance. (((Graffiti x Zuzana) x Queen in Calico) x Rei Momo) X Instructor. Muska 1998.

INTEGRA (Glenn Corlew, TB, R. 1988). Cooley 1992.

INTENSE EMOTIONS (Sterling Innerst, R. 1999). Sdlg. 3972-5. TB, 36" (91 cm), ML. S. bright yellow; style arms maroon bronze; F. red, 1/2" bright yellow edge; beards bronze tipped yellow; slight musky fragrance. Springhouse X Smart Aleck.

INTERESTING EXPRESSION (Sterling Innerst, R. 1995). Sdlg. 3708-2. TB, 36" (91 cm), M. S. medium yellow; style arms yellow brown; F. yellow ground, marked brown; beards yellow orange to bronze. Point Made X Gigolo. Innerst 1996.

INTERPLANET (John C. Taylor, R. 1998). Sdlg. UL 12-1. LA, 39" (100 cm), M. Light yellow; signals yellow. Dancing Vogue X RL 41-2: (N61-A: (unknown red sdlg. x Koorawatha) x Margaret Lee). Rainbow Ridge 1999/2000.

IN THE CHIPS (Harold Stahly, R. 1993). Sdlg. 87-1. IB, 24" (61 cm), EM. S. white, infused light yellow at midrib; F. bright golden yellow; beards yellow to red; slightly ruffled. Marmalade Skies X Dash Away. Stahly 1993.

IN THE DARK (Sterling Innerst, R. 1990). Sdlg. 2336-3. TB, 36" (91 cm), ML. Black; beards purple black; slight fragrance. By Night X Swazi Princess.

IN THE GLOAMING (Leslie Donnell, R. 1998). Sdlg. 95-3-2. TB, 35" (89 cm), ML. S. golden brown, gold on reverse; F. golden brown, gold center patch; beards golden brown; pronounced sweet fragrance. Liqueur Creme X Speculator.

IN THE MIST (Barry Blyth, R. 1996). Sdlg. B89-3. IB, 25" (64 cm), ML. S. icy blue; F. icy blue overlaid blue lavender and light olive, deepening around beard, haft veining olive; beards deep burnt tangerine. Esoteric X Electrique. Tempo Two 1996/97.

IN THE MOOD (Schreiner, R. 1994). Sdlg. AA 1726-A. TB, 36" (91 cm), ML. Ruffled flamingo pink (RHS 36A), white center around tangerine beards. Electrabrite X T 1791-A: (Far Corners x Enchanted World). Schreiner 1994.

IN THE RED (Harold Stahly, R. 1995). Sdlg. 1-5. SDB, 11" (28 cm), M. S. red (deeper than RHS 178A); style arms red; F. red (near 46A), maroon (deeper than 183A) center spot; beards pale violet at end merging from light yellow to yellow in throat; ruffled. Plum Perfect X Little Annie. Stahly 1995.

IN THE STARS (Barry Blyth, R. 1999). Sdlg. E88-14. TB, 38" (97 cm), EM. S. white, slight pink midrib flush; F. soft pastel rose pink, 1/4" white band, slight rose tan haft blending; beards tangerine, base white; slight fragrance. Crazy For You X About Town. Tempo Two 1999/2000.

IN TOTO (Carl Boswell, AB, R. 1989). Adamgrove 1993.

IN TOUCH (Ben Hager, R. 1999). Sdlg. MD5686DpPk. MDB, 4-7" (10-18 cm), EML. Pink self; beards cream, tangerine in throat; open S., arched F. Wee Me X MD5149TyPk: ((((Tiny Apricot x (((Prodigy x ((Red Lilli x Pogo) x Regards)) x 2562: (Pink Amber x Pink Cushion)) x 2873: (Buttercup Charm x 2562))) x ((2562 x Buttercup Charm) x 2873)) x (Pet sib x (Pet sib x Tiny Apricot))) x Tiny Cherub).

INVASION FORCE (Sharon McAllister, R. 1992). Sdlg. 88-16-A. AB (OGB-), 16" (42 cm), E. S. pale silvery blue; F. soft yellow ground blushed burgundy, linear burgundy signal; beards yellow, tipped burgundy. Hidden Talents X (Lillibright x unknown). McAllister 1992.

INVASION IN PINK (Carl Boswell by Barbara Schmieder, R. 1993). Sdlg. 84-79-I. IB, 18-20" (45-51 cm), EM. S. and style arms clear light pink (RHS 36C); F. pale pink (36D) in center, shading to light pink (36C) at haft and edge; beards tangerine pink (28B) in throat and on hair tips on paler pink base toward end; slight sweet fragrance. Inv. Buffy, April Melody, Yum-Yum, Campus Flirt, Java Dove, Java Charm, Palisades, Little Lynn X Pink Cushion. Markham 1993.

INVENTION (Harald Mathes, R. 1994). AB (OGB), 20" (50 cm), E. Red violet, F. with black signal; beards blue. Anacrusis X sib. Aril Society 1995.

INVINCIBLE (Vernon Wood, R. 1991). Sdlg. 90-17. CA, 12-15" (30-38 cm), M. S. white ground, some yellow (RHS 12B) deep in center, red purple (78) fringe at tip; F. white ground, some yellow deep in center, red violet (72A) flush and lines over upper third, slightly flushed blue (105D) at tip; ruffled. Fort Point X Encircle. Stockton 1995.

INVOCAZIONE (Ladislav Muska, R. 1996). Sdlg. DFSH-02. TB, 36" (91 cm), ML. Ruffled, heavily laced pinkish salmon self; beards tangerine; slight fragrance. Deep Fire X (Sky Hooks x Beverly Sills). Muska 1996.

IN YOUR DREAMS (Lynda Miller, R. 1999). Sdlg. 4694A. TB, 38" (97 cm), M. S. deep cream, midrib washed orchid violet; style arms dark cream, orchid midrib; F. orchid violet, upper haft gold; beards blue, white in throat, hairs tipped cream to gold; slight musky fragrance. Edith Wolford X Phenomenon.

IO (Jane McKnew, R. 1994). Sdlg. 89-7. TB, 36" (91 cm), M. Yellow (RHS 9B) with faint white flash below beards; beards white, tipped orange, white horn; pronounced fragrance. Copper Lace X Hands Up. Friendship 1999.

IRENE BENTON (B. Charles Jenkins, R. 1993). Sdlg. C18-29B. SPU, 35-41" (89-104 cm), M. S. and style arms lavender; F. yellow, faintly edged lavender, ruffled and frilled. Ila Crawford X Ruffled Canary. Shepard Iris 1993.

IRENE FRANCES (Gerald Richardson, R. 1994). Sdlg. 86-29-1. TB, 32" (81 cm), ML. Coral pink, F. with cream pink area radiating from beard; beards white, tipped tangerine. Old Flame X Eastertime. Rainbow's End 1995.

I REPEAT (Joan Roberts, R. 1998). Sdlg. 791-2. TB, 29" (74 cm), EM & RE. Heavily ruffled medium blue violet, F. with white blaze around pale yellow beard; slight sweet fragrance. Twice Delightful X Joan's Pleasure. Friendship 1998.

IRGEN (Irina Driagina, R. 1995). Sdlg. 2-51. TB, 35" (90 cm), EM. Light blue self; beards yellow. Parentage unknown. Driagina 1983.

IRIDESCENT BRONZE (B. Charles Jenkins, R. 1995). Sdlg. BH63A. SPU, 26-34" (66-86 cm), ML. Greyed orange (RHS 176C) self, yellow glow in signal area; iridescent effect from certain angles. Purple Reign X Janice Chesnik.

IRISH LAUGHTER (Chet Tompkins, R. 1992). Sdlg. 84-23. TB, 38" (97 cm), EML-VL. Heavily ruffled white; beards lemon white. ((Irish Linen x Herald Angel) x (Radiant Bride x Fay white sdlg.)) X (((Ribbon Round x Cup Race) x (Blanc de Chine x Ivory Plumes)) x Fine China). Fleur de Lis 1992.

IRISH MASCARA (Jo Tunney, R. 1992). Sdlg. F5/88. AB (OGB), 20-22" (51-56 cm), EM. S. soft lavender (RHS 92D) shading to buff (12B/C) with green infusion at midrib, deeper lavender and buff veining, buff edge; style arms gold buff, crests stippled green with distinct green (129B) veining; F. buff overlaid rose lavender stippled maroon and green, maroon and cream stripes around beard; beards buff, tipped maroon. Heart Stealer X Enchanted Hour.

213

#IRISH MIST (David Silverberg, TB, R. 1984). Not introduced or distributed; name released.

IRISH MIST (Currier McEwen, R. 1999). Sdlg. T(9)91/55. SIB (tet.), 30" (76 cm), EML. S. white; style arms white, midrib tinted pale greenish yellow (RHS 4D); F. white tinted light green (140D) and veined sap green (150C), hafts and signals sap green with darker (150A) veining; ruffled. Harpswell Prelude X White Encore.

IRISH MOSS (Bennett Jones, R. 1993). Sdlg. 442-1. SDB, 12" (30 cm), M. S. persian blue (HCC 647/3); F. persian blue (647/1) edging around fern green brushed-on pattern; beards deep violet blue; slight fragrance. 392: (Sun Doll x Dixie Pixie) X Bedford Lilac. Bennett Jones 1994.

IRISH SPIRIT (Richard Morgan, R. 1997). Sdlg. L397-G. LA, 26" (66 cm), M. S. blue; F. blue, large greenish yellow lancehead signal. L100X: (Winter's Veil x Acadian White) X L65-A: (Everett Caradine x Clyde Redmond). Redbud Lane 1999.

IRIS LAUVAIN (Ron Busch, R. 1991). Sdlg. 8354/2. TB, 36" (91 cm), M. Pink, F. with purple blush; beards tangerine. Parentage unknown. Busch 1992.

IRLEV (Irina Driagina, R. 1995). Sdlg. 1-84. TB, 33" (85 cm), EM. Blue white self; beards yellow. Parentage unknown. Driagina 1983.

IRMGARD (Manfred Beer, R. 1991). Sdlg. MB 12/80D. TB, 41" (105 cm), M. Orchid pink; beards red. Champagne Music X Fond Wish. Gartencenter Kania 1991.

IRON BUTTERFLY (Perry Dyer, R. 1998). Sdlg. 90-154A. TB, 40-42" (102-107 cm), ML. S. ochre yellow, midrib flushed tan; style arms ochre yellow infused tan; F. blended tan, rosewood, brick red and magenta, orchid flash below beard; beards old gold, 1/2" to 1" red orange horn. Conjuration X Enchanting.

IRON EAGLE (George Sutton, R. 1999). Sdlg. H-214. TB, 37" (94 cm), ML & RE. S. off-white, antique gold midrib; style arms pale lavender white; F. pale lavender white, near light grey; beards antique gold, confederate blue base and horn; slight musky fragrance. Cloud Baron X Dashing.

IRWELL ANGEL (Ron Busch, R. 1999). Sdlg. 93D3-70. SDB, 11" (28 cm), M. S. white, flushed cream; F. yellow, edged white, metal brown blush around beard; beards yellow, tipped blue. Parentage unknown.

IRWELL DELIGHT (Ron Busch, R. 1999). Sdlg. 93D34-87. SDB, 12" (31 cm), ML. S. pale lavender; F. old gold; beards lavender. Parentage unknown.

IRWELL GOBLIN (Ron Busch, R. 1999). Sdlg. 93D33-88. SDB, 12" (31 cm), M. S. old gold; F. light violet, veined medium violet, red veining around blue beard. Parentage unknown.

IRWELL GOLDEN CHARM (Ron Busch, R. 1999). Sdlg. 93D37-71. SDB, 12" (31 cm), M. S. lemon; F. lemon yellow, tan shoulders, beards yellow. Parentage unknown.

IRWELL LAKESIDE (Ron Busch, R. 1999). Sdlg. 93-103. SDB, 12" (31 cm), M. S. deep lavender; F. golden tan, deep lavender wire edge; beards blue. Parentage unknown.

IRWELL ROYAL (Ron Busch, R. 1997). Sdlg. L10. TB, 36" (91 cm), M. S. purple; F. rich velvety purple; beards bronze; ruffled, flared; slight fragrance. Parentage unknown.

ISABELLA-ROSE (R. E. Nichol by Jean Nichol, R. 1997). Sdlg. N195. TB, 37" (94 cm), M. S. pale lavender violet (RHS 85D), midrib infused deep violet (93A); F. deep violet; beards pale gold, hairs tipped blue; ruffled. Pascoe X Warleggan.

ISABELLINA (Sydney B. Mitchell by Philip Edinger, R. 1999). TB, 38" (97 cm), EM. Pale creamy flesh pink; beards tangerine. 29-33-1: (26-223-1: ((((*mesopotamica* x Oriflamme) x Gaviota) x Soledad) x (Sherbert x Esplendido)) x 26-13: ((Argentina x Mme. Cheri) x (Alcazar x Esplendido))) X W. R. Dykes. In circulation since 1930's and appearing in parentages.

I SAID YEAH (Tom Burseen, R. 1999). Sdlg. 95-162A. TB, 36" (91 cm), EM S. bluish pink; F. lighter blue pink; beards pink, long pink spoon; ruffled; slight fragrance. 93-442: (Amelia's Orchid X Stingray) X Mauvelous.

I SEEK YOU (Augusto Bianco, R. 1999). Sdlg. 797. TB, 32" (82 cm), ML. S. blue pearl; style arms beige pearl; F. amber cinnamon, center touched lilac; beards rust, base mustard; pronounced spicy musky fragrance. ((Beachgirl x (Borderline x Peaches n' Topping)) x (Olympiad x Peach Spot)) X Electrique.

ISE HOMARE (Society for Japanese Irises, R. 1992). JI (3 F.), 31½" (80 cm), ML. S. white with purple edge and markings; F. purple veined white, signal yellow. Parentage and hybridizer unknown. Introduced in Japan prior to 1940.

ISEJI-NO-HARU (Kamo Nursery by Society for Japanese Irises, R. 1999). JI (3 F.), 36" (91 cm), M. Light pink. Hime Kagami X Sakura Komachi. Kamo Nursery 1987.

ISLAND CHARM (J. T. Aitken, R. 1991). Sdlg. 84T21. BB, 26" (66 cm), ML. Ruffled lemon yellow, white flash around yellow orange beards. (Sunshine Express x Brown Lasso) X (Sunshine Express x Summer Love). Aitken's Salmon Creek 1991.

ISLAND DANCER (George Shoop, R. 1991). Sdlg. 85-5-1. TB, 36" (91 cm), M. S. brown; F. orange; beards tangerine. Hawaiian Queen X 82-3 brown: (Orange Burst x Early Surprise). Shoop 1991.

ISLAND GOSSIP (Barry Blyth, R. 1996). Sdlg. A151-3. TB, 36" (91 cm), ML. S. apricot to buff; F. rose to burgundy rose, lighter centerline; beards rich apricot; sweet fragrance. Painted Blue X Impressionist. Tempo Two 1996/97.

ISLAND GYPSY (Barry Blyth, R. 1975). Sdlg. E369-1. TB, 34" (86 cm), ML. S. tan gold; F. reddish tan; beards old gold. Twilight Harmony X Barcelona. Tempo Two 1976/77.

ISLAND HOLIDAY (James Gibson, TB, R. 1969). Cooley 1970.

ISLANDS CHEER (Tony Huber, R. 1998). Sdlg. 95-Wn-12. SPEC (*versicolor*), 28" (70 cm), E. S. white, veined violet blue (RHS 90C); style arms violet blue, bordered pink and white; F. violet blue (90B), signal veined yellow and surrounded by white zone veined violet blue (90B); slight sweet fragrance. AC-012: (AC-0 12 ex, collected Anticosti Island, x unknown) X 90-522 white veined purple: (HA-89-49, near-white from Magdalena Islands, x white Laurentian *versicolor*).

ISLAND SONG (Francis Rogers, TB, R. 1989). Meadowbrook 1991.

ISLAND SUNSET (Schreiner, R. 1992). Sdlg. W 735-A. TB, 36" (91 cm), M. S. apricot pink (RHS 26C); F. apricot yellow (23C); beards tangerine; ruffled. Erleen Richeson X Olympic Challenge. Schreiner 1992.

ISLAND SURF (J. T. Aitken, R. 1994). Sdlg. 86T85. TB, 34" (86 cm), M. S. medium violet, midrib flushed deeper; F. light violet, deeper flush below deep violet beard. Memorable X Olympiad. Aitken's Salmon Creek 1994.

ISLA SERLE (Harry Foster, R. 1991). Sdlg. R36/87. SIB (tet.), 34" (86 cm), ML. S. pale violet blue (RHS 93C); style arms azure, feathered; F. rich pacific blue (93A), pale green signal; ruffled. Harpswell Happiness X Dear Dianne. V. H. Humphrey 1995.

ISLAY (Revie Harvey, R. 1991). Sdlg. 85/M/QM. SPEC-X (evansia), 34" (86 cm), L. S. pale orchid pink; style arms pale pink, deeper midrib, fimbriated; F. pale orchid pink, violet signal lines from hafts, pale gold crests. *I. milesii* X Question Mark. Hilmary Catton 1991.

ISLE AH CUNDEE (Clifton Kunde, R. 1993). Sdlg. 85-8-1R. TB, 33" (84 cm), EM & RE. S. light lilac (RHS 76A) over white ground; F. cream white ground edged darker lilac (87C), greyed red (181A) haft markings; beards yellow orange, tipped near-white. Parentage unknown.

ISN'T IT ROMANTIC (Barbara Roberts, R. 1999). Sdlg. CB 57-6. TB, 36" (91 cm), ML. Medium lavender violet, F. with small white area at beard increasing with age, leaving wide lavender violet edge; beards tangerine, lavender violet at end; ruffled; pronounced sweet fragrance. Chapel Bells X PC 86-12: (Pearl Chiffon x Spanish Lace).

ISN'T THIS SOMETHING (Allan Ensminger, R. 1992). Sdlg. 186-68. TB, 28" (71 cm), ML. Carmine rose (HCC 21/3) with amethyst violet (35/1) stripes and splashes; beards brick red (16/1); ruffled; slight fragrance. Go Around X 81-44: ((Doodle Strudel x (69-50: ((Valimar x (Patience x Apricot Luster)) x Peachy Creamy) x Royal Belle)) x (Dream Lover x (64-33: ((Champagne Velvet x Lake Tahoe) x Dutch Doll) x Rococo))). Varigay 1993.

ISOLDE JANN (Manfred Beer, R. 1999). Sdlg. MB 1/87. TB, 39" (100 cm), M. Lightly ruffled cinnamon (RHS 165C), F. with light greyed purple (186C) blaze; beards cadmium orange (23A); spicy fragrance. Nanni F. X San Jose.

ISO-NO-ASAKAZE (Shuichi Hirao by Society for Japanese Irises, R. 1993). JI (6 F.), 48" (122 cm), L. Ruffled dark red violet with white halo and short white veins, signal yellow; style arms tipped and edged red violet, multiple. Parentage unknown. Hirao prior to 1985.

ISPOVED (Adolf Volfovich-Moler, R. 1999). Sdlg. 151. TB, 45" (115 cm), EM. S. light raspberry purple; style arms pale cardinal red, midrib brighter; F. bright raspberry purple, lighter edge, cream brown markings around yellow beard and on hafts; ruffled; laced; slight fragrance. Pink Sleigh X Vdokhnoveniye. Volfovich-Moler 1999.

ISTANBUL (Monty Byers, TB, R. 1989). Moonshine 1990.

IT AIN'T SO (Tom Burseen, R. 1999). Sdlg. 95-266A. TB, 36" (91 cm), ML. S. violet (RHS 88B); F. dark violet (89C), blackish sheen; beards mustard, with long narrow violet petaloid ending in small spoon; ruffled; slight fragrance. Hunk X Thornbird. T.B.'s Place 1999.

ITALIAN AFFAIR (John C. Taylor, R. 1998). Sdlg. UL15-2. LA, 43" (110 cm), ML. Purple violet, light buff edge and reverse; signals yellow; style arms buff; heavily ruffled. Dancing Vogue X Dural Dreamtime.

ITAZIPEJUTA (L. J. Duffy, R. 1992). Sdlg. WI-35-81. SPEC (*setosa*), 30-36" (76-91 cm), E. Purple red with white streaking at base of F.; style arms pale rose, purple mid-streak; buds purple. Selection of *I. setosa interior* collected 1981 near Fairbanks, Alaska.

IT HAPPENS (John Durrance, R. 1990). Sdlg. D89-164. TB, 32" (81 cm), M. Blend of creamy light yellow with red, brown, and purple streaks. Parentage unknown. Long 1993.

IT IS (Barry Blyth, R. 1995). Sdlg. B34-6. SDB, 10" (25 cm), VE-EML. S. cocoa tan, midrib infused violet; F. cocoa tan, hafts violet tan, deep violet rose chevron blaze; beards white to lavender, tangerine in throat. Z15-4, Fairy Favours sib, X Z24-1, Volts sib. Tempo Two 1995/96.

ITRIEL (Viktor Koroliov, R. 1995). Sdlg. S-18-86K. TB, 39" (100 cm), E. S. white; F. white, tinted lilac; beards yellow; ruffled; pronounced sweet fragrance. New Snow X unknown. Koroliov 1990.

IT'S A BEAUTY (Sara Doonan, R. 1992). Sdlg. 85-7. TB, 36" (91 cm), ML-VL. Lacy pink (RHS 50D); wide self beards; slight sweet fragrance. Chanteuse X Sunday Chimes. Sunset Iris Garden 1992.

IT'S A BOY (Dorman Haymon, LA, R. 1989). Deep South Garden 1990.

IT'S A GIGGLE (Barry Blyth, R. 1998). Sdlg. F3-3. IB, 20-22" (51-56 cm), VE-EM & RE. S. ochre tan, reddish burgundy midrib and base; F. reddish burgundy, 1/4" ochre tan edge; beards lavender, hairs tipped bronze except at outer end. Celsius X Talk. Tempo Two 1998/99.

IT'S A TRY (Alison Nicoll, R. 1999). Sdlg. N95T6:5. TB, 32" (81 cm), E. S. purple, fading to blue at edge; style arms blue; F. light blue, purple wash; beards gold, tipped blue. In Town X Honky Tonk Blues. Richmond Iris 1999/2000.

IT'S COOL (John C. Taylor, R. 1991). Sdlg. OL 143-1. LA, 39" (100 cm), EM. Pale mauve (RHS 69D), veined darker mauve; style arms green and mauve. OL 101-1: (Joel Fletcher x Limited Edition) X Helen Naish. Rainbow Ridge 1991/92.

IT'S DELICIOUS (Barry Blyth, R. 1996). Sdlg. B140-1. TB, 38" (96 cm), ML. Lacy light orange apricot; beards tangerine orange. Legato X Romantic Mood. Tempo Two 1996/97.

IT'S LILAC TIME (Peter Jackson, R. 1997). Sdlg. LWM1. LA, 34" (87 cm), ML. S. pale lilac, soft lilac center wash; style arms cream, tipped soft lilac; F. soft lilac, fine yellow line signal; lightly ruffled; slight fragrance. Watch Out X Malibu Magic. Iris Acres 1997/98.

#IT'S MAGIC (Edyth Burns, TB, R. 1954). Stock destroyed, not introduced. Name released.

IT'S MAGIC (William Maryott, R. 1994). Sdlg. S161HORN. TB, 36" (91 cm), M. S. bright medium sunfast yellow; F. bright medium yellow, darkening toward hafts with white flash in middle; beards bright yellow, big, with yellow horn. Lemon Fever X Blowtorch. Maryott 1995.

IT'S WILD (Joseph Ghio, CA, R. 1989). Bay View 1990.

ITTOO (Ed Matheny III, R. 1996). Sdlg. J:02-03-93. JI (6 F.), 37" (94 cm), EM. Blue, wide lavender rim, signals yellow with white halo; style arms white, tipped lavender. Nemurijishi X Sapphire Star. Ed's Iris 1997.

IVAN-DA-MARIYA (Nina Miroshnichenko, R. 1996). TB, 31" (78 cm), M. S. white, tinted lilac; F. light violet; beards white at end, yellow to dark yellow in throat; ruffled; pronounced spicy fragrance. Parentage unknown. Miroshnichenko 1988.

IVAN SHISHKIN (V. & N. Gordodelovy, R. 1995). Sdlg. 77. TB, 32" (80 cm), EM. Orange, tinted lettuce green; beards red; ruffled. Parentage unknown. Gordodelovy 1978.

IVAN TURGENEV (V. & N. Gordodelovy, R. 1995). Sdlg. 137. TB, 37" (95 cm), E. S. rose; style arms yellow; F. cowberry rose, light brown haft striations; beards brown. Parentage unknown. Gordodelovy 1981.

I'VE GOT RHYTHM (Schreiner, R. 1998). Sdlg. EE 975-A. TB, 38" (97 cm), EM. S. lilac purple (RHS 70A), slight creamy center; style arms lilac purple; F. creamy yellow (13D) ground, distinct lilac purple plicata edging; beards tangerine. Footloose X AA 2191-C: (Y 252-1: ((Cozy Calico x Grape Accent) x Capricious) x Gigolo). Schreiner 1998.

IVEY LOU (Louise Smith, R. 1993). Sdlg. 85-40. TB, 36" (91 cm), EM. Medium pink self; beards deep pink; pronounced sweet fragrance. Parentage unknown.

IVOR KNOWLES (F. Knowles by Ruth Knowles, R. 1991). Sdlg. G3. CA, 12" (30 cm), ML. S. white, veined and fringed violet blue (RHS 92B); F. soft blue violet bitone effect; slightly ruffled. Parentage unknown. V. H. Humphrey 1992.

IVORY AND RED (Austin Morgan, R. 1990). TB, 36" (91 cm), EML. S. ivory; F. red, edged ivory; beards red. Parentage unknown. Iris Test Garden 1990.

IVORY BLUSH (Schreiner, R. 1998). Sdlg. DD 935-1. TB, 38" (97 cm), M. S. and style arms soft salmon (RHS 27B); F. pink overlaid amber yellow (18C); beards tangerine, pink at end; ruffled. Lovely Glow X V 476-A: (Carved Angel x Paradise). Schreiner 1998.

IVORY BUTTONS (Ben Hager, R. 1993). Sdlg. MD5496IvSp. MDB, 5½" (13 cm), EM. S. ivory; F. ivory white, light brown spot; beards white. Sib to Fragment. Adamgrove 1997.

IVORY FASHION (A. & D. Willott, R. 1996). Sdlg. 94-16. MDB, 5" (13 cm), EM. Creamy white, F. with small red brown rayed spots separated by white blaze extending from beard; beards white, changing to cream, orange in throat; lightly ruffled. Daisy Fresh X What Not. Willott 1996.

IVORY FAUN (Chet Tompkins, R. 1992). Sdlg. 83-49. TB, 36" (91 cm), ML. Ruffled blend of pale tan, ivory and dull green; beards faun brown. (((Angel's Touch x Wayward Angel) x (Valverde x Carillon Belles)) x ((Pink Pussycat x Emerald Echo) x (Dragon Lady x Ovation))) X ((Mint Meringue x Dragon Lady) x (Emerald Echo x Diplomat)). Fleur de Lis 1992.

IVORY GODDESS (Frederick Kerr, R. 1997). Sdlg. 905301. TB, 35" (89 cm), M. S. ivory; style arms yellow; F. white in center shading to ivory edge, hafts darker; beards dark yellow; ruffled; slight fragrance. Gypsy Woman X Silverado. Rainbow Acres 1997.

IVORY WAY (Barry Blyth, R. 1995). Sdlg. A70-4. TB, 36" (91 cm), ML. S. pure cream, some lemon veining; F. cream, light lemon reverse; beards cream; foliage base very deep purple; pronounced sweet fragrance. Liqueur Creme X Taffeta Bow. Tempo Two 1995/96.

IWAI-NO-NISHIKI (Shuichi Hirao by Society for Japanese Irises, R. 1997). JI (6 F.), 35" (90 cm), M. Red violet with white flecks, small white halo around yellow signal. Parentage unknown. Introduced in Japan, 1959.

IYUNSKAYA MELODIYA (Sergey Loktev, R. 1999). Sdlg. 94-R14-1E. BB, 24" (60 cm), VE-E. S. pale yellow, midrib whitish cream; style arms yellow, paler midrib; F. pale lilac edged pale lemon, brown-patterned yellow hafts with bordeaux spots on lower portion; beards yellow, pale lilac at end. (Pink Blue Genes x unknown) X unknown.

IZMOROZ (Yuri Pirogov, R. 1997). Sdlg. 92-2C. TB, 37" (95 cm), M. White ground, pale blue plicata edge; style arms white; beards violet, base yellow; slight fragrance. Spinning Wheel X "Depeche Mode": (Rancho Rose x Sketch Me). Pirogov 1997.

IZU-NO-UMI (Shuichi Hirao by Society for Japanese Irises, R. 1993). JI (3 F.), 36" (91 cm), M. S. blue violet (RHS 94C); style arms same, with white center; F. blue violet (94C) with white veins extending almost to edge, yellow signal suffused green. Parentage unknown. Hirao prior to 1985. Also in commerce as "Izo-no-Umi".

JABAL (Sterling Innerst, R. 1992). Sdlg. 3544-6. SDB, 15" (38 cm), M. S. medium yellow; F. white; beards cream. Syllable X Dash Away. Innerst 1993.

JACARANDA FESTIVAL (Kevin Nilsen, R. 1992). Sdlg. 71-87-1. TB, 32" (82 cm), ML. Heavily ruffled violet blue; beards blue. Parentage unknown. Iridescence 1992/93.

JACARANDA LAD (Heather Pryor, R. 1996). Sdlg. 17/92-A. LA, 40" (102 cm), M. Soft jacaranda blue, veined darker, F. with bright lime green steeple signal; style arms jacaranda blue, cream side rim; lightly ruffled. Sea Wisp X Spanish Ballet. Iris Haven 1997/98.

JA CEE (Donovan Albers, SDB, R. 1989). Albers, Borbeleta Gardens 1990.

JACIVA (Chad Harris, R. 1991). Sdlg. 85JA3. JI (6 F.), 42" (107 cm), ML. Sanded blue lavender, lemon yellow signal, very fine white rim; style arms and petaloids white, edged lavender blue; ruffled. Knight in Armor X Marx 7507. Aitken's Salmon Creek 1992.

JACK ATTACK (John C. Taylor, R. 1993). Sdlg. RL 3-1. LA, 51" (130 cm), EM. S. light purple; F. purple, strong yellow signal; ruffled. C'est Bonne X Margaret Lee. Rainbow Ridge 1993/94.

JACK DUNDERMAN (Mary Louise Dunderman, R. 1992). SPEC (*versicolor*), 18" (46 cm), L. Blue purple, fewer than usual F. markings. Selected *I. versicolor* sdlg., parentage unknown.

JACK REYNOLDS (Ed Attenberger, R. 1996). Sdlg. 92-02-06. TB, 36" (91 cm), M. S. and style arms medium yellow; F. orchid purple, edged tan buff, hafts buff yellow lined white; beards yellow orange. Rare Gold X Gold Galore.

JACKS ARE BETTER (Helen Cochran, R. 1997). Sdlg. 94-02-A. TB, 36" (91 cm), M. S. blue violet, deeper midrib flush; style arms blue violet; F. pale blue violet; beards yellow, blue tip; ruffled; slight spicy fragrance. Bubble Up X Modern Times. Stockton 1998.

JACKS ARE WILD (Joseph Ghio, R. 1998). Sdlg. PD-222J2. CA, 10" (25 cm), M. S. light rosewood; F. rosewood, lightening to dusty rose, violet halo signal around gold throat. PF-160V3: (PJ-164-X, San Andreas sib, x PH-228T2: (PJ-164A x National Anthem)) X PF-191W3: ((Los Californio x San Andreas) x Sierra Dell). Bay View 1998.

#JACQUELINE (J. Salter, TB, R. 1868) and (Eugene Dunphe, TB, 1921). Marked as obsolete in 1939 Check List; name released.

JACQUELINE (William Plotner, R. 1999). TB, 38" (97 cm), L. S. silky dark violet (blend of RHS 89C and 95B), darker veining; style arms slightly darker; F. bluish black violet (103B), centerline and edge matching S.; beards dark blue violet base, hair tips varying from silvery white at end to light yellow in center, yellow in throat; slight spicy fragrance. 87-403: (By Night x Study in Black) X 87-401: (Swazi Princess x Study in Black). Wildwood Gardens 1999.

JACQUIE J (Hilmary Catton, R. 1990). Sdlg. C849-3. BB, 26½" (68 cm), EM. Azure blue, F. with dark wine ray pattern; beards pale blue, tipped white. Open Sky X Mystique. Hilmary Catton 1991.

JAC-Y-DO (Harry Foster, R. 1990). Sdlg. J333/85. SIB (tet.), 36" (91 cm), EM. S. rich purple blue; F. deep rich navy blue, kingfisher blue spot in center, silver edge, soft beige signal edged white. Silver Edge X Hubbard.

JADE EAST (Bob Thomason, R. 1993). Sdlg. BT 8511A. SDB, 9" (23 cm), EM. White with green overlay, lavender infusion at base; beards light blue; slight fragrance. Jade Mist X Joyous Isle. Okie Iris 1999.

JADE MAID (J. T. Aitken, R. 1996). Sdlg. 91M43. SDB, 12" (31 cm), M. S. greenish yellow; F. greenish yellow, washed burgundy red; beards frosted blue. Jade Jewels X unknown. Aitken's Salmon Creek 1996.

JADE MOON (Lois O'Brien, R. 1996). Sdlg. 91-24A. TB, 36" (91 cm), ML. Greenish cream self; beards soft yellow, hairs tipped white; slight sweet fragrance. Envy X OB 85-69A: (Key Lime x OB 83-20A: (Soap Opera x Carriage Trade)). O'Brien Iris 1997.

JADE STONE (O. D. Niswonger, R. 1994). Sdlg. SDB 26-91. SDB, 15" (38 cm), M. Olive green with darker spot around light blue beards. SDB 20-87: (C. Palmer 72-59: ((Wilma V x unknown) x Little Titan) x H. Nichols 8109A: (April Anthem x Passport)) X Adoring Glances. Cape Iris 1994.

JADE WIZARD (A. & D. Willott, R. 1990). Sdlg. 88-40. SDB, 12" (30 cm), M. Ruffled ecru, F. with olive halo; beards blue. Geauga Lake X 84-51: (Royal Silk x Michael Paul). Willott 1991.

JADRIAN (Bob Thomason, R. 1993). Sdlg. BT 8626A. SDB, 12" (30 cm), EM. S. yellow tinted green, base plum; F. pale yellow, hafts gold brown; beards orange, tipped white; slight fragrance. Jade Mist X Hee Haw. Okie Iris 1994.

JAI DEE (Bob Thomason, R. 1993). Sdlg. BT 8811B. SDB, 11" (28 cm), EM. S. medium violet; F. medium violet, hafts veined white, deep red violet around beard; beards orange, tipped lavender; slight fragrance. Dove Wings X Tortuga. Okie Iris 1994.

JAILLANAIS (Christian Lanthelme, R. 1997). Sdlg. 5A91. MDB, 7" (18 cm), M. S. light beige, base flushed violet; style arms ochre; F. light ochre brown; beards violet, ochre hair tips and in throat. Stockholm X unknown. Lanthelme 1998.

JAI'S SURPRISE (Indra Belford, R. 1997). Sdlg. 89A-2-9123. TB, 36" (91 cm), EML. S. pale orchid; style arms lavender, edges yellow; F. burgundy; beards burgundy, hairs tipped tangerine, long burgundy horn at times fuzzy or with long spoon; lightly ruffled; slight fragrance. Camelot Rose X Horned Tantalizer.

JAMES BOND (Marky Smith, R. 1995). Sdlg. 9007A. SDB, 14" (36 cm), EM. Ruffled cadet blue blend (RHS 92C to 188C), F. with olive bronze (195A) halo surrounding beard; beards bronze (195A), navy blue (94B) at end; pronounced sweet fragrance. Dark Vader X Chubby Cheeks. Aitken's Salmon Creek 1996.

JAMES F. BALLARD (Bob Thomason, R. 1992). Sdlg. BT 8933H. TB, 32" (81 cm), M. White, thin yellow rim, F. with yellow hafts; beards deep orange; slight spicy fragrance. Simply Pretty X Christmas Time.

JAMES FRANKLIN CLAY (Louise Smith, R. 1992). TB, 35½" (90 cm), M. Slightly ruffled white self; beards yellow, 3/4" white horn. Parentage unknown.

JAMES P. (Mary Dunn, R. 1994). Sdlg. M84-889-3. TB, 37" (94 cm), ML. Ruffled silvery french blue violet, deeper on edge of F.; beards matching violet. Crystalyn X Gaulter 81-70: (Portrait of Larrie x Carriage Trade). M.A.D. Iris 1995.

JAMMY PRINTS (LeRoy Meininger, R. 1997). Sdlg. I.F. 89. TB, 30" (76 cm), M. S. light blue, blue violet streaks and spots mainly on outer 1/2"; style arms light blue; F. blue violet forming dark veined pattern, irregular violet marginal band; beards blue violet, tipped gold; variable pattern; slight sweet fragrance. Island Fiesta X (Purple Pepper x Purple Streaker). Monument, Woodland Iris 1997.

JANET HINES (Thom Ericson, R. 1995). Sdlg. 88G94-21. TB, 35" (89 cm), EM. S. light blue (RHS

97C), mottled sky blue; style arms light blue, slightly deeper center rib; F. medium blue (93B); beards orange, blue at end; slight musky fragrance. Christmas Time X Rancho Rose.

JANET HUTCHINSON (Graeme Grosvenor, R. 1993). JI (6 F.), 50" (127 cm), EM. Heavily ruffled white, heavily suffused rose pink; tufted center. Rose Tower X Frilled Enchantment. Rainbow Ridge 1993/94.

JANET LANE (Cy Bartlett, R. 1997). Sdlg. C93-17. BB, 25" (63 cm), M. Ruffled light, bright lemon yellow, F. slightly darker; beards cream yellow; slight sweet fragrance. Nichol M133: (Elizabeth Poldark x Loveday) X Simply Pretty.

JANET SUE (Jim Hedgecock, R. 1996). Sdlg. A-13-1. TB, 30" (76 cm), ML. Medium pink self; beards reddish pink; ruffled, lightly laced; slight sweet fragrance. C.Q. 82-1: (Angie Quadros x Homecoming Queen) X Birthday Gift. Comanche Acres 1998.

JANIANS WAY (Mrs. D. J. Hossack, R. 1996). SDB, 9" (23 cm), M. Old gold; beards gold, dusted brown. Surprise Orange X Little Buccaneer.

JAN KATZ (A. & D. Willott, R. 1997). Sdlg. W 91-335. IB, 23" (59 cm), EM. S. and style arms light peach; F. medium apricot blending to light peach at edge, slight white halo near beard; beards bright orange, cream at end; ruffled, flared. Barney's Delight X Coral Beads. Willott 1997.

JAPANESE HARMONY (Currier McEwen, R. 1994). Sdlg. T(4)85/93A. JI (3 F.) tet., 32" (80 cm), ML. S. violet blue (RHS 84A), 1/8" white edge; style arms pure white; F. white, yellow (7B) signal, greenish yellow (2B) veins. Blueberry Rimmed X T(1)80/134: ((Muffled Drums x unknown) x unknown). Eartheart, Seaways 1994.

JAPANESE MARBLE (Currier McEwen, R. 1994). Sdlg. 85/20. JI (3 F.), 48" (120 cm), M. S. marbled blue purple (RHS 88A) heavily splashed off-white; F. same, more heavily splashed, golden yellow (12A) signal. Purple Plus X 80/165: ((Muffled Drums x unknown) x unknown). Eartheart, Seaways 1994.

J. ARTHUR NELSON (Frank Foster, R. 1990). Sdlg. 8552B. TB, 35½" (90 cm), M. S. medium yellow; F. medium yellow gold, slightly lighter around deep yellow beard; ruffled, lightly flared; slight spicy fragrance. Lemon Lyric X Gold Galore.

JASPER COUNTY (John Gass, R. 1999). Sdlg. 20-90-60. TB, 34" (86 cm), ML. Copper, F. lighter around burnt orange beard; slight fragrance. Copper Classic X Malaysia. Rainbow Chasers 1999.

JATINWANE (Calvin Helsley, R. 1993). Sdlg. 93-5. SIB, 30" (76 cm), M. S. blue violet (RHS 92A); style arms red violet (87A), blue violet (92A) midrib; F. darker blue violet (94B), small white signal veined blue violet. Wing on Wing X Mabel Coday. Helsley 1997.

JAUNTY DANCER (Barry Blyth, R. 1997). Sdlg. D72-1. TB, 36" (92 cm), EM. S. light tan brown; F. white, faint bluish lavender blush, sharp 1/4" golden brown border, yellow hafts; beards bright gold; pronounced fragrance. Ivory Way X B132-2: (Holiday Lover x Love Comes). Tempo Two 1997/98.

JA WOHL (Bob Thomason, SDB, R. 1988). Okie Iris 1990.

JAYCEE (John Clive Russell, R. 1996). Sdlg. S-SH 93/1. TB, 36" (91 cm), M. S. icy lavender white, midrib buff; style arms buff; F. icy lavender white, paler center; beards white, tipped buff, 3/4" white horn; ruffled. Silverado X Sky Hooks.

JAY R (Robert Dunn, R. 1991). Sdlg. B87-1021-X. TB, 36" (91 cm), M. S. buckskin tan, slight deep cordovan red stain up midrib; F. velvety deep cordovan red, blue flash at tip of buckskin tan beard; ruffled. B80-744-A: (Tarde x P. T. Barnum) X M80-706-A: (Charro x Cavalier). M.A.D. Iris 1992.

JAZZ CHAMPS (Darlene Pinegar, R. 1999). Sdlg. TGY-93-79C. TB, 34" (86 cm), M. Dark violet self; beards dark violet, dark gold in throat; ruffled, flared; pronounced sweet fragrance. Titan's Glory X Then Again.

JAZZ ECHO (Donald Denney by James McWhirter, R. 1991). Sdlg. D79-18-1. TB, 36" (91 cm), M. S. tan gold; F. brownish red tan; beards gold, tipped mustard; slight fragrance. All That Jazz X D81-56: (Spectacular Bid x Gypsy Caravan). Cottage 1991.

JAZZED UP (Schreiner, R. 1994). Sdlg. AA 1462-1. TB, 42" (107 cm), ML. S. white (RHS 155D); F. rosy lavender (80C); beards white; lightly ruffled. S 269-O: (Mill Valley x I 686-1: (E 242-A: (Lilac Champagne sdlg. x ((Alpenrose x Whole Cloth) x Cashmere)) x Breaking Dawn)) X Lullaby of Spring. Schreiner 1994.

JAZZ FESTIVAL (Schreiner, R. 1990). Sdlg. T 710-1. TB, 40" (102 cm), ML. S. buff cream (RHS 199A); style arms soft yellow, rosy light purple lip; F. rosy violet (72B); beards yellow, tipped lavender; ruffled. K 155-F: (F 246-A: (Breaking Dawn x Y 1740-CC: (Amethyst Flame x ((Lavanesque x Opal Beauty) x Wonderment))) x H 387-1, Navajo Blanket sib) X R 309-L: (L 828-A: (Chapeau x Bold Hour) x Lorilee). Schreiner 1990.

JAZZ HOT (Heather Pryor, R. 1994). Sdlg. 60/90-8. LA, 35" (89 cm), ML. Smoky red (RHS 181A) edged white, bright yellow raised steeple signal on all petals, pale yellow reverse; style arms green, yellow center rib and smoky red tips. Gladiator's Gift X Desert Jewel. Lone Star 1997, Iris Haven 1997/98.

JAZZ ME BLUE (Schreiner, R. 1993). Sdlg. Y 23-1. TB, 38" (97 cm), M. Billowy ruffled blue (RHS 96B); beards yellow, tipped blue. N 124-A: (J 20-A: (Sapphire Hills x G 30-A: ((Pacific Panorama x Parisian Blue) x Sapphire Hills)) x J 21-9: (Sailor's Dance x G 30-A)) X T 283-1: (Land o' Lakes x Pledge Allegiance). Schreiner 1993.

JAZZ STAR (Thomas Wight, BB, R. 1989). Wight's Iris 1990.

JAZZY RAZZY (Monty Byers by Phyllis Dickey, R. 1998). Sdlg. G55-1. TB, 30" (76 cm), ML. Deep red raspberry; beards red orange, raspberry horn. D54-1B: (Blowtorch x Mulled Wine) X D50-1, unknown.

JEAN BUSH (Dorman Haymon, R. 1994). Sdlg. 87-88-1. LA, 36" (91 cm), M. S. red with yellow halo and large irregular yellow signal; style arms creamy yellow; F. red with yellow halo, large yellow sunburst signal; edges serrate. 29-85-1: (Teresa Margaret x (Uptight x Lucile Holley)) X 111-86-1: (Easter Tide x Swamp Flame). Lone Star 1994.

JEAN COLLINS (Hector Collins, R. 1990). Sdlg. 1985/SP 10. SPU, 55" (140 cm), M. S. white, lined gold; F. white, yellow area in throat lined gold, white signal; slight fragrance. Parentage unknown. Frances Love, Lynette Black 1995/96.

JEAN ERICKSON (Colin Rigby, R. 1993). Sdlg. PCN 56. CA, 12-14" (30-36 cm), M. S. light blue violet, red violet midrib; F. light blue violet, dark red violet signal and few veins, light blue wash below signal area. Canyon Snow X PCN 12: (Meek 269 x Sierra Sapphire Third). Portable Acres 1993.

JEAN MARIE (Lloyd Zurbrigg, R. 1994). Sdlg. KK 5-1-1. TB, 34" (86 cm), M. S. pure white; style arms white; F. light yellow; beards yellow; ruffled. Borderline X Champagne Elegance. Friendship 1995.

JEANNE LOUTZ (Jean-Jacques Francois, R. 1998). Sdlg. 2-11(95). TB, 35" (90 cm), EM. S. very light yellow, darker toward top; style arms light yellow; F. dark yellow, lighter border, brown shoulder veining; beards orange. Superstition X Champagne Elegance.

JEANNINE'S PRIDE (Willy Hublau, R. 1996). Sdlg. B5. JI (6 F.), 24-28" (60-70 cm), M. Silvery white, edged and dotted light violet, signal golden yellow; style arms white, edged lavender pink. Sdlg. X Lady in Waiting.

JEAN'S DELIGHT (Jean Collins by Hector Collins, R. 1990). Sdlg. 82/S6. SIB, 26" (65 cm), L. S. pale lavender marked and veined deeper lavender blue; style arms icy blue, deeper center markings; F. pale lavender edge, deepening toward center, golden yellow hafts with creamy edge, veined and spotted violet purple; ruffled. Foretell X unknown.

JEEPERS CREEPERS (George Sutton, R. 1997). MDB, 5" (13 cm), VE-E & RE. S. white, 1/4" stitched and dotted wistaria blue (RHS 92B) edge, blue stripes and dots on midrib; style arms wistaria blue (92D); F. white, stitched wistaria blue (92B) at hafts and to end of beard; beards white, hairs tipped wistaria blue, changing to orange in throat; lightly ruffled; slight sweet fragrance. Dunlin X Chubby Cheeks.

JEHOSAPHAT'S RELIANCE (Pete McGrath, R. 1998). Sdlg. McAB 93-43-P-B. AB (OGB), 24" (61 cm), M. S. light lilac blue fading near-white, light pink effect; F. white, washed light rose lilac, aging to light pink effect, rouge burgundy signal dotted at haft; beards light violet to lilac, hairs tipped mustard. Heart Stealer X Seraph's Jewel. Aril Society 1998.

JE NAYE (Ken Durio, R. 1992). Sdlg. PAT #12. LA, 30-36" (76-91 cm), L. S. very dark violet; self style arms with appendages; F. darker velvety violet, yellow cathedral signal. Bandito X Ann Chowning. Louisiana Nursery 1997.

JENNA (Barry Blyth, R. 1998). Sdlg. E56-1. IB, 20" (51 cm), VE-EML. S. light apricot; F. 3/8" slightly darker apricot edge, creamy white center area; beards bright tangerine, 1/4" white end; slight fragrance. Say Hello X Yes. Tempo Two 1998/99.

JENNIFER MARY (Heather Collins, R. 1994). Sdlg. 80-6. CA, 20" (50 cm), EML. S. pinkish lavender, midrib blue; F. deeper pink lavender, pale lavender signal, wine veining around gold flash; petal edges waved to curled; musky fragrance. Parentage unknown.

JENNIFER'S WISH (Nancy Burrows, TB, R. 1989). Stornaway Gardens 1990.

JENNY E (Manfred Beer, R. 1991). Sdlg. MB 28/84A. TB, 43" (110 cm), M. S. white; F. medium blue; beards yellow, tipped light blue. Lemon Brocade X Beauty Crown. Gartencenter Kania 1991.

JENNY ELF (Thom Ericson, R. 1995). Sdlg. 89GD-09. AB (OGB-), 21" (53 cm), EM. S. and style arms reddish plum purple (RHS 83A) with deep purple veining; F. bright reddish plum (79C), darker veining deepening near beard; beards deep reddish black, tipped brownish red; slight spicy fragrance. Cherry Garden X Martha Mia.

JENNY LYNN (Tom Burseen, R. 1999). Sdlg. 95-229A. TB, 37" (94 cm), EM. Pearled light pink (RHS 62D), style arms washed yellow; beards white, hairs tipped red orange; ruffled, laced; sweet fragrance. 93-110A: (Change of Pace x Dawn Sky) X Lotta Plicata.

JENNY MARIE (Shirley Sylvia, R. 1997). Sdlg. 1. SPU, 16-28" (41-70 cm), ML. S. pale lemon, tinged green; style arms cream to pale lemon; F. yellow; lightly ruffled. Just Janelle sdlg. X unknown -- possibly Frost.

JEREMIAH (Bob Thomason, R. 1991). Sdlg. 8635A. SDB, 10" (25 cm), EM. S. lemon yellow; F. gold, lighter hafts and rim; beards orange, tipped white. Runaway X unknown. Okie Iris 1993.

JEREMY BRIAN (Brian Price, SDB, R. 1975). British Iris Society 1981.

JEREMY POLDARK (R. E. Nichol, R. 1992). Sdlg. J25-1. TB, 36" (91 cm), E. Ruffled blue violet (RHS 93B) self; beards yellow gold. (Intuition x (Annabel Jane x Mystique)) X (Full Tide x Intuition).

JERRY DALE REIN (Bob Thomason, R. 1993). Sdlg. BT 9034C. BB, 22" (56 cm), ML. S. white, yellow wire rim; F. red brown, lighter edge; beards orange, tipped yellow; slight fragrance. Boy o' Boy X Trudy.

JESSE MAC (Mary Miller, R. 1992). Sdlg. M-61-10B. MDB, 8" (20 cm), E. Cream with green signal below yellow beards. Gold Sprite X Green Spot.

JESSE'S EDITION (George Sutton, R. 1998). Sdlg. E-100. BB, 26" (66 cm), ML & RE. S. blue purple (near RHS 102A), white midrib with blue purple line and few specks; style arms blue purple; F. white, 5/8" blue purple edge and stippling; beards yellow orange, base light blue purple; ruffled; pronounced sweet fragrance. Rare Edition X Jesse's Song. Sutton 1999.

#JESSICA (Salter, TB, 1878). Marked as obsolete in 1939 Check List; name released.

JESSICA (Polly Black, R. 1995). Sdlg. MT21-35W. TB, 36" (91 cm), E. Ruffled white self, green hint around beard; beards orange, tipped white. Purple plicata sdlg. X unknown. Polly Black 1995.

JESSICA ANN (Ingeborg Hempel, R. 1998). TB, 38" (96 cm), L. S. and style arms white; F. white, diamond dusted, lemon yellow on upper half; beards white, hairs tipped yellow, deep yellow in throat; slight fragrance. Leda's Lover X Sunshine Song. Holly Lane 1998.

JESSICA'S JADE (T. J. Betts, R. 1990). Sdlg. 718J. LA, 43" (109 cm), E. S. violet blue (RHS 87A); style arms pale green; F. white, heavily veined violet blue (87A), bright green signal. Mac's Blue Heaven X La Perouse.

JESSICA'S JOLLIFICATION (J. Owings Rebert, R. 1999). Sdlg. CB-97-7. SIB, 28" (71 cm), M. Violet blue self, F. with copper signal. Parentage unknown.

JESSIE'S CHORUS (Polly Black, R. 1992). Sdlg. WG5-16P. TB, 30" (76 cm), E. S. delicate orchid; F. white, fringed delicate orchid; beards white-tipped; slight fragrance. Jesse's Song X unknown. Polly Black 1992.

JESSIE'S STAR (Chris Vizvarie, R. 1991). Sdlg. 86-7A. SDB, 10" (25 cm), E. Ruffled violet blue (RHS 97D); beards yellow, tipped blue; pronounced sweet fragrance. Serenity Prayer sib X Pale Star. Last Scent Farm 1991.

JESTER'S MOTLEY (Janet Hutchinson, R. 1991). SPEC (*laevigata*), 22-26" (56-65 cm), M. S. and style arms medium purple, blotched, striped and veined rich fuchsia in irregular pattern overall; F. same, white signal and small pale yellow line. Parentage unknown. Rainbow Ridge 1995/96.

JE T'AIME (Lilly Gartman, R. 1990). Sdlg. 86-2W. TB, 38" (97 cm), ML. Ruffled white; beards soft coral. Critic's Choice X Status Seeker. Roris 1994.

JET STREAM (Luella Danielson, AR (OH), R. 1989). Aril Society, Pleasure Iris 1990.

JEVER DOPPELDECKER (Uwe Knoepnadel, R. 1990). JI (6 F.), 39" (100 cm), M. White, yellow signal. Sdlg. X sdlg. Friesland Staudengarten 1990.

JEVER HARLEKIN (Uwe Knoepnadel, R. 1990). SIB (sino-sib), 23½" (60 cm), M. Dark blue violet, F. with large white spot, small yellow brown signal. Sino-sib sdlg. X unknown. Friesland Staudengarten 1990.

JEVER SILBERPFEIL (Uwe Knoepnadel, R. 1990). SIB (sino-sib), 18" (45 cm), EM. Light yellow, F. with some veining, yellow signal. Sino-sib sdlg. X unknown. Friesland Staudengarten 1990.

JEVER VULKAN (Tomas Tamberg by Uwe Knoepnadel, R. 1990). SPEC-X (cal-sib), 31½" (80 cm), EM. Light yellow melon with heavy burgundy veining, intense orange F. center, orange signal. Parentage unknown. Friesland Staudengarten 1990.

JEWEL BEACH (Chun Fan, R. 1990). Sdlg. 86-19. TB, 37" (93 cm), E. S. white, slight yellow lacing at upper edge; F. lightly ruffled white with golden yellow flush; beards yellow (RHS 13A) tipped lighter; slight fragrance. Cup Race X Coral Beauty.

JEWEL BRIGHT (Nora Scopes, SDB, R. 1983). British Iris Society 1987.

JEWELER'S ART (Carol Lankow by J. T. Aitken, R. 1993). Sdlg. 0-H-15-2. SDB, 12" (30 cm), M. S. amethyst violet; F. red, blending to black at hafts; beards amethyst; slight fragrance. Cherry Pop X (Cherry Tart x Cheery Cherry). Aitken's Salmon Creek 1993.

JEWEL OF JAKARTA (Chris Vizvarie, R. 1997). SDB, 12" (30 cm), E & RE. Ruffled medium dark lavender self; beards dark lavender; slight sweet fragrance. Sigh X Mama Big Bucks. Last Scent Farm 1998.

JEWELRY (Ben Hager, R. 1991). Sdlg. SD4999Wh/YBlBds. SDB, 11½" (29 cm), M. S. white tinged cream and blue at base; style arms blue white; F. medium yellow; beards light blue. Naiad X SD4449: ((((Joy Bringer x Ornament) x ((Sunny Heart x ((Evening Storm x Welch H-501) x (Sulina x Melodrama))) x (Blueberry Muffins x Peanuts))) x Flirty Mary) x 4018GrSp). Adamgrove 1991.

JEZIÓRKO (Lech Komarnicki, R. 1998). Sdlg. 93/4/6 Sib 2. SIB, 36-38" (91-97 cm), EML. Deep blue violet, white F. blaze. Parentage unknown (28 chr. group); seed from British Iris Society seed exchange.

J. FINDLEY (Bob Thomason, R. 1998). Sdlg. BT 94-030B. TB, 32" (81 cm), EM. S. rose lavender veined darker lavender; style arms lavender, edged yellow; F. light lavender, darker toward rose lavender edge, hafts gold; beards gold; laced; slight spicy fragrance. Lace Jabot X Mary Frances.

JIFFY (Ben Hager, R. 1995). Sdlg. MD4972YRdSp. MDB, 5-6" (13-15 cm), EML. S. and style arms yellow; F. dark red, precise yellow border; beards yellow. AMD4465TlVar: (Little You x (Inca Toy x (BU67 x Atomic Blue))) X MD4475Am: (Ditto sib x MD3409BlAm: ((((Orange Caper x Puppet) x (Rickshaw x Lilli-Var)) x Wink) x (((Rickshaw x Lilli-Var) x Bongo) x (Russet Dot x (Rickshaw x Lilli-Var))))). Adamgrove 1995.

JILJILYAH (David Shahak by Arnold Ferguson, selector, R. 1997). Sdlg. RxPM#1. AR (OH), 17" (43 cm), E. S. silver blue, darker blue veining; style arms rose, tipped violet; F. brown with green cast, lightly veined overall giving sanded appearance; beards yellow, split around signal; slight fragrance. Ravid X Princess Maya. Grandview Iris Patch 1997.

JILLIAN MASON (Brian Price, IB, R. 1988). David Austin Roses 1992.

JILL ROSALIND (B.L.C. Dodsworth, TB, R. 1976). British Iris Society 1981.

JIM (Gerald Richardson, R. 1994). Sdlg. 87-35-5. TB, 38" (97 cm), M. S. pale blue white; style arms lavender blue; F. white, light lavender blue plicata markings on hafts; beards creamy white; slight fragrance. 81-18-2: (Victoria Falls x Mary Frances) X He-Man Blues. Rainbow's End 1994.

JIM ELWICK (G. F. Wilson, R. 1992). Sdlg. 46-89TTWM-G. AB (OGB), 32" (81 cm), EM. S. clear pale pink, bright orange yellow rib; F. russet, paling toward edge, pale yellow rim, few brown black lines radiating from beard; beards yellow, tipped brown; slight sweet fragrance. Turkish Tangent X Warrior's Mantle.

JIM FRAZIER (Graeme Grosvenor, R. 1997). Sdlg. V12-1. TB, 36" (91 cm), M. S. lavender white, center darker; F. dark lavender, large lighter outer edge; beards pale yellow to lavender white; heavily ruffled; slight fragrance. Delirious X Timescape.

JIMMY'S SMILE (Francis Rogers, R. 1996). Sdlg. C-55-B. TB, 32" (81 cm), M. S. light lavender blue (RHS 91B); F. white ground, 3/8" purple to violet blue (93B) edge, speckled purple haft veining; beards purple, tipped greyed gold; ruffled; sweet fragrance. Everything Plus X Island Song. Meadowbrook 1996.

JOAN GRACE (Mary Tubbs, R. 1994). Sdlg. WD-4. TB, 36" (91 cm), M. Clear yellow, F. edged faint white; beards pale yellow; tailored; sweet fragrance. Sun King X Wartime.

JOAN MORITZ (Marguerite Hagberg, SDB, R. 1988). Hillcrest 1990.

JOAN'S PARTY (Tom Burseen, R. 1999). Sdlg. 95-65B. TB, 36" (91 cm), M. Heavily ruffled peach (RHS 29C); style arms golden apricot; beards creamy apricot, with purple petaloid ending in large peach flounce; slight fragrance. Flute Enchantee X Air Up There.

JOAN'S PLEASURE (Lloyd Zurbrigg, R. 1992). Sdlg. HH 22-1-1. TB, 26-31" (66-79 cm), M. S.

brownish blend; F. bright lavender, edged S. color, white hafts and around pale yellow beard; heavily ruffled; slight fragrance. Soap Opera X Summer Olympics. Avonbank 1993.

JOAN TREVITHICK (Currier McEwen, R. 1991). Sdlg. 84/128. JI (3 F.), 34" (85 cm), EML. Pink (RHS 77D), darker (77B) down center of F., signal yellow (12C). (Rose Queen x self) X (Rose Queen x self). Pope's Perennials, Seaways 1992.

JOAQUIN LADY (LeRoy Meininger, R. 1997). Sdlg. Sor 3. TB, 36" (91 cm), EM. S. rose mauve, midrib lavender; style arms peach, center rib lavender; F. velvety rose violet, pale lavender edge; beards burnt orange; lightly ruffled; slight sweet fragrance. Sorceress X Malaguena. Monument, Woodland Iris 1997.

JOE COOL (J. T. Aitken, R. 1991). Sdlg. 85M64. SDB, 10" (25 cm), ML. S. white; F. light blue, rimmed white, slight yellow haft wash; beards orange, tipped yellow. (Solar Flight x Cotton Blossom) X B. Jones 334-2: ((Solar Flight x 255: (Melon Honey x (Roberts 65-R-11 x 201))) x (Wright L20 x 255-1)). Aitken's Salmon Creek 1991.

JOE VIAL (Chet Tompkins, R. 1992). Sdlg. 84-83C. TB, 38" (97 cm), EML. Lilac self; beards lilac lemon. (Astolat x Amadeus) X Silver Silence. Fleur de Lis 1991.

JOHANN STRAUSS (V. & N. Gordodelovy, R. 1995). Sdlg. 106. TB, 33" (85 cm), EM. Pink, tinted lilac, F. with brown haft striations; style arms cream; beards red; ruffled. Parentage unknown. Gordodelovy 1981.

JOHN (Allan Ensminger, IB, R. 1989). Varigay 1990

JOHN E. VOIGHT (Clarence Protzmann, TB, R. 1988). Protzmann 1990.

JOHN HOEHNER (Joseph Hoage, R. 1993). Sdlg. H82-42-2. TB, 36" (91 cm), ML. Pale blue; beards dark blue. Portrait of Larrie X Song of Norway. Long 1995.

JOHN KEARNEY (Sterling Innerst, R. 1993). Sdlg. 2752-1. TB, 36" (91 cm), ML. S. yellow; F. red; beards bronze; slight fragrance. Show Biz X P. T. Barnum. Innerst 1994.

JOHNNY REB (Roger Nelson, R. 1992). Sdlg. RN 86-4BF. TB, 37" (94 cm), ML. S. greyed wine (near RHS 184C); F. brighter greyed wine (183B/C) with white spray haft pattern; beards greyed orange (163A); ruffled, pleated; slight musky fragrance. Lorilee X Freckle Face. Iris Country 1994.

JOHN PAUL JONES (Allan Ensminger, R. 1997). Sdlg. 390-21. TB, 35" (89 cm), ML. S. veronica violet (HCC 639); style arms and F. white; beards mandarin red. 84-53: (((Oos and Ahs x Rancho Rose) x 78-77: (Pink Sleigh x Karen Christine)) x (Firewater x (sib x Blue Too))) X 87-48: (((Infatuation x Entourage) x (78-77 x (78-77 x 77-54: ((((((Helen McGregor x Pink Formal) x My Happiness) x (Frost and Flame x Belle Meade)) x Stepping Out) x (Faydy Girl x sib)) x Rancho Rose)))) x 84-53).

JOHN TAYLOR (John D. Taylor by Carilla Taylor, R. 1998). Sdlg. JDT Cream. SDB, 12" (30 cm), M. S. cream; F. white, bleeding to cream at edge; beards sky blue. Probably -- Bibury X Sarah Taylor. Kelways 1998.

JOHN WOOD (John Wood by Everette Lineberger, R. 1997). SPEC (*versicolor*), 32" (81 cm), M. S. medium maroon, darker veining; style arms violet, rib darker; F. velvety deep red violet, gold signal, white ray pattern; stems black. Parentage unknown. Quail Hill 1998.

JOIE DE VIVRE (Heather Pryor, R. 1995). Sdlg. 60/90-22. LA, 35" (89 cm), ML. Heavily ruffled deep rose, flushed purple, reverse paler; raised yellow steeple signal on all petals. Gladiator's Gift X Desert Jewel. Lone Star 1997, Iris Haven 1997/98.

JOINT VENTURE (Sharon McAllister, R. 1990). Sdlg. 84-3A-1. AB (OGB-), 29" (74 cm), EM. S. amethyst violet (near RHS 85A); F. greyed yellow (opening darker than RHS 161A), flushed reddish grey, near-black underlay around beard to fainter near edge; beards brown black tipped brown (redder than 200A). Lovely Blanche sib X Edith Seligmann. McAllister 1992.

JOLI COEUR (Jean Cayeux, R. 1993). Sdlg. 8258 B. TB, 34" (86 cm), ML. S. white; F. lilac pink; beards red tangerine. Scintillation X (Metropolitan x Loudoun Lassie). Cayeux 1992.

JOLIETTE (Tony Huber, R. 1998). Sdlg. 94-035. SPEC-X (versata), 33" (85 cm), ML. S. violet (RHS 83C); style arms violet (83B), bordered pink on white; F. dark violet (83B), bright yellow signal; slight fragrance. EX-DW-13 *versicolor*, inv. dwarf High Laurentian *versicolor*, X purple *I. ensata* sdlg.

JOLLY JOEY (Carol Lankow by J. T. Aitken, R. 1993). Sdlg. 0-J4-11. MDB, 5" (13 cm), M. S. straw yellow; F. light blue; beards yellow orange; slight fragrance. (That's Right x Rain Dance) X Maya Mint. Aitken's Salmon Creek 1993.

JOLLY JUMBUK (John Baldwin, R. 1994). Sdlg. 88-5G. TB, 36" (91 cm), M. S. greyed orange (RHS 163C); F. velvety greyed purple (187C); beards deep yellow; slight spicy fragrance. Show

Biz X 82-75D: (((70-61M: ((((((Helen McGregor x Pink Formal) x Happy Birthday) x Hamblen H53-27E: ((Helen McGregor x Radiation) x Palomino)) x Glittering Amber) x Rippling Waters) x Sunset Snows) x (66-72D: ((((Party Dress x Ethereal Minstrel) x Palomino) x (Happy Birthday x Whole Cloth)) x ((Happy Birthday x Whole Cloth) x Hamblen H53-27E)) x (Melodrama x Rippling Waters))) x (70-61M x (70-61M x 70-59A: (66-72J x ((Mary Randall x Melodrama) x ((Happy Birthday x Hamblen H53-27E) x (Happy Birthday x Whole Cloth))))))) x ((70-61F x 70-59A) x (70-61M x 70-59A))).

JONABLUE (Alphonse Van Mulders, R. 1991). Sdlg. 35/89. TB, 38" (71 cm), M. Azure self, intensifying darker in center; beards white. New Moon X Blue Luster. Jardinart-Van Mulders 1992.

JONNYE'S MAGIC (Lois Rich by James Whitely, R. 1992). Sdlg. R84-26. AB (OGB), 32" (81 cm), ML. White ground, heavily striped violet, small lavender signal; style arms deep purple; beards dark. R79-152E: (R77-121B: ((R71-130F: (R69-146D: (William Mohr x (Jallah Effendi x ((OBK44 x *I. auranitica*) x Grand Vizier))) x (Welcome Reward x ((Bagdad Beauty x Orchid and Flame) x Kalifa Hirfa))) x (Kerr 55-3-0 x blue TB)) x (Mohr Pretender x R71-130A)) x ((Kelita Adah x JGA-AM) x (Clark sdlg. x Cayenne Capers))) X R79-138H: (R77-121B x (Welcome Reward x R69-164C)). Aril Patch 1992.

JO PETE (Duane Meek, R. 1993). Sdlg. 63-1-6. TB, 34" (86 cm), ML. S. sky blue; F. blue white paling to white; beards blue; ruffled. D. Denney 81-47-1: (Winterscape x Regents' Row) X White Linen. D & J Gardens 1993.

JORDAN BRUAT (Christian Lanthelme, R. 1997). TB, 35" (90 cm), M. S. and style arms orange; F. orange, small blue white spot at base of beard, shoulders dark orange, veined; beards orange yellow. Parentage unknown. Lanthelme 1996.

JOSEPHINE SHANKS (John C. Taylor, R. 1990). Sdlg. OL 107-1. LA, 47" (120 cm), M. Fluted deep pink (RHS 52D), lighter edge and reverse; signals yellow, veined green. Gentleman X Limited Edition. Rainbow Ridge 1992/93.

JOSIE'S PEARL (T. J. Betts, R. 1990). Sdlg. 181C. LA, 47" (119 cm), M. S. creamy white (RHS 11D); style arms lime yellow; F. creamy white (11B) infused lavender when fresh, green signal tipped orange; ruffled. 941A: (Ila Nunn x unknown white) X 938A: (Deneb x Shrimp Creole).

JOURNEY (Betty Wilkerson, R. 1996). Sdlg. F30-CoBr. TB, 38" (97 cm), ML. Red (RHS 60A) self; beards deep old gold. Her Royal Highness X Inferno. Bridge in Time 1996.

JOY BOAT (Ben Hager, R. 1997). Sdlg. IB6092-Or. IB, 20" (51 cm), M & RE. Orange self; beards tangerine. T5541PerOr: (T4549RfApOr, Gratuity sib, x Guadalajara) X SD5200SalOr, unknown.

JOYCE DIANE (Francis Rogers, R. 1991). Sdlg. F651-0. TB, 33" (84 cm), M. S. red purple (RHS 62D), slightly lighter at top; F. greyed purple fading to 62D on edge, tan and white veining below beard; beards orange, tipped lighter orange; ruffled; slight fragrance. Bonbon X Coral Beauty. Meadowbrook 1992.

JOYCE DONALDSON (Graeme Grosvenor, R. 1997). Sdlg. U185-1. TB, 36" (91 cm), M. White self; beards red; slight fragrance. M2-1: (Mollie Savell x Lady Friend) X First Movement. Rainbow Ridge 1999/2000.

JOYCE LORRAINE (Francis Brenner, R. 1992). Sdlg. B-78-B. TB, 28" (71 cm), ML. S. peach (RHS 29D); F. cadmium orange (23A); beards tangerine. Parentage unknown.

JOYCE MEEK (Melba Hamblen, R. 1990). Sdlg. H84-04A. TB, 34" (86 cm), EML. Creamy amber, F. bordered deep amber; beards burnt sienna tipped violet. H75-20A: (Touche x Sienna Star) X Nancy Glazier. Mission Bell 1991.

JOYCOS COLLOR (Willy Hublau, R. 1996). Sdlg. C7. JI (6 F.), 32" (80 cm), E. White, yellow signal, light yellow (RHS 7A) rays; style arms light primrose yellow (4D); stamens forming flags at top. B22 X Japanese import. Delmez Gardens 1998.

JOYFUL CHARM (Richard Morgan, R. 1994). Sdlg. L527-R. LA, 32" (81 cm), EM. Rose pink, yellow steeple signal. L 262-P: (This I Love x Parade Music) X This I Love. Redbud Lane 1997.

JOY JOY JOY (Allan Ensminger, R. 1995). Sdlg. 90-36. TB, 36" (91 cm), ML. S. white; F. royal purple with 3/8" white border; beards yellow, hairs tipped white. 181-57: (Pink Sleigh x 78-6D: (((64-12: (((Helen McGregor x Pink Formal) x My Happiness) x (Frost and Flame x Belle Meade)) x Stepping Out) x (Faydy Girl x sib)) x (Oos and Ahs x Charmed Circle))) X Jazzebel. Varigay 1996.

JOY JUNCTION (Tom Burseen, R. 1992). Sdlg. 8-133X. TB, 33" (84 cm), EM. S. tan, blended purple; F. white, 1" brilliant washed red purple (RHS 78A) edge; beards yellow, tipped lavender; ruffled; sweet fragrance. New Cool sib X 5-174: (Theatre x Capricious). T.B.'s Place 1993.

JOYOUS MORN (Schreiner, R. 1992). Sdlg. T 1619-A. TB, 37" (94 cm), EML. S. dusty rose (RHS 58D); F. rose apricot (33D); beards tangerine; ruffled, laced. Roselene X R 367-A: (Dawn Glory x J 215-A: ((Annabel Lee x (Gracie Pfost x T 889-1)) x (((Amethyst Flame x (Amethyst Flame x Alpenrose)) x Lilac Supreme) x Warm Laughter sib))). Schreiner 1992.

JOY PETERS (William Ackerman, JI, R. 1988). Nicholls Gardens 1990.

JUAN VALDEZ (William Maryott, TB, R. 1989). Maryott 1993.

JUBAL (Sterling Innerst, R. 1992). Sdlg. 3537-10. SDB, 14" (36 cm), M. Moss green self; beards blue. 2249-17: (Jared x Dixie Pixie) X 2843-1: (Jared x 1559-2: (Melon Honey x Soft Air)). Innerst 1993.

JUBILÉ RAINIER III (Richard Cayeux, R. 1998). Sdlg. 90170 A. TB, 32" (80 cm), M. S. orange apricot; F. red faintly shaded brown; beards bright orange red. Supersimmon X 8254 A: (Pink Game x Marmalade). Cayeux 1999.

JUDEAN OASIS (James Whitely, R. 1994). Sdlg. W88-83. AB (OGB), 27" (70 cm), ML. S. white, midrib yellow; style arms yellow; F. pale yellow, small dark mahogany signal; beards yellow. Syrian Moon X V. Wood 88-10: (Onlooker x self). Aril Patch 1994.

JUDEAN SANDS (Lois Rich by James Whitely, R. 1991). Sdlg. R84-7M. AB (OGB+), 10-11" (25-28 cm), ML. S. cream white ground veined violet, violet midrib; style arms brown violet; F. cream white, dark rust brown lines at center, veined brown around edge and shoulders, wide brown wine signal; beards brown. R69-283B: (((*I. gatesii* x *I. hermona*) x Bagdad Beauty) x R65-12C) X R80-27: (R75-205G x R74-114).

JUDGEMENT (John C. Taylor, R. 1998). Sdlg. UL 24-2. LA, 39" (100 cm), M. S. white, veined light red purple; style arms buff; F. red purple, buff edge and reverse, signal yellow; ruffled. Gladiator's Gift X Screen Gem.

JU DOU (Bob Thomason, R. 1993). Sdlg. BT 8624A. SDB, 11" (28 cm), E. Deep red violet, F. with plum hafts; beards deep purple. Regards X Plum Perfect. Okie Iris 1994.

#JUD PAYNTER (R. E. Nichol, TB, R. 1984). Stock destroyed; name released.

JUD PAYNTER (R. E. Nichol, R. 1991). Sdlg. L100-1. TB, 41" (104 cm), EM. S. rosy magenta; F. pale peach, 3/8" rosy magenta edge, white area around tangerine beard; ruffled. D42-1: (Roundup x Smoke Rings) X G42-9: (Rancho Rose x Keppel 77-111M, Gigolo sib). Iris Garden 1993.

JUDY BROWN (Bob Thomason, R. 1993). Sdlg. BT 9011A. TB, 31" (79 cm), ML. S. light plum; style arms yellow, crests plum; F. deep maroon red, yellow hafts veined deep maroon, small white area around tangerine beard; spicy fragrance. Jamari X Michelin.

JUDY MOGIL (James McWhirter by Abram Feuerstein, R. 1999). Sdlg. J92-316. TB, 32" (81 cm), M. Lavender blue, irregular lighter streaks; style arms pale blue; beards whitish, tipped yellow in throat, sometimes missing; novelty flat form; foliage purple-based. Proud Tradition X Alaskan Seas. Stockton 1997.

JUDY'S BLUE GARLAND (Chris Vizvarie, R. 1992). Sdlg. JBG-1. IB, 21" (52 cm), M. Pale to light blue self; beards medium blue; slight sweet fragrance. Parentage unknown. Last Scent Farm 1992.

JUDY TUNINK (Bob Thomason, R. 1993). Sdlg. BT 8713A. IB, 22" (56 cm), M. Soft yellow, F. with lemon hafts, white centerline; beards white; musky fragrance. Avanelle X Posy Parade.

JUEGO (Chet Tompkins, TB, R. 1959). Correction of spelling (JUGEO) in 1959 Check List.

JULIA STRAWN (Kirk Strawn, R. 1993). Sdlg. S-1985. LA, 35" (89 cm), M. S. violet (RHS 87B); style arms pale yellow (4D); F. darker violet (87A), bright yellow (6A) signal. C'est Magnifique X Charjoy's Mike. Bois d'Arc 1996.

JULIA VENNOR (R. E. Nichol by Jean Nichol, R. 1998). Sdlg. S 290-10. TB, 34" (86 cm), M. Yellow ochre (RHS 165D), F. with deeper central blotch, pale yellow hafts; style arms pale gold; beards lemon yellow; ruffled, frilled; slight fragrance. M 136-2: (((Cambodia x Liz) x Catalyst) x (Luscious Lemon x Starring Role)) X M 133-4: (Elizabeth Poldark x Loveday).

JULIE ELIZABETH (Louise Smith, R. 1991). Sdlg. 83-83. TB, 34" (86 cm), M. Ruffled and waved cream, light yellow hafts; beards deep orange to lighter orange; slight sweet fragrance. Arctic Fury X unknown.

JULIE STANTON (Robert Jeffries, R. 1991). Sdlg. J84-3 Y/W/A. TB, 42" (107 cm), ML. S. mimosa yellow (HCC 602/1), light lavender at base; F. very light mimosa yellow, darker (602/1) edge, light blue dart below beard; beards cadmium orange tipped light blue; slight fragrance. Fringed Lace X Song of Norway. Bar K Iris, Kansas Rainbow Garden 1991.

JUMBO JACK (Charles Okken, R. 1993). Sdlg. Bh-9. TB, 35" (89 cm), EM. S. glossy deep violet; F. deeper violet, violet signal; slight fragrance. Big Valley X Dusky Challenger. Misty Hill 1995.

JUMNA (C. G. White by Philip Edinger, R. 1999). AB, 36" (91 cm), E. S. violet, veined darker; style arms violet; F. violet, veined and dotted darker violet, violet black signal; beards black; form globular. Parentage unknown. Tom Craig 1949.

JUMP FOR JOY (Ben Hager, R. 1997). Sdlg. SP5507#6PchPk. TB, 36" (91 cm), M. Peach pink to pink self; beards tangerine, orchid horn or spoon. T5056PkBlBds: (Terra Bella sib x (Come to Me sib x (Birthstone x Sky Hooks))) X T5250PkBlBds: (((((Carved Cameo x Picture Pink) x (Orchid Song x Vanity)) x Magic) x ((Orchid Song x Vanity) x (Ice Sculpture x (Pink Taffeta x (One Desire x Adorable You))))) x Enchanting). Cooley 1999.

JUMPING JUPITER (Barbara Wight, R. 1996). Sdlg. 90-31. TB, 30" (76 cm), EM. Light naples yellow (RHS 11C) self; beards darker yellow (11A), dark yellow horn or spoon; slight spicy fragrance. 87-5: (Horned Sunshine x Moon Star) X 86-17: (Financier x Horned Sunshine). Wight's Iris 1997.

JUMP TO BLUE (Ladislav Muska, R. 1995). Sdlg. TGGB-11. TB, 40" (102 cm), M. Ruffled velvety blue black; beards deep blue; sweet fragrance. Titan's Glory X Glory Bound. Muska 1993.

JUNA SOMERO (Izidor Golob, R. 1997). Sdlg. 7613-19. TB, 32" (80 cm), E. S. old gold, veined light brown; style arms yellow; F. brown red on golden yellow base, rim yellow; beards yellow; lightly ruffled; slight sweet fragrance. Wine and Roses X Peking Summer. Peroma 1997.

JUNEAU RUTH (Louise Smith, R. 1991). Sdlg. 77-129. TB, 36" (91 cm), EM. S. white; F. purple, white hafts; beards pale yellow; pronounced sweet fragrance. Parentage unknown.

JUNGER FALTER (Artur Winkelmann, R. 1992). Sdlg. AW 92. SIB, 23½" (60 cm), ML. S. white; F. light yellow aging white; ruffled. Butter and Sugar X Zitroneneis.

JUNGFER BLAUBART (Lothar Denkewitz, R. 1995). Sdlg. N-85-hge-1. SDB, 13½" (35 cm), M. S. clear yellow; style arms white; F. yellow, enamel finish; beards clear blue, bushy; slight sweet fragrance. From sdlgs.: (Laced Lemonade x Snow Elf) linebred, F3. Von Zeppelin 1997.

JUNGLE CAT (Monty Byers, R. 1990). Sdlg. E55-101. TB, 36" (91 cm), EM & RE. S. variable from creamy light orange to orange-toned peach pink, lower inside third speckled rose brown; F. variable from creamy light orange to orange-toned peach pink, overlaid rose brown stripes halfway down, diffusing to soft blended wash over lower half; beards red orange; heavily ruffled and laced; slight musky fragrance. Grace Thomas X C-1-1: (Spirit of Memphis x Sky Hooks). Moonshine 1991.

JUNGLE DUSK (Chet Tompkins, R. 1993). Sdlg. 83. TB, 38" (97 cm), ML-VL. Smooth deep blend of regimental blue and windsor violet, touched deeper kingfisher violet blended chocolate at hafts; beards dark violet. Inv. Intermezzo, Mountain Music, sdlgs. X Revival Meeting. Fleur de Lis 1993.

JUNGLE EDEN (Margaret Hale, R. 1996). Sdlg. H-70-A. MTB, 24-26" (61-66 cm), E. S. and style arms red; F. red, velvety black overlay; beards orange, touched brown; slight musky fragrance. Jungle Shadows X H-66-A: (Manna Marie x Edenite).

JURASSIC PARK (Larry Lauer, R. 1995). Sdlg. 89-7-2. TB, 36" (91 cm), EM. S. and style arms canary yellow; F. blended lavender blue purple, yellow veining and edging; beards yellow, tipped blue purple; slight sweet fragrance. Best Bet X 87-29: (Edith Wolford x Denney 81-5-1: ((Regents' Row sib x Winterscape) x Midnight Love Affair)). Stockton 1995.

JUST A CROC (Brad Kasperek, R. 1996). Sdlg. 93RM-5A. SDB, 10" (25 cm), EM. S. and style arms light butterfly blue (RHS 106C), yellow green (193A) midrib; F. blue green (112A) ground, medium butterfly blue (106B) spot, hafts pea green (149C); beards lavender blue; ruffled; slight fragrance. Chubby Cherub X Perfume. Zebra 1997.

JUSTA DELIGHT (Marilyn Fleming, R. 1999). Sdlg. W 3 87. JI (6 F.), 33" (83 cm), M. White ground, fine purple veining, signal yellow; style arms ivory, tip white; petite size. Parentage unknown. Glenleigh Iris 1999/2000.

JUSTA DREAM (Stan Dexter by Marie Ingersoll, R. 1990). Sdlg. 1983/275. TB, 36" (91 cm), ML. Ruffled blue orchid with few lines on F.; beards white, tipped orchid blue. 1979B, unknown, X Silver Years. Ingersoll's Iris 1991.

JUST A FLIRT (David Miller, R. 1998). Sdlg. 92-1A. SDB, 12" (31 cm), M. Soft light yellow, F. with darker ray pattern fanning out from light yellow midrib; beards white, pale blue cast; slight sweet fragrance. Blue Line X 85-6A: (Sapphire Gem x Ice Chalet). Long 1999.

JUSTA OLDER CLAXTON (Harry Wolford, R. 1995). Sdlg. CO8+R05-1. TB, 32-34" (81-86 cm), M. S. rose raspberry, white stitching in central area; F. white, tinted chartreuse, with 1/2" heavy rose raspberry edging; beards orange, tipped blue; slight sweet fragrance. Chartreuse Ruffles X Rippling Rose.

JUST A SMIDGEN (Opal Wulf, R. 1995). Sdlg. 28-2-92. MTB, 14-16" (36-41 cm), E. S. pale blue; F. dark blue; beards yellow, hairs tipped white. Lucky Charm X STGO: (Striking Gold x unknown).

JUST A SNIGGLET (Opal Wulf, R. 1995). Sdlg. 28-3-92. MTB, 19-21" (48-53 cm), EM. S. warm golden pink; F. deep burgundy red; beards yellow. Lucky Charm X STGO-B-88: (Striking Gold x unknown). Wulf's Backachers 1999.

JUST A SNIPPET (Opal Wulf, R. 1995). Sdlg. 28-1-92. MTB, 16-18" (41-46 cm), M. S. pale lavender; F. deep warm purple, pale lavender veining across shoulders and down halfway on sides; beards yellow, hairs tipped white. Lucky Charm X STGO-B-88: (Striking Gold x unknown). Wulf's Backachers 1999.

JUST A WHISPER (Myrtle Wolff, BB, R. 1988). Hildenbrandt's Iris 1990. Change of classification from IB to BB.

JUSTA WISH (Richard Morgan, R. 1997). Sdlg. MTB-2-B. MTB, 21" (53 cm), E. S. white; F. violet, heavily lined and edged white; beards yellow. Sparkling Chablis X Welch's Reward. Redbud Lane 1998.

JUST BECAUSE (Marty Schafer/Jan Sacks, R. 1994). Sdlg. S86-27-2. SIB, 30" (76 cm), M. Ruffled medium blue violet (RHS 94B to 94D), very small white signal on F.; style arms with bluer midribs, turquoise side-ribs and darker blue violet edge; slight fragrance. Purple Prose X Springs Brook. Joe Pye Weed 1994.

JUST BETWEEN FRIENDS (Lynn Bausch, SDB, R. 1989). Garden of the East Wind 1990.

JUST DANCE (Barry Blyth, R. 1995). Sdlg. B95-1. IB, 20" (51 cm), VE-EM. S. creamy buff tan, midrib flushed pink apricot; F. creamy buff tan; beards white, tipped tangerine in throat. Buzz Me X Electrique. Tempo Two 1995/96.

JUST DO IT (Lynda Miller, R. 1993). Sdlg. 23989A. TB, 34" (86 cm), EM. S. apricot; F. maroon red violet, apricot hafts and lines around tangerine orange beard, apricot signal. 12784A: (Mandolin x Queen in Calico) X Gigolo. Miller's Manor 1995.

JUST FOR FUN (Lynda Miller, TB, R. 1989). Miller's Manor 1990.

JUST FOR SOPHIE (Richard Ernst, R. 1998). Sdlg. M103-10. TB, 35" (89 cm), M. S. deep pink; style arms pink; F. pink, slightly lighter at end of tangerine beard, darker pink veining. Confectionary X HD175A: (D175-7: ((Cheesecake x (Countryman x Outreach)) x Piping Hot) x Shoop 73-4). Cooley 1998.

JUST FOR YOU (Shirley Spicer, R. 1996). Sdlg. SS 10/2/85. TB, 33" (84 cm), M. S. butterscotch gold; F. light butterscotch gold, white near orange beard; ruffled; sweet fragrance. Summer Sun X May Melody. Waimate 1997/98.

JUST HELENE (Joseph Mertzweiller, R. 1990). LA, 36" (91 cm), M. S. blue yellow blended ground, heavily veined dark blue purple; style arms greenish; F. yellowish ground veined light blue, green yellow signal; musky fragrance. Harland K. Riley X unknown. Cordon Bleu 1991.

JUST IMAGINE (Janet Hutchinson, R. 1998). Sdlg. WH/OP/ST. LA, 41" (104 cm), ML. S. white, veined lilac, green base; style arms pale lime green, white crests lightly veined lilac; F. white, sanded and veined lilac (RHS 76A), white line edge, green and white reverse, signal medium yellow, short, broad, raised green centerline extending outward; lightly ruffled, picotee edge; slight fragrance. White Heaven X Our Parris.

JUSTINE MARGARET (Carl Jorgensen, R. 1990). Sdlg. 84-P-2B. BB, 26" (66 cm), ML. S. shell pink (HCC 516/3); F. shell pink (516/2); beards french rose (520); ruffled, laced; slight fragrance. Summit Sweetie X Cozy and Warm. Long 1990.

JUSTIN'S JOY (Dana Borglum, R. 1993). Sdlg. F117-1. BB, 24" (61 cm), M. Maroon red; beards old gold. Red Lion X self. Borglum's Iris 1995.

JUSTIN TYME (Chet Tompkins, R. 1990). Sdlg. 83-59. TB, 38" (97 cm), ML. S. colonial white infused cream; F. powder blue; beards lemon, tipped blue. (((Lord Baltimore x Cool River) x (Gentility x Dream Lover)) x (Lord Baltimore x Dream Lover)) X (Out Yonder x Cool River). Fleur de Lis 1990.

JUST JANELLE (Shirley Sylvia, R. 1996). Sdlg. 1. SPU, 46" (117 cm), M. S. cream honey; F. honey overlaid gold, lighter toward edge, bronze veining in shade; buds bronze. Imperial Bronze X Big Cloud. Tempo Two 1997/98.

JUST MAGIC (Barry Blyth, R. 1990). Sdlg. V71-3. TB, 36-38" (91-97 cm), EML. S. icy white with blue flush flowing through; F. creamy ice white; beards white. Perfect Couple X Pledge Allegiance. Tempo Two 1990/91.

JUST MEE (Lloyd Zurbrigg, R. 1990). Sdlg. MEE. TB, 35" (89 cm), VE. White ground marked violet. Parentage unknown -- possibly Earl of Essex X self. Avonbank 1991.

JUST MY STYLE (Richard Ernst, R. 1999). Sdlg. NJF168-2-3A. TB, 34" (86 cm), ML. Ruffled pink, berry and fuchsia blend, S. with deeper midrib, style arms with paler crests, F. with paler edge, deeper shoulders; beards tangerine; slight spicy fragrance. JF168-2-3A: (((Irene Nelson x Honest Pleasure) x Gaulter 81-17, inv. Irene Nelson) x ((Irene Nelson x Sun Fire) x Friday Surprise)) X After the Dawn. Cooley 1999.

JUST ONE LOOK (Chet Tompkins, R. 1995). Sdlg. 89-57. TB, 38" (99 cm), M. Lavender self; beards lavender. (((Intermezzo x Mendenhall sib) x Intermezzo) x ((Priscilla x Midwest Gem) x Matula)) X ((Easy Grace x self) x Grand Waltz). Fleur de Lis 1995.

JUST TERRIFIC (Ian Barry, R. 1997). Sdlg. 12-J-11. TB, 42" (106 cm), M. Violet blue self; beards dark blue. Perfect Couple X Titan's Glory.

JUTRZENKA (Lech Komarnicki, R. 1998). Sdlg. 93/4-19D. SDB, 15" (38 cm), M. Ruffled light apricot, S. with rosy basal infusion, F. with darker haft veining, small bluish white area below beard; beards white, red in throat; slight sweet fragrance. Kandi Moon X Tart.

JUTTA (Manfred Beer, R. 1999). Sdlg. MB 36/90 X. TB, 35" (90 cm), M. S. and style arms greyed yellow (RHS 150B), campanula violet midrib; F. campanula violet, warm brown (174B) shoulders; beards saffron yellow (21A); lightly ruffled; pronounced fragrance. Edith Wolford X Sweet Musette.

JUTTA EXNER (Pavel Nejedlo, R. 1998). Sdlg. HQAC-90-1. TB, 38" (97 cm), M. S. light orange; style arms orange; F. orange brown, edged deeper; beards bright orange; ruffled. Homecoming Queen X Art Center. Lukon 1998.

KABLUEY (Bob Bauer/John Coble, R. 1999). Sdlg. S93G-2. SIB, 30" (76 cm), M. S. (12-15) dark blue violet; style arms absent; F. (9-12) dark blue violet, white blaze, yellow in throat; multipetal hose-in-hose form: 3 F. and 6 S., then additional 3-6 F., 6-9 S. S89A-1: (Shirley Pope x (Sultan's Ruby x Hollingworth sdlg.)) X "Uzushio". Ensata Gardens 1999.

KADAICHA (Barry Blyth, R. 1990). Sdlg. W25-2. IB, 20" (51 cm), M. S. biscuit tan; F. bright rosy violet, deepening to brown below around hafts; beards old gold to light bronze. Kinetic X (Chinese Treasure x Beachgirl). Tempo Two 1990/91.

KADAINSKI PROVAL (Galina Zinoviyeva, R. 1998). Sdlg. 596-6. TB, 32" (80 cm), ML. S. rose; style arms yellow; F. dark rose centered blue violet, brown hafts, brown-veined cream around yellow beard, light lilac median line; F. held above horizontal; sweet fragrance. Pipes of Pan x Loreley. Zabaykalsi 1998.

KAE PRINCE (Elyse Hill, R. 1998). Sdlg. EJ 27-3-91. TB, 34" (86 cm), M. S. and style arms aster violet (RHS 87B); F. plum purple (79A), 1/4" violet rim; shoulders striped white; beards red orange; heavily ruffled; slight sweet fragrance. EJ 3-7-89: (Liaison x Lightning Ridge) X Spin-off. O'Brien Iris 1999.

KAHUNA (Marky Smith, R. 1999). Sdlg. 96-27. IB, 23" (58 cm), M. S. chestnut brown (RHS 177A); style arms gold, brass midrib, gold crests; F. lighter chestnut (166A), darker and redder center spot, gold line pattern around beard; beards spanish orange (26A); ruffled. 93-36B: ((Twilight Blaze x Magician's Apprentice) x Star Fleet) X Minidragon.

KAIOSEI (Shuichi Hirao by Society for Japanese Irises, R. 1997). JI (3 F.), 35" (90 cm), ML. S. medium violet, white and grey flecking and streaking; style arms white, crests light violet with small white markings; F. medium violet, heavy white and grey flecking and streaking, yellow signal with white halo. Parentage unknown. Introduced in Japan, 1961.

KAIPARA HARBOUR (Mrs. M. P. May, R. 1994). Sdlg. 205. SIB, 28" (70 cm), EM. S. light blue; F. light blue, shaded light violet on hafts, signals light violet. Swank X Castlegrace.

KAIPARA MAGIC (Mrs. M. P. May, R. 1994). Sdlg. 547. SIB, 21" (52 cm), M. S. slightly lighter than F.; F. medium blue with conspicuous white edge, white signal veined blue. Parentage unknown.

KAITLIN (Dorothy Guild, MTB, R. 1989). Guild 1990.

KAIZAIKU (Shuichi Hirao by Society for Japanese Irises, R. 1995). JI (3 F.), 28" (70 cm), E. S. not visible; style arms red violet; F. dark to medium red violet, paling to very light red violet toward edges, twisting around styles and not fully opening. Parentage unknown. Introduced in Japan, 1969.

KAKA (Frances Love, R. 1993). Sdlg. 25-10-5. SDB, 15" (37 cm), M. Orange self; beards deep orange; slight fragrance. Parentage unknown.

KALEIDOSHOW (Lorena Reid, R. 1992). Sdlg. 87J2-G8-1. JI (6 F.), 42-48" (107 cm), M. White ground with striking maroon pattern and narrow maroon edge, small white area around dark gold signal; style arms white, tipped pale violet. Summer Splash X Freckled Geisha. Laurie's Garden 1992.

KALIFA'S HORN (Robert Annand, R. 1995). Sdlg. 89-18A. AB (OGB-), 38" (97 cm), ML. S. orchid lavender, flecked darker; style arms lavender bronze; F. orchid lavender, flecked, paler below beard and with pale yellow haft infusion; beards bronze, lavender horn; ruffled. Sky Hooks X (William Mohr x Kalifa Gulnare). Stockton 1995.

KALIFA'S ROBE (Ben Hager, AB, R. 1989). Aril Society, Melrose 1990.

KALISTI (Ladislav Muska, R. 1999). Sdlg. 99-EWCE-07. TB, 36" (91 cm), M. S. pinkish rose; style arms pink; F lavender, washed orchid, 1/2" deep lavender rim; beards orange; ruffled, crinkled; sweet fragrance. ((Edith Wolford x Celebration Song) x "Erebuni": (Thriller x ((Vandal Spirit x Okavango) x (Simple Pleasures x Tropicana Doll)))) X "Svitanie": ((Don Epifano x "Bozenka") x La Dentelle).

KALLI STATHAKIS (Robert Fabel-Ward, R. 1991). Sdlg. H10-89VW. LA, 36" (91 cm), M. Very pale violet, large yellow signal. (Bertha Fabel x Francis Kingdon-Ward) X (Sinyaya Ptitsa x Evangelist Billy Graham).

KAMIJI-NO-HOMARE (Toyokazu Ichie by Society for Japanese Irises, R. 1995). JI (3 F.), 30" (76 cm), M. S. rich purple (RHS 77A); style arms light violet (84C), edging and large tufts of very dark violet (83A); F. rich violet (83C), veined darker (83A), giving brighter (83A) overall effect, signals rich yellow (12B). Yamataikoku X Minokotobuki. Introduced in Japan, 1980.

KAMORA (Mary Dunn, R. 1992). Sdlg. M84-855 CT. TB, 38" (97 cm), M. S. rosy copper rose; F. rosy copper with heavy copper area at hafts and by copper beards. California Classic X Spring Fling. M.A.D. Iris 1993.

KANGARILLA (Ivar Schmidt, R. 1995). Sdlg. PC 89-AF. CA, 15" (38 cm), ML. S. pale creamy apricot, midribs veined chocolate brown; style arms creamy apricot; F. creamy apricot, signal yellow, heavy chocolate veining. Nayook X unknown. Iris Acres 1995/96.

KANSAS CITY BLUES (Robert Jeffries, R. 1991). Sdlg. J84-15-A. TB, 30" (76 cm), EM. S. pale sea lavender violet, darker midrib, sea lavender violet (HCC 637/1) base; F. sea lavender violet, lighter area around beard; beards red orange, tipped lavender; ruffled; slight sweet fragrance. Vivien X J77-3-LB: ((Lovely Letty x Whole Cloth) x Shipshape). Bar K Iris 1992.

KAPRIZ FORTUNY (V. & N. Gordodelovy, R. 1996). Sdlg. 417. TB, 37" (95 cm), M. S. bright golden orange, shaded brown at base; F. raspberry red edged light yellow, hafts shaded yellow; beards orange; ruffled; slight fragrance. Parentage unknown. Gordodelovy 1990.

KARAKUMY (Adolf Volfovich-Moler, R. 1995). Sdlg. 103. TB, 39" (100 cm), EM. S. bright yellow; F. bright yellow, light brown striations; beards yellow; ruffled. Buttercup Bower X Babbling Brook. Volfovich-Moler 1996.

KARAMINKA (Rita Caldwell, TB, R. 1988). Tempo Two 1991/92.

KARA NOELLE (Carol Lankow, R. 1990). Sdlg. 4F50-3. IB, 20" (51 cm), M. Creamy white, F. with soft yellow hafts; beards pale blue, tipped orange yellow; slight sweet fragrance. Sun Dappled X Loveshine. Aitken's Salmon Creek 1991.

KARATE (Ladislav Muska, R. 1997). Sdlg. IB-CAST-03. IB, 22" (56 cm), EM. S. white ground, heavily marked lilac blue; style arms light brown; F. white ground, wide lilac blue peppering; beards yellow; ruffled, lightly laced. "Carina": (Angelic Inspiration x Laced Lemonade) X Sun Toasted. Muska 1997.

KAREN MADDOCK (W. F. Longley, TB, R. 1964). V. H. Humphrey 1993.

KAREN MAREE (Leslie Donnell, R. 1998). Sdlg. 94-1-7. TB, 39" (100 cm), E. S. pallid wistaria blue (RHS 92C); F. pale wistaria blue (92A); beards yellow and orange; sweet fragrance. (Kerrie's Kirtle x Scotch Blend) X Olympiad.

KARIN (Karl Mildenberger, R. 1990). Sdlg. 7/77. SIB, 33½" (85 cm), M. Blue; style arms light blue. Mountain Lake X White Swirl. Waechter 1991.

KARIN LEIGH (Louise Smith, R. 1992). TB, 45" (114 cm), EM. White self; beards orange, tipped yellow; slight spicy fragrance. Parentage unknown.

KARMEN DANCE (Adolf Volfovich-Moler, R. 1995). Sdlg. V-36. TB, 43" (110 cm), M. Heavily ruffled and laced violet red; beards blue violet. Rippling Waters X Sable Night. Volfovich-Moler 1992.

KASHMIRI SONG (Ben Hager, R. 1992). Sdlg. S978LtLvBl. SPU, 38" (89 cm), M. Light lavender blue, small pale yellow signal. S717Wh: (((Golden Lady x Driftwood) x Windfall) x Ila Crawford) X S795WWh: (Clarke Cosgrove x (Media Luz x Marilyn Holloway)).

KASHTANKA (Viktor Sheviakov, R. 1996). Sdlg. 7c8. TB, 32" (80 cm), ML. S. light yellow orange, inconspicuous light ginger brown plicata markings; F. cream yellow, maroon brown edge, darker and wider on hafts; beards yellow orange; ruffled; slight spicy fragrance. Dancers Veil X Radiant Apogee. Sheviakov 1996.

KASKADE (Harald Moos, R. 1991). Sdlg. 894/488A. TB, 36" (90 cm) M. Bluish white; beards gold yellow. (Pagan x Spartan) X Precious Moments. Schoeppinger 1993.

KASUMI-NO-KOROMO (Shuichi Hirao by Society for Japanese Irises, R. 1995). JI (6 F.), 33" (85 cm), E. F. lavender, with large white halo and veining extending 1/2 to 2/3 way down petal; style arms white, slight lavender on edge of crest. "Daisekkei" X Shino-no-Ome. Introduced in Japan, 1957.

KATE FRYER HARRIS (Berthe Conarty, R. 1998). Sdlg. C-95-5A. SDB, 10½" (27 cm), M. S. white ground, wide border and midrib lavender; style arms lavender, tan midrib, buff tan crests; F. white ground dotted lavender, narrow tan edge, lavender lines extending down from beard; beards tan, lavender base; slight sweet fragrance. MH/SF 861: (Melon Honey x Solar Flight) X Gigglepot. Ambrosia Gardens 1999.

KATE LINKERTON (Erhard Woerfel, R. 1990). Sdlg. 19/84. TB, 39" (100 cm), E. White; beards yellow. Azucena X Soft Moonbeam. Hochheimer 1991.

KATHLEEN KAY NELSON (Ben Hager, R. 1992). Sdlg. T4840-3Bl. TB, 35" (89 cm), ML. Deeply fluted dark violet blue; beards light yellow. Tinted Crystal X T3702: (Silver Flow x Ruffled Ballet). Melrose 1993.

KATHLEEN MARY (Cy Bartlett, R. 1999). Sdlg. C95-103. SIB (tet.), 30" (75 cm), ML. Lightly ruffled and flared white, F. with lemon yellow heart, lemon signal. Harpswell Happiness X McEwen T(6)78/118B, sib.

KATHRIN (Manfred Beer, R. 1998). Sdlg. MB 15/85 Y. TB, 33" (85 cm), M. Purple violet (RHS 80A) self; style arms lighter (80D); beards red (40B); pronounced fragrance. Ringo X Metropolitan. Mon Jardin 1998.

KATHY'S JOY (Francis Rogers, R. 1991). Sdlg. F-656-K. TB, 32" (81 cm), L. S. violet blue (RHS 97A); F. light blue (98C) veined dark blue; beards yellow, tipped blue; heavily ruffled; sweet fragrance. AT2A: (Song of Norway x Lady Marie) X FR-80-20-E: (Lacy Snowflake x (Jakarta x Stepping Out)). Meadowbrook 1992.

KATHY TRAPHAGAN (Marle Smith, R. 1994). TB, 36" (91 cm), M. Light purple, F. paling slightly in center; beards white, gold in throat; lightly ruffled. Douce France X Raspberry Frills.

KATIE (Ken Durio, R. 1992). Sdlg. BC PAD 3#8. LA, 36" (91 cm), ML. S. white, full violet mid-stripe and veining; style arms white, full violet center; F. light violet, veined full violet, gold yellow cathedral signal; ruffled; slight spicy fragrance. Clara Goula X unknown. Louisiana Nursery 1997.

KATIE BETH (Alice Bouldin, R. 1990). Sdlg. B-5-89. LA, 32" (81 cm), ML. S. light lavender, lighter in center; F. deep lavender. Parentage unknown.

KATIE-KOO (Cy Bartlett, R. 1993). Sdlg. C91-32. IB, 20" (51 cm), M. S. deep violet purple; F. slightly darker; beards grey, yellow in throat; waved, lightly ruffled; slight sweet fragrance. Gossip X Snowbrook. Kelways 1997.

KATIE PIE (Barry Blyth, R. 1998). Sdlg. D69-3. TB, 34" (86 cm), EM. Ruffled and laced clear pink, F. lighter and with small white area; beards saturn red, outer 1/2" white with hairs tipped pastel lilac; slight fragrance. Letter From Paris X Spring Tidings. Tempo Two 1998/99.

KATIE'S CHOICE (Francis Rogers, R. 1997). Sdlg. C228-B. IB, 24" (61 cm), M. S. lobelia blue (RHS 91C), white (155B) at base; style arms lighter lobelia blue (91D); F. white ground, 1/4" lobelia blue (91D) edge and striping changing to gold at haft; beards gold, deeper in throat, base violet blue; sweet fragrance. Island Song X Chubby Cheeks. Meadowbrook 1998.

KATINKA (Nora Scopes, CA, R. 1988). V. H. Humphrey 1992.

KATINKA FRANZ (Abram Feuerstein, R. 1999). Sdlg. 92-460. TB, 34" (86 cm), M. Dark violet blue self; beards blue. Alexander's Ragtime Band X Dusky Challenger. Stockton 1997.

KATMANDU (Joseph Ghio, R. 1990). Sdlg. 85-69R. TB, 40" (102 cm), ML. S. red orange; F. green orange; beards tangerine. 82-37W, Esmeralda sib, X Guadalajara. Bay View 1991.

KATY BECCA (Bernard Hamner, R. 1995). TB, 32" (81 cm), E. S. white; F. yellow (RHS 12A); beards yellow orange (14A); ruffled. Snow Summit X Borderline. Hamner's Iris 1995.

KAUKLIAR (Ladislav Muska, R. 1997). Sdlg. S-MNTN-07. SDB, 14" (36 cm), M. Lightly laced light lilac blue velvety bitone; style arms lavender blue; beards blue; sweet fragrance. ((Mini-Plic x Negro Blues) x (Marvelous Magic x Top Jovial)) X Negro Blues. Muska 1997.

KAYLEIGH-JAYNE LOUISE (R. E. Nichol by Jean Nichol, R. 1996). Sdlg. N175-2. TB, 32" (81 cm), M. S. pale yellow, darker base; F. pale ginger, pale blue blaze; beards gold; ruffled. Doctor Behenna X Loveday.

KEEKA DO (Labriano Anaya, R. 1991). Sdlg. 21A-84. TB, 28" (71 cm), M. Lilac, deep lavender blaze; beards deep bronze; sweet fragrance. Muted Melody X Garnet Sport. Rancho de la Flor de Lis 1991.

KEEP 'EM GUESSING (Gustav Seligmann by Sharon McAllister, AB (OGB), R. 1988). Aril Society, McAllister 1991.

KEEP THE PEACE (Graeme Grosvenor, R. 1998). Sdlg. V60-X. TB, 38" (96 cm), M. S. light blue violet; F. blue violet, edged light blue; beards blue violet, yellow in throat; heavily ruffled. Silverado X Timescape. Rainbow Ridge 1998/99.

KEIKO'S WORLD (Larry Johnson, R. 1996). Sdlg. JO87-8. TB, 36" (91 cm), M. Ruffled dark blue (RHS 99B/C to 98A), F. with small whitish stripe at tip of beard; beards light blue (108C). Dusky Challenger X Swirling Seas. Cooley 1997.

KEIRITH (Jean Witt, R. 1997). Sdlg. 91-07-G9. MTB, 17-20" (43-51 cm), M. S. pale yellow, lightly freckled pale lavender; style arms very pale yellow; F. white, dotted and veined lavender, reverse yellow; beards yellow, hairs tipped brown; lightly ruffled; slight fragrance. Susan Bliss X *I. astrachanica*. Aitken's Salmon Creek 1998.

KELLEY'S CHOICE (Richard Morgan, R. 1991). Sdlg. L380-A. LA, 28" (71 cm), M. Yellow, edged rose, signal yellow. Town Council X Shines Brightly. Bois d'Arc 1993.

KELLY LYNNE (Chun Fan, R. 1995). Sdlg. F91-640-A. TB, 34 (86 cm), ML. S. violet (RHS 85C); F. white, with 1" violet rim; beards orange, hairs tipped light violet; ruffled, lightly laced; slight sweet fragrance. Lingering Love X Knots Landing. Fan's Iris 1998.

KELWAY RENAISSANCE (Cy Bartlett, R. 1997). Sdlg. (C-IT)(C-EF)2. TB, 36" (91 cm), L. S. bright rose madder; F. bright dark wine red, white dart below tangerine beard; ruffled; spicy fragrance. ((Carnaby x In Tempo) x (Carnaby x Evening Frolic)) X sib. Kelways 1998.

KENAI LADY (Norma Barnard, R. 1997). Sdlg. NB 91-306P. CA, 14" (36 cm), EML. Ruffled very pale butter yellow, F. with bright yellow lance signal. Seed from Shepard Iris Garden. Parentage unknown. Paradise Iris 1997.

KEN BASTOW (Ed Pickin, R. 1995). Sdlg. 84/A/2. AR (RH), 18" (46 cm), M. S. and F. slate blue, lighter markings at edge; beards yellow. *I. hoogiana alba* X *I. stolonifera* hybrid.

KENDRICK FARRIES (Bob Thomason, R. 1993). Sdlg. BT 8805C. SDB, 12" (30 cm), ML. S. light plum; F. darker plum, white veined pattern around beard; beards white, orange in throat; slight fragrance. Plum-Plum X Regards. Okie Iris 1999.

KEN'S CHOICE (Leslie Donnell, R. 1994). Sdlg. 87-15-7. BB, 24-25" (61-64 cm), L. S. grading from grey edge to violet blue (RHS 92B) at midrib, violet blue (91A) inside; style arms violet blue (92A); F. violet (83C) plicata edge on white; beards orange, tipped blue; slight sweet fragrance. Light at Eventide X 82-5-11: (Kerrie's Kirtle x Hampton Harmony).

KENTUCKY CAJUN (Samuel Norris, R. 1994). Sdlg. T-88-AH. LA, 30" (76 cm), M. S. violet blue (RHS 89C); violet blue style crests lighter toward base; F. darker violet blue (89A/B), well defined gold signal; flaring, ruffled. Professor Ike X Mertzweiller JM 2-85: (JM 66-8 x Mentida). Lone Star 1995.

KENTUCKY FROST (Mark Cook, R. 1996). Sdlg. 101. SPEC (*pseudacorus*), 25" (64 cm), ML. Pale greenish white (RHS 157D), F. with yellow (3D) signal narrowly edged brown (200C); slight sweet fragrance. Parentage unknown; seed from British Iris Society (S.S. and J. Group) seedbank.

KENTUCKY MOONBEAM (Mark Cook, R. 1995). SPEC (*pseudacorus*), 16" (41 cm), M. Greenish yellow (RHS 1C), F. with orangish brown (177B) signal markings at haft. Parentage unknown; seed from British Iris Society seed exchange.

KENTUCKY SKIES (Ken Mohr, R. 1990). Sdlg. L-92. TB, 37" (94 cm), M. S. cool white tinted soft blue; F. medium sky blue; beards soft lemon, tipped white. Dutch Girl X (Sea of Galilee x (Cup Race x Tufted Cloud)). Pacific Coast Hybridizers 1990.

KENTUCKY WOMAN (Schreiner, R. 1997). Sdlg. AA 1666-A. TB, 36" (91 cm), ML. Orient pink (RHS 36B), F. aging to white in center; beards tangerine rose; lightly ruffled, laced. S 567-B: (M 434-A: (Pink Angel x ((Pink Horizon x Flaming Heart) x Pink Taffeta)) x Blushing Pink) X Electrabrite. Schreiner 1997.

KERMIT (Allan Ensminger, IB, R. 1989). Varigay 1990.

KERSTIN (Manfred Beer, R. 1991). Sdlg. MB 27/83B. TB, 37" (95 cm), M. S. light blue; F. dark blue violet; beards light blue. Gala Madrid X Dutch Master. Gartencenter Kania 1991.

KEVIN JOSEPH (Clyde & Anna Hahn, R. 1996). Sdlg. 94-6-C. SIB, 29" (74 cm), EM. S. white, tinted purple; style arms white; F. purple, tinted maroon red wine. Parentage unknown. Hahn's Rainbow 1996.

KEVIN'S THEME (Frederick Kerr, R. 1993). Sdlg. 88-17-1. TB, 38" (97 cm), ML. S. ivory yellow with blue violet center flush; F. blue violet, lightening to white around beard; beards yellow, tipped blue violet; ruffled; slight musky fragrance. Edith Wolford X Lullaby of Spring. Rainbow Acres 1993.

KEY LARGO (Marvin Granger, LA, R. 1987). Faggard 1991.

KHAMDENG (Bob Thomason, R. 1991). Sdlg. 8811A. SDB, 10" (25 cm), EM. S. light yellow; F. white, yellow hafts and marks; beards dark yellow, tipped white. Dove Wings X Tortuga. Okie Iris 1993.

KHMUROYE UTRO (Nina Miroshnichenko, R. 1996). TB, 35" (90 cm), M. Ruffled smoky light blue; style arms yellow, crests blue; beards yellow, paler at end; slight spicy fragrance. Parentage unknown. Miroshnichenko 1985.

KHUDOZHNIK SURIKOV (V. & N. Gordodelovy, R. 1995). Sdlg. 206. TB, 33" (85 cm), EM. S. red orange; style arms yellow, brown center; F. red orange, yellow haft striations; beards bright brown. Parentage unknown. Gordodelovy 1980.

KICKAPOO SPEARS (Jim Hedgecock, R. 1991). Sdlg. 87-76-1. TB, 34" (86 cm), M. S. rose pink; F. orchid pink, blue blaze; beards yellowish orange, with violet horn or flounce; ruffled, laced, flared; slight sweet fragrance. Spooned Blaze X Eastertime. Comanche Acres 1992.

KID CREEK (Floyd Dyer, R. 1992). Sdlg. D-63-88-D. SDB, 13½" (35 cm), M. S. blue violet; F. white, overlaid blue violet, violet-veined hafts; beards yellow, tipped blue; ruffled; slight musky fragrance. Cindy Mitchell X D-32-82-D: (Melon Honey x Lenna M). Four Cedars 1992.

KID'S CLOTHES (Tom Burseen, R. 1993). Sdlg. 9-215C. TB, 34" (86 cm), ML. S. tannish orange (RHS 29C), serrate; F. white ground with red purple speckling more concentrated toward red purple edge; beards mustard, tipped orange; ruffled; musky fragrance. Point Made X 6-146: (Rio de Oro x Noon Siesta). T.B.'s Place 1994.

KID STUFF (Ben Hager, MDB, R. 1989). Melrose 1990.

KILIMANDSCHARO EXPRESS (Georg Emke, R. 1997). TB, 35" (90 cm), M. S. ochre brown; style arms brown; F. violet blue to pinkish blue, ochre brown edge; beards yellow orange; waved. Rustler X Timescape. Emke 1998.

KILLDEER (Dana Borglum, R. 1995). SPU, 40" (107 cm), M. S. and style arms plum red; F. deeper plum red, gold signal; ruffled. Parentage unknown; seed from SIGNA. Borglum's Iris 1997.

KILNDOWN (Ann Olley, R. 1999). SPEC (*unguicularis*), 8-10" (20-25 cm), EML. Variable ground color methyl violet (RHS 85C) to hyacinth blue (91A), darker pansy violet (83A) striped and streaked markings; style arms deeper hyacinth blue (91B), slight plum flush; broken color pattern. Parentage unknown.

KIMBOSHI (Hisaharu Ueki by Society for Japanese Irises, R. 1993). SPEC-X, 20" (51 cm), E. S. light yellow; F. slightly lighter yellow, dark yellow signal patch with brown markings. *I. pseudacorus* X *I. ensata*, white. Ueki 1971.

KIMMELFARBER (Sterling Innerst, R. 1991). Sdlg. 3379-1. IB, 27" (69 cm), M. Dark blue, darker blue F. spot; beards blue; slight musky fragrance. Scented Nutmeg X 2815-1: (Little Episode x Pippi Longstockings). Innerst 1992.

KINDER SCOUT (B.L.C. Dodsworth, R. 1995). Sdlg. 89 TT. TB, 44" (112 cm), M. Ruffled magenta self; beards pink; sweet fragrance. Paradise Bird X Mulled Wine.

KIND KAREN (Donald Spoon, R. 1995). Sdlg. 88-18. TB, 31" (79 cm), M. S. pink, infused peach; style arms burnt golden yellow; F. lavender and yellow blend, edged rose peach, hafts darker and veined yellow; beards golden yellow (RHS 13A); ruffled, laced. Homecoming Queen X Persian Berry. Winterberry 1998.

KING CLOVIS (Eric & Bob Tankesley-Clarke, R. 1994). Sdlg. 88A-XFL-RE. SPEC (*I. pseudacorus*), 36" (91 cm), EM & RE (June/MO). Brilliant yellow with brown signal. *I. pseudacorus* #88 X self. Adamgrove 1994.

KINGDOM COME (Tom Burseen, R. 1999). Sdlg. 95-216B. TB, 36" (91 cm), ML. S. canary yellow (RHS 9C); F. cream white, edges washed canary, hafts gold; beards golden tan, with long filamentous horn and/or spoon; heavily ruffled; musky fragrance. 91-363: (Magic x Fundango) X Classy Chassy.

KING IN CALICO (Cloyd McCord, R. 1996). Sdlg. 82-60-1. TB, 38" (97 cm), E. S. pale lavender, 1/4" brown border; style arms pale lavender and bright yellow; F. light lavender stripes, 1½" white center blaze, 1/4" yellowish rim; beards bronze; spicy fragrance. Queen in Calico X self. McCord 1997.

KINGLY WHITE (D. Steve Varner, R. 1993). Sdlg. 9060. SIB, 30" (76 cm), M. Ruffled white self. King of Kings X 5200: ((Steve x Ausable River) x Ode to Love). Illini Iris 1993.

KING OF ANGELS (Monty Byers by Phyllis Dickey, R. 1996). Sdlg. F41-2. TB, 40" (102 cm), ML. Crystalline white self; beards yellow, large shaggy horn and flounce. D177-1: (Song of Norway x Pronghorn) X Titan's Glory. Misty Hill 1996.

KING OF FIRE (Cloyd McCord, R. 1996). Sdlg. 90-62. TB, 38" (97 cm), M. Ruffled and laced red; beards yellow; spicy fragrance. Clearfire X Gallant Moment.

KING REX (Kirk Strawn, R. 1993). Sdlg. M-1985. LA, 31" (82 cm), E. S. grey purple (RHS 85C); style arms red purple (59A); F. red purple (59A), yellow (7A) signal. Mighty Rich X President Hedley. Bois d'Arc 1996.

KING'S BOUNTY (Bernard Hamner, R. 1995). TB, 36" (91 cm), E. Ruffled yellow orange (RHS 6A) self; beards yellow orange (14A). Danger X King's Ruby. Hamner's Iris 1995.

KING'S DREAM (John C. Taylor, R. 1994). Sdlg. RL 68-1. LA, 56" (140 cm), ML Ruffled and laced rose burgundy, lemon edges and reverse, green line signal. OL 137-4: (Dazzling Star x Helen Naish) X Margaret Lee. Rainbow Ridge 1996/97.

KING'S SIGNET (Robert Jeffries, R. 1991). Sdlg. J83-D3-KS. SDB, 11" (28 cm), EM. Royal purple (HCC 834/1), darker royal purple F. spot; beards dark blue; slight sweet fragrance. Sapphire Jewel X Baby Baron. Bar K Iris, Kansas Rainbow Garden 1991.

KING TUSH (Brad Kasperek, R. 1997). Sdlg. 92B-57W. TB, 38" (97 cm), L. S. azalea pink (RHS 39D), splashed indian lake (58A) and spinel red (54C/D); style arms azalea pink; F. azalea pink with pinkish white stripes, infrequent splashes of indian lake and spinel red; beards bright medium orange; ruffled; slight fragrance. Tiger Honey X Raspberry Fudge. Zebra 1997.

KINKAJOU SHREW (Brad Kasperek, R. 1999). Sdlg. 94B-18A. TB, 38" (97 cm), EM. S. red purple (RHS 72B), white streaking with occasional red purple dot; F. darker beetroot purple (71A), white streaking, light golden yellow hafts; beards cadmium orange, large; ruffled; pronounced fragrance. Gnus Flash X Footloose.

KINNANE (Cyril Field, R. 1992). Sdlg. CF4. MTB, 16" (41 cm), L. S. yellow with red streaks at haft; F. red brown, thin yellow border, red lines on yellow ground at beard area; beards yellow; lower 2" of foliage stained red. Joseph's Coat sport.

KIOWA ROSE (Jim Hedgecock, R. 1992). Sdlg. C-84-9-1. TB, 36" (91 cm), M. S. dark pink; F. dark pink with lighter center and hafts; beards bright reddish orange; ruffled; pronounced sweet fragrance. Kiowa Rose X 73-13: (Touche x 70-20). Comanche Acres 1993.

KIRIGAMINE (Kiyoro Yoshie by Society for Japanese Irises, R. 1995). JI (3 F.), 33" (85 cm), M. Deep red violet self. Parentage unknown. Introduced in Japan, 1966.

KIRK STRAWN (Neil Bertinot, R. 1993). Sdlg. PV81-2. LA, 42" (107 cm), E. S. lilac purple (RHS 70A); style arms dark red purple (59B); F. ruby red (61A), yellow (13B) signal. Olivier Monette X Ann Chowning.

KIRRAWEE (Graeme Grosvenor, R. 1998). Sdlg. V60-D. TB, 38" (96 cm), M. White self, faintly flushed lavender; beards white, yellow in throat; slight fragrance. Silverado X Timescape. Rainbow Ridge 1998/99.

KIRSTEN MARRIOTT (C. M. Anderson, R. 1990). TB, 29" (73 cm), ML. Laced apricot orange; beards deep apricot; slight sweet fragrance. Spanish Gift X Mandolin.

KISS FROM ABOVE (Marie Murdy, R. 1994). Sdlg. D-4-3-91. TB, 28" (71 cm), M. Ivory cream to cream self, golden shoulders; beards orange; slight fragrance. Horned Lace X Winter Olympics.

KISS ME QUICK (Barry Blyth, R. 1996). Sdlg. D8-3. SDB, 15" (38 cm), ML. S. light pink; F. white, 1/4" light pink plicata edge; beards white, hairs tipped tangerine. Smoky Trail X A44-2, Razoo sib. Tempo Two 1996/97.

KISS OF HONEY (Sharon McAllister, R. 1996). Sdlg. 91-36-11. AB (OGB-), 30" (76 cm), M. S. soft honey yellow, faint violet basal flush; style arms soft honey yellow; F. soft honey yellow delicately veined and dotted tannish violet in throat and in V-shaped area around beard; beards mustard and rust mixture. Altogether Lovely X Persian Smoke. McAllister 1996.

KISS OF KISSES (Frederick Kerr, R. 1997). Sdlg. 915901B. TB, 35" (89 cm), M & RE. S. lemon yellow; style arms yellow; F. white, wide yellow hafts, 1/4" dark reddish edge infusing and lightening toward center to form 1" band; beards medium yellow; slight musky fragrance. Peach Picotee X 882801: (Gypsy Woman x Condottiere). Rainbow Acres 1997.

KISS THE DAWN (Frederick Kerr, R. 1994). Sdlg. 89-03-02. TB, 35" (89 cm), M. S. pinkish red violet; F. peach pink, veined darker, with distinct pinkish red violet edge; beards red orange; ruffled, lightly laced; slight fragrance. Feminine Wiles X Prom Night. Rainbow Acres 1994.

KITA-NO-SEIZA (Ho Shidara, R. 1999). SIB, 28" (71 cm), M. S. absent; style arms medium to dark blue violet; F. multiple (6), medium to dark blue violet, large white signal, veined. Parentage unknown. Ensata Gardens 1997.

KITAYSKI FARFOR (Oleg Amekhin, R. 1996). Sdlg. YAP-2. JI (6 F.), 30" (75 cm), M. Light purple, thickly veined purple violet. Sakura-Gawa X double sdlg. Amekhin 1996.

KITCHEN MUSIC (Richard Morgan, R. 1994). Sdlg. L599-BC. LA, 30" (76 cm), M. S. yellow with red midrib; F. red, orange yellow steeple signal. Parade Music X L233-N: ((Delta King x Gold Reserve) x Chowning 77-6: (Ann Chowning x Mockers Song)). Redbud Lane 1996.

KITCHEN SINK TOO (Tom Burseen, R. 1995). Sdlg. 1-64A. TB, 35" (89 cm), EM. S. lemon, flushed gold; style arms slightly darker; F. lemon ground washed gold, shoulders golden brown; beards yellow; ruffled, laced; sweet fragrance. 9-395: (Sterling Stitch x (Trousseau Lace x Wings of Dreams)) X 9-354: (Villa Splendor x (Date Bait x (Laced Cotton x Curtain Call))). T.B.'s Place 1996.

KIT FOX (Lowell Baumunk, R. 1998). Sdlg. 92SCJm-1. SDB, 12" (31 cm), M. S. white, midrib with some yellow veining, few green veins; style arms white; F. mahogany, rim white; beards white, blending to yellow in throat. Sass with Class X Jazzamatazz. Baumunk 1999.

KITTEN (Keith Keppel, R. 1997). Sdlg. 91-25F. SDB, 14" (36 cm), EM. S. blended pyrethrum yellow (M&P 11-L-2) and absinthe yellow (12-J-2); style arms pyrite yellow (12-L-3), edges and lip flushed lavender; F. blended goldenrod (10-L-5), lime yellow (11-L-5) and bistre green (12-L-5), deeper toward center; beards wistaria violet (41-E-8), tipped bronze in throat; lightly ruffled. Jade Jewels X Chanted. Keppel 1998.

KITTY D (Dorman Haymon, LA, R. 1989). Deep South Garden 1990.

KITTY DYER (Perry Dyer, R. 1998). Sdlg. 91-235A. TB, 30" (76 cm), ML. S. and style arms light citron yellow; F. ice white, 1/4" citron yellow band; beards light to medium yellow; lightly ruffled. Vida X Spring Satin. Contemporary 1999.

KITTY LACK (Hooker Nichols, TB, R. 1989). Hillcrest 1995.

KIWI BIRD (Edwin Hill, R. 1998). Sdlg. ED 14-17-91. TB, 34" (86 cm), M. S. greenish yellow (RHS 1B), midribs blue lavender; style arms blue lavender; F. violet blue (97B), greenish yellow rim; beards blue, blue horn; heavily ruffled; slight fragrance. Sky Hooks X Evening Mist. O'Brien Iris 1999.

KIWI CAPERS (O. D. Niswonger, SDB, R. 1989). Cape Iris 1990.

KIWI CHEESECAKE (O. D. Niswonger, R. 1998). Sdlg. 58-95. TB, 33" (84 cm), M. S. white; style arms and F. greenish yellow; beards tangerine. Violet Dawson X unknown. Cape Iris 1998.

KIWI GOLD (Hector Collins, R. 1990). Sdlg. 1985 SP 18. SPU, 51" (130 cm), M. S. bright yellow, gold centerline; F. bright yellow, gold lines from hafts, yellow signal; slight fragrance. Parentage unknown. Frances Love, Lynette Black 1995/96.

KIWI SLICES (O. D. Niswonger, SDB, R. 1989). Cape Iris 1990.

KIWI WINE (O. D. Niswonger, R. 1995). Sdlg. SDB 18-91. SDB, 12" (31 cm), M. S. and style arms light burgundy; F. burgundy, light burgundy rim; beards blue. Kiwi Slices X unknown. Cape Iris 1996.

KIYUKSA (L. J. Duffy, R. 1992). Sdlg. WI-67-85. SPEC (*setosa*), 30-36" (76-91 cm), E. Wine with white streaking at base of F.; style arms light rose, wine mid-streak and crest area; buds deep wine. Selection of *I. setosa interior* collected 1985 near Fairbanks, Alaska.

KLEINE MOEWE (Lothar Denkewitz, R. 1995). Sdlg. N-88-pl 4. SDB, 8½" (22 cm), VE. S. white ground, slightly marked intense violet; style arms violet; F. white, intense violet markings in throat, very small plicata edge; beards pale violet, golden yellow in throat; pronounced spicy fragrance. Bodderlecker X Scribe. Von Zeppelin 1997.

KLEVER KEN (J. Owings Rebert, R. 1999). Sdlg. CB-97-6. SIB, 24" (61 cm), M. Violet blue bitone, S. midrib darker, F. with slight beige haft marking. Parentage unknown.

KLINGON PRINCESS (Chuck Chapman, R. 1996). Sdlg. 91-180-3. SDB, 9" (23 cm), M. S. yellowish khaki, light violet wash; style arms yellowish khaki; F. yellowish khaki, citrine yellow edges and throat veining; beards dark violet, hairs tipped bronze; ruffled. Chubby Cheeks X Bantam. Chapman Iris 1997.

KLONDIKE LIL (Vernon Wood, R. 1993). Sdlg. 90-90. TB, 32-33" (81-84 cm), EM. Ruffled buttercup yellow (RHS 15A); beards orange. Bourbon X Flaming Victory. Stockton 1994.

KLOUN (Adolf Volfovich-Moler, R. 1998). Sdlg. V-157. TB, 37" (95 cm), M. S. light purple blended yellow orange; style arms light purple, orange edge; F. blended yellow orange, indistinct light purple centerline; beards yellow; ruffled, laced; pronounced fragrance. Chartreuse Ruffles X Mary Frances. Volfovich-Moler 1999.

KNIGHT'S TREASURE (John C. Taylor, R. 1994). Sdlg. RL 17-2. LA, 46" (115 cm), M. S. pink heavily suffused rose violet; style arms rosy violet; F. rose violet, green line signal surrounded by yellow; ruffled. Lina X Margaret Lee. Rainbow Ridge 1995/96.

KNIGHT TEMPLAR (Barry Blyth, R. 1993). Sdlg. Y6-10. TB, 36" (91 cm), VE-EM. S. spectrum violet; F. slightly darker with plush blackish finish; self beards; slight fragrance. Sib to Imprimis. Tempo Two 1993/94.

KNOCK 'EM DEAD (Richard Ernst, R. 1993). Sdlg. F169-22. TB, 38" (97 cm), M. S. butter yellow, edged creamy white; F. lavender blue with slight brownish cast on golden yellow cream edge, buff reverse; beards yellow; heavily ruffled. Sib to Competitive Edge. Cooley 1993.

KNOCK QUIETLY (Sterling Innerst, R. 1999). Sdlg. 3988-1. TB, 36" (91 cm), M. White; style arms cream; beards white to cream; slight fragrance. Lady Madonna X Missy Yorktowne. Innerst 1999.

KNOTS LANDING (Chun Fan, R. 1990). Sdlg. F85-42. TB, 37" (94 cm), M. S. white; F. greenish white (RHS 157D), translucent ruffles; beards orange yellow, blending to white tip; slight fragrance. Vanity X Dream Date. Fan's Iris 1993.

KOBAI-NO-KAORI (Seiro Yoshie by Society for Japanese Irises, R. 1993). JI (3 F.), 27" (70 cm), E. S. white, edged red violet; style arms white, tipped red violet; F. red violet, large white center and white veining, signal yellow. Parentage unknown. Yoshie 1981.

KODIAK (Connell Marsh, TB, R. 1985). C. Marsh 1990.

KOKI-NO-IRO (Society for Japanese Irises, R. 1997). JI (6 F.), 35" (90 cm), M. Red violet, yellow signal, extra petaloids often present; style arms white, red violet crests. Parentage and hybridizer unknown. Introduced in Japan prior to 1920.

KOKOPELLI (Hyram Ames, R. 1996). Sdlg. A942. TB, 30" (76 cm), M. S. dark maroon red, midrib darker; style arms dark maroon red; F. maroon black, slightly lighter edge; beards bronze; ruffled, laced; slight spicy fragrance. Quanah Parker X A905: (Blackout x A845, pollen parent of Quanah Parker).

KOKYO-NO-HARU (Society for Japanese Irises, R. 1993). JI (3 F.), 32" (81 cm), E. S. light pink; F. ruffled light pink, yellow signal. Parentage and hybridizer unknown. Appeared in commerce in Japan after 1945.

KOLYBELNAYA PESNIA (Viktor Sheviakov, R. 1996). Sdlg. 20d1b. TB, 30" (75 cm), ML. S. light rose violet, midrib lighter; style arms golden yellow; F. bordeaux, narrow light rose violet edge, white striations near bright yellow beard; slight sweet fragrance. Heather Hawk X Latin Lover. Sheviakov 1997.

KOMA TSUNAGI (S. Goto by Society for Japanese Irises, R. 1995). JI (3 F.), 30" (76 cm), M. S. light phlox purple (RHS 75C); style arms paler (75D) with darker tufts (75B); F. pale (75D) ground with some veining, darker sanding (75A) giving effect of (75D). Parentage unknown. Introduced in Japan prior to 1980.

KOM-BANWA (Ed Matheny III, R. 1995). Sdlg. J:00-05-93. JI (6 F.), 36" (91 cm), ML. Reddish violet veined deeper, edged silver, splashed silver white; signal daisy yellow (RHS 12A) surrounded by victorian violet (90B) halo; style arms violet. Geisha Gown X Glitter and Glamour. Ed's Iris 1996.

KONA BLUSH (J. T. Aitken, R. 1990). Sdlg. 82M110. BB, 20" (51 cm), M. S. tan flushed pink; F. creamed coffee tan blending smoothly into charcoal brown spot; beards russet orange. (Post Time x Light Cavalry) X Post Time. Aitken's Salmon Creek 1990.

KONA CATTLEYA (William Maryott, R. 1998). Sdlg. S236A. TB, 30" (76 cm), ML & RE. White self, hafts yellow; beards yellow, prominent; tightly ruffled edges. Radiant Energy X Lemon Fever.

KONA NIGHTS (J. T. Aitken, R. 1992). Sdlg. 82M107. BB, 26" (66 cm), M. S. light violet; F. deep velvety purple black, edged lighter; beards dark. Hellcat X TA79-80: ((Warm Laughter x Dusky Evening) x Mystique). Aitken's Salmon Creek 1992.

KONGOJYO (Shuichi Hirao by Society for Japanese Irises, R. 1993). JI (6 F.), 36" (90 cm), L. Blue violet (RHS 90A) with white blaze and veining around prominent yellow signal; style arms blue violet, near-white center. Parentage unknown. Hirao 1971. Also in commerce as "Kongoujou".

KONNICHIWA (Ed Matheny III, R. 1999). Sdlg. J:03-12-93. JI (6 F.), 36" (91 cm), M. Reddish violet with broken white lines, yellow signal with white halo; style arms white, crests purple. Cascade Spice X Midsummer Reverie.

KOOL KNIGHT (Mary Dunn, R. 1995). Sdlg. M989-D. TB, 36" (91 cm), M. S. and style arms light green gold; F. blue violet, tiny light edge; beards brown to bronze. Edith Wolford X Colorbration. M.A.D. Iris 1998.

KOREAN BEAUTY (Darlene Pinegar, R. 1997). Sdlg. FT-2-1. TB, 32" (81 cm), ML. S. creamy white, narrow light yellow edge, midrib flushed pink; style arms creamy white; F. pinkish mauve, cream centerline, very narrow light yellow edge, hafts apricot, white near beard and under pinkish mauve haft marking; beards coral orange; lightly ruffled, laced; slight sweet fragrance. Fancy Tales X Spiced Custard. Spanish Fork 1997.

KOREAN CUTIE (Darlene Pinegar, R. 1995). Sdlg. FT-2-5. TB, 31" (79 cm), ML. S. white; style arms white, narrowly edged yellow; F. lavender blue, yellow gold shoulders and edge, white area around beard; beards dark coral orange; lightly ruffled; slight sweet fragrance. Fancy Tales X Spiced Custard. Spanish Fork 1996.

KORNBLUMENBLAUCHEN (Eberhard Fischer, R. 1993). Sdlg. 6. TB, 27" (70 cm), M. Waved medium blue self; beards blue; slight sweet fragrance. Parentage unknown. Camehl 1993.

KOROHO (Society for Japanese Irises, R. 1993). JI (6 F.), 32" (81 cm), ML. Tailored white with slightly greenish veins, yellow signal with greenish cast. Parentage unknown. Shuho-en (Japan) between 1923 and 1930.

KOROLEVA BALA (Viktor Sheviakov, R. 1996). Sdlg. 7b11a. TB, 30" (75 cm), ML. S. pale rose violet; F. deep rose violet; beards yellow to light brown; ruffled, horizontally flared; slight sweet fragrance. Rippling Waters X Latin Lover. Sheviakov 1997.

KOSHI-NO-OTOME (Society for Japanese Irises, R. 1995). JI (3 F.), 33" (85 cm), EM. S. light pinkish lavender; style arms pinkish lavender, centered white; F. medium pinkish lavender, deep yellow signal. Parentage unknown. Introduced in Japan prior to 1990.

KOSHUI NO ASA (Hiroshi Shimizu by Carol Warner, R. 1998). JI (9 F.), 32" (81 cm), M. Sky blue. "Mizuumi No Sei" X "Aizoshi". Draycott 1998.

KOTARE (Frances Love, R. 1991). MTB, 18" (46 cm), E. Wine self. Gingerbread Man X Picayune.

KOTIONOK (Mariya Kaulen, R. 1999). Sdlg. YA 2/46. JI (6 F.), 26" (65 cm), L. Rose lilac aging to pale rose, yellow signal; style arms (6) heavily ruffled rose lilac. Parentage unknown.

KOZASA GAWA (Shuichi Hirao by Society for Japanese Irises, R. 1993). JI (3 F.), 32" (81 cm), M. S. lavender violet edged lighter; styles violet; F. pale blue violet, veined dark violet, signal yellow. Parentage unknown. Hirao prior to 1980.

KRAEHENWINKEL SHOW (Harald Moos, R. 1996). Sdlg. 88/800A. TB, 32" (80 cm), M. Waved bright copper red, pinkish influence; beards orange. (Glendale x Lady Friend) X (Mary Todd x Post Time). Moos 1997.

KRANITZ'S ALIBI (Jim Hedgecock, R. 1993). Sdlg. 83-396-7. TB, 34" (86 cm), M. S. ruffled pale blue; F. pale blue, white area by white beard; ruffled, lightly laced, fluted. Victoria Falls X Navy Strut. Comanche Acres 1994.

KRASKI OSENI (Viktor Koroliov, R. 1999). Sdlg. S 85-93K. BB, 26" (65 cm), M. S. tan yellow; style arms yellow, crests light brown; F. yellow ground, heavy claret streaking and centerline; beards yellow, paler at end; pronounced sweet fragrance. Siva Siva X Cliffs of Dover. Koroliov 1999.

KRASNA VASILISA (Ladislav Muska, R. 1996). Sdlg. KAFI-01. TB, 40" (102 cm), ML. S. tannish terracotta red; F. washed light lavender, wide cocoa tan band; beards orange; heavily ruffled, laced; sweet fragrance. "Kakaova Kader": (Kilt Lilt x Laced Cotton) X ("Fialovy Kvet": (Windsor Rose x Laced Cotton) x Don Epifano). Muska 1996.

KRASNOLESNY (Sergey Loktev, R. 1999). Sdlg. 94-L15E-R37. SDB, 13" (32 cm), M. Olive to brown, F. with bordeaux brown spot veined darker, light yellow marking around yellow beard, style arms with lilac dash. Jade Stone X unknown. Loktev 1999.

KREOLKA (Nina Miroshnichenko, R. 1996). TB, 43" (110 cm), M. S. yellow; F. red brown, light brown yellow edge; beards yellow; pronounced spicy fragrance. Parentage unknown. Miroshnichenko 1978.

KRESTONOSETS (Viacheslav Gavrilin, R. 1999). Sdlg. 96-114. TB, 33" (85 cm), EM. S. light yellow; style arms yellow; F. light violet, hafts tan yellow, two violet stripes from yellow mustard beard to lower edge, narrow light yellow rim; lightly laced and ruffled. Fiesta Time X Pledge Allegiance.

KRIEGHOFF (Tony Huber, R. 1992). Sdlg. KR-F-030-04. SPEC (*versicolor*), 20" (50 cm), E. S. light purple; F. deep red purple (RHS 71A), white center veined dark purple, bright yellow signal veined deep purple; slight sweet fragrance. Selection of *I. versicolor* collected in Laurentian Mountains, Canada. Dominion Seed House, Horticlub 1999.

KRILL (Jill Copeland, R. 1997). Sdlg. LT-YPW/RS. SPEC (*pseudacorus*), 24" (61 cm), M. Light yellow (RHS 2A), F. with heavily veined henna red (176A) signal appearing solid; foliage red-based. Parentage unknown.

KRIMHILDE (Jan Stillhammer, R. 1993). TB, 28" (71 cm), M. S. pink; F. blue, rimmed coffee brown; waved. Pink Angel X unknown. Stillhammer 1996.

KRISTALLPALAST (Eberhard Fischer, R. 1993). Sdlg. 4. TB, 39" (100 cm), M. Waved pink to peach pink, hafts peach yellow; beards red, wide; pronounced fragrance. Pink Magic X Christmas Time. Mattuschka 1993.

KRISTEN FRANCIS (Mark Grumbine, R. 1999). Sdlg. 95-11-1. TB, 34" (86 cm), M. S. goldenrod yellow deepening to orange base; F. white ground, violet wedge in center, reddish brown hafts yellow under orange beard. Touche X Superstition.

KRISTINA MARIE (Carl & Ruth Schulz, TB, R. 1989). Wild Mountain Thyme 1990.

KROEPCKE (Harald Moos, R. 1990). Sdlg. 86/696A. TB, 29½" (75 cm), M. Light brown violet, hafts medium brown. Cream Taffeta X Royal Trumpeter. Schoeppinger 1993.

KRONSBERG (Harald Moos, R. 1994). Sdlg. 91/A10.1. TB, 31" (80 cm), M. Gold yellow self; beards reddish orange; ruffled. Bischofshol X Flaming Victory. Moos 1995.

KRYPTON (Josef Dudek, R. 1999). Sdlg. 96-ExVA-1. TB, 41" (105 cm), M. Ruffled and laced aster violet (RHS 78C) self, style arms with lighter crests, F. with lighter area around beard; beards orange red, end lighter; slight sweet fragrance. Extravagant X Visual Arts.

KRYZHINKA (Borys Pravdyvy, R. 1999). Sdlg. 6D62-3. SDB, 13" (33 cm), ML. S. blue white, slightly purple midrib, darker base; style arms blue white; F. blue white, greenish white spot veined brown and edged purple on lower edge, greenish outer edge; beards white, hairs tipped lemon yellow on outer half; ruffled. Lemon Wine X Gingerbread Man.

KUESTENNEBEL (Lothar Denkewitz, R. 1995). Sdlg. N-83-br.am 1. SDB, 13½" (35 cm), M. S. bluish, center cream to greenish yellow; style arms white; F. olive brown, edged cream; beards bluish, tipped yellow; slight sweet fragrance. ((Snow Elf x Adrienne Taylor) x (Blueberry Muffins x (Toskanerprinz x Scot Cream))) X Irish Lilt. Von Zeppelin 1997.

KUITPO (Ivar Schmidt, R. 1995). Sdlg. PC 90-32. CA, 12" (30 cm), EM. S. mushroom pink, midrib infused gold, red pink veining; style arms mushroom pink; F. very large butter yellow signal surrounded by narrow band of red pink, fine pencil edge of mushroom pink. Big Money X Azaz. Iris Acres 1995/96.

KUMARI (Nora Scopes, R. 1990). Sdlg. 14PCA. CA, 12" (30 cm), ML. S. crimson; F. crimson to ruby. Banbury Gem sdlg. X Big Wheel.

KUPARI (Eric & Bob Tankesley-Clarke, R. 1994). SPEC (*pallida*), 26" (66 cm), M. White self devoid of haft markings; beards white; slight sweet fragrance. Collected at Kupari, Dalmatia; distributed by Randolph prior to 1960 and in commerce as *I. pallida* Y5A and as "White Mutant".

KWANZAA (Rob Stetson, R. 1999). Sdlg. RS 93G-3. TB, 30" (76 cm), EM. Candy apple red; beards old gold, red base; slight sweet fragrance. Spartan X Ruth Porter Waring.

KYOKKO (Koji Tomino by Society for Japanese Irises, R. 1992). JI (3 F.), 36" (90 cm), EM. Light pink, veined deep rose, yellow signal. Parentage unknown. Tomino 1957.

KYOKUSHO (Shoji Nishiguchi by Society for Japanese Irises, R. 1995). JI (6 F.), 35" (90 cm), M. White ground, streaked and dotted red violet, signal yellow; style arms white with large white crests streaked and dotted red violet. Parentage unknown. Introduced in Japan prior to 1990.

KYOMAI (Yoshio Mitsuda by Society for Japanese Irises, R. 1993). JI (3 F.), 32" (81 cm), VE-EM. S. red violet (RHS 79C) edged silver white; style arms white with cream center, red violet crests; F. heavily sanded red violet (80A) with appearance of white veins and silver white edge, yellow signal tinted green; ruffled. Parentage unknown. Mitsuda prior to 1985. Also known as "Kyou-Mai".

KYOTO (Joseph Ghio by Roris Gardens, R. 1993). Sdlg. 84-168X. TB, 37" (94 cm), EM. S. pastel orchid, slightly darker midrib base; F. medium orchid lavender, slightly lighter around red-tipped beard; ruffled, lightly laced. Divinity X Electrabrite. Roris 1993.

KYRUS (Erhard Woerfel, R. 1990). Sdlg. 13/86. TB, 43" (110 cm), L. S. dark blue violet; F. black violet; beards blue, brown in throat. (Adalgisa x Despina) X self. Hochheimer 1991.

K YUBILEYU ILIYICHA (Irina Driagina, R. 1996). Sdlg. 004. TB, 45" (115 cm), E. Whitish pink self; beards orange red; slight fragrance. Parentage unknown. Driagina 1970.

LA BAMBA CARA (Ladislav Muska, R. 1996). Sdlg. DELM-11. TB, 38" (97 cm), ML. S. pale rose lavender; F. white, light nut brown band; beards orange; laced; spicy fragrance. (Don Epifano x Lady Madonna) X (Don Epifano x Geniality). Muska 1993.

LABRASKA (Tony Huber, R. 1999). Sdlg. 94-007. SPEC-X, 27" (70 cm), E. S. whitish, small and tubular; style arms deep amethyst violet (RHS 84A), edged white; F. amethyst violet (84A/C), white spot signal. *I. setosa interior*, wine red, from NARGS seed, "Farm Park", from Fairbanks, Alaska, X Point Riche.

LABYRINTH OF DOTS (Ladislav Muska, R. 1999). Sdlg. 98-CQDF-01. TB, 36" (91 cm), M. S. deep cream, lilac veining; style arms medium mustard cream; F. vanilla yellow ground, wide intricate cream-lilac dotted network, lilac centerline; beards mustard; slight fragrance. (((Calicoball x Queen in Calico) x Nejedlo DERRSM-89-2, Spacelight Sketch sib) x (Zuzana x Scattered Dots)) X Funny Bird. Muska 1999.

LACED BUFFO (Ladislav Muska, R. 1997). Sdlg. IB-HOHO-03. IB, 24" (61 cm), M. S. light yellow; style arms deeper yellow; F. light buff; beards yellow, light blue at end; heavily laced; sweet fragrance. Honey Lace X (Laced Lemonade x Honey Lace). Muska 1996.

LACED SUNSHINE (D. L. Shepard, R. 1999). Sdlg. 97028-9309. SPU, 46-52" (117-132 cm), M. S. cream, yellow infusion; style arms cream white, midrib yellow; F. gold yellow, laced cream white edge. Giuseppe X Purple Reign. Shepard Iris 1999.

LACE LEGACY (Doris Greenwood by J. T. Aitken, R. 1992). Sdlg. G83A-1. TB, 34" (86 cm), M. Heavily laced light apricot orange, paling to white around bright orange beards; slight fragrance. Parentage unknown. Aitken's Salmon Creek 1992.

LACE RINGS (Nathan Rudolph by Loleta Powell, R. 1992). Sdlg. 85-63. TB, 34" (86 cm), ML. Snow white, laced yellow edge. Carved Canyon X 82-35: (78-01 x Love Scene). Powell's Gardens 1993.

LACKAWANNA (Tom Burseen, R. 1999). Sdlg. 95-305A. TB, 36" (91 cm), ML. S. maize pink, fine yellow rim; F. tannish maize, hafts brown; beards bronze, with long fuzzy purple horn. Thornbird X Quiet Elegance.

LACY ADVENTURE (Tom Burseen, R. 1991). Sdlg. 8-6E. TB, 37" (94 cm), M. Ruffled and heavily laced burnt orange (RHS 173C); beards orange; spicy fragrance. Homecoming Queen X 3-435: (Rancho Rose x Meda Lee). T.B.'s Place 1992.

LACY BERRY (Hall Bradshaw, R. 1993). Sdlg. 91-14. TB, 38" (97 cm), E. Lightly ruffled, heavily laced violet (RHS 88D), F. with maroon shoulders; beards tangerine; slight fragrance. New Frontier X Persian Berry. Kary Iris 1994.

LACY HAGOOD (Ed Attenberger, R. 1999). Sdlg. 92-08-10. TB, 36" (91 cm), M. Light orchid pink, S. shaded darker, F. with lighter center; beards reddish orange; ruffled, laced; slight sweet fragrance. Extravagant X Starcrest.

LACYLADY (Norma Barnard, R. 1995). Sdlg. 91-NB-64P. CA, 12-16" (31-41 cm), M. S. butter cream, red lavender (RHS 70B) wash and rays; style arms butter cream, red lavender markings; F. butter cream, red lavender rays and edge, pale cream outer rim, lavender wash around gold signal; lacy. Parentage unknown; seed from Shepard Iris Garden.

LACY LUCY (John Wight, R. 1995). Sdlg. S87-20A. SPU, 56" (142 cm), EM. S. yellow (RHS 14B); F. yellow (14A), yellow orange (15A) line signal halfway to margin; ruffled, laced. S79-4B, Imperial Yellow sib, X Imperial Yellow.

LACY MOON (Howard Shockey, R. 1990). Sdlg. 86-245-A. TB, 38" (97 cm), M. Heavily laced medium yellow; beards tangerine; slight spicy fragrance. 82-235-4A: (80-222-H: ((Carved Cameo x Summer Love) x Flaming Day) x Lunar Flounce) X Flaming Victory. Arilian Acres 1991.

LACY PRIMROSE (Joseph Hoage, R. 1992). Sdlg. H 87-74-1. TB, 34" (86 cm), ML. Primrose yellow, darker yellow edge; F. veined lighter; beards burnt orange; ruffled, laced. Ruffles Supreme X Bride's Halo. Long 1993.

LACY TUTU (Lynda Miller, TB, R. 1989). Miller's Manor 1990.

LA DARK (Carl Boswell, R. 1999). Sdlg. 99-87-1. IB, 22" (56 cm), L. S. deep purple; F. and style arms blackish purple; beards dark purple. (Plum Plum x Balkana Baby) X Black Flag. Adamgrove 1999.

LA DE DA (Allan Ensminger, R. 1997). Sdlg. 92-100. IB, 22" (56 cm), ML. Pastel mauve (HCC 433), streaked white; style arms pastel mauve; beards blue, red tip; slight fragrance. 88-44: (Painted Plic x 82-27: (Ruffled Surprise x Morning Sunshine)) X Chanted. Varigay 1998.

LA DENTELLE (Ladislav Muska, R. 1996). Sdlg. LMDE-07. TB, 36" (91 cm), ML. Heavily laced light lavender, bordered light brown; beards yellow; pronounced fragrance. (Lady Madonna x Don Epifano) X Laced Cotton. Muska 1995.

LADIES' NIGHT (Lloyd Zurbrigg, R. 1997). Sdlg. KK 12-1-1. TB, 39" (99 cm), M. Violet-toned red black, smooth F. hafts redder; beards red black. Holy Night X Lady Friend. Friendship 1997.

LADY ANN (James D. Stadler, TB, R. 1989). Celestial Gardens 1990.

LADY AUTUMN (Norma Barnard, R. 1996). Sdlg. NB-91-31-PE-RE. CA, 13-14" (33-36 cm), M & RE. S. and style arms red purple, lighter toward center of bloom; F. darker red purple, gold signal with purple edge and white halo, white F. rim at tip; ruffled. Parentage unknown; seed from Sharon McAllister.

LADY BIRD JOHNSON (Clarence Mahan, R. 1991). Sdlg. 686-1. TB, 34" (86 cm), ML. Lightly ruffled and laced light wistaria blue (RHS 92D); beards blue violet (92A); slight fragrance. Laced Cotton X Blue Zipper. Iris Pond, Stockton 1996.

LADY BUTTERFLY (B. Charles Jenkins, R. 1994). Sdlg. BA72H. SPU, 42-49" (107-124 cm), E. Heavily ruffled and frilled pale yellow self, yellow signal. Lively One X Candle Lace. Shepard Iris 1994.

LADY CELESTA (Bernard Hamner by Shepard Iris Garden, R. 1994). Sdlg. 89-27. TB, 38" (97 cm), M. Pale blue white self; beards dark blue. (Song of Norway x Sea Spell) X Evening Echo. Hamner Iris, Shepard Iris 1994.

LADY DAY (Carol Lankow, IB, R. 1989). Kirkland Iris 1990.

LADY DOUBLELOON (Norma Barnard, R. 1997). Sdlg. NB 91-117P. CA, 16" (41 cm), EM. S. and style arms golden yellow, veined gold, laced; F. dark gold, golden yellow rim, large gold signal with light brown rays at top and bottom; ruffled. Parentage unknown; seed from Shepard Iris Garden. Paradise Iris 1997.

LADY DRAGON (Leo Barnard, R. 1996). Sdlg. L-91-77 W-B. TB, 40" (107 cm), ML. S. white, slight tan at base; style arms white; F. white, pale blue rib at hafts; beards blue white, orange in throat, fuzzy blue forked horn or spoon; ruffled; slight sweet fragrance. Twice Thrilling X Borderline. Paradise Iris 1996.

LADY ESSEX (Lloyd Zurbrigg, R. 1990). Sdlg. V 46 SEPT. TB, 34" (86 cm), M & RE (Sept./VA). S. white with slight violet markings; style arms deep violet; F. white with few violet markings, more at hafts; beards light yellow. R 26 Wide: (Needlecraft x Earl of Essex) X R 3 Substance: (Cross Stitch x Earl of Essex). Avonbank 1991.

LADY FIRE (James Gibson by Cooley's Gardens, R. 1993). Sdlg. 6-0B. TB, 32" (81 cm), EM. S. brick red; F. white ground with brick red markings and 1/8" wide stripe extending from orange beard. Parentage unknown. Cooley 1992.

LADY FIREWORKS (Norma Barnard, R. 1997). Sdlg. NB 91-47PE. CA, 16" (41 cm), EM. Velvety red purple, F. with large gold signal with purple rays. Parentage unknown; seed from Shepard Iris Garden.

LADY HAWKE (William Plotner, TB, R. 1989). Wildwood Gardens 1994.

LADY JAN (W. E. Doehne, R. 1992). Sdlg. 3-85-10. TB, 31" (79 cm), M. S. white with lavender peppering; style arms lavender purple; F. white, edged lavender, heavy plicata pattern at hafts; beards gold, tipped white; sweet fragrance. Bewitched X unknown. Holly Lane 1993.

LADY JEAN (Tom Burns, R. 1997). Sdlg. TR-HNY-1G. TB, 30" (76 cm), EM & RE. S. rosy violet; style arms rosy violet, yellow base; F. white, rosy violet border; beards white, tipped yellow in throat; ruffled, lightly laced; slight sweet fragrance. Tennison Ridge X Happy New Year. Stockton 1997.

LADY JETFIRE (Norma Barnard, R. 1997). Sdlg. NB 91-305P. 16-18" (41-46 cm), ML. Red black self, F. velvety. Parentage unknown; seed from Shepard Iris Garden.

LADY JEWELL (Norma Barnard, R. 1996). Sdlg. NB-94-1P. CA, 12-14" (31-36 cm), E. S. warm cream, purple midrib and rays on inner surface; style arms warm cream, lined purple; F. cream, lavender center wash, yellow signal with purple halo, purple rays radiating toward cream rim; lightly ruffled. Lacylady X self.

LADY JULIET (Hooker Nichols, TB, R. 1989). Hillcrest 1994.

LADY LAREE (Ann Barrows, R. 1999). Sdlg. 93-G-1. TB, 40" (107 cm), M. S. heavily washed violet (RHS 86A/B), some white near midrib; style arms violet; F. white, 5/8" violet edge, some dotting, small rays at beard; beards violet, gold in throat; ruffled; slight sweet fragrance. Everything Plus X unknown.

LADY LAVENDALE (Jim Hedgecock, R. 1991). Sdlg. 82-68-5. TB, 34" (86 cm), M. Laced and ruffled violet, lightening at beard; beards silver, yellow in throat; slight sweet fragrance. Glendale X Navy Strut. Comanche Acres 1992.

LADY LILAC (Currier McEwen, R. 1990). Sdlg. T(2)82/123(2). SIB (tet.), 32" (80 cm), VE-EM. S. and feathered styles forming white cup with 3 large purple spots at bottom; F. pink lilac (RHS 81D), darker around green signal, lighter at edge, hafts green; ruffled. T(1)76/38B: (Lavender Light x Augury) X T(1)76/38K, sib. Pope's Perennials, Seaways 1991.

LADY LONGHORN (Leo Barnard, R. 1997). Sdlg. L 91-77 PF. TB, 36" (91 cm), ML. S. creamy apricot shading to vanilla at top; style arms creamy apricot; F. blended apricot, vanilla rim; beards brick orange, small apricot area at end continuing as long apricot horn usually ending in spoon; heavily ruffled; slight fragrance. Borderline X Twice Thrilling.

LADY MARILYN (Graeme Grosvenor, R. 1993). Sdlg. M2-1. TB, 38" (97 cm), E. Lightly ruffled dark rose red; beards red. Mollie Savell X Lady Friend. Rainbow Ridge 1993/94.

LADY OF LEONESS (Donald Spoon, R. 1997). Sdlg. 91-40A. TB, 34" (86 cm), ML. Ruffled pale lavender blue, deeper at petal base; beards pale lavender blue; flared. Silverado X Honky Tonk Blues.

LADY OF MIDDLEBURG (Donald Spoon, R. 1998). Sdlg. 90-189. TB, 32" (81 cm), ML. Ruffled snow white; F. with golden yellow on each side of tangerine beard; flared. Sienna Waltz X Woodland Rose. Winterberry 1998.

LADY OF SKYE (Norma Barnard, R. 1997). Sdlg. NB 91-133P. CA, 14-16" (36-41 cm), EML. S. and style arms pale lavender blue, blue veining; F. pale lavender blue, lavender blue veining, white rim and area around narrow gold signal; ruffled; slight fragrance. Parentage unknown; seed from Shepard Iris Garden. Paradise Iris 1997.

LADY OF SUBSTANCE (Donald Spoon, R. 1996). Sdlg. 89-133. TB, 31" (79 cm), M. White, infused lavender, pale green wash; beards white, hairs tipped yellow, yellow in throat; ruffled, laced; slight fragrance. Laced Cotton X Grand Waltz.

LADY'S BLUSH (D. L. Shepard, R. 1992). Sdlg. 88007. LA, 40" (102 cm), M. Pale butterscotch tan, finely veined dark butterscotch, F. with gold yellow steeple signal with butterscotch veins radiating outward. Ila Nunn X Bobbie Lou. Shepard Iris 1992.

LADY WALPOLE (Marty Schafer/Jan Sacks, R. 1996). Sdlg. S90-62-4. SIB, 32" (81 cm), EM. S. light blue violet (RHS 91B/C) edged lighter, dark center wash; style arms light blue violet, blue midrib; F. light blue violet, darker (90A/B) veining and wash intensifying at shoulders and around small dark-veined white signal; lightly ruffled. S88-7-1: (Lady Vanessa x Springs Brook) X S86-12-2: (Springs Brook x Warburton ARV82-4: ((Atoll x Ruffled Velvet) x Ruffled Velvet)). Joe Pye Weed 1996.

LADY WINIFRED BEARDSLEY (Labriano Anaya, R. 1991). Sdlg. 84-6A. TB, 42" (107 cm), M. S. hot pink; F. pink apricot, white signal, burgundy brown stripes on hafts; beards bright red; pronounced sweet fragrance. Almost Provocative X Crowd Pleaser. Rancho de la Flor de Lis 1991.

LAEMMERWOLKEN (Lothar Denkewitz, R. 1995). Sdlg. M-85-ge-am 2. IB, 20" (50 cm), M. S. white, light cream center; style arms white; F. clear yellow, veined yellow; beards ceam; slight spicy fragrance. Baroque Prelude X Sonnentrude. Von Zeppelin 1997.

LAFAYETTE HONEY (Dorman Haymon, R. 1999). Sdlg. FBxV-5-83. LA, 30" (76 cm), M. Ruffled tan, veined lavender; F. with green gold steeple signal, occasional line signal on S.; style arms brownish tan. Fading Beauty X Valera.

LAFCADIO HEARN (George Bush, R. 1997). Sdlg. 12-0-8. JI (3 F.), 15" (38 cm), M. S. and style arms white, edged crimson; F. with yellow signal, large white halo streaking into wide crimson border; flared. Parentage unknown; seed from Japan.

LAKE JANET (Beryl Pederick, R. 1994). Sdlg. 1. TB, 33" (84 cm), E. Cobalt blue self; beards gold. Parentage unknown.

LAKE KEUKA (Dana Borglum, R. 1991). Sdlg. D-4-34-1. SIB, 31" (79 cm), M. S. violet blue (RHS 95C); style arms aqua; F. violet blue (95B) edged lighter (95D); ruffled. Gulls Way X Outer Loop. Abbey Gardens 1994.

LAKE MEAD (James McWhirter by Abram Feuerstein, R. 1996). Sdlg. J89-110-1. TB, 34" (86 cm), EM. Heavily ruffled medium blue violet self; beards lavender, yellow in throat; pronounced spicy fragrance. Navajo Jewel X Winterscape. Stockton 1996.

LAKE NIKLAS (Eckard Berlin, SIB, R. 1981). British Iris Society 1997.

LAKE OUACHITA (Richard Morgan, R. 1992). Sdlg. L2-88-K. LA, 26" (66 cm) M. Light blue, small yellow steeple signal. L56-A, Angel Mist sib, X Bayou Waters. Redbud Lane 1992.

LAKE PARK (Bob Brown, R. 1994). Sdlg. 85-18. TB, 37" (94 cm), M. Ruffled dark purple, whiter around purple beards. Park Lane X Titan's Glory. Stockton 1994.

LAKE QUINALT (Colin Rigby, R. 1999). Sdlg. 75. CA, 18" (46 cm), M. Ruffled medium blue with slight lavender flush, F. with white signal veined gold; style arms medium blue flushed white, yellow markings. (Meek 281 x purple sdlg. from Ghio line) X Meek 369, inv. *I. munzii*.

LAKE REPRISE (Walter Moores, TB, R. 1989). Moores 1990.

LAKE SENECA (Dana Borglum, R. 1999). Sdlg. LKNS 1. SIB, 32" (81 cm), ML. S. bluebird blue (RHS 94A); style arms gentian blue (94D); F. cornflower blue (95A), obscure small yellow signal; lightly ruffled, F. arched. Lake Keuka X Seneca Night Sky.

LAKE SYLVIA (Richard Morgan, R. 1991). Sdlg. L436-B. LA, 24" (61 cm), M. Medium blue, orange yellow signal. (Everett Caradine x Clyde Redmond) X Trail of Tears. Bois d'Arc 1993.

LAKOTA WARRIOR (Darlene Pinegar, R. 1997). Sdlg. BCT-1-C. TB, 36" (91 cm), ML. S. and style arms dark golden brown; F. yellow at hafts, marked rust, solidifying and blending to oxblood, edged lighter; beards yellow orange; lightly ruffled; pronounced sweet fragrance. Barbary Coast X Witch of Endor. Spanish Fork 1998.

LAKOTA WIND (Jim Hedgecock, R. 1995). Sdlg. 84-72-6. TB, 34" (86 cm), M. S. wine maroon; F. white ground, wide band and center streak of lighter wine; beards burnt orange, white base; ruffled, lightly laced; slight musky fragrance. Roundup X Smoke Rings. Comanche Acres 1996.

LAMBADA (Lilly Gartman by Roris Gardens, R. 1993). Sdlg. 87-14-O. TB, 36" (91 cm), VE-E. Tangerine orange self; beards tangerine red. 82-2-2: (Preface x Lady Friend) X Orange Celebrity. Roris 1993.

LAMB'S SHARE (Mitch Jameson, R. 1996). Sdlg. 6-87. TB, 32" (81 cm), M. S. and style arms pastel yellow gold; F. white; beards yellow; ruffled; slight fragrance. Edith Wolford X Song of Spring. Knee-Deep in June 1997.

LAMÉ ARRAY (Darlene Pinegar, R. 1999). Sdlg. C-93-195A. TB, 32" (81 cm), ML. Ruffled and lightly laced pinkish orange, narrow yellowish edge; beards dark coral orange; slight sweet fragrance. Capricious X Tangerine Dream.

LA MER (Gerald Richardson, R. 1994). Sdlg. 87-22-5. TB, 37" (94 cm), EM. S. pale blue white; F. light blue, fading smoothly to pale blue rim; beards blue white; slight fragrance. Olympiad X Royal Crusader. Rainbow's End 1994.

LAMORNA (Nora Scopes, R. 1990). Sdlg. 5/114A. TB, 35-36" (89-91 cm), ML. S. pale lavender, aging white; F. deeper blue lavender, darker edge; beards cream yellow; lightly ruffled, flared. 1/184: (Focus x Dachstein) X 1/186A: (Como Surprise x Focus). V. H. Humphrey 1995.

LA MOUETTE (Philip Cook, R. 1999). JI (3 F.), 36-42" (90-105 cm), EML. S. white, 2" length; style arms pure white, midrib cream; F. white, 3½"-4" length, yellow signal. Parentage unknown; misnamed Japanese import.

LAMOYNE (Jim Hedgecock, R. 1990). Sdlg. 84-95-1. TB, 35" (89 cm), M. S. pale pink; F. pink, large white blaze; beards pale reddish orange; slight sweet fragrance. Cherry Sundae X Vanity. Comanche Acres 1991.

LANAI (Joseph Ghio, R. 1997). Sdlg. 92-73K4. TB, 36" (91 cm), EML. S. lemon, strong pink midrib infusion; F. lemon, pink outpouring from heart; beards yellow. Enhancement X 89-11P2: (87-134Y: (Esmeralda x ((((Veneer sib x (Capitation x Coffee House)) x sib) x (Tropica sib x ((Flareup x Indian Territory) x 76-37F: (Ballet in Orange x 73-122Z: (Hi Top x ((Ponderosa x Travel On) x Peace Offering)))))) x ((((Flareup x 73-122Z) x 76-37F) x (Preface sib x (Old Flame x Pink Angel))) x ((((Ponderosa x Honey Rae) x ((((Commentary x Claudia Rene) x Claudia Rene) x Ponderosa) x (Ponderosa x New Moon))) x Homecoming Queen) x Orangerie)))) x 86-117F3: ((Winning Note x Caption sib) x Memoirs)). Bay View 1998.

LANCER (Howard Shockey, R. 1994). Sdlg. 90-112-BZ. AB (OGB), 28" (71 cm), M. Medium light orchid violet, F. with very large and sharp near-black pointed signal; beards old gold. Seraph's Jewel X Queen Sheba. Arilian Acres 1995.

LAND OF COTTON (Mary Dunn by Joseph Ghio, R. 1999). Sdlg. L240-1A. LA, 38" (97 cm), ML. Creamy white, yellow line signal; style arms green, tipped white, upraised. Lina X L166-2: (Delta Dawn x Gourmet).

LAND OF ENCHANTMENT (Sharon McAllister, R. 1992). Sdlg. 84-2-2. AB (OGB) 28" (71 cm), EM.

S. lilac; F. soft chrome yellow, heavily blushed oxblood, giving overall dark adobe brick effect, signal area heavily dotted and veined burgundy. Thunderstorm X Shades of Sunset. McAllister 1992.

LAND O' MAGIC (Floyd Dyer, R. 1993). Sdlg. D-253-86-B. BB, 26" (66 cm), M. S. yellow green blend, pink at base; F. yellow green blend with peach tint on hafts; beards deep orange; ruffled; musky fragrance. Marilyn C X Saber Dance. Four Cedars 1993.

LANG (Carl & Mabel Bacon, R. 1990). Sdlg. SB-85-1. SIB, 25" (64 cm), M. S. dark violet blue (RHS 89A); style arms lighter (89D); F. very dark violet blue, gold signal. Blue Pennant X unknown. Old Douglas Perennials 1991.

LANGPORT MINSTREL (Kelways, R. 1995). IB, 22" (56 cm), M. Cream, F. with bronze patch; beards gold. Parentage unknown. Kelways 1968.

LANGPORT PHOENIX (Cy Bartlett, R. 1997). Sdlg. C91-42. IB, 18" (46 cm), M. S. sky blue, violet midrib; F. deep violet; beards blue; ruffled; slight sweet fragrance. Violet Lass X Amadora. Kelways 1998.

LANGPORT SNOW (Kelways, R. 1995). IB, 16" (41 cm), M. White self; beards white. Parentage unknown. Kelways 1972.

LANGPORT STORM (Kelways, R. 1995). IB, 18" (45 cm), M. Smoky chartreuse, F. with red brown patch; beards cream, yellow in throat. Parentage unknown. Kelways 1970

LANGPORT SYLVIA (Cy Bartlett, R. 1998). Sdlg. C91-47. IB, 24" (61 cm), ML. S. silvery white; F. white, washed pale blue lavender, hafts greenish yellow; beards yellow; ruffled. Gossip X Snowbrook. Kelways 1998.

LANGPORT VISTA (Kelways, R. 1995). IB, 20" (51 cm), M. Pale blue self; beards white to pale blue. Parentage unknown. Kelways 1968.

LANGPORT WARRIOR (Kelways, R. 1995). IB, 18" (45 cm), ML. Magenta violet, F. with darker patch; beards gold. Parentage unknown. Kelways 1970.

LANGPORT WREN (Kelways, R. 1995). IB, 22" (56 cm), ML. Red black self; beards brown.Parentage unknown. Kelways 1973.

LANGTHORNS PINK (P. & D. Cannon by Jennifer Hewitt, R. 1996). SIB, 31" (78 cm), EM. Small-flowered light lavender pink (RHS 87D), F. with cream edge and creamy yellow signal. Parentage unknown. Langthorns Plantery prior to 1987.

LA NINA (Joseph Ghio, R. 1999). Sdlg. PB-321X. CA, 10" (25 cm), ML. Soft lavender, yellow-veined signal. PD-243-Q3, Cross Purpose sib, X PD-201D2: (Candid x Local Girl). Bay View 1999.

LAPORTE COUNTY (J. Braddock, TB, R. 1988). Correction of spelling (LAPORTE COUNTRY) in 1989 Check List.

L'APPAT (Ladislav Muska, R. 1996). Sdlg. COCO-06/B. TB, 38" (97 cm), EM. S. light brownish lilac; F. light lilac lavender, maroon band; beards orange; heavily ruffled, laced; slight fragrance. (Coral Magic X "Fialovy Kvet": (Windsor Rose x Laced Cotton)) X (Coral Magic x Etty). Muska 1996.

LAPWING (Jim & Vicki Craig, R. 1999). Sdlg. AH98A2. IB, 25" (63 cm), M. S. muted lavender; style arms medium beige; F. deeper lavender, shoulders reddish; beards bronze yellow; foliage heavily based red purple. 67X1: (Gala Madrid x *I. aphylla* S2) X 38Y6: (Payoff x 14T116: (7M4, Sunshiny sib, x Puppy Love)). J. & V. Craig 1999.

LARA (Jim Hummel, R. 1990). Sdlg. 83-21G. TB, 30" (76 cm), ML. Magenta rose (RHS 186C), F. with salmon (27A) haft blush; beards rose red (171B). Social Register X Tide Mark. Bumble Bee Gardens 1991.

LARAMIE (Chet Tompkins, R. 1996). Sdlg. 93-33F. TB, 34" (86 cm), ML. S. copper gold undertoned smoky orchid; style arms smoky orchid blended coppery orange; F. blended rose, violet and copper; beards copper to violet blue; ruffled. (((Burgermeister x Intermission) x Extravaganza) x (Graduation x Syncopation)) X (Megabucks x Up and Coming). Fleur de Lis 1996.

LAREN JOY (Ed Matheny III, R. 1995). Sdlg. 11-05-91. TB, 34" (86 cm), M. S. and style arms white; F. purple, edged lavender, white area around beard; beards white, yellow in throat. Sweet Reflection X Victoria Falls. Ed's Iris 1996.

LARK ABOUT (Barry Blyth, R. 1990). Sdlg. V55-1. TB, 38" (97 cm), VE-EM. S. lavender grey; F. white, 1/2" lavender violet edge; beards old gold. Charmed Life X Gigolo. Tempo Two 1990/91.

LARK ASCENDING (Ben Hager, R. 1994). Sdlg. T5533TITWh. TB, 48" (122 cm), ML. White self;

beards bright tangerine. T5251TWh: (((T3852LcPrT: ((((Babson M131-4 x Morning Breeze) x Jody) x Tiburon) x (((Gay Adventure x Sass 55-349: ((((Melitza x (Flora Zenor x Sea Shell)) x sib) x 49-81, unknown) x My Happiness)) x Keppel 68-52: (Jones 743 x (Marquesan Skies x Babbling Brook))) x Caro Nome)) x T3616, pollen parent of Good Show) x O. Brown 78-1B4: (Snowy Wonderland x (Spring Bride x Royal Coachman))) x DuBose DU200-20TWh: (My Valentine x Condottiere)) X T5226WTWh: (DuBose DU200-20TWh x Skyblaze). Cooley 1996.

LARK RISE (Cy Bartlett, R. 1993). Sdlg. CM.GH. TB, 38" (97 cm), ML. S. greyed blue lavender; F. deep blue lavender; beards grey blue, yellow in throat; ruffled, slightly serrate. (Cherished Memory x Chico Maid) X Gunnar Hannestad. British Iris Society, Sutton 1999.

LARUE BOSWELL (Vernon Wood, R. 1997). Sdlg. 93-92. TB, 36" (91 cm), M. Light pink (RHS 56B) self; beards red tangerine. Sib to Pink Quartz. Stockton 1998.

LASCIVIOUS DREAMS (Sterling Innerst, R. 1994). Sdlg. 2953-B-50. TB, 36" (91 cm), M. Full dark peach self; beards peach; spicy fragrance. Catalyst X Idol's Dream. Innerst 1995.

LA SELVA BEACH (Joseph Ghio, R. 1993). Sdlg. PG-133H. CA, 11" (28 cm), M. S. gold; F. gold, maroon signal darkening to black in center with dark lines extending to edge. Bottom Dollar sib X It's Wild. Bay View 1994.

LASER (Pierre Anfosso, R. 1990). Sdlg. P 83 38B. TB, 33½" (85 cm), ML. Laced ochre red; beards orange. (Carmen X x Marmalade) X Mulled Wine. Iris in Provence 1990.

LA SERENISSIMA (Nora Scopes, R. 1993). Sdlg. 9S147. TB, 37" (94 cm), ML. Pale blue lilac, F. shaded deep blue in throat; beards deep cobalt; sweet fragrance. 5/122: ((sdlg. x Pink Angel) x Bewick Swan) X Icelandic Moon.

LASER PRINT (Paul Black, R. 1997). Sdlg. A114YY. IB, 25" (63 cm), EM. S. white, wide light violet band and midrib; style arms pale violet white; F. white, wide medium violet band, darker at edge, dark purple dart at tip of dark blue purple beard. Privileged Character X Polar Seas. Mid-America 1997.

LASER SHOW (John C. Taylor, R. 1991). Sdlg. OL 108-2. LA, 47" (120 cm), ML. S. marbled cream and magenta mauve; style arms light mauve magenta and cream; F. darker magenta, rimmed cream, signal yellow with green line. Lucile Holley X Dazzling Star. Rainbow Ridge 1991/92,

LASKOVOYE SOLNYSHKO (Viktor Sheviakov, R. 1995). Sdlg. 22 1E 18. TB, 32" (80 cm), ML. S. light yellow, green midrib; F. cream white, light yellow edge, tan hafts; beards yellow, orange in throat; ruffled; musky fragrance. "Solnechny" X Broadway Star. Sheviakov 1997.

LASKOVY VECHER (Nina Miroshnichenko, R. 1996). TB, 39" (98 cm), ML. Blue, tinted violet, F. with large light blue spot around violet blue beard; slight sweet fragrance. Parentage unknown. Miroshnichenko 1978.

LAS LOMAS (Joseph Ghio, CA, R. 1989). Bay View 1990.

LASSOED (Barry Blyth, R. 1997). Sdlg. D100-1. TB, 42" (107 cm), EM. S. white, allover rosy patterning; F. pure white, lightly stitched 1/2" rosy lavender edge, hafts and upper edge dotted and lined deeper rosy lavender to magenta, violet dart below beard; beards white, tipped tangerine; slight fragrance. Turner KH91-3-1: (Bama Berry x Holiday Lover) X B147-2: (Billows x Harmonics). Tempo Two 1997/98.

LASSO LANE (Mildred Wasmundt, R. 1992). Sdlg. 82-25. BB, 26" (66 cm), ML. S. bronze brown (near RHS 165B); F. violet (near 76A/B) aging lighter, greyed orange (165B) 1/4" edge, shoulders and signal; beards lemon gold; ruffled. Brown Lasso X Drury Lane. Long 1994.

LAST BLAST (Tom Burseen, R. 1995). Sdlg. 0-96D. TB, 36" (91 cm), L. S. pinkish plum (redder than RHS 73B); style arms tan; F. maize (tanner than RHS 179D), browner petal edges; beards pinkish red; ruffled. 7-203: (Tangerine Dream x Copper Lace) X Role Model. T.B.'s Place 1996.

LAST CHANCE (Schreiner, 1999). Sdlg. CC 1300-B. TB, 40" (102 cm), VL. S. buff peach (RHS 158C); style arms buff peach, creamy yellow base; F. blue lavender (92B); beards tangerine, tip and base white; ruffled. T 730-2: (K 1206-1: (((Fairy Rose x Rippling Waters) x ((Amethyst Flame x sdlg.) x (Celestial Snow x (First Violet x Snowy Heron sib)))) x G 297) x Heather Blush) X Song of Spring. Schreiner 1999.

LAST EMPEROR (Larry Gaulter by Cooley's Gardens, R. 1990). Sdlg. 82-1-7A. TB, 36" (91 cm), ML. Lightly ruffled royal blue purple; self beards. Inv. sdlgs. from His Lordship lines. Cooley 1990.

LASTING MEMORY (Kenneth Fisher, R. 1993). Sdlg. 91-10. MTB, 22" (56 cm), M. S. medium purple; F. royal purple; beards orange, tipped light yellow. (Consummation x unknown) X unknown. Aitken's Salmon Creek 1994.

LASTING ROMANCE (J. T. Aitken, R. 1999). Sdlg. 91T60. TB, 38" (97 cm), EML-VL. S. and style arms soft apricot; F. white, 1/4" soft apricot rim; beards soft apricot; slight fragrance. (Peach Float x Irene Nelson) X Romantic Mood. Aitken's Salmon Creek 1999.

LASTING SNOW (Shirley Paquet, R. 1994). Sdlg. JP 86 1. JI (3 F.), 47" (119 cm), VE. White self. Parentage unknown; seed from JI seed exchange. Pecan Grove Gardens 1996.

LAST LIGHT (Edwin Hill, R. 1998). Sdlg. ED 27-14-91. TB, 34" (86 cm), M. Greyed red (RHS 181A), F. with tan shoulders; style arms tan; beards red orange; slight fragrance. Red Lion X Samurai Warrior. O'Brien Iris 1999.

LAST SONG (Lyle Fort by Dona Fort, R. 1997). Sdlg. 89-537-DO. TB, 36" (91 cm), M. Heavily ruffled, lightly laced orchid self; beards white, hairs tipped yellow orange; slight sweet fragrance. 83-139-B: (82-28-E: (Misty Miss x Laced Cotton) x Wide Hips) X Wide Hips.

LAST TANGO (Oscar Schick, R. 1999). Sdlg. 91-20L02. TB, 38-40" (97-102 cm), L. S. cream, base infused light peach; style arms and F. creamy yellow; beards bright orange; heavily laced; slight spicy fragrance. Love Scene X Perils of Pauline.

LA STUPENDA (Heather Pryor, R. 1994). Sdlg. 57/90-5. LA, 38" (96 cm), ML. S. soft rose, darker rose border, green yellow center wash; style arms bright lime green, fringed deep rose; F. rose pink, darker rose border, green yellow center wash, green line signal; ruffled. Desert Jewel X Noble Planet. Rainbow Ridge 1995/96.

LASZKA (Lech Komarnicki, R. 1998). Sdlg. 93/4-24G. SDB, 12" (30 cm), ML. S. light yellow aging near white, veins light yellow; style arms light yellow; F. large red spot, yellow rim; beards yellow; pronounced sweet fragrance. Windbeam X Sam.

LATE DATE (Larry Ernst by Keith Keppel, R. 1999). Sdlg. 34-62. TB, 36" (91 cm), L-VL. S. and F. bright violet blue, shading to white in central area; beards white, tipped orange in throat. 19-59: (Sweet Refrain x Silvertone) X Lovely Letty. Cooley 1967.

LATE FOR SCHOOL (Heidi Blyth, R. 1995). Sdlg. BH 80-2. SDB, 14" (36 cm), ML-VL. S. light violet blue; F. rosy burgundy with 3/8" lighter violet blue edge; beards lavender, tipped mustard; sweet fragrance. Zing Me X Taja. Tempo Two 1995/96.

LATE NIGHT (Lynda Miller, R. 1990). Sdlg. 10584A. SDB, 13" (33 cm), EM. S. violet; F. ruffled blue black, paler edge, blue lines at haft, full violet rib; beards bluebird blue tipped gold; slight sweet fragrance. Jennie Grace X unknown. Miller's Manor 1991.

LATER ON (Opal Brown, R. 1994). Sdlg. 83-1F3. TB, 36" (91 cm), VL. Ruffled, flared pink (RHS 55D) self; beards orange red (33B). Chanteuse X 78-6A50: ((Dawn Flight x Winter Olympics) x (Pink Sleigh x Sweet 'n' Lovely)). Brown's Sunnyhill 1994.

LA TOYA (Ladislav Muska, R. 1997). Sdlg. PAGE-01. TB, 34" (86 cm), EM. Ruffled, heavily laced deep rose salmon self; style arms old rose; beards red orange; slight fragrance. (Paradise x Geniality) X Invocazione. Muska 1996.

LAUGHING BUDDHA (Kirk Strawn, R. 1993). Sdlg. NN-1985. LA, 38" (71 cm), M. S. yellow (RHS 3D) lightly veined greyed green (198D); style arms yellow (3B); F. yellow (3B), darker yellow (13A) signal. Sun Fury X Charjoy's Ann. Bois d'Arc 1996.

LAUGHINGSTOCK (Pat Otterness, R. 1999). Sdlg. 9697-2X34-011. TB, 32" (81 cm), EM. S. mimosa yellow (RHS 88/C); F. white, 1/2" mimosa yellow edge, yellow shoulder veining; beards bright yellow, bushy; lightly ruffled. Aphrodisiac X Silverado.

LAUGH LINES (Joseph Ghio, R. 1998). Sdlg. 92-51U. TB, 36" (91 cm), EML. S. almost solid wine purple; F. white ground, overall wine purple lining; beards red. Decipher X Epicenter. Bay View 1999.

LAURA LOUISE (Joseph Mertzweiller by Rusty Ostheimer, R. 1990). Sdlg. JP-3-83. LA, 28" (71 cm), ML. Yellow orange (RHS 14B), signal yellow orange (17A). Parentage record lost, but inv. President Hedley. Bois d'Arc 1990.

LAURA STRAWN (Kirk Strawn, R. 1993). Sdlg. 11-1985. LA, 43" (109 cm), ML. S. violet blue (RHS 90D); style arms yellow (11B); F. darker violet blue (89D), yellow (7A) signal. Justa Reflection X Lafitte's Retreat.

LAUREN ELIZABETH (Jim Hedgecock, R. 1995). Sdlg. A-13-3. TB, 36" (91 cm), M. Medium pink self, lighter area near reddish pink beards; ruffled, laced; slight musky fragrance. C-82-1: (Angie Quadros x Homecoming Queen) X Birthday Gift. Comanche Acres 1996.

LAURENTIAN SUNSET (Tony Huber, R. 1998). Sdlg. 94-055 (Cr. 92-52). SPEC-X (biversata), 28" (70 cm), EM. S. purplish violet (RHS 80C); style arms deeper (80B), bordered pink and white; F. purple violet (80B), bordered campanula violet (82B), signal bright yellow surrounded by white and yellow veins. Mirabel Glow X Riopelle.

LAVA FLOW (Dana Borglum, R. 1995). JI (3 F.), 29" (74 cm), M. S. blue purple; style arms and F. white with blue purple veins, F. with small yellow signal. Parentage unknown. Borglum's Iris 1997.

LAVALIER (Opal Brown, R. 1994). Sdlg. 81-4D16. BB, 26" (66 cm), M. Lightly ruffled mauve (HCC 633/1) self; beards light tangerine, base mauve. Persian Gown sib X sib. Brown's Sunnyhill 1994.

LA VALSE (Ben Hager, R. 1994). Sdlg. T5431DpPchSh. TB, 36" (91 cm), M. Smooth deep peach self; beards tangerine. T4235PkCr/Lv: (Merry Madrigal x Mother Earth) X Adventuress. Cooley 1995.

LAVA MOONSCAPE (LeRoy Meininger, R. 1998). Sdlg. 91-MI-5. TB, 34" (86 cm), EM. S. white, pink center flush, green veining; style arms white flushed pink on edge and midrib; F. pale lavender, hafts marked mauve, narrow flesh pink rim; beards carrot orange; ruffled. Matinee Idol X unknown. Monument, Woodland Iris 1998.

LAVENDER BELLE (George Sutton, R. 1998). Sdlg. G-103. BB, 26" (66 cm), ML. Ruffled sea lavender violet (RHS 85D), veined darker; beards lobelia blue (91C), hairs tipped yellow in throat; slight sweet fragrance. G-15: (Winterscape x Sky Hooks) X Ensign. Sutton 1999.

LAVENDER BLEACH (Tony Huber, R. 1999). Sdlg. 94-43. SPEC-X (versata), 28" (70 cm), ML. S. white, fine lavender veining; style arms white bordered clear lilac, crests lined lobelia blue (91C); F. white shaded lavender by means of close very fine veining, elongate bright yellow signal. *I. versicolor* 616 white X *I. ensata* (6 F.) white.

LAVENDER BLUSH (Kirk Strawn, R. 1993). Sdlg. J-1985. LA, 38" (97 cm), M. S. violet (RHS 86C); style arms yellow orange (14C) blushed purple; F. greyed orange (lighter than 177D), signal yellow orange (14A). Justa Reflection X Easter Tide.

LAVENDER DESIRES (Albert Faggard, LA, R. 1986). Faggard 1992.

LAVENDER DILLY (Barbara Wight, R. 1998). Sdlg. 92-4. IB, 25" (64 cm), ML. S. and F. light lavender; style arms white, edged yellow; beards greenish yellow, small dark purple horn; slight sweet fragrance. Twice Thrilling X Jazz Star. Wight's Iris 1998.

LAVENDER DUET (Evelyn Kegerise, BB, R. 1989). Evelyn Kegerise 1991.

LAVENDER FAIR (Robert Hollingworth, R. 1999). Sdlg. 96T8B5. SIB (tet.), 30" (76 cm), E. S. and style arms light lavender and blue mix; F. medium lavender, large ivory signal; ruffled. 92K1B8: (88W8D1: ((Wizardry x Sunburst Blue) x Fourfold Lavender) x 85B4C3: (Jewelled Crown x (Windwood Spring sib x 78N6: (McEwen T(4)72/10 x unknown)))) X Somebody Loves Me.

LAVENDER ICE (Dorothy Cantwell, R. 1997). Sdlg. 320-19. TB, 34-36" (86-91 cm), M. S. pale lobelia blue (near RHS 91D), darker hyacinth blue (91A) midrib and base; style arms lobelia blue (91C), lip hyacinth blue; F. silvery pale violet blue (91D); beards white; ruffled. Silverado X Incantation. Mahalo Iris 1999.

LAVENDER ICICLE (LeRoy Meininger, R. 1999). Sdlg. 91-44-C. TB, 36" (91 cm), EM. Lightly ruffled and crinkled white, light lavender tint; beards orange, fuzzy lavender horn. Silverado X Twice Thrilling. Monument, Woodland Iris 1999.

LAVENDER LULLABY (Jim Hedgecock, R. 1992). Sdlg. 82-68-3. TB, 36" (91 cm), M. Ruffled and laced blue violet, lighter silvery area by silvery blue violet beards; slight sweet fragrance. Glendale X Navy Strut. Comanche Acres 1993.

LAVENDER PARADE (Barry Blyth, R. 1993). Sdlg. EQ-1. SPU, 38-40" (97-102 cm), M. S. lilac lavender; F. yellow, veined lilac lavender, white outer ground with lilac lavender wire edge. Equality X self. Tempo Two 1993/94.

LAVENDER PARK (Graeme Grosvenor, R. 1998). Sdlg. V12-2. TB, 38" (96 cm), VE-EM. S. pale lavender, midrib darker; F. dark lavender, edges lighter; beards pale yellow; heavily ruffled. Delirious X Timescape. Rainbow Ridge 1998/99.

LAVENDER PINSTRIPE (Ray Lyons, R. 1998). Sdlg. LY-90-7-M. BB, 22" (56 cm), ML. White ground, lavender pinstripe veining; beards light yellow. Orchid Pinstripe X LY-85-6-1: (Rancho Rose x LY-80-15-5: (Petite Posy x (Petite Posy x Pink Sleigh))).

LAVENDER PRINCESS (Betty Squires, R. 1992). Sdlg. 87-43-B. TB, 34" (86 cm), ML. Laced lavender self; beards yellow, tipped lavender, 1½" lavender horn; sweet fragrance. Happy Bride X Lavender Queen.

LAVENDER PUP (B. Charles Jenkins, R. 1994). Sdlg. BA01D. SPU, 35-47" (89-119 cm), M. Pale lavender with yellow signal blending to deeper lavender; F. margin wavy. Color Focus X Diminuendo. Shepard Iris 1995.

LAVENDER SACHET DORATHY (Louise Smith, R. 1991). Sdlg. 76-401. TB, 29" (74 cm), EM. Lavender; beards white, tipped orange; slight sweet fragrance. Parentage unknown.

LAVENDER STIPPLES (Anna Mae Miller, R. 1990). Sdlg. 85-49-8. SIB, 30" (76 cm), ML. S. white with few violet (RHS 88B) lines; F. white, infused and veined violet (88B). Esther C.D.M. X Almost a Melody. Old Douglas Perennials 1991.

LAVENDER THRILLS (Herbert Holk, R. 1996). Sdlg. 28011. TB, 36" (91 cm), ML. Ruffled and laced rose lavender (RHS 76A to 77C), F. with lighter area below shrimp beard. 9812: (Dance Music x Orchidarium) X 9829: (Sandy Rose x Just Married). Cal-Dixie 1997.

LAVENDER TROUBADOUR (Jim Hedgecock, TB, R. 1989). Comanche Acres 1990.

LAVENDER WARRIOR (Jim Hedgecock, R. 1993). Sdlg. A-13-4. TB, 37" (94 cm), M. Laced and ruffled rose lilac with lighter area around bright orange beards. Quadros 82-1: (Angie Quadros x Homecoming Queen) X Birthday Gift. Comanche Acres 1994.

LAVENDER WAVES (B. Charles Jenkins, R. 1995). Sdlg. BJ21J. SPU, 38" (97 cm), M. Light lavender, F. with large yellow signal; waved form. Janice Chesnik X Lively One. Shepard Iris 1996.

LA VIE EN ROSE (Cayeux, R. 1999). Sdlg. 89108 A. TB, 35" (90 cm), M. Dark rose, F. with small white area below bright coral pink beard. Eden X Helene C.

LAVINA ZHIZNI (Viacheslav Gavrilin, R. 1999). Sdlg. 95-48-1. TB, 33" (85 cm), M. S. white tinted light violet; style arms ice white; F. violet, light violet white patterning on upper half; beards light mustard, hairs tipped light violet; ruffled. Taj Regis X unknown.

LAVISH LOVER (Barry Blyth, R. 1996). Sdlg. B139-1. TB, 38" (97 cm), VE-EM. S. bright coral apricot peach; F. blended peach coral, orchid around beard, hafts rosy tan, blended rosy tan 3/8" edge; beards bright orange tangerine; pronounced sweet fragrance. Legato X Stratagem. Tempo Two 1996/97.

LAZYBONES (Bob Thomason, R. 1992). Sdlg. BT 8947B. SDB, 10" (25 cm), E. S. white; F. pale yellow, fading toward edge, hafts veined darker; beards white; slight musky fragrance. Stockholm X Love. Okie Iris 1999.

LDINKA (V. & N. Gordodelovy, R. 1996). Sdlg. 126. TB, 30" (75 cm), M. Light blue self; beards orange; slight fragrance. Parentage unknown. Gordodelovy 1987.

LEADING LIGHT (George Shoop by Keith Keppel, R. 1998). Sdlg. 92-18. TB, 36" (91 cm), M. S. primrose yellow (M&P 10-J-4), base shaded peach (10-C-5); style arms primrose yellow; F. lemon yellow (10-K-3), small white center spot; beards mikado orange (2-B-12); lightly ruffled; slight sweet fragrance. 89-7: ((Orange Burst x Fancy Lady) x yellow sdlg.) X Private Treasure. Keppel 1999.

LEAH ISABEL (Shirley Spicer, R. 1996). Sdlg. SS 10/4/85. TB, 37" (94 cm), M. S. lemon, ruffled cream edge; F. pale cream, soft lemon frilled edge and reverse, dark lemon hafts, blue flush below yellow beard; slight sweet fragrance. Summer Sun X May Melody. Waimate 1997/98.

LEAH TRADED (Bernice Miller, R. 1990). Sdlg. LT90. BB, 23½" (69 cm), E & RE (Sept./AL). Ruffled orchid lavender; beards yellow; slight fragrance. Late Lilac X Dorcas Lives Again. Garden of the Enchanted Rainbow 1990.

LEANNA (LeRoy Meininger, R. 1997). Sdlg. Q-C 90-3. TB, 30" (76 cm), EM. Heavily ruffled white ground plicata, S. densely peppered lavender, F. with heavily peppered 3/4" lavender edge; style arms medium lavender; beards gold, tipped lavender; pronounced sweet fragrance. Queen in Calico X unknown (probably Jesse's Song, possibly Purple Pepper). Monument, Woodland Iris 1997.

LEAPING DOLPHIN (Ben Hager, TB, R. 1989). Roris 1992.

LEARN (Sterling Innerst, R. 1990). Sdlg. 3390-1. SDB, 10" (25 cm), ML. Warm pink; beards white, tipped cream. 2875-1: ((Betsey Boo x Cherub Tears) x (Soft Air x Pink Cushion)) X Bright Vision. Innerst 1990.

LE CYGNE (Melba Hamblen, TB, R. 1989). Roris 1992.

LEE'S BLUE (Bob Bauer/John Coble, R. 1993). Sdlg. S85C-2. SIB, 30" (76 cm), M. S. light blue with some violet shading; style arms light blue with darker blue midrib; F. medium light blue ground (91A), veined darker blue (94A), large white blaze around yellow signal; ruffled. S82C-2 X blue sdlg. Ensata Gardens 1994.

LEGACY OF LOVE (Katharine Steele, R. 1992). Sdlg. 861-12730. SIB, 20" (51 cm), ML. Silvery lavender blue self, including style arms. Pink Haze X unknown. Draycott 1995.

LEGATO (Barry Blyth, R. 1991). Sdlg. X140-2. TB, 38" (96 cm), ML. Vibrant metallic orange, few plicata markings around bright saturn orange beards. Latin Lark X (Edna's Wish x Orangerie). Tempo Two 1991/92.

LEGENDS OF FALL (George Sutton, R. 1998). Sdlg. G-37. TB, 36" (91 cm), EM & RE. S. violet purple (RHS 77A) blended darker; style arms violet purple; F. white, allover violet purple wash; beards violet purple, hairs tipped bronze; ruffled; slight sweet fragrance. Titan's Glory X Violet Classic. Sutton 1999.

LEGIONARY (Robert Dunn, R. 1992). Sdlg. B87-1018-3. TB, 38" (97 cm), M. S. blue; F. blue with reddish violet cast; beards pale yellow. B84-882: (Bubbling Over x Blue Maxx) X Crystalyn. M.A.D. Iris 1993.

LEILANA KAI (Cleo Palmer, R. 1990). Sdlg. 8622. IB, 22" (56 cm), EM. S. pink; F. pink, white hafts, pale violet red veining; beards light reddish pink; ruffled; sweet fragrance. Mlle. Modiste X 8102: (Miss Oklahoma x (Dove Wings x ((Wilma V x unknown) x Little Titan))). Palmer's Iris 1991.

L'ELEGANCE (Ben Hager, R. 1997). Sdlg. SD6007PlPk. SDB, 12½" (32 cm), EM. Clear light true pink self; beards bluish white at end, tipped tangerine in midsection, tangerine in throat. Play Pretty X Pretty Cute. Adamgrove 1998.

L'ELY (Ladislav Muska, R. 1995). Sdlg. LWLM-03. TB, 37" (94 cm), M. Heavily laced pinkish lavender, nut brown rim; beards light yellow; sweet fragrance. Louise Watts X Lady Madonna. Muska 1994.

#LE MIROIR (Krelage, Bulbous). Marked as obsolete in 1939 Checklist; name released.

LE MIROIR (Ladislav Muska, R. 1995). Sdlg. SLSR-01. TB, 38" (97 cm), M. S. pink; F. cream, banded pink; beards tangerine; laced; sweet fragrance. "Slahacka": (Buffy x Silver Shower) X Social Register. Muska 1995.

LEMON CHESS (Walter Moores, R. 1995). Sdlg. 88-17. TB, 36" (91 cm), ML. Ruffled creamy light yellow self; beards golden; slight sweet fragrance. Silent Screen X Catalyst. Moores 1996.

LEMON COOLER (John Gass, R. 1996). Sdlg. G81. TB, 36" (91 cm), M. Ruffled and laced lemonade yellow, F. paler in center; beards yellow; slight fragrance. Honor Bound X Anna Belle Babson. Rainbow Chasers 1997.

LEMON CRYSTAL (Donovan Albers, R. 1990). Sdlg. 8907. SDB, 15" (38 cm), M. S. chartreuse green (HCC 663/2) flushed lavender inside base; F. uranium green (63/3) edged chartreuse green, heavy veining radiating around white beard. Parentage unknown. Redbud Lane 1991.

LEMON CURD (W. & A. Godfrey, 1999). Sdlg. TBDA. SDB, 12" (31 cm), M. S. butter cream; F. deep lemon, butter cream rim; beards deep orange, white at end; ruffled. Tweety Bird X Dash Away. Hermit Medlars Walk 1999.

LEMON DEW (Richard Ernst, R. 1998). Sdlg. KF125-M. TB, 34" (86 cm), EM. S. and style arms lemon yellow; F. white ground, lemon yellow markings; beards lemon yellow, white at end. F125 series: (Edna's Wish x Wild Jasmine) X sib. Cooley 1998.

LEMON DILEMMA (Lawrence Johnsen, R. 1992). Sdlg. VF 87-1. SPU, 48" (122 cm), ML. S. blue violet; style arms blue violet, darker blue violet crests; F. bright yellow, narrow rim veined light blue violet. Vintage Year X Far Out. Shepard Iris 1993.

LEMON FEVER (William Maryott, TB, R. 1988). Correction of parentage. H26A: ((Carved Cameo x Wings of Dreams) x Ghio 76-257X: (Entourage x Homecoming Queen)) X G128A, Radiant Energy sib.

LEMON FIRE (Ladislav Muska, R. 1996). Sdlg. ANGE-10. TB, 38" (97 cm), ML. Heavily laced light lemon yellow self; beards orange, lemon yellow at end; sweet fragrance. ("Andel": (Laced Cotton x Fabulous Frills) x Geniality) X "Lemon Star". Muska 1996.

LEMON GUMDROP (Bernard Hamner by Shepard Iris Garden, R. 1992). Sdlg. 87-96. TB, 36" (91 cm), M. S. deep rich yellow; F. white, edged yellow; beards orange; ruffled, laced. (Creme de Creme x Sun Circle) X Bride's Halo. Hamner Iris, Shepard Iris 1992.

LEMON LOLLIPOP (Donald Spoon, R. 1996). Sdlg. 90-8-118. TB, 30" (76 cm), EM & RE (Oct./VA). Brilliant yellow, darker yellow shoulders, paler area below beard; beards orange yellow, darker in throat; ruffled, lightly laced; slight sweet fragrance. Lemon Reflection X 87-65: (Hindenburg x Lemon Reflection).

LEMON LOVE (Barbara Wight, R. 1990). Sdlg. 86-18. TB, 28" (71 cm), E. Lightly ruffled and laced pastel lemon yellow, white below light lemon beard; pronounced sweet fragrance. Financier X Snow Canyon. Wight's Iris 1990.

LEMON MAGIC (Elmer Williams, R. 1997). Sdlg. 7-89. TB, 35" (89 cm), EM & RE. Ruffled lemon yellow self; beards yellow, lemon horn. Howdy Do X Sky Hooks. Permian Basin Iris Society 1999.

247

LEMON ON ICE (Chuck Chapman, R. 1994). Sdlg. 87-G. SDB, 10" (25 cm), M. S. light yellow; F. white, light yellow lines in throat; beards white, tipped yellow. Parentage unknown. Chapman Iris 1994.

LEMON PETTICOAT (Heather Pryor, R. 1996). Sdlg. 40/90-4. LA, 38" (97 cm), E. S. and F. lemon white, bright orange line signal, more heavily veined on F.; style arms canary yellow (RHS 9C); ruffled; heavily textured and dimpled. Alluvial Gold X Gladiator's Gift. Iris Haven 1997/98.

LEMON POP (Larry Lauer, IB, R. 1989). Cottage 1990.

LEMON SILENCE (Barry Blyth, R. 1993). Sdlg., A138-3. TB, 36" (91 cm), EML. S. lemon yellow; F. white, 1/4" blended yellow edge; beards bright yellow; sweet fragrance. Billows X X127-1: ((Hush at Twilight x ((Love Chant x Festive Skirt) x (Caramba x Pink Ember))) x (Edna's Wish x Orangerie)). Tempo Two 1994/95.

LEMON SORBET (Heather Pryor, R. 1995). Sdlg. 40/90-B. LA, 35" (89 cm), EM. Lightly ruffled pale yellow (RHS 23D), orange centerline signal, veined; style arms pale yellow. Alluvial Gold X Gladiator's Gift. Rainbow Ridge 1996/97.

LEMON SPRINGS (Geoff Austin, R. 1998). Sdlg. EWS-1495. TB, 29" (75 cm), M. S. and style arms lemon; F. creamy lemon; beards lemon; ruffled; slight sweet fragrance. Edith Wolford X Silverado. Austland 1998/99.

LEMON TABLE (B. Charles Jenkins, R. 1994). Sdlg. C24-29A. SPU, 36" (91 cm), M. Pale lemon yellow with darker signal. Ping and Pang (lavender blue) X Ruffled Canary.

LEMON TEASE (George Shoop, R. 1990). Sdlg. 86-53. IB, 18" (46 cm), E. Ruffled lemon, deep yellow F. spot; beards yellow; slight fragrance. Spring Dancer X Pink Caper. Shoop 1990.

LEMON TOUCH (B. Charles Jenkins, R. 1995). Sdlg. BA67B. SPU, 38-45" (97-114 cm), ML. Lacy lemon yellow self, signal darker yellow. Candle Lace X Finally Free. Shepard Iris 1995.

LEMON UP (Tom Magee, R. 1991). Sdlg. 8420B. BB, 27" (69 cm), M. Ruffled light lemon yellow, lighter F. blaze; beards gold, tipped light lemon; slight fragrance. Eastertime X 8113E: (768: (((Above All x Fuji's Mantle) x (Mary Randall x Strike Me Pink sib)) x ((Strike Me Pink x Fair Luzon) x Pink Sleigh)) x Mandolin). Long 1994.

LEMON WHIP (Carol Lankow by J. T. Aitken, R. 1993). Sdlg. 4H55-1. IB, 22" (56 cm), ML. S. white; F. lemon yellow; beards white, tipped yellow; slight fragrance. Sun King X Loveshine. Aitken's Salmon Creek 1993.

LEMON WINE (Cy Bartlett, R. 1994). Sdlg. D/E-A1. IB, 20" (51 cm), EM. Clear light lemon, F. with burgundy thumbprint; beards yellow to orange; lightly waved and ruffled; slight sweet fragrance. (Diligence x Eyebright) X Arden sib. Sutton 1994.

LEMON ZEST (Kevin Vaughn, R. 1998). Sdlg. F-32-1. LA, 24-28" (61-71 cm), VE-EM. S. bright lemon yellow aging to creamy lemon with lemon green veins; style arms electric green; F. bright lemon yellow, intense electric green signal area; heavily ruffled, lightly serrate. Heavenly Glow X Vermilion Queen.

LEMPERG PURPLE (Eric & Bob Tankesley-Clarke, R. 1994). SPEC, 20-22" (51-56 cm), M. Deep purple, F. slightly deeper; beards white, orange in throat; pronounced sweet fragrance. Origin unknown; distributed by Hanselmayer from the Lemperg-Mayr-Melnhof collection, Frohnleiten, Austria, prior to 1960; in commerce as *I. croatica* C2.

LENA BAKER (Frederick Kerr, R. 1998). Sdlg. 911102. TB, 36" (91 cm), M. S. bright yellow; F. medium yellow, wide golden yellow hafts shading to white at beard, dark red 3/4" marginal band; beards golden yellow; ruffled; slight sweet fragrance. 881713: (Edith Wolford x Lullaby of Spring) X 880803: (Alpine Castle x Gypsy Woman). Rainbow Acres 1998.

LENA MAE (George Slade, R. 1991). Sdlg. 87-12-1. TB, 35" (89 cm), M. Ruffled dark red purple (RHS 83B); beards dark tangerine; slight sweet fragrance. Naughty But Nice X Graduation.

LENINGRADSKIYE NOCHI (Nina Miroshnichenko, R. 1996). BB, 27" (70 cm), M. Light blue self; beards light blue at end, changing to light yellow, to yellow in throat; pronounced spicy fragrance. Parentage unknown. Miroshnichenko 1987.

LENKORAN (George Rodionenko by Tom & Ellen Abrego, R. 1994). SPU, 45½" (115 cm), M. S. light blue violet (RHS 96C); F. white, heavily veined and edged light blue violet (96C), golden signal; thin form. Inv. *I. klattii.* Chehalem Gardens 1985.

LENORA PEARL (Hooker Nichols, BB, R. 1988). Hillcrest 1990.

LENTEN PRAYER (Schreiner, R. 1998). Sdlg. CC 369-2. TB, 36" (91 cm), M. Beetroot purple (RHS 71A) self; beards bishops purple. T 850-2: (K 400-1: (Cranberry Ice x ((Dream Time sib x Mulberry Wine) x (Skywatch x (Amethyst Flame x Silvertone)))) x K 946-A: (Hayride x Burnt Toffee sib)) X Jazz Festival. Schreiner 1998.

LEO HEWITT (Jennifer Hewitt, R. 1994). Sdlg. T8311. SIB (tet.), 33" (84 cm), M. S. medium to dark blue violet, veined darker; F. deep blue violet with variable fine gold edge, gold signal; tailored, flared, standards upright. Sdlg. (parentage unknown, from McEwen seed) X Silver Edge. British Iris Society 1995.

LEONA CHARLENE (Harry Wolford, R. 1995). Sdlg. PO7+001-1. TB, 30-32" (76-81 cm), ML. Lightly ruffled white self; beards white, tipped yellow; slight sweet fragrance. Playgirl X Ocean Swells.

LEONTYNE (Graeme Grosvenor, R. 1998). Sdlg. J97-1. TB, 33" (84 cm), ML. Apricot, F. lighter around red beard; slight fragrance. Memoirs X Bubble Up.

LEO NYNE (Chet Tompkins, R. 1992). Sdlg. 85-10. TB, 37" (94 cm), ML. Bright taffy tan gold blend, F. edged vivid rosy copper; beards yellow. ((Elegant Era x Summer Serenade) x (Summer Serenade x Candle Power)) X (Wayward Angel x (Tinsel Town x Ovation)). Fleur de Lis 1991.

LEO'S CHOICE (C. T. Claussen, R. 1991). Sdlg. 82-6-1. BB, 24" (61 cm), EM. S. pale blue lavender, base dark lavender; F. blue lavender, darker haft veining; beards dark lavender; slight fragrance. Night Hawk X Song of Norway. Wagontrail Acres 1992.

LEO'S LORT-CHEN (Leo T. Clark by Sharon McAllister, R. 1992). AB (OGB+), 28" (72 cm), EM. S. yellow; F. darker yellow, burgundy signal; beards yellow. Chenik Aga X *I. lortetii*. Aril Society 1992.

LEOTA D (Floyd Dyer, R. 1992). Sdlg. D-279-88-D. SDB, 13" (33 cm), M. S. pale violet with green tint at top; F. red brown, edged blue; beards blue; slight musky fragrance. D-134-83-D: (Fire One x Gingerbread Man) X D-132-83-D: (D-32-72-D x Blue Pools). Four Cedars 1992.

LEPRECHAUN'S KISS (Barry Blyth, R. 1993). Sdlg. W149-3. SPU, 22-24" (56-61 cm), M. Brown with darker overlay on lower portion of F.; style arms brown gold. Satinwood X self. Tempo Two 1993/94.

LEPRECHAUN'S PURSE (Chuck Chapman, R. 1999). Sdlg. 89-50-2. SDB, 12" (31 cm), M. S. pale greenish cream, pastel green midrib, scalloped margin; F. light greenish cream, yellow green lined spot; beards light violet, orange in throat. Mrs. Nate Rudolph X Loveshine. Chapman Iris 1999.

LESLIE DAWN (Darlene Pinegar, R. 1992). Sdlg. A-2-1. TB, 32" (81 cm), M. S. solid medium red purple on outside, apricot inside with red purple dotting; style arms red purple, apricot inside base; F. white ground, heavy dark red purple striping starting at apricot hafts and becoming solid at edge; beards burnt orange; ruffled; slight sweet fragrance. Anon X Rancho Rose. Spanish Fork 1993.

LESNAYA FIALKA (V. & N. Gordodelovy, R. 1995). Sdlg. 229. TB, 32" (80 cm), EM. Purple violet, white striations near beard; beards blue, brown in throat. Parentage unknown. Gordodelovy 1986.

LESSON (Sterling Innerst, R. 1990). Sdlg. 3235-5. SDB, 10" (25 cm), ML. Full blue; beards white, tipped yellow. Rain Dance X 1583-1: ((Gentle Smile x Mystic Symbol) x (Gentle Smile x Stockholm)). Innerst 1990.

LET IT RIDE (Oscar Schick, R. 1998). Sdlg. 93-20K04. TB, 30" (76 cm), M. Lightly ruffled grey blue, F. with buff yellow shoulders; beards deep orange; slight musky fragrance. Twilight Blaze X 90-04A16: (Tide's In x Blue Maxx). Stockton 1998.

LET IT SHINE (Eugene Hunt by Sharon McAllister, R. 1990). Sdlg. ORB 89-3. AB (OGB+), 29½" (75 cm), EM. S. barium yellow (near RHS 10B); F. sulphur yellow (near 7A), signal burgundy black (darker than 187A); beards bright yellow, tipped tangerine. Leo's Lort-Chen X Esther's Son. Aril Society 1990.

LETMENTERTAINU (Tom Burseen, R. 1995). Sdlg. 0-137B. TB, 35" (89 cm), EM. S. and style arms orange, washed reddish lavender (RHS 39A); F. white, edges red lavender (39A), orange burst at hafts; beards orange, tipped yellow; ruffled, heavily laced; spicy fragrance. Romantic Mood X Fundango. T.B.'s Place 1995.

LET ME SEE (William Ackerman, JI, R. 1989). Nicholls Gardens 1990.

LETNI VECHER (Adolf Volfovich-Moler, R. 1995). Sdlg. 136. TB, 39" (100 cm), EM. S. violet; F. violet, hafts brown; beards yellow, violet at end; heavily ruffled, laced. Victoria Falls X Karmen Dance. Volfovich-Moler 1997.

LET'S BOOGIE (Schreiner, R. 1997). Sdlg. BB 1814-A. TB, 37" (94 cm), EM. S. and style arms creamy peach (RHS 193); F. beetroot purple (71A), 1/8" cream white mid-stripe; beards tangerine. Sweeter Than Wine X V 248-A: (Latin Lady x (Craig #41, unknown, x Breaking Dawn)). Schreiner 1997.

LET'S ELOPE (Barry Blyth, R. 1993). Sdlg. Z31-2. IB, 24" (61 cm), EM. S. vibrant coral rose pink, slightly violet at midrib; F. similar with light tannish rose overlay, slight violet flush below saturn red beard; sweet fragrance. Shiralee X Chanted. Tempo Two 1993/94.

LET'S PRETEND (Monty Byers, TB, R. 1989). Moonshine 1990.

LETTER FROM PARIS (Barry Blyth, R. 1997). Sdlg. A63-D. TB, 36" (92 cm), ML. Medium to light pink, slightly paler central F. area; beards tangerine; slight sweet fragrance. Dance Man X Rembrandt Magic. Tempo Two 1997/98.

LETUCHI GOLLANDETS (Sergey Loktev, R. 1999) Sdlg. 94-R13-5B. TB, 34" (86 cm), VE-EM. Blue violet, F. with whitish area around beard; beards yellow, white at end. Master Touch X Lilac Treat.

LEUTENBACH (Wolfgang Heuss, R. 1990). Sdlg. 208/83. MDB, 6-8" (15-20 cm), M. Very light blue with dark grey blue veins. Parentage unknown.

LEVITY (J. T. Aitken, R. 1991). Sdlg. 86M47. IB, 18" (46 cm), E. White ground, 3/8" medium blue plicata band on S. and F.; beards deep violet. Chubby Cheeks X Jesse's Song. Aitken's Salmon Creek 1991.

LEWISDALE (Robert Harding, R. 1992). Sdlg. EF-SFP A. TB, 39" (100 cm), VE-E. Apricot self; beards tangerine. Elysian Fields X Starfrost Pink. Iris Acres 1993/94.

LIAM JOHNS (John Carter, R. 1999). SPEC (*laevigata*), 24" (61 cm), ML. S. white, grey midrib; style arms mauve grey, broad white upturned tips; F. white fading and becoming almost translucent with grey veining, giving grey effect overall. Parentage unknown.

LIBERTY LIGHT (Robert Dunn, R. 1996). Sdlg. B1038C. TB, 38" (97 cm), M. S. creamy ivory, pastel lilac plicata edge; style arms cream; F. ivory, cream haft, pastel lilac edge; beards yellow. Vibrations X My Way. M.A.D. Iris 1997.

LIBRA STAR (Walter Moores, R. 1998). Sdlg. 88-29-C. TB, 34" (86 cm), M & RE. Ruffled medium violet blue, F. with white spot; beards yellow, white at end; slight spicy fragrance. Victoria Falls X Fall Spotlight. Moores 1999.

LICENSE TO CHILL (Chris Vizvarie, R. 1994). TB, 35" (89 cm), L. Soft light blue self; beards light blue; slight sweet fragrance. Song of Norway X Bill Jones sdlg. Last Scent Farm 1994.

LICHTERFELDIUS (Tomas Tamberg, R. 1997. SIB, 50-60" (125-150 cm), M. S. and style arms medium blue; F. white, blue line pattern. *I. sibirica* X unidentified blue. Joe Pye Weed 1997.

LIDIYA (V. & N. Gordodelovy, R. 1995). Sdlg. 75. TB, 32" (80 cm), ML. S. pastel pink; F. cream, paler in center; beards red cream at end; ruffled. Parentage unknown. Gordodelovy 1976.

LIFE OF RILEY (James McWhirter, R. 1992). Sdlg. J88-15-4. TB, 36" (91 cm), M. S. peach; F. rose tan; beards bright red; ruffled; slight fragrance. Cameo Concert X Role Model. Cottage 1993.

LIGHT AND AIRY (Joyce Meek, R. 1995). Sdlg. 55-2-6. TB, 33" (84 cm), ML. S. white with 3/4" red violet plicata rim; F. white, very narrow red violet rim, widening near hafts; beards white, faintly tipped coral; ruffled. (Deanna Darcy x Candace) X Lingering Love. D & J Gardens 1995.

LIGHTED LANTERN (Tom Magee, TB, R. 1986). Long 1991.

LIGHTED SIGNAL (B. Charles Jenkins, R. 1990). Sdlg. C26-36E. SPU, 40-48" (102-122 cm), M. Blue purple, small yellow signal uniquely diffused at edge. Ping and Pang (white) X Terra Nova. Shepard 1991.

LIGHTHOUSE BEACON (Cleo Palmer, R. 1992). Sdlg. 8900. MDB, 5" (13 cm), E. S. white; F. white, very pale blue spot aging fainter. Parentage unknown. Palmer's Iris 1992.

LIGHT LAUGHTER (Nora Scopes, IB, R. 1984). British Iris Society 1987.

LIGHTLY TOUCHED (Jean Peyrard by Connie Hansen, R. 1991). SIB (sino-sib), 30-36" (76-91 cm), L. S. milky white; style arms pale yellow; F. milky white to ivory with slight violet venation, touch of violet along lower half of edge, yellow throat. *I. clarkei* X *I. delavayi*. Laurie's Garden 1992.

LIGHT 'N EASY (O. D. Niswonger, R. 1994). Sdlg. SDB 32-90. SDB, 12" (30 cm), M. Pale blue grey with chartreuse influence, pale brown spot around white beards; beards white, tipped yellow. Sib to Jade Stone. Cape Iris 1994.

LIGHTNING BOLT (Joseph Ghio, R. 1992). Sdlg. 86-64T. TB, 35" (89 cm), EML. S. rose wine; F. electric blue, blending to rose wine at edge; beards red. 83-9E: ((Act of Love x Lady Friend) x ((Entourage x Homecoming Queen) x Mulled Wine)) X Stratagem. Bay View 1993.

LIGHTNING QUICK (Mary Dunn by Joe Ghio, R. 1998). Sdlg. 237-8. LA, 36" (91 cm), M. Medium yellow self. Rich and Famous X Natural Wonder. Bay View 1998.

LIGHTNING SPEED (Joseph Ghio, R. 1996). Sdlg. PE-172-H2. CA, 13" (33 cm), EM. S. solid deep gold; style arms buff gold; F. gold, heavily lined and patterned henna, gold hairline edge. Sib to Gordola. Bay View 1996.

LIGHTNING STREAK (James Gibson by Cooley's Gardens, R. 1993). Sdlg. 9-2Z. TB, 34" (86 cm), EM. S. caramel over orange ground; F. orange yellow ground with red brown plicata pattern simulating stripes, red brown plicata edge; beards yellow orange; lightly ruffled. Yellow Brick Road X 45-0, Mountain Melody sib. Cooley 1992.

LIGHTNING STRIKE (Anthony Lange, R. 1994). Sdlg. 4-88-15. TB, 30" (76 cm), M & RE. S. violet (near RHS 86A); style arms violet; F. velvety purple violet (near 82) with metallic overlay, edged S. color, veining around beards; beards old gold, white base, broad purple violet flounce; lightly ruffled; pronounced sweet fragrance. Sky Hooks X Spinning Wheel. Camicot Acres 1997.

LIGHT OF HEAVEN (Chet Tompkins, R. 1999). Sdlg. 93-16A. TB, 36" (91 cm), ML-VL. S. and style arms creamy yellow; F. dark chrome yellow to antique gold; beards dark chrome yellow. Sib to Smash Hit. Fleur de Lis 1999.

LIGHT REBUFF (Raymond Smith, R. 1990). Sdlg. 7703BR. TB, 30" (76 cm), M & RE. S. pale orange yellow (Munsell 7.5YR 9/4) with slight pink cast; F. pale orange yellow veined green; beards yellow, tipped tangerine; ruffled; slight fragrance. 7511B: (Lemon Mist x Moonlight Duet) X 7426A: (6703BF x Fay 62-10: (Orchid Brocade x Morning Breeze sdlg.)). R. G. Smith 1992.

LIGHTS CAMERA ACTION (Lowell Baumunk, R. 1999). Sdlg. 94HBEE-15. TB, 37" (94 cm), M. S. and style arms deep lavender, slight lighter blending; F. cream white ground and reverse, brick red near hafts blending into lavender and buff yellow to form large spot pattern, lavender centerline, 1/2" cream white edge with narrow lavender picotee outer rim; beards yellow orange. Honky Tonk Blues X Ecstatic Echo.

LIGHT SHOW (Keith Keppel, R. 1990). Sdlg. 84-93A. TB, 34" (86 cm), M. S. sunflower yellow (M&P 9-L-4); F. citron yellow (10-J-2) ground, 1/16" clear margin, remainder dot washed garnet brown (6-L-9) to peony red (6-J-6) forming almost solid rayed pattern; beards cadmium yellow (9-L-9). 82-42F, Jitterbug sib, X 79-102C: (72-34A: (Caramba sib x (66-24A: ((Taholah x (Gene Wild x Majorette)) x Ballyhoo sib) x (High Life x 66-24H))) x Broadway). Keppel 1991.

LIGHTS OF ARABIA (Lois Rich by James Whitely, R. 1994). Sdlg. R84-67. AB (OGB), 29" (74 cm), ML. S. bright butter yellow, strong midribs; F. bright butter yellow, mahogany signal; beards yellow. R80-151B: (Sunset Dunes x ((((*I. atropurpurea* x *I. jordana*) x Pink Formal) x ((R69-108 x Welcome Reward) x (Welcome Reward x (R62-OB-1D x Kalifa Hirfa))))) X R80-118F: (Sand Etching x (((CR64-12C: inv. Iman Onco, *I. lortetii, I. auranitica, I. barnumae,* W83-O) x Mishawaka))). Aril Patch 1994.

LILAC HILL (Barry Blyth, R. 1993). Sdlg. Z31-1. IB, 22" (56 cm), M. S. mulberry; F. white, heavily stitched mulberry, deeper centerline; beards white, tangerine in throat; sweet fragrance. Shiralee X Chanted. Tempo Two 1993/94.

LILAC N' ICE (Barry Blyth, R. 1993). Sdlg. A44-13. SDB, 14" (36 cm), VE-EM. S. lavender lilac, slight white midrib area; F. white, 1/8" dotted and stitched lavender lilac edge; beards lavender, tangerine in throat; slight fragrance. (Cupid's Cup x Yipee sib) X Chanted. Tempo Two 1993/94.

LILAC SERENADE (Bernard Pryor, R. 1999). Sdlg. 32/92-P. LA, 40" (102 cm), EM. S. soft methyl violet (RHS 85C), yellow line signal; style arms pallid lavender, midrib white; F. soft methyl violet, raised yellow steeple signal; ruffled. Volcanic Wildfire X Charlotte's Tutu.

LILAC TOPPER (Stan Dexter by Marie Ingersoll, R. 1995). Sdlg. 7-37-8. TB, 38" (97 cm), EM. S. lilac rose; F. wine maroon shading to yellowish maroon, edged lavender tan; beards yellow. Beachgirl X 1980-99C: (Coral Magic x unknown). Ingersoll's Iris 1996.

LILAC VALE (Chet Tompkins, R. 1993). Sdlg. 87-83. TB, 38" (97 cm), EML. Waved bright lilac rose with blue infusion; beards lilac rose tinted blue. ((Easy Grace x Emissary) x (Lombardy x Easy Grace)) X Silver Silence. Fleur de Lis 1993.

LILAC WALTZ (Robert Harding, TB, R. 1983). Iris Acres 1993/94.

LILLA ALBERTA (Donald Spoon, R. 1995). Sdlg. 92-249. TB, 34" (86 cm), M. S. and style arms lavender, darker veining; F. plum, thin lavender edge, hafts veined white; beards tangerine orange, white at end; ruffled, laced. 89-114A: (Sweet Musette x Femme Fatale) X 87-22C: (Queen in Calico x Gentle Edith). Winterberry 1998.

LILLA'S GLOVES (Donald Spoon, R. 1995). Sdlg. 86-30G. TB, 32" (81 cm), EM & RE (Oct./VA). Ruffled lavender (RHS 88A/B) self, darker texture veining; beards lavender, hairs tipped yellow, entirely yellow in throat; ruffled. Violet Miracle X Quiet Times. Winterberry 1997.

LILLA'S LACE (Donald Spoon, R. 1995). Sdlg. 93-24A. TB, 32" (81 cm), ML. Bright peachy golden yellow; F. with large lighter central area; beards darker yellow; heavily ruffled, laced. Sweetheart Ring X (Orien x Romantic Mood).

LILLA'S STRIPES (Donald Spoon, R. 1995). TB, 32" (81 cm), EM & RE (Sept./VA). S. and style arms plum lavender; F. white ground, plum lavender border, thin dark stripes and wide center stripe; beards white, hairs tipped yellow, all yellow in throat; ruffled. Lilla's Gloves X Violet Miracle. Winterberry 1997.

LILLIAN (J. R. Allen, R. 1993). Sdlg. S11J. TB, 30" (76 cm), M. S. medium blue violet; F. light to medium blue violet; beards yellow, tipped white; slight fragrance. Victoria Falls X Rebecca Anne. Allen Iris 1997.

LILLIAN LINDSEY STEWART (Bob Thomason, R. 1992). Sdlg. BT 8926G. TB, 32" (81 cm), M. Medium red violet self; beards deep blue; slight sweet fragrance. Mary Frances X Cranberry Ice.

LILLIAN WHITE (Eugene Hunt by Sharon McAllister, R. 1991). Sdlg. ORB 90-2. AB (OGB), 28" (72 cm), EM. S. very pale amethyst, aging white; F. ivory, aging white, burgundy veined signal; beards gold. ((Esther the Queen x Dove Song) x (Esther's Son x (*I. lortetii* x Chenik Aga))) X Esther's Son. Aril Society, McAllister 1991.

LILLIE NORWETA (Kirk Strawn, R. 1993). Sdlg. 27-1985. LA, 43" (109 cm), M. S. violet blue (RHS 90C); style arms violet blue (94C); F. darker violet blue (89D), yellow (12A) signal. King Creole X Just For Joe. Bois d'Arc 1996.

LILO (Manfred Beer, R. 1991). Sdlg. MB 12/80A. TB, 37" (95 cm), M. Pink violet; beards red. Champagne Music X Fond Wish. Gartencenter Kania 1991.

LILTING (Monty Byers, R. 1990). Sdlg. G48-1. TB, 34" (86 cm), EM & RE. S. smooth silvery oyster white; F. snow white, hafts and edge stitched light red violet; beards white, tipped cinnamon gold. Rosy Cloud X C-52-3: (Garden Grace x Hager horned violet sdlg.: (Moon Mistress x Meek horned sdlg.)). Moonshine 1991.

LILTING LAURA (Anna Mae Miller, SIB, R. 1989). Old Douglas Perennials 1990.

LILY MY LOVE (Barry Blyth, R. 1999). Sdlg. E88-17. TB, 34" (86 cm), VE-EM. S. pastel oyster lavender pink; F. deeper, with pinkish tan overlay deepest at hafts, giving pink grey effect; beards light tangerine, outer 1/4" tipped lavender; musky fragrance. Crazy For You X About Town. Tempo Two 1999/2000.

LIMA (Joseph Ghio, R. 1994). Sdlg. 90-33U. TB, 40" (102 cm), EML. Brassy gold self with greenish cast; beards bronze. Caracas X Opportunity. Bay View 1995.

LIMBO (J. R. Ellis, SPEC-X, R. 1988). British Iris Society 1995.

LIME AND LAVENDER (Cyril Field, R. 1992). Sdlg. CF12. TB, 29" (72 cm), M. Pale lavender with lime yellow appearing at random; style arms same; beards yellow. (Corsage x Humoresque sdlg.) X (Crazy Clown x sdlg.).

LIME DASH (T. J. Betts, R. 1993). Sdlg. 326A. LA, 36" (91 cm), EM. Lightly ruffled creamy yellow (RHS 5C), strongly veined green, long green signal; style arms green. Inez Conger X 826H: (Ila Nunn x tan sdlg.).

LIME FIZZ (Schreiner, TB, R. 1968). Schreiner 1969.

LIME FROSTED (Dana Borglum, R. 1993). Sdlg. C-1-7. TB, 32" (81 cm), M. S. white; F. white with lime green veining, ruffled; beards yellow, tipped white. A62-1: (white sdlg. x Visual Arts) X A61-1: ((Neon Rainbow x Piping Hot) x Wedding Candles).

LIMEHEART (Marjorie Brummitt, SIB, R. 1968). Correction of introductory data. Orpington Nurseries 1970.

LIME RUFFLES (William Maryott, R. 1995). Sdlg. TM196N. SDB, 10" (25 cm), M. Ruffled greenish white; beards greenish white. Starlight Waltz X Jazzamatazz. Maryott 1996.

LIME SMOOTHY (J. T. Aitken, R. 1997). Sdlg. 91M2. SDB, 10" (25 cm), M. S. white; F. light lime yellow; beards white; ruffled. (Stockholm x Combo) X ((Blue Trinket x Cotton Blossom) x Rain Dance). Aitken's Salmon Creek 1997.

LIME SODA (B.L.C. Dodsworth, R. 1997). Sdlg. EB 90 EE. TB, 42" (107 cm), M. S. pale yellow; F. white, edged yellow; beards yellow; ruffled. Edale X Early Light.

LIME SORBET (R. C. Brown, R. 1998). SPEC (*pseudacorus*), 30" (76 cm), M. S. and F. yellow; all new foliage creamy lime green, darkening to green with age. *I. pseudacorus* "Variegata" X unknown.

LIME SUPERB (John Gass, R. 1996). Sdlg. G-90. TB, 36" (91 cm), M. S. lemon lime; style arms light lemon lime; F. lemon lime, very slight paling in center; beards pale yellow; heavily ruffled, laced; spicy fragrance. Anna Belle Babson X Honor Bound. Rainbow Chasers 1997.

LINCOLN HIGH REUNION (Albert Buchholz, R. 1992). Sdlg. 31. TB, 29-32" (74-83 cm), M. Lightly ruffled white; beards yellow orange; slight fragrance. Social Whirl X Well Endowed.

LINCOLN IMP (J. R. Dodsworth, R. 1990). Sdlg. EB132. CA, 12" (30 cm), L. Lilac, F. with burgundy throat. Parentage unknown.

LINCOLN'S REWARD (Colin Fidock, R. 1997). Sdlg. F96-3. AB (OGB), 15" (38 cm), E. S. lavender, midrib darker; style arms bright lemon, frilled faint lavender edge; F. lemon, fading to pale lavender at edge, signal chocolate brown with edge tinged reddish; beards lemon, hairs tipped chocolate. Turkish Heart X Close Contact.

LINDA LEIGH (Donald Spoon, R. 1995). Sdlg. 90-184. TB, 35" (89 cm), ML. Ruffled, laced light gold orange self, F. with lighter central area; beards orange, long and large. Grand Prix X Filoli. Winterberry 1996.

LINDA LOU (Betty Wyss, R. 1997). Sdlg. 8946-8. MTB, 22" (56 cm), M. S. and F. white ground, rose pink plicata lines and dotting, heavier in S.; style arms yellow; beards white, hairs tipped yellow, all yellow in throat. Lively Rose X unknown. Stockton 1997.

LINDA MARY (Joan Cooper, SIB, R. 1988). Cooper's Garden, Redbud Lane 1990.

LINDA'S BLUE LINEN (William Phillips by Francis Scott Key Iris Society, R. 1992). Sdlg. 87-28. TB, 40" (102 cm), M. Blue violet self; beards yellow, tipped white. Mary Frances X unknown. Francis Scott Key Iris Society 1993.

LINDA WEST (Peter Hutchinson by Lorena Reid, R. 1991). SPEC (*pseudacorus*), 30-42" (76-107 cm), M & RE. S. ivory white; F. ivory white, yellow signal, few grey vein lines. Collected, origin unknown. Laurie's Garden 1991.

LINDIS (G. F. Wilson, R. 1991). Sdlg. 21-89MSO-D. AB (OGB), 27½" (70 cm), EM. S. pale blue, lightly veined, bright rose buff rib; F. smooth blend of pale buff and pale violet rose, small dark maroon signal; beards brown, lightly tipped cream; pronounced fragrance. Mainstream X Onlooker. Pleasure Iris 1993.

LINDSAY (Bob Brown by Abram Feuerstein, R. 1999). TB, 36" (91 cm), M. Silver lavender blend, F. with bronze shoulders; beards lavender. 8523: (Collage x 81-41: (((Pink Taffeta x Buffy) x Monaco) x self)) X unknown. Stockton 1997.

LINE DANCE (O. D. Niswonger, R. 1999). Sdlg. SDB 10-94. SDB, 12" (31 cm), M. S. pale blue, blended beige, white ground; style arms light blue blended beige; F. white ground, light blue blended beige plicata; beards blue to purple. SDB 29-91: (Chubby Cheeks x 10-88: (Auburn Valley x unknown)) X unknown. Cape Iris 1999.

LINGERING LAVENDER (Richard Ernst, R. 1991). Sdlg. F106-1. TB, 36" (91 cm), ML. S. lavender infused antique gold; F. cool lavender; beards yellow; ruffled; slight sweet fragrance. Syncopation X Champagne Duo. Cooley 1991.

LINGERING RAINBOW (Chet Tompkins, R. 1993). Sdlg. 115A. TB, 38" (97 cm), ML. Ruffled and laced iridescent blend of pearl, pink, cream and orchid with overtones of lilac and milky blue; beards deep lilac. Sdlgs. inv. Air Bubbles, Easy Grace, Ovation, Nile Flower. Fleur de Lis 1993.

LINGERING SPRING (Ben Hager, R. 1991). Sdlg. T4660RfWhLa. TB, 36" (91 cm), VL. Deeply ruffled white; beards white, yellow in throat. T3917RfBl, Edith Wolford blue sib, X Tinted Crystal. Melrose 1992.

LIOGKI MIRAZH (Nina Miroshnichenko, R. 1997). TB, 28" (71 cm), M. S. pale claret brown; F. lilac, edged pale claret brown, hafts yellow with dark claret brown beneath; beards lilac white, hairs tipped yellow; slight spicy fragrance. Parentage unknown. Miroshnichenko 1996.

LION CHIEF (Donald Spoon, R. 1998). Sdlg. 90-207. TB, 34" (86 cm), ML. Velvety rich red maroon self; style arms red maroon; beards maroon, brushed burnt golden yellow; ruffled, flared. Chief George X Red Lion. Winterberry 1998.

LIONHEART (Donna Aldridge, R. 1998). Sdlg. LV. SPEC (*pseudacorus*), 42" (107 cm), M. Deep rich yellow, F. spade-shaped, with dark signal markings forming perfect burgundy red heart with deeper chrome yellow inlay. Selected from naturalized colony at Lawrence, KS.

LION KING (Bob Bauer/John Coble, R. 1996). Sdlg. J89U-5. JI (9 F.), 40" (107 cm), M. Ruffled, rose (RHS 77A) edge with wide white center, white veining to near edge, hidden yellow signal; style arms white, multiple and upright, crests tipped violet. Frosted Pyramid X Frilled Enchantment. Ensata Gardens 1996.

LION'S SHARE (Mitch Jameson, R. 1991). Sdlg. 11-87. TB, 40" (102 cm), M. S. lemon cream; F. ivory white; beards yellow; ruffled; sweet fragrance. Moon's Delight X Tide's In. Knee-Deep in June 1992.

LIPPISCHER SCHUETZE (Siegmar Goerbitz, R. 1997). Sdlg. 9003 A2. TB, 41" (105 cm), M. Violet blue; beards yellow, blue at end. Augenweide X Five Star Admiral. Goerbitz 1998.

LIPTOV (Josef Dudek, R. 1997). Sdlg. 91-ExRi-1. TB, 37" (95 cm), M. S. and style arms coral rose (RHS 76D); F. deep wine red (80A), edged coral rose, hafts marked rose wine; beards red orange, large; ruffled, laced; slight sweet fragrance. Extravagant X Ringo. Josef Dudek 1998.

LISA JANE (George Shoop, R. 1992). Sdlg. 86-56. SDB, 10" (25 cm), M. Peach pink self; beards red tangerine; slight fragrance. Pink Caper X Sunny Heart. Shoop 1992.

LISA MARIE (Polly Black, R. 1996). Sdlg. GR14-20-IL. TB, 36" (91 cm), M. S. pinkish lilac; F. lilac, slightly darker shoulders and centerline; beards coral; slight fragrance. Squeeze Louise X Welcome Stranger.

LISBON ANTIGUA (Frank Foster, R. 1998). Sdlg. 8751GA. TB, 30" (76 cm), M. S. and style arms yellow (nearest RHS 22C); F. dark brownish maroon (near 187A) overlaid velvety black maroon (near 200A), yellow reticulations beside orange gold beard; slight musky fragrance. 8556V: (Flash Fire x Villain) X sib 8556B.

LIST MIOBIUSA (Sergey Loktev, R. 1998). Sdlg. 94-R11-15C. BB, 24" (60 cm), EM. S. grey, slight olive veining and narrow rim, pale violet base; style arms yellowish grey; F. pale lilac veined olive, grey pencil rim, grey tint below beard, hafts mustard; beards yellow, grey white base; sweet fragrance. "Uroda" X Drevni Rim. Loktev 1998.

LITHUANIAN AMBER (V. Zliobiene by Edmundas Kondratas, R. 1999). SIB, 41" (105 cm), VE. S. white, upright; style arms white; F. pale yellow, hafts deep yellow brown, yellow signal blending paler down F. Parentage unknown.

LITTLE BEV (Barry Blyth, R. 1996). Sdlg. B34-4. SDB, 10" (25 cm), VE. Salmcn pink, F. with white area around beard; beards pastel lavender, bright tangerine in throat; slight fragrance. Z15-4, Fairy Favours sib, X Z24-1, Volts sib. Tempo Two 1996/97.

LITTLE BLUEBOY (Arthur Blodgett, R. 1994). Sdlg. M88-11. MDB, 8" (20 cm), E. Dark blue violet; self beards. 553: (Tortuga x unknown) X D84-07: ((Haiku x 731) x (731 x Mrs. Nate Rudolph)).

LITTLE BLUE-EYES (John Weiler, R. 1993). Sdlg. 88-10-2RE. SDB, 11" (28 cm), ML & RE. Medium clear yellow with slightly darker yellow spot on F.; beards lavender blue; slight sweet fragrance. 85-16-1RE: (Leprechaun's Delight x (79-39-3RE: (((Yellow Wave x 70-95-2: (Brighteyes x Grace Note)) x 74-3-1: (Cartwheel x 70-95-6)) x Chariots) x 79-20-1RE: ((70-95-3 x Gingerbread Man) x Stockholm))) X 84-47-6RE: ((((Ruby Contrast x Little Blackfoot) x ((70-95-3 x Bronze Babe) x 74-3-1)) x Pink Amber) x (79-39-3RE x 79-20-1RE)). Rialto 1993.

LITTLE BLUE SPARKLER (Sarah Tiffney, R. 1995). Sdlg. TS80-2. SIB, 27" (69 cm), EM. S. violet blue (RHS 93C), faint darker (93B) veining; style arms violet blue (93C), darker (93B) midrib, edges and crest; F. cream, deeper violet blue (93A) veining, centerline and edging; slender fountain-effect foliage. *I. sibirica* sdlg., sib to Snow Prince. Pope's Perennials 1996.

LITTLE BLUETS (John Weiler, R. 1992). Sdlg. 87-57-1RE. SDB, 12" (30 cm), ML & RE. Tailored medium blue self; beards cream; pronounced sweet fragrance. 85-28-2RE: ((Third Charm x Plum-Plum) x (Third World x Third Charm)) X 85-32-2RE: ((Twink x Third Charm) x Muchacha). Rialto 1992.

LITTLE BOW PINK (Don Delmez, R. 1998). Sdlg. SP-4. JI (3 F.), 38" (97 cm), EM. Pink, F. with yellow signal; S. upright. Iseji-no-Haru X Hime Komachi. Delmez Gardens 1998.

LITTLE BREEZE (Floyd Dyer, R. 1994). Sdlg. D33-87D. MDB, 4½" (11 cm), M. S. red violet blend, darker near haft; F. light red violet, darker around yellow beard. D20-81D: (Bloodspot x unknown) X D1-77D, unknown. Four Cedars 1994.

LITTLE BRIDGET (Shirley Spicer, R. 1996). Sdlg. SS 2/5/85. SDB, 7-9" (17-23 cm), L. Pale lavender blue, F. purple in center; beards soft blue; sweet fragrance. Stormy Eyes X Profiteer. Waimate 1997/98.

LITTLE CAILLET (Ken Durio, R. 1996). Sdlg. VI-B87. SPEC-X, 25" (64 cm), M. S. full orchid blue, veined wistaria blue, light lavender blue edging; style arms lilac, edged white; F. wistaria blue veined deeper, some light violet blue between veins; signal full golden yellow and green, with chocolate veining, mid-stripe and edge; base of foliage and scapes suffused maroon; slight spicy fragrance. *I. virginica* light blue X Bayou Rouge. Louisiana Nursery 1998.

LITTLE CLOWN (Mary Louise Dunderman, R. 1991). Sdlg. HH396. MTB, 24" (61 cm), L. S. orange (RHS 28B); F. bright red orange (179A), orange signal; beards orange. Welch brown MTB sdlg.: (C309 x black sdlg.) X DD522 light brown: (AA197 rose: (Y485 coral pink x Carolyn Rose) x Z370 rose pink). Ohio Gardens 1993.

LITTLE DRUMMER BOY (A. & D. Willott, R. 1997). Sdlg. W 94-49. MDB, 4" (10 cm), E. Lightly ruffled white, large violet F. spot; beards cream. W 91-85: (Pittance x W 79-13: (Greenlee GX-2: ((White Mite x self) x (*I. pumila alba* x Hanselmayer)) x Buttons)) X W 92-6: (Kuban *pumila* #205 x Daring Eyes). Willott 1997.

LITTLE EDENITE (Cleo Palmer, R. 1990). Sdlg. 8708. SDB, 15" (38 cm), E. Dark reddish black, hafts slightly lighter; beards violet base, hairs tipped brown. Demon X 7630: (Bloodspot x Cherry Garden). Palmer's Iris 1990.

LITTLE EGYPT (Allen Harper, MTB, R. 1986). Harper's Garden 1986.

LITTLE FIRECRACKER (Chuck Chapman, R. 1997). Sdlg. 92-213-3. SDB, 15" (38 cm), M. S. and style arms light butterscotch orange; F. dark butterscotch orange, edged lighter; beards bright tangerine red; slight fragrance. 87-22-44: (Mister Roberts x Solar Flight) X 90-214-1: ((Melon Honey x Pulse Rate) x Orange Tiger). Chapman Iris 1997.

LITTLE FREAK (John Steel by Roger Nelson, R. 1999). BB, 22" (56 cm), M. S. absent; F. (6) white, neatly marked fine medium violet plicata edge; beards medium yellow; flat form. Parentage unknown; diploid. Rainbow Hybridizing Gardens 1959.

LITTLE FRILLS (B. Charles Jenkins, R. 1995). Sdlg. AZ81B. SPU, 25" (64 cm), E. S. violet blue; style arms creamy white, edged violet; F. creamy white, edges tinted violet, yellow signal; ruffled. Color Focus X self. Shepard Iris 1998.

LITTLE HONEY-BUNNY (Opal Wulf, R. 1996). Sdlg. 1093. MTB, 16" (41 cm), ML. S. and style arms aureolin yellow (RHS 12A); F. yellow, ruby red (59A) veining and spot at end of cadmium orange (23A) beard. Grandpa's Girl X Snickerdoodle. Wulf's Backachers 1998.

LITTLE ITCH (Rolla Eich, R. 1998). Sdlg. E-93-1. SDB, 8-10" (21-25 cm), E. Bright sulphur yellow, F. with olive green haft veins becoming gold in blade; beards bright powder blue. Raspberry Whip X unknown.

LITTLE JESTER (B. Charles Jenkins, R. 1990). Sdlg. B1-21C. CA, 10" (25 cm), ML. Pale rosy magenta, style arms and S. veins darker, F. with rosy magenta surrounding prominent yellow orange blaze. Big Money X Mission Santa Cruz. Portable Acres 1991.

LITTLE JOHN (Donald Spoon, R. 1995). Sdlg. 90-59A. TB, 34" (86 cm), M. S. lavender pink, darker lavender arched veining; style arms lavender pink; F. lavender, white centerline; beards tangerine, tipped lavender; ruffled, laced. Damsel X Queen Dorothy. Winterberry 1996.

LITTLE LARRIKIN (Janet Hutchinson, R. 1998). Sdlg. GL/B/2. LA, 33" (84 cm), ML. S. pale lemon yellow, veined and flushed grey lavender; style arms medium lemon, pale green wash; F. pale lime yellow, heavily veined lavender, lavender flush, small medium yellow signal; heavily ruffled; flower small, foliage fine; slight fragrance. Glowlight X unknown.

LITTLE LOLLIPOP (Nora Scopes, R. 1990). Sdlg. 1/52C. BB, 20" (51 cm), EM. S. very pale pink; F. pale pink, hafts flushed apricot; beards pink; ruffled, flared; sweet fragrance. Little Dolly Daydream X Sunset Star.

LITTLE MARY SUNSHINE (Elvan Roderick, BB, R. 1989). Roderick Iris 1990.

LITTLE MERMAID (Tom Magee, R. 1992). Sdlg. 8534B. IB, 20" (51 cm), M. Pale shell pink, F. with ivory radiating from beard; style arms lighter pink; beards ivory, tipped red. 8033C: (Mountain Sunbeams x 7513F, Wedding Cake sib) X Shrimp. Long 1994.

LITTLE MISTY (Jim & Vicki Craig, R. 1990). Sdlg. 42V11. MTB, 23" (58 cm), E. S. pale greyed lavender; F. medium lavender blue; beards yellow, tipped pale lavender blue; slight sweet fragrance. Payoff X 11R4, Reformation sib. J. & V. Craig 1990.

LITTLE MOO (Ruby Buchanan by John Wood, R. 1992). SIB, 10" (25 cm), L. Violet blue (RHS 94A) self. Parentage unknown. John Wood 1993.

LITTLE MOONBEAM (John Wight, R. 1998). Sdlg. J93-11-1. SDB, 13½" (34 cm), EM. Lightly ruffled sulphur yellow (RHS 6B), F. with maroon red lines radiating within deeper yellow spot; beards white, hairs barely tipped orange. Kentucky Bluegrass X J85-6-5: (Ruffled Shamrock x Moon Over Shiraz). Wight's Iris 1998.

LITTLE NUTKIN (Heather Pryor, R. 1994). Sdlg. 66/90-1. LA, 26" (66 cm), ML. Heavily ruffled and slightly reflexed tan brown, all petals with yellow signal with raised orange line; style arms light tan infused rosy pink, crests yellow. Gladiator's Gift X self. Rainbow Ridge 1995/96.

LITTLE PAPOOSE (D. Steve Varner, R. 1992). Sdlg. 3189. SIB, 20" (51 cm), M. Deep red grape, wide white signal; slight fragrance. Rare Jewel X Kismet. Illini Iris 1992.

LITTLE POLITICIAN (Floyd Dyer, R. 1996). Sdlg. D-16-91-1. IB, 20" (51 cm), M. S. yellow tan, violet marking; F. pale yellow, violet center overlay; beards yellow. Cindy Mitchell X Wings of Dreams. Dyer's Garden 1996.

LITTLE PRINCESS (Nora Scopes, R. 1991). Sdlg. 8/111. BB, 24" (61 cm), M. S. white; F. white, shadowed purple; beards tangerine; sweet fragrance. 1/52: (Little Dolly Daydream x Sunset Star) X Magic Man.

LITTLE RASCAL (Jim & Lucy Fry, MDB, R. 1988). J & L Iris 1991.

LITTLE RHYME (Marty Schafer/Jan Sacks, R. 1990). Sdlg. SP85-2-1. SPEC (*versicolor*), 12" (30 cm), M. S. white, yellow near heart; style arms white, yellow green in heart; F. white, green hafts, yellow signal veined green. Parentage unknown. Joe Pye Weed 1991.

LITTLE ROCK CELEBRITY (Henry Rowlan by Comanche Acres, R. 1997). Sdlg. 87-T-2. MTB, 19" (48 cm), EM. S. white ground, wide lavender blue band; F. white ground, narrow stitched lavender blue edge; beards white, yellow in throat; slight sweet fragrance. Parentage unknown. Comanche Acres 1998.

LITTLE ROCK PRINCESS (Henry Rowlan by Comanche Acres, R. 1995). Sdlg. 85-MTB-6. MTB, 17" (43 cm), M. S. yellowish white, reddish brown veins; F. white, reddish brown veins; beards yellow. Parentage unknown. Comanche Acres 1995.

LITTLE RUSSIAN (Vernon Wood, R. 1995). Sdlg. 93-64. CA, 10" (25 cm), M. S. golden yellow, flushed ruby red; style arms yellow; F. golden yellow, ruby red spot and lines. Ohlone X 91-45: (89-7: (Roaring Camp x 87-9, from sdlgs. of unknown parentage) x Riva).

LITTLE SNOWBALL (Adolph Vogt, JI, R. 1985). Ensata Gardens 1990.

LITTLE SNOWMAN (Adolph Vogt, JI, R. 1981). Tranquil Lake Nursery 1990.

LITTLE SONG (Floyd Dyer, R. 1991). Sdlg. D-116-85-D. SDB, 13" (33 cm), M. S. pale blue violet, slight yellow overlay; F. brown, very pale blue violet edge; beards yellow brown, tipped blue; slight sweet fragrance. Star Boy X D-39-79D: (((Orange Bantam x Knick-Knack) x self) x ((Brassie x Blue Denim) x self)). Four Cedars 1991.

LITTLE SPLASH (B. Charles Jenkins, R. 1997). Sdlg. BF17F. SPU, 29" (74 cm), E. S. creamy white, base blending to yellow; style arms creamy white; F. creamy white, large yellow central area leaving 1/4" margin; lightly ruffled. Bali Bali X Elixir. Shepard Iris 1997.

LITTLE SPRINKLE (Chris Vizvarie, R. 1992). Sdlg. RT-66. SDB, 9" (23 cm), M. S. yellow, edge dusted plum; F. yellow, darker plum plicata peppering; beards yellow orange; slight sweet fragrance. Parentage unknown. Last Scent Farm 1992.

LITTLE SPRITZER (Don Delmez, R. 1998). Sdlg. SMIN-1. JI (3 F.), 22" (56 cm), M. S. violet purple; style arms purple; F. white, veined purple, signal yellow. Chitose Hime X unknown. Delmez Gardens 1998.

LITTLE TAJ (Barry Blyth, R. 1994). Sdlg. A22-2. SDB, 12" (30 cm), EML. S. tan-champagne flushed pink; F. same, rosy hafts, white area around beards and blue violet blaze down midline; beards deep tangerine, blue violet on outer 1/4"; slight fragrance. Moondawn X Merry Dance. Tempo Two 1994/95.

LITTLE TILGATES (Brian Price, R. 1994). Sdlg. BPP88/9/E. CA, 12" (30 cm), M. S. peach; F. peach, lightly marked radiant center. From sdlgs. inv. Ghio line. V. H. Humphrey 1997.

LITTLE TOBY (B. Charles Jenkins, R. 1992). Sdlg. B1-21B. CA, 16" (41 cm), M. S. light maroon; F. dark maroon, yellow flash with two yellow lines extending almost full length of F. Big Money X Mission Santa Cruz. Portable Acres 1992.

LITTLE TREASURE (Bernard Pryor, R. 1997). Sdlg. 66/90-2. LA, 28" (71 cm), ML. S. soft burnt caramel rose; style rims caramel rose, yellow center rib and fringe; F. darker burnt caramel rose, darker veining; yellow line signals larger on F.; ruffled. Gladiator's Gift X self. Iris Haven 1999/2000.

LITTLE VIOLET CHARM (George Sutton, R. 1995). Sdlg. C-30. SDB, 11" (28 cm), EM & RE. S. and style arms violet (RHS 87A); F. blended plum purple (79A) and violet; beards violet blue (96D), whitish base; ruffled; slight sweet fragrance. Plum Perfect X Third Charm. Sutton 1997.

LITTLE VIXEN (Alan McWhirter, SDB, R. 1988). Last Scent Farm 1991.

LITTLE ZIPPER (Graeme Grosvenor, R. 1999). Sdlg. V93-B. BB, 25" (63 cm), ML. White overlaid blue violet; F. with darker blue violet perimeter; beards mustard; slight fragrance. Zipper Stitch X Worth Ethic sib.

LIUBASHA (Viacheslav Gavrilin, R. 1999). Sdlg. 94-627-4. TB, 34" (87 cm), ML. S. pink, midrib rose; style arms warm pink; F. rose violet in center blending to rose with narrow pink rim; beards tangerine orange, pinkish white at end, with rose violet spoon. Fiesta Time X Starcrest.

LIUBOV ORLOVA (V. &. N. Gordodelovy, R. 1996). Sdlg. 17. TB, 35" (90 cm), L. S. cream; F. pink, shaded white near red beard; ruffled; pronounced fragrance. Parentage unknown. Gordodelovy 1983.

LIVE COALS (O. D. Niswonger, R. 1993). Sdlg. SDB 65-91. SDB, 14" (36 cm), ML. S. yellow;

F. maroon sharply banded yellow; beards white base, yellow hair tips. Splash of Red X Jazzamatazz. Cape Iris 1993.

LIVELY LISA (C. T. Claussen, R. 1991). Sdlg. 82-12. TB, 30" (76 cm), E. S. light lemon yellow; F. white, edged lemon; beards deep yellow; ruffled, lightly laced; slight fragrance. Buttered All Over X Dancing Fairy. Wagontrail Acres 1992.

LIVING FREE (Barry Blyth, R. 1999). Sdlg. E103-4. TB, 36" (91 cm), VE-EM. Pinkish peach, F. with light rose overlay; beards bright tangerine; pronounced musky fragrance. B142-2, Power of One sib, X B178-2: (Wild Vision x Imprimis). Tempo Two 1999/2000.

LIVING LEGACY (James Gibson by Cooley's Gardens, R. 1993). Sdlg. 10-2A. TB, 36" (91 cm), EM. S. violet infused amber yellow; F. white ground, violet burgundy plicata markings, lighter blending on edge, violet burgundy midrib; beards bright yellow. 28-4I, Inspiration Point sib, X Broadway. Cooley 1993.

LIVING PICTURE (Ben Hager, R. 1998). Sdlg. T5920RsOcEa. TB, 35" (89 cm), E. S. and style arms orchid; F. orchid white ground, overblended light orchid deepening at center; beards white, tipped yellow except at end; ruffled, laced. T5382Bl: (High Tech x T4679RevBi, Garden Escort sib) X T5364LvBl/Wh: (High Tech x Timescape). Cooley 1999.

LIVING RIGHT (Richard Ernst, R. 1991). Sdlg. F120-2. TB, 35" (89 cm), ML. S. medium lavender purple, midrib paler; F. clean near-white, infused medium lavender rim; beards tangerine; ruffled, lightly laced. Afternoon Delight X Gaulter 81-17, inv. Irene Nelson. Cooley 1991.

LIZA LAUGHING (Nancy Burrows, TB, R. 1989). Stornoway Gardens 1990.

LIZZIE (Frances Love, R. 1991). SIB, 15" (38 cm), M. Royal blue. Parentage unknown. Seed from Currier McEwen.

LIZZOO (Ken Durio, R. 1992). Sdlg. ORS WEB #5. LA, 28" (71 cm), ML. S. light yellow, heavily marked with dark orange veining, dark orange mid-stripe, yellow edge; F. very dark orange, full golden yellow signal, full yellow markings between veins, light yellow green reverse. Charlie X President Hedley. Louisiana Nursery 1995.

LLANA (Allan Ensminger, R. 1995). Sdlg. 188-4. SDB, 9" (23 cm), M. S. and style arms barium yellow (HCC 503/3); F. barium yellow, ruby red (827) spot pattern; beards chrome yellow, tipped barium yellow. 285-3. (Do-Si-Do x 83-6: ((Boo x Sweet 'n Neat) x (Miss Region Twenty-One x (Eye Shadow x Reath 6-64)))) X 85-8: (Small Flash x Sweet 'n Neat).

LLANGORS (Harry Foster, SIB, R. 1989). V. H. Humphrey 1995.

LLOYD'S CHOICE (Joan Roberts, R. 1997) Sdlg. 525-8. TB, 36" (91 cm), ML. S. purple, base rosier; F. purple, hafts rosier; beards purple; ruffled. Titan's Glory X Mulled Wine. Friendship 1997.

LLYN BRIANNE (Harry Foster, SIB, R. 1986). V. H. Humphrey 1995.

LOADED (Tom Burseen, R. 1991). Sdlg. 8-123C. TB, 35" (89 cm), E. S. light brownish red (RHS 181D), some tan in heart; F. red (redder than 185A), white spray pattern by yellow beard; ruffled, laced, flared. 5-179A: (Flower Show x Mandolin) X Pulse Rate Date sib. T.B.'s Place 1995.

LOCAL COLOR (Keith Keppel, R. 1995). Sdlg. 89-79B. TB, 40" (107 cm), M. S. roman purple (M&P 44-K-10); style arms slightly lighter (42-K-9); F. dark purple (47-L-12), narrow violet (42-JK-8) edge, slight white patterning near beard; beards orange vermilion (2-G-12). Witches' Sabbath X Gallant Rogue. Keppel 1996.

LOCAL DANCER (Daniel Thruman, R. 1997). Sdlg. 97-381. TB, 38" (97 cm), M. S. blue violet; style arms violet; F. red purple, purple centerline, light lavender marginal band, hafts veined white and purple; beards yellow; ruffled; sweet fragrance. Into the Night X Grand Waltz.

LOCAL GIRL (Joseph Ghio, R. 1995). Sdlg. PF-171P2. CA, 14" (36 cm), L. Blended violet, mauve and apricot, F. with violet signal. PH-266Y: (Las Lomas x Aftershock sib) X Villa Montalvo. Bay View 1995.

LOCAL MOTION (Tom Burseen, R. 1990). Sdlg. 4-203F. TB, 35" (89 cm), M. S. white, yellow midrib and center; F. violet blue (RHS 91C); beards yellow; heavily ruffled. Ringo X Bubbling Over. T.B.'s Place 1991.

LOCAL YOKEL (Bob Thomason, SDB, R. 1988). Okie Iris 1994.

LOCHEYNORT (B.L.C. Dodsworth, R. 1991). Sdlg. EB 86BB. TB, 40" (102 cm), M. Ruffled pale blue, base darker; beards white. High Peak X Sullom Voe. British Iris Society 1997.

LOFTY CLOUD (Polly Black, R. 1992). Sdlg. SR1-5W. TB, 40" (102 cm), E. Heavily laced white, touched green near orange beards. Real Adventure X White Lightning. Polly Black 1992.

LOFTY DREAMS (Evelyn Robarts, R. 1992). Sdlg. 505-1. TB, 35-37" (89-94 cm), M. Ruffled pale blue white; beards medium blue; slight sweet fragrance. Blue Zipper X Song of Norway. Stahly 1992.

LOFTY ELEGANCE (John Wood, R. 1992). Sdlg. W-120-89. SIB, 30" (76 cm), M. S. lilac (RHS 76C), veined imperial purple (76A); style arms lilac (76C); F. imperial purple (76A) veined violet (88A). Pink Haze X Lavender Bounty. John Wood 1993.

LOGANBERRY WINE (A. & D. Cadd, R. 1999). Sdlg. 86-91-3. TB, 38" (97 cm), M. S. light violet, deeper center and midrib; style arms yellow to violet; F. deep reddish purple, white lines radiating from beard; beards white, to yellow in throat; pronounced sweet fragrance. Royalist X Wild Berry.

LOIS PARRISH (Paul Black, R. 1997). Sdlg. 88116B. TB, 34" (86 cm), ML. S. medium lilac; style arms violet lilac, crests laced; F. medium lilac, center paler pearly lilac; beards lilac at end, changing to cream, yellow in throat; heavily laced; pronounced sweet fragrance. Bubbling Lace X O. K. Corral. Mid-America 1997.

LOIS SETSER (Ed Matheny III, R. 1999). Sdlg. L:00-03-96. LA, 38" (97 cm), L. S. light pinkish lavender; style arms cream; F. pinkish lavender, yellow signal; slight musky fragrance. Rosebery X unknown.

LOLLAPALOOSA (Allan Ensminger, R. 1992). Sdlg. 86-19. TB, 30" (76 cm), M. Rose purple (HCC 533); beards vermilion (18/1). 81-50: (Infatuation x Entourage) X Christa. Varigay 1993.

LOLOKI (Barry Blyth, R. 1995). Sdlg. A44-22. SDB, 12" (30 cm), VL. Pink with bluish cast, F. with lavender blue chevron below beard; beards blue lavender on end, tangerine in throat; ruffled. V7-5, Gigolette sib, X Chanted. Tempo Two 1995/96.

LO MOMMO (Ladislav Muska, R. 1996). Sdlg. DOLA-07. TB, 34" (86 cm), EM. Heavily laced medium cream vanilla self; beards light orange; pronounced sweet fragrance. (Don Epifano x Lady Madonna) X Lady Madonna. Muska 1996.

LONDONDERRY (Keith Keppel, R. 1995). Sdlg. 91-41C. IB, 24" (61 cm), EM. S. and style arms pastel pinkish lilac (M&P 42-B-8); F. same, paling to near-white center; beards cool white, lightly tipped lemon and tangerine in throat; ruffled. Gatty T-1-2: ((Nefertiti x Playgirl) x Presence) X Chanted. Keppel 1996.

LONELY HEARTS (Keith Keppel, R. 1998). Sdlg. 91-86H. TB, 36" (91 cm), EM. S. peachbloom (M&P 2-BC-9), flushed rhodenite pink (43-G-1); style arms pinkish salmon (10-A-6), golden apricot (10-F-6) margin; F. peach (9-A-5) ground, 3/4" shaded and dotted cygnet purple (45-L-7) band; beards coral orange (1-J-11); ruffled; pronounced musky fragrance. Dawn Sky X Screen Play. Keppel 1999.

LONELY STREET (Duane Meek, R. 1997). Sdlg. 17-11-1. TB, 35" (89 cm), ML. S. dark red; F. deeper dark red, near red black; beards mustard bronze; ruffled. Rancho Grande X ((Spartan x Santana) x Bridget's Choice). D & J Gardens 1997.

LONE RANGER (Tom Magee, R. 1990). Sdlg. 8637A. TB, 35" (89 cm), E. S. light blue violet; F. darker blue violet, light blue blazed around beard; beards tangerine, tipped light blue violet; ruffled; sweet fragrance. Glory Thunder X Graduation. Long 1998.

LONESOME DOVE (Frederick Kerr by Stockton Iris Gardens, R. 1994). Sdlg. 87-29. TB, 35" (89 cm), ML. S. apricot; F. lighter apricot, deeper hafts; beards tangerine; heavily ruffled, lightly laced; slight fragrance. Moon's Delight X Speculator. Stockton 1994.

LONESOME STRANGER (Richard Ernst, R. 1994). Sdlg. HA103-1. TB, 40" (102 cm), M. Ruffled bluish white with pale blue stripe extending from beards; beards blue, tipped white. A101-3: (Song of Norway x Inheritance) X Wings of Doves. Cooley 1994.

#LONE STAR (Mrs. W. H. Benners, TB, R. 1931). Not introduced; name released.

LONE STAR (Farron Campbell, R. 1997). Sdlg. 93-182-A. LA, 30-36" (76-91 cm), ML. Soft blue lavender, light lavender violet veining, yellow crest on white ground; style arms light green base, midrib cream, heavily flushed and tipped blue lavender; cartwheel form with six F. and no S.; lightly ruffled. *I. hexagona* X Clara Goula. Lone Star 1997.

LONGHORN (George Sutton, R. 1996). Sdlg. G19-A. TB, 40" (107 cm), ML. S. white, hint of lavender pink; style arms white; F. white, hint of pink; beards white, ending in 3" white filamentous horn; ruffled, lightly laced; slight spicy fragrance. Sweet Musette X Twice Thrilling.

LONGING (Barry Blyth, R. 1994). Sdlg. A55-1. IB, 25" (63 cm), VE-EML. S. smoky apricot salmon with faint violet flush, slight veining on F. hafts; beards burnt tangerine, lavender on outer 1/2". Impish X Electrique. Tempo Two 1994/95.

LONG'S PEAK (John Durrance, R. 1994). Sdlg. D90-124V. TB, 42" (107 cm), ML. Grape purple, F. with white haft markings; beards yellow. Parentage unknown. Long 1994.

LONGUE VUE (Dorman Haymon, R. 1999). Sdlg. 31-92-1. LA, 38" (97 cm), M. S. white, overlaid pale silver to lavender, some olive veining; F. same, aging white, yellow gold signals going into olive veins; style arms cream white; heavily ruffled, laced; slight sweet fragrance. Easter Tide X Dural White Butterfly.

LOOK AGAIN (B. Charles Jenkins, R. 1990). Sdlg. B5-D. SPU, 31-43" (79-109 cm), EM. Purple, unique star-pointed signal. Equality X Ada Perry. Shepard Iris 1991.

#LOOK AT ME (Hooker Nichols, SDB, R. 1974). Not introduced; name released.

LOOK AT ME (Ladislav Muska, R. 1999). Sdlg. 99-WMSC-05. TB, 35" (89 cm), M. S. white, flushed lavender; style arms lavender; F. light lavender; beards yellow, lavender horn; ruffled, laced; slight fragrance. ((White Crow x Mys Horn) x "Snorri") X Conjuration.

LOOKING FOR LOVE (Richard Ernst, R. 1999). Sdlg. N105-J. TB, 37" (94 cm), ML. Ruffled deep pink, pale pink S. highlights and F. edge; beards pink to orange. Magharee X HD175-D: (D175: ((Cheesecake x (Sumptuous x Sandberry)) x Piping Hot) x self). Cooley 1999.

LOOKIN' UP (Polly Black, R. 1993). Sdlg. GR15-27. TB, 40" (102 cm), M. S. pure white; F. white, lightly brushed yellow on haft; beards orange; slight fragrance. White Stallion X White Lightning. Polly Black 1993.

LOOKOUT POINT (Paul Black, R. 1996). Sdlg. 88134A. TB, 35" (89 cm), M. S. buff pink, slight violet midrib infusion; style arms buff pink; F. violet, hafts darker, whitish area around beard; beards coral, with 1" fuzzy violet horn; slight spicy fragrance. Dream a Little X 8636C: (Frances Gaulter x Sky Hooks). Mid-America 1996.

LORD FAIRFAX (Donald Spoon, R. 1999). Sdlg. 92-142A. TB, 36" (91 cm), ML. S. near-white, light violet blue basal and midrib toning; style arms same; F. violet blue (RHS 94A), paling (94D) at edges; beards light violet blue, hairs tipped yellow; ruffled, flared. Son of Dreams X Sheer Bliss.

LORD OLIVIER (Graeme Grosvenor, R. 1990). Sdlg. O12-3. TB, 37" (94 cm), ML. Heavily ruffled blue purple; beards white tipped blue violet. Bubbly Mood X Titan's Glory. Rainbow Ridge 1993/94.

LORE (Barry Blyth, R. 1998). Sdlg. E37-1. SDB, 10" (25 cm), VE-EM. S. pink, midrib and base flushed light violet; F. lighter pink, whitish area around tangerine beard; slight fragrance. Cuddle Me X B25-1: (Z7-2, Toy Kingdom sib, x Z24-1, Volts sib). Tempo Two 1998/99.

LORENA CRONIN (Art Cronin, R. 1991). Sdlg. M-1. SIB, 27" (69 cm), VE. S. and style arms purple; F. white, bright blue lines around edge, darker blue centerline, blue haze at end of F., inconspicuous yellow signal. Parentage unknown. Ensata Gardens 1996.

LORI SUZANNE (Ed Matheny III, R. 1992). Sdlg. 01-03-88. TB, 36" (91 cm), M. Champagne pink (RHS 65D); beards red, purple horn; slight fragrance. Sky Hooks X Varga Girl. Ed's Iris 1993.

LOS COYOTES Tom Burseen, R. 1992). Sdlg. 7-275A. TB, 35" (89 cm), EM. S. brilliant pure golden yellow (brighter than RHS 21A); F. golden yellow ground with bright red (near 46B) streaks and veining, fine yellow edge; beards gold; ruffled; spicy fragrance. 4-103: (Theatre x Dazzling Gold) X 4-74: (Prosperity x Sun Toasted). T.B.'s Place 1993.

LOST FOR WORDS (Heather Pryor, R. 1997). Sdlg. 27/92-A. LA, 35" (89 cm), EM. S. and F. soft mars orange (RHS 31D), edges blushed rosy pink, reverse pale, maroon line signal and veining; style arms lemon, blushed pink; lightly ruffled. 31/90-1: (Myra Arny x Lucy Payens) X Volcanic Wildfire. Lone Star 1998.

LOTTA PLICATA (Tom Burseen, R. 1995). Sdlg. 0-75A. TB, 37" (94 cm), EM. S. golden maize; style arms golden tan; F. creamy yellow, broad burgundy rim; beards golden orange, prominent; ruffled; slight musky fragrance. 7-70A: (Foolish Fancy x (Wild Berry x Medieval)) X Make Mine Misty. T.B.'s Place 1996.

LOTUS LAND (Keith Keppel, R. 1998). Sdlg. 92-97B. TB, 36" (91 cm), M. S. miniature pink (M&P 2-AB-8); style arms buff pink (9-B-3); F. creamier buff pink (9-AB-4); beards soft melon (2-F-10), paler (2/3-A-9) at end; ruffled; pronounced musky fragrance. 89-29A: (Social Event x Femme Fatale) X 90-113A: (Social Event x Bubble Up). Keppel 1999.

LOU ANNE (Ruth Wilder, R. 1995). Sdlg. WW2. SIB, 36-38" (91-97 cm), M. Pale pink edged white, edging on F. 1/4" wide. Pink Haze X Pink Haze sdlg. Quail Hill 1996.

LOU BEET (Lou Ehrcke, R. 1997). Sdlg. 102935. TB, 36" (91 cm), M. S. near mallow purple (RHS 72C); F. beetroot purple (71A), faintly edged S. color, hafts conspicuously marked; beards greyed orange (169A); ruffled, lightly laced; slight musky fragrance. Parentage unknown. Ehrcke 1998.

LOU BEN (Jack Worel, R. 1993). Sdlg. 19-20-4. TB, 34" (86 cm), M. Ruffled dark blue violet, white blaze below dark blue violet beards; slight sweet fragrance. St. Louis Blues X Cosmic Dance. Holly Lane 1993.

LOUD WHISPER (Chet Tompkins, R. 1995). Sdlg. 90-73. TB, 39" (99 cm), ML. Vivid lilac cerise; style arms lilac cerise to pale lilac, tinged yellow; beards lilac, touched yellow. ((Emissary x Untamed) x (Night Lightning x Enchanted Land)) X (Air Bubbles x Dark Twilight). Fleur de Lis 1995.

LOUISA'S SONG (Barry Blyth, R. 1999). Sdlg. E148-1. TB, 42" (107 cm), EM. S. lilac orchid; F. red lavender to orchid lavender, 1/4" blended lilac orchid edge; beards bright tangerine; ruffled, laced; slight sweet fragrance. Cloud Berry X About Town. Tempo Two 1999/2000.

LOUIS D'OR (Richard Cayeux, R. 1995). Sdlg. 8920 A. TB, 32" (80 cm), M. Bright golden yellow to cadmium yellow, F. with light brown lines around yellow beard. Dazzling Gold X Broadway. Cayeux 1996.

LOUISE CLAY SMITH (Louise Smith, R. 1992). Sdlg. 84-178. TB, 34" (86 cm), M. Ruffled peach self; beards pink; pronounced sweet fragrance. Spirit of Memphis X Mt. Cook a'Dawning.

LOUISE TODD (James McWhirter, R. 1994). Sdlg. J89-104. TB, 38" (97 cm), ML. S. orchid blue; style arms lavender blue; F. white; beards orchid lavender; heavily ruffled; slight fragrance. Winterscape X Honky Tonk Blues. Stockton 1995.

LOUISE WHITE (Joy White, R. 1999). SPEC-X (cal-sib), 24" (60 cm), M. S. amethyst violet (RHS 84B aging 84C); style arms buff yellow (161C) overlaid and aging amethyst violet (84B); F. magenta rose (186D), edges paling to background of buff yellow (161C) at edge, hafts deeper buff yellow (161B), plum (79B) patch in center below gold haft signal. Parentage unknown; seed from Tomas Tamberg. Otepopo 1999/2000.

LOUISE WITH LACE (Lois O'Brien, R. 1995). TB, 38" (96 cm), ML. Frosty white self; beards white, pale cream midsection, pale gold in throat; ruffled, laced; slight sweet fragrance. Snow Jade X Wedding Vow. O'Brien Iris 1995.

LOUISON (Calvin Helsley, R. 1998). Sdlg. 92-1. SIB, 28" (71 cm), M. Lightly ruffled rosy wine red, F. with large white signal. Mabel Coday X War March. Helsley 1998.

LOU PEACH (Lou Ehrcke, R. 1997). Sdlg. 102936. TB, 33" (84 cm), M. Peach (RHS 29C), F. washed light magenta rose (186A); beards greyed orange (169A); lightly laced; slight musky fragrance. Parentage unknown. Ehrcke 1998.

LOUQSOR (Pierre Anfosso, R. 1990). Sdlg. P 82 S 10A. SPU, 39" (100 cm), M. S. white; F. bright yellow, edged white. Equality X (Marilyn Holloway x Fort Ridge). Iris en Provence 1990.

LOVE AGAIN (George Sutton, R. 1996). Sdlg. G-39RE. TB, 38" (97 cm), EM & RE. Ruffled violet blue (RHS 90C), F. with lighter area around beard; beards orange, tipped violet at end. Recurring Ruffles X Best Bet.

LOVE BLUSH (Howard Shockey, R. 1990). Sdlg. 86-252-A. TB, 36" (91 cm), M. S. peach, strong central pink flush; F. milk white, lacy peach rim; beards cerise; sweet spicy fragrance. Parfait Delight X 82-212-4A: (80-213-E: (Money x Gold Trimmings) x ((Carved Cameo x Summer Love) x (Pink Angel x Valentina)). Arilian Acres 1991.

LOVE BY CANDLELIGHT (Perry Dyer, R. 1999). TB, 28" (71 cm), ML. S. and style arms cream white, flushed butter yellow; F. medium apricot flushed butter yellow, white spray pattern radiating from deep apricot orange beard. Sport of Lighted Within.

LOVE COMES (Barry Blyth, R. 1994). Sdlg. Z82-1. TB, 36" (91 cm), EML. Mulberry magenta, slightly lighter area around burnt tangerine beards, tannish hafts; slight fragrance. U82-B: (Edna's Wish x Orangerie) X P115-A: ((Love Chant x Festive Skirt) x (Caramba x Pink Ember)). Tempo Two 1994/95.

LOVE DART (Ben Johnson, R. 1997). Sdlg. A49-B. TB, 41" (104 cm), ML. S. white, edges flushed pale blue violet; style arms pale blue violet; F. medium blue violet; beards pale blue violet, yellow orange in throat, ending with medium blue violet horn; ruffled; slight sweet fragrance. Rapture in Blue X Conjuration.

LOVEDAY (R. E. Nichol, R. 1992). Sdlg. K82-1. TB, 37" (94 cm), M. S. white; F. white, inconspicuous gold hafts; beards white shading to gold in throat; ruffled. Gatty K52: (((Princess x Grand Waltz) x Bonbon sib) x Paradise sib) X Demelza. V. H. Humphrey 1993.

LOVE DIVINE (Ed Matheny III, R. 1995). Sdlg. 11-04-91. TB, 37" (94 cm), EM. S. and style arms white, tinted blue (RHS 92D); F. purple (79B) with silver edge; beards white, orange in throat. Sweet Reflection X Victoria Falls. Ed's Iris 1996.

LOVE JOY (Donovan Albers, R. 1990). Sdlg. 8365. SDB, 9½" (24 cm), M. Cream, veined uranium green (HCC 63/2) around beard; beards yellow, tipped lavender; slight fragrance. Joyful X unknown. Adamgrove 1991.

LOVE KRISTIN (Donovan Albers, R. 1990). Sdlg. 8219. SDB, 9" (23 cm), M. Royal purple (HCC 834); beards gold; slight fragrance. Mrs. Nate Rudolph X Wee Bee. Redbud Lane 1991.

LOVE LINES (Betty Wilkerson, R. 1996). Sdlg. D34-1. TB, 38" (97 cm), EM. Pale blue (RHS 100C), F. with darker blue (98A) stripes; beards white. Latest Style X Glistening Icicle.

LOVELORN (Ben Hager, TB, R. 1989). Melrose 1990.

LOVELY DAWN (Keith Keppel, R. 1997). Sdlg. 91-86A. TB, 34" (86 cm), EM. S. light pink (M&P 1-CD-7); style arms light pink, lavender midrib flush; F. pinkish cream (9-A-2), solid 3/4" cattleya (42-H-6) border; beards pale pinkish coral (9-B-6) to pinkish orange (9-G-11) in throat; ruffled; sweet fragrance. Dawn Sky X Screen Play. Keppel 1998.

LOVELY FRAN (John Weiler by Joan Roberts, R. 1999). Sdlg. 88-135A-RE. TB, 36" (91 cm), EML & RE. S. light blue violet; F. white, edges stitched and stippled dark blue violet; beards yellow, blue violet at end; ruffled; slight sweet fragrance. Double Up X 85-292-2: (Avalon Bay x Earl of Essex). Friendship 1999.

LOVELY JENNIFER (Darlene Pinegar, R. 1992). Sdlg. MF-1-2. TB, 33" (84 cm), M. Medium plum, F. with lighter bluish area around and below beard; beards yellow orange, tipped lavender; ruffled. Mary Frances X Warm Laughter. Spanish Fork 1993.

LOVELY LOOKOUT (Albert Faggard, LA, R. 1986). Faggard 1992.

LOVELY LOYCE (D. Steve Varner, R. 1993). Sdlg. V2096. TB, 32" (81 cm), EM. S. light violet blue; F. white; beards white, tipped red; lightly ruffled. Pearl Chiffon X Battle Fury. Illini Iris 1994.

LOVELY NIGHT (Cloyd McCord, R. 1996). Sdlg. 33-93. TB, 38" (97 cm), M. Very dark purple self; beards purple; musky sweet fragrance. Raven's Roost X Midnight Hour. McCord 1996.

LOVELY PEGGY (George Slade, R. 1990). Sdlg. 85-28-PK. TB, 36" (91 cm), ML. Hot pink; beards shrimp red. Frosty Jewels X Helen's Pick. Wyle Wynde 1990.

LOVELY SPRING (Cloyd McCord, R. 1991). Sdlg. 85-6. TB, 36" (91 cm), M. S. light yellow; F. light lavender, light yellow signal; beards yellow; sweet fragrance. 82-1: (Chorus Girl x Custom Made) X 84-1: (Last Call x American Sweetheart). McCord 1991.

LOVE ME DO (Bernard Pryor, R. 1996). Sdlg. 35/92-E. LA, 32" (81 cm), ML. S. and F. cerise red, pronounced white rim and reverse, bright yellow green steeple signal surrounded by yellow and white spray; heavily ruffled. Volcanic Wildfire X Spanish Ballet. Lone Star 1998.

LOVE MELODY (A. & D. Willott, R. 1993). Sdlg. 91-136. SDB, 10" (25 cm), M. S. light red violet; F. pale red violet, deeper flush around beard, amber flush on hafts; beards light yellow, tipped pale violet; ruffled. Raspberry Whip X 84-35: ((Mister Roberts x Fresh Face) x Coral Wings). Willott 1993.

LOVE ME TENDER (Akihiko Terada, R. 1995). Sdlg. 241-89-6. TB, 36" (91 cm), M. Ruffled light pink self; beards orange, tipped white. Anna Belle Babson X Pink Jade. Roris 1996.

LOVE MOTIF (Franklin Carr, TB, R. 1986). Carr 1990.

LOVE OF PINK (Cloyd McCord, R. 1996). Sdlg. 06-93. TB, 35" (89 cm), M & RE. Ruffled and laced pale pink; beards light orange; sweet fragrance. Pink Swan X Quadros' Pride.

LOVE OF TERESA (Akihiko Terada, R. 1998). Sdlg. 180-2. TB, 38" (97 cm), M. S. light orchid; F. darker orchid; beards bright orange; pronounced musky fragrance. Condottiere X Exotic Melody. Roris 1998.

LOVER'S CHARM (Richard Ernst, R. 1994). Sdlg. JF169-11-6. TB, 34" (86 cm), M. S. light apricot peach (RHS 19C/20C) blended pink; style arms slightly darker apricot peach; F. white, blended apricot peach shoulders and rim; beards orange red; heavily ruffled; slight sweet fragrance. Different World X F123-2: (Afternoon Delight x Edna's Wish). Cooley 1995.

LOVER'S CONCERTO (A. & D. Willott, R. 1999). Sdlg. W 92-229. TB, 36" (91 cm), ML. Shell pink (RHS 37C), F. with white area around beard; beards nasturtium red (32B); ruffled. Beverly Sills X Master Gardener.

LOVER'S LANE (Barry Blyth, R. 1991). Sdlg. Y4-5. TB, 38" (97 cm), VE-E. S. pure white; F. heavily ruffled champagne to pastel apricot; beards apricot tangerine. Sib to Breezes. Tempo Two 1992/93.

LOVER'S REUNION (Chun Fan, R. 1996). Sdlg. F91 616 BB. TB, 31" (79 cm), EML. S. silvered velvety red purple (RHS 59A); style arms amber; F. cream ground streaked yellow, greyed purple (187B) edge; hafts stippled golden yellow and purple; beards orange yellow; ruffled, lightly laced; slight sweet fragrance. Oh Babe X Mel's Honor. Fan's Iris 1998.

LOVE SPRING (Jim & Vicki Craig, R. 1990). Sdlg. 34T30. TB, 38" (96 cm), ML. Heavily ruffled white ground plicata, 1 cm pale lavender blue stitched band; style arms lavender; beards yellow, tipped pale lavender. Gentle Rain X (Odyssey x (Stepping Out x Deborah Suzanne)). J. & V. Craig 1990.

LOVE TOKEN (Ben Hager, R. 1997). Sdlg. SD6004PkFlrSh. SDB, 10" (25 cm), EML. Clear pink; beards white, tipped tangerine. SD5203YBrt: (((Ceremony x Today's Fashion) x My Sheba) x (My Sheba x ((3393: (2885Y: (Blonde Doll x (Pink Amber x Pink Cushion)) x ((Pink Amber x Pink Cushion) x Buttercup Charm)) x Pet sib) x ((((Pink Cushion x Roberts 65-R-28) x (Pink Amber x Pink Cushion)) x 2885) x 3393)))) X Opal Wings. Adamgrove 1997.

LOVE VENDOR (William Simon, TB, R. 1986). Stahly 1993.

LOVE YA (Oren Campbell, R. 1991). LA, 34" (86 cm), M. S. red purple (RHS 73); F. darker (72A/B), gold signal. (Myra Arny x This I Love) X Colorific.

LOVING (Joyce Meek, R. 1993). Sdlg. 270-2-6. TB, 30" (76 cm), M. S. peach pink; F. peach, large ivory area around tangerine beard; heavily ruffled. Tamara Anne X Paradise. D & J Gardens 1993.

LOVIN' SPOONFUL (Lynn Bausch, SDB, R. 1989). Garden of the East Wind 1992.

LOW COUNTRY (Nora Scopes, R. 1994). Sdlg. 8/30. IB, 22" (56 cm), M. S. medium blue; F. deep violet blue; beards blue. Tan Tingo X Zeeland.

LOWELL STORM (Chet Tompkins, R. 1992). Sdlg. 86-28. TB, 40" (102 cm), ML-VL. S. aniline blue; F. dark midnight violet; beards blue bronze. (((Cool River x Cimbay) x (Cimbay x River Hawk)) x (Patent Leather x (Cool River x Cimbay))) X River Hawk. Fleur de Lis 1991.

LOW LIFE (J. T. Aitken, R. 1995). Sdlg. 90M13. SDB, 14" (36 cm), EM. Cream ground heavily suffused burgundy; style arms violet; beards russet. Chubby Cheeks X Tricks. Aitken's Salmon Creek 1995.

LOW PROFILE (Joseph Ghio, R. 1997). Sdlg. 93-74Q4. BB, 20" (51 cm), ML. Dark orange self; beards red. Gartman G90-1-bright: ((Natural Beauty x Ice Ballet) x Forbidden Fruit) X 90-110A: ((Bogota x Guadalajara) x Quito). Bay View 1998.

LOW SPIRITS (Keith Keppel, R. 1993). Sdlg. 87-60A. BB, 26" (66 cm), EM. S. reddish violet (M&P 43-F-6) with salmon buff (10-B-3) edge; F. velvety prunella purple (44-K-11), paler veining, narrow white jade (10-A-2) side border, golden orange (9-J-7) hafts, warm white area around beard; beards capucine buff (9-E-5) merging to reddish orange (1-A-2) in throat. 84-22C: ((((68-39F: (66-35C: ((Irma Melrose x Tea Apron) x ((Full Circle x Rococo) x Tea Apron)) x April Melody) x 68-39D) x 74-52A: ((Joy Ride x Roundup) x (April Melody x (66-35B x April Melody)))) x (Mistress x 75-98B, Peccadillo sib)) x (Goddess x (74-35C, Mistress sib, x 74-52A))) X 82-45A: (77-111Q, Gigolo sib, x 78-70A, Rosy Cloud sib). Keppel 1994.

LUC DE GRAS (Ladislav Muska, R. 1999). Sdlg. ZCQR-09. TB, 37" (94 cm), M. S. light cream veined light creamy brown; style arms cream; F. cream ground, 1" cinnamon dotted border; beards mustard; sweet fragrance. Zuzana X ((Calicoball x Queen in Calico) x Rei Momo). Muska 1998.

LUCIE ANDRY (Donald Spoon, R. 1992). BB, 22" (56 cm), M & RE (Sept./VA). Lightly ruffled white self; beards lemon yellow; slight sweet fragrance. Winter Olympics X Spinning Wheel. Winterberry 1997.

LUCILLE (Robert Reed, R. 1998). Sdlg. EWS 1-92. TB, 40" (102 cm), ML. S. soft yellow; F. lavender, shoulders yellow, subtle yellow edging; beards gold. Edith Wolford X Starcrest. Anderson Iris 1999.

LUCILLE RICHARDSON (Gerald Richardson, R. 1991). Sdlg. 86-26-1. TB, 33" (84 cm), EM. S. pale greyed lavender (RHS 85C); style arms lavender, flushed orchid; F. rich orchid lavender (81A), paler halo pattern around beard; beards orchid lavender, tipped pale lavender; slight fragrance. Mary Frances X 84-38-1: ((Mystique x Rainbow's End) x Mystique). Fort Iris 1992.

LUCINDA BOYD (George Slade, R. 1995). Sdlg. 90-W-A. TB, 38" (97 cm), M. Pale orchid pink, F. fading to cream pink at center; beards bright orange; sweet fragrance. Beverly Sills X Helen's Pick.

LUCIOLE (Laure Anfosso, R. 1990). Sdlg. L 83 10B. TB, 33½" (85 cm), M. Ruffled bluish white aging pure white; beards light orange, blue horn. Beverly Sills X Sky Hooks. Iris en Provence 1990.

LUCKY DOLL (Bernard Hamner, R. 1991). Sdlg. 87-17. TB, 32" (81 cm), M. S. pink; F. white, edged yellow; beards tangerine; heavily ruffled. Arctic Blond X Blushing Diana. Shepard Iris 1991.

LUCKY DRAW (Richard Ernst, R. 1994). Sdlg. JF169-7. TB, 35" (89 cm), M. S. clear medium golden yellow; style arms golden yellow; F. brassy mustard yellow, shoulders and rim blended caramel; beards medium yellow; ruffled; slight spicy sweet fragrance. Sdlgs. inv. Afternoon Delight, Ringo. Cooley 1995.

LUCKY GUY (Frederick Kerr, R. 1998). Sdlg. 9072A. TB, 36" (91 cm), M. S. and style arms dark reddish brown; F. golden yellow, wide diffuse reddish brown edge; beards gold. Moon's Delight X Gold Country. Rainbow Acres 1998.

LUCKY LEMON (William Maryott, R. 1990). Sdlg. L180A. TB, 37" (89 cm), M. S. nearly pure white; style arms white, crests yellow; F. medium yellow, white wire rim, slightly paler near beard; beards yellow orange in throat, white tip; ruffled, flared. H115B, Frosted Buttercup sib, X Frosted Buttercup. Maryott 1990.

LUCKY STRIPES (Francis Rogers, R. 1994). Sdlg. F638-P. TB, 36" (91 cm), M. S. greyed orange (RHS 174B), lighter (174D) at base; F. yellow ground, greyed purple (183B) plicata streaking and striping; beards yellow orange; sweet fragrance. Rancho Rose X unknown. Meadowbrook 1995.

LUCRETIA (Louise Smith, R. 1992). BB, 25" (64 cm), EM. S. light blue; F. dark blue; beards dark blue; pronounced sweet fragrance. Parentage unknown.

LUCY ANNE (Graeme Grosvenor, R. 1999). Sdlg. V91-B. TB, 36" (91 cm), M. Apricot, F. slightly darker; beards tangerine. Move On sib X Bogota. Rainbow Ridge 1999/2000.

LUCY PAYENS (John C. Taylor, R. 1990). Sdlg. OL 113-1. LA, 59" (150 cm), E. S. light greyed red (RHS 179D) marbled darker (179A); F. dark greyed red (179A), lighter edge and reverse. Koorawatha X Dazzling Star. Rainbow Ridge 1992/93.

LUCY'S CHARM (J. Griffin Crump, R. 1997). Sdlg. 952U1. TB, 45" (114 cm) EM. S. and style arms honey mocha; F. bright lavender center blending to honey mocha edge, shoulders gold; beards yellow; ruffled, laced; slight sweet fragrance. Yvonne Burt X Opportunity.

LUCY'S LEGACY (Heather Pryor, R. 1997). Sdlg. 16/93-P. LA, 32" (81 cm), ML. S. soft pink blushed rose, cream rim, pale reverse; style arms bright butter yellow; F. deep cherry red, cream rim, pale reverse, raised lime green steeple signal surrounded yellow; ruffled. Ginger Fudge X Never Say.

LUELLA DEE (G. F. Wilson, R. 1996). Sdlg. 19-90TSOL-A. AB (OGB) 32" (81 cm), E. S. pale violet, lightly veined violet, midrib gold; F. cream, lightly veined and dotted violet, large soft brown signal; beards wide, grey, hairs tipped orange. (Tuesday Song X Holden Ho5) X Onlooker. Aril Society, Pleasure Iris 1997.

LUKENVIZ (Lothar Denkewitz, R. 1990). Sdlg. N-80-hbl-1. SDB, 10½" (26 cm), M. S. pale lavender; F. whitish lavender; beards bluish white to deep yellow; pronounced sweet fragrance. Sky and Snow X unknown. Von Zeppelin 1992.

LUKE'S EMBER (T. J. Betts, R. 1996). Sdlg. 822C. LA, 36" (91 cm), E. S. dark red purple (RHS 183A), veined; style arms dark red; F. dark red purple (187B), veined, gold spear signal. Carioca Carnival X 938B: (Deneb x Shrimp Creole).

LULI-ANN (Cy Bartlett, R. 1998). Sdlg. C93/6. SDB, 11" (27 cm), M. White ground, hyacinth blue plicata marking; beards white, yellow in throat; lightly waved, ruffled; slight fragrance. (Menton x Dunlin) X Concord Touch.

LUMALITE (J. T. Aitken, R. 1995). Sdlg. 88M3A. SDB, 14½" (36 cm), EM. S. white; style arms yellow; F. yellow, flushed green, rim white; beards red. (Pumpkin Center x B. Jones 334-2: ((Solar Flight x 255: (Melon Honey x M229)) x (Wright L20 x 255))) X (Greenwood yellow sdlg. x Princess of Love). Aitken's Salmon Creek 1995.

LUMINA (Allan Ensminger, R. 1990). Sdlg. 85-43. BB, 26" (66 cm), ML. Wistaria blue (HCC 640/1) at edge, lightening to near-white at center; beards white. Edge of Winter X 81-22: (79-74: (Firewater x 75-55: ((Faydy Girl x sib) x sib)) x sib). Varigay 1991.

LUMINIST (Elyse Hill, R. 1998). Sdlg. EJ 10-13. CA, 6" (15 cm), M. Heavily ruffled intense yellow, veined gold. Wild Time X unknown.

LUMINOSITY (Monty Byers, R. 1990). Sdlg. D73-103. TB, 36" (91 cm), M & RE. Opening medium canary yellow and immediately lightening to luminous yellow cream with brighter yellow heart; beards bright yellow; ruffled; slight musky fragrance. Grace Thomas X Vanity. Moonshine 1991.

LUNA NUOVA (Augusto Bianco, R. 1999). Sdlg. 212-95. TB, 35" (88 cm), M. Lemon yellow, F. slightly pearled in center; style arms lemon; beards golden yellow; slight musky fragrance. 643: (424: (Classico x Gold Trimmings) x 420: (Candlegleam x Jolt)) X 651: (411: (Lovely Glow x Planned Treasure) x Honky Tonk Blues).

LUNAR ECLIPSE (J. T. Aitken, R. 1993). Sdlg. 86PC9A. CA, 12" (30 cm), M. S. light violet with dark center, white rim; F. dark violet, ruffled white rim, near-black signal. Parentage unknown. Aitken's Salmon Creek 1993.

LUNAR EXCURSION (Colin Hill, R. 1999). Sdlg. CH4-94-A. TB, 38" (97 cm), ML. Bright lemon, F. with white blaze; style arms lemon, crests laced; beards saturn red, 1/2" upright white to light yellow horn; slight sweet fragrance. Lemon Custard X Horned Tantalizer. I.poppin' Irises 1999.

LUNAR FLAME (Howard Shockey, R. 1991). Sdlg. 87-207-A. TB, 36" (91 cm), M. Yellow (RHS 13B), F. with lighter center area; beards orange red (33A); pronounced sweet fragrance. Flaming Victory X 80-221-3C: ((Carved Cameo x Summer Love) x Beige Melody). Arilian Acres 1992

LUNAR FROST (Keith Keppel, R. 1995). Sdlg. 91-50A. IB, 23" (58 cm), M. S. and style arms white; F. white, 1/2" spot of cadmium lemon (M&P 9-L-1) to aureolin (10-L-2); beards white, yellow in throat; ruffled; pronounced sweet fragrance. Over Easy X Overjoyed. Keppel 1996.

LUNE BLEUE (Michèle Bersillon, R. 1999). Sdlg. 9713F. TB, 31" (78 cm), M & RE. S. and style arms lavender blue; F. white, lightly tinted lavender blue; beards white and pale blue; heavily waved, F. horizontal; slight fragrance. Edge of Winter X Pledge Allegiance.

LUNETTE (Nora Scopes, R. 1997). Sdlg. 00/171. TB, 36" (91 cm), ML. S. yellow, lightly sanded copper; F. yellow, white central patch, slight copper haft markings; beards deep yellow; sweet fragrance. Torchlight Tattoo X Aunt Agatha.

LUNNOYE OBLAKO (Nina Miroshnichenko, R. 1996). TB, 35" (90 cm), M. S. white, edged light cream; style arms yellow; F. white, edged yellow; beards yellow; slight sweet fragrance. Parentage unknown. Miroshnichenko 1981.

LUSCIOUS LASS (Jim & Vicki Craig, R. 1990). Sdlg. 8T32. IB, 22" (56 cm), L. S. oxblood red; F. medium oxblood red, hafts marked golden yellow and brown; beards dark yellow. (En Route x Maroon Caper) X (Sacred Mountain X *I. aphylla* "Werckmeister"). J. & V. Craig 1990.

LUSTIGE HANNOVERANER (Harald Moos, R. 1996). Sdlg. 86/603A. TB, 34" (86 cm), M. Waved medium pink self; beards orange. Vanity X Mulled Wine. Moos 1997.

LUXOR GOLD (Schreiner, R. 1998). Sdlg. DD 722-1. TB, 38" (97 cm), M. Lightly ruffled canary yellow (RHS 9A) self; beards orange yellow. Cote d'Or X Bold Gold. Schreiner 1998.

LUXURY LOVER (Chet Tompkins, R. 1992). Sdlg. 87-4. TB, 34" (86 cm), ML. S. amber; F. claret purple with heavy brown undertone; beards bronze. ((Cimbay x Tanya) x (Camelot Rose x Cimarron Strip)) X ((Cimbay x Cosmopolitan) x (Wayward Angel x Camelot Rose)). Fleur de Lis 1991.

LYDIA SAFAN-SWIASTYN (Mitch Jameson, R. 1999). Sdlg. L-2-90. TB, 36" (91 cm), ML. S. and style arms yellow; F. bluish purple; beards golden yellow. Doo Dah X 22-87: (Edith Wolford x 1-84: (Cabaret Royale x Son of Star)).

LYDIA'S LOVE (John C. Taylor, LA, R. 1989). Rainbow Ridge 1990/91.

LYME TYME (Virginia Messick, R. 1995). Sdlg. M88-99. TB, 36" (91 cm), ML. S. rosy yellow; F. lime, hafts bronze; beards bronze; ruffled. Fortunata X Copper Lace. Messick 1997.

LYNDA DIANNE CARR (Bob Thomason, R. 1992). Sdlg. BT-8807B. TB, 36" (91 cm), M. S. pale lilac; F. rose violet, white upper half heavily veined rose violet and gold; beards tangerine; slight sweet fragrance. Vanity X Mary Frances.

LYNDAL (Hilmary Catton, R. 1991). Sdlg. C849-4. BB, 20" (51 cm), EM. Ruffled pale sky blue, shading to white at hafts; beards white. Open Sky X Mystique. Catton 1991.

LYRIC DANCE (Kevin Nilsen, R. 1995). Sdlg. KJN 000-1. TB, 39" (98 cm), E. S. cream, tinged and veined pink; F. red violet, lighter edge; beards orange. Parentage unknown -- possibly inv. Tomorrow's Child. Iridescence 1995/96.

LYRIQUE (Barry Blyth, R. 1996). Sdlg. B110-2. BB, 20" (51 cm), ML. S. silvery blue lilac; F. silvery blue lilac, strong burgundy plum signal split in center, coming halfway down fall, small white area on either side of bronze beard; standards erect, open. Zing Me X Divine. Tempo Two 1996/97.

MABEL C (George Slade, R. 1991). Sdlg. 85-23-T. TB, 35" (89 cm), M. Ruffled and laced lilac violet (near RHS 87C); beards orange, tipped yellow. Laced Cotton X Flip Side.

MABLE LAURA CLAY (Louise Smith, R. 1992). Sdlg. 84-6. TB, 29" (74 cm), M. Slightly ruffled peach pink self; beards pink red. Unknown X Love With Lace.

MACARENA (Virginia Messick, R. 1996). Sdlg. M89-119. TB, 37" (94 cm), M. Ruffled peach orange self; beards orange bronze; slight fragrance. Voltage X M87-70: (Autumn Blush x Edna's Wish). Messick 1997.

MACHO MUCHACHO (David Miller, R. 1999). Sdlg. 93-20 WYE. BB, 24" (61 cm), M. S. maroon, midrib shaded brown gold; style arms rosy brown, highlighted gold; F. slightly deeper maroon, extensive marking over upper portion; beards bronze gold; musky fragrance. 86-6A: (81-1B: (Dutch Chocolate x Sandberry) x Henna Accent) X Canyon de Chelly.

MAD ABOUT YOU (Heather Pryor, R. 1995). Sdlg. 56/90-1. LA, 30" (76 cm), EM. S. maize yellow (RHS 21D); style arms and F. saffron yellow (21C); raised green steeple signal on F., yellow green veining on all petals; ruffled. Designer's Dream X Gladiator's Gift. Lone Star 1998.

MADAME BOVARY (Larry Lauer, R. 1992). Sdlg. L85-2-2. TB, 38" (97 cm), M. Heavily ruffled pale orchid pink blend; beards yellow, tipped orchid; slight fragrance. Feminine Wiles X Wedding Party. Cottage 1993.

MADAME FROTH (Mitch Jameson, R. 1994). Sdlg. 1-87-A. TB, 34-38" (86-97 cm), M. S. and style arms lavender orchid; F. rose violet; beards coral, rose violet to white at base, hairs tipped coral to white; ruffled; slight sweet fragrance. Laced Wonder X Song of Spring. Knee-Deep in June 1995.

MADAM PRESIDENT (Hugh Thurman, R. 1998). Sdlg. 92-18-1. MTB, 23" (58 cm), L. S. and style arms canary yellow (RHS 9B); F. light amethyst violet (84C) veined imperial purple (78B), yellow rim; beards golden yellow; sweet fragrance. Bumblebee Deelite X unknown.

MAD DASH (Sigrid Asmus, SDB, R. 1988). Aitken's Salmon Creek 1991.

MADEIRA (Schreiner, R. 1993). Sdlg. W 130-1. TB, 38" (97 cm), M. S. wine purple (RHS 79C); F. velvety deeper wine purple (79A); beards purple. Spectacular Bid X Titan's Glory. Schreiner 1993.

MADELEINE SPRING (Cy Bartlett, R. 1998). Sdlg. C95-21. BB, 26" (66 cm), ML. S. white, light blue violet plicata wash; F. white, heavy blue purple rim; beards white, blue white in throat; ruffled; sweet fragrance. Seaport X (Concord Touch x Orinoco Flow).

MADISON AVENUE (Roy Bohrer, R. 1992). Sdlg. 89-RB. TB, 36" (91 cm), M. S. light blue violet; F. dark violet, edged lighter with hash markings, light violet centerline; beards yellow orange; slight spicy fragrance. Love Child X Ruffled Ballet.

MADISON COUNTY (James McWhirter by Abram Feuerstein, R. 1997). Sdlg. 89-83-2. TB, 34" (86 cm), M. S. violet, blending to blue violet at edge; F. deep reddish violet; beards violet; ruffled; slight sweet fragrance. Cranberry Crush X 87-77-2: (Winterscape x Larry Gaulter). Stockton 1997.

MADONNA RIDGE (Joseph Ghio, R. 1999). Sdlg. PB-234L4. CA, 12" (31 cm), ML. Soft shell pink self. PE-202-C2: (PG-185Y: (PI-MIX-Y, unknown, x PI-MIX-A, unknown) x Charter Member sib) X PD-201D2: (Candid x Local Girl). Bay View 1999.

MAGAKI-NO-TOMO (Society for Japanese Irises, R. 1993). JI (3 F.), 29" (75 cm), E. Light blue violet veined darker, signal yellow; style arms deep blue violet with white center; S. about 1/3 size of F. and giving appearance of being little F. Parentage unknown. Introduced in Japan prior to 1939.

MAGELLAN (Roger Nelson, R. 1994). Sdlg. RN 86-73BY. TB, 36" (91 cm), ML. S. icy blue violet (RHS 92D to 93D); F. deep violet blue (93B to 94B), aging lighter, with small spray pattern around gold orange beard; pronounced musky fragrance. Navy Strut X RN 84-40L: (Tumblin' Dice x Social Hour). Iris Country 1994.

MAGENTA MOMENT (Calvin Helsley, R. 1993). Sdlg. 88-1. SIB, 36" (91 cm), M. Lightly ruffled magenta red, very slight white signal. Pink Haze X "Corey's Pink". Helsley 1992.

MAGGIE BARON (Agnes Frech, R. 1997). Sdlg. 1191. TB, 36" (91 cm), EM. S. old rose; style arms gold; F. cranberry red, large triangular white blaze with red lines radiating from yellow beard; ruffled; pronounced sweet fragrance. Crinoline X Heather Blush.

MAGGIE BELFORD (Indra Belford, R. 1997). Sdlg. 89A-1-9124. BB, 26" (66 cm), EM. S. tan yellow, veined orchid, orchid-blushed border at tip, aging pinkish; style arms pale lavender, edges blended yellow; F. burgundy violet edged pale tan, hafts white with yellow edge, overall red brown tracery; beards white base, golden orange hair tips, 3/4" white to amethyst fuzzy horn; lightly ruffled and laced; slight sweet fragrance. Camelot Rose X Horned Tantalizer.

MAGGIE SHARP (Jim Hedgecock, R. 1991). Sdlg. 83-26-1. TB, 34" (86 cm), M. Heavily laced and ruffled pure white; beards white; slight sweet fragrance. Lacy Snowflake X Madeira Belle. Comanche Acres 1992.

MAGICAL ENCOUNTER (Schreiner, R. 1999). Sdlg. FF 944-A. TB, 35" (89 cm), EML. Deep shrimp pink (RHS 73C); beards bright salmon pink. CC 484-A: (S 367-A: (Renaissance Faire x ((((Amethyst Flame x (Halolight x Savage)) x (Amethyst Flame x Silvertone)) x (Rippling Waters x (((((Chantilly x Midwest Gem) x Cherie) x (Lapham sdlg. x (Chantilly x Midwest Gem))) x Pretty

Carol) x Fay 57-73))) x Country Lilac)) x T 1756-A: (Far Corners x Laurel Park)) X Dreamsicle. Schreiner 1999.

MAGIC BUBBLES (A. & D. Willott, R. 1994). Sdlg. 91-351. IB, 24" (61 cm), M. Ruffled and laced coral pink; beards coral. Pink Bubbles X 88-135: (Coral Wings x Magic). Willott 1994.

MAGIC BUS (Larry Lauer, R. 1999). Sdlg. 494-1. TB, 36" (91 cm), ML. S. mimosa yellow (RHS 8B); style arms mimosa yellow, crests with faint wistaria blue; F. ivory rimmed mimosa yellow, shoulders darker; beards wistaria blue at end, lemon yellow center, cadmium orange in throat; pronounced sweet fragrance. Brocaded Gown X Hager T5056: (Terra Bella sib x (Come to Me sib x (Birthstone x Sky Hooks))).

MAGIC CHILD (Barry Blyth, R. 1995). Sdlg. B82-1. IB, 18-20 " (46-51 cm), EM. S. pastel blue white; F. lavender blue, shaded lighter toward edge, deeper blue haft marking; beards white, tipped tangerine; slight sweet fragrance. Melodic X Electrique. Tempo Two 1995/96.

MAGIC DRAGON (Ben Hager, R. 1997). Sdlg. SD5968Br/YPc. SDB, 10" (25 cm), EML. S. yellow; F. intense deep yellow, dark brown plicata edging; beards pale yellow, hairs tipped deep yellow. Input X In Limbo.

MAGIC DREAM (Lin Flanagan, R. 1999). Sdlg. 87045-1. AB (OGB), 26" (66 cm), M. S. light violet; style arms blended violet and tan; F. light violet and tan blend; round black violet signal at end of black beard, ruffled and slightly recurved; slight fragrance. Onlooker X Tornado Warning.

MAGIC FOUNTAIN (George Shoop, R. 1993). Sdlg. 87-18. TB, 36" (91 cm), M. Medium deep pink, lightly ruffled F.; beards pink; slight fragrance. Blushing Duchess X Modern Story. Shoop 1993.

MAGICIAN'S APPRENTICE (William Maryott, TB, R. 1988). Maryott 1989.

MAGICIAN'S MASTERPIECE (LeRoy Meininger, R. 1999). Sdlg. PP-05. TB, 32" (81 cm), M. S. rich gold, brown edge; style arms gold, midrib lavender; F. red brown, bright violet flash below beard; beards white, hairs tipped carrot; slight sweet fragrance. Party Parfait X Gladys Austin. Monument, Woodland Iris 1999.

MAGIC JEWEL (Donovan Albers, SDB, R. 1989). Redbud Lane 1991.

MAGIC PALETTE (Chun Fan, R. 1994). Sdlg. F91-616-B. TB, 33" (84 cm), EM. S. sulphur yellow, faintly dotted and veined pale violet; F. yellow ground, sanded and streaked vivid red violet, sulphur yellow edge, darker red violet center stripe; beards yellow orange; slight sweet fragrance. Oh Babe X Mel's Honor. Fan's Iris 1997.

MAGIC RAIMENT (Frederick Kerr, R. 1993). Sdlg. 87B-29-1. TB, 38" (97 cm), ML. Ruffled and fluted medium yellow, white area around medium yellow beards. Moon's Delight X Speculator. Rainbow Acres 1993.

MAGIC RAY (Hilmary Catton, SDB, R. 1987). Wyuna 1987.

MAGIC SEA (Lois Belardi, R. 1999). Sdlg. BT-97. CA, 14" (36 cm), ML. Ruffled delphinium blue with crystalline edge, F. with 3/4" turquoise signal with darker blue halo. NOR-4: (Sea Gal x (Miramar x Sierra Dell)) X (Age of Chivalry x Marine Magic).

MAGIC SHOW (Keith Keppel, R. 1994). Sdlg. 87-28D. TB, 36" (91 cm), EM. S. maple (M&P 11-E-4) softly and evenly overlaid rose blush (12-A-7 to 5-F-3); F. sulphur yellow (10-J-1), 5/8" light marginal suffusion of rose blush, hafts overlaid garnet red (6-K-6); beards chrome yellow (9-L-7); ruffled. Rosarita X 82-40D: ((Santana x Anon) x Rustic Dance). Keppel 1994.

MAGIC STYLE (John C. Taylor, R. 1994). Sdlg. RL 35-E. LA, 50" (127 cm), M. S. violet suffused on paler pink violet ground; style arms cream; F. violet purple, lighter edge, green line signal edged yellow; ruffled, fluted. Wine and Dine X Margaret Lee. Rainbow Ridge 1996/97.

MAGIC WISH (Ben Hager, TB, R. 1989). Melrose 1990.

MAGNETIC (John C. Taylor, R. 1996). Sdlg. UL 19-5. LA, 47" (120 cm), ML. S. cream, pink edge and central rib; style arms buff, rose pink blush; F. buff, rose pink spray-pattern edge, yellow signal; ruffled; slight fragrance. Desert Jewel X Dural Dreamtime. Rainbow Ridge 1997/98.

MAGNIFICENT OBSESSION (Sharon McAllister, R. 1993). Sdlg. 89-1-30. AB (OGB-), 30" (75 cm), M. S. pearl grey, very fine yellow veining; F. apricot buff lightly washed plum red, signal oxblood red; beards yellow. Sostenique X Tribe of Judah. McAllister 1993.

MAGYAR MEDLEY (Philip Edinger, R. 1998). Sdlg. PEVar. SPEC-X, 10-12" (25-31 cm), L. S. and style arms aureolin yellow (RHS 12A); F. white, veined red brown (173A) overall; beards yellow. *I. variegata*, Welch clone, X Varibo. Adamgrove 1999.

MAHARISHI (Keith Keppel, R. 1990). Sdlg. 82-39B. TB, 35" (89 cm), M. S. buff peach (M&P 10-A-2/3), buff cream (9-C-3) at edge; F. capucine buff (9-E-5) with wide dotted band plus crushed violets (45-G-5) centerline; beards cowslip (10-J-9), white base. 77-112A: (Rancho

Rose x 75-113B: (71-12C, Flamenco sib, x (68-17B, Roundup sib, x April Melody))) X Rustic Dance. Keppel 1990.

MAHOGANY LORD (Barry Blyth, R. 1993). Sdlg. ET-3. SPU, 44" (112 cm), EM. Chocolate brown with purple glow, slight gold radiation on F. Ethic X self. Tempo Two 1993/94.

MAHPIYASKA (L. J. Duffy, R. 1992). Sdlg. WI-30-79. SPEC (*setosa*), 36-40" (91-102 cm), E. White with yellow streaking, lemon yellow at base of F.; style arms white; buds white, sometimes overtoned pale blue. Selection of *I. setosa interior* collected 1979, near Fairbanks, Alaska.

MAID OF LORRAINE (Cherry Harwood by J. J. Melgers, R. 1993). TB, 36" (92 cm), M. S. lightly laced light violet, center white; F. white, wide ruffled light violet edge, violet central stripe, brownish violet reverse; beards white, tipped gold; slight sweet fragrance. Theatre X Bayberry Candle.

MAID OF NORWAY (Nora Scopes, R. 1990). Sdlg. 5/68C. TB, 37" (94 cm), ML. Pale blue, beards deeper; sweet fragrance. Song of Norway X Cobweb Morning.

MAID SO PRETTY (Opal Wulf, R. 1998). Sdlg. 15-92-2. TB, 34" (86 cm), EML. S. white, inner midrib violet; style arms white, midrib violet; F. deep violet (RHS 86A) paling to wide violet blue (90C) rim, white ray halo around upper beard; beards yellow, white at end; ruffled, fluted; slight sweet fragrance. Ellen Mae X In Town. Wulf's Backachers 1999.

MAIKO (Society for Japanese Irises, R. 1992). JI (6 F.), 36" (91 cm), M. White with red purple edging and plicata markings, signal yellow; style arms white, tipped red purple. Parentage unknown. Originated at Shuho-en prior to being imported into U.S. in 1973. Supercedes 1939 Check List entry "Mai-ko", which mis-identifies Mr. Uyeki as originator. Uyeki of Yokohama Nursery obtained many irises from Shuho-en and was the first to export Maiko to the U.S.

MAINE CHARM (Currier McEwen, R. 1994). Sdlg. JT(2)83/110. JI (6 F.) tet., 30" (76 cm), M. Blue white brushed blue (RHS 92C), giving effect of (92C) on outer half; signals green (143B) when fresh, aging to lighter yellow green (154A); style arms blue white with blue (92C/D) tufts, tufted petaloids on anthers; wide, very ruffled. T(1)76/66(1): (Jewelled Sea x Returning Tide) X T(1)72/40(21): (sdlg., F3 from Hirao seed, x Garden Caprice).

MAIN SEQUENCE (G. F. Wilson, R. 1992). Sdlg. 48-90SMO-K. AB (OGB), 28" (70 cm), EM. S. pale oyster white veined light yellow; F. clear yellow gold, heart-shaped maroon brown signal; beards yellow; sweet fragrance. Syrian Moon X Onlooker. Potterton & Martin 1995.

MAINSTAY (James Burch, R. 1990). Sdlg. 41-9. BB, 26½" (67 cm), ML. Light pink (RHS 38D); beards red (41B). 74-14-1: (Winona H. x Kimberlina) X Frosty Jewels. Burch Iris 1991.

MAI OGI (Shuichi Hirao by Society for Japanese Irises, R. 1992). JI (6 F.), 36" (90 cm), M. Red purple ground, white center with radiating bold white veins, greenish yellow signal; style arms white, edged and tipped red purple; ruffled. Parentage unknown. Hirao 1957.

MAIRI (Nora Scopes, SDB, R. 1977). British Iris Society 1987.

MAIRI'S WEDDING (Marty Schafer/Jan Sacks, R. 1999). Sdlg. 92-61-1. SIB, 24" (61 cm), M. Creamy white, style arms with yellow midrib, F. with yellow blending to small yellow signal; small flower; slight fragrance. S89-5-10: (Forrest McCord x Isabelle) X Careless Sally. Joe Pye Weed 1999.

MAISHOJO (Shuichi Hirao by Society for Japanese Irises, R. 1993). JI (6 F.), 32" (81 cm), M. Large dark red violet (darker than RHS 77A), signal yellow; style arms 1½", red violet (76B) edged and tipped darker. Parentage unknown. Hirao 1965.

MAISON (Mary Dunn, R. 1997). Sdlg. L216-1. LA, 34" (86 cm), M. Ruffled mauve pink self, greenish yellow finger signal; style arms tinged pink, light edge and heart. L157-3: (Elusive Butterfly x L95-5: (Ila Nunn x Professor Ike)) X Gladiator's Gift. Bay View 1997.

MAJÁK (Zdeněk Seidl, R. 1998). Sdlg. EFRF19. TB, 33" (85 cm), EM. Rich cerise purple, hafts white; style arms mauve purple; beards purple; slight sweet fragrance. Eagle's Flight X Raspberry Frills.

MAJESTIC SUMMIT (Carl Jorgensen, R. 1998). Sdlg. 92-LP-1H. TB, 32" (81 cm), ML. S. heliotrope (HCC 636/1); style arms poppy red (16) base, heliotrope crest; F. heliotrope, lighter around poppy red beard; ruffled, laced; pronounced sweet fragrance. 90-LP-1: (85-P-6J: (Colorado Winter Morning x (Summit Lady x Flaming Star)) x 85-P-12: (Summit Love x Flaming Pink)) X 85-P-9: ((75-P11-6A, Summit Love sib, x 73-P11-2: (((Court Ballet x Garden Party) x Java Dove) x DeForest 72-9)) x Cozy and Warm).

MAJOR MEET (John C. Taylor, R. 1998). Sdlg. UL 34-4. LA, 47" (120 cm), ML. S. light red purple; style arms red purple; F. red purple, yellow signal; ruffled. Poseidon's Pool X Helen Naish.

MAKE BELIEVE MAGIC (Chet Tompkins, R. 1994). Sdlg. 88-17. TB, 37" (94 cm), ML. S. white, blended wine rose edge; F. white, edged wine, rose and violet; beards red. (Hamblen 71-154D: (Betty Simon plic sib x sib) x (Jet Fire x Tinsel Town)) X (Blushing Butterfly x Capricious). Fleur de Lis 1994.

MAKEBELIEVE WORLD (Mary Dunn, R. 1993). Sdlg. L166-2. LA, 35" (89 cm), M. S. lilac lavender; style arms green and ivory; F. deeper lilac lavender, yellow spear-shaped signal; ruffled. Lavender Ruffles X self. Bay View 1993.

MAKE MINE MISTY (Tom Burseen, R. 1990). Sdlg. 5-374A. TB, 36" (91 cm), M. S. very light salmon pink (RHS 27B); F. ivory, light violet (85C) blended edge; beards tangerine; ruffled; sweet fragrance. Social Butterfly X Capricious. T.B.'s Place 1991.

MAKES SCENTS (John Durrance, R. 1996). Sdlg. D86-131. TB, 36" (91 cm), ML. S. and style arms light silvery lavender (near RHS 92); F. dark lavender (87C), light silvery lavender around yellow beard; lightly ruffled; pronounced sweet fragrance. Song of Spring X "Silver Lady". Long 1996.

MAKING SMALL TALK (Jim Hedgecock, R. 1999). Sdlg. A-29-1. BB, 26" (66 cm), ML. Laced and ruffled medium yellow; F. with subdued white blaze at golden yellow beard; pronounced sweet fragrance. Rose Caress X 83-46: (Temple Gold x Carolina Gold). Comanche Acres 1999.

MAKING WAVES (Ben Hager, R. 1999). Sdlg. T5902FltLtBl. TB, 37" (94 cm), M. Light to medium blue; beards white, hairs tipped yellow except at end. Neptune's Cloak X Busy Being Blue. Cooley 1999.

MALA MAJA (Izidor Golob, R. 1997). Sdlg. 8901-07. SDB, 10" (25 cm), EM. S. light bluish violet, base darker, midrib olive green; style arms light blue; F. pale ochre and yellow on near-white; beards heavenly blue; pronounced sweet fragrance. 8511-03: (First Lilac x Gingerbread Man) X Irish Sea. Peroma 1997.

MALARKY (Barry Blyth, R. 1994). Sdlg. Z29-1. IB, 20" (51 cm), ML. S. tan beige with violet midrib flush; F. white, 3/4" medium to bright violet plicata edge, darker centerline, bright white area around blue lavender beard; slight fragrance. Armada X Moocha. Tempo Two 1994/95.

MALIBU MAGIC (John C. Taylor, R. 1990). Sdlg. OL 133-1. LA, 43" (110 cm), M. S. violet blue (RHS 97D) veined darker (97A); F. violet blue (97B) veined darker (97A), narrow yellow green crest signal. Flight of Fantasy X Helen Naish. Rainbow Ridge 1990/91.

MALIBU WILDFIRE (A. & D. Willott, R. 1994). Sdlg. 92-190. IB, 26" (66 cm), M. S. light apricot orange; F. bright medium orange; beards orange coral; ruffled. Barney's Delight X Coral Beads. Willott 1995.

MALINDA (Austin Morgan, R. 1990). TB, 36" (91 cm), EML. S. light purple; F. dark purple; beards purple. Parentage unknown. Iris Test Garden 1990.

MALINOVKA (Viacheslav Gavrilin, R. 1999). Sdlg. 1-16-3-94. TB, 36" (92 cm), EM. Heavily ruffled red violet tinted raspberry pink, F. with light wine red rays; beards orange, light blue at end; slight fragrance. Superstition X unknown. Gavrilin 1999.

MALINOVY RASSVET (Viktor Sheviakov, R. 1997). Sdlg. 10a7a. TB, 30" (75 cm), M. Red violet self, tinted crimson; beards cream at end, yellow orange midsection, red orange in throat; slight sweet fragrance. Amethyst Flame X Mary Randall. Sheviakov 1997.

MALLORY KAY (Larry Johnson, R. 1998). Sdlg. J089-6-1. TB, 38" (97 cm), M. Dark red self; beards red maroon, base violet. Harlem Hussy X Maroon Velvet. Cooley 1998.

MALLOW DRAMATIC (Joseph Gatty by Keith Keppel, R. 1995). Sdlg. X45-2. TB, 36" (91 cm), M. S. pinkish cattleya orchid (M&P 42-J-6); style arms pinkish orchid (42-G-3); F. pinkish cattleya orchid (42-I-6), bluer and paler (41-D-6 to 41-B-4) in upper center; beards flamingo (2-I-11), pinkish white base; slight sweet fragrance. Coming Up Roses X Designing Woman. Keppel 1996.

MALTBY DREAM (Ralph & Fran Walster, R. 1990). Sdlg. 7-1986D. TB, 32" (81 cm), M. S. lightly ruffled royal purple; F. deep velvety purple, white hafts veined purple; beards light yellow, tipped white. Raziza X Glory Bound. Walsterway 1991.

MALY LORD (Lech Komarnicki, R. 1999). Sdlg. 93/4-27A. SDB, 10" (25 cm), EM. S. and style arms violet blue; F. deeper violet blue, darker center, velvet texture; beards violet blue; lightly ruffled. People Pleaser X unknown.

MALY PIEDESTAL (Ladislav Muska, R. 1996). Sdlg. DFMF-05. TB, 40" (102 cm), ML. S. light lavender; F. white, light cocoa brown band; beards light canary yellow; heavily ruffled; pronounced fragrance. (Don Epifano x "Fialovy Kvet": (Windsor Rose x Laced Cotton)) X (Monte Albano x Fontana di Trevi). Muska 1996.

MAMIE AND IRISH (Louise Smith, R. 1991). Sdlg. 76-133. TB, 38" (97 cm), EM. Ruffled white; beards green, tipped white; slight sweet fragrance. Bosky Dell X unknown.

MAN ABOUT TOWN (Barry Blyth, R. 1998). Sdlg. D64-6. TB, 40" (102 cm), EM. S. buff to biscuit deepening to rose midrib, creamy lemon infusion; F. old rose, blended lighter to tannish edge, small white area around beard, tiny blue blaze; beards white, hairs tipped lemon; spicy fragrance. Plume d'Or X A153-5, Cafe Risque sib. Tempo Two 1998/99.

MANAGUA (Joseph Ghio, R. 1993). Sdlg. 88-113D. TB, 36" (91 cm), EML. Opaque orange self; beards tangerine. 85-189U2: (Esmeralda x Stratagem sib) X Caracas. Bay View 1994.

MANCUNIAN (Anne Blanco White, selector, R. 1996). JI (3 F.), 30" (76 cm), ML. S. white ground, heavy purple veining; F. white ground, dark violet veining. Parentage and origin unknown.

MANDARIN CHOCOLATE (Dorothy Steele, TB, R. 1989). Rancho de la Flor de Lis 1990.

MANDATE (James Burch, R. 1997). Sdlg. 50-17. TB, 36" (91 cm), ML. S. light orient pink (RHS 36A); F. lighter orient pink (36B); beards mandarin red (40B). Frosty Jewels X Symmetry. Comanche Acres 1998.

MANDELA (Joseph Ghio, R. 1998). Sdlg. 93-113H2. TB, 32" (81 cm), ML. S. light lavender pink, midrib flushed deeper lavender; F. deep lavender pink; beards tangerine. 90-12Q3: (Pink Ballerina x (Newlywed x Caption)) X 91-35pk, Boudoir sib. Bay View 1999.

MANDY G (Manfred Beer, R. 1991). Sdlg. MB 16/84. TB, 36" (90 cm), L. Very dark wine red, F. velvety; beards yellow. Swazi Princess X Superstition. Gartencenter Kania, Von Zeppelin 1992.

MANGO ENTREE (Barry Blyth, R. 1996). Sdlg. B222-1. TB, 38" (97 cm), ML. Honey apricot, slight veining near apricot tangerine beards; heavily ruffled. Castaway X Stratagem. Tempo Two 1996/97.

MANGO KISS (Barry Blyth, R. 1993). Sdlg. Z2-1. SDB, 10" (25 cm), ML. Vibrant orange, F. with darker orange overlay; beards orange, outer 1/4" white, tipped yellow. (Fifi x (Peach Eyes x Kandi Moon)) X X25-7, Cupfull sib. Tempo Two 1994/95.

MANGO TANGO (Joseph Ghio by Maryott's Gardens, R. 1995). Sdlg. 85-70-I4. TB, 37-38" (94-97 cm), M. Heavily ruffled soft melon orange (RHS 24B); beards orange. 82-37W, Esmeralda sib, X 83-88-C3, Stratagem sib. Maryott 1996.

MANI PULITE (Augusto Bianco, R. 1998). Sdlg. 486. TB, 36" (91 cm), EM. S. and style arms blended beige bronze, violet suffusion; F. violet, smoky cream edge; beards golden orange based white, lavender at end; purple-based foliage; slight spicy fragrance. Edith Wolford X (Betty Simon x Shenanigan). Iride 1997.

MANISTEE LADY (Ray Lyons, R. 1998). Sdlg. LY-84-32-2. TB, 37-40" (94-102 cm), M. S. violet; F. white ground, 1/2" violet plicata band; beards violet, gold in throat; ruffled. Focus X Petite Queen. Long 1998.

MANIT (Bob Thomason, R. 1991). Sdlg. 8702A. SDB, 11" (28 cm), EM. Off-white, hafts gold; beards orange, tipped white; slight fragrance. Angel Baby X Solar Flare. Okie Iris 1993.

MANITOU MAIDEN (Jim Hedgecock, R. 1999). Sdlg. 84-1-S. TB, 36" (91 cm), M. S. dark blue, shaded purple; F. dark blue, hafts purple; beards burnt gold, long dark blue horn; heavily ruffled. Sky Hooks X Soul Music. Comanche Acres 1999.

MANNEKIN PIS (Ladislav Muska, R. 1999). Sdlg. 98-MCAS-07. TB, 36" (91 cm), L. Medium amethyst; style arms light amethyst tipped cream tan; beards bright orange with long amethyst flounce; slight fragrance. ((Mys Horn x Calicoball) x (Amethyst Smile x Sky Hooks)) X Sentimental Mood. Muska 1999.

MANOR BORN (Virginia Messick, R. 1994). Sdlg. M87-26. TB, 38" (97 cm), M. Ruffled, laced and deeply scalloped bright lavender rose; beards light lavender; slight fragrance. Winterscape X Nordic Prince. Messick 1994.

MANTIYA KARDINALA (Viktor Sheviakov, R. 1996). Sdlg. 10c14. TB, 32" (80 cm), M. Dark red violet self; beards light yellow, cream white at end; ruffled; slight sweet fragrance. Heather Hawk X Pipes of Pan. Sheviakov 1997.

MANTRA (Joseph Ghio, R. 1992). Sdlg. PH-287-S2. CA, 19" (48 cm), ML. S. velvety red purple, light orchid edge; F. velvety red purple, orchid edge on top third, solid black signal. National Anthem X (Rare Reward x Western World). Bay View 1993.

MANUSCRIPT (James Burch, TB, R. 1988). Burch Iris 1990.

MANYCH (Galina Shevchenko, R. 1995). MDB, 6" (16 cm), E. S. rich blue; F. purplish blue; beards orange, light blue at end; lightly ruffled; slight sweet fragrance. From *I. pumila* sdlgs. Shevchenko 1992.

MANY THANKS (Larry Gaulter by Cooley's Gardens, R. 1990). Sdlg. L83-1. TB, 37" (94 cm), ML. Ruffled soft blue, F. paler below blue white beard. Portrait of Larrie X Victoria Falls. Cooley 1989.

MAPLECREST (Myrtle Holden by Glenn Stoneking-Jones, R. 1999). Sdlg. CIR6-5264-09-18-1998). TB, 30" (76 cm), EM. Dark blue, style arms veined bronze; beards orange; slight sweet fragrance. Parentage unknown.

MAPLE FROST (A. & D. Willott, R. 1994). Sdlg. 84-102. SDB, 12" (30 cm), ML. S. light yellow, washed taupe; F. cream, edged light yellow, dotted tan especially on hafts; beards yellow; lightly ruffled. 78-239: (Triple Touch x Gibson TB brown plicata sdlg.) X 79-87: (Ginger Tart x Gunga Din). Willott 1994.

MAPLE TREAT (Opal Brown, R. 1995). Sdlg. 91-8E4. TB, 28" (71 cm), M. S. medium brown (RHS 166A); style arms medium brown; F. lighter brown, paler (166D) below beard; beards deep gold, thick; ruffled. Caliph X Indian Capers. Brown's Sunnyhill 1995.

MARA (Barry Blyth, R. 1993). Sdlg. Z34-1. IB, 24" (61 cm), ML. Pallid pink, white area around soft palest pink beards. Tiffany Time X Chanted. Tempo Two 1993/94.

MARBLE CAKE (John C. Taylor, R. 1993). Sdlg. RL 27-1. LA, 55" (140 cm), EM. S. cream, heavily and irregularly marked pinkish purple; F. purple, yellow signal. Old South X Margaret Lee. Rainbow Ridge 1993/94.

MARBRE BLEU (Jean Cayeux, R. 1993). Sdlg. 84109 F. TB, 35" (89 cm), ML. S. white, waved; F. bright blue, white center veined bright blue; beards tangerine. (Condottiere x Delphi) X (Alizes x (Condottiere x Lunar Rainbow)). Cayeux 1993.

MARCELLA PARKER (George Slade, R. 1991). Sdlg. 87-9-1. TB, 35" (89 cm), ML. S. pale purple violet (near RHS 77D); F. darker (near 77B); beards coral, tipped white; sweet fragrance. Lovely Kay X (Etched Amoena x Pink Sleigh).

MARCELLO (Bob Thomason, R. 1991). Sdlg. 8712A. SDB, 10" (25 cm), E. S. yellow gold; F. darker yellow gold with hint of brown, lighter toward dark gold rim; beards orange, tipped white; slight fragrance. Cosmos X Bugler Boy. Okie Iris 1993.

MARCEL TURBAT (Jean Cayeux, R. 1993). Sdlg. 7813 A. TB, 35" (89 cm), EM. Ruffled bright orange apricot self; beards tangerine. Piroska X (6583 A x Flaming Star). Cayeux 1990.

MARCHE TURQUE (Pierre-Christian Anfosso, R. 1991). Sdlg. PC 86 2B. TB, 35½" (90 cm), EM. S. gold; F. velvety deep garnet red; beards antique gold. Piper's Flute X (Shaman x Sostenique). Iris en Provence 1991.

MARCUS PERRY (Amos Perry by Jennifer Hewitt, R. 1997). SIB, 30" (76 cm), EM. S. blue violet (RHS 94A), short, upright; style arms blue violet; F. slightly deeper blue violet, darker veins, signal white veined blue violet. Parentage unknown. Perry's Hardy Plant Farm, ca. 1930.

MARCY MICHELE (Larry Lauer, R. 1995). Sdlg. L89-78-1. TB, 36" (91 cm), ML. Orchid self; beards white, tipped yellow. L86-34-1: (Brandy x Roselene) X Opening Act. Stockton 1996.

MARENOVAYA ROZA (Viktor Sheviakov, R. 1996). Sdlg. 20c21a. TB, 30" (75 cm), EM. S. cream white ground, plum red plicata markings; F. white, plum red edge; beards red brown; ruffled; slight sweet fragrance. Stepping Out X Matinata. Sheviakov 1996.

MARFA'S SUNSHINE (Joseph Shapiro, R. 1999). TB, 28-30" (71-76 cm), ML. Bright lemon yellow, F. with small white blaze increasing in size on later blossoms; beards orange; slight spicy fragrance. Startler X Gold Galore.

MARGANIT (David Shahak, R. 1992). Sdlg. 5-85-III. AR (OH), 17" (43 cm), M. S. yellow (RHS 10B), lightly veined darker; F. yellow (12B), orange signal; beards yellow. (*I. urmiensis* yellow sdlg. x *I. samariae* yellow sdlg.) X sib. Aril Society, Tira Nurseries 1993.

MARGARET BARRY (Wayne Barry, R. 1998). Sdlg. WB-95-6-2. AB (OGB-), 14" (36 cm), E. S. light peach; style arms peach; F. darker peach, fuchsia signal; beards orange, hairs tipped yellow. WB-91-1-1: (Sheik x Pixie Princess) X self.

MARGARET BEAUFORT (Lucy Burton, R. 1993). Sdlg. L86-BK-8. BB, 23" (58 cm), ML. Violet (near RHS 91A) with rosy tints, slightly darker texture veining; beards lemon, gold in throat. Louise Hopper X Miss Nellie. Burton 1994.

MARGARET HELEN (Lloyd Zurbrigg, R. 1994). Sdlg. KK 126. TB, 36" (91 cm), ML. Medium violet blue self; beards medium violet blue, some hairs tipped yellow, with self-colored long horn or spoon. HH 102-3-2: ((Shipshape x Trumpet Concerto) x (Victoria Falls x (Grand Dame x Summer Holidays))) X Scented Bubbles. Friendship 1995.

MARGARET INEZ (George Sutton, R. 1995). Sdlg. H-1. TB, 36" (91 cm), EM. Ruffled neyron rose (RHS 56A) self; beards pink, pinkish white base, ending in neyron rose spoon; slight sweet fragrance. Sweet Musette X Twice Thrilling. Sutton 1999.

MARGARET LEE (John C. Taylor, LA, R. 1989). Rainbow Ridge 1991/92.

MARGARET VIOLA WHITE (Lloyd Zurbrigg, R. 1992). Sdlg. T 28-2. TB, 37" (94 cm), M. White, hint of violet blue; beards violet. O 223 W bb: (G 53 'Dave' x Art of Raphael) X Song of Norway. Avonbank 1992.

MARGARITA ROYAL (Mary Dunn, R. 1996). Sdlg. 2031B. TB, 37" (94 cm), L. S. light violet blue; style arms light blue violet; F. deeper red violet, small light violet blue edge; beards light blue, yellow in throat. Royalist X Mary D. M.A.D. Iris 1998.

MARGE HAGBERG (Donovan Albers, SDB, R. 1989). D. Albers, Redbud Lane 1990.

MARGE M (George Sutton, R. 1990). Sdlg. 4-2-RA. TB, 34" (86 cm), M. Ruffled violet blue (RHS 92A), paler around beard; beards violet blue, tipped white; slight sweet fragrance. 81-6A: (Happy Birthday x Pink Taffeta) X 81-6, sib. Sutton 1991.

MARGINAL WAY (Robert Sobek, R. 1993). Sdlg. 84MT11C. MTB, 25" (64 cm), M. S. violet (near RHS 85B); F. pansy purple (near 83A) with texture veining overall but particularly on haft, violet inner rim with thin purple outer rim; beards tipped lemon. Consummation X Carolyn Rose. Joe Pye Weed 1991.

MARGIT (Manfred Beer, R. 1991). Sdlg. MB 18/84A. TB, 43" (110 cm), M. S. white; F. medium blue; beards yellow. Navajo Blanket X Metropolitan. Gartencenter Kania 1991.

MARIAH (Schreiner, R. 1995). Sdlg. W 440-B. TB, 35" (89 cm), ML. Light blue (RHS 100B) self; beards white. Sib to Rapture in Blue. Schreiner 1995.

MARIE CHUARD (Tony Huber, R. 1998). Sdlg. 1 95-212. SPEC-X (reensata), 49" (124 cm), M-VL. S. purple (RHS 79C); style arms white centered violet, changing to purple violet (80B), violet blue (90B) crests; F. purple (79B changing to 79C), large very bright yellow signal with darker midline extension; slight sweet fragrance. 92-257 versata: (90 PPK-068 *versicolor* x purple and pink *I. ensata* sdlg.) X Royal Burgundy.

MARIE FLORE (Jean Cayeux, R. 1990). Sdlg. 76110 A. TB, 34" (85 cm), L. S. light apricot; F. white, narrowly bordered apricot; beards bright orange; ruffled. Symphonette X Peach Frost. Cayeux 1987.

MARIE KALFAYAN (Lawrence Ransom, R. 1994). Sdlg. 87/66-15. TB, 32" (80 cm), M. Light mauve, veined darker; style arms mauve white; F. light mauve with whiter central area, darker veining; beards cadmium orange, whiter at end; ruffled, lightly laced, lacerated; slight sweet fragrance. Coup de Coeur X Lady Friend. Iris au Trescols 1995.

MARIE M (Jack Fitzgerald, R. 1992). TB, 34" (86 cm), M. S. light lavender lilac, paler midrib; F. white ground with rosy lavender lilac plicata markings, narrow edge of S. color; beards orange; slight sweet fragrance. Parentage unknown.

MARIE MY LOVE (O. D. Niswonger, R. 1996). Sdlg. 52-93. TB, 36" (91 cm), M. Cool white self; beards white, pale yellow at base. Tinted Crystal X 54-89: (Elvis Presley x Bridal Fashion). Cape Iris 1997.

MARIENWERDER (Harald Moos, R. 1990). Sdlg. 86/611G. TB, 31½" (80 cm), L. Peach undertoned orange; beards red orange. (Rosa Heimann sdlg. x Vanity) X (Flaming Light x Fresno Calypso). Schoeppinger 1993.

MARILYN ASHLEY (Jim Hedgecock, R. 1998). Sdlg. F-26-2. TB, 33" (84 cm), M. Heavily laced and ruffled baby pink, F. with creamy pink center; beards red orange, large, sometimes with short lavender pink horn; slight sweet fragrance. Lucille Em X Pink Diablo. Comanche Acres 1999.

MARINA RASKOVA (Irina Driagina, R. 1995). Sdlg. 6-74. TB, 32" (82 cm), EM. S. pink; F. dark pink, lilac striations; beards red; ruffled. Parentage unknown. Driagina 1978.

MARINAZUL (Christian Lanthelme, R. 1997). TB, 39" (100 cm), M. Marine blue self; beards gold, blue at base. Parentage unknown. Lanthelme 1996.

MARINE MAGIC (Lois Belardi, R. 1994). Sdlg. 093-1. CA, 15" (38 cm), M. Dark delphinium blue, F. center deeper. Sea Gal X SDT-2: ((Pacific High x Del Rey) x (Spring Daze x California Mystique)). Bay View 1995.

MARINER'S VICTORY (Alphonse Van Mulders, R. 1990). Sdlg. 122.6/85. TB, 38" (97 cm), M. Ruffled spectrum violet. Ceremony Violet X Silver Point. Jardinart-Van Mulders 1989.

MARIPOSA AUTUMN (Richard Tasco, R. 1999). Sdlg. 92-25-06-RE. TB, 32" (81 cm), EM & RE. S. rosy violet, white showing in center; style arms rosy violet, edges lemon yellow; F. white ground, rosy violet band; beards white base, hairs tipped violet at end, tipped gold in throat; lightly ruffled; slight sweet fragrance. Jesse's Song X Earl of Essex. Superstition 1999.

271

MARIPOSA SKIES (Richard Tasco, R. 1995). Sdlg. 89-05-02-RE. TB, 33" (84 cm), EM & RE. S. pale blue, blue violet basal flush; F. medium blue violet, slightly lighter edge; beards white. 8717: (Wedding Vow x Violet Miracle) X Glistening Icicle. Superstition 1996.

MARITIMA GEM (Ben Hager, SPU, R. 1989). Melrose 1990.

MAR JAN (Harry Bishop, R. 1990). Sdlg. SI-B-U-10-E. SPEC (*versicolor*), 26" (66 cm), M. S. wine red (RHS 71A); style arms white, rib wine red; F. wine red (71A) aging paler (71B or lighter), yellow white signal. *I. versicolor* Kermesina X unknown. Joe Pye Weed 1993.

MARKAKOL (Leonard Venivitin, R. 1995). TB, 37" (95 cm), M. S. white, red brown basal dots; F. white, greenish brown haft markings; beards white at end, merging from yellow to orange in throat. Parentage unknown. Venivitin 1993.

MARK ALLEN (J. R. Allen, TB, R. 1989). Allen Irises 1992.

MARKSMAN (Marky Smith, R. 1997). Sdlg. 93-11M. SDB, 13" (33 cm), M. S. hot orange (between RHS 21C and 163C); style arms pale orange, crest hot orange; F. faintly smoked hot orange (22A to 163A); beards vermilion (30A); ruffled; slight spicy fragrance. Tweety Bird X B. Jones 415-5: ((((Melon Honey x Wright L32) x (229-2 x Melon Honey)) x Pumpkin Center) x Orange Dazzler sib). Aitken's Salmon Creek 1999.

MAR MONTE (Joseph Ghio, R. 1991). Sdlg. PI-178M3. CA, 21" (53 cm), ML. White base, medium blue overlay, slight gold signal. Miramar X Idylwild. Bay View 1992.

MARONGLA (Kevin Nilsen, R. 1992). Sdlg. 8-86-1. TB, 35" (88 cm), EM. S. creamy tan blend, rose midrib; F. deeper tan, overlaid rose aging tan, lighter edge; beards red. Beachgirl X Lady Friend. Iridescence 1992/93.

MAROON MOON (Donald Spoon, R. 1995). Sdlg. 90-204-64. TB, 35" (89 cm), ML. Maroon self; beards maroon; lightly ruffled, flared. Study in Black X Time Lord.

MAROON NUGGET (Carl Boswell, R. 1991). Sdlg. 26-80-S. SDB, 12" (30 cm), M. S. light old gold; style arms old gold, lined green; F. maroon, old gold edge; beards gold. Middlebury X Plum-Plum. Adamgrove 1992.

MAROON PRINCE (Ed Pickin, R. 1995). Sdlg. T87/BB/7. AB (OG) tet., 18" (46 cm), E. S. light grey ground, maroon veining; F. light grey ground, maroon veining and spots; beards dark maroon. Holden HR6T: (CHj105 x Hn29h-T) X Holden HR17T: (Norris T-N79A6 x Norris T-N78R1).

MAROUBRA (Graeme Grosvenor, R. 1996), Sdlg. S75-1. TB, 40" (102 cm), ML. Violet self; beards blue violet; slight fragrance. Bubbly Mood X Breakers. Rainbow Ridge 1996/97.

MARQUEE (Monty Byers, TB, R. 1989). Moonshine 1990.

MARRIS (Sterling Innerst, R. 1995). Sdlg. 4172-1. IB, 19" (48 cm), M. S. gold; style arms yellow gold to white; F. gold, brown feathered spot around orange gold beard. Spin-Off X Smart. Innerst 1996.

MARSHAL POKRYSHKIN (Irina Driagina, R. 1996). Sdlg. 75-29. TB, 33" (85 cm), EM. Cream pink self; beards red. K Yubileyu Iliyicha X unknown. Driagina 1975.

MARSHAL ZHUKOV (Viktor Sheviakov, R. 1995). Sdlg. 20 E 18. TB, 30" (75 cm), L. S. brownish violet; F. dark red violet with light violet centerline, cream hafts; beards yellow orange; ruffled; spicy fragrance. Radiant Apogee X Arabi Pasha.

MARSHMALLOW DREAM (D. L. Shepard, R. 1996). Sdlg. 95026-8915. TB, 35" (89 cm), EML. Heavily ruffled pure white self; beards yellow gold. Irish Butter X Exotic Melody. Shepard Iris 1996.

MARSIANIN (Adolf Volfovich-Moler, R. 1995). Sdlg. V-12. TB, 39" (100 cm), L. Lightly ruffled orange red self; beards dark yellow. Broadway Star X Vitafire. Volfovich-Moler 1992.

MARTHA FIRCH (Ed Attenberger, R. 1996). Sdlg. 90-04-23. TB, 36" (91 cm), ML. Ruffled, lightly laced bright golden yellow, F. with small white spot below yellow beard; slight sweet fragrance. Acapulco Gold X Lemon Mist.

MARTHA-JANE (Nell Wilson, R. 1999). Sdlg. 95-12. TB, 38" (96 cm), M. Ruffled salmon, F. with brick red haft netting; beards red; slight musky fragrance. Lady Friend X Starfrost Pink.

MARTHA P (Louise Smith, R. 1991). Sdlg. 86-34. TB, 36" (91 cm), EM. S. rich yellow; F. golden bronze; beards gold; slight sweet fragrance. Parentage unknown.

MARTHA'S GOLD (J. T. Aitken, R. 1991). Sdlg. 85M61. TB, 35" (89 cm), ML. Intense yellow gold, 1/4" deeper gold F. edge; beards yellow orange; slight sweet fragrance. Brown Lasso X Maid of Orange. Aitken's Salmon Creek 1991.

MARTHA SMITH (Labriano Anaya, AB, R. 1989). Rancho de la Flor de Lis 1990.

MARTHE JOSEPH (Alphonse Van Mulders, R. 1990). Sdlg. 210-85. TB, 38" (97 cm), M. S. gentian blue; F. darker, ruffled. Victoria Falls X Tuxedo. Jardinart-Van Mulders 1990.

MARTHELLA (Hooker Nichols, TB, R. 1989). Hillcrest 1995.

MARTHELLA'S CHOICE (Cleo Palmer, IB, R. 1989). Palmer's Iris 1990.

MARTIAL ARTS (Perry Dyer, R. 1999). Sdlg. 94-8A. SDB, 9" (22 cm), EML. Glowing plum violet, F. with deep violet flash below deep purple beard; style arms plum violet; waved. Nut Ruffles X Chanted.

MARTIAN REFLECTIONS (Clarence Protzmann, TB, R. 1989). Protzmann 1990.

MARTI CORT (Harry Wolford, R. 1994). Sdlg. S55T16-A94. TB, 34" (86 cm), EM. S. white, yellow midrib blush continuing to hafts, edges lightly laced yellow; F. white, lightly laced yellow edge, ruffled; beards soft yellow, tipped white; slight sweet fragrance. Sterling Blush X Tres Elegante.

MARTILE ROWLAND (Howard Bushnell, R. 1999). Sdlg. 90-0-2. TB, 36-38" (91-97 cm), E. Ruffled and laced lemon yellow, F. fading to white around uniform fire engine red orange beard; slight spicy fragrance. 86-LL: (Lighted Within x Christmas Time) X 86-AA6n: (Christmas Time x Flaming Victory).

MARTINI MIST (Robert Dunn, R. 1994). Sdlg. B84-852A. TB, 36" (91 cm), M. S. light tan, olive green cast, slight violet midrib stain; F. tan washed violet, olive green cast; beards mustard; ruffled. Bourbon X Evening Mist. M.A.D. Iris 1996.

MARTOVSKI SNEG (Viktor Koroliov, R. 1995). Sdlg. S-6-86K. TB, 35" (88 cm), EM. White, tinted pale blue; beards white at end, yellow, to dark yellow in throat; slight sweet fragrance. New Snow X unknown. Koroliov 1995.

MARVELL GOLD (James Waddick, R. 1991). LA, 30" (76 cm), M. Yellow self. *I. fulva* collected 1932 near Marvell, Arkansas, by Frank Chowning. Redbud Lane 1986.

MARY CARSON (Bob Thomason, R. 1991). Sdlg. BT-8807A. TB, 28" (71 cm), ML. Light coral pink, F. with white area around deep coral beard; ruffled; slight fragrance. Vanity X Buffy. Okie Iris 1999.

MARY CONSTANCE (Cy Bartlett, R. 1994). Sdlg. C91-35. IB, 25" (63 cm), M. Blue violet self; beards blue; ruffled; slight sweet fragrance. Violet Lass X Amadora. Sutton 1995.

MARY ELLEN NICHOLS (Hooker Nichols, TB, R. 1988). Hillcrest 1990.

MARY ESTELLE (Lloyd Zurbrigg, R. 1991). Sdlg. KK 84-1-2. TB, 35" (89 cm), VE. Heavily ruffled light blue; beards bright medium blue, white touch at tip. HH 12-2-2: (Howdy Do x Song of Norway) X J. Moffitt 84-16/17-12-1: (Song of Norway x (Magic Memories x Key Lime)). Friendship 1995.

MARY G (Rusty Ostheimer, R. 1991). Sdlg. Bit-P-85. LA, 34" (85 cm), ML. Pinkish lavender (RHS 65A), yellow signal surrounded by white area. This I Love x unknown. Bois d'Arc 1991.

MARY JEAN REYNOLDS (Ed Attenberger, R. 1996). Sdlg. 92-01-03. TB, 37" (94 cm), M. S. and style arms creamy white to light peach pink; F. light peach pink, creamy white in center, suffused light lavender edge; beards bright reddish orange; slight sweet fragrance. Peach Picotee X Entourage.

MARY JOHNS (Leslie Donnell, BB, R. 1987). Iris Acres 1993/94.

MARY LOUISE (Kirk Strawn, R. 1996). Sdlg. 48-1985. LA, 38" (97 cm), M. S. methyl violet (RHS 85B); style arms pale lilac (76D); F. deep lilac (76A), indian yellow (17A) signal. Charles Arny III X Easter Tide.

MARY LOUISE MICHIE (Anna Mae Miller, R. 1995). Sdlg. 85.20.24. SIB, 32" (81 cm), EM. S. lavender (RHS 84C), shaded pink; style arms white, flushed pink; F. darker rose lavender (77B). Aqua Whispers X Lavender Bounty. Ensata Gardens 1996.

MARY LUSTER (William & Mary Grise, R. 1996). Sdlg. ML3. TB, 36" (91 cm), EM. Ruffled blue violet (RHS 90A), F. with 1/2" white wash around beard; beards white, deep yellow in throat; slight musky fragrance. Victoria Falls X Master Touch. Parkwood 1996.

MARY McKENNA (John Durrance by Anne Bobel, R. 1999). Sdlg. D1-2-32. BB, 21" (53 cm), M. S. pale lavender; F. lavender, brick red blaze overlay, lavender rim; beards yellow. Parentage unknown.

MARY NEAL (Louise Smith, R. 1993). Sdlg. 85-90. TB, 37" (94 cm), EM. White self; beards yellow, tipped white; slight sweet fragrance. Parentage unknown.

MARY R (Revie Harvey, SDB, R. 1989). Hilmary Catton 1991.

MARY'S COLOR (Bernard Hamner by Shepard Iris Garden, R. 1994). Sdlg. 89-21. TB, 38" (97 cm), ML. Mauve plum with grey cast, F. with white blaze around orange-red beard; ruffled. Blushing Diana X Melissa Sue. Hamner Iris, Shepard Iris 1994.

MARY'S MARVEL (Mary Dunn by Joseph Ghio, R. 1998). Sdlg. 239-6. LA, 36" (91 cm), EM. Rosy red with yellow rim, yellow spear signal; style arms green. Midnight Drama X self. Bay View 1999.

MARY WALLS (Bob Thomason, R. 1992). Sdlg. BT-8922C. IB, 20" (51 cm), E. S. bright yellow; F. darker yellow with white haft pattern, light yellow centerline; beards fuzzy lavender, tipped orange in throat; pronounced sweet fragrance. Favorite Song X Hat Trick. Okie Iris 1994.

MARY WINIFRED (Cyril Field, R. 1992). Sdlg. CF3. TB, 29" (72 cm), M. S. palest lavender; style arms white, thin yellow centerline; F. white; beards yellow, ending in lavender horn and white flounce. Horned white sdlg. X Flounced Frivolite.

MARZIE JOAN (Cyril Field, R. 1992). Sdlg. CF1. TB, 32" (81 cm), M. Salmon saffron self; beards fiery orange, saffron flounce. Horned pink sdlg. X Happy Birthday.

MASAI WARRIOR (Francis Rogers, R. 1998). Sdlg. C-106-H. TB, 30" (76 cm), E. S. oxblood red (RHS 183B); style arms hazelnut brown (166C); F. plum purple (79A), white spray pattern beside beard, yellow spray pattern on haft; beards indian yellow (17A); ruffled; slight fragrance. Chippewa Brave X Gallant Rogue. Meadowbrook 1999.

MASCARA BRUSH (John Marchant, R. 1990). Sdlg. 3187. CA, 10" (25 cm), M. Creamy white ground completely overlaid royal purple (HCC 834) leaving 1/16" white edge; F. lightly ruffled. Sdlg. X sdlg.

MASCHTEICH (Harald Moos, R. 1991). Sdlg. 81-124C. TB, 36" (90 cm), E. Medium blue violet; beards white yellow. Navy Strut X Sailor's Dance. Schoeppinger 1992.

MASCOT (Joseph Ghio, R. 1997). Sdlg. PF-185-I2. CA, 16" (41 cm), L-VL. Red black self, rosewater halo on all petals, fuchsia black petal reverse; style arms violet. Mantra X PH-230D3: (San Andreas sib x National Anthem). Bay View 1997.

MASKED BANDIT (Keith Keppel, R. 1997). Sdlg. 91-68B. IB, 26" (66 cm), EM. S. blended greyed mauve (M&P 54-F-3) to wineberry (55-H-4) shading to khaki (13-J-7) on outer third, speckled colonial buff (10-G-2) in center; style arms buckthorn brown (13-L-8), edged brass (11-L-6); F. chrome lemon (9-K-2) ground heavily marked velvety port wine (56-J-12) to dahlia purple (55-J-12), almost solid except for blaze and haft striping; beards sudan brown (14-C-12) to burnt umber (15-A-12); heavily ruffled; pronounced sweet fragrance. 88-28A: (Jitterbug x Hot Streak) X Gatty W37-19, Quote sib. Keppel 1998.

MASTERFUL (John C. Taylor, R. 1998). Sdlg. UL 10-2. LA, 43" (110 cm), ML. S. marbled light and darker purple violet; style arms same, variable; F. darker purple violet, signal yellow; ruffled. Concours d'Elegance X First Favourite.

MASTER GARDENER (A. & D. Willott, R. 1990). Sdlg. 84-196. TB, 38" (96 cm), M. Ruffled peach, F. with slightly deeper edge; beards orange. Mandolin X 80-102: (Silver Shower x Far Corners). Willott 1991.

MASTERMIND (Lilly Gartman, R. 1990). Sdlg. 84-28L. TB, 38" (97 cm), M. Lavender aging to pale lavender in petal centers, F. with yellow shoulder blush; beards yellow. Classico X 180-10A: (Soap Opera x Ghio 76-63C: (Joyce Terry x Entourage)). Roris 1995.

MASTER PLAN (Keith Keppel, R. 1994). Sdlg. 88-61A. TB, 35" (89 cm), M. S. purplish rose (M&P 54-FG-8 to 55-H-8), slight cream infusion at base; style arms blended buff red (6-H-2); F. purplish rose (55-H-9) 1/2" border, cream to ivory ground; beards brownish brick (5-B-12), fire red (1-F-12) in throat; ruffled; pronounced sweet fragrance. 82-11K: ((Rancho Rose x (71-12C, Flamenco sib, x (68-17B, Roundup sib, x April Melody))) x Gigolo) X 85-65A: (Ever After x Lorilee). Keppel 1995.

MASTER SLEUTH (Hooker Nichols, IB, R. 1988). Hillcrest 1993.

MASUMU-NO-SORA (Yoshio Mitsuda by Society for Japanese Irises, R. 1993). JI (6 F. + extra petaloids), 37" (94 cm), ML. Silvery violet (RHS 88B) ground and edge, darker violet halo and veining, irregular yellow signal; style arms violet, lighter midrib. Parentage unknown. Mitsuda prior to 1988.

MATAMORE (Pierre Anfosso, R. 1990). Sdlg. P 82 24D. TB, 31½" (80 cm), ML. Ruffled maroon red; self beards. Spartan X Post Time. Iris en Provence 1990.

MATENE (Frances Love, R. 1993). Sdlg. G.W. 92/11/5. SIB, 23" (59 cm), ML. S. purple; F. purple, white ray pattern, lavender signal with purple midrib; fluted. Parentage unknown.

MATHILDE (Virginia Messick, R. 1997). Sdlg. M92-82. TB, 36" (91 cm), M. Ruffled mauve self; beards slightly darker mauve. Silverado X M88-20: (Winterscape x (Navy Strut x Bubbling Over)).

MATISSE (Tony Huber, R. 1992). Sdlg. 1DM-Bar-08. SPEC (*versicolor*), 36" (90 cm), E. S. violet blue (RHS 92A) veined darker; F. dark violet blue (89C), large white center and dark violet veins; slight sweet fragrance. Selected *I. versicolor* collected on Magdalen Islands, Quebec, Canada.

MATRIX (Earl Hall by Lloyd Zurbrigg, R. 1990). Sdlg. 86-144-5SC. TB, 36" (91 cm), M & RE (Sept./VA). S. cream veined pale cinnamon, giving self effect; F. near-white, creamy yellow rim, cinnamon hafts, suggestion of pale violet texture veining and violet centerline; beards white, tipped cream. Violet Miracle X Brother Carl. Avonbank 1991.

MATSUZAKA TSUKASA (Society for Japanese Irises, R. 1994). JI (3 F.), 27½" (70 cm), M. S. white, edged red violet; style arms white, red violet on crests; F. red violet, large white veins. Parentage unknown. Old Edo variety from Meiji period (1869-1912).

MATTY (Frances Love, R. 1993). Sdlg. 25/10/1. MDB, 5" (14 cm), M. S. gold, deep maroon markings deep in haft area; F. gold, deeper toward center; beards gold, tipped white; sweet fragrance. Ana X self.

MATUSHKA (Viacheslav Gavrilin, R. 1998). Sdlg. 6-5-3-94. TB, 37" (95 cm), VE. S. and style arms white, shot lilac; F. lilac, hafts darker, indistinct lilac white border; beards orange, lilac at end, with hairs tipped white; ruffled; slight fragrance. Eagle's Flight X unknown. Gavrilin 1999.

MAUI GOLD (J. T. Aitken, R. 1992). Sdlg. 86M21. IB, 25" (64 cm), ML. Sunflower yellow; beards light orange; slight fragrance. Winterbourne X Solar Flight. Aitken's Salmon Creek 1992.

MAUI MAGIC (J. T. Aitken, R. 1991). Sdlg. 84T25B. BB, 26" (66 cm), M. Ruffled intense deep purple; beards deep purple; pronounced sweet fragrance. Memorable X Orbiter. Aitken's Salmon Creek 1991.

MAUI SURF (J. T. Aitken, R. 1990). Sdlg. 84T25A. BB, 26" (66 cm), ML. Light blue violet; self beards; heavily ruffled. Memorable X Orbiter. Aitken's Salmon Creek 1990.

MAUNA KEA (Chet Tompkins, R. 1992). Sdlg. 84-88. TB, 38" (97 cm), EML. Ruffled ivory white with lemon undertone, edged sky blue; beards yellow, tipped blue. Sib to Hawaiian Halo. Fleur de Lis 1991.

MAUNA LOA BABY (Berthe Conarty, R. 1999). Sdlg. C95-7E. SDB, 9" (23 cm), M. S. and style arms bright orange; F. purple, rimmed pale orange; beards vivid tangerine. 23-951: (Baby Pink x (Melon Honey x Solar Flight)) X Pele.

MAUNGATI (Judith Neilson, R. 1998). Sdlg. JN/1. SDB, 8½" (21 cm), M. S. pale blue, green infusion; F. tannish brown infused yellow, fine 1/4" pale blue rim; beards blue; pronounced sweet fragrance. Parentage unknown. Otepopo 1999/2000.

MAURICE (Bob Thomason, R. 1993). Sdlg. BT-8805B. SDB, 9" (21 cm), ML. Greyed lavender self; beards violet; slight fragrance. Plum-Plum X Regards. Okie Iris 1999.

MAURICE POPE (John White, R. 1993). Sdlg. 2. SIB, 36" (91 cm), EM. S. dark violet (RHS 86A); style arms red violet (83C to 77A); F. dark violet (86A) with greenish hafts, white signal. Janet K. Merrill X Shirley Pope. Pope's Perennials 1996.

MAUVE LADY (Carl Boswell, R. 1999). Sdlg. 123-87-T. TB, 40" (107 cm), EM. S. light mauve pink; style arms mauve; F. pale mauve pink, dark mauve pink marginal band; beards orange. Invasion in Pink X (Sinaloa x Mais Oui). Adamgrove 1999.

MAUVE PALLET (Alphonse Van Mulders, R. 1990). Sdlg. 42/84. TB, 38" (97 cm), M. Ruffled rosy lavender. Grand Waltz X Victoria Falls. Jardinart-Van Mulders 1990.

MAUVE SNOWTOP (Lorena Reid, R. 1994). Sdlg. 8sp2D. SPEC-X (sibtosa), 24-30" (61-76 cm), EM. S. palest lavender aging white; style arms white, palest lavender midrib; F. mauve pink, inconspicuous gold, brown and white signal. Pink Haze X *I. setosa alba*. Laurie's Garden 1994.

MAVERICK'S GAME (Lynda Miller, R. 1996). Sdlg. 100991. TB, 32" (81 cm), L. S. medium old gold, slight violet midrib flush; style arms medium old gold; F. violet plum, edged red brown; beards dark gold, light blue base; slight musky fragrance. 6087A: (5384: (Spartan x unknown) x Mulled Wine) X Graduation. Miller's Manor 1997.

MAVIS WAVES (Mitch Jameson, R. 1992). Sdlg. 1-88-A. TB, 34-38" (86-97 cm), ML. S. pink; F. lavender blue edged lavender; beards cream tangerine tipped blue. Sophistication X Graduation. Knee-Deep in June 1994.

MAXINE PERKINS (Sharon McAllister, R. 1995). Sdlg. 85-3-16. AB (OGB), 28" (71 cm), M. S. white ground, reddish violet midrib and 1/2" veined rim; style arms golden yellow, reddish violet midrib and crest; F. soft ivory yellow ground, intense reddish violet dotting around beard, reddish violet veining on inner half and 1/2" rim; beards mustard and maroon mixture. Boaz X Jean Ralls. McAllister 1996.

MAXINE'S LOVE (Cloyd McCord, R. 1991). Sdlg. 80-5. TB, 37" (94 cm), E. Light apricot; beards orange; sweet fragrance. 82-1: (Chorus Girl x Custom Made) X 84-1: (Last Call x American Sweetheart). McCord 1991.

MAYA MAKITA (Audrey Machulak, R. 1992). Sdlg. 79-45-26. MDB, 6½" (17 cm), M. S. laced pure white; F. white blending to deep blue violet, lightly laced white edge; beards white, tipped blue; slight fragrance. 50-77-3: (Bit o' Sky x unknown) X 76-49-3: (Peanuts x unknown). Miller's Manor 1992.

MAYA MEADOW (Audrey Machulak, R. 1991). Sdlg. 79-27-17. MDB, 7-¾" (19 cm), M. S. bright green yellow; F. green yellow blending to gold, small red spot, bright yellow rim; beards orange. Nu-Nu X unknown. Miller's Manor 1991.

MAYA MOROCCO (Audrey Machulak, R. 1990). Sdlg. 15-79-9. SDB, 11" (28 cm), M. Greyed purple, F. with lighter rim; beards gold; slight sweet fragrance. ((Sunny Heart x unknown) x sib) X unknown. Miller's Manor 1990.

MAYA-O-MAYA (Audrey Machulak, R. 1990). Sdlg. 76-32-2. SDB, 13" (33 cm), M. Greyed yellow green, F. with gold wash around gold beard. Puppet X unknown. Miller's Manor 1990.

MAYBE AN ANGEL (Barry Blyth, R. 1996). Sdlg. A144-1. TB, 38" (97 cm), ML. S. light blue, deeping at midrib and base; F. pastel blue, deepening at haft; beards blue white. Just Magic X Honky Tonk Blues. Tempo Two 1996/97.

MAYBE BABY (Tom Burseen, R. 1993). Sdlg. 8-116B. TB, 36" (91 cm), M. S. apricot (RHS 39C), toasted edge; F. creamy orange (27A), toasted hafts and edge; beards bright orange red; lightly ruffled, laced; sweet fragrance. Delirious X Montevideo. T.B.'s Place 1994.

MAYBE LARISSA (Shirley Sylvia, R. 1997). Sdlg. 3. SPU, 28" (71 cm), M. S. purple; style arms mauve to purple; F. yellow, edged and veined purple. Highline Lavender X Fergy's Poetry.

MAY FRILLS (D. C. Anderson, TB, R. 1988). Brown's Iris Garden 1990.

MAYLA (Kirk Strawn, R. 1993). Sdlg. P-1985. LA, 41" (104 cm), M. S. lavender purple (RHS 78D); style arms yellow (11D) with light purple; F. darker lavender purple (78C), bright yellow (8A) signal. Mighty Rich X President Hedley. Bois d'Arc 1996.

MAYNARD E. HARP (J. Owings Rebert, R. 1996). Sdlg. AHB-2. SIB, 33" (84 cm), M. Violet red self, F. with white signal, deep yellow hafts. Parentage unknown.

MAY THIRTY-FIRST (A. J. Farrington, SDB, R. 1986). British Iris Society 1987.

MAYWOOD HERITAGE (J. Owings Rebert, R. 1996). Sdlg. FY-R-1. SIB, 28" (71 cm), M. Deep purple, slight ivory signal pattern; S. very erect. Parentage unknown.

McARTHUR PARK (Georg Emke, R. 1996). TB, 34" (86 cm), M. Medium blue, F. with lighter edge; beards whitish. Honky Tonk Blues X Timescape.

McCORD'S FIRE (Cloyd McCord, R. 1994). Sdlg. 86-6-A. TB, 38" (97 cm), M. Ruffled red self; beards pale yellow; pronounced sweet fragrance. Clearfire X War Sails. McCord 1994.

McCORD'S GOLD (Cloyd McCord, R. 1992). Sdlg. 66-1. TB, 40" (102 cm), M. Ruffled and laced dark yellow gold, small white spot below orange beards; pronounced sweet fragrance. Homecoming Queen X 73-13: (Angie Quadros x Homecoming Queen). McCord 1992.

McCORD'S PRIDE (Cloyd McCord, R. 1992). Sdlg. 86-04. TB, 36" (91 cm), L. S. pale rose lavender, 1/8" near-white edge; F. darker rose lavender, 1/8" near-white edge, reddish veins around yellow beard; ruffled; sweet fragrance. Beauty Crown X 83-6: (Entourage x Homecoming Queen). McCord 1992.

McCORD'S QUEEN (Cloyd McCord, R. 1994). Sdlg. 85-2-1-A. TB, 36" (91 cm), E. S. and style arms pale rose lavender; F. white ground, 1/4" lavender-trimmed edge, lavender on upper portion, pale yellow around red beard; ruffled, laced; pronounced sweet fragrance. Homecoming Queen X 76-13: (Beauty Crown x Homecoming Queen). McCord 1994.

McCRAE MOON (Leslie Donnell, R. 1998). Sdlg. 94-8-1. TB, 38" (97 cm), E. Pallid blue, F. lined; beards pale yellow; slight sweet fragrance. Affaire X Mt. Bogong.

McKENZIE VIOLET (Lorena Reid, R. 1995). Sdlg. DL opG91-5F. SIB (sino-sib), 36" (91 cm), ML. S. medium violet; style arms light violet, pale midrib; F. medium violet, signal near-black with single white centerline. Dotted Line X unknown. Laurie's Garden 1995.

McNEAL BLUE (Louise Smith, R. 1992). TB, 42" (107 cm), EM. Tailored deep blue; beards yellow; pronounced sweet fragrance. Parentage unknown.

MEADOWBROOK BEAUTY (Francis Rogers, R. 1996). Sdlg. F-737-A. TB, 32" (81 cm), M. Ruffled, lightly laced white self; beards orange; sweet fragrance. Triple Crown X F215-L: (Bonbon x Rancho Rose). Meadowbrook 1996.

MEADOW CREEK (Opal Brown, R. 1996). Sdlg. 91-8B. TB, 38" (97 cm), M. Pale blue self; beards lobelia blue and black. 88-2A: (Grecian Skies x Skyblaze) X Codicil. Brown's Sunnyhill 1997.

MEADOW FROST (Richard Morgan, R. 1991). Sdlg. L255-W. LA, 20" (51 cm), M. White, green yellow signal; style arms green. Bayou Waters X Finders Keepers. Redbud Lane 1993.

MEADOWLARK SERENADE (Francis Rogers, R. 1991). Sdlg. F-503-H. TB, 30" (76 cm), M. S. yellow (RHS 162); F. white ground, greyed orange (163B) plicata markings and solid 1/8" edge; beards gold; ruffled; slight fragrance. Dirndl X Bengal Tiger. Meadowbrook 1993.

MEADOW NYMPH (Ben Hager, R. 1993). SD5116WGrSf. SDB, 12" (30 cm), ML. Chartreuse yellow; self beards. Willow Mist X SD4931RndGr: ((((SD2669A: ((Sunny Heart x (697: (Evening Storm x Welch H501) x 1289: (Sulina x Melodrama))) x (Blueberry Muffins x Peanuts)) x Jane Taylor) x Mrs. Nate Rudolph) x SD4018AGrSf: (((((697 x 1289) x Zing) x Golden Fair) x April Fool) x Baby Blessed)) x ((((Joy Bringer x Ornament) x SD2669GrSp) x Flirty Mary) x SD4018AGrSf)). Adamgrove 1994.

MEADOWS MAGIC (Ivar Schmidt, R. 1995). Sdlg. PC 90-34. CA, 11" (28 cm), ML. S. eggyolk yellow; style arms butter yellow, frilled and pleated; F. eggyolk yellow, signal bold gold. Big Money X Azaz. Iris Acres 1995/96.

MEADOW SONG (A. & D. Cadd, R. 1999). Sdlg. 6-91-4. TB, 36-38" (91-97 cm), E. S. and style arms soft lemon yellow; F. light reddish lavender, pale chocolate blended border, brown shoulder marking, small velvety white blaze around soft yellow beard; heavily ruffled; slight sweet fragrance. Baja Bandit X Well Endowed.

MEAGAN ELIZABETH (Bob Brown, R. 1990). Sdlg. 8517. TB, 34" (86 cm), EML. S. light purple violet (RHS 81D); F. slightly darker purple violet (81C); beards orange, tipped violet; ruffled; slight fragrance. 827: (Orchid Blush x Sunday Chimes) X 8131: (Orchid Blush x Mary Frances). Cottage 1991.

MEAN STREAK (Allan Ensminger, R. 1994). Sdlg. 85-34. TB, 38" (97 cm), ML. Very light peach (HCC 512/3) with all flower parts variegated with pansy violet (033/1) streaks and splashes; beards tipped violet. Karen Christine X 83-76: (78-77: (Pink Sleigh x 75-18: (((((Helen McGregor x Pink Formal) x My Happiness) x (Frost and Flame x Belle Meade)) x Stepping Out) x (Faydy Girl x sib))) x (78-77 x (75-18 x Rancho Rose))). Varigay 1995.

MECHTA (Irina Driagina, R. 1996). Sdlg. 4-12. TB, 33" (85 cm), EM. Cream pink self; beards orange red. Parentage unknown. Driagina 1969.

MECHTA YELENY (Viktor Koroliov, R. 1997). Sdlg. S78-93K. TB, 32" (80 cm), M. S. light brown, center lemon; style arms yellow brown; F. white ground, claret brown plicata edge; beards rich yellow; slight sweet fragrance. Siva Siva X Cliffs of Dover. Koroliov 1997.

MEDITERRANO (Ladislav Muska, R. 1995). Sdlg. EXSH-03. TB, 40" (102 cm), ML. Ruffled medium blue self; beards gold, long blue horn. (Extravagant x "Curro") X Sky Hooks. Muska 1995.

MEETA ARETA (Tom Burseen, R. 1995). Sdlg. 7-103A. TB, 36" (91 cm), EM. S. white, heavily washed lavender (RHS 78C); style arms lavender; F. white, heavily washed darker lavender (78A); beards yellow, tipped white; ruffled, heavily laced; sweet fragrance. Lavish Lace X Villa Splendor. T.B.'s Place 1995.

MEETING OF DOTS (Ladislav Muska, R. 1999). Sdlg. 98-CCGC-03. TB, 38" (97 cm), M. S. yellow tan, washed lilac; style arms yellow tan; F. cream yellow ground banded and stippled raspberry violet; beards orange; ruffled, lightly laced; slight fragrance. ((Calliope's Dream x Spacelight Sketch) x (Queen in Calico x Graffiti)) X Colortart. Muska 1999.

MEGABRIGHT (B. Charles Jenkins, R. 1995). Sdlg. AX68C. SPU, 40" (107 cm), EM. S. creamy white, blended yellow in center; F. creamy white, blending to large yellow signal. Elixir X A8-15B: (Clarke Cosgrove x Forty Carats). Shepard Iris 1997.

MEGABUCKS (Chet Tompkins, R. 1990). Sdlg. 85-43. TB, 38" (97 cm), ML. S. blended flame yellow and capucine gold; F. brilliant fuchsia rose blended with copper red, shimmering blue haze; beards flame copper. ((Gypsy Lullaby x Fifth Avenue) x (Cosmopolitan x Dutch Master)) X Up and Coming. Fleur de Lis 1990.

MEGA CHARM (Stan Dexter by Marie Ingersoll, R. 1994). Sdlg. 106X7-84-82 B. TB, 34" (86 cm), M. S. orchid; F. white, edged darker orchid; beards yellow. 1980-99C: (Coral Magic x Mabel Helland) X 1980-10-B: (Vanity x Focus). Ingersoll's Iris 1995.

MEGAGOLD (B. Charles Jenkins, R. 1995). Sdlg. BC58A. SPU, 39-45" (99-114 cm), M. Ruffled golden yellow self. Janice Chesnik X A33-28D: (Struttin' x Protege). Shepard Iris 1996.

MEGAN DIANE (Carl Jorgensen, R. 1995). Sdlg. 85-P-1E. TB, 36" (91 cm), M-VL. S. shrimp red (HCC 616/3); style arms shrimp red, long, laced; F. shrimp red (616/2); beards shrimp red (616);

ruffled; slight spicy fragrance. 83-P-1: (Beverly Sills x Summit Sweetie) X Custom Made. Long 1995.

MEGGLETHORP (Sterling Innerst, R. 1990). Sdlg. 3379-4. IB, 19" (48 cm), ML. Light blue, F. with dark blue spot; beards light blue. Scented Nutmeg X 2815-1: (Little Episode x Pippi Longstockings). Innerst 1991.

MEGGS (Graeme Grosvenor, R. 1999). Sdlg. V23-A. TB, 36" (91 cm), ML. Pink self; beards red; sweet fragrance. Larcenist X Bogota.

MEGHAN'S CHOICE (Herbert Holk, R. 1996). Sdlg. 8277. TB, 32-36" (81-91 cm), EM. S. white; F. white, small peach area on hafts; beards shrimp, white at tip; ruffled, lightly laced; slight sweet fragrance. 8138: ((White Raiment x Angel Unawares) x (White Lightning x Georgia Girl)) X Chosen One. Cal-Dixie 1997.

MEHETABEL (Lois Rich, AB, R. 1984). Correction of spelling (MEHETABLE) in 1989 Check List.

MELANA ROSA (David Miller, R. 1999). Sdlg. 93-8D. TB, 36" (91 cm), ML. Violet purple (RHS 77A) self; beards burnt orange; slight musky fragrance. Ever Anew X Ignition.

MELANCHOLY MAN (Roger Nelson, R. 1994). Sdlg. RN 86-37BK. TB, 35" (89 cm), M. Silvery violet blue (near RHS 87A) with deeper (77A) thumbprints on F.; self beards, tipped orange; pronounced sweet fragrance. Neil Diamond X Lorilee. Iris Country 1994.

MELANIE ANN (Donald Spoon, R. 1997). Sdlg. 89-144B. TB, 38" (97 cm), ML. S. light rose pink; style arms rose pink; F. white ground, light rose pink plicata markings; beards tangerine; ruffled, flared. Poet X Sweet Anita. Winterberry 1997.

MELANIE STEUERNAGEL (Manfred Beer, R. 1999). Sdlg. MB 35/90A. TB, 28" (72 cm), M. S. and style arms yellow green (RHS 152D); F. white to greyed yellow (162B) ground, oxblood (183A) toward outer portion with light warm brown (177D) edge, remainder heavily covered with red purple (72A) speckling; beards bronze yellow (163A), red purple (72A) base; lightly ruffled; pronounced fragrance. Edith Wolford X Condottiere.

MELANIS FLOWER (Harald Moos, R. 1999). Sdlg. 97/77C. TB, 35½" (90 cm), M. Waved dark red brown self; beards copper. Lady Friend X Buchholzer Glut.

MELANKHOLIYA (Viktor Sheviakov, R. 1995). Sdlg. 21A 16B. TB, 37" (95 cm), ML. Lightly ruffled dark brownish violet, F. with creamy white striations. Siva Siva X Arabi Pasha. Sheviakov 1997.

MELBA HAMBLEN (Ben Hager, R. 1992). Sdlg. T4531PchPk/DpM. TB, 38" (96 cm), M. S. peach pink, blending of orchid spreading partway out from midrib; F. deep maroon, narrow light peach edge; beards bronze tangerine. T4133OcPk/Pr: (Piper's Flute x Color Splash) X Adventuress. Melrose 1992.

MELERI (Maureen Foster, R. 1991). Sdlg. 7A6. TB, 37" (94 cm), M. S. white ground, overall mulberry (RHS 60A) wash; F. clean white ground, 1½" ripe loganberry (185B) border and centerline; beards squirrel brown; ruffled, fluted, and flared; fragrant. Wild Berry X Flamenco.

MELLOW FELLOW (Lucy Burton, R. 1993). Sdlg. L86-BK-22. BB, 22-23" (56-58 cm), M. S. tawny yellow; F. cream blending to tawny yellow edge, buff texture veining at center and on hafts; beards medium yellow; ruffled. Louise Hopper X Miss Nellie. Burton 1995.

MELLOW MAGIC (Paul Black, R. 1991). Sdlg. 84279A. TB, 36" (91 cm), L. S. flesh pink rib diffusing to bluish mauve edge; style arms flesh pink; F. warm white around cocoa pink beard, blending to light mauve pink; ruffled; slight sweet fragrance. Chartreuse Ruffles X Undersea Adventure. Mid-America 1992.

MELLOW MAUVE (Kirk Strawn, R. 1993). Sdlg. BBB1985. LA, 37" (93 cm), M. S. purple (77C); style arms yellow, blushed pink; F. darker purple (77B), yellow orange (14A) signal. Clara Goula X Easter Tide. Bois d'Arc 1996.

MELODIC (Barry Blyth, R. 1991). Sdlg. X8-2. SDB, 14-15" (36-38 cm), ML. Smoky peach, bluish rose thumbprint on F.; beards tangerine, outer ¼" pastel blue. Oladi X (Peach Eyes x Kandi Moon). Tempo Two 1991/92.

MELON RITA (Mary Dunn by Robert Dunn, R. 1998). Sdlg. M2001-11. TB, 36" (91 cm), EM. Heavily ruffled orange buff with pink cast; style arms orange buff; beards burnt orange. Pulsar X 867YF, Gardenlite sib. M.A.D. Iris 1999.

MEL'S HONOR (Mel Leavitt by Chun Fan, R. 1997). Sdlg. P89-102. TB, 35" (89 cm), E. S. violet purple; F. rich cream ground, rich violet purple sanding, dotting and center stripe; beards orange, violet at end; slight spicy fragrance. Parentage unknown. Fan's Iris 1998.

MELTDOWN (Kevin Nilsen, R. 1990). Sdlg. 6-84-1. TB, 36" (91 cm), EM. Ruffled orange apricot blend, slightly paler under orange beards. Mandolin X Lady Friend. Iridescence 1990/91.

MELTED BUTTER (Chun Fan, R. 1992). Sdlg. F-19-86. TB, 39" (99 cm), ML. S. white infused butter yellow on midrib; F. white, butter yellow spray extending halfway down, yellow pleated edge; beards bright orange yellow (RHS 17A), 1/2" melted butter tip; slight sweet fragrance. Cup Race X Coral Beauty. Fan's Iris 1994.

MELTING POINT (Tom Burseen, TB, R. 1989). T.B.'s Place 1990.

MELTING POT (Lawrence Ransom, R. 1994). Sdlg. 89/27-16. SDB, 10" (25 cm), M. S. dark copper yellow, frosted gold; F. dark burnt sienna lower portion, edged copper brown, copper yellow shoulders, cream eyelash pattern; beards orange, bluish white base. Dekho sib X Zounds. Iris au Trescols 1995.

MELTON RED FLARE (Thompson & Morgan by Keith Sangster, R. 1997). Seed strain. SIB, 36-43" (91-110 cm), M. S. wine red; F. lighter red wine, pale wine red signal with darker veins; slight fragrance. Selection from seedling lines. Thompson & Morgan 1989 as "Red Flare".

MEMO (Joseph Gatty, R. 1990). Sdlg. S47-1. IB, 20" (51 cm), M. S. dark chrome lemon (M&P 9-L-2); F. same, paling to white patch, inconspicuous tanner haft shading (11-L-5); beards dandelion (9-L-4) to golden glow (9-L-6), white base; pronounced sweet fragrance. Muchacha X Broadway. Keppel 1991.

MEMORIES OF MOM (Dana Borglum, R. 1995). Sdlg. D-2-22. TB, 33" (84 cm), ML. Lavender, F. paling in center with age; beards tangerine red. B-52: (Vanity x Ovation) X Chapel Bells.

MEMPHIS BASH (Carl Boswell, IB, R. 1989). Adamgrove 1997.

MEMPHIS MEMORY (D. Steve Varner, SIB, R. 1989). Illini Iris 1990.

MENDOCINO BANNER (Joseph Grant II, R. 1992). CA, 18" (46 cm), M. S. white, imperial purple (HCC 33) central sliver; six style arms dark imperial purple; F. white, prominently veined imperial purple, narrow white rim, faint yellow signal. *I. douglasiana* clone collected about 500 yards from coastline, central Mendocino County, California.

MENDOCINO BLUE (Robert & Janet Canning, R. 1999). Sdlg. 93-02D-PCN. CA, 11" (28 cm), M. S. hyacinth blue (RHS 91B) with darker (91A) veining; F. slightly darker wistaria blue (92B) with darker (92A) halo and veining, turquoise midrib wash. Parentage unknown; sdlg. purchased at Mendocino Coast Botanic Garden, California.

MENDOCINO GOLD (Robert & Janet Canning, R. 1999). Sdlg. 93-01C-PCN. CA, 7" (18 cm), M. S. indian yellow (RHS 17D), darker veining; F. darker indian yellow (17C), darker veining, haft area greyed orange (171A) with darker veining, orange white (159A) center ribbing. Parentage unknown; sdlg. purchased at Mendocino Coast Botanic Garden, California.

MENESTREL (Lawrence Ransom, R. 1994). Sdlg. 88/12-8. TB, 32" (81 cm), M. S. blended bronze and purple; F. light violet, edged brown; beards orange yellow; ruffled, laced. Soap Opera X 85/13-11: (Vanity x Raspberry Ripples). Iris au Trescols 1995.

MEN IN BLACK (Larry Lauer, R. 1998). Sdlg. 88-122-3. TB, 34" (86 cm), ML. Ruffled blackish purple, F. with deep lavender central flush; beards deep purple, hairs tipped mustard, changing to mustard central section, bright yellow in throat; slight sweet fragrance. Witches' Sabbath X Black Fantasy. Stockton 1998.

MENTON (A. J. Farrington, SDB, R. 1988). British Iris Society 1989.

MERCEDES OLSEN (Bennett Jones, R. 1990). Sdlg. 86-15-1. TB, 36" (91 cm), M. S. canary yellow (HCC 2/2); F. white, canary yellow hafts and 1/4" crinkled edge; beards fiery red; slight fragrance. 81-17: ((Orange Harvest sib x 74-36-2: ((Bright Butterfly x Shoop 60-11) x Hayride) x (sdlg. x Rhoda Anne sib))) x Gold Galore) X 84-7: ((Shoop 76-33 x (((May Dancer x Elizabeth Stuart) x Bright Sunset) x (69-31-18 x Sunrise Point sib))) x 81-20, inv. Bright Life, Orange Glory, sdlgs.). Bennett Jones 1991.

MERCI BEAUCOUP (Mary Dunn, R. 1994). Sdlg. 165-1. LA, 35" (89 cm), M. Smooth smoky lilac violet, yellow line signal. Joel Fletcher X self. Bay View 1994.

MER DU SUD (Richard Cayeux, R. 1997). Sdlg. 8989C. TB, 32" (80 cm), M. Sea blue self; beards light blue. Dusky Challenger X Pledge Allegiance. Cayeux 1997.

MERIT (Kenneth Fisher, R. 1996). Sdlg. 94-5. MTB, 20" (51 cm), E. S. and F. with white central area surrounded by lavender spots, blending to brown border; beards orange. V7: (Ozark Sky x 80-J: (Slim Jim x Dainty Damsel)) X B6: ((Spanish Coins x White Canary) x (White Canary sdlg. x Spanish Coins)). Aitken's Salmon Creek 1996.

MERLIN'S TUNE (Barry Blyth, R. 1998). Sdlg. E48-1. IB, 22" (56 cm), EML. S. light violet, small white area; style arms lavender and white; F. white, 3/8" medium violet stitched edge; beards bright mustard orange; slight fragrance. C29-Y: (A30-5, Imbue sib, x A14-8, Noble Toff sib) X B146-2: (Larkabout x Divine). Tempo Two 1998/99.

MERLOT (Schreiner, R. 1999). Sdlg. EE 297-B. TB, 37" (94 cm), ML. Blended hyacinth violet and cherry red (RHS 59A); style arms violet and red, lip yellow; beards violet, hair tips yellow at end. Cannonball X Mulberry Punch. Schreiner 1999.

MERRY DANCE (Barry Blyth, R. 1992). Sdlg. X8-1. SDB, 15" (39 cm), VE. Icy blue, F. with rosy brown area halfway down; beards lavender blue, tangerine in throat. Oladi X (Peach Eyes x Kandi Moon). Tempo Two 1992/93.

MERRY LIFE (Barry Blyth, R. 1990). Sdlg. W35-3. IB, 20" (51 cm), EML. S. rose with tan infusion; F. creamy white, 1/2" burgundy rose plicata border, light burgundy rose centerline; beards tangerine. (Cupid's Cup x (Sniffs 'n' Sneezes x Hammered Copper)) X Entrancement. Tempo Two 1990/91.

MERRY MAIDS (Donald Spoon, R. 1997). Sdlg. 88-14B. TB, 34" (86 cm), ML. Ruffled, lightly laced pink self; beards darker pink. Anna Belle Babson X Loveboat.

MERRY MASQUE (Mary Dunn, R. 1993). Sdlg. M87-1002A. TB, 38" (97 cm), M. S. white with tiny plicata markings around edge, violet blue midrib stain; style arms very deep blue violet; F. white ground with tiny violet blue plicata markings; beards white; ruffled. Fancy Face X Windsurfer. Roris 1995.

MESA PEARL (Bob Bauer/John Coble, R. 1993). Sdlg. S85B-1. SIB, 30" (76 cm), L. S. pale lavender (RHS 76C) veined blue (104C); style arms near-white, turquoise midrib; F. pale lavender (76C) with darker veins and lighter edge, small cream signal streak. S82F-21: (Temper Tantrum x unknown) X Esther C.D.M. Ensata Gardens 1994.

MESA SNOW (John Gass, R. 1996). Sdlg. G120. TB, 33" (84 cm), M. Ruffled white self; beards pale yellow; pronounced sweet fragrance. Honor Bound X Victoria Falls. Rainbow Chasers 1997.

MESCAL (Jim & Vicki Craig, R. 1996). Sdlg. YU17. TB, 40" (102 cm), L. S. light lemon yellow, center paler; style arms bright yellow; F. warm white, 1/4" lemon yellow rim, medium yellow plicata veins and dotting at haft; beards yellow; ruffled, lightly laced; slight sweet fragrance. Parentage unknown -- possibly inv. Debutante Ball, Flaming Light, plicata sdlgs. J. & V. Craig 1996.

MESCALERO CHIEF (Jim Hedgecock, R. 1993). Sdlg. 84-1-Q. TB, 40" (103 cm), M. S. dark purple; F. dark maroon at hafts with dark electric blue ray patterns extending to dark maroon edge; beards burnt gold, 1" blue horn; ruffled; slight sweet fragrance. Sky Hooks X Soul Music. Comanche Acres 1994.

MESHACK (Mitch Jameson, R. 1997). Sdlg. 2-88-A. TB, 34" (86 cm), ML. Violet, undertoned chestnut, F. with blue haze; beards fat, white with violet hair tips, orange in throat. Sophistication X Graduation. Knee-Deep in June 1998.

MESILLA MORN (Sharon McAllister, AB (OGB), R. 1985). Aril Society 1992.

MESMERIZER (Monty Byers, R. 1990). Sdlg. E101-1. TB, 36" (91 cm), M. Ruffled white; beards tangerine red with large uplifted frilly white flounce terminating in pale green button pompon. B37-12: (Sky Hooks x Condottiere) X Branching Out. Moonshine 1991.

MESSENGER (Sterling Innerst, R. 1994). Sdlg. 3578-4. IB, 19" (48 cm), M. White ground plicata trimmed purple; beards purple, tipped bronze; slight fragrance. Point Made X Chubby Cheeks. Innerst 1995.

MESSIAH (Chet Tompkins, R. 1999). Sdlg. 95-19. TB, 38" (97 cm), EML. Smooth deep orange self; beards deep chrome orange. Rip Snorter X Marmalade. Fleur de Lis 1999.

METAMORPHIC MAGIC (Tom Burseen, R. 1997). Sdlg. 93-339A. TB, 35" (89 cm), EM. S. light grey lavender; style arms darker grey lavender; F. cream ground, washed and streaked purple, heavier at edge; beards maize; ruffled. Step Beyond X Dawn Sky. T.B.'s Place 1997.

METEORIC RISE (Heather Pryor, R. 1999). Sdlg. 56/90-E. LA, 47" (120 cm), ML. Ruffled golden yellow, lime green line signal on all petals; style arms yellow. Designer's Dream X Gladiator's Gift.

MEXICAN MOTH (Chet Tompkins, R. 1993). Sdlg. 87-19-60. TB, 36" (91 cm), EML. S. greenish buff with coppery tint; F. blended brownish orange, oxblood red and black; beards mustard, tipped dark brown. Inv. Licorice Stick, Bermuda High, Dusky Dancer, Gypsy Lullaby X ((Uproar x 80-70A) x Swahili). Fleur de Lis 1993.

MEXICAN TILE (Kirk Strawn, R. 1993). Sdlg. 37-1984. LA, 37" (93 cm), L. S. dark greyed orange (RHS 174C); style arms darker (176D); F. greyed red (178B), yellow orange (16A) signal. Sun Fury X Shrimp Louis.

MEZZA CARTUCCIA (Augusto Bianco, R. 1998). Sdlg. 580. IB, 24" (60 cm), EML. S. blue grey, central area flushed wine; style arms grey; F. violet; beards lilac to sky blue, gold in throat; slight spicy fragrance. (Pacific Tide x Touch of Bronze) X Chubby Cheeks. Iride 1998.

MEZZOTINTO (Ladislav Muska, R. 1999). Sdlg. CFQC-07. TB, 36" (91 cm), M. S. rose lavender, broad light maroon rim; style arms yellow; F. white ground, widely and heavily sanded maroon; beards yellow; ruffled, lightly laced; spicy fragrance. (("Cocoa Foam" x Queen in Calico) x (Calicoball x Rei Momo)) X Jesse's Song. Muska 1998.

MIAH JANE (Tom Parkhill, R. 1999). Sdlg. 91-1304. TB, 36" (91 cm), ML. Heavily ruffled light blue self; beards yellow, white at end; slight fragrance. Breakers X Tide's In.

MICANTE (L. J. Duffy, R. 1999). Sdlg. WI-84-95. SPEC (*setosa*), 24-30" (61-76 cm), M. Lavender (RHS 69D), F. with yellow and purple basal veining; style arms pale yellow and white, lavender pencil-line midstripe, lavender crests; recurved form; purple-toned 2- to 3-branched stalks. Collected from wild 6½ miles SE of Fairbanks, Alaska, Nordale Road area, 1995.

MICHAEL DEWAYNE (Clyde & Anna Hahn, R. 1996). Sdlg. 91-11-C. TB, 29" (74 cm), EM. S. and style arms yellow; F. yellow, white in center; beards orange, tipped yellow; slight sweet fragrance. Sunkist Frills X Time Piece. Hahn's Rainbow 1996.

MICHAEL FREDERICK STEVENS (J. Owings Rebert, R. 1997). Sdlg. UG-F1. SIB, 28" (71 cm), M. S. violet blue; F. slightly deeper, maroon brown to ivory hafts and signal. Parentage unknown.

MICHAEL'S ANNA MAY (Oscar Schick, R. 1999). Sdlg. 91-15-G01. TB, 38" (97 cm), M. Ruffled light pink (RHS 62D) self; beards tangerine pink; slight musky fragrance. Delirious X 89-13D: (Winterscape x Titan's Glory).

MICHELE RENE (Ed Matheny III, TB, R. 1989). Ed's Iris 1992.

MICHELLE RENEE STEVENS (J. Owings Rebert, R. 1996). Sdlg. UG-3. SIB, 28" (71 cm), M. Soft pinkish blue, F. with small ivory signal, few lemon haft marks. Parentage unknown.

MICHELLE STADLER (James Stadler, R. 1990). Sdlg. H33/13. BB, 24" (61 cm), EM. S. deep coral pink; F. medium coral pink; beards deep pink; ruffled, lightly laced; slight spicy fragrance. Pink Bubbles X Memphis Delight. Celestial Gardens 1991.

MICHILLINDA (Carl Milliken by Philip Edinger, R. 1999). TB, 40" (102 cm), ML. Ruffled cream ground plicata overlaid light pink, dotted dark rose markings; beards dark yellow. Parentage unknown. Milliken 1950.

MICRO CHIP (Ben Hager, SDB, R. 1989). Melrose 1990.

MICRO MINI (A. & D. Willott, R. 1999). Sdlg. W 95-28. MDB, 4" (10 cm), E. Light yellow, F. with large maroon spot; beards cream deepening to yellow in throat. W 91-85, Wee Ghost sib, X W 92-6: (Kuban *pumila* #205 x Daring Eyes).

MIDARE ITO (Koji Tomino by Society for Japanese Irises, R. 1993). JI (3 F.),30" (76 cm), EM. S. lavender, paling to near-white; style arms white, crests lavender; F. light lavender, aging near-white, white halo; S. often drop after opening, giving appearance of 3 large and 3 smaller F. Parentage unknown. Tomino prior to 1970.

MIDAS PLUSH (Barry Blyth, R. 1990). Sdlg. W21-A. IB, 22" (56 cm), EM. Brilliant gold; beards chrome gold. It's Love X Catalyst. Tempo Two 1990/91.

MIDINETTE (Lawrence Ransom, R. 1999). Sdlg. 92/114-A. IB, 27" (68 cm), M. S. raw sienna blended pale lilac; style arms soft yellow, ridge and base white; F. rosy lilac center conspicuously veined white, light raw sienna edge, yellower hafts peppered brown, white area around beard; beards cream white, brushed orange in throat. Violet Lulu X Classmate.

MIDNIGHT CALLER (Monty Byers, TB, R. 1989). Moonshine 1990.

MIDNIGHT CAPER (Francis Rogers, R. 1998). Sdlg. C-115-A. TB, 30" (76 cm), M. S. and style arms dark plum purple (RHS 79A); F. near-black; beards violet blue (93A); ruffled; sweet fragrance. Night Ruler X Blackout. Meadowbrook 1999.

MIDNIGHT CHILD (George Sutton, R. 1998). Sdlg. G-85C. SDB, 12" (31 cm), EM & RE. S. and style arms plum purple (darker than RHS 79A), F. with darker thumbprint; beards near wistaria blue (92A), hairs tipped lighter; ruffled; slight sweet fragrance. Sigh X Chanted.

MIDNIGHT DANCER (Schreiner, R. 1991). Sdlg. S 107-A. TB, 36" (91 cm), EM. Purple black; beards black; ruffled, flared. M 229-2: ((B 1072-1: ((Allegiance x N 364-1) x (R 1199-1 x Black Swan)) x Navy Strut) x (C 276-A: ((R 808-E x Black Swan) x Matinata) x Navy Strut)) X I 181-1: ((Black Swan x S 529-H, Tuxedo sib) x Navy Strut). Schreiner 1991.

MIDNIGHT DRAMA (John C. Taylor, R. 1990). Sdlg. OL 142-1. LA, 43" (110 cm), EM. Ruffled violet (RHS 86B), lighter reverse, yellow signal on S. and F. M24-4: (C'est Si Bon x Charles Arny III) X Helen Naish. Rainbow Ridge 1990/91.

MIDNIGHT FRAGRANCE (Stephen Stevens by Clyde Hahn, TB, R. 1989). Hahn's Rainbow 1990.

MIDNIGHT FROST (Stan Dexter by Marie Ingersoll, R. 1993). Sdlg. 7-118A. TB, 38" (97 cm), M. Reddish blue purple, blue line below beards; beards yellow, tipped blue. Lord Jeff X Grape Charm. Ingersoll's Iris 1994.

MIDNIGHT HUSTLE (William Plotner, R. 1992). Sdlg. 83-35-2. TB, 36" (91 cm), ML. S. campanula violet (RHS 84A/82D), veined slightly darker; F. dark canterbury violet (86A) lightening to broad campanula violet edge; beards violet, tipped bronze; slight spicy fragrance. (Lilac Wine x Navajo Blanket) X Total Authority. Wildwood Gardens 1990.

MIDNIGHT JOURNEY (Lois Rich by James Whitely, R. 1994). Sdlg. R69-1B. AR (RC), 14" (36 cm), EM. S. orchid ground veined dark violet; F. blackish, darker black signal; beards yellow orange. Persian Pansy X CR64-19A: ((((*I. lortetii* x (K47-18 x *I. gatesii*)) x ((*I. susiana* x *I. gatesii*) x *I. nazarena*)) x ((*I. helenae* x (*I. auranitica* x Charon)) x (K53-44LB x Judean Cream))). Aril Patch 1994.

MIDNIGHT MADONNA (Robert Dunn, R. 1995). Sdlg. B2011-4. TB, 36" (91 cm), EM. Heavily ruffled very dark purple black, F. with velvety texture; beards dark purple. B1006: (Skyship x Sea Wolf) X Mystic Warrior. M.A.D. Iris 1996.

MIDNIGHT MIST (Paul Black, R. 1995). Sdlg. 87134C. SDB, 14" (36 cm), E. S. very wide red violet plicata band, small white central area; style arms purple; F. white near beard, red violet luminata wash over center, darker red violet plicata band; beards white, violet in throat; slight spicy fragrance. Chubby Cheeks X 84238F: (Oriental Blush x Sniffs 'n' Sneezes). Mid-America 1995.

MIDNIGHT MOONLIGHT (Lowell Baumunk, R. 1999). Sdlg. 94X10-10. TB, 35" (89 cm), EM. S. white; style arms white, highlighted lavender; F. dark purple, edge slightly lighter, white area around beard patterned with purple lines; beards mustard, base white. Tempting Fate X 92TFRW-3: (Twist of Fate x Ride the Wind).

MIDNIGHT OASIS (Lois Rich by James Whitely, R. 1992). Sdlg. R80-148B. AB (OGB), 25" (64 cm), ML. S. deep purple black veined darker; style arms deep purple black; F. velvety deep purple black, black signal; beards black. R74-84C: (R69-101F: (Kerr 55-3-0 x TB blue) x R66-35L: ((Kerr K54-8-0 x Judean Raven) x *I. antilibanotica*)) X Othmani. Aril Patch 1992.

MIDNIGHT OIL (Keith Keppel, R. 1997). Sdlg. 91-174A. TB, 36" (91 cm), M. Black self, darker than eggplant (M&P 48-H-12), F. with slight velvet finish; style arms darker than port (56-E-12); beards grape (47-JL-12); slight sweet fragrance. 88-45C: ((Snowbrook x Blackout) x 84-93B, Light Show sib) X Before the Storm. Keppel 1998.

MIDNIGHT RIVAL (Lawrence Johnsen, R. 1992). Sdlg. VYCW 89-3. SPU, 48" (122 cm), ML. S. dark amethyst purple; style arms purple, edged lighter, deep purple crests; F. deepest amethyst purple with velvety brown overlay, small yellow signal; ruffled. Vintage Year X Crow Wing. Shepard Iris 1993.

MIDNIGHT SPIRIT (Richard Morgan, R. 1992). Sdlg. L597-D. LA, 21" (54 cm), E. Dark blue violet (RHS 89A), yellow line signal. Full Eclipse X Trail of Tears. Redbud Lane 1992.

MIDNIGHT THUNDERSTORMS (Chun Fan, R. 1996). Sdlg. F90-88. TB, 35" (89 cm), ML-VL. Ruffled pure deep velvety violet (RHS 86A); beards violet blue; pronounced spicy fragrance. Chico Maid X Dusky Challenger.

MIDNIGHT WINE (Lorena Reid, R. 1992). SPEC (*laevigata*), 14-20" (36-51 cm), M. S. very deep maroon; style arms slightly lighter; F. very deep maroon, white slash signal extending about halfway from styles. Regal X unknown. Laurie's Garden 1992.

MIDRIB MAGIC (D. L. Shepard, R. 1999). Sdlg. 96004-9309. SPU, 45-52" (114-132 cm), ML. S. pale violet, gold splash on inner side; style arms lavender and dark violet, yellow rib; F. dark golden yellow, dark violet centerline, 1/2" pale violet edge. Giuseppe X Purple Reign. Shepard Iris 1999.

MIDSUMMER HAPPINESS (Currier McEwen, R. 1990). Sdlg. 85/95F. JI (6 F.), 39" (98 cm), ML. Blue (RHS 95C/D) with clean white lines extending to edge, rich yellow (13B) signal; style arms tufted, stamens petaloid; ruffled. White Parachute X Continuing Pleasure. Pope's Perennials, Seaways 1991.

MIDSUMMER NIGHT'S DREAM (Lowell Baumunk, R. 1998). Sdlg. 92BBWA-7. IB, 17" (43 cm), M & RE. Dark purple self; beards dark purple. Best Bet X What Again. Baumunk 1999.

MIDSUMMER'S EVE (Donald Spoon, R. 1997). BB, 27" (69 cm), ML & RE. S. and style arms pink;

F. peach pink, darker veining; beards tangerine; lightly ruffled, flared. Immortality X Enchanted World. Winterberry 1999.

MIDWEST STAR (Cleo Palmer, R. 1992). Sdlg. 89119. IB, 22" (56 cm), L. S. light orange, midrib flushed yellow and pinkish; F. light orange yellow, hafts veined peach, slightly darker toward tip; beards red orange tipped paler. Parentage unknown. Palmer's Iris 1992.

MIGHTY DARK (B. Charles Jenkins, R. 1998). Sdlg. BH44F. SPU 36-40" (91-107 cm), ML. Near-black self overtoned maroon, small yellow veined signal. Purple Reign X C17-7C: (Highline Honey x Crow Wing). Shepard Iris 1999.

MIGHTY MAUVE (Eleanor McCown, R. 1991). Sdlg. 87-12. SPU, 49" (125 cm), M. S. pale mauve with tan influence; F. deep reddish mauve, lighter ruffled edge, gold signal heavily veined and speckled mauve. 82-15, white, X 79-10: (75-2 x Ripe Wheat). Cordon Bleu 1991.

MIKHAIL LERMONTOV (V. & G. Gordodelovy, R. 1995). Sdlg. 25. TB, 32" (80 cm), M. S. orange red, yellow basal striations; style arms brown; F. orange red, yellow haft striations; beards brown. Parentage unknown. Gordodelovy 1979.

MIKIE ANN (Carl Boswell, R. 1991). Sdlg. 76-84-4S. SDB, 9" (23 cm), EM. S. pale smoky plum, edged light plum; F. red maroon, edged pale plum; beards light orchid. Cute Stuff X Plum Spot. Adamgrove 1992.

MIKIKO (Tomas Tamberg, R. 1993). Sdlg. 8406-1. SIB, 31½" (80 cm), M. White self. Sdlg. X Creme Chantilly. V. H. Humphrey 1995.

MILANO (William Maryott, R. 1995). Sdlg. TM198RE. SDB, 10" (25 cm), M & RE. S. bright yellow; F. maroon, 1/4" bright yellow rim; beards yellow. Sunstrip X Jazzamatazz. Maryott 1996.

MIL BYERS (Monty Byers by Phyllis Dickey, R. 1997). Sdlg. EM 92-1. TB, 30" (76 cm), E & RE. Peach self; beards orange; slight sweet fragrance. Parentage unknown. Misty Hill 1997.

MILDRED ANNE (Frederick Kerr, R. 1997). Sdlg. 905307. TB, 38" (97 cm), ML. S. very pale rose lavender, aging white; style arms white, pale rose lavender lip; F. medium rose lavender, lighter edge and beside beard; beards white, yellow in throat; slight sweet fragrance. Gypsy Woman X Silverado. Rainbow Acres 1997.

MILDRED MAE (Harry Wolford, R. 1993). Sdlg. P7C8-1. TB, 38" (97 cm), EML. Lightly ruffled light pink tan with 3/4" blue streak at tip of beards; beards orange, tipped blue; sweet fragrance. Playgirl X Chartreuse Ruffles.

MILLENNIUM (Chet Tompkins, R. 1999) Sdlg. 93-117A. TB, 38" (97 cm), ML. S. bright chamois; F. darker chamois ground heavily obscured by brownish red wash blending to electric blue violet toward center; beards white, blue at end. ((Clarion Call x Starkist) x (Soaring Kite x Royal Rage)) X Soaring Spirits. Fleur de Lis 1999.

MILLENNIUM BUG (A. & D. Willott, R. 1999). Sdlg. W 96-23. MDB, 8" (20 cm), M. Pale blue, edges tinted green, F. with deeper green haft veining and small blue violet spot around light orange beard; style arms pale blue. Elfin Magic X unknown.

MILLENNIUM FALCON (Brad Kasperek, R. 1998). Sdlg. 94B-23C. TB, 38" (97 cm), M. S. light wistaria blue (RHS 92A), silver white (155D) streaks; style arms violet blue; F. rich royal blue (89B), silver white streaks; beards orange, hairs tipped blue; broken color pattern; ruffled; slight fragrance. Gnus Flash X 92B-49Z: (Batik x 89B-42E: (Rustic Dance x Maria Tormena)).

MILLENNIUM MELTDOWN (Jim Hedgecock, R. 1999). Sdlg. F-9-B. TB, 34" (86 cm), M. S. medium red; F. velvety dark red, narrow medium red band; beards burnt gold; lightly laced, ruffled. Spanish Tile X 83-132-1: (Fairlight x unknown).

MILLION MILES (Roger Nelson, TB, R. 1987). Iris Country 1991.

MILTA (Viacheslav Gavrilin, R. 1999). Sdlg. 924-621-4. TB, 33" (84 cm), M. S. and style arms light yellowish lilac; F. light yellowish lilac, whitish lilac below beard, hafts yellow, edge light tan yellow; beards orange, yellow at end; ruffled. Fiesta Time X Starcrest.

MILY DRUG (Viktor Sheviakov, R. 1995). Sdlg. 12 A 4. TB, 29" (72 cm), ML. S. pinkish violet; F. violet purple; beards tangerine; ruffled, laced. Rippling Waters X Latin Lover. Sheviakov 1997.

MIND BEND (Duane Meek, R. 1995). Sdlg. 150-1-5. TB, 35" (89 cm), EM. S. solid light maroon; F. pale apricot ground, patterned streaking from cinnamon beard to very wide irregular dark maroon border; ruffled. (Mistress x Lingering Love) X Wild Berry. D & J Gardens 1995.

MIND READER (Keith Keppel, R. 1992). Sdlg. 86-18B. TB, 36" (91 cm), E. S. mignon violet (M&P 43-G-7) irregularly shaded over pale (43-B-1/2) ground, paler edge; F. deeper (43-J-9) becoming darker (44-K-11) and slightly velvety in center with conspicuous pale veining, white (43-B-1/2) area by beards and 1/8" edge; beards white, tipped pale lemon; pronounced sweet fragrance. Sib to Spirit World. Keppel 1994.

MIND'S EYE (Barry Blyth, R. 1994). Sdlg. A98-2. TB, 34" (86 cm), EM. S. pure white; F. peachy apricot, 1/4" laced white edge; beards bright saturn red; slight fragrance. Lover's Lane X X90-A: ((So Rare x (Ringo x Color Bash)) x Town Clown). Tempo Two 1994/95.

MING (Marky Smith, R. 1997). Sdlg. 89-52F. IB, 25" (64 cm), M. S. clear dresden yellow (RHS 5A), green midrib; style arms clear yellow, midrib cream; F. shoulders dresden yellow (5A), slightly lighter (5B) rim, small cream white (4D) center and median stripe; beards cream white at end, strong yellow in throat; lightly ruffled; pronounced sweet fragrance. Violet Lulu X Keppel 84-15B, pollen parent of Spirit World. Aitken's Salmon Creek 1998.

MINI-AGNES (Thelma Naylor, SDB, R. 1988). British Iris Society 1995.

MINI BIG HORN (Robert Annand, R. 1998). Sdlg. 91-28A. SDB, 15" (38 cm), M. S. old gold; style arms old gold, midrib violet; F. purple blue flushed maroon on upper portion, 1/16" old gold edge; beards yellow orange blending to 1/2" purple horn. (Escape Artist x Frosted Olives) X Gladys Austin. Forest Ranch 1998.

MINI CHAMPAGNE (George Sutton, R. 1997). Sdlg. G-95. BB, 25" (64 cm), ML & RE. S. white, midrib blended peach; style arms white and apricot; F. peach (RHS 29C); beards soft orange, white at end; ruffled; slight sweet fragrance. F-245: (E-133: (Cloudless Sunrise x Brown Lasso) x (2-14 x Frizzy Lizzy)) X F-261: (E-133 x (Blazing Sunrise x Gypsy Wings)). Sutton 1998.

MINIDRAGON (Marky Smith, R. 1996). Sdlg. 93-06A. SDB, 13" (33 cm), M. S. silky dark port wine (RHS 187A); style arms old gold, red violet midrib; F. black burgundy, darker than S.; beards tangerine (32A); lightly ruffled; slight sweet fragrance. Asmus 85-72A: (Mad Dash x Little Annie) X Shoop red: (Torchy x Bright Chic). Aitken's Salmon Creek 1998.

MINIKIN (Allan Ensminger, R. 1991). Sdlg. 85-13. MDB, 7" (18 cm), L. S. violet, cream midrib; F. yellow, edged cream; beards violet. People Pleaser X 183-4: (280-4: ((75-2: (Born Free x 69-8) x Gingerbread Man) x 78-3) x 180-8: (73-1 x (Tumwater x 73-1))). Varigay 1998.

MINI-LAVENDER (Thelma Naylor, R. 1995). Sdlg. 89/2. MDB, 6" (15 cm), L. S. lavender blue; F. lavender blue, deeper near beard; beards white, gold in throat. 82/3/2: (Jeremy Brian x 77/8/3 lavender blue) X unknown.

MINI MIGHT (John Weiler, R. 1992). Sdlg. 87-48-3RE. SDB, 10" (25 cm), M & RE. S. light yellow; F. slightly darker; beards lavender blue; slight sweet fragrance. 85-4-4: ((75-101-8RE: (70-95-3: (Brighteyes x Grace Note) x Gingerbread Man) x Chariots) x (76-1-1: (Ruby Contrast x Little Blackfoot) x sib) X 84-43-5RE: (((((Yellow Wave x 70-95-2) x 74-3-1: (Cartwheel x 70-95-6)) x Chariots) x (75-101-10 x Stockholm)) x ((76-1-15RE x ((70-95-3 x Bronze Babe) x 74-3-1)) x Pink Amber)). Rialto 1992.

MINI SONG (Barry Blyth, R. 1992). Sdlg. X31-6. SDB, 10" (25 cm), VE. S. smoky orchid rose pink; F. creamy smoky pink, lavender flash below beard; beards tangerine, outer 1/2" lavender. Yipee X Camarilla. Tempo Two 1992/93.

MINITREND (B. Charles Jenkins, R. 1995). Sdlg. BA01P. SPU, 28-32" (71-81 cm), EM. S. light violet, blended ivory at base; style arms violet, edged ivory; F. ivory ground, yellow signal radiating yellow lines changing to violet, forming narrow violet edge. Color Focus X Diminuendo. Shepard Iris 1997.

MINI WABASH (Riley Probst, R. 1993). Sdlg. 89PQX37OP2. MTB, 22" (56 cm), ML. S. white; F. dark violet blue (RHS 89A) overlaid on white ground creating effect of purple veins radiating from yellow beard, slight lighter purple rim. Pretty Quirky X Ornate Pageant. Miller's Manor 1996.

MIN MIN (Hilmary Catton, R. 1990). Sdlg. 801-4. IB, 16" (40 cm), ML. Bright mustard yellow, hafts deeper; beards bronze. Zing X Marsh Light. Wyuna 1991/92.

MINNESOTA PINKS (Jack Worel, R. 1999). Sdlg. PG2. TB, 32" (81 cm), M. Light venetian pink (RHS 49C), S. with peach midrib flush, F. with slightly lighter center, slightly darker hafts; style arms peach pink; beards light orange, light pink at end, a few hairs tipped violet. (Paradise x Pink Blue Genes) X (Paradise x (Good Morning America x Song of Norway)). Holly Lane 1999.

MINNOW (Jim & Vicki Craig, R. 1999). Sdlg. C1X44. SPEC (*aphylla*), 10" (25 cm), L. Deep violet self; beards lighter violet. *I. aphylla* 61-56A X Aphylla Wine-Red.

MINOKOTOBUKI (Koji Tomino by Society for Japanese Irises, R. 1993). JI (3 F.), 30" (76 cm), M. Bright red violet with white margins; style arms red violet. Parentage unknown. Tomino prior to 1980.

#MINTAKA (G. Bunyard, TB, R. 1927). Listed as obsolete in 1939 Check List; name released.

MINTAKA (Jim Hummel, R. 1990). Sdlg. JH 80-34M. BB, 22½" (57 cm), M. White infused light cornflower blue (HCC 742/3), some darker veining on S.; beards cornflower blue (742/1). 78-13B: (Navy Strut x Sea Bright) X Blue Luster. Bumble Bee Gardens 1991.

MINTED GOLD (Barry Blyth, R. 1999). Sdlg. F112-2. IB, 25" (64 cm), M-VL. S. gold; F. slightly deeper gold; beards orange gold. Aura Light X Celsius. Tempo Two 1999/2000.

MIRABEL GLOW (Tony Huber, R. 1998). Sdlg. 94-052. SPEC-X (versata), 28" (70 cm), ML.S. purple red (RHS 84A); style arms centered aster violet (87C), bordered mauve and white; F. violet (88A) aging to aster violet (87C) on second day, bright yellow signal with white extension line; slight spicy fragrance. 90-XDom 031: (Belle Promesse x self) X pink *I. ensata* sdlg.

MIRA MAR GOLD (Nell Wilson, R. 1994). Sdlg. 90-2. TB, 35" (89 cm), L. Gold self; beards orange; pronounced sweet fragrance. ((Rainbow Gold x Royal Gold) x Royal Gold) X Sun City.

MIRANA (Manfred Beer, R. 1994). Sdlg. MB 4/85A. TB, 29" (75 cm), EM. Lightly waved yellow orange (RHS 15B); beards orange (28A), tipped lighter. Skyfire X Orange Empire. Baumschule Mattuschka 1994.

MIRAZH (V. & N. Gordodelovy, R. 1995). Sdlg. 27. TB, 37" (95 cm), M. Lemon yellow tinted lettuce green, brown striations at base of S. and on F. hafts; beards orange. Parentage unknown. Gordodelovy 1993.

MIR DLIA DVOIKH (Sergey Loktev, R. 1999). Sdlg. 93-R13-7A. TB, 28" (71 cm), EML. S. light yellow; style arms dark yellow, midrib pale violet; F. purple violet, blue lilac central spot, cream hafts with claret brown patterning; beards yellow, white base at end. Arc Above X Siva Siva. Loktev 1999.

MIR-DRUZHBA (V. & N. Gordodelovy, R. 1995). Sdlg. 30. TB, 32" (80 cm), M. White, tinted pink, base of S. and F. hafts striated brown; beards orange, cream at end. Parentage unknown. Gordodelovy 1979.

MISCHA (Barry Blyth, R. 1997). Sdlg. D34-7. SDB, 14" (36 cm), ML. S. apricot tan, deeper violet midrib flush; F. white ground, apricot tan outer margin, dotted and veined violet hafts and inner margin; beards white, lavender at end, tangerine in throat. Bee's Knees X A7-1: (Merry Dance x Mini Song). Tempo Two 1997/98.

MISCHIEF MAKER (Bernard Pryor, R. 1997). Sdlg. 35/92-D. LA, 32" (81 cm), EM. S. and F. soft pink (RHS 63C) with white rim, darker pink veining; signals lime yellow, veined lime, surrounded by darker pink; style arms soft lemon; ruffled. Volcanic Wildfire X Spanish Ballet. Lone Star 1998.

MISS ANDREA (Lin Flanagan, R. 1993). Sdlg. 85014-4. AB (OGB-), 24" (61 cm), M. S. pale violet amber blend; F. amber flushed pale violet; beards yellow; ruffled; slight fragrance. Vanity X 78001-6: (Thunderstorm x Mayfest). Aril Society 1994.

MISS ATLANTA (David Mohr, R. 1990). TB, 32" (81 cm), VE-E. S. medium azalea pink; F. lighter azalea pink, paling to cream pink around tangerine beard; slight fragrance. Blushing Diana sib X (Sun City x Temple Gold). Pacific Coast Hybridizers 1990.

MISS BUFFALO (Anna Rettig, R. 1997). Sdlg. AR-090. JI (3 F.), 23" (58 cm), M. S. white, narrow magenta edge; style arms white, flushed violet; F. white, light blue violet wash, chartreuse green (RHS 154B) signal. Parentage unknown. A & M Perennials 1998.

MISS BUTTERWORTH (Jim Hedgecock, R. 1993). Sdlg. 84-3-6. TB, 36" (91 cm), M. Ruffled and laced creamy yellow; beards bright gold. Baroque Prelude X Moonstruck. Comanche Acres 1994.

MISS CARLA (John D. Taylor, IB, R. 1985). British Iris Society 1989.

MISS CAROL (J. R. Allen, R. 1993). Sdlg. KV1. TB, 32" (81 cm), EM. S. white with bluish tinge at base; F. white; beards pale yellow, tipped light blue; ruffled; slight fragrance. R3A: (Sapphire Hills x Rebecca Anne) X Rebecca Anne. Allen Iris 1997.

MISS COLLEEN (Lin Flanagan, AB (OGB-), R. 1989). Aril Society 1991.

MISS DAISY (Donald Sorensen, R. 1998). Sdlg. S-95-10-1. TB, 34" (86 cm), M. S. light barium yellow (RHS 10D); style arms light primrose yellow (4D) to cream; F. creamy white (155A), medium naples yellow (11B) haft, very light violet extending from beard to center; beards violet blue (91D) at end changing to light aureolin yellow (12C), chrome yellow (15C) in throat; heavily ruffled; pronounced sweet fragrance. World Class X Caption.

MISS GERTIE'S BONNET (Dorman Haymon, R. 1999). Sdlg. 81-92-2. LA, 44" (119 cm), M. S. cream, edged lavender, veined brown; style arms dark lavender, tipped lavender cream; F. light lavender, edged dark lavender, veined brown, gold steeple signal outlined brown; ruffled, strongly flared; slight sweet fragrance. Charlie's Karen X All Agaze.

MISSION IMPOSSIBLE (George Sutton, R. 1998). Sdlg. G-19-F. TB, 36" (91 cm), EML. S. and style arms neyron rose (RHS 55C), S. veined darker; F. imperial purple (near 78A); beards orange, pale rose at end, extending as white petaloid with rose spoon; ruffled; slight spicy fragrance. Sweet Musette X Twice Thrilling. Sutton 1999.

MISSION SANTA CLARA (Joseph Ghio, R. 1992). Sdlg. PH-265C. CA, 10" (25 cm), EM. S. crimson red; style arms buff red; F. crimson red, neon violet signal, buff red hairline edge. San Felipe sib X (((Big Wheel x (Pacific Moon x California Native)) x Montara sib) x San Gregorio). Bay View 1993.

MISSISSIPPI BLUES (James McWhirter by Abram Feuerstein, R. 1999). Sdlg. 92-126-6. TB, 32" (81 cm), EM. Medium blue self; beards yellow; foliage purple-based. Prince of Tides X Quintessence.

MISS JESSICA (Don Nebeker, R. 1997). Sdlg. N 1148-1. TB, 36" (91 cm), EM. S. white ground overlaid cream, 1/4" dark violet stitched edge; style arms dark violet, prominent; F. white touched cream, 1/4" dark violet stitched edge; beards tangerine; ruffled; slight fragrance. N 1033-3: (Rare Treat x N 816-14: (Beyond x Capricious)) X N 1031-1: (Gigolo x N 816-14). Zebra 1997.

MISS KAY (J. R. Allen, R. 1992). Sdlg. 88B. TB, 32" (81 cm), ML. Heavily ruffled and fluted white; beards pale yellow, tipped pale blue; slight sweet fragrance. Probably --- (Jack R. Dee x Full Tide) X Vows Renewed. Allen Iris 1997.

MISS LAURA (Lin Flanagan, R. 1997). Sdlg. 83002-1. AB (OGB), 22" (56 cm), E. S. pale cream; style arms pale violet; F. pale cream blended violet pink; beards blended violet and orange; ruffled, semi-recurved; slight fragrance. Thunderstorm X 80003-1: (Desert Dove x Rare Spice).

MISS LEMON (Phyllis Dickey, R. 1996). Sdlg. PD 44-1. TB, 35" (89 cm), ML. S. soft lemon yellow; F. soft lemon yellow, washed white, dark yellow edging; beards yellow; slight sweet fragrance. Playgirl X Dusky Challenger. Misty Hill 1996.

MISS LUCIE (George Slade, R. 1990). Sdlg. 85-28-C. TB, 35" (89 cm), M. Red purple (near RHS 64A), F. shoulders edged tan; beards bright tangerine; slight sweet fragrance. Frosty Jewels X Helen's Pick. Wyle Wynde 1990.

MISS OCHAROVANIYE (V. & N. Gordodelovy, R. 1995). Sdlg. 53. TB, 39" (100 cm), ML. S. light pink, base tinted lilac; style arms light lilac edged yellow; F. light pink, tinted lilac, brown haft striations; beards red; ruffled. Parentage unknown. Gordodelovy 1984.

MISSOULA (Allan Ensminger, R. 1996). Sdlg. 193-1. SDB, 12" (31 cm), ML. S. flax blue (HCC 642/3), midrib darker (642/1); F. flax blue, mineral violet (635) spot pattern; beards purple, brown at end; slight fragrance. Zing Me X 91-4: (85-3: (Do-Si-Do x ((Boo x Sweet 'n Neat) x (Miss Region Twenty-One x (Eye Shadow x Reath 6-64)))) x Chubby Cheeks).

MISSOURI AUTUMN (O. D. Niswonger, R. 1996). Sdlg. Sp 16-93. SPU, 40" (102 cm), M. Light brown self. Sp 6-80: (Far Out x Redwood Supreme) X unknown. Cape Iris 1997.

MISSOURI CLOUDS (O. D. Niswonger, R. 1995). Sdlg. Sp 1-93. SPU, 42" (107 cm), M. White, F. with yellow blush. Sp 4-88: (Sp 6-80: (Far Out x Redwood Supreme) x unknown) X Chocolate Fudge. Cape Iris 1996.

MISSOURI DREAMLAND (O. D. Niswonger, R. 1999). Sdlg. Sp 1-94. SPU, 42" (107 cm), M. Blended yellow and rose, style arms lightly touched violet; F. yellow, blended rose toward edge. Sp 8-88: (Sp 6-80: (Far Out x Redwood Supreme) x unknown) X Firemist. Cape Iris 1999.

MISSOURI IRON ORE (O. D. Niswonger, R. 1996). Sdlg. SP 5-94. SPU, 42" (107 cm), M. S. dark purple, infused red; style arms purple, infused red brown; F. red brown, infused purple. Mary's Beau Brummel X Sultan's Sash. Cape Iris 1997.

MISSOURI LAKES (O. D. Niswonger, R. 1994). Sdlg. Sp 2-86. SPU, 38" (97 cm), M. S. light blue; F. light blue, yellow blaze. Missouri Streams X unknown -- probably self. Cape Iris 1994.

MISSOURI METEOR (Jim Hedgecock, R. 1995). Sdlg. C-82-2-D. TB, 34" (86 cm), M. Medium orange, lighter area by bright orange beards; ruffled, lightly laced; slight sweet fragrance. Four Leaf Clover X Replay. Comanche Acres 1996.

MISSOURI MIST (O. D. Niswonger, R. 1999). Sdlg. 71-95. TB, 38" (97 cm), M. S. and style arms dark blue; F. pallid blue; beards orange tangerine, base and end white. Honky Tonk Blues X Upside Down. Cape Iris 1999.

MISSOURI MOONLIGHT (O. D. Niswonger, R. 1996). Sdlg. Sp 4-94. SPU, 40" (102 cm), M. Light yellow self. Sp 8-88: (Sp 6-80: (Far Out x Redwood Supreme) x unknown) X Firemist. Cape Iris 1997.

MISSOURI ORANGE (O. D. Niswonger, R. 1998). Sdlg. Sp 2-94. SPU, 42" (107 cm), M. Golden orange, F. with deeper golden orange signal. Goldmania X Destination. Cape Iris 1998.

MISSOURI RAINBOWS (O. D. Niswonger, R. 1996). Sdlg. Sp 4-93. SPU, 40" (102 cm), M. S. and style arms medium blue; F. medium blue, paling and becoming almost white at edge of yellow blaze. Missouri Rivers X Olinda. Cape Iris 1997.

MISSOURI RIVERS (O. D. Niswonger, SPU, R. 1989). Cape Iris 1990.

MISSOURI ROSE (Jim Hedgecock, R. 1995). Sdlg. C-82-3-rose. TB, 34" (86 cm), M. S. rose pink; F. rose, paler hafts and center streak; beards bright tangerine orange; ruffled, laced; slight sweet fragrance. Beauty Crown X Homecoming Queen. Comanche Acres 1995.

MISSOURI SMILE (O. D. Niswonger, R. 1999). Sdlg. 45-95. TB, 36" (91 cm), M. S. and style arms mauve pink; F. lighter mauve pink; beards blue at end, tangerine and blue midsection, sienna in throat. Sky Blue Pink X 46-92: (Pink Blue Genes x Fontaine). Cape Iris 1999.

MISSOURI SPRINGS (O. D. Niswonger, R. 1994). Sdlg. Sp 2-91. SPU, 40" (102 cm), ML. Deep blue, F. with small yellow signal. Sp 1-86: (Missouri Streams x unknown -- probably self) X *I. demetrii*. Cape Iris 1994.

MISSOURI STAR (O. D. Niswonger, R. 1998). Sdlg. Sp 8-94. SPU, 42" (107 cm), M. S. lavender blue; style arms blue; F. lavender blue, medium yellow signal. Sp 1-86: (Missouri Streams x unknown) X unknown. Cape Iris 1998.

MISSOURI SUNSET (O. D. Niswonger, R. 1995). Sdlg. Sp 6-92. SPU, 42" (107 cm), M. Yellow, F. with deeper gold signal. Parentage unknown. Cape Iris 1996.

MISS PIGGY (Tom Burseen, R. 1997). Sdlg. 1-127B. TB, 35" (89 cm), ML. S. dark plum purple (RHS 79A); style arms black; F. blackish burgundy, white haft striations; beards gold; ruffled; sweet fragrance. 9-153: ((Afternoon Delight x Sooner Serenade) x Burnt Crisp) X 9-220: (Bluid x Quite Quaint). T.B.'s Place 1997.

MISS PORTERVILLE (George Sutton, R. 1997). Sdlg. G-94. TB, 37" (94 cm), ML & RE. Ruffled deep velvety plum purple self; beards plum purple; slight sweet fragrance. Holy Night X Blue Anew. Sutton 1998.

MISS PRETTY (Mel Leavitt, R. 1991). Sdlg. M-90-1. TB, 39" (99 cm), M. S. white; F. white ground splashed red, edged white; beards yellow, tipped white. H-77-M: (Ringo x Cloudless Sunrise) X H-80-P: (Spinning Wheel x Sterling Stitch).

MISS SARA (Darlene Pinegar, R. 1992). Sdlg. PNS-2-2. TB, 30½" (77 cm), M. S. medium pink, edged lighter peach pink; F. toasted pink, hafts veined darker; beards dark coral orange; lightly ruffled, laced; slight sweet fragrance. Earlirose X Queen in Calico. Spanish Fork 1993.

MISS SEDONA (Tom Magee, R. 1991). Sdlg. 8534A. IB, 27" (69 cm), M. Ruffled salmon pink; beards salmon orange; slight fragrance. Garden Frock sib X Shrimp. Long 1993.

MISS SUNSHINE (George Shoop, R. 1994). Sdlg. 86-50. SDB, 9" (23 cm), M. Lemon yellow, F. with darker yellow spot; beards yellow; ruffled. New Kid X Sunny Honey. Keppel 1995.

MISS SWEET (Stan Dexter by Marie Ingersoll, R. 1992). Sdlg. I-85-37. TB, 34" (86 cm), M. Creamy coral, F. hafts yellow tan; beards tangerine. Exotic Flare X Melon Supreme. Ingersoll's Iris 1993.

MISS VERRET (Richard Goula, R. 1992). Sdlg. G-85-R1. LA, 36" (91 cm), ML. Ruffled bright rose red, large bright yellow signal; slight spicy fragrance. Freddie Boy X Ann Chowning. Gatewood Gardens 1993.

MISTER CROTHERS (Bruce Clark, R. 1999). Sdlg. 96-191. TB, 37" (95 cm), ML. S. red purple; style arms buff yellow and purple; F. dark red purple, violet centerline; beards blue base and at end with hairs tipped yellow, yellow in throat. Tintinara X Supreme Sultan.

MISTER NICE GUY (Leo Barnard, R. 1997). Sdlg. L 91-96A. TB, 38-40" (97-102 cm), EML. S. and style arms blue white; F. velvety blue lavender, metallic sheen, narrow blue white rim; beards light lavender blue, hairs tipped bronze in throat; ruffled; slight fragrance. Silverado X Latin Rock. Paradise Iris 1997.

MISTICO (Thomas Burch, R. 1995). Sdlg. ACXC-1. TB, 35" (89 cm), M. Ruffled pale lavender (paler than RHS 91D) aging white; style arms lavender at base; beards white, yellow in throat; slight sweet fragrance. America's Cup X Cruzin. Burch Fields 1996.

MISTIE'S AUDIENCE (Jim Hedgecock, R. 1993). Sdlg. JM-85-4-1. TB, 33" (84 cm), M. S. white; F. pale blue, lighter area around bright golden orange beard, gold hafts; ruffled, laced. White Lightning X Chinese Treasure. Comanche Acres 1994.

MISTIGRI (Richard Cayeux, R. 1993). Sdlg. 8709 A. IB, 22" (56 cm), M. S. light blue; F. white, veined and edged blue; beards blue. Purple Fringe X Spinning Wheel. Cayeux 1993.

MISTRESS PERRY (Colin Rigby, R. 1993). SPEC-X, 6-8" (15-20"), M. Lightly ruffled full medium yellow, F. veined darker. Fairy Chimes X yellow *I. innominata* grown from collected seed (from SPCNI or SIGNA). Portable Acres 1993.

MISTS OF AVALON (Ken Mohr, R. 1990). TB, 37" (94 cm), M. S. light lavender blue; F. medium to dark lavender blue, smoother overlay of light lavender blue on shoulders; beards pale lemon, tipped white; slight fragrance. (Mystique x (Coolhead x Margarita)) X Mystic Waters sib. Pacific Coast Hybridizers 1990.

MISTY LADY (Gary Sides, R. 1994). Sdlg. D32-F20B. TB, 32" (81 cm), M & RE (Oct.). S. pale lavender; F. blue violet; beards blue violet tipped yellow; ruffled, lightly laced; slight sweet fragrance. AP46-D11B: (Corn Harvest x Vanity) X Graduation. Miller's Manor 1994.

MISTY MAY (Jim Hedgecock, R. 1993). Sdlg. 83-88-1. TB, 34" (86 cm), M. S. pale blue; F. darker blue with pale blue border, white plicata markings at hafts and by pale yellow beard; ruffled, laced and fluted. Unknown plicata sdlg. X Ballyhoo. Comanche Acres 1994.

MISTY MEMORIES (Calvin Helsley, R. 1990). Sdlg. 88-2. SIB, 26" (66 cm), M. S. light blue violet veined dark blue violet; style arms blue violet veined brilliant blue; F. smoky blue violet, 1/4" lighter blue violet edge, gold signal; ruffled. Parentage unknown. Helsley 1996.

MISTY MOISTY MORNING (Opal Wulf, R. 1998). Sdlg. 46-93-3. SDB, 15" (38 cm), EML. S. violet blue (RHS 97C) deepening at base, green midrib; style arms violet blue; F. violet blue, brown (199) spot on upper third around beard; beards brown, purple tip; pronounced sweet fragrance. Morning Show X Posy Parade.

MISTY OPAL (Nora Scopes, R. 1995). Sdlg. 7/173 B. TB, 36" (91 cm), M. S. mauve, shot tan; F. golden tan, shot and edged mauve; beards orange brown. Torchlight Tattoo X 1/147 B: (Launching Pad x (Cambodia x Western Wind)).

MISTY REFLECTIONS (Hooker Nichols, IB, R. 1988). Hillcrest 1992.

MITZU SAKURA (Shuichi Hirao by Society for Japanese Irises, R. 1993). JI (6 F.), 27" (70 cm), EM. Pink (RHS 69B), yellow signal with rib; style arms cream with slight midrib. Parentage unknown. Hirao ca. 1980.

MIX AND MATCH (Paul Black, R. 1991). Sdlg. 89U25. TB, 33" (84 cm), M. S. white rib blending to pale yellow with plum brown plicata markings around edge, gilt gold rim at top; style arms violet edged yellow gold, crests brassy violet; F. warm white, plum brown plicata markings at hafts, brassy gold edge halfway around, lime yellow band around lower half; beards yellow, tipped white at end; ruffled, laced. Bronze Fawn X Glitz 'n Glitter sib. Mid-America 1992.

MIXED REVIEWS (Hooker Nichols, TB, R. 1989). Hillcrest 1994.

MIXTURE (Graeme Grosvenor, R. 1993). Sdlg. R12-1. TB, 38" (97 cm), EM. S. white, heavily suffused rose pink; F. white, edged and dotted rose pink, plum hafts; beards orange yellow; ruffled. Beyond X N6-2: (Goddess x ((Elsedina x (Rondo x (Quetta x Ribbon Round))) x Bonifay)). Rainbow Ridge 1993/94.

MIYAKO NISHIKI (Shuichi Hirao by Society for Japanese Irises, R. 1994). JI (6 F.), 36" (91 cm), ML. Silvery ground with light purple and lavender stippling. Parentage unknown. Introduced in Japan ca. 1970.

MIYOSHINO (Koji Tomino by Society for Japanese Irises, R. 1992). JI (3 F.), 27" (70 cm), EML. Pink self. Parentage unknown. Introduced by Tomino prior to 1975.

MIYUKI (Shuichi Hirao by Society for Japanese Irises, R. 1994). JI (9 F.), 27½" (70 cm), EM. White self, usually with 9 F., upper F. partially erect appearing almost like S. Parentage unknown. Introduced in Japan 1962.

MIZ MARY (Virginia Messick, R. 1995). Sdlg. M 87-65. TB, 37" (94 cm), M. S. blended tan and peach pink; F. tan, washed pink, gold at hafts; beards gold. Spring Fling X Flower Show. Messick 1995.

MIZU-NO-HIKARI (Shuichi Hirao by Society for Japanese Irises, R. 1995). JI (3 F.), 39" (100 cm), M. S. lavender; style arms white, lavender crests; F. lavender, small white halo and veins. Parentage unknown. Introduced in Japan 1975.

MIZUTAMA BOSHI (Shuichi Hirao by Society for Japanese Irises, R. 1993). JI (6 F.), 36" (91 cm), M. Very pallid red violet giving appearance of white with red violet veins, signal yellow; style arms deep red violet, edged white. Parentage unknown. Hirao prior to 1980.

MOANA (Ivar Schmidt, R. 1995). Sdlg. PC 90-15. CA, 13" (33 cm), ML. S. pale plum, midrib deeper; style arms slightly paler plum; F. plum red, paler fine edging, small gold signal with darker plum veining. Big Money X Azaz. Iris Acres 1995/96.

MOBY GRAPE (Larry Lauer, R. 1998). Sdlg. 91-212-1. TB, 36" (91 cm), ML. Ruffled reddish purple self; beards layered purple, orange and white, orange in throat; slight sweet fragrance. 86-20-5: (Nancy Glazier x Brandy) X 88-120-3: (Quiet Riot x Sweet Musette). Stockton 1998.

MOCHACCINO (Keith Keppel, R. 1998). Sdlg. 91-53B. SDB, 12" (31 cm), M. S. lime yellow

(M&P 11-L-5) lightly shaded rose quartz (53-B-3); style arms goldenrod (10-L-5) to lime yellow; F. tennis (12-L-6) to deep stone (13-L-7), slight rosy (54-B-3) shading forming 1/2" band, 5/8" unmarked oyster white blaze; beards blue white at end, cadmium yellow (9-L-8) in throat; slight sweet fragrance. Quote X Gatty W37-9, sib. Keppel 1999.

MOCHA MELODY (Alphild Lind, R.1992). Sdlg. 87-AL-77. CA, 20" (51 cm), EM. S. cream with berry midrib 2/3 way down; F. medium berry, feathering to cream rib. Simply Wild X Wild Party.

MODERN MAJOR GENERAL (Abram Feuerstein, R. 1997). Sdlg. 92-460-1. TB, 36" (91 cm), M. S. blue; F. bluish purple, slight whitish area under beard; beards blue, bronze in throat; ruffled; slight sweet fragrance. Alexander's Ragtime Band X Dusky Challenger. Stockton 1997.

MODERN MUSIC (John Nelson by Bryce Williamson, R. 1995). TB, 37" (94 cm), M. Straw orange, flushed pinkish orange at midrib; F. straw orange; beards tangerine red; heavily laced. Inv. Buffy, Hayride, Avanti, Wenatchee Valley, Glacier Sunset, Pink Taffeta. Pacific Coast Hybridizers 1990.

MODERN PRINCESS (Chun Fan, R. 1996). Sdlg. F90-142. TB, 35" (89 cm), M. S. violet (RHS 86B), midrib streaked white; F. white ground, 3/4" violet rim, faint dotting inside rim; beards yellow orange, hairs tipped violet; slight sweet fragrance. F87-31D: (Loop the Loop x Quiet Times) X Last Waltz.

MODERN TIMES (Joseph Gatty, R. 1991). Sdlg. S22-2. TB, 34" (86 cm), M. S. bluish white (M&P 41-AB-2) deepening in center and base to pale lilac (41-BC-5); F. cool white (41-A-1); beards white, tipped lemon in throat; pronounced sweet fragrance. N57-2A, Royal Elegance sib, X Classic Profile. Keppel 1992.

MODRÉ PONDĚLI (Zdeněk Seidl, R. 1997). Sdlg. 89-PAMD/3. TB, 41" (105 cm), M. S. and style arms light violet blue (RHS 97C); F. violet blue (93A); beards orange, violet blue at end; ruffled; slight sweet fragrance. Pledge Allegiance X Misty Dawn. Seidl 1997.

MODRÝ KRYSTAL (Josef Dudek, R. 1997). Sdlg. 91-PAVA-1. TB, 36" (90 cm), M. Heavily ruffled, laced dark blue violet (RHS 90A) self; beards blue, yellow in throat; slight spicy fragrance. Pledge Allegiance X Visual Arts. Josef Dudek 1998.

MOEKE (Koen Engelen, R. 1999). Sdlg. 95.003. TB, 31" (78 cm), ML. Crystal pink, F. with small creamy white central area; beards tangerine; ruffled, lightly laced; slight sweet fragrance. (Enthralling Pink x Vanity) X Social Register. Engelen 1999.

MOGUL (Joseph Ghio, R. 1991). Sdlg. 85-199H3. TB, 38" (97 cm), M-VL. S. violet, blending to apricot tan; F. apricot, mauve undertone; beards yellow. 82-78V4: (80-181Z: ((Indian Territory sib x (Capitation x Coffee House)) x sib) x 80-46: ((Financier x 76-37F: (Ballet in Orange x 73-122Z: (Hi Top x (Ponderosa x Travel On) x Peace Offering)))) x ((Flareup x Indian Territory) x 76-37F))) X Guadalajara. Bay View 1992.

MOHAWK BRAVE (Jim Hedgecock, R. 1990). Sdlg. 84-72-1. TB, 32" (81 cm), M. S. wine red, some white at midrib; F. white, wide wine red plicata border; beards golden bronze. Roundup X Smoke Rings. Comanche Acres 1991.

MOHRIC BUTTERFLY (Sharon McAllister, R. 1998). Sdlg. 90-11-3. AB (OGB-), 28" (71 cm), EM. S. pale blue violet ground, faint blue violet veining; style arms greenish buff; F. greenish buff ground veined burgundy to rust, intense burgundy dotting around golden brown beard. Mohric Art X Boaz. McAllister 1998.

MOI SNOVIDENIYA (Viktor Koroliov, R. 1999). Sdlg. STG10-95K. TB, 43" (110 cm), M. S. blue, tinted violet; style arms blue; F. blue, hafts streaked violet; beards blue, hairs tipped white; ruffled; pronounced spicy fragrance. Titan's Glory X Lunar Fire. Koroliov 1998.

MOJAVE (Bob Brown, R. 1993). Sdlg. 8824. TB, 36" (91 cm), M. S. muted golden yellow with lavender infusion; F. brownish tan green; beards gold; slight fragrance. Sugar Daddy X (Golden Dynasty x Catalyst). Cottage 1993.

MOJAVE SUNRISE (John Wight, R. 1995). Sdlg. S85-21A. SPU, 52" (132 cm), EM. S. light yellow heavily veined and infused bluish violet, giving tan effect; F. slightly darker yellow, bluish violet striations, orange line signal. Adobe Sunset X Butter Paddle. Wight's Iris 1998.

MOK (Frances Love, R. 1991). SPU, 54" (137 cm), L. Mushroom; musky fragrance. Parentage unknown; seed from Jack Vennor.

MOLTEN LAVA (A. & D. Willott, R. 1992). Sdlg. 88-20. SDB, 12½" (32 cm), EM. S. dark red violet; F. velvety bright dark red violet; beards bronze; ruffled. Nachos X Pilgrims' Choice. Willott 1992.

MOMENT (Barry Blyth, SDB, R. 1986). Correction of parentage. (Cupid's Cup x Tiger Rouge) X Capricornia.

MOMENTOUS OCCASION (George Sutton, R. 1999). Sdlg. H-116. TB, 33" (84 cm), EML. S. and style arms white, edged and sanded violet blue (RHS 88B); F. clean white, 1/4" dotted and striped violet blue edge; beards gold, 1" white filament with white-ground flounce marked violet blue; ruffled; slight sweet fragrance. Momentum X Rock Star.

MOMIJIGARE (Mototeru Kamo by Society for Japanese Irises, R. 1995). JI (6 F.), 35" (90 cm), M. F. deep red violet; style arms converted to petaloids with white center and light red violet crest. Parentage unknown. Introduced in Japan 1979.

MOMIJI YAMA (Shuichi Hirao by Society for Japanese Irises, R. 1992). JI (9+ F.), 30" (79 cm), L. Red violet, yellow signal; multipetal peony form. Parentage unknown. Hirao prior to 1985.

MOMOGASUMI (Toyokazu Ichie by Society for Japanese Irises, R. 1995). JI (3 F.), 28" (71 cm), M. S. lavender pink (RHS 75B), edges darker (77B); style arms (75D), tufts (77B); F. ground light lavender pink (75D), veined darker (75A), giving overall effect of (75B), signal rich yellow (12B). "Hatsugoromo" X "Sekishun". Introduced in Japan ca. 1989.

MOMOMATSURI (Kamo Nursery by Society for Japanese Irises, R. 1999). JI (3 F.), 35" (90 cm), EM. S. deep pink; style arms pink; F. deep pink. Miyoshino X "Kyokusui-no-Uta". Kamo Nursery 1987.

MON ANGE (Lawrence Ransom, R. 1995). Sdlg. 90/317-1. IB, 20" (50 cm), M. Ruffled warm white self, lightly veined pale yellow; beards white, tipped orange in throat, bushy; slight sweet fragrance. High Ho Silver X Frosted Angel. Iris au Trescols 1996.

MONARCH QUEEN (Bernard Hamner by Shepard Iris Garden, R. 1993). Sdlg. 87-11. TB, 48" (122 cm), EM. S. subdued violet blue (RHS 87B); F. lighter (87D); beards yellow, ending in silver; heavily ruffled. Bubbling Over X Blue Gloss. Hamner Iris, Shepard Iris 1993.

MON BLEU (Nora Scopes, R. 1992). Sdlg. 9S90. TB, 35" (89 cm), M. Ruffled pale sapphire blue, heart deeper; beards deep blue; sweet fragrance. Jack R. Dee X 5/68D: (Song of Norway x Cobweb Morning).

MONDAY-MONDAY (Roger Nelson, R. 1992). Sdlg. RN 86-79BT. TB, 29" (74 cm), EML. Smooth bright deep lavender blue (RHS 93B/C), F. with lighter area near beard; beards deep lavender blue, some gold orange deep in throat; ruffled, pleated; pronounced sweet fragrance. Venus and Mars X Pledge Allegiance. Iris Country 1993.

MONET (Tony Huber, R. 1992). Sdlg. 88-LWY-04. SPEC (*versicolor*), 24" (60 cm), E. S. lilac (RHS 85A), veined darker; F. pale violet (92A), large white center area veined violet, signal yellow. Selected *I. versicolor* sdlg., parentage unknown.

MONET'S BLUE (Schreiner, R. 1998). Sdlg. CC 146-1. TB, 37" (94 cm), M. Ruffled light blue (RHS 93D) self; beards white. Rapture in Blue X Oregon Skies. Schreiner 1998.

MONET'S LADY (Barry Blyth, R. 1998). Sdlg. D83-1. TB, 36" (91 cm), ML. S. white, slight lemon at midrib; F. gold; beards gold; sweet fragrance. A139-2, China Walk sib, X Aura Light. Tempo Two 1998/99.

MONET'S MAGIC (Heather Pryor, R. 1995). Sdlg. 60/90-13. LA, 35" (89 cm), M. Ruffled deep maroon (RHS 187A), raised orange signal pattern, beige petal reverse; style arms deep maroon tipped beige. Gladiator's Gift X Desert Jewel. Iris Haven 1999/2000.

MONEYMAKER (John C. Taylor, R. 1998). Sdlg. UL 19-9. LA, 43" (110 cm), ML. S. buff, edged light purple violet; style arms buff, green base, purple violet backing; F. peach tan blending to purple violet edge, yellow green signal. Desert Jewel X Dural Dreamtime. Rainbow Ridge 1998/99.

MONGOLIUS (Tomas Tamberg, R. 1998). SPEC, 56-60" (142-152 cm), EM. S. blue; F. blue, white signal. Unknown, from seed collected in Mongolia, distributed by BIS seed exchange. Schoeppinger 1998.

MONI (Manfred Beer, R. 1992). Sdlg. EWMB 6/82A. TB, 36" (90 cm), E. Ice blue; beards gold yellow, tipped ice blue; sweet fragrance. ((Outreach x New Moon) x Ermine Robe) X Cranberry Ice. Beer 1994.

#MONICA (Bliss 1919, TB). Marked as obsolete in 1939 Check List; name released.

MONICA (Loleta Powell, R. 1994). Sdlg. 93-26. IB, 25" (64 cm), EM. S. creamy white; style arms yellow; F. lemon yellow; beards yellow; pronounced sweet fragrance. Obligato X unknown. Powell's Gardens 1996.

MONIQUE'S CHILD (Tomas Tamberg, R. 1997). SPEC (*versicolor*), 20" (51 cm), M. S. violet blue; F. dark violet blue, small signal. *I. versicolor* sdlg. X Mysterious Monique. Schoeppinger 1997.

MON NATALI (Ladislav Muska, R. 1997). Sdlg. S-WGHP-06. SDB, 13" (33 cm), M. S. cream, touched gold; style arms cream; F. ivory cream; beards white, tipped light gold; ruffled, lightly laced; sweet fragrance. White Gem X Hazel's Pink. Muska 1992.

MONOLOGUE (Bryce Williamson, R. 1993). Sdlg. 2086-2. TB, 36" (91 cm), M. S. soft lavender blue with slightly darker plicata markings at edge; F. white ground with medium to dark lavender blue plicata edge; slight fragrance. Centre Court X Simile. Pacific Coast Hybridizers 1994.

MONPANSIYE (Viacheslav Gavrilin, R. 1999). Sdlg. 94-4103. TB, 33" (85 cm), ML. S. and style arms pink; F. light rose lilac, paler below tangerine beard. Color Splash X Starcrest.

MONSIEUR-MONSIEUR (Jean Segui, R. 1998). TB, 35" (90 cm), EM. Plum purple (RHS 79A) self; beards mustard yellow; slight fragrance. Trapel X Seven Hills. Iris de Thau 1994.

MONTE ALBANO (Ladislav Muska, R. 1995). Sdlg. SESS-03B. TB, 37" (94 cm), M. Laced white; beards orange. Sunshine Express X Silver Shower. Muska 1992.

MONTEREY SNOW (B. Charles Jenkins, R. 1992). Sdlg. B30-34H. CA, 14" (36 cm), M. Ruffled white with small yellow flash. Santa Rita X Western Movie. Portable Acres 1992.

MONTY DUANE (Betty Wyss, R. 1999). Sdlg. 89Z-15. MTB, 22" (56 cm), M. S. and style arms white; F. white ground, overlaid with lavender stripes radiating from beard, pale lavender rim; beards yellow orange. Parentage unknown.

MONTY'S SWEET BLUE (Monty Byers by Phyllis Dickey, R. 1994). TB, 36" (91 cm), M. Dark blue violet; beards yellow, tipped light blue, dark blue violet flounce or horn; pronounced sweet fragrance. Scented Bubbles X Starship. Misty Hill 1994.

MOOD SWING (Joseph Ghio, R. 1996). Sdlg. 92-15N3. TB, 36" (91 cm), EML. S. smoky violet pink; F. apricot peach; beards tangerine. 90-21Y, pod parent of Blonde Bombshell, X Island Dancer. Bay View 1997.

MOODY HUES (Barry Blyth, R. 1998). Sdlg. E36-3. SDB, 14" (36 cm), EM. Blended lavender blue, S. with washed effect, F. with slightly deeper centerline, small white area around beard; beards tangerine, outer 3/8" lavender blue. A44-2, Bee's Knees sib, X Little Bev. Tempo Two 1998/99.

MOONDAWN (Barry Blyth, R. 1991). Sdlg. X23-1. SDB, 14" (36 cm), VE-E. Grey, infused tan, F. rosy brown at hafts and with lavender blue centerline; beards lavender blue, tangerine in throat. (Peach Eyes x Kandi Moon) X Moment sib. Tempo Two 1991/92.

MOON DRIFT (Chet Tompkins, R. 1992). Sdlg. 80-118A. TB, 34" (86 cm), ML. Fluted colonial to mimosa cream; self beards. ((Tinsel Town x Tahiti Sunrise) x (Primrose Path x Cool Comfort)) X ((Tinsel Town x Leda's Lover) x (Christmas Time x ((Royal Gold x Ovation) x Ming Porcelain))). Fleur de Lis 1992.

MOONGLADE (Keith Keppel, R. 1997). Sdlg. 92-13A. IB, 18" (46 cm), EM. S. slate purple (M&P 46-J-6), veined and blended paler greyed mauve (45-F-4), extreme base flushed pyrethrum yellow (11-L-2); style arms greyed lavender to light lemon; F. hortensia (47-L-12) to prune purple (46-L-11) paling to small lavender (43-C-5) edge, white spot in heart; beards white, tipped chrome yellow (9-L-7) in throat; lightly ruffled; slight sweet fragrance. Gemstar X 86-18A, Spirit World sib. Keppel 1998.

MOON IN NETS (Ladislav Muska, R. 1999). Sdlg. 98-DZCL-02. TB, 36" (91 cm), M. S. creamy yellow, light brown lilac veining; style arms brown; F. cream yellow ground, 1/2" cinnamon brown dotted edge; beards yellow mustard; heavily ruffled, laced; slight fragrance. Spacelight Sketch X (Zuzana x Calicoball). Muska 1999.

MOONLIGHT BECOMES YOU (Leslie Donnell, R. 1995). Sdlg. 91.14.11. TB, 31" (78 cm), M. Off-white self; beards light yellow; pronounced sweet fragrance. (Lilac Lustre x Soul Kiss) X Caroline Penvenon.

MOONLIGHTING (A. & D. Willott, R. 1990). Sdlg. 88-70. SDB, 11" (28 cm), M. Ruffled light greenish yellow; beards blue and yellow. Nachos X Pilgrims' Choice. Willott 1991.

MOONLIGHT INTERVAL (William Plotner, R. 1992). Sdlg. 84-215. TB, 36" (91 cm), M. S. white; style arms moonlight yellow; F. white, yellow hafts and reverse; beards yellow; ruffled. Pretty Please X Stately Mansions. Wildwood Gardens 1989.

MOONLIGHT MADNESS (Sharon McAllister, R. 1996). Sdlg. 86-4-1. AB (OGB+), 28" (71 cm), L. S. white ground heavily veined and washed lustrous blue violet, appearing almost solid; style arms blended red violet, blue violet and brown violet; F. very dark blended blue violet, red violet and brown violet; beards brownish violet. Sal-Leo-Five X Rebecca's Veil. McAllister 1996.

MOONLIGHT SKETCH (Pavel Nejedlo, R. 1998). Sdlg. DERRSM-90-1. TB, 38" (97 cm), M. S. blended silver, grey and lavender; style arms lilac brown; F. cream ground heavily speckled yellow, brown and lavender on upper half, wide silvery lavender edge; beards mustard; slight sweet fragrance. Desert Echo X (Rancho Rose x Sketch Me). Lukon 1998.

MOONLIT LACE (Connell Marsh, R. 1994). Sdlg. 85-26-6-C. TB, 37" (94 cm), ML. S. white center, washed lilac lavender toward edge, midrib lavender; style arms heavily fringed lavender and white; F. crystalline white, 1/4" lilac lavender veined rim; beards lavender-tipped white, tipped orange in throat; slight fragrance. Laced Cotton X Dancing Lady.

MOONLIT THEATRE (Riley Probst, R. 1991). Sdlg. 86TX2MS1. TB, 36" (91 cm), ML. S. light violet blue (RHS 91B); F. dark violet blue (94A), white flash and fancy streaking; beards lemon yellow. Theatre X Moonlit Sea. Manchester Garden 1994.

MOON LOVE (Tom Magee, TB, R. 1989). Long 1994.

MOON MAID (Steve Moldovan, R. 1996). Sdlg. 32-69. IB, 20" (51 cm), E. S. cream white, shot gold; F. cream white, gold beside beard; beards lemon gold; ruffled. Gleaming Gold X 63-47: ((Sorority Girl sib x Whole Cloth) x (Sorority Girl sib x self)). Introduced under invalid name "Moon Maiden". Moldovan 1979.

MOON PEARL (Nora Scopes, R. 1997). Sdlg. PC 106. CA, 15" (38 cm), M. White, F. with cream yellow central flush. Parentage unknown.

MOONRAKER (George Sutton, R. 1997). Sdlg. F-32 ARSA. TB, 36" (91 cm), ML. S. and style arms golden yellow; F. white, veined golden yellow, gold shoulders, 1/2" yellow gold rim; beards gold, 1" white horn; ruffled; slight sweet fragrance. Quasar X Come to Me. Sutton 1998.

MOON SHRINE (Ben Hager, R. 1993). Sdlg. S885LtY. SPU, 42" (107 cm), M. Fluted light yellow self. Parentage unknown. Cordon Bleu 1994.

MOON SILK (Harold Stahly, R. 1990). Sdlg. 85-1-A. SIB, 28" (71 cm), M. S. and style arms creamy white; F. widely flared pale yellow, orange yellow signal, small yellow green veins radiating outward; ruffled. Super Ego X Sally Kerlin. Stahly 1991.

MOON SPREE (Barbara Wight, R. 1993). Sdlg. 87-6. IB, 16" (41 cm), EM. Light pale yellow (RHS 8C); beards light yellow (8B), short 1/4" horns; slight sweet fragrance. Horned Sunshine X Dresden Gold. Wight's Iris 1993.

MOR (David Shahak, R. 1992). Sdlg. S-T-81-127 IV. AR (OH), 28" (72 cm), M. S. violet purple (RHS 77A), heavily veined; F. heavily veined red purple (59A), signal black purple; beards dark purple. *I. samariae* X (*I. mariae* x *I. hermona*). Aril Society, Tira Nurseries 1993.

MORNING MAIL (Barry Blyth, R. 1998). Sdlg. E148-3. TB, 38" (96 cm), EM. Orchid lilac self; beards tangerine. Cloud Berry X About Town. Tempo Two 1998/99.

MORNING MOOD (Keith Keppel, R. 1997). Sdlg. 91-85A. TB, 35" (89 cm), EM. S. buff peach (M&P 9-A-4); style arms apricot (10-F-7), lavender midrib; F. cream white ground, 3/16" amaranth purple (44-L-8) edge and hafts, golden apricot (10-G-6) haft suffusion; beards bittersweet pink (9-A-8), flame (1-C-12) in throat; ruffled; pronounced sweet fragrance. Dawn Sky X Platform. Keppel 1998.

MORNING PEACOCK (Daniel Thruman, R. 1997). JI (6 F.), 35" (89 cm), M. Violet blue (RHS 97A/B) lines on white; style arms violet blue. Southern Son X Continuing Pleasure.

MORNING PRINCESS (Ed Matheny III, R. 1994). Sdlg. 01-02-93. TB, 32" (81 cm), EM. S. shell white (RHS 159D); F. reddish purple, edged orchid (76C); beards zinnia yellow (14A); slight spicy fragrance. Sweet Reflection X Rustic Dance. Ed's Iris 1995.

MORNING RED (George Slade, R. 1990). Sdlg. 84-30-1. TB, 32" (81 cm), ML. S. buff pink; F. dark red violet; beards orange. Watermelon Wine X Capricious. Wyle Wynde 1990.

MORNING'S BLUSH (Evelyn Jones, R. 1993). Sdlg. I89-28-1. SDB, 14" (36 cm), M. S. lemon yellow (HCC 4/1); F. nasturtium orange (610/2) with rosy blush, blending to lemon yellow edge; beards brilliant indian orange (713). I85-2-6: ((Rhoda Anne x unknown) x ((Solar Flight x 255: (Melon Honey x pink sdlg.)) x (Wright L20 x 255))) X 415-1: (((Solar Flight x ((Roberts 65R11 x (pink IB sdlg. x sdlg.)) x Melon Honey)) x Pumpkin Center) x Orange Dazzler). Bennett Jones 1994.

MORNING SMILE (Jim & Vicki Craig, R. 1997). Sdlg. 63X38. IB, 22" (60 cm), M. Ruffled white self; beards white, pale yellow in throat; slight sweet fragrance. Sib to Departure. J. & V. Craig 1997.

MOROZ I SOLNTSE (Sergey Loktev, R. 1999). Sdlg. 94-R11-12G. TB, 32" (80 cm), EML. S. light yellow, slightly darker edges; style arms yellow, lighter midrib and crests; F. white, light yellow hafts and edge; beards yellow, orange in throat. Master Touch X Gold Galore. Loktev 1999.

MORRIS (A. & D. Willott, SDB, R. 1982). Willott 1990.

MORSE CODE (Lynda Miller, R. 1996). Sdlg. 4689. TB, 33" (84 cm), L. White ground, dark lavender near-solid edge and dotting; style arms dark lavender, yellow gold midrib; beards gold, lavender base. 3586A: (Anon x Queen in Calico) X 3386A: ((Odyssey x Petite Posy) x Laced Cotton). Miller's Manor 1997.

MORSKOY PRIBOY (Adolf Volfovich-Moler, R. 1997). Sdlg. V-141. TB, 29" (75 cm), ML. S. blended blue white; style arms pale violet, edge lighter; F. blue white highlighted cream, hafts light yellow; beards lavender with light yellow hair tips, light yellow in throat; heavily ruffled, laced; slight fragrance. Pink Sleigh X Laced Cotton. Volfovich-Moler 1999.

MORWENNA (R. E. Nichol, TB, R. 1984). Sutton 1991.

MOSHIO-NO-KEMURI (Shuichi Hirao by Society for Japanese Irises, R. 1994). JI (9+ F.), 28" (71 cm), EM. Red violet flecked and splashed white; style arms white with red violet edges and crests (sometimes converted to extra petaloids). Sport of Ushio-No-Kemuri. Introduced in Japan ca. 1981.

MOSKOVSKI BAMBUK (Viacheslav Gavrilin, R. 1998). Sdlg. 4-12-2-94. TB, 33" (85 cm), M. S. pink, midrib darker; style arms pink, tinted raspberry; F. light raspberry, pink edge, white veining and pattern around red beard; lightly ruffled; slight fragrance. Fiesta Time X Starcrest. Gavrilin 1999.

MOSTAR (Eric & Bob Tankesley-Clarke, R. 1994). SPEC, 25" (64 cm), L. Blue violet self; beards light yellow; pronounced sweet fragrance. Collected at Mostar, Bosnia; distributed prior to 1980 and in commerce as *I. pallida cengialti* "Mostar".

MOSTEST (John Durrance, R. 1990). Sdlg. D83-27. BB, 24" (61 cm), EM. Ruffled bright gold. Frills X Golden Apple. Long 1990.

MOST STUNNING (Ed Roberts, R. 1992). Sdlg. 921. TB, 32" (81 cm), M. S. light lilac, yellow at base; F. red, edge lighter; beards yellow; slight fragrance. Stunning X Lilac Wine. Ed Roberts 1994.

MOST WANTED (Polly Black, R. 1995). Sdlg. PA3-2PL. TB, 30" (76 cm), M. S. medium purple, some white showing in center; F. white ground, wide purple rim, purple dots in center; beards bright orange; sweet fragrance. Southern Comfort X purple plicata sdlg. Polly Black 1995.

MOTHER EVE SMILES (Bernice Miller, R. 1991). Sdlg. MES91. TB, 37" (94 cm), M & RE (Oct./AL). S. light yellow; F. white, edged light yellow; beards golden orange; ruffled; slight fragrance. Radiant Angel X (Radiant Angel sib x Summer Whitewings). Garden of the Enchanted Rainbow 1991.

#MOTHER GOOSE (Shiloh, TB, R. 1929). Shown as obsolete in 1939 Check List; name released.

MOTHER GOOSE (Ben Hager, R. 1999). Sdlg. SD6170Pk/PkBf. SDB, 14" (36 cm), EM. S. and style arms pink, undertoned pale orange; F. pink, upper hafts tinged buff; beards bright flame, bushy. Playful sib X Orange Tiger. Adamgrove 1999.

MOTHER MARSHMALLOW (James McWhirter by Abram Feuerstein, R. 1997). Sdlg. 89-94-1. TB, 34" (86 cm), ML. Ruffled white self; beards white, tipped yellow in throat; pronounced sweet fragrance. Denney 79-174: (Regents' Row sib x Winterscape) X Navajo Jewel. Stockton 1997.

MOTHER OF ANGELS (Cloyd McCord, R. 1996). Sdlg. 85-62-01. TB, 36" (91 cm), E. S. and style arms light apricot; F. pale blue, 1/2" dark blue margin; beards white to lemon; ruffled; sweet fragrance. Maxine's Love X Princess Maxine.

MOTHER'S LITTLE HELPER (Richard Ernst, R. 1994). Sdlg. JF169-5. TB, 35" (89 cm), ML. Lightly ruffled orange, S. with slight pale pink infusion on midribs, F. with darker shoulders; beards orange red; slight sweet fragrance. Probably -- F169-5, Competitive Edge sib, X F169-19, sib. Cooley 1995.

MO-TOWN SISTER (Gordon Nicholson, R. 1998). Sdlg. 53-94. TB, 36-38" (91-97 cm), M. S. light grape juice; style arms same, golden inner glow; F. velvety deep tokay grape, thin white rim, white area near beard peppered deep grape; beards orange, deepening in throat, white at end and on base of hairs; heavily ruffled; slight musky fragrance. Flights of Fancy X unknown. Woodland Iris 1999.

MOTTO (Joseph Gatty by Keith Keppel, R. 1992). Sdlg. W37-6. SDB, 12" (30 cm), EM. S. white ground, 1/4" solid gentian blue border; F. white, slightly deeper (M&P 43-F-10) and narrower solid border; beards blue white at end, cadmium orange (9-L-10) in throat; pronounced sweet fragrance. Chubby Cheeks X S48-4, Toy Clown sib. D & J Gardens 1993.

MOUNTAIN ECHO (Schreiner, R. 1997). Sdlg. BB 1173-A. TB, 38" (97 cm), ML. S. and style arms blue lavender (RHS 91B); F. blue lavender, tan 1/4" margin and shoulders, white spot around orange beard; ruffled; slight fragrance. M 436-1: ((((Amethyst Flame x Pretty Carol) x Brilliant Star) x Launching Pad) x ((Dream Spun x Crinoline) x April Melody)) X Precious Moments. Schreiner 1997.

MOUNTAIN HEATHER (Opal Brown, TB, R. 1988). Roris 1990.

MOUNTAIN LIGHTNING (Ken Mohr, R. 1992). TB, 34" (86 cm), ML-VL. Heavily ruffled dark blue violet; beards lemon white; slight musky fragrance. ((Cup Race x Babbling Brook) x Five Star Admiral) X God Bless. Pacific Coast Hybridizers 1992.

MOUNTAIN MAJESTY (Joseph Ghio, R. 1994). Sdlg. 88-20-C2. TB, 36" (91 cm), ML. Deep purple self with blackish sheen; beards violet; scalloped ruffling. Peace and Harmony X Darkside. Bay View 1995.

MOUNTAIN SHADOWS (Opal Brown, R. 1996). Sdlg. 90-3F4. TB, 38-40" (97-102 cm), EM. S. and style arms blended violet (RHS 84B); F. slightly deeper, white area below soft lavender beard; ruffled. Lorilee X unknown. Brown's Sunnyhill 1997.

MOUNT EMMONS (Luzon Crosby by Philip Edinger, R. 1999). TB, 40" (102 cm), ML. Flared white self; beards yellow. Snow Carnival X (Snow Flurry x Cloud Castle). Tell's Iris Gardens 1955; listed as "Mt. Emmons".

MOUSE (Donald Spoon, R. 1996). Sdlg. 88-35C. BB, 18" (46 cm), M & RE (Oct./VA). S. and style arms butter yellow; F. butter yellow, oval purple spots, maroon veining on brighter yellow hafts; beards yellow; ruffled, flared; slight fragrance. Winter Olympics X Spinning Wheel. Winterberry 1997.

MOUSTACHE (Barry Blyth, R. 1995). Sdlg. B67-2. SDB, 15" (38 cm), VE. S. lemon; F. lemon, 1/8" band of deeper lemon around lower half, white signal with brown halo circle broken at lowest point; beards white; slight sweet fragrance. Honey Haze X Scat. Tempo Two 1995/96.

MOVEALONG (John C. Taylor, R. 1998). Sdlg. UL 14-3. LA, 43" (110 cm), ML. S. and style arms light tan; F. light tan, darker midrib and around yellow signal. Dancing Vogue X Watch Out. Rainbow Ridge 1999/2000.

MOVE ON (Graeme Grosvenor, R. 1993). Sdlg. R30-1. TB, 42" (107 cm), EM. Ruffled apricot self; beards red. First Movement X N14-13: (Goddess x Words and Music). Rainbow Ridge 1993/94.

MOVE OVER (W. Terry Varner, R. 1995). Sdlg. Q-356. MTB, 20" (51 cm), L. Blue purple self; beards white. Velvet Bouquet X N-318 blue self: (Blue Twinkle x J-311 light blue: (MLD 0-144 light blue x Velvet Bouquet)). Ohio Gardens 1995.

MOVIE MAGIC (Ken Mohr by Bryce Williamson, R. 1994). Sdlg. Q-250-C. TB, 36" (91 cm), ML. Medium azure blue with silvery area below blue white beards; slight fragrance. Bubbling Over X 4-2. Pacific Coast Hybridizers 1994.

MOY GIMENEY (Nina Miroshnichenko, R. 1996). TB, 43" (110 cm), M. Milky white self; beards white at end, yellow in throat. Parentage unknown. Miroshnichenko 1977.

MOYOMAZORA (Kamo Nursery by Society for Japanese Irises, R. 1995). JI (6 F.), 35" (90 cm), M. White, amethyst veins and dusting; style arms white, edged and tipped medium amethyst. Parentage unknown. Introduced in Japan, Kamo Nursery.

MOYO VDOKHNOVENIYE (V. & N. Gordodelovy, R. 1995). Sdlg. 220. TB, 32" (80 cm), M. Ruffled light blue, brown yellow striations near beard; beards blue white at end (with small white horn), yellow in center, orange in throat. Parentage unknown. Gordodelovy 1980.

MOY SHKIPER (Viacheslav Gavrilin, R. 1999). Sdlg. 94-453. TB, 33" (85 cm), ML. S. cream, midrib tinted violet; style arms cream, tinted violet; F. red raspberry violet, indistinct cream rim; beards mustard, yellow at end; ruffled. Darkside X unknown.

MT. BOGONG (E. S. Fankhauser, R. 1991). Sdlg. 10-83-A. TB, 40" (102 cm), M. Ruffled medium blue; beards white, tipped lemon. Wedding Vow X Victoria Falls. Tempo Two 1992/93.

MT. BULLION (Vernon Wood, R. 1991). Sdlg. 89-9. CA, 12-13" (30-33 cm), E. S. yellow (RHS 13B); F. slightly darker yellow (13A); ruffled. 87-19, unknown, X Different Drummer. Portable Acres 1992.

MT. SINAI AFLAME (Bernice Miller, R. 1992). Sdlg. MSA93. TB, 36" (91 cm), EM & RE. Lightly ruffled garnet crimson with scarlet highlights; beards bronze; sweet fragrance. Reblooming red sdlg. X Sheba's Queen. Comanche Acres, Garden of the Enchanted Rainbow 1993.

MT. ZION (Howard Shockey, R. 1992). Sdlg. 87-123-B. AB (OGB+), 16" (41 cm), M. S. violet blue (near RHS 91C); F. greyed yellow (near 162D), large greyed red (near 179B) signal; beards greyed orange (163C). Heart Stealer X 84-12-7A: (Shah Kebir x (Hetira x (Aril Sanctum x Judean Snow))). Arilian Acres, Aril Society 1992.

MUCH OBLIGED (Ben Hager, R. 1992). Sdlg. T4662BchLvBl. TB, 36" (92 cm), M. Full lavender plum, lighter silvery cast in center of F. below blue white beard. T3705Bl: (T3466, Unfurled Flag sib, x Freedom Road) X T3702: (Silver Flow x Ruffled Ballet). Melrose 1992.

MUDBUG (Patrick O'Connor, R. 1999). Sdlg. 91-3. LA, 28" (71 cm), M. S. medium purple, 2-3 darker lengthwise lines extending halfway; style arms red purple; F. medium purple, yellow orange line signal centered in large white thumbprint signal overlaid with purple veining. Dr. Dormon X *I. brevicaulis*. Bois d'Arc 1999.

MUGGLES (Sterling Innerst, R. 1999). Sdlg. 5022-1. SDB, 14" (36 cm), ML. White, F. with brown feathered spot; beards orange tipped white; slight musky fragrance. 4672-2, Orknies sib, X Orange Dazzler.

MUKADDAM (Ladislav Muska, R. 1995). Sdlg. SHCK-02. TB, 38" (97 cm), ML. Heavily ruffled maroon lavender self; beards orange, long blue spoon; spicy fragrance. (Sky Hooks x "Cipkovana Krinolina": (After All x Grand Waltz)) X Sky Falls. Muska 1994.

MULBERRY ECHO (William Maryott, R. 1997). Sdlg. W134A. TB, 37" (94 cm), EM & RE. Lightly ruffled cerise maroon (RHS 72A) self; beards orange; slight spicy fragrance. M154A: (J5-Smooth: (Ghio 80-5, unknown, x (Ghio 76-175, Paris Original sib, x Ghio 76-257-X: (Entourage x Homecoming Queen))) x Lady Friend) X Cherry Glen. Maryott 1997.

MULBERRY INN (David Miller, R. 1992). Sdlg. DM85-1C. TB, 32-34" (81-86 cm), M. S. dark mulbery purple (RHS 77A); F. white ground, 1/2" dark mulberry edge; beards bronze orange; slight fragrance. Roundup X Crinoline. Long 1993.

MULBERRY PUNCH (Schreiner, R. 1992). Sdlg. 1986 #25. TB, 38" (99 cm), ML. Ruffled cerise purple (RHS 77A); beards blue purple. Parentage unknown. Schreiner 1992.

MULBERRY RIM (Stan Dexter by Marie Ingersoll, R. 1991). Sdlg. 227-83-110. TB, 38" (97 cm), M. S. cream, mulberry overlay; F. cream, mulberry edge and slight plicata marking, small white area near yellow beard; sweet fragrance. April Melody X Coral Surf. Ingersoll's Iris 1992.

MULBERRY SOUFFLE (Darrell Weikle, R. 1995). TB, 34-38" (86-96 cm), M. Bright mulberry, overtoned blue, F. paling to near-white at beard; beards light mulberry, golden orange in throat; ruffled; sweet fragrance. Bubble Bath X Dark Triumph. Weikle's Wonderland 1995.

MULBERRY TEMPLE (Barry Blyth, R. 1993). Sdlg. Z34-6. IB, 22" (56 cm), M. Bright mulberry with white area around beards; beards tangerine, outer tip lavender; slight sweet fragrance. Tiffany Time X Chanted. Tempo Two 1993/94.

MULBERRY VELVET (Loleta Powell, R. 1994). Sdlg. 90-26. TB, 36" (91 cm), EML. Heavily ruffled mulberry self; beards bronze red; pronounced sweet fragrance. (Camelot Wine x Crushed Berries) X Camelot Wine. Powell's Gardens 1996.

MUNCHKIN MAID (Don Boen, IB, R. 1984). Billie's Iris Garden 1990.

MUNICH BLUE (Eric & Bob Tankesley-Clarke, R. 1994). SPEC, 22" (56 cm), M. Dark violet blue self; beards white, tipped orange; pronounced musky fragrance. Seed from Munich Botanic Garden; distributed prior to 1970 and in commerce as *I. pallida illyrica* "Munich".

MUPPET MADNESS (Paul Black, R. 1991). Sdlg. 87137B. SDB, 12" (30 cm), M. S. white ground, heavy red purple irregular wash and plicata markings; F. white ground, edge heavily banded and marked red purple, turning to sanded red purple wash in center; beards white, tipped purple. Chubby Cheeks X 85319B: (Gentle Air x Chubby Cheeks). Mid-America 1991.

MURASAKI JISHI (Shichiro Maeda by Society for Japanese Irises, R. 1994). JI (6 F.), 36" (90 cm), EM. Lavender violet veined deeper; style arms lavender violet. Parentage unknown. Maeda 1958.

MURASAME (Mototeru Kamo by Society for Japanese Irises, R. 1994). JI (3 F.), 38" (97 cm), M. S. white, edged lavender; style arms white; F. white, brushed lavender, signal bright gold. Parentage unknown. Introduced in Japan 1979.

MURMUR (Barry Blyth, R. 1997). Sdlg. D2-1. SDB, 10-12" (26-30 cm), VE-M. S. creamy lemon; F. creamy lemon, deeper creamy lemon apricot thumbprint, 1/8" brighter lemon edge; beards tangerine, white at end; slight fragrance. Fairy Favours X Carats. Tempo Two 1997/98.

MURPHY'S LAW (Bennett Jones, R. 1995). Sdlg. 509-1. SDB, 13" (33 cm), M. S. white; F. citron green (HCC 763); beards poppy red (16). Cinderella X 433-5: (Orange Tiger x Pumpkin Center).

MURRAH MEMORIAL (Augusto Bianco, R. 1998). Sdlg. 418. TB, 34" (86 cm), ML. Ruffled pure white self; beards white, yellow in throat. Olympiad X Precious Moments. Contemporary, Iride 1998.

MURRAY BRIDGE (Leslie Donnell, R. 1999). Sdlg. 92-2-5. TB, 30-32" (76-81 cm), L. S. light salmon (RHS 27A); F. cadmium orange (23D), lined, with darker (23C) intensification at throat; beards indian orange (32A); pronounced sweet fragrance. (Hampton Horizon x Flaming Victory) X Hampton Glory.

MUSAK (Nora Scopes, R. 1992). Sdlg. PC31. CA, 12" (30 cm), M. S. crimson magenta; F. crimson, yellow signal lined crimson. Cramoisie X Popinjay.

MUSE (Marky Smith, R. 1996). Sdlg. 92-14M. SDB, 14" (36 cm), M. S. dusty mauve (RHS 186D to 75C), aging pinker; style arms smoky greyed peach, midrib blue violet; F. smoky peach (greyer than 179), faint violet center wash when fresh, gold brown shoulder wash; beards smoky opera pink (180C), vermilion in throat; ruffled; pronounced sweet fragrance. Pink Caper X Chanted. Aitken's Salmon Creek 1997.

MUSE'S FIRE (Ken Mohr, R. 1993). Sdlg. P-163-A. TB, 34" (86 cm), EM. S. smoky dark orchid lavender flushed pink at midrib; F. smoky dark orchid lavender, pink shoulder infusion; beards tangerine red; slight fragrance. Spellmaker X Love Magic. Pacific Coast Hybridizers 1993.

MUSE'S VISIT (Ray Rogers, R. 1998). Sdlg. DCSF-3. TB, 38" (97 cm), ML. S. brownish violet; style arms light violet and dark gold; F. bright violet, aging with central blue cast, hafts bronze, 1/4" brownish violet rim; pronounced sweet fragrance. Dusky Challenger X Star Fleet.

MUSHKETIOR (Viacheslav Gavrilin, R. 1999). Sdlg. 96-138. TB, 36" (91 cm), EM. S. blue violet, brown base; style arms brownish blue violet; F. bright blue violet, light violet below beard; beards mustard orange, blue at end; heavily ruffled. Fiesta Time X Pledge Allegiance.

MUSIC (Keith Keppel, R. 1998). Sdlg. 94-23A. SDB, 12" (31 cm), EM. S. apricot buff (M&P 10-D-4) shaded peach buff (10-A-4); style arms deeper buff apricot (10-C-6); F. light apricot buff (9-E-3) ground, rubient (55-L-8) haft and shoulder veining, lightly dotted and veined edge; beards fire red (1-F-12), white-based hairs at end; ruffled. Tweety Bird X 91-7A: (Gigolette x Fairy Lore). Keppel 1999.

MUSIC LOVER (Bryce Williamson, R. 1993). Sdlg. 3985. TB, 38" (97 cm), ML. S. cattleya orchid, strong peach midrib infusion; F. cattleya orchid, washed peach from shoulders; beards tangerine; heavily laced; slight fragrance. Love Poem X Love and Desire. Pacific Coast Hybridizers 1992.

MUSIC MAESTRO (Barry Blyth, R. 1990). Sdlg. V73-2. TB, 34-36" (86-91 cm), EM. Medium blue to ultramarine; beards medium blue. Pledge Allegiance X Swirling Seas. Tempo Two 1990/91.

MUSKOKA SUNSET (Lloyd Zurbrigg, R. 1999). Sdlg. LL 89D 'Last Orange'. TB, 38" (97 cm), M. Orange to orange apricot self; beards orange apricot. HH 15-1-1: (Lady Friend x Beverly Sills) X HH 9-1-2: (Fresno Frolic x Mabel Andrews).

MUSTARD SURPRISE (A. Theodore Mueller, R. 1994). Sdlg. 89-91. TB, 28-30" (71-76 cm), M. S. mustard yellow; style arms lighter blend of yellow; F. mustard yellow, slightly lighter center; beards deep bright yellow. Unknown purple sdlg. X Minted Halo. Mueller's Garden 1994.

MUST UNITE (Graeme Grosvenor, R. 1998). Sdlg. U76-1. TB, 39" (99 cm), ML. Purple self; beards blue purple. Holy Night X Larry Gaulter. Rainbow Ridge 1999/2000.

MUTED MULBERRY (A. & D. Willott, R. 1994). Sdlg. 88-76. SDB, 14" (36 cm), M. Lightly ruffled muted full red violet; beards yellow, tipped violet. Drambuie X Ecru Echo. Willott 1995.

MUTE SWAN (B.L.C. Dodsworth, TB, R. 1985). British Iris Society 1990.

MUZYKALNY MOMENT (Sergey Loktev, R. 1998). Sdlg. 94-R11-16A. SDB 12" (29 cm), VE-ML. S. pale yellow, whitish edge; style arms pale yellowish white; F. white, lightly touched lemon yellow at end, hafts veined lemon yellow; beards yellow, white at end and orange in throat. Lemon Puff X unknown. Loktev 1998.

MY BILL (Ruth Goebel, R. 1995). Sdlg. ABRM. TB, 37" (94 cm), ML. Purplish violet (darker than RHS 80A), F. with wine to blackish edge, slight lace; beards yellow, blue at tip. Georgia Girl X Charcoal.

MY BLUE HEART (Opal Brown by Margaret McCrae, R. 1998). Sdlg. 85-3A10. TB, 32" (81 cm), M. S. chicory blue (M&P 41/42-B-7), base shaded violet (42-I-9); style arms slightly lighter blue (41-B-6/7); F. chicory blue, campanula violet (42-J-10) overlay near middle of beard and shading to below beard, hafts rosier violet (41-J-8); beards lobelia blue (42-J-12), hairs tipped lighter; lightly ruffled; pronounced sweet fragrance. 73-6A7: (70-1A1: ((Goodness x 63-9B2: (Scharff 57-34-1: (Sweet Alice Lee x Blue Throat) x Blue Miller)) x (63-9B9 x Winter Olympics)) x Eagle Harbor) X Song of Norway.

MY CAM (Frances Love, R. 1993). Sdlg. 25-10-2. IB, 20" (53 cm), E. S. sunshine yellow; F. white speckled lavender, sunshine yellow signal, frilly gold edge; beards white; slight fragrance. Parentage unknown.

MY CHARTREUSE GREENIE (Ruby Short, R. 1994). Sdlg. 1437gr. TB, 28" (71 cm), M. Lacy lemon chartreuse self; beards yellow green. Rainbow Gold X Ultrapoise. Ruby Short 1994.

MY DELIGHT (Ben Hager, R. 1996). Sdlg. SD6015. SDB, 12" (31 cm), M. Pink self; beards light tangerine. SD5473WRfPkSh: (5130: ((Ceremony x Today's Fashion) x (((2919: (2563-0: (Pink Cushion x Roberts 65-R-28) x (Frosty Lemonade x Pink Cushion)) x 2920: (2563-0 x (Pink Amber x Pink Cushion))) x 3420: (2920 x 2885: (Blonde Doll x 2562: (Pink Amber x Pink Cushion)))) x

My Sheba sib)) x 4905: ((3393Pk: (2885 x (2562 x Buttercup Charm)) x (2919 x Pet)) x (Gigglepot x ((3393Pk x Pet) x (3420 x 3393)))))) X Pretty Cute. Adamgrove 1996.

MY ELLA (Pat Otterness, R. 1999). Sdlg. 9697-12X4-105. TB, 29" (74 cm), M. Ruffled pale methyl violet (RHS 85C) self; beards golden yellow, blue at end. Edith Wolford X Blue Aristocrat.

MY ETCHINGS (Sharon McAllister, R. 1998). Sdlg. 85-3-18. AB (OGB), 28" (71 cm), M. S. white ground heavily veined, dotted and washed brownish violet except on clear patch along midrib; style arms golden yellow, reddish violet midrib and crests; F. soft yellow ground veined and dotted brownish violet; beards mixed mustard and maroon. Boaz X Jean Ralls. McAllister 1998.

MY FRIEND CHELSEA (Tom Burseen, R. 1999). Sdlg. 95-266B. TB, 35" (89 cm), ML. S. and style arms pale lilac (RHS 76D); F. violet (83C); beards white, tangerine in throat, violet spoon; ruffled, strongly flared; spicy fragrance. Hunk X Thornbird.

MY FRIEND DICK (Richard Butler by M. D. Faith, R. 1998). Sdlg. RCB#1. LA, 35" (89 cm), M. Currant red, bold golden yellow signal. Ann Chowning X self.

MY FRIEND JONATHAN (Bernice Miller, R. 1996). TB, 36" (91 cm), EM & RE (Aug.-Nov./AL). Bright fuchsia and brick blend, veined chocolate; beards bronze; lightly ruffled, faintly laced. Sheba's Queen X H. Wright sdlg.: (Emma Louisa x Magic Melody). Garden of the Enchanted Rainbow 1994.

MY GINNY (Donald Spoon, R. 1995). Sdlg. 92-164. TB, 30" (76 cm), ML. S. and style arms pearl pink; F. purplish pink border grading smoothly to large pink central area; beards bright tangerine, white at end, cherry red in throat; ruffled, lightly laced, flared. (Sweet Musette x Femme Fatale) X (Winifred Ross x My Katie).

MY GIRL (Schreiner, R. 1991). Sdlg. S 540-2. TB, 38" (97 cm), ML. Ruffled pink (RHS 62D), F. with white center; beards tangerine, tipped white. H 370-B, unknown, X Carved Angel. Schreiner 1991.

MY GOLD (B. Charles Jenkins, SPU, R. 1989). Shepard Iris 1992.

MY HEROINE (John Baldwin, R. 1994). Sdlg. 85-2C. TB, 33" (84 cm), ML. Ruffled peach pink (RHS 29D); beards deep pink; slight spicy fragrance. Precious Moments X 80-11A: (Vanity x (Como Queen x Pink Angel)). Tempo Two 1997/98.

MY IMPULSE (B. Charles Jenkins, R. 1994). Sdlg. C18-11E. SPU, 47-60" (119-152 cm), M. S. purple; F. yellow, veined bronze, wavy bronze edge, gold signal. Ila Crawford X Eurasia. Shepard Iris 1994.

MY JAYNE (Barry Emmerson, R. 1998). Sdlg. BE 94/22/11. TB, 38" (97 cm), M. S. light blue violet, midrib deeper; style arms light blue violet; F. red violet; beards pallid blue; lightly ruffled; slight fragrance. High Peak X BE 92/17/12: (Kingsland Royale x Scopes sdlg.: (Alec Howe x China Seas)).

MY JODIE (Donald Spoon, TB, R. 1989). Winterberry 1995.

MY LINE (Mary Dunn, R. 1992). Sdlg. M83-817E. TB, 38" (97 cm), M. S. white with wide deep violet band, violet midrib stain; style arms deep violet; F. deep violet, large white zone at beard area; beards pale yellow, tipped white. Ghio 77-70: ((Premonition sib x Mystique) x Barletta) X Fancy Face. M.A.D. Iris 1993.

MY LITTLE GIRL (Kevin Nilsen, R. 1991). Sdlg. 6-84-2. TB, 38" (96 cm), EM. Pale creamy apricot, F. with small white area below orange beard; lightly ruffled. Lady Friend X Mandolin. Iridescence 1991/92.

MY LITTLE LUCY (Hilmary Catton, R. 1993). Sdlg. C826-1. MDB, 6" (15 cm), EM. S. white; F. gold with distinct white edge; beards cream, tipped yellow. Chalk Mark X L. Delaney sdlg.

MY LITTLE PAPOOSE (Marie Murdy, R. 1992). Sdlg. D-5-89. BB, 26" (66 cm), M. Ivory cream, golden yellow shoulders; beards light orange, short ivory cream horn; slight fragrance. Parentage unknown. My Starz Iris 1998.

MY MAUVE (Mitch Jameson, R. 1993). Sdlg. 19-87. TB, 34-38" (86-97 cm), M. S. rosy mauve; F. lavender, edged rosy mauve, rose maroon intensification on cream at hafts; beards cream and purple, tipped orange. Song of Spring X (Cabaret Royale x Son of Star). Knee-Deep in June 1994.

MY PLEASURE (Evelyn Robarts, R. 1994). Sdlg. 615-1. TB, 32-33" (81-83 cm), ML. S. clear pink; F. pink, overlaid rose violet; beards tangerine pink, tipped bright pink, slight horn at tip; slight sweet fragrance. 71 pink horned sdlg.: ((Pink Taffeta x Schiaparelli) x (#40 horned sdlg. x Pink Sleigh)) X 22-B peach sdlg.: (Holiday House x Far Corners). Stahly 1994.

MY PRETTY VALENTINE (Richard Ernst, R. 1996). Sdlg. HA141-B4. TB, 35" (89 cm), EM. Ruffled pink (near RHS 62D) self; beards orange pink; slight sweet fragrance. A141-3: (Cheesecake x R79-108: (Sumptuous x Sandberry)) X D175: (A141-3 x Piping Hot). Cooley 1997.

MYRTLE'S MEMORY (Margery Fenton, R. 1994). Sdlg. M.F.1. TB, 39" (99 cm), EM. S. white, broadly edged light violet; F. white, pale violet rim, light violet lines beside beard; beards pale yellow, tipped blue; slight spicy fragrance. Cambodia X (Cambodia x Song of Erin).

MY SEA SPRAY (Craig Carroll, R. 1995). Sdlg. 89-B-C. LA, 33-34" (84-86 cm), M. S. deep mauve, veined brown; F. mauve, veined, with white spray pattern, yellow signal. (Gypsy Moon x Marie Caillet) X unknown.

MY SHADOW (Tom Magee, TB, R. 1988). Long 1990.

MYS HORN (Ladislav Muska, R. 1999). Sdlg. SSSI-03. TB, 36" (91 cm), M. Ruffled, heavily laced pure white; beards light yellow with long white spoon; slight fragrance. (((Laced Cotton x Sky Hooks) x Soissons) x (Sky Hooks x Illulisat)) X Soissons. Muska 1998.

MY SISTER ROSIE (Marie Murdy, R. 1994). Sdlg. D-4-6-91. TB, 28" (71 cm), M. Creamy yellow; style arms cream; beards orange with creamy yellow horn. Horned Lace X Winter Olympics.

MY SOUVENIR (Jim & Vicki Craig, R. 1998). Sdlg. AH24C74. MTB, 22" (56 cm), E. S. pallid lavender, near white; style arms pale lavender; F. white, edge tinted light lavender, light veining; beards yellow; slight sweet fragrance. 38Y11: (Payoff x (7M4, Sunshiny sib, x Puppy Love)) X AH72A3: (37X10, Sailing Free sib, x 23V1: (Little Sunrise x Abridged Version)). J. & V. Craig 1998.

MYST (Barry Blyth, R. 1997). Sdlg. C222-2. TB, 36" (92 cm), VE-E. S. oyster grey, fine oyster cream netting; F. smoky lavender orchid shot light brown, giving grey effect; beards bronze; slight sweet fragrance. Aztec Burst X Witching. Tempo Two 1997/98.

MYSTERIOUS BALANCE (Paul Black, R. 1996). Sdlg. 90U1. TB, 38" (97 cm), M. S. and style arms warm white; F. white, blue violet blended edge; beards cream yellow; ruffled. Glitz 'n Glitter X 8767C: (Precious Moments x 85-143C: ((Magic Candle x Anon) x (Starfrost Pink x Spinning Wheel))). Mid-America 1996.

MYSTERIOUS MONIQUE (Uwe Knoepnadel, SPEC, R. 1986). Joe Pye Weed 1992.

MYSTERIOUS STRANGER (Chet Tompkins, R. 1994). Sdlg. 73-69. TB, 38" (97 cm), M. Yellow blended blue green; beards yellow. Inv. sdlg. lines X (Hamblen 71-154D: (Betty Simon plic sib x sib) x Hushabye Time). Fleur de Lis 1994.

MYSTERY BLUSH (Gary Sides, R. 1996). Sdlg. F46-H1. TB, 36" (91 cm), E & RE. Heavily ruffled light blush pink; style arms medium pink; beards pink, tipped blue; slight sweet fragrance. Misty Lady X October Splendor. Sides 1999.

MYSTERY MUSIC (William Simon by Elizabeth Simon, R. 1991). Sdlg. 21-44-33. TB, 34" (86 cm), ML. Ruffled velvety deep maroon red; self beards. Garnet Robe X Soldier's Chorus. Stahly 1992.

MYSTERY SONG (William Simon, TB, R. 1986). Stahly 1993.

MYSTERY STORY (Darlene Pinegar, R. 1994). Sdlg. SW-4-1. TB, 35" (89 cm), ML. S. cream ground heavily flushed greyed plum, darker greyed plum edge and midrib; style arms plum brown; F. white center blending to creamy yellow, darker greyed plum haft markings and 1/2" plicata edge, short dark greyed plum line under beard; beards old gold, tipped greyed plum; ruffled; pronounced sweet fragrance. Spinning Wheel X Grape Freeze. Spanish Fork 1995.

MYSTIC GLOW (Kenneth Fisher, R. 1994). Sdlg. 92-1. MTB, 19" (48 cm), M. S. light yellow; F. cream, yellow cast; beards yellow. TM6: ((Ting-a-ling x (Pharaoh's Daughter x Puppy Love)) x unknown) X TC4: (Pink Kewpie x Puppy Love). Aitken's Salmon Creek 1995.

MYSTIC LACE (J. T. Aitken, R. 1990). Sdlg. 84T39. TB, 36" (91 cm), VE. S. light violet flushed deeper at midrib; F. deep violet, white spot around white beard; laced; pronounced sweet fragrance. 81-55: (Laced Cotton x Mystique) X Sea Wolf. Aitken's Salmon Creek 1990.

MYSTIC LAGOON (A. & D. Willott, R. 1990). Sdlg. 86-87. SIB, 24" (61 cm), M. Lightly ruffled violet blue, deeper hafts, inconspicuous signal; style arms violet blue, blue midrib. Parentage unknown. Willott 1991.

MYSTIC LOVER (George Sutton, R. 1999). Sdlg. G-108. TB, 36" (91 cm), ML. S. white, trace of violet (RHS 86) on midrib; style arms pale violet; F. dark violet (93A); beards bronze, violet base, short dark violet horn; slight sweet fragrance. F-39: (Mystique x Sky Hooks) X F-64: (Antigua Soleil x Egyptian).

MYSTIC MINARET (John Baldwin, R. 1994). Sdlg. 88-2B. TB, 32" (81 cm), ML. S. cream pink, pale violet midrib; F. light grey violet, white area around tangerine beard; slight fragrance. Nefertiti X My Heroine.

298

MYSTIC PLUM (A. & D. Willott, R. 1999). Sdlg. W 99-19. SDB, 12" (30 cm), M. S. ecru, base flushed violet; style arms ecru; F. medium violet; beards blue, greyed yellow in throat; ruffled. W 96-32: (W 88-3: (W 83-92: (Gay Parasol x (Greenlee GX-2 x Buttons)) x Pilgrims' Choice) x unknown) X Chubby Cheeks.

MYSTIC POTION (Barry Blyth, R. 1996). Sdlg. A49-1. IB, 24" (61 cm), EM. S. smoky mushroom pink, midrib flushed lavender; F. smoky mushroom pink overlaid rosy lavender, rosy lavender veining near navy black beard. Chanted X Electrique. Tempo Two 1996/97.

MYSTIC RITES (Barry Blyth, R. 1992). Sdlg. X85-2. TB, 35" (89 cm), ML. S. beige pink, slight lavender flush at midrib; F. bright rosy magenta; beards vivid tangerine; slight fragrance. Street Dancer X Mulled Wine. Tempo Two 1992/93.

MYSTIC SMILE (Cleo Palmer, SDB, R. 1989). Palmer's Iris 1990.

MYSTIC'S MUSE (Schreiner, R. 1993). Sdlg. W 600-A. TB, 36" (91 cm), ML. Bright pink (RHS 38C) self; beards tangerine. S 364-1: (M 851-1: ((Rippling Waters x (Annabel Lee sib x Claudia Rene)) x ((Annabel Lee x (Gracie Pfost x T 889-1)) x (((Amethyst Flame x (Amethyst Flame x Alpenrose)) x Lilac Supreme) x Warm Laughter sib))) x H 941-B, unknown) X N 528-A: (K 475-B: (Elizabeth Stuart x (Pink Horizon x (One Desire x Esther Fay))) x Pinafore Pink). Schreiner 1993.

MYTHS AND DREAMS (Barry Blyth, R. 1999). Sdlg. E165-1. SPU, 38" (97 cm), ML. S. soft powder blue lilac; style arms more mauve; F. soft powder blue lilac, lemon yellow spreading signal, some light violet veining; ruffled. Noble Roman X "Touareg". Tempo Two 1999/2000.

MY VAGABOND (Barry Blyth, R. 1992). Sdlg. Y6-8. TB, 36-38" (91-97 cm), VE-M. S. light violet, some deeper veining; F. plush velvety violet, 1/8" bleeding light violet edge; beards white, tipped mustard; sweet fragrance. Sib to Imprimis. Tempo Two 1992/93.

MY WAY (Mary Dunn, R. 1994). Sdlg. M84-947A. TB, 37" (94 cm), M. S. white ground, french lilac plicata markings; F. white, texture veined, edged french lilac; beards yellow, tipped french lilac; laced. Patterns X Laced Cotton. M.A.D. Iris 1995.

NACHTFALTER (Vera Matthe, R. 1990). Sdlg. VM 80-21-1. TB, 36" (90 cm), M. Lightly ruffled greyed purple (RHS 187A), F. blending lighter (187B) in center, shoulders blending from greyed purple (183A) to greyed orange (166A); beards bronze (near 167A); slight spicy fragrance. "Faust" X Barcelona.

NACRE ART (Stan Dexter by Marie Ingersoll, R. 1994). Sdlg. A37-86-165 BB. TB, 38" (97 cm), ML. Pale orchid, aging silver blue, with few orchid lines on F.; beards brown yellow, tipped purple. 83-24: (Logan's Run x Peppermint) X Pink 'n' Mint. Ingersoll's Iris 1995.

NADEZHDA BUDUSCHEGO (Nataliya Khimina, R. 1999). Sdlg. 95-12. TB, 32" (82 cm), EM. S. white, cream edge; style arms cream yellow; F. chocolate brown, white central spot; beards yellow. Floorshow X Tennessee Gentleman.

NADEZHDA ROLLER (V. & N. Gordodelovy, R. 1995). Sdlg. 12. TB, 35" (90 cm), L. Ruffled pink, tinted orange, F. with light brown rim and haft striations; beards red, light yellow at end. Parentage unknown. Gordodelovy 1987.

NADEZHDINY SNY (Viktor Sheviakov, R. 1996). Sdlg. 20b3. TB, 30" (75 cm), ML. S. light salmon pink; F. salmon pink, light salmon pink edge; beards yellow pink; slight fragrance. Latin Lover X Limelight. Sheviakov 1996.

NADEZHDY (Irina Driagina, R. 1995). Sdlg. 75-19. TB, 45" (115 cm), M. Lightly ruffled pinkish cream self; beards red. Parentage unknown. Driagina 1979.

NAFFASINA (Ladislav Muska, R. 1997). Sdlg. S-ELLZ-01. SDB, 14" (36 cm), M. Light ice blue, F. flushed lilac blue around beard; style arms light blue; beards orange, hairs tipped blue. (El Naffasa x Laced Lemonade) X (Demon x Queen's Pawn). Muska 1997.

NAGAREBOSHI (Ho Shidara, R. 1999). SIB, 27" (69 cm), M. S. absent; style arms dark blue violet; F. multiple (6), dark blue violet, white signal. Parentage unknown. Ensata Gardens 1997.

NAMPARA (R. E. Nichol, TB, R. 1984). British Iris Society 1987.

NANCY KAY (Francis McVicker, R. 1994). Sdlg. 8931. TB, 39" (99 cm), EM. S. medium blue violet (RHS 91A); style arms light blue, near-white in center; F. deeper blue violet (90C), white speckling around beard, brown haft lines; beards white, tipped gold in throat; ruffled; slight sweet fragrance. Millrace X Victoria Falls.

NANCY LOUVIERE (Ed Matheny III, TB, R. 1989). Ed's Iris 1991.

NANCY ROSE (D. L. Shepard, R. 1999). Sdlg. 97026-9301. SPU, 48-52" (122-132 cm), M. S. purple, base of midrib yellow; style arms purple, edged white; F. purple, medium gold signal veined purple on lower portion. Giuseppe X Custom Design.

NANCY'S TREASURE (Ed Matheny III, R. 1996). Sdlg. 28-01-91. TB, 40" (107 cm), E. S. dusty lavender; F. maroon, edged dusty lavender, white area lined maroon around mustard beard. Parentage unknown. Ed's Iris 1997.

NANGKITA (Ivar Schmidt, R. 1995). Sdlg. PC 89-AP. CA, 13" (33 cm), M. Pastel rich creamy apricot, F. with large yellow signal. Nayook X unknown. Iris Acres 1995/96.

NANNI F (Manfred Beer, R. 1991). Sdlg. MB 5/78. TB, 39" (100 cm), M. Smoky yellow, F. with large white violet spot; beards yellow. Cosmopolitan X Nachtfalter. Gartencenter Kania 1991.

NANNY RIDER (Truman Scarborough, R. 1995). Sdlg. 2-90-C2a. TB, 33" (84 cm), M. Near-black, with velvety purple overlay, some lighter marking on F. haft; style arms lavender; beards golden bronze; pronounced spicy to musky fragrance. Parentage unknown, black X dark purple. Scarborough's Backyard Garden 1998.

NAOMI OF MARA (E. S. Fankhauser, AB, R. 1989). Tempo Two 1990/91.

NARIHIRA (Shuichi Hirao by Society for Japanese Irises, R. 1992). JI, (6 F.), 39" (100 cm), M. Deep velvety red purple. Parentage unknown. Hirao 1960.

NASHA MASHA (Viacheslav Gavrilin, R. 1996). SDB, 10" (25 cm), ML. Light yellow, stitched and dotted lilac, F. also edged light yellow, green pattern under white spot below beard; beards lilac, light blue at end, hairs tipped orange; slight fragrance. Chanted X Chubby Cheeks. Gavrilin 1999.

NATACHA DELVAUX (Alphonse Van Mulders, R. 1990). Sdlg. 223-18-86. TB, 38" (97 cm), M. Ruffled blue white; beards white. Tahiti Sunrise X Dentelle Rose. Jardinart-Van Mulders 1989.

NATASCHA N. (Pavel Nejedlo, R. 1998). Sdlg. CACPMDDGG-89-1. TB, 42" (107 cm), ML. S. and style arms rich pink; F. light pink, edged darker; beards coral pink; ruffled, lightly laced; slight sweet fragrance. (Carved Angel x Carved Pink) X (Miss Dolly Dollars x Grecian Gown). Lukon 1998.

NATE RUDOLPH (Nathan Rudolph by Loleta Powell, R. 1992). Sdlg. 88-07. TB, 28" (71 cm), EML. Lightly ruffled pure pink; beards deep pink. Parentage unknown. Powell's Gardens 1993.

NATIONAL ANTHEM (Joseph Ghio, CA, R. 1989). Bay View 1990.

NATIONAL VELVET (Lowell Baumunk, R. 1998). Sdlg. 94X10-18. TB, 33" (84 cm), M. S. pale lavender; style arms light lavender, infused purple; F. dark purple, narrow lavender edge; beards yellow. Tempting Fate X 92TFRW-3: (Twist of Fate x Ride the Wind).

NATIVE WINE (Elaine Hulbert, R. 1997). SPEC (*virginica*), 30" (76 cm), ML. S. wine red; style arms white, slight red center brushing; F. wine red, large yellow signal with inconspicuous whitish border and wine veining; leaf bases red purple; slight sweet fragrance. Parentage unknown.

NATURAL CHARM (Joseph Ghio by William Maryott, R. 1997). Sdlg. 89-121-Z. TB, 35" (89 cm), M. Shell pink (RHS 37B aging to 37D); beards blue pink; slight fragrance. 85-153-T3, Birthday Greetings sib, X 86-103-R2: (Romantic Mood x 82-156-H2, pollen parent of Birthday Greetings). Maryott 1997.

NATURAL GRACE (Barry Blyth, R. 1998). Sdlg. D87-2. TB, 38" (96 cm), ML. Ruffled silvery blue self, slightly deeper S. midrib and base, some burgundy tan around hafts; beards lavender, hairs tipped mustard; slight fragrance. Vanda Song X Plume d'Or. Tempo Two 1998/99.

NATURAL REFLEXION (Mary Dunn, R. 1996). Sdlg. M940-3. TB, 36" (91 cm), M. S. warm white, blue plicata flecking; style arms warm white, violet center; F. warm white, flecked and stained deep violet; beards blue, hairs tipped mustard. Patterns X Charmed Life. M.A.D. Iris 1997.

NATURAL WONDER (John C. Taylor, R. 1990). Sdlg. OL 116-1. LA, 51" (130 cm), M. Fluted greyed purple (RHS 186C), yellow signal with green veining on S. and F.; cartwheel form. Koorawatha sib X unknown. Rainbow Ridge 1990/91.

NAUGHTY NOTIONS (Tom Burseen, R. 1993). Sdlg. 9-203R. TB, 34" (86 cm), ML. S. light creamy apricot with lemon tints (near RHS 24D); F. white, edged creamy apricot; beards tangerine orange; laced, tightly ruffled; sweet fragrance. Role Model X 4-192: (Lavish Lace x Embellishment). T.B.'s Place 1994.

NAVA (Augusto Bianco, R. 1999). Sdlg. 450. SDB, 10" (26 cm), EM & RE. s. wistaria; style arms wistaria and beige; F. blended yellow and ochre; beards orange; slight spicy fragrance. Fairy Footsteps X Small Flash. Iride 1998. Introduced as "Neva".

NAVAJO CORAL (D. L. Shepard, R. 1996). Sdlg. 88007-8605. LA, 36-40" (91-107 cm), ML. S. sandy coral, deep coral centerline; style arms greenish yellow; F. deeper coral, spear-shaped yellow gold signal with 1/4" dark coral red outline. Ila Nunn X Bobbie Lou. Shepard Iris 1996.

NAVAJO GOLD (Jim Hedgecock, R. 1990). Sdlg. 83-46-1. TB, 32" (81 cm), M. Heavily laced and ruffled bright gold; beards bright gold; slight fragrance. Temple Gold X Carolina Gold. Comanche Acres 1991.

NAVAJO NIGHT (Jim Hedgecock, R. 1997). Sdlg. 83-40-3. TB, 31" (79 cm), ML. S. lightly laced purple black; F. red black, slight purple blaze by burnt brown beard; ruffled; slight sweet fragrance. Superstition X Soul Music. Comanche Acres 1998.

NAVAJO PRINCESS (D. L. Shepard, R. 1999). Sdlg. 89514. LA, 35" (89 cm), ML. S. light lavender, burgundy veining, darker centerline; style arms light burgundy; F. burgundy, veined darker, large yellow signal. Parentage unknown. Shepard Iris 1999.

NAVAJO ROSE (D. L. Shepard, R. 1992). Sdlg. 88009. LA, 42" (107 cm), M. Rose red, veined darker red, dark gold steeple signal. Bobbie Lou X Creole Flame. Shepard Iris 1992.

NAVY BAND (Eric & Bob Tankesley-Clarke, R. 1999). Sdlg. 463A. BB, 26" (66 cm), M. White ground plicata edged dark blue violet; style arms dark blue violet; beards with dark blue hair tips, bronze and white lower layers; slight sweet fragrance. Goddess X Everything Plus. Adamgrove 1997.

NAVY BLUE GEM (Marty Schafer/Jan Sacks, R. 1998). SPEC (*cristata*), 4" (10 cm), ML. Dark blue violet, bright white signal bordered very dark blue, light yellow central crest, two side crests white. Parentage unknown. In commerce prior to 1985 as "Dark Blue Violet" (Laurie's Garden), 1997 as "Navy Blue" (Joe Pye Weed's Garden).

NAVY BLUES (Robert Dunn, R. 1993). Sdlg. B-87-1003Z. TB, 37" (93 cm), E. Ruffled very dark navy blue violet; beards dark violet. Allstar X Busy Being Blue. M.A.D. Iris 1994.

NAVY SEAL (Graeme Grosvenor, R. 1998). Sdlg. U31-2. TB, 37" (95 cm), M. Navy blue self; beards dark navy blue violet; slight fragrance. Breakers X Lord Olivier.

NAVY TRIM (Calvin Helsley, R. 1993). Sdlg. 91-7. SIB, 30" (76 cm), E. Blue violet (RHS 96D) edged and lightly veined navy blue (89B), white signal veined blue (89D); style arms violet blue (97B), darker midrib. Mabel Coday X D. S. Varner S060: (Marlya x Steve).

NEAR AND DEAR (Frederick Kerr, R. 1996). Sdlg. 90-72-05. TB, 36" (91 cm), M. Heavily ruffled, lightly laced dark yellow; beards dark yellow; slight fragrance. Moon's Delight X Gold Country. Rainbow Acres 1996.

NEARLY SO (Stan Dexter by Marie Ingersoll, R. 1992). Sdlg. 84-83-30. TB, 34" (86 cm), M. S. white; F. clear medium yellow with white lines; beards yellow, tipped white. Tranquil Star X Wedding Candles. Ingersoll's Iris 1993.

NEAR MYTH (J. T. Aitken, R. 1998). Sdlg. 91M25. SDB, 14" (36 cm), M. S. white; F. white, bright yellow spot; beards white, yellow in throat. Lankow 0H18 ((Aitken 80-22 x Dixie Pixie) x (Inscription x M. Wright L85: (Blue Trinket x Cotton Blossom))) X Pele. Aitken's Salmon Creek 1998.

NEAT PLEATS (Tom Burseen, R. 1990). Sdlg. 6-268A. TB, 34" (86 cm), ML. S. very light pinkish cream; F. very light mint green cream; beards white, tipped tangerine; heavily ruffled, fluted, and pleated; musky fragrance. Ace of Lace sib X Glory Bound. T.B.'s Place 1994.

NEAT TRICK (John W. White, R. 1994). Sdlg. JKMxSP-1. SIB, 35" (89 cm), EM. S. near blue violet (RHS 89C); style arms lighter and bluer (93C to 93D); F. dark blue violet (89A), splashed white, with pale yellow green signal. Janet K. Merrill X Shirley Pope. Pope's Perennials 1997.

NEBBIOLO (Lawrence Ransom, R. 1999). Sdlg. 89/51-14. TB, 32" (80 cm), ML. S. light cobalt violet, base paler; style arms pale cobalt violet, edge and crests yellower; F. deep garnet violet, edge paler, upper third white ground netted garnet; beards vermilion orange, mid-layer garnet, base white; pronounced spicy sweet fragrance. 86/74-2: (Pink Taffeta x Needlecraft) X Queen in Calico.

NEBRASKA SKIES (Connell Marsh, TB, R. 1987). C. Marsh 1990.

NECTAR (Keith Keppel, IB, R. 1989). Keppel 1990.

NECUKE (Ladislav Muska, R. 1997). Sdlg. AFLC-02. TB, 38" (97 cm), M. Ruffled, heavily laced pinkish peach, F. with white center; style arms rose pink; beards burnt orange; sweet fragrance. (Aphrodisiac x Lady Madonna) X Pan-Pink. Muska 1997.

NEDDA (Erhard Woerfel, R. 1990). Sdlg. 21/84B. TB, 43" (110 cm), E. White; beards tangerine. Snowmound X Montego Bay. Hochheimer 1991.

NEDOTROGA (Viktor Sheviakov, R. 1996). Sdlg. 18e1. TB, 30" (75 cm), ML. S. creamy peach pink, pale violet midrib; F. deep rose violet, brownish hafts; beards yellow brown; slight fragrance. Rippling Waters X Latin Lover. Sheviakov 1997.

NEFERTITI'S DAUGHTER (O. D. Niswonger, TB, R. 1989). Cape Iris 1991.

NEGOTIATOR (Chet Tompkins, R. 1997). Sdlg. 93-85C. TB, 40" (102 cm), ML-VL. Medium blue, whitish undertoning more apparent in heart; beards pale lemon white, tinted blue. Honky Tonk Blues X (Frost Alert x Fuji Skies). Fleur de Lis 1997.

NEGRA MODELO (George Sutton, R. 1998). Sdlg. G-85-B. SDB, 13" (33 cm), EM & RE. Ruffled black and violet blend, F. with black thumbprint; beards blue violet, bronze in throat; slight sweet fragrance. Sigh X Chanted. Sutton 1999.

NEGRO BLUES (Ladislav Muska, R. 1997). Sdlg. S-MOQP-02. SDB, 13" (33 cm), M. Laced purplish red black self; style arms red black; beards violet blue; sweet fragrance. Monkey X Queen's Pawn. Muska 1992.

NELL'S SUNDAE (Stan Dexter by Marie Ingersoll, R. 1991). Sdlg. 180-82-46. TB, 32" (81 cm), M. Ruffled pinkish rose melon, small white flash below pink red beard; slight fragrance. 1979-8 X Pink Taffeta. Ingersoll's Iris 1992.

NELSON BAYS (Alison Nicoll, R. 1999). Sdlg. N95T6:10. TB, 36" (91 cm), E. S. purple; style arms blue; F. purple, medium blue edge; beards gold, tipped blue; slight sweet fragrance. In Town X Honky Tonk Blues. Richmond Iris 1999/2000.

NEMURIJISHI (Society for Japanese Irises, R. 1992). JI (9-12 F.), 37" (95 cm), E. White ground heavily sanded light blue violet, signal yellow. Parentage unknown. Seiko-en (Japan) prior to 1940.

NEON COWBOY (Hall Bradshaw, R. 1996). Sdlg. 91-02. TB, 42" (107 cm), M. Lightly ruffled reddish black, F. with mauve rim, white spray pattern below beard; beards yellow, violet at end. Superstition X Queen in Calico. Superstition 1998.

NEON MOON (Marvin Granger, R. 1994). Sdlg. 92-UNK10. LA, 25" (64 cm), M. Tailored pure white, greenish yellow signals; slight fragrance. Parentage unknown.

NEON PIXIE (Lynda Miller, SDB, R. 1988). Miller's Manor 1990.

NEON RUBY (D. L. Shepard, R. 1992). Sdlg. 88006. LA, 40" (102 cm), M. S. light rose red; style arms brick red; F. brick red, veined darker, 1/16" pale yellow edge, neon green yellow signal. Bobbie Lou X Creole Flame. Shepard Iris 1992.

NEON SMOKE (Hooker Nichols, R. 1994). TB, 34" (86 cm), ML. S. blended smoky greyed tan heliotrope; F. ruffled blended greyed petunia purple, darker area around dark bronze brown beard. Puget Sound X Dazzling Gold. Hillcrest 1996.

NEON TROLL (Hooker Nichols, R. 1992). Sdlg. 8812B. IB, 18" (46 cm), EML. S. yellow; F. deep neon yellow, sometimes edged slightly lighter; beards orange; lightly ruffled; sweet fragrance. Academy Awards X Marmalade Skies. Hillcrest 1993.

NEPTUNE'S CLOAK (Ben Hager, TB, R. 1989). Roris 1992.

NEREID (Nora Scopes, R. 1999). Sdlg. 06/54. TB, 36" (91 cm), M. S. pallid hyacinth blue, base deeper; F. pale hyacinth blue, hafts deep hyacinth, greenish center; beards blue. Airs Above Ground X 01/26: (4/53: (0/165B, Demoiselle sib, x -- possibly Easter Dream) x Sea Music).

NESSIE (Lynda Miller, R. 1998). Sdlg. 692B. SDB, 11-12" (28-31 cm), M. S. creamy green, smoky deep lavender solid border and dotted center; style arms cream, green edge; F. creamy green, violet plicata band, outer green band; beards light blue, white-based old gold to gold in throat. 3587B: (Smidget x Sniffs 'n' Sneezes) X Chubby Cheeks. Miller's Manor 1998.

NESTLING (Ben Hager, R. 1996). Sdlg. MD5152WYBrSp. MDB, 4" (10 cm), EM. S. clear medium yellow; style arms yellow; F. clear yellow, chestnut brown spot; beards orange, yellow base; slight sweet fragrance. MD4473B: (((((((Seventh Heaven x Jones 157) x (Frenchi x Pagoda)) x ((Norah x Thisbe) x sib)) x A. Brown D-138Y: (Little Charmer x unknown)) x (Dinky x A. Brown D-789-12)) x MD3739WWhYHft: (Pet sib x Tiny Apricot)) x (MD3739CrYel x (Pet sib x Tiny Apricot))) X MD3428BlAm, Ditto sib. Adamgrove 1997.

NEUE BULT (Harald Moos, R. 1990). Sdlg. 86/6020A. TB, 35½" (90 cm), M. Bright red brown, yellowish hafts; beards golden yellow. War Sails X Desert Lilac. Moos 1991.

NEUTRINO (Barry Blyth, R. 1997). Sdlg. D34-4. SDB, 14" (36 cm), EML. S. bright lavender magenta; F. white, 1/4" lavender magenta edge, small line below beard, hafts deeper rosy magenta; beards vivid bright tangerine; slight sweet fragrance. Bee's Knees X A7-1: (Merry Dance x Mini Song). Tempo Two 1997/98.

NEVER SAY (John C. Taylor, R. 1993). Sdlg. RL 58-2. LA, 51" (130 cm), M. S. creamy pink, irregularly flushed magenta; F. magenta pink with light rim, yellow signal with distinct green line; ruffled. OL 113-1: (Koorawatha x Dazzling Star) X Margaret Lee. Rainbow Ridge 1993/94.

NEVER SAY NEVER (George Sutton, R. 1999). Sdlg. H-130. TB, 37" (94 cm), ML. S. and style arms white, tinted pale lavender; F. off-white; beards orange, lavender horn; ruffled; slight musky fragrance. Tinted Crystal X Mesmerizer.

NEW AGE (Ken Mohr, R. 1992). TB, 36" (91 cm), M. Heavily ruffled and laced lavender violet; beards white, tipped lemon; slight musky fragrance. Added Praise X Grand Waltz. Pacific Coast Hybridizers 1991.

NEW BEGINNING (Jim Hedgecock, R. 1990). Sdlg. C-83-10-1. TB, 30" (76 cm), M. S. white; F. peach pink; beards reddish pink; ruffled, laced. Java Charm X Little Susie. Comanche Acres 1991.

NEW CENTURION (Schreiner, R. 1993). Sdlg. W 861-1. TB, 39" (99 cm), EM. Smooth deep carmine red (RHS 46A); beards bronze. Cayenne Pepper X Distant Fire. Schreiner 1993.

NEW CENTURY (Graeme Grosvenor, R. 1999). Sdlg. V111-1. TB, 36" (91 cm), M. S. pale blue; F. medium blue violet, lighter edge; beards yellow, tipped blue violet. T18-2: (Silverado x Honky Tonk Blues) X Zipper Stitch sib. Rainbow Ridge 1999/2000.

NEW CHALLENGE (Graeme Grosvenor, R. 1997). Sdlg. R5-4. TB, 36" (91 cm), ML. Purple self; beards blue violet; ruffled; pronounced sweet fragrance. Silverado X Dusky Challenger. Rainbow Ridge 1997/98.

NEW COOL (Tom Burseen, R. 1990). Sdlg. 6-153T. TB, 36" (91 cm), M. S. tannish yellow; F. white, faint red brown plicata margin; beards bright yellow; heavily ruffled; musky fragrance. 4-103D: (Theatre x Dazzling Gold) X Oh Babe. T.B.'s Place 1991.

NEW DAWNING (Richard Ernst, R. 1990). Sdlg. F112-6. TB, 36" (91 cm), M. S. lemon yellow; F. white, edged yellow; beards yellow; ruffled. Afternoon Delight X Gaulter 80-74, pink sdlg. from Claudia Rene lines. Cooley 1990.

NEW FLAME (Augusto Bianco, R. 1999). Sdlg. 808. TB, 34" (86 cm), ML. Texture-veined milky white self; beards cream, hairs tipped carrot; slight spicy fragrance. Quarta Caravella X (Candlegleam x Jolt).

NEW GLORY (John Knaus, TB, R. 1989). Knaus 1990.

NEW LEAF (Joseph Ghio, R. 1996). Sdlg. 91-65X2. TB, 32" (81 cm), M. S. pink, rosy violet midrib brushing; style arms pink; F. plush maroon, red purple edge, white area around beard; beards tangerine, white at end. Sib to Skipalong. Bay View 1997.

NEW LOVER (Barry Blyth, R. 1994). Sdlg. A60-2. TB, 42" (107 cm), ML. S. pastel lemon yellow; F. creamy white, lemon gold hafts; beards gold, deeper in throat; pronounced sweet fragrance. Dance Man X Elegant Blue. Tempo Two 1994/95.

NEW MAGIC (Floyd Dyer, R. 1994). Sdlg. D220-86D. SDB, 13" (33 cm), M. S. violet to tan at top edge; F. dark red, blending to tan edge; beards yellow, lightly tipped blue; slight sweet fragrance. Small Music X Ice Chalet. Four Cedars 1994.

NEW MEXICO (Polly Black, R. 1996). Sdlg. WGI-1. TB, 39" (99 cm), L. Deep bright gold self; beards deep orange. Alaskan Sunset X Magic Candle.

NEW MEXICO SUNSHINE (Sara Doonan, R. 1990). Sdlg. 84-29-4. TB, 36" (91 cm), ML. Lightly ruffled bright chromium yellow; self beards; slight fragrance. Tut's Gold X Money. Sunset Iris 1991.

NEW ORDER (Mary Dunn, R. 1993). Sdlg. M84-939Z. TB, 36" (91 cm), M. S. ivory cream, very faintly shaded lilac when fresh; F. ruffled ivory cream, very pale lilac plicata edge and pastel plicata markings around pale yellow beard. Go Around X Fiction. M.A.D. Iris 1994.

NEW PROSPECT (Cleo Palmer, R. 1992). Sdlg. 8970. SDB, 13" (33 cm), M. Oyster shell white, F. with yellowish hafts and shoulder veining; beards red, tipped blue. 8560: (Gigglepot x 82-11: ((Dove Wings x 7259) x ((Baria x Carpathia) x Dove Wings))) X Dorothy Howard. Palmer's Iris 1992.

NEW REVUE (Chet Tompkins, R. 1992). Sdlg. DByY. TB, 38" (97 cm), ML. S. creamy white; F. pastel apricot orange; beards bright red. Sdlgs. inv. Lamplit Hour, Shannopin, Pinnacle, Whole Cloth, Orange Parade, Sass 36-19, Candle Power. Fleur de Lis 1992.

NEWSTEAD GOLD (Beryl Pederick, R. 1994). Sdlg. 5. TB, 33" (83 cm), EM. Aureolin yellow (HCC 3) self; beards orange; slight fragrance. Sound of Gold X Joyce Terry.

NEW TUNE (Graeme Grosvenor, R. 1993). Sdlg. R2-BB. TB, 36" (91 cm), ML. Ruffled blue self; beards yellow, tipped white. Silverado X Skyblaze. Rainbow Ridge 1995/96.

NEW VISTA (B. Charles Jenkins, R. 1992). Sdlg. C4-17B. SPU, 35-49" (89-124 cm), M. S. and style arms light purple; F. ivory ground with plicata pattern of purple lines intensifying at edge. Blue Lassie X Highline Honey. Shepard Iris 1995.

NEW VOGUE (Heather Pryor, R. 1997). Sdlg. 56/90-10. LA, 38" (97 cm), EM. S. and F. barium yellow (RHS 10C), golden yellow line signal; style arms lime green, tipped yellow; ruffled. Designer's Dream X Gladiator's Gift. Lone Star 1998.

303

NEW WRINKLES (Tom Burseen, R. 1991). Sdlg. 6-48A. TB, 36" (91 cm), M. S. violet (RHS 87A); F. violet (87A) edge fading to creamy violet center; beards cream, tipped orange; ruffled, heavily laced; sweet fragrance. Tres Elegante X Secret Cove. T.B.'s Place 1994.

NEW YORK CITY (Frank Foster, R. 1990). Sdlg. 8430A. TB, 38½" (98 cm), M. S. cream with yellow; F. cream white, edged yellow; beards yellow; slight fragrance. Jeweled Starlight X Temple Gold.

NEXT MILLENNIUM (Joseph Ghio, R. 1999). Sdlg. 93-90C. TB, 32" (81 cm), ML. S. creamy white, light yellow halo; style arms white, edged gold; F. blackish red purple, yellow sunburst around red beard. Sib to Snowed In.

NEXT STEP (Bryce Williamson, R. 1995). Sdlg. 2091. TB, 36" (91 cm), EM. S. light to medium delft blue, marked blue white at midrib base; style arms medium delft blue; F. white ground, precise stitched and sanded medium to dark delft blue edge, shoulders dark delft blue, stitched and sanded "V" around soft blue beard. Rare Treat X Monologue. Stockton 1998.

NEXT TIME ROUND (Graeme Grosvenor, R. 1999). Sdlg. U122-1. TB, 35" (89 cm), ML. White with lavender influence, F. with darker hafts; beards red, blue violet at end; slight fragrance. Perils of Pauline X Dance Music.

NEZHNOST (Irina Driagina, R. 1996). Sdlg. 2-28. TB, 31" (78 cm), E. White self, tinted light blue; beards light yellow; pronounced fragrance. Parentage unknown. Driagina 1971.

#NIAGARA (Joyce Ragle, TB, R. 1955). Stock destroyed and name released.

NIAGARA (Akihiko Terada, R. 1997). Sdlg. S-252-89-6. TB, 36" (91 cm), M. marine blue self; beards white, tipped yellow; pronounced spicy fragrance. Silverado X Pacific Tide. Roris 1997.

NIAGARA POWER (Anna Rettig, R. 1995). Sdlg. AR-110. JI (3 F.), 36" (91 cm), ML. S. violet (RHS 82C); style arms purple violet (82A), nearly vertical; F. purple violet (82C), intensifying in center (84A), radiating into veins; narrow medium yellow signal. Parentage unknown. A & M Perennials 1995.

NICE NIECE (Tom Burseen, TB, 1989). T.B.'s Place 1992.

NICK'S JOY (John & Helen Kinnamon, R. 1998). Sdlg. 91-1. TB, 30" (76 cm), M. S. and style arms cream; F. cream, throat yellow; beards orange, gold at end. Going My Way X Ruffled Ballet.

NICK'S NUGGET (T. J. Betts, R. 1995). Sdlg. 117C. LA, 38" (96 cm), EM. S. yellow (RHS 12B); style arms yellow; F. yellow (11A), orange streak signal; ruffled. Carioca Carnival X 930A: (Ila Nunn x Shrimp Creole).

NICODEMUS (Nora Scopes, R. 1991). Sdlg. 1/189. TB, 38" (97 cm), L. S. mahogany red; F. deep black red, velvety finish; ochre beard. Dark Rosaleen X Superstition.

NICOLA JANE (R. E. Nichol by Jean Nichol, R. 1996). Sdlg. Q15. TB, 32" (81 cm), M. S. light blue, infused white; F. with wide deep violet (RHS 89B) edge bleeding into white ground; beards pale gold; lightly ruffled. Probably -- Seaport X unknown.

NIGERIAN RASPBERRY (Brad Kasperek, R. 1994). Sdlg. 91B-71A. TB, 36" (91 cm), M. Raspberry cream (RHS 54C) ground with red purple (58A) and purple (77A) splashes; beards deep orange; ruffled. Maria Tormena X Bygone Era. Zebra 1995.

NIGHT ANGEL (J. T. Aitken, R. 1996). Sdlg. 87J27. JI (6 F.), 34" (86 cm), ML. Purple, light violet rays; style arms deep purple edged white,multiple, forming prominent cluster. Dancing Waves X Electric Rays. Aitken's Salmon Creek 1996.

NIGHT ATTACK (Joseph Ghio, R. 1992). Sdlg. 88-17G. TB, 40" (102 cm), EM. S. blue purple; F. black with blue purple hairline edge; beards tangerine, tipped purple. Tempting X In Town. Bay View 1993.

NIGHT CANYON (Polly Black, R. 1992). Sdlg. ESA8-13P. TB, 40" (102 cm), E. Solid deep reddish purple; self beards; slight fragrance. Dark Triumph X unknown. Polly Black 1992.

NIGHT FIRES (Sterling Innerst, R. 1992). Sdlg. 2949-9. TB, 34" (86 cm), M. Dark blue; beards red; slight fragrance. Firewater X Midnight Fire. Innerst 1993.

NIGHT FLAME (J. T. Aitken, R. 1992). Sdlg. 81-52. TB, 44" (112 cm), ML. S. glossy red black; F. black; beards black, tipped mustard. Superstition X Haida Dancer. Aitken's Salmon Creek 1992.

NIGHT FLASH (Tony Huber, R. 1998). Sdlg. 95-140 (93-536). SPEC-X, 43" (110 cm), ML. S. blue violet (RHS 89C); style arms violet (88C), crests aster violet (87B); F. violet blue, signal bright yellow, small dull yellow and purplish halo; slight sweet fragrance. 92-136: ((90 Dom-024: (Nouvel Age x Belle Promesse) x self) x 90 Dom-024) X Purple Parasol.

NIGHT GAME (Keith Keppel, R. 1995). Sdlg. 89-79Q. TB, 42" (107 cm), ML. S. eggplant (M&P 48-H-12) to fluorite violet (46-L-12); style arms mellowglow (10-I-6), hortensia (47-L-12) rib; F.

velvety blackish purple (deeper than 48-H-12), narrow prune purple (46-L-11) edge; beards brick orange (11-H-12), violet base; slight sweet fragrance. Witches' Sabbath X Gallant Rogue. Keppel 1996.

NIGHT HAWK'S DREAM (Merle Roberts, R. 1999). Sdlg. J-126B. TB, 36" (91 cm), ML. S. and style arms white; F. medium dark blue; beards white, hairs tipped pale yellow in throat. Columbia Springs X Ride the Wind.

NIGHT IN CAMELOT (Mary Dunn by Robert Dunn, R. 1999). Sdlg. M1094-9. TB, 36" (91 cm), EM. Ruffled self, apricot over golden rose; beards apricot to golden rose; slight sweet fragrance. M827-B: (M662-2: (Charro x (Ponderosa x Tambourine)) x M80-717: (Charro x Show Biz)) X Sweet Musette.

NIGHT MAGIC (Eleanor Kegerise, TB, R. 1989). Eleanor Kegerise 1991.

NIGHT RULER (Schreiner, R. 1990). Sdlg. T 75-B. TB, 39" (99 cm), M. S. dark purple (RHS 79A); F. black (202A); beards black; ruffled. I 198-B: (D 791-J: (A 671-1: ((Black Onyx x N 371-1) x Grand Ball sib) x Matinata) x Navy Strut) X K 1300-B: (Miriam Steel x Ermine Robe). Schreiner 1990.

NIGHTS OF GLADNESS (Richard Ernst, R. 1990). Sdlg. 84x2. TB, 36" (91 cm), EML. Lightly ruffled velvety black purple; beards purple, tipped mustard, pale yellow in throat. Interpol X unknown. Cooley 1990.

NIGHT SQUALL (Darlene Pinegar, R. 1994). Sdlg. AM1-1-1C. TB, 33" (84 cm), ML. S. dark wine, slightly lighter midrib; style arms dark wine; F. velvety blackish wine, slightly lighter edge, white area with wine markings around beard; beards old gold, tipped dark purple; ruffled; slight sweet fragrance. AM1-1-1: (April Melody x Spinning Wheel) X Capricious. Spanish Fork 1995.

NIGHT STALKER (Jim Hedgecock, R. 1993). Sdlg. 83-62-1. TB, 36" (91 cm), ML. Ruffled purple black with velvety sheen on fluted F.; beards purple, gold in throat; slight sweet fragrance. Superstition X unknown. Comanche Acres 1994.

NIGHT THIEF (William Plotner, R. 1992). Sdlg. 86-601-1. TB, 38" (97 cm), EM. Ruffled dark russian violet (darker than RHS 88A); beards dark purple; slight sweet fragrance. Ovation X Beverly Sills. Wildwood Gardens 1991.

NIGHT TO REMEMBER (Richard Ernst, R. 1996). Sdlg. N104-3. TB, 35" (89 cm), ML. Ruffled dark blue black (RHS 103A/B); beards blue purple (89A to 99A). Before the Storm X Raven's Quote. Cooley 1997.

NIGHT VISION (Duane Meek, R. 1993). Sdlg. 723-1-1. TB, 36" (91 cm), ML. S. light red black; F. dark red black; beards black, tipped bronze. Deep Fire X Cherry Smoke. D & J Gardens 1993.

NIHONKAI (Shuichi Hirao by Society for Japanese Irises, R. 1992). JI (6 F.), 36" (90 cm), M. Royal violet with white splashes, yellow signal. Parentage unknown. Hirao 1957.

NIJI-NO-TOMOE (Society for Japanese Irises, R. 1994). JI (3 F.), 39" (100 cm), E. S. white with red violet rim; style arms white, some red violet on edge; F. with large white center radiating into red violet on outer portion. Old Edo type; parentage unknown. Believed hybridized by Matsudaira Shoo prior to 1856.

NIKOLAY FEDIAYEV (Viacheslav Gavrilin, R. 1996). Sdlg. 94-76-1. TB, 37" (95 cm), M. S. straw to light lemon yellow; style arms yellow; F. patterning of dark red brown on violet base, lightening to orange and light yellow toward beard, 1/3" yellow rim; beards light blue at end, orange in throat, hairs tipped light yellow; slight fragrance. Fiesta Time X Swazi Princess. Gavrilin 1999.

NIKOLCHANKA (Viktor Sheviakov, R. 1995). Sdlg. 22D 18. TB, 35" (90 cm), M. S. blue violet; F. reddish violet, violet brown hafts, white markings near orange brown beard. Winner's Circle X Rippling Waters. Sheviakov 1995.

NIKOLSKI SUVENIR (Viktor Sheviakov, R. 1995). Sdlg. 10D 3A. TB, 30" (75 cm), L. S. white ground, dotted lilac violet; F. white ground, sparsely dotted lilac, narrow lilac violet edge; beards orange, brown at end; ruffled. Latin Lover X Stepping Out. Sheviakov 1995.

NISHIKIORI (Hiroshi Shimizu by Carol Warner, R. 1997). JI (6 F.), 36" (91 cm), ML. Bright red violet, streaked and mottled white, small yellow and white signal; style arms red violet and white, prominent terminal tufts. Saigyozakura X "Myogisan". Draycott 1997.

NITA'S BELLE (Mark Grumbine, R. 1999). Sdlg. 95-15-1. TB, 32" (81 cm), M. S. persimmon orange paling to yellow orange edge; F. maroon, 1/8" yellow orange band; beards red orange; ruffled, lightly laced. Taco Belle X Glazed Orange.

NITAYA (Bob Thomason, R. 1991). Sdlg. BT 8719B. SDB, 11" (28 cm), EM. S. light yellow; F. golden brown, white centerline; beards orange, tipped white; slight fragrance. Marmalade Skies X (Tan Lace x (Gingerbread Man x Solar Flight)). Okie Iris 1993.

NITSUA (Ivar Schmidt, R. 1995). Sdlg. EN B 89/1. JI (6 F.), 25" (64 cm), M. Rich magenta pink, white flash around long daffodil yellow signal, green in throat, short white veins extending outward; style arms white, edged magenta pink. Time and Tide X unknown. Iris Acres 1995/96.

NOARLUNGA (Ivar Schmidt, R. 1995). Sdlg. PC 89-AB. CA, 15" (38 cm), M. S. soft buff-mushroom; F. dusky pink fading to mushroom at edge, deeper pink veining, round bold gold signal; ruffled. Nayook X unknown. Iris Acres 1995/96.

NO BIKINI ATOLL (Richard Ernst, R. 1996). Sdlg. JF120-8-7. TB, 38" (97 cm), M. S. clear medium pink, blended deeper toward midrib; style arms clear medium pink; F. deep pink, smoky cast, edges blended lighter; beards orange, whitish pink at end; lightly ruffled. Rhapsody in Bloom X F104-1: ((Irene Nelson x Sunfire) x Friday Surprise). Cooley 1996.

NOBILITY'S BLUE (Stan Dexter by Marie Ingersoll, R. 1992). Sdlg. 7-118B. TB, 38" (97 cm), ML. Purple blue, F. darker in center, with hash marks; beards yellow, tipped blue. Lord Jeff X 1983-149: (Grape Charm x Ritchie sdlg.). Ingersoll's Iris 1993.

NOBLE CONTESSA (Barry Blyth, R. 1998). Sdlg. E88-5. TB, 36" (91 cm), M. S. lilac, deeper texture veining; F. bright magenta plum, 1/8" lilac edge; beards tangerine; sweet fragrance. Crazy For You X About Town. Tempo Two 1998/99.

NOBLE IMAGE (Eleanor Kegerise, R. 1990). Sdlg. 83-84. TB, 34" (86 cm), M. Ruffled bright medium blue; beards blue. Parentage unknown. Eleanor Kegerise 1991.

NOBLE KNIGHT (Mary Dunn by Robert Dunn, R. 1999). Sdlg. M2168-A. TB, 36" (91 cm), EM. S. butterfly blue; style arms butterfly blue, purple stripe; F. plum purple, white splash at hafts; beards old gold, white at end; slight spicy fragrance. Royalist X Tempting Fate.

NOBLE LADY (Lynda Miller, R. 1999). Sdlg. 4494B. TB, 33" (84 cm), M. S. and style arms pale pink; F. slightly paler pink, rose haft lines; beards tangerine, small orchid horn. Christa X Pagan Pink. Miller's Manor 1999.

NOBLE PLANET (John C. Taylor, R. 1990). Sdlg. OL 137-8. LA, 47" (120 cm), ML. Ruffled light yellow (RHS 11D) veined yellow; style arms yellow. Dazzling Star X Helen Naish. Rainbow Ridge 1990/91.

NOBLE ROMAN (Barry Blyth, R. 1993). Sdlg. EQ-2. SPU, 48" (122 cm), ML. S. lavender blue; F. gold, light filigree netting, 1/4" lavender blue edge. Equality X self. Tempo Two 1993/94.

NOBLESA (Ladislav Muska, R. 1997). Sdlg. AVLB-03. TB, 38" (97 cm), ML. Ruffled and laced light apricot vanilla, F. with deep cream flush near bright orange beard; style arms cream; sweet fragrance. (Aphrodisiac x Vanilla Lace) X Peach Boom. Muska 1997.

NOBLE TOFF (Barry Blyth, R. 1994). Sdlg. A14-3. SDB, 14" (36 cm), EM. S. medium violet; F. deeper medium violet, deeper plush violet thumbprint; beards tangerine in throat, deeper lavender on outer 1/2"; slight sweet fragrance. Smoky Imp X Chanted. Tempo Two 1994/95.

NOBLE TROLL (Hooker Nichols, R. 1991). Sdlg. 8624B. SDB, 12" (30 cm), EML. S. medium violet purple suffused and dotted white near base; F. white solidly edged and dotted dark violet purple, blue dotting on each side of beard; beards gold, tipped blue; ruffled. Court Magician X (Pink Kitten x (Happy Mood x Kiss)).

NOBODY'S CHILD (Isobel Simpson, R. 1993). Sdlg. I.S. 89-21. SPEC (evansia), 11½" (28 cm), EML. S. light lavender blue, edged paler; F. pale lavender blue, royal blue at end of crest, olive brown to deep blue spots; sweet-musky fragrance. Parentage unknown. Simpson 1994.

NOBORI-RYU (Society for Japanese Irises, R. 1994). JI (9 F.), 30" (76 cm), M. Pale violet (RHS 85D) ground with deep purple (89C) veins, yellow signals; stigmas normal, but anthers converted to 3 inner petals with no pollen. Old Edo variety; parentage and hybridizer unknown. Introduced in Japan prior to 1930.

NOC A DEN (Zdeněk Seidl, R. 1999). Sdlg. 93-ToFltN/4. TB, 35" (89 cm), EM. S. and style arms light blue; F. dark purplish blue, light silver dusted hafts; beards mustard, base deep blue; ruffled; slight sweet fragrance. Twist of Fate X Into the Night.

NOCH BEZ TEBIA (Viktor Sheviakov, R. 1995). Sdlg. 22S 10A. TB, 28" (72 cm), M. S. very dark violet; F. violet black; beards dark blue; ruffled. Allegiance X Pink Taffeta. Sheviakov 1997.

NOCHNAYA BABOCHKA (Viacheslav Gavrilin, R. 1999). Sdlg. 94-1117. TB, 31" (78 cm), M. Heavily ruffled black purple self; beards black purple. Darkside X Swazi Princess.

NOCHNAYA SERENADA (Nina Miroshnichenko, R. 1996). TB, 33" (85 cm), EM. S. lilac; F. dark violet, lilac edge, whitish hafts patterned brown; beards yellow; slight sweet fragrance. Parentage unknown. Miroshnichenko 1980.

NOCHNOY DOZOR (Viktor Koroliov, R. 1999). Sdlg. STG3-95K. TB, 45" (115 cm), EM. S. and style arms blue violet; F. blue violet, hafts marked brown; beards blue, brown in throat, hairs tipped white on end; lightly ruffled; pronounced sweet fragrance. Titan's Glory X Lunar Fire. Koroliov 1998.

NOCHNOYE RANDEVU (Sergey Loktev, R. 1996). TB, 28" (72 cm), EM. Bordeaux violet, slight cream influence at base of S. and hafts; beards orange; pronounced spicy fragrance. Parentage unknown. Loktev 1996.

NO CONTEST (William Maryott, R. 1995). Sdlg. TM196WHBL. SDB, 10" (25 cm), M. S. light yellow; F. medium to deep lavender blue, 1/4" light yellow rim; beards yellow. Starlight Waltz X Jazzamatazz. Maryott 1996.

NO DOWN PAYMENT (Paul Black, R. 1996). Sdlg. A61D. TB, 33" (84 cm), L. S. warm pink; F. buff, heavy warm pink laced edge; beards warm pink; slight musky fragrance. Victorian Frills X Ruth Black. Mid-America 1996.

NOEL AIDAN (Harry Foster by Maureen Foster, R. 1993). Sdlg. R91. SIB (tet.) 36" (91 cm), ML. Ruffled very bright deep ultramarine blue (RHS 95A), F. with very prominent silver edge, small white signal; style arms violet blue (90A), violet (87B) in heart, crests large and ruffled. Harpswell Happiness X Dear Dianne.

NO GREATER LOVE (Barbara Roberts, R. 1999). Sdlg. GG 33-4. TB, 36" (91 cm), E. Ruffled light to medium pink; F. with slight white central area; beards coral red; slight sweet fragrance. Grecian Gown X Vanity.

NO JIVE (Tom Burseen, R. 1991). Sdlg. 7-39A. TB, 36" (91 cm), M. S. creamy ground washed orange brown (RHS 166C); F. creamy yellow ground heavily veined and streaked orange brown (166A); beards yellow gold; ruffled; slight fragrance. Rustic Dance X 4-56: (Grape Accent x Bronco Brown). T.B.'s Place 1992.

NOMARCHOS (Ladislav Muska, R. 1996). Sdlg. CMCK-03. TB, 40" (102 cm), ML. Ruffled, heavily laced smoked steel to silver self; beards orange; pronounced fragrance. (Coral Magic x "Cipkovana Krinolina": (After All x Grand Waltz)) X Constantino. Muska 1996.

NOMINEE (Mary Dunn, R. 1995). Sdlg. M1062A. TB, 36" (91 cm), ML. S. rosy tan; style arms copper; F. cordovan fancy pattern, slight markings at tip of golden beard; ruffled. Freestyle X Hamblen 82-42B. M.A.D. Iris 1997.

NONCONFORMIST (Sharon McAllister, R. 1998). Sdlg. 90-19-8. AB (OGB+), 24" (61 cm), EM. S. pale blue violet; style arms greenish buff, midrib blue; F. greenish buff almost covered by rust stippling; beards bronze. Werckmeister's Beauty X Whirlwind Tour. McAllister 1998.

NOOBINNA (Kevin Nilsen, R. 1992). Sdlg. 11-88-1. TB, 36" (91 cm) EM. S. butterscotch gold; F. deep claret, edged tan, tan centerline; beards orange, tinged bronze; ruffled. (Mandolin x Lady Friend) X Ken Ware.

NOOKSACK BEAUTY (Stan Dexter by Marie Ingersoll, R. 1990). Sdlg. 83-223A. TB, 34" (86 cm), M. Dark raspberry rose, gold around hash markings; beards rose orange. Klondike Kate X Mulled Wine. Ingersoll's Iris 1990.

NORA EILEEN (Gerald Richardson, R. 1994). Sdlg. 89-97-1. TB, 39" (99 cm), M. Wine red magenta, F. with violet flash by violet beard; slight fragrance. 87-20-1: (Master Touch x 85-35-2: (((Bluebell Lane x 69-27-2: (((Limelight x Jake) x unknown) x Dress Suit)) x (Rockette x Blue Luster)) x Titan's Glory)) X Ever After. Rainbow's End 1994.

NORDDEUTSCHER WINTER (Harald Moos, R. 1999). Sdlg. 93/B48 AZ. TB, 35½" (90 cm), M. Waved white, F. with small pale yellow haft area; beards yellow. Maerkisch Weiss X Fine China.

NORDICA (William Maryott, R. 1991). Sdlg. M120A. TB, 37" (94 cm), M. Heavily ruffled pure white; beards red, prominent. Radiant Energy X Oktoberfest. Maryott 1992.

NORDIC ICE (Howard Shockey, R. 1992). Sdlg. 88-234-C. TB, 35" (89 cm), M. S. white, slight blue flush inside lower portion; F. white, inconspicuous green veining; beards blue, heavily frosted white; ruffled; slight sweet fragrance. Silverado X 85-220-7B: (El Morado x High Flight). Arilian Acres 1993.

#NORDIC NYMPH (Lilly Gartman, TB, R. 1981). Stock destroyed and name released 1993.

NORDIC YULE (Carl Jorgensen, R. 1995). Sdlg. 87-Wrb-3. TB, 30" (76 cm), ML. Ruffled pure white self, infusion of vermilion at hafts; style arms white; beards vermilion (18); pronounced sweet fragrance. 5-Wrb-2: (Christmas Rubies x 2-P11-4D) X 2-P11-4D: (Summit Sweetie x Triple Crown). Long 1995.

NOREEN'S DELIGHT (D. L. Shepard, R. 1998). Sdlg. 95049-8709. TB, 38" (97 cm), ML. S.

lavender white; F. dark violet blue, blue white central area; beards white, hairs tipped yellow. Twice Blue X Quintessence. Shepard Iris 1998.

NORMA JEAN (John Durrance, R. 1991). Sdlg. D86-44. TB, 36" (91 cm), ML. Ruffled hot pink. Coral Satin X Custom Made. Long 1991.

NORMA L (Gordon Loveridge, R. 1990). Sdlg. L83-16. SIB (sino-sib); 30" (76 cm), M. S. creamy yellow; F. creamy white, violet haze toward hafts, violet veins radiating from hafts. *I. clarkei* X *I. delavayi* white hybrid.

NORMANDY BAY (William Plotner, TB, R. 1989). Wildwood Gardens 1990.

NORMA VALERIE (Ron Busch, R. 1995). Sdlg. 89170/1. SDB, 10" (25 cm), E. S. lemon; F. lavender, flushed lemon when fresh; beards lemon; sweet fragrance. Combo X seedling.

NORTHERN FLAME (Monty Byers, TB, R. 1989). Moonshine 1990.

NORTHERN JEWEL (Schreiner, R. 1991). Sdlg. AA 1246-C. IB, 23" (58 cm), E. Cream white (RHS 158D), yellow shoulder markings; beards yellow. Parentage unknown. Schreiner 1991.

NORTHERN MIST (Harold Stahly, R. 1996). Sdlg. 91-40. TB, 33" (84 cm), M. S. and style arms white; F. white, blending to narrow blue border; beards pale yellow; ruffled; slight sweet fragrance. Celestial Dream X Classic Treasure. Stahly 1996.

NORTHERN PINK (Tomas Tamberg, R. 1995). Sdlg. SSTT 359. SPEC-X (tet.), 31" (80 cm), M. S. pale lavender pink, small; F. lavender pink. Converted tetra-sibtosa V: (Pink Haze x lavender *I. setosa*) X converted tetra-sibtosa IV: (Pink Haze x lavender *I. setosa*). Schoeppinger 1995.

NORTHERN VALENTINE (Chuck Chapman, R. 1995). Sdlg. 92-525-1. SPEC (*setosa*), 20" (51 cm), E. Blue violet self; F. heart-shaped, semi-flaring, with small whitish signal. *I. setosa canadensis* X *I. setosa*, seed from SIGNA. Chapman Iris 1997.

NORTH PACIFIC SEAS (Larry Johnson, R. 1996). Sdlg. J089-23-1. TB, 38" (97 cm), M. S. and style arms dark violet blue (RHS 95B); F. dark violet blue (95A); beards white, hairs tipped silvery blue; ruffled; moderate sweet fragrance. Fair Dinkum X Many Thanks. Cooley 1996.

NORTH POLE (Jim Hedgecock, R. 1995). Sdlg. 83-31-1. TB, 32" (81 cm), M. S. pale blue white; F. medium blue, near-white by beard; beards pale blue, yellow in throat; ruffled, laced; pronounced sweet fragrance. Navy Strut X Margarita. Comanche Acres 1995.

NORTHWARD HO (Lloyd Zurbrigg, R. 1990). Sdlg. GG 82. TB, 37" (94 cm), M & RE (Sept./VA). S. and F. white ground, strawberry pink markings on edges; beards pale yellow. P 14-Oct.: (English Cottage x unknown) X Re-Treat. Avonbank 1991.

NORTHWEST PRIDE (Schreiner, R. 1993). Sdlg. W 167-A. TB, 39" (99 cm), M. S. white (RHS 155B); F. light sky blue (97B); beards white; lightly ruffled. Stormy Night X Royal Crusader. Schreiner 1993.

NORTHWEST PROGRESS (Schreiner, R. 1997). Sdlg. 1988 #25. TB, 34" (86 cm), EM. S. and style arms light blue (RHS 93D); F. dark violet black (103A); beards yellow, dark violet at end; slight fragrance. Parentage unknown. Schreiner 1997.

NOSTALGIYA (Viktor Sheviakov, R. 1995). Sdlg. 21A 16A. TB, 35" (90 cm), ML. S. violet brown; F. dark violet brown, blue violet midrib, cream white haft striations; beards yellow brown; ruffled. Siva Siva X Arabi Pasha. Sheviakov 1997.

NOTABLE (Joseph Ghio, R. 1990). Sdlg. 86-84Y3. TB, 38" (97 cm), L-VL. Toasted melon, blue blaze and red shoulders on F.; beards tangerine. Stratagem X 83-58J: ((Dream Affair x (Artiste x Tupelo Honey)) x (Copper Classic x 76-110BB: ((Malaysia x Carolina Honey) x (Hi Top x ((Ponderosa x Travel On) x Peace Offering))))). Bay View 1991.

NOTHING BUT NET (O. D. Niswonger, R. 1995). Sdlg. 63-93. TB, 34" (86 cm), M. Lilac, hint of pink darker in S.; beards sienna, blue at tip. Blue Chip Pink X Hamblen H81-54H, Fontaine sib. Cape Iris 1996.

NOTHING TO LOSE (Richard Ernst, R. 1993). Sdlg. HR8545-2. TB, 36" (91 cm), M. S. creamy white with lemon yellow infusion on midrib; F. light to medium violet, deeper center; beards yellow; ruffled; slight sweet fragrance. R8545: (Edith Wolford x Merry Madrigal) X unknown. Cooley 1992.

NOTORIOUS (Joseph Ghio, R. 1990). Sdlg. 84-216P4. TB, 36" (91 cm), ML. S. pink; F. pink sunburst blending to wide purple edge; beards tangerine. Geniality X 81-32U: (Fancy Tales x Entourage). Bay View 1991.

NOUVEL AGE (Tony Huber, R. 1992). Sdlg. DOM-F-2-01. SPEC-X, 29½" (75 cm), M. S. purple violet (RHS 86B); F. darker purple violet (86A), white and yellow pointed signal. Oriental Touch X *I. versicolor* sdlg. Dominion Seed House, Horticlub 1997.

NOVA AT MIDNIGHT (Carl Boswell, TB, R. 1989). Adamgrove 1992.

NOW AND FOREVER (Heather Pryor, R. 1997). Sdlg. 29/91-C. LA, 35" (89 cm), M. S. soft lavender (RHS 85B), purple veining, white reverse; style arms soft lime green, lavender tip; F. soft lavender, purple veining, white rim and blush near lime green steeple signal; lightly ruffled. Cammeray X Classical Note. Iris Haven 1997/98.

NO WAY JOSE (Tom Burseen, TB, R. 1989). T.B.'s Place 1990.

NOW HEAR THIS (Heather Pryor, R. 1994). Sdlg. 55/90-5. LA, 36" (91 cm), ML. S. deep rose pink (RHS 58A); style arms ruby red, yellow centerline creating star effect; F. darker ruby red (59A), green reverse, raised yellow dagger signal; ruffled. Gladiator's Gift X Designer's Dream.

NUGENT'S GOLD (Stan Dexter by Marie Ingersoll, R. 1993). Sdlg. A3-7-87A. TB, 34" (86 cm), EM. Yellow, with strong purplish hash markings shading to brown at edge of F.; beards yellow. Freda Laura X Orangerie. Ingersoll's Iris 1994.

NUKA (Ken Durio, R. 1992). Sdlg. PAD-3-PATH. LA (tet.), 26" (66 cm), M. S. full violet blue, edged cream, light yellow line signal; F. full violet, edged cream, large yellow gold signal radiating outward; pronounced spicy fragrance. Bowie X (Bowie x Godzilla). Louisiana Nursery 1995.

NURSE NANCY (Paul Black, R. 1993). Sdlg. 90189A. SDB, 14" (36 cm), E. S. pale lemon yellow; style arms pale yellow; F. white, pale yellow reverse; beards gold, tipped white; ruffled. Bunny Hop X 84211A: (824A, Chubby Cheeks sib, X 824D, sib). Mid-America 1993.

NUTCOTE (Heather Pryor, R. 1999). Sdlg. 9/93-A. LA, 38" (97 cm), E & RE. Ruffled ice blue (RHS 97D) with green line signal, F. with additional faint green veining, bright orange line signal extending 3/4 petal length; style arms lemon, with green and purple midrib blush. Sinfonietta X 16/90-1: (Koorawatha x Alluvial Gold).

NUTFIELD BLUE (H. R. Jeffs, SPEC-X, R. 1989). Stillingfleet Lodge Nurseries 1995.

NUT RUFFLES (Carol Lankow by J. T. Aitken, R. 1992). Sdlg. 0H15-1. SDB, 12" (30 cm), M. S. smooth chocolate brown; F. similar with charcoal brown spot, small cream spot at base of bronze beard; ruffled. Cherry Pop X 0F3-1: (Cherry Tart x Cheery Cherry). Aitken's Salmon Creek 1992.

OAKLANDS AMETHYST (Peter Jackson, R. 1999). Sdlg. LAW6. LA, 35" (90 cm), M. S. medium amethyst; style arms light amethyst, center darker; F. rosy amethyst (RHS 83B); gold line signal surrounded by lighter triangular area; lightly ruffled. All Agaze X Watch Out. Iris Acres 1999/2000.

OAKLANDS JEWELL (Peter Jackson, R. 1997). Sdlg. LDD1. LA, 44" (112 cm), EM. S. soft violet, veined and washed deeper violet; style arms cream, tipped soft violet; F. medium violet, fine lighter edge; yellow steeple signal with green centerline; ruffled; pronounced fragrance. Dural White Butterfly X Delta Dove. Iris Acres 1997/98.

OASIS BROADBEACH (Leslie Donnell, R. 1994). Sdlg. 87-3-3. TB, 28" (71 cm), M. Yellow with white F. blaze; beards yellow base tipped orange; slight fragrance. Speculator X Tintinara.

OBA (Hiroshi Shimizu by Carol Warner, R. 1999). JI (6 F.), 34" (86 cm), ML. White ground mottled pink, darker at shoulders and edge, large yellow green signal; style arms large, white tipped pink. Yuki Arashi X "Sakura-no-Sei". Draycott 1998.

OBAN (Harry Foster, SIB, R. 1989). V. H. Humphrey 1995.

OBA OBA (Mary Dunn, R. 1991). Sdlg. M84-925. TB, 35" (89 cm), M. S. white ground stitched rosy magenta purple, almost solid edge; F. white ground, rosy magenta stitching almost to edge; beards whitish, yellow deep in throat; ruffled. Momentum X Ghio 77-70: (Premonition sib x (Mystique x Barletta)). M.A.D. Iris 1992.

O'BRIEN'S CHOICE (Joyce Meek, R. 1996). Sdlg. 86-5-1. TB, 38" (97 cm), M. Greenish yellow, small ivory blaze in F.; beards bronze. P. T. Barnum X Brandy. D & J Gardens, O'Brien Iris 1996.

OBVIOUS HEIR (John C. Taylor, R. 1991). Sdlg. OL 137-5. LA, 43" (110 cm), M. Heavily ruffled milk white, olive green veining and signal on S. and F. Dazzling Star X Helen Naish. Rainbow Ridge 1991/92.

OCEAN CLOUDS (Bernard Hamner by Shepard Iris Garden, R. 1992). Sdlg. 87-8. TB, 36" (91 cm), E. Soft blue white, F. widely banded sky blue; beards white, tipped yellow; heavily ruffled. Dutch Girl X Glistening Icicle. Hamner Iris, Shepard 1992.

OCEAN FURY (Harold Stahly, R. 1990). Sdlg. 84-25. TB, 32" (81 cm), M. S. deep blue (RHS 93A); F. slightly deeper blue (89A); beards blue; ruffled; slight sweet fragrance. Deep Pacific X ((Ivy League x River Patrol) x Navy Strut). Stahly 1991.

OCEAN GOING (John C. Taylor, R. 1998). Sdlg. UL 8-8. LA, 47" (120 cm), M. S. blue violet;

style arms white, tipped blue violet; F. blue violet, lighter edge, yellow signal surrounded by white. C'est La Mote X First Favourite. Rainbow Ridge 1998/99.

OCEANIC LASS (Kevin Nilsen, R. 1995). Sdlg. 97-87-1. TB, 35" (90 cm), EM. S. pale blue; style arms blue and white; F. sky blue, deeper veining; beards light yellow. Dutch Girl X Sea Haven. Iridescence 1995/96.

OCEAN JEWELS (Opal Brown, R. 1995). Sdlg. 91-16E6. TB, 36" (91 cm), M. S. and style arms palest pink; F. deeper pink; beards tangerine; ruffled. Orangerie X 84-1A3: (Satin Bow x Symphonette). Brown's Sunnyhill 1995.

OCEANSIDE VIEW (Hooker Nichols, R. 1991). Sdlg. 8894A. TB, 36" (91 cm), M-VL. Ruffled light blue, base of S. slightly darker; beards yellow and white. Seeker X Song of Spring. Hillcrest 1992.

OCELOT (Joseph Ghio, R. 1997). Sdlg. 93-2Q. TB, 36" (91 cm), EM. S. peach; F. maroon with blackish sheen; beards tangerine. Chinese New Year X Romantic Evening. Bay View 1998.

OCHAROVANIYE (V. & N. Gordodelovy, R. 1995). Sdlg. 3. TB, 32" (80 cm), M. Ruffled white self, tinted pink; beards pinkish red. Parentage unknown. Gordodelovy 1982.

OCTOBER EVE (T. J. Betts, R. 1997). Sdlg. 025A. LA, 31" (78 cm), ML. S. amethyst violet (RHS 84C); style arms cream; F. amethyst violet, darker veining, creamy central infusion, signal faint orange on cream. Deeper Echo X Evelyn Boon.

OCTOBER SKY (Larry Lauer, R. 1999). Sdlg. 542-3R. TB, 34" (86 cm), EM & RE. S. white, hyacinth blue cast; style arms hyacinth blue; F. wistaria blue, white flash around beard; beards blue, tipped white at end and yellow in middle, solid orange in throat; pronounced spicy fragrance. Speeding Again X Waterworld.

OCTOBER SPLENDOR (Gary Sides, R. 1994). Sdlg. C11-F11B. BB, 27" (69 cm), M & RE (Oct./TN). Ruffled, lightly laced pink self; beards tangerine; pronounced sweet fragrance. Christa X AP22-C1Re: (Returning Peace x Vanity). Sides 1997.

ODA VESNE (Nina Miroshnichenko, R. 1996). TB, 43" (108 cm), M. Salmon pink, small whitish spot below orange red beard; slight sweet fragrance. Parentage unknown. Miroshnichenko 1976.

ODIHAM (R. J. Henley, R. 1994). Sdlg. O3. SPEC (*laevigata*), 12-18" (30-45 cm), M. Medium blue, white signals; six-petaled form; foliage striped green and white. *I. laevigata variegata* X *I. laevigata* (six-petaled).

ODILE (Lawrence Ransom, R. 1996). Sdlg. 90/258-9. SDB, 13" (33 cm), ML. S. medium pink; style arms light pink, crests medium pink; F. medium pink, center paler pink to cream white; beards white, brushed tangerine in throat; spicy sweet fragrance. Cupid's Cup X My Sheba. Iris au Trescols 1997.

ODYSSEUS (Sterling Innerst, R. 1993). Sdlg. 2812-1. JI (6 F.), 36" (91 cm), M. White with subtle reddish blue lines radiating from yellow signal to slight bluish red edge. Jocasta X Iapetus. Iris Pond 1994.

OEDIPUSSI (Harald Moos, TB, R. 1989). Schoeppinger 1990.

OFF BROADWAY (Walter Moores, R. 1991). Sdlg. 85-32-C. TB, 34" (86 cm), EM & RE (Nov./MS). S. deep gold; F. cream to white ground, maroon plicata markings blending to solid brown edge; beards mustard; ruffled. Broadway X ((Drifting Confetti x Queen in Calico) x (Queen in Calico x Blue Tempest)). Moores 1992.

OFF COLOR JOKE (Paul Black, R. 1997). Sdlg. A68C. TB, 34" (86 cm), EM. S. grey white, blended light pinkish grey in center, slight violet midrib infusion; style arms pinkish grey, violet center; F. with medium dark violet central blot washed lighter toward grey white margin, hafts tan with light brown sanding; beards burnt orange, hairs tipped violet; ruffled; slight musky fragrance. Witches' Sabbath X In Town. Mid-America 1997.

OFFENHAM (John D. Taylor, TB, R. 1986). V. H. Humphrey 1992.

OFFERING (Glenn Corlew, R. 1992). Sdlg. SP-13A. SPU, 46" (117 cm), M. Intensely ruffled creamy yellow with quince undertones, very slightly deeper yellow signal. Ila Crawford X (Dawn Candle x Archie Owen). Bay View 1992.

OFF SHE GOES (Marty Schafer/Jan Sacks, R. 1998). Sdlg. S92-75-1. SIB, 28" (71 cm), EM. S. light lavender (RHS 91C/D) with violet (86D) dappling, 1/8" warm white (159D) rim; style arms pearly warm white, pale yellow curls and midrib, wide; F. lavender (91B/C), violet dappling, 1/4" warm white rim changing to gold at shoulders; signal pale yellow to gold with brick speckles and lavender veins, prominent; ruffled. S89-16-1: (Reprise x Mad Magenta) X S89-9-2: (Isabelle x Silver Illusion). Joe Pye Weed 1998.

OFFSHORE FLOW (Mary Dunn, R. 1997). Sdlg. L 213-1. LA, 35" (89 cm), M. Blue violet self, lighter fall area, green finger signal; style arms centered rosy violet. Boy Crazy X Malibu Magic. Bay View 1997.

OGI-NO-MATO (Toyokazu Ichie by Society for Japanese Irises, R. 1995). JI (3 F.), 36" (91 cm), M. S. white, edged violet blue (RHS 93B); style arms white, edged violet, tufted; F. light violet blue (94B/C) with clean white lines, signal rich yellow (13B). Parentage unknown. Introduced in Japan ca. 1984.

OH BE JOYFUL (Ray Lyons, R. 1993). Sdlg. 85-18-E. TB, 32" (81 cm), ML. Heavily ruffled and laced pale pink; beards medium pink. Playgirl X Blushing Lady. Long 1995.

OH JAMAICA (Schreiner, R. 1995). Sdlg. BB 797-1. TB, 40" (102 cm), ML. S. buff tan (RHS 173D) with violet midrib; F. maroon (187B); beards orange. 1983 #2, unknown, X T 1488-1: (M 912-AA: (((October Ale x Hi Top) x ((Wild Ginger x Taste of Honey) x Y 866-A: ((Olympic Torch x Brass Accents sib) x (((A 115 x Casa Morena) x Inca Chief) x Dark Chocolate)))) x Copper Nugget) x San Jose). Schreiner 1995.

OH JAMES (Barry Blyth, R. 1995). Sdlg. A137-2. TB, 42" (107 cm), EML. Iridescent orange self; beards matching. X140-1, Legato sib, X X127-1: (S128-A: (Hush at Twilight x P115-A: ((Love Chant x Festive Skirt) x (Caramba x Pink Ember))) x U82-B, Samurai Silk sib). Tempo Two 1995/96.

OH KATZ (A. & D. Willott, R. 1990). Sdlg. 80-47. SDB, 11" (28 cm), M. S. pale yellow; F. creamy white, lemon hafts, edge lightly washed lemon; beards blue white, lemon in throat; ruffled. Erie Islands X 78-126: (Cherished x Greenlee GX-9, white *pumila*). Willott 1990.

OHLONE (Joseph Ghio, CA, R. 1989). Bay View 1990.

OH MY BUBBLES (Graeme Grosvenor, R. 1996). Sdlg. O-12-4. TB, 37" (95 cm), M. White self; beards white. Bubbly Mood X Titan's Glory. Rainbow Ridge 1996/97.

OH THOSE GENES (Eugene Hunt by Sharon McAllister, R. 1998). Sdlg. JR-MoM-1. AB (OGB), 28" (71 cm), M. S. soft ivory ground, faint blue violet veining more intense toward edge; style arms yellowish ivory; F. yellowish ivory ground, veined and washed soft red violet, V-shaped area of burgundy stippling on ivory; beards mixed yellow and burgundy. Jean Ralls X Mary of Magdala. McAllister 1998.

OJOHNNYO (Heather Collins, SDB, R. 1984). Wyuna 1987.

OKANAGAN BLIZZARD (Berthe Conarty, R. 1992). Sdlg. DR/RW 864. TB, 30-33" (76-84 cm), ML. S. white; F. white, hafts light yellow; beards yellow; ruffled; diamond dusted; slight sweet fragrance. Debby Rairdon X Rippling Waters. Monashee Perennials 1994.

OKANAGAN LASS (Berthe Conarty, R. 1992). Sdlg. DR/RW 851. TB, 32-40" (81-102 cm), M. S. cream, light gold (RHS 11D) veining; F. white, canary yellow (9C) at hafts and reverse; beards yellow (14B); ruffled; slight sweet fragrance. Debby Rairdon X Rippling Waters. Monashee Perennials 1993.

OKANAGAN PEACH (Berthe Conarty, R. 1998). Sdlg. C-94-5A. TB, 37" (94 cm), M. S. pale peach, darker texture veining; F. medium peach, pale peach edging, cream flash below tangerine beard, darker peach veining from haft to near end of F.; slight spicy fragrance. Marmalade Skies X C-941: (Lacy Lu x (Debby Rairdon x Wine and Roses)).

OKANAGAN SEASHELL (Berthe Conarty, R. 1999). Sdlg. C94-1C. TB, 30" (76 cm), M. S. medium shell pink; style arms darker pink, midrib apricot; F. peach; beards tangerine; slight sweet fragrance. Emergency Response X Marmalade Skies.

OKANAGAN TWILIGHT (Berthe Conarty, R. 1998). Sdlg. C-95-16L. TB, 38" (97 cm), M. S. medium blue violet, diamond dusted; F. slightly lighter blue violet, white area with violet veining below coral beard; ruffled; pronounced spicy fragrance. SR/FK 941: (Surf Rider x unknown yellow and white with tangerine beard) X (Silver Shower x Sea Venture).

OKARITA (Revie Harvey, R. 1990). RS/WV/83. TB, 42" (107 cm), EML. White self, F. fluted; beards white, tipped gold; slight fragrance. Regalaire sdlg. X Wedding Vow. Hilmary Catton 1991.

OKAVANGO (Ladislav Muska, R. 1997). Sdlg. TCLM-10. TB, 38" (97 cm), M. S. light azurine; style arms light lavender blue; F. beetroot black, wide light azurine border; beards burnt tangerine; ruffled, laced; slight fragrance. Tomorrow's Child X Lady Madonna. Muska 1994.

O. K. CORRAL (Paul Black, R. 1991). Sdlg. 8633D. TB, 32" (81 cm), L. S. greyed red violet (RHS 87C); styles edged apricot, pink violet crests; F. pearly violet white (85C) blending to greyed red violet (87C) edge, amber orange (173C) thumbprint on hafts; beards bright deep orange; ruffled. Extravagant X Roller Coaster. Mid-America 1992.

OKIE DOKIE (Bob Thomason, SDB, R. 1988). Okie Iris 1999.

OKLAHOMA KITTY (Marvin Granger, R. 1990). Sdlg. 82-8. LA, 28" (71 cm), M. S. light pink; F. bright medium pink, small greenish yellow line signal; slight fragrance. BR77-23: (69-1: ((BQ64-24 x Louisiana Sambo) x King of Clubs) x Charlie's Michele) X 75-15, unknown. Faggard 1992.

OKLAHOMA SCISSORTAILS (Bob Thomason, R. 1992). Sdlg. BT 8921C. IB, 22" (56 cm), E. S. pale yellow; style arms dark yellow, bright yellow crests; F. white, thin yellow rim, yellow brown hafts; beards yellow; slight musky fragrance. Avanelle X Harlow Gold.

OKTIABRSKOYE SOLNTSE (Nina Miroshnichenko, R. 1996). BB, 27" (68 cm), M. Salmon orange self; beards red; pronounced spicy fragrance. Parentage unknown. Miroshnichenko 1990.

OLADI (Barry Blyth, SDB, R. 1986). Correction of parentage. (Cupid's Cup x Tiger Rouge) X Capricornia.

OLBA (Kevin Nilsen, R. 1995). Sdlg. 46-87-2. TB, 41" (104 cm), EM. Deep brownish red self; beards deep yellow. Lady Friend X Burgundy Brown. Iridescence 1995/96.

OLD BLACK MAGIC (Schreiner, R. 1996). Sdlg. AA 401-A. TB, 36" (91 cm), EM. Lightly ruffled coal black (RHS 202A) self; beards yellow; pronounced sweet fragrance. Midnight Dancer X Back in Black. Schreiner 1996.

OLD BLUE EYES (Chet Tompkins, R. 1990). Sdlg. 83-47. TB, 37" (94 cm), EM. Ruffled rich indigo blue. (((Diplomat x Satin Sound) x (Diplomat x Restless Waves)) x (((Sapphire Shore x Deep Space) x Diplomat) x Land o' Lakes)) X Sheer Bliss. Fleur de Lis 1990.

OLD DEVIL MOON (Joseph Hoage, R. 1998). Sdlg. H 87-22-1. TB, 36" (91 cm), L. S. creamy orange; F. burnt orange, white spot; beards red, orange at end. Modern Story X China Dragon. Long 1998.

OLD FASHIONED GIRL (Sharon McAllister, R. 1993). Sdlg. 85-9-1. AB (OGB-), 30" (76 cm), M. S. white, lightly veined violet, more intense around edge; F. white, burgundy veins flanking burgundy beard, finely veined burgundy edge. Hunt sdlg.: ((KBKG5: (Kalifa Baltis x Kalifa Gulnare) x Esther the Queen) x Tuesday Song) X Asha Michelle. McAllister 1993.

OLD FRIEND (Ralph & Fran Walster, R. 1990). Sdlg. 6-1986F. TB, 30" (76 cm), ML. S. creamy cinnamon; F. warm maroon, white hafts; beards yellow. Shaft of Gold X Silver Years. Walsterway 1991.

OLD LOYALTIES (Sterling Innerst, R. 1995). Sdlg. 3500-5. TB, 36" (91 cm), M. S. medium pink; style arms blue; F. medium blue; beards blue bronze. Deserving Treasure X 2417-10: (Heavenly Harmony x Loudoun Princess). Innerst 1996.

OLD MONEY (James Burch, R. 1994). Sdlg. 48-7. TB, 33" (84 cm), EM. Yellow gold (RHS 14B) with currant red (46A) flecks at base of F.; beards darker yellow orange (17A). 45-4: (Echo Madrid x Seven Hills) X Bama Berry. Burch Iris, Comanche Acres 1994.

OLD MONTEREY (Joseph Ghio, R. 1992). Sdlg. PH-276A2. CA, 12" (30 cm), ML. S. deep ruby garnet; F. ruby garnet, light rose hairline edge, dark red signal. Hot Blooded X PJ-171T2: ((San Gregorio x (Montara sib x Mission Santa Cruz sib)) x Latin Blood). Bay View 1993.

OLD SANTA FE (Tom Magee, R. 1995). Sdlg. 8823. TB, 42" (107 cm), M. S. russet tan, midribs golden tan; style arms gold tan; F. russet tan, reddish tan at extreme end, purple blaze surrounding white centerline extending from gold beard, haft markings gold. Syncopation X 8223: (Mountain Sunbeams sib x Astro Flash).

OLD SOUTH BALL (Dorman Haymon, LA, R. 1989). Deep South Garden 1990.

OLD TIMES SAKE (Sharon McAllister, R. 1998). Sdlg. 90-36-2. AB (OGB-), 30" (76 cm), EM. S. soft yellow, few golden veins; style arms golden yellow; F. soft yellow ground blushed pinkish rust, brownish burgundy area framing yellow orange beard. Brandy Sipper X Sunrise in Glory. McAllister 1998.

OLENKA (Viktor Sheviakov, R. 1996). Sdlg. 20d2. TB, 32" (80 cm), ML. S. bright yellow; F. rich yellow, cream yellow patterning; beards rich yellow; ruffled; slight spicy fragrance. Radiant Apogee X Fairy Fable. Sheviakov 1996.

OLEZHKA (Viktor Sheviakov, R. 1997). Sdlg. 21d15b. IB, 22" (55 cm), EM. Ruffled dark claret violet self; beards yellowish brown; slight spicy fragrance. "Uroda" X Demon. Sheviakov 1997.

OLGA K. (Eberhard Fischer, R. 1999). Sdlg. 8. TB, 39" (100 cm), M. Waved light lavender blue self, F. with small white area around beard; beards white, yellow in throat. Victoria Falls X Sapphire Hills.

OLGIDA (Viacheslav Gavrilin, R. 1998). Sdlg. 4-13-4-94. TB, 36" (92 cm), M. S. and style arms yellow; F. lilac edged darker, 1/2" yellow brown rim, hafts yellowish, indistinct white spot below beard; beards yellow, white at end; ruffled, laced. Fiesta Time X Starcrest. Gavrilin 1999.

OLIMPIYSKI (Irina Driagina, R. 1996). Sdlg. 4-14. TB, 28" (72 cm), VE. Yellow self; beards orange red; pronounced sweet fragrance. Parentage unknown. Driagina 1972.

OLIVE BRANCH (Richard Ernst, R. 1990). Sdlg. A136-1. TB, 35" (89 cm), EM. S. soft yellow shaded olive; F. orange tan on olive ground; beards mustard; lightly fluted. Desert Echo X Patina. Cooley 1990.

OLIVE FROLIC (Jayne Ritchie, R. 1998). Sdlg. 91-19-12. SDB, 11" (28 cm), M. S. chartreuse ground heavily washed olive green; style arms chartreuse, tipped lettuce green; F. chartreuse ground, olive green plicata edge, grey violet centerline; beards gold, hairs tipped bronze; ruffled; slight sweet fragrance. 87-1-2: (Sam x Auburn Valley) X Chubby Cheeks. Ritchie 1998.

OLIVE GARDEN (Paul Black, R. 1996). Sdlg. A501A. SDB, 13" (33 cm), VE. S. and style arms lime green; F. yellow olive central area, lime green edge; beards violet, mustard in throat and on hair tips; pronounced spicy fragrance. Toy Boat X Earliglo. Mid-America 1996.

OLIVE REFLECTION (Raymond Smith, R. 1990). Sdlg. 7809BR. TB, 28" (71 cm), M & RE. S. antique white with olive cast; style arms darker; F. antique white; beards yellow; ruffled. 7410CR: (4972 x Winter Olympics) X (Earl Roberts x Earl Roberts sdlg.). R. G. Smith 1992.

OLNEY BELLE (Richard Sparling, R. 1994). MDB, 6" (15 cm), EM. S. white; F. white, blue spot; beards white. Parentage unknown. Miller's Manor 1995.

OLOROSO (Lawrence Ransom, R. 1999). Sdlg. 90/417-2. TB, 36" (91 cm), M. S. deep cadmium yellow, edges toned orange; style arms deep cadmium yellow; F. blended yellow ochre and raw sienna, slight pale lilac flush below dark orange beard; pronounced musky fragrance. Speculator X 87/161-2: ((Heartbreaker x Vanity) x Opium).

OLYMPARICO (Bryce Williamson, R. 1990). TB, 36" (91 cm), VE-E. Cream white, soft cream yellow haft infusion; beards cream yellow; slight fragrance. (Vernal Falls x White Lightning) X Dream Affair. Pacific Coast Hybridizers 1990.

OLYMPIC ODYSSEY (Mary Dunn by Robert Dunn, R. 1998). Sdlg. M2149A. TB, 36" (91 cm), M. S. pale lilac; style arms lilac; F. white, very small deeper lilac edge; beards pale yellow; heavily ruffled. Patterns X Handshake. M.A.D. Iris 1999.

OLYMPIC PERFORMANCE (George Sutton, R. 1996). Sdlg. G-77RE. TB, 37" (94 cm), EM & RE. S. white with yellowish cast; style arms cream white, edged yellow; F. aureolin (RHS 12A/B), 1/4" white ribbon half-way down; beards cadmium orange; ruffled. Olympic Rings X Sunny Shoulders.

OLYMPIC RINGS (Walter Moores, TB, R. 1989). Moores 1990.

OMAMORI (Mary Ann Zurek, TB, R. 1988). Rancho de la Flor de Lis 1990. Incorrectly listed as OMANORI in 1989 Check List.

OMAR'S EYE (Carl Boswell, R. 1995). Sdlg. 127-87-2-AM. AB (OGB), 8" (20 cm), L. S. light lavender veined darker, white at base; F. white blending to light lavender at edge, violet veining from beard, small violet signal; beards white, tipped orange. Dunlin X L. Rich sdlg.: ((*I. atropurpurea* x (*I. mariae* x Judean Cream)) x (*I. stolonifera* x ((*I. lortetii* x *I. susiana*) x *I. nazarena*))).

OMAR'S GOLD (Carl Boswell, R. 1995). Sdlg. 95-90-AM. AB (OGB-), 18" (45 cm), M. S. yellow; F. golden yellow, black line signal; beards gold. 110-75-AS: (Puppet Baby x Moon Spot) X Onlooker. Adamgrove 1996.

OMAR'S VALOR (Carl Boswell, R. 1995). Sdlg. 45-79-AM. AB (OGB), 14" (36 cm), E. Violet maroon, F. with small maroon line signal; beards brownish maroon. (Jewel of Omar x Syrian Moon) X Onco G Plus. Adamgrove 1995.

OMINOUS STRANGER (Sterling Innerst, R. 1992). Sdlg. 3103-7. TB, 34" (86 cm), M. S. muted yellow, trimmed muted purple and dotted with tiny brown spots; F. muted yellow, trimmed muted purple, tiny brown dots all over; beards bronze, trimmed blue white; slight fragrance. Point Made X sib. Innerst 1993.

O MY GOLD (Timothy Stanek, R. 1994). Sdlg. 88-34-Gold. TB, 38" (97 cm), ML. S. yellow orange (RHS 15A); F. yellow orange (17B) deepening (17A) near hafts; beards orange (25A); lightly laced. Yukon Fever X Glazed Gold. Eight Mile Grove 1994.

ON BENDED KNEE (Sharon McAllister, R. 1998). Sdlg. 87-6-10. AB (OGB), 28" (71 cm), M. S. pale blue violet ground, lightly marked with fine blue violet veining; style arms buff; F. buff ground, few deep burgundy lines around burgundy black beard. Granted Wish X Sunrise in Glory. McAllister 1998.

ON BROADWAY (Calvin Helsley, R. 1999). Sdlg. 98-1. SIB, 30" (76 cm), EM. Vibrant purple (RHS

89A/B), F. with blended cornflower blue (95B) area below very slight dull white signal; ruffled. Mabel Coday X War March.

ONCE AGAIN (John Weiler by Joan Roberts, R. 1998). Sdlg. 84-87-2RE. TB, 35" (89 cm), EM & RE. Smooth light blue self; beards cream; slight sweet fragrance. Summer Holidays X (That Scentsation x Sweetwater). Friendship 1998.

ONCO G PLUS (Carl Boswell, AB (OGB-), R. 1989). Adamgrove, Aril Patch 1991.

ONE AND ONLY (Roy Bohrer, R. 1992). Sdlg. 98-MSLB. TB, 30" (76 cm), ML. S. pale lavender; F. dark violet, veined white, red violet hafts; beards lavender; slight sweet fragrance. 86-MSLB: (Majorette x St. Louis Blues) X Grand Waltz.

ONE LITTLE PINKIE (John Durrance, R. 1992). Sdlg. D86-56. BB, 26½" (68 cm), M. Bright coral pink; beards reddish coral. Paradise X Custom Made. Long 1992.

ONE MORE TIME (Allen Harper, SDB, R. 1989). Harper's Garden 1990.

ONESFORALL (Chet Tompkins, R. 1996). TB, 38" (97 cm), ML. Ruffled velvety white, yellow flush at base of S. and on upper F.; beards yellow. (Lux Aeterna x Majestic Moonlight) X First Interstate. Fleur de Lis 1996.

ONESFORFUN (Chet Tompkins, R. 1996). Sdlg. 93-71. TB, 38" (97 cm), EML. S. and style arms ivory to cream gilt, blended pink; F. pale watermelon rose, undertoned brass; beards pinkish rose, yellow base. (Heavenly Body x Magharee) X (Live Music x Turnabout). Fleur de Lis 1996.

ONESFORHER (Chet Tompkins, R. 1996). Sdlg. 91-26. TB, 39" (99 cm), M-VL. S. creamy ivory tinted wine; style arms lilac wine blended white; F. ivory ground, sanded, dotted and bordered vivid lilac cerise; beards golden pink; ruffled. ((Starkist x Rendezvous) x (Summer Sandman x inv. Rosy Veil)) X (Playing Around x Strawberry Swirl). Fleur de Lis 1996.

ONESFORHIM (Chet Tompkins, R. 1996). TB, 38" (97 cm), M-VL. S. corona gold; style arms gold, tinted orange bronze; F. orange bronze; beards orange. (Apollodorus x Smart Aleck) X (Apollodorus x Dance Fever). Fleur de Lis 1996.

ONESFORME (Chet Tompkins, R. 1996). Sdlg. 92-87. TB, 37" (94 cm), M-VL. Ruffled smoky pink; beards pink. (Facsimile x Special Delivery) X (Melissa Sue x Angel's Touch). Fleur de Lis 1996.

ONESFORU (Chet Tompkins, R. 1996). Sdlg. 91-101. TB, 38" (97 cm), ML. Chalky blue self; beards blue white, light yellow base. (Silverado x Frost Alert) X Fuji Skies. Fleur de Lis 1996.

ON GOLDEN POND (Perry Dyer, R. 1998). Sdlg. 94-77A. IB, 18" (46 cm), ML. Full golden yellow self; beards deep gold, bushy. Tulare X Bright Chic.

ONLY YOU (Barry Blyth, R. 1997). Sdlg. B147-3. TB, 30-32" (76-81 cm), ML. S. lemon, cream at midrib, deeper at top; F. bright white ground, 1/4" pastel blue lavender stitched margin, deeper rosy brown hafts; beards white, tipped lemon in throat; pronounced sweet fragrance. Billows X Harmonics. Tempo Two 1997/98.

ONO SUNSET (Carole Vossen, R. 1992). Sdlg. 2-37. AB (OGB+), 16" (40 cm), EM. S. pale lilac with slightly darker veining, golden amber midrib line and style arms; F. golden amber, veined slightly darker, rust red veins on light ground around rust red signal; beards gold. L. Rich onco sdlg., parentage unknown, X Falcon Flight. Aril Society 1992.

ON THE BAYOU (Kevin Vaughn, R. 1997). Sdlg. E-8-3. LA, 32-36" (81-91 cm), ML. S. amethyst violet (RHS 84C), dark orchid (83B) veining; style arms near-white, dark orchid midrib and crest; F. dark orchid, edged white; lightly ruffled, laciniated. Kay Nelson X Jazz Ballet.

ON THE BORDER (William Maryott, R. 1998). Sdlg. U155VAR. BB, 18-25" (46-64 cm), M. S. bright lemon yellow (RHS 13B); style arms yellow; F. dark maroon (darker than 59A), 1/8" yellow band; beards bright yellow orange. S142B: (Jitterbug x P121B: ((G999 x Sound of Gold) x Sound of Gold)) X sib, S142A. Maryott 1999.

ON THE BOULEVARDE (Barry Blyth, R. 1999). Sdlg. D88-C. TB, 38" (97 cm), ML Heavily ruffled silvery white with blue cast; beards lemon, white base; sweet fragrance. Vanda Song X Some Are Angels. Tempo Two 1999/2000.

ON THE EDGE (Joseph Ghio, CA, R. 1989). Bay View 1990.

ON THE WILDSIDE (Joseph Ghio, R. 1991). Sdlg. PI-200U3. CA, 12" (30 cm), L. Golden bronze brushed and dusted deep brown, deep brown signal. PK-321A: (((Banbury Candy x Simply Wild) x (Native State sib x Emigrant)) x (Elberta Peach sib x (Going West x Mission Santa Cruz))) X Mists of Time. Bay View 1992.

ON TRUST (Graeme Grosvenor, R. 1996). Sdlg. R2-2. TB, 35" (90 cm), M. Blue purple self; beards white, hairs tipped yellow. Silverado X Skyblaze. Rainbow Ridge 1996/97.

ON WINGS (Beryl James, R. 1992). Sdlg. B.J.1. BB, 21" (53 cm), ML. S. pale blue white, midrib flushed pastel pink (RHS 56D); F. pale blue white, flushed paler pastel pink; beards pale tangerine, tipped white; ruffled, laced. Wings of Dreams X Showtime. Rainbow Ridge 1993/94.

OOH LA LA (Allan Ensminger, R. 1993). Sdlg. 88-14. SDB, 13" (33 cm), ML. S. sulphur yellow (HCC 142); F. canary yellow; beards blue. 85-12: (((77-24, Ten sib, x 73-1: ((Spring Salute x ((Patience x Welch N503) x (Jungle Shadows x *I. pumila*))) x (((Jungle Shadows x *I. pumila*) x sib) x ((Jungle Shadows x Cretica) x Kavan 11-66)))) x (Tumwater x 73-1)) x 83-4: (Jillaroo sib x (78-4 x Limpid Pools sib))) X 85-13, What Again sib. Varigay 1994.

OOLAY (Barry Blyth, R. 1993). Sdlg. Z31-4. IB, 25" (64 cm), EM. S. apricot, slight violet infusion; F. creamy white, 1/4" apricot edge, few lilac plicata markings around hafts and beard, faint violet centerline; beards tangerine, outer 1/2" white. Shiralee X Chanted. Tempo Two 1993/94.

OPAL BROWN (Duane Meek, R. 1996). Sdlg. 57-6-0. TB, 35" (89 cm), M. S. snow white, base flushed apricot; style arms white; F. deep apricot, lighter below beard, irregular white margin; beards deep melon; ruffled. Magharee X Champagne Girl. D & J Gardens 1996.

OPALETTE (Barry Blyth, R. 1993). Sdlg. Z30-2. IB, 18" (46 cm), ML. Pastel cream, slight pink flush; beards white, tipped tangerine; slight fragrance. Coral Light X Impish. Tempo Two 1993/94.

OPAL'S LEGACY (Joseph Hoage, R. 1992). Sdlg. 85-17-1. TB, 33" (84 cm), ML. S. lightly ruffled pale lavender; F. laced pale lavender; beards red. Pink Bubbles X Coral Flush Long 1993.

OPAL WINGS (Ben Hager, R. 1992). Sdlg. SD5199PkYRm. SDB, 14" (36 cm), M. Ruffled off-white, flecked and blended pink and yellow; self beards, tangerine in throat. Sib to Cuddle Up. Adamgrove 1993.

OPAQUE SKY (Donovan Albers, R. 1993). Sdlg. 8717-A. SDB, 11" (28 cm), M. Light blue with pink infusion; beards white; slight fragrance. Brown Doll X B. Jones M212-2, white Queen's Pawn sib. Adamgrove 1994.

OPENING ACT (Larry Lauer, R. 1990). Sdlg. L85-2-1. TB, 35" (89 cm), L. Orchid; beards orange; slight sweet fragrance. Feminine Wiles X Wedding Party. Cottage 1991.

OPENING DAY (Larry Lauer, R. 1999). Sdlg. 373-7. SDB, 12" (31 cm), E. Lightly ruffled dark violet purple self; beards dark violet purple; pronounced sweet fragrance. Pacific Destiny X Chicory Charm.

OPENING VERSE (Chet Tompkins, R. 1996). Sdlg. 93-49B. TB, 38" (97 cm), EML. S. flame gold; style arms lilac blended gold; F. blended cream, gold and violet blue; beards dark gold. (Judie x Burgermeister) X (Shenanigan x Burgermeister). Fleur de Lis 1996.

OPERA BOUFFE (Lawrence Ransom, R. 1991). Sdlg. 86/30. TB, 38" (97 cm), M. S. creamish yellow, style arms, crests more yellow; F. white, edged yellow, fine brown haft veining, cream yellow reverse; beards yellow; ruffled. Debby Rairdon X Spirit of Memphis. Iris au Trescols 1992.

OPPORTUNITY (Keith Keppel, TB, R. 1989). Keppel 1990.

OPPOSITES ATTRACT (Sharon McAllister, R. 1995). Sdlg. 81-3-1. AB (OGB), 28" (71 cm), EM. S. pale grey, violet cast when fresh; style arms deep yellow gold; F. buttercup yellow (near RHS 7B), dime-size spot of intense reddish brown veining surrounding beard tip; beards light cadmium orange (near 23B), buttercup yellow base. Welcome Reward X Esther the Queen. McAllister 1995.

OPULENCE (Elaine Bessette, R. 1996). Sdlg. PCXB 93-07. CA, 17" (43 cm), ML. S. tapestry rose (RHS 182D), veined rosewood (187B), 1/32" pale cream (lighter than 19D) edge; style arms creamy pale yellow (19D), tips and crests washed pale tapestry rose; F. deeper tapestry rose (182C), darker (184B) central pattern wash, dark rosewood (187A) veins, 1/32" pale cream edge, green (147C) central streak. PCXB-91-23, from sdlgs., parentage unknown, X unknown. Iris Gallery 1998.

ORA BURTON (Melba Hamblen, R. 1991). Sdlg. 85-21A. TB, 32" (81 cm), ML. S. light blue (RHS 83D); F. near purple (77B), lighter area around beard; beards henna, tipped violet. Gift of Dreams X ((Sophistication x Henna Accent) x Magic). Mission Bell 1992.

ORAGEUX (Richard Cayeux, R. 1995). Sdlg. 8905 C. IB, 22" (55 cm), M. S. copper yellow; F. red black; beards copper. Rabbit's Foot X Broadway. Cayeux 1996.

ORANGE ALA MODE (Leo Barnard, R. 1997). Sdlg. L 91-22EO. TB, 36" (91 cm), ML. S. warm white, shaded apricot at base; style arms warm white, apricot edge; F. bright orange, narrow white rim, white veining near beard, maroon flecking or streaking; beards red, base orange, bushy and prominent; ruffled, laced; slight fragrance. Flamingo Way X Borderline. Paradise Iris 1997.

ORANGE BLOSSOM SPECIAL (Schreiner, R. 1999). Sdlg. CC 796-1. TB, 36" (91 cm), L. Bright

315

cadmium orange (RHS 23A); beards tangerine; ruffled; sweet fragrance. Hawaiian Queen X W 621-10: (T 842-A: (M 973-A: (((M1212-1 x Snowy Heron) x (Mary Randall x Amethyst Flame)) x (((Inca Chief x Lady Albright) x ((Miogem x Oriental Glory) x (Harriet Thoreau sdlg. x Savage))) x ((Halolight x Inca Chief) x Brass Accents sib))) x ((Lilac Supreme x Rippling Waters) x (Lilac Snow x Lilac Supreme))) x K 390-H: (Meggie x (Carnaby sib x (((Alpenrose x Amethyst Flame sib) x Prairie Clover) x Claudia Rene)))) x Hula Girl). Schreiner 1999.

ORANGE BLOTTER (Tom Burseen, R. 1993). Sdlg. 0-46B. TB, 32" (81 cm), ML. S. orange; F. orange ground, maroon purple veining becoming almost solid at edge; beards bright orange; ruffled; slight fragrance. Along the Way X 6-30R: (Lawrence of Arabia x (Vaudeville x Porta Villa)).

ORANGE CHIPS (J. T. Aitken, R. 1990). SDB, 10" (25 cm), EM. Medium orange; beards coral red; slight fragrance. Live Jazz X 82M38: (unknown x B. Jones M-304). Aitken's Salmon Creek 1990.

ORANGE DAWN (Alec Howe by Sidney Linnegar, TB, R. 1981). Correction of parentage: Aurelian X May Melody. V. H. Humphrey 1992.

ORANGE DAZZLER (Bennett Jones, R. 1991). Sdlg. 384-2. SDB, 12" (30 cm), M. Deep orange; beards red; slight fragrance. 378: (((Melon Honey x Wright L32) x (229-2 x Melon Honey)) x Pumpkin Center) X 331-4: ((Wright L32 x 255: (Melon Honey x 229: (Roberts 65R11 x (pink IB x *I. pumila* "Blazek")))) x (Solar Flight x 255)). Bennett Jones 1992.

ORANGE DESIGN (O. D. Niswonger, R. 1994). Sdlg. SDB 11-91. SDB, 11" (28 cm), M. Light orange, deeper near hafts; beards white, tipped orange. Straw Hat X Ballet Slippers. Cape Iris 1994.

ORANGE DRAGON (Leo Barnard, R. 1997). Sdlg. L 91-76F. TB, 38" (97 cm), ML. Ruffled apricot orange blend; beards red orange, apricot at end, extending as orange horn; slight fragrance. Twice Thrilling X Borderline. Paradise Iris 1997.

ORANGE DREAMS (O. D. Niswonger, R. 1998). Sdlg. 57-95. TB, 34" (86 cm), M. Orange self; beards orange. Orange Slices X Good Show. Cape Iris 1998.

ORANGE EMBERS (Howard Shockey, R. 1992). Sdlg. 88-236-A. TB, 34" (86 cm), M. S. orange (near RHS 28C), strongly flushed rose pink on lower central area; F. orange (near 28C); beards orange red (33B), large. 86-253-A: (Parfait Delight x Piping Hot) X Classic Edition. Arilian Acres 1993.

ORANGE ENSEMBLE (Jim Hedgecock, R. 1993). Sdlg. 84-6-B. TB, 34" (86 cm), M. Ruffled, lightly laced pale orange self; beards reddish orange, wide; pronounced sweet fragrance. Sun Fire X Mandolin. Comanche Acres 1994.

ORANGE FALL (Cloyd McCord, R. 1996). Sdlg. 006-1-A-C. TB, 36" (91 cm), E. Ruffled and laced pale orange lavender blend; beards bright orange; spicy fragrance. Goblin Autumn X Angie Quadros. McCord 1996.

ORANGE FALTER (Vera Matthe, R. 1990). Sdlg. VM 83-7A. TB, 39" (100 cm), M. S. orange (RHS 26B), light pinkish midrib glow; F. orange (24A/B), lighter orange yellow (18B) blaze around orange (28A) beard; lightly laced. Fresno Calypso X Piping Hot.

ORANGE FLIRT (William Maryott, R. 1990). Sdlg. L176N. TB, 36" (91 cm), M. Lightly ruffled deep red orange; beards deep mandarin red. H108Bst: (Fresno Frolic x Hindenburg) X J22D: (Hindenburg x (Homecoming Queen x Coffee House)). Maryott 1990.

ORANGE FURNACE (Loleta Powell, R. 1995). Sdlg. 93-11. TB, 30" (76 cm), M-VL. Vivid orange self; beards deeper orange; ruffled; slight sweet fragrance. Fireside Glow X Fame. Powell's Gardens 1996.

ORANGE GUMDROPS (O. D. Niswonger, R. 1995). Sdlg. SDB 1-92. SDB, 10" (25 cm), E. Orange self; beards orange. Pink Caper X Lankow 2A28-3: (Spring Bonnet x Wright L85: (Blue Trinket x Cotton Blossom)). Cape Iris 1996.

ORANGE HORNS (Ladislav Muska, R. 1996). Sdlg. QCSS-08/B. TB, 36" (91 cm), M. S. pale lavender; F. burgundy red, narrow lavender edge; beards orange, long orange horn; slight fragrance. ((Queen in Calico x Sky Hooks) x Sky Falls) X Tropicana Doll. Muska 1996.

ORANGE IMPACT (Duane Meek, R. 1997). Sdlg. 214-1-1. TB, 34" (86 cm), ML. Ruffled, lightly laced bright deep orange self; beards slightly deeper orange, bushy. Orange Surprise X Orange Star. D & J Gardens 1997.

ORANGE JEWELIUS (David Miller, R. 1990). Sdlg. DM 84-2A. TB, 36" (91 cm), ML. S. creamy orange; F. orange blended yellow, slight pink tones; beards red. Beverly Sills X Sun Fire. Long 1991.

ORANGE JUBILEE (Schreiner, R. 1993). Sdlg. AA 1147-A. TB, 38" (97 cm), M. Heavily ruffled orange (RHS 21B) self; beards tangerine. S 659-1, Outrageous Fortune sib, X S 494-C: (Vanity x M 1119-1: (G 1292-B: (((Puriri x Whole Cloth) x Prairie Clover) x Distant Chimes) x Loudoun Charmer)). Schreiner 1993.

ORANGE MOTIF (Cleo Palmer, R. 1993). Slg. 8835. SDB, 11" (28 cm), M. S. light orange; F. light orange, slightly darker peachy orange halo; beards orange; slight sweet fragrance. 8526: ((7607 x (7416 x Dove Wings)) x (Show Baby x ((Prophecy x Lenna M) x Dove Wings))) X 8527, Dorothy Howard sib. Palmer's Iris 1993.

ORANGE ORDER (B.L.C. Dodsworth, R. 1995). Sdlg. EB 142C. TB, 36" (91 cm), L. Ruffled orange self; beards tangerine. Orange Dawn X Fresno Calypso. British Iris Society 1999.

ORANGE OUTRAGE (Bennett Jones, R. 1994). Sdlg. 451-2. SDB, 12" (30 cm), M. Marigold orange (HCC 11/1) self; beards deep red; slight fragrance. Sib to Desert Orange. Aitken's Salmon Creek 1995.

ORANGE PETALS (O. D. Niswonger, R. 1991). Sdlg. IB 13-88. IB, 25" (64 cm), M. S. pinkish orange; F. orange; beards orange. Oriental Blush X unknown. Cape Iris 1991.

ORANGE POP (Larry Lauer, R. 1998). Sdlg. 91-189. BB, 26" (66 cm), ML. Ruffled orange self; beards orange; pronounced sweet fragrance. Role Model X Gratuity. Lauer's Flowers 1998.

ORANGE PRIDE (Cloyd McCord, R. 1992). Sdlg. 86-02. TB, 38" (97 cm), M. Ruffled light orange; beards red; sweet fragrance. Angie Quadros X 73-13: (Angie Quadros x Homecoming Queen). McCord 1992.

ORANGE RINGS (Nathan Rudolph by Loleta Powell, R. 1992). TB, 35" (89 cm), EML. Ruffled white, edged orange; beards orange. Parentage unknown. Powell's Gardens 1992.

ORANGE SORBET (Lyle Fort, R. 1990). Sdlg. 87-38-A. TB, 36" (91 cm), M. S. pink orange; F. creamy orange; beards tangerine red, large; ruffled, laced; slight fragrance. (Opal Brown 78-1F1, Art Center sib, x Mandolin) X (Snowy Wonderland x Tut's Gold). Fort Iris 1991.

ORANGE SOUFFLÉ (B.L.C. Dodsworth, R. 1998). Sdlg. EB 98 HH. TB, 40" (100 cm), M. Ruffled orange self; beards red orange; slight fragrance. Orange Order X Good Show.

ORANGE SPANGLES (Barry Blyth, R. 1998). Sdlg. E4-6. SDB, 9" (22 cm), ML. S. bright burnt orange, erect; F. bright burnt orange, slightly deeper area and veining around beard, creamy white center; beards bright tangerine, faint lavender at end; pronounced sweet fragrance. Little Bev X Desert Country. Tempo Two 1998/99.

ORANGE SUNBURST (Jim Hedgecock, R. 1995). Sdlg. 84-6-0. TB, 34" (86 cm), M. Medium orange, F. with white sunray pattern by bright reddish orange beard; ruffled, laced; pronounced sweet fragrance. Sun Fire X Mandolin. Comanche Acres 1995.

ORANGE SUNRISE (Ed Matheny III, R. 1994). Sdlg. 07-02-93. TB, 31" (79 cm), M. S. mandarin orange (RHS 24D); cream petaloids between mandarin orange style arms; F. misty orange (29B); beards goldfish orange (25A); slight sweet fragrance. Peach Bisque X Porta Villa. Ed's Iris 1995.

ORANGE SURPRISE (Duane Meek, R. 1996). Sdlg. 70-5-2. TB, 34" (86 cm), ML. Ruffled deep bright orange self; beards deeper orange, bushy. Fresno Flash X Marmalade. D & J Gardens 1996.

ORANGE TREAT (Bernard Hamner, R. 1990). Sdlg. 84-22. TB, 37" (94 cm), M. Ruffled orange (RHS 26B); beards tangerine; slight fragrance. (Chief Redskin x Peach Sundae) X (Party Parfait x Beauty Crown). Hamner Iris 1990.

ORANZHEVOYE NEBO (Viktor Sheviakov, R. 1995). Sdlg. 4D1. TB, 29" (72 cm), ML. Ruffled, laced yellow orange self; beards bright orange. "Gold Linder" X Pink Taffeta. Sheviakov 1992.

ORCHIDEA SELVAGGIA (Augusto Bianco, R. 1999). Sdlg. 480. TB, 34" (85 cm), EM. S. cameo rose; style arms rose; F. light rose, center near-white, hafts striped bilberry; beards orange; slight spicy fragrance. Queen in Calico X Shenanigan. Iride 1997.

ORCHID ENSEMBLE (Opal Brown, R. 1992). Sdlg. 82-20D2. TB, 30" (76 cm), M. S. magnolia (RHS 70D); F. violet (84A/B), orient pink (36C) signal; beards jasper red (39A), fine; ruffled. 76-2A30: (Peach Float x Instant Charm) X 78-3B5: (Old Flame x 73-11A27: ((Grandiflora x Arctic Flame) x Buffy)). Brown's Sunnyhill 1992.

ORCHID ICING (Sara Doonan, R. 1990). Sdlg. 83-29-1. TB, 34" (86 cm), ML. S. orchid, lightly laced slight beige edge; style crests orchid, creamy yellow edge; F. orchid, creamy white blaze below beard; beards gold in throat, end white; heavily ruffled; slight sweet fragrance. Armistice X Lorilee. Sunset Iris 1991.

ORCHID PINSTRIPE (Ray Lyons, TB, R. 1988). Long 1991.

ORCHIDS FOR HER (Donald Sorensen, R. 1998). Sdlg. S-91-23-5. TB, 33" (84 cm), M. S. orchid (RHS 80C), paling to orchid white midrib; style arms light orchid (76B); F. orchid (80C), white haft area blending to light orchid (76C) in center; beards dawn pink (49A), end section white with hairs tipped pink; pronounced sweet fragrance. Grecian Pearl X Varga Girl.

ORCHID SPLENDOR (John Knudtson, R. 1994). Sdlg. 94-10-Ro. TB, 33" (84 cm), M. Rose orchid, F. with white zonal area around beard; beards orange base, hairs tipped white; slight sweet fragrance. Beverly Sills X Lorilee.

OREGOLD (Bennett Jones, SDB, R. 1989). Bennett Jones 1990.

OREGON SKIES (Schreiner, R. 1991). Sdlg. Y 119-1. TB, 34" (86 cm), EM. Ruffled light blue (RHS 97B); beards white, tipped yellow. S 50-1: (Sapphire Hills x M 95-2: (((Tufted Cloud sib x ((Sparkling Waters x Sierra Skies) x Music Maker)) x Tufted Cloud) x K 968-A)) X Scandia Delight. Schreiner 1991.

ORETI LEMON (Noel Lapham, R. 1991). Sdlg. 61-1. SDB, 12" (30 cm), M. S. pale lemon; F. bright lemon, brown haft markings; beards brown. Butter Pecan X unknown. Waimate 1997/98.

ORETTA'S SHADOW (John Durrance, R. 1991). Sdlg. D84-22. TB, 36" (91 cm), ML. Ruffled medium blue purple. Prince of Peace X Sexton 53-75. Long 1991.

ORIENTAL BOUQUET (William Ackerman, R. 1990). Sdlg. A3-10-111. JI (10 P. + 6 petaloids), 22" (56 cm), ML. Very pale violet blue (RHS 91D) ground, veined very dark violet blue (89A), heavier around green yellow (1A) signal; style arms eight, veined violet blue (90A). D4-10-86, inv. sdlgs. from Seiko-en Nursery X self. Nicholls Gardens 1991.

ORIENTAL DANCER (Daniel Thruman, R. 1997). JI (3 F.), 34" (86 cm), M. S. amethyst, distinct white edging; style arms white with violet blue; F. violet blue (90B), yellow signal, veining to F. edge. Oriental Classic X Japanese Pinwheel.

ORIENTAL DAWN (Tony Huber, R. 1999). Sdlg. 95-123. SPEC-X (versata), 32" (80 cm), EML. S. violet (RHS 86D), midrib white; style arms pure white; F. violet (86B/D), large bright yellow signal bordered violet purple on white halo. *I. versicolor* 524 X *I. ensata* 183.

ORIENTAL DESIGN (Donald Spoon, R. 1997). Sdlg. 90-180. TB, 34" (86 cm), ML. S. light rose pink; style arms light rose pink to peach pink; F. darker rose pink, prominent darker and lighter streaks half way down petal to solid intense rose pink area; beards tangerine, deeper in throat; ruffled, lightly laced, flared. Oriental Imagery X Enchanted World. Winterberry 1997.

ORIENTAL EXPRESS (Daniel Thruman, R. 1997). JI (6 F.), 36" (91 cm), EM. Violet (RHS 83B), outer portion lighter violet (88A), lined, signal yellow with light white margin; style crests violet, lined, white in center. Oriental Classic X Japanese Pinwheel.

ORIENTAL FLAIR (Opal Brown, R. 1990). Sdlg. 82-20B1. TB, 34" (86 cm), M. Ruffled and fluted spanish orange (RHS 29C) with pink influence in S.; beards greyed orange (169B). 78-10C1: (Mystic Vision x Neon Magic) X 79-3J1: (Old Flame x (Spring Bride x Royal Coachman)). Brown's Sunnyhill 1990.

ORIENTAL JEWEL (William Ackerman, R. 1999). Sdlg. B5-1. JI (3 F.), 34-36" (86-91 cm), M. S. plum purple (RHS 79A); style arms white center, purple margins and lips; F. plum purple at bright yellow signal, shading to paler (79D) margins; very crinkled texture. Samurai Crest X Wine Ruffles.

ORIENTAL MYSTERY (Daniel Thruman, R. 1997). JI (6 F.), 34" (86 cm), M. Violet blue (RHS 97C) overall brushing; style arms violet blue. Southern Son X Continuing Pleasure.

ORIENTAL PONGEE (Franklin Carr, TB, R. 1986). Franklin Carr 1993.

ORIENTAL SILK (Jim Hedgecock, R. 1992). Sdlg. 84-48-6. TB, 34" (86 cm), ML. Reddish violet, F. with golden brown hafts; beards orange; heavily laced, ruffled; slight sweet fragrance. Sky Hooks X Swazi Princess. Comanche Acres 1993.

ORIENTAL TOUCH (Tony Huber, R. 1992). Sdlg. DOM-F1. SPEC-X (versata), 40½" (105 cm), M. S. medium violet (RHS 88B); F. darker medium violet (88A), short central line near pointed light creamy yellow signal tip. X1X, *versicolor* sdlg., X purple *ensata* sdlg. W. H. Perron 1993.

ORIGIN (Graeme Grosvenor, R. 1998). Sdlg. U109-1. TB, 37" (94 cm), ML. Pink self; beards tangerine; pronounced fragrance. Natural Beauty X Bubble Up. Rainbow Ridge 1998/99.

ORILLIA'S RING (Jean Witt by J. T. Aitken, R. 1991). Sdlg. 85-03-45. MTB, 18" (46 cm), ML. S. medium butter yellow; F. white, edged yellow with brown plicata markings. Spanish Coins X unknown. Aitken's Salmon Creek 1991.

ORINOCO FLOW (Cy Bartlett, BB, R. 1989). Sutton 1993.

ORIOLE OAK (Carl & Ruth Schulz, TB, R. 1989). Wild Mountain Thyme 1990.

ORKNIES (Sterling Innerst, R. 1996). Sdlg. 4672-4. SDB, 14" (36 cm), M. Medium pink self; beards orange, tipped white; slight musky fragrance. 3891-1: (3598-2: ((Jared x (Melon Honey x Soft Air)) x Delicate Pink) x 3524-6: (2875-2: ((Betsey Boo x Cherub Tears) x (Soft Air x Pink Cushion)) x Tillie)) X 4129-1: (3526-6: (2875-2 x Delicate Pink) x 3524-6). Innerst 1999.

ORNATE (Lloyd Zurbrigg, R. 1999). Sdlg. NN 32-9-2. TB, 34" (86 cm), ML. Light orchid pink; beards bright red orange, bright purple at beginning of 1/2" horn covered with purple fuzz. Flying X Godsend.

OR NOIR (Lawrence Ransom, R. 1995). Sdlg. 86/33-3. IB, 24" (60 cm), M. S. dark red violet; F. darker red violet, blackish sheen; beards bronze gold. Demon X Sign of Leo. Iris au Trescols 1996.

ORO DE SONORA (Floyd Wickenkamp, R. 1990). Sdlg. SP-84-3. SPU, 54" (137 cm), ML. Gold, narrow orange stripe on F. midrib; waved, F. ruffled. Butter Paddle X McCown ruffled gold sdlg. Shepard Iris 1991.

OSAKA (Joseph Ghio, R. 1991). Sdlg. 85-20N2. TB, 42" (107 cm), EM. S. white, cream toward midrib; F. maroon red, slight violet blaze; beards yellow. 83-73K: (Success Story x (Fancy Tales x Alpine Castle)) X 83-33G: (((Entourage x (Carved Cameo x Louise Watts)) x Marauder sib) x Bristo Magic). Roris 1993.

OSAY CANUC (Tom Burseen, R. 1999). Sdlg. 95-323A. TB, 36" (91 cm), M. S. pure white; F. white, with purple lines darkest at beard and lighter at edge; beards carrot red, fuzzy white horn with tan hairs at tip. 93-444: (91-297: ((Edna's Wish x Rosecraft) x (Iris Irene x Classic Capers)) x 91-124: (Ample Charm x Hello Hobo)) X Godsend.

OSENNEYE NEBO (Mariya Kaulen, R. 1999). Sdlg. YA 2/14. JI (6 F.), 32" (80 cm), E. Ruffled blue violet sprinkled light blue, yellow signal surrounded by blue area; style arms blue violet. Parentage unknown.

OSENNI VECHER (Viktor Koroliov, R. 1996). Sdlg. C3-89K. TB, 35" (90 cm), M. S. smoky violet; style arms yellow, light violet crests; F. red violet, bronze violet edge, white yellow hafts shaded violet; beards yellow; pronounced sweet fragrance. Music Maker X Jersey Beauty. Koroliov 1993.

OSHO KUN (Society for Japanese Irises, R. 1993). JI (6 F.), 36" (90 cm), L-VL. Blue violet, signal yellow. Parentage unknown. Very old cultivar, registered to correct information in 1939 Check List. Introduced in Japan prior to 1900.

OSLO (Carl Jorgensen, R. 1999). Sdlg. 90-5-2B. TB, 30" (76 cm), EML. S. very pale hyacinth blue, darkening (HCC 40/2) at base; style arms very pale hyacinth blue; F. very pale hyacinth blue, deeper haft veining, yellow green cast around beard; beards hyacinth blue (40/1), faintly yellow in throat, wide; ruffled; pronounced sweet fragrance. Song of Norway X Summit Easter. Long 1999.

OSMOSE (Lawrence Ransom, R. 1996). Sdlg. 90/220-4. SDB, 10" (25 cm), M. White, F. with diffuse light blue violet spot bisected by white centerline; beards white. Bright Moment X Frosted Angel. Iris au Trescols 1996.

OSOCALES (Joseph Ghio, R. 1995). Sdlg. PF-188X. CA, 15" (38 cm), E. Golden orange, F. with maroon signal veining over petal. Eagle Eyes X PH-266K: (Las Lomas x Aftershock sib). Bay View 1995.

O'SO PRETTY (Evelyn Kegerise, R. 1992). Sdlg. 86-725. TB, 31-32" (79-81 cm), EM. S. lilac-tinted white, fading white; F. tinted lilac, fading to white in center, edged deep lilac; beards white, tipped lilac; ruffled; slight sweet fragrance. Sultry Miss X 83-454: ((Actress x Cozy Carol) x Rosabelle V). Evelyn Kegerise 1993.

OSTENTATIOUS (Joseph Ghio, R. 1997). Sdlg. 93-132Y. TB, 38" (97 cm), ML. S. black cherry; F. bright gold ground, maroon marginal band with dotting inside band, white area around sienna beard. 91-68-tricolor: ((((Chuckles x (Goddess x (Rancho Rose x ((Flareup x Osage Buff) x (Vanity x Anon))))) x ((((Handiwork x (Gay Parasol x Mystique)) x Goddess) x (Gem of Sierra x ((((Ponderosa x Honey Rae) x ((((Claudia Rene x Commentary) x Claudia Rene) x Ponderosa) x (Ponderosa x New Moon))) x Osage Buff) x (Vanity x Anon)))) x Gigolo)) x Power Surge) x Chatter) X Epicenter. Bay View 1998.

OSTROGOTH (Jean Peyrard by Lawrence Ransom, R. 1993). Sdlg. PB88/2. TB, 35" (90 cm), M. S. blended light violet and milk chocolate brown; F. light violet center, milk chocolate edge, ochre yellow shoulders; beards orange, long white horn; ruffled, lightly laced, flaring. Sky Hooks X Golden Encore. Iris au Trescols 1994.

OSTRY WHITE (Eric & Bob Tankesley-Clarke, R. 1994). SPEC (*aphylla*), 6-8" (15-20 cm), E. Cold white self; beards pale yellow. Collected at Mt. Ostry, Bohemia; distributed by Blazek prior to 1971 and in commerce as *I. aphylla* B66-2.

OTEPOPO HONEY (Gwenda Harris, R. 1996). SIB, 43" (110 cm), M & RE. S. white; style arms pale yellow; F. pale yellow deepening to yellow hafts faintly marked brown. Parentage unknown; seed from New Zealand Iris Society. Otepopo 1996/97.

OTIMESE (Frank Foster, R. 1998). Sdlg. 8906 GN. TB, 36" (91 cm), M. Orchid blue self; beards lavender; slight fragrance. Mary Frances X Alabama Bound.

OTOME KAGAMI (Mototeru Kamo by Society for Japanese Irises, R. 1993). JI (6 F.), 28" (71 cm), EM. Light lavender pink, signals yellow; style arms white, edged and tipped pink. Parentage unknown. Kamo 1972.

OTTEPEL (Adolf Volfovich-Moler, R. 1995). Sdlg. 44. TB, 39" (100 cm), E. S. light purplish brown, white center; F. light purplish brown border, white central spot; beards yellow, cream at end; ruffled. Dancers Veil X Rippling Waters. Volfovich-Moler 1992.

OURAGAN (Richard Cayeux, R. 1995). Sdlg. 89212 B. TB, 32" (80 cm), M. Bright medium blue self; beards pale blue, milky white at end. Memphis Blues X Sapphire Hills. Cayeux 1996.

OUR DOROTHY (Bernard Pryor, R. 1997). Sdlg. 41/93-F. LA, 38" (97 cm), ML. S. pale lemon, cyclamen pink rim; style arms apricot, blushed cyclamen pink; F. lemon apricot, wide suffused cyclamen pink rim, lime yellow steeple signal outlined maroon; flower color changing to pink with age. 62/90-1: (Frank Chowning x Desert Jewel) X Heather Pryor.

OUR HOUSE (Graeme Grosvenor, R. 1999). Sdlg. V14-3. TB, 36" (91 cm), M. Laced lavender mauve; beards orange, tipped mauve; sweet fragrance. Eidolia X Perils of Pauline. Rainbow Ridge 1999/2000.

OUR REQUEST (Duane Meek, R. 1991). Sdlg. 227-1-4. TB, 35" (89 cm), ML. S. cream, flushed yellow gold at midrib; F. yellow gold, discreet brown peppering around edge, large central cream area; beards yellow gold; heavily ruffled. 242-1-7: (Orange Plush x Grecian Gown) X Desert Echo. D & J Gardens 1991.

OUR TRACY (Clyde Hahn, R. 1995). Sdlg. 91-1-C. TB, 38" (97 cm), M. Light rose pink self; beards matching; slight sweet fragrance. Dorothy Palmer X D. Palmer 4975-A: (Trade Winds x Mlle. Modiste). Hahn's Rainbow 1995.

OUTBURST (Robert Sobek, R. 1990). Sdlg. 82S82. SDB, 13" (33 cm), M. S. lavender blended gold; F. off-white, mostly covered with rusty brown veined spot pattern; beards white, tipped orange. Soft Air X 79S5: (Flapjack x Baby Toes). Joe Pye Weed 1990.

OUTLAW (Keith Fillmore, R. 1993). Sdlg. 8607-2. IB, 22" (56 cm), M. S. mauve violet with darker violet midrib; F. deep violet, edged lighter, bright purple line below beard; beards mustard yellow, tipped light violet. Blue Sapphire X unknown. Bar K Iris 1993.

OUTLINE (G. F. Wilson, R. 1994). Sdlg. 41-90TSO-D. AB (OGB), 30" (76 cm), EM. S. orchid pink, slightly darker veining, orange rib; F. blended tannish rose pink, large maroon black signal outlined carmine; beards brown; slight fragrance. (Tuesday Song x Holden Ho5 arilbred) X Onlooker. Pleasure Iris, Potterton & Martin 1995.

OUT OF CONTROL (William Maryott, R. 1994). Sdlg. S110C. TB, 34-35" (86-89 cm), ML. Purple with maroon influence, splashed or flecked white; beards light blue; lightly ruffled; sweet fragrance. Colours X Batik. Maryott 1995.

OUT OF FOCUS (Paul Black, R. 1991). Sdlg. 86418A. IB, 26" (66 cm), M. S. white rib, slight pale blue violet plicata markings, wide icy blue violet band; F. white, widely banded with violet plicata markings; beards white, tinted blue; pronounced musky fragrance. 83303F: (Focus x Magic Candle) X Chubby Cheeks sib. Mid-America 1992.

OUT OF WORK (Graeme Grosvenor, R. 1999). Sdlg. V81-1. TB, 36" (91 cm), M. S. blue; F. purple; beards light blue; slight fragrance. Work Ethic X T4-2: (Navy Waves x Snowbrook). Rainbow Ridge 1999/2000.

OUTRAGE (Lawrence Ransom, R. 1997). Sdlg. 90/247-16. SDB, 9" (22 cm), ML. S. creamy yellow, darker veining; F. amber, more yellow at edge, hafts yellow; beards white, hairs tipped orange, with long amber horns, thin and hairless or fat and hairy; pronounced fragrance. Clay's Caper X Peyrard PB88/1-1: (Planet Iris x *pumila*). Iris au Trescols 1998.

OUT STAND DISH (Tom Burseen, R. 1997). Sdlg. 93-47A. TB, 35" (89 cm), ML. S. white, midrib yellow; style arms white; F. golden yellow (RHS 17C), white center stripe; beards yellow; ruffled, flared; pronounced spicy fragrance. Snow Moon X Wings of Gold. T.B.'s Place 1998.

OVERDRAWN (Paul Black, R. 1998). Sdlg. A114WW. IB, 26" (66 cm), E. S. white, overall violet fancy wash; style arms violet; F. white ground, heavy red violet fancy wash, darker edge, white area around beard with dark purple dart, short lines; beards dark purple, white base; ruffled; slight spicy fragrance. Privileged Character X Polar Seas. Mid-America 1998.

OVER EASY (Carol Lankow, SDB, R. 1989). Kirkland Iris 1990.

OVER EXPOSED (Tom Burseen, R. 1991). Sdlg. 7-193X. TB, 35" (89 cm), EM. S. clean white, faint violet blue (RHS 98C) picoteed edge; style arms dark blue (99A); F. clean white, faint violet blue at hafts; beards grey; ruffled. Victoria Falls X 5-318: (Exotic Isle x Barletta). T.B.'s Place 1992.

OVER FENCE GENEROSITY (Charles Arny, LA, R. 1985). Bois d'Arc 1992.

OVER IN GLORYLAND (Robert Hollingworth, R. 1992). Sdlg. 85B3B10. SIB (tet.), 34" (86 cm), M. S. dark royal purple; F. velvety dark royal purple, cream blaze; ruffled. 82J2C6(T), Jewelled Crown sib, X 81A3A4: ((Dreaming Spires x unknown) x (Cambridge x unknown)). Windwood Gardens 1993.

OVERJOYED (Joseph Gatty by Keith Keppel, R. 1993). Sdlg. W32-1. TB, 35" (89 cm), M. S. oyster white (M&P 10-B-1); F. shoulders near chrome lemon (9-L-2), lighter edge reed yellow (10-H-2), center marguerite yellow (10-C-1); beards cream at end, deepening to sunflower (9-L-4) to goldenrod (10-L-5) in throat; ruffled. Perfect Interlude X Sunny and Warm. Keppel 1994.

OVERNIGHT SENSATION (Schreiner, R. 1995). Sdlg. W 167-B. TB, 39" (99 cm), ML. S. and style arms light blue white (RHS 97D); F. medium blue (94B); beards blue at end, white base and in throat. Stormy Night X Royal Crusader. Schreiner 1995.

OVERNIGHT SUCCESS (Joseph Ghio, R. 1996). Sdlg. LA 93-233A. LA, 36" (91 cm), EM. Plush red purple self, contrasting gold signals. High Pitch X Margaret Lee. Bay View 1997.

OVERSEAS (Joseph Ghio, R. 1993). Sdlg. 86-14-I. TB, 38" (97 cm), ML. True medium blue self; beards blue. Sea of Joy X 82-124-Z2, Inaugural Ball sib. Roris 1994.

OVER THE BLUES (Barry Blyth, R. 1995). Sdlg. A64-1. TB, 38" (97 cm), ML. S. light blue, slightly deeper toward midrib; F. medium violet blue; beards blue violet. Physique X Blues Brothers. Tempo Two 1995/96.

OVER THE HILL (Gordon Nicholson, R. 1996). TB, 42" (107 cm), M. Lavender self; style arms slightly deeper lavender; beards soft yellow; petal edges serrated; pronounced spicy fragrance. Snow Flurry X unknown. Woodland Iris 1996.

OVER THE RAINBOW (Darlene Pinegar, R. 1994). Sdlg. BC-1-2. BB, 27" (70 cm), ML. S. light blue white aging pure white; style arms white; F. gold shoulders with reddish brown markings, medium orchid center, light gold inner edge; light gold inner edge, light blue white outer edge; beards deep yellow; ruffled; pronounced sweet fragrance. Bayberry Candle X Latin Lover. Spanish Fork 1995.

OVER THERE (Mary Dunn, R. 1991). Sdlg. L110-5. LA, 36" (91 cm), M. Medium blue violet, lime line signal; F. ruffled. C'est Chic X Easter Tide. Bay View 1992.

OVER THE TOP (John C. Taylor, R. 1996). Sdlg. SL 59-1. LA, 47" (120 cm), ML. S. cream, purple spray pattern; style arms cream, blushed purple; F. purple, light edge, signal yellow, recurved form; slight fragrance. Paul Payens X OL 137-9: (Dazzling Star x Watch Out).

OWYHEE AMETHYST (Lucille Pinkston, R. 1996). Sdlg. 88-1-C. TB, 36" (91 cm), ML. S. white, tinged orchid; style arms white; F. white, washed and streaked amethyst, lighter wire rim; beards yellow; slight fragrance. Wild Jasmine X unknown. Sand Hollow 1997.

OWYHEE DESERT (Lucille Pinkston, R. 1996). Sdlg. 88-1-A. TB, 36" (91 cm), ML. S. and style arms white; F. rusty brown, washed gold, white ray pattern from beard area, yellow halo, white wire rim; beards light yellow, deeper in throat; slight fragrance. Wild Jasmine X unknown. Sand Hollow 1997.

OZARK DREAM (Kenneth Fisher, R. 1991). Sdlg. TV4 (88-8). MTB, 22" (56 cm), L. S. medium violet; F. dark purple; beards cream. 25-24A: (Quirky x Buenita) X 2E: (Pharaoh's Daughter x Puppy Love). Aitken's Salmon Creek 1992.

OZARK EVENING (Kenneth Fisther, R. 1990). Sdlg. 88-1. MTB (tet.), 22" (56 cm), EM. Light pink; beards apricot. Pink Kewpie X Puppy Love. Aitken's Salmon Creek 1991.

OZARK JEWEL (Kenneth Fisher, R. 1991). Sdlg. 89-5 (B6). MTB, 19" (48 cm), M. S. white edged lemon yellow; F. lemon yellow; beards orange, fading yellow. B3: ((Sherwin-Wright x Ice Fairy) x Spanish Coins) X L3: (Spanish Coins x (Purple Heather x White Canary)). Aitken's Salmon Creek 1992.

OZARK SKY (Kenneth Fisher, MTB, R. 1988). Kirkland Iris 1990.

OZERO KENON (Galina Zinoviyeva, R. 1998). Sdlg. 603-1. TB, 33" (83 cm), M. S. snow white; style arms white; F. blue white, brown haft veining, light blue centerline; beards orange; flat form. Broadway Star X Kangchenjunga. Zabaykalski 1998.

OZHERELIYE (Viacheslav Gavrilin, R. 1998). Sdlg. 4-2-52-94. TB, 35" (90 cm), M. S. and style arms light violet; F. light lilac violet, paler below beard; beards light lilac, hairs tipped orange; ruffled. Rolling Thunder X Breakers. Gavrilin 1999.

OZHIDANIYE (Mariya Kaulen, R. 1999). Sdlg. YA/2/18. JI (6 F.), 28" (70 cm), E. Heavily ruffled blue violet, yellow signal; style arms blue violet. Parentage unknown.

OZONE ALERT (Tom Burseen, R. 1997). Sdlg. 92-495A. TB, 36" (91 cm), M. S. light grey (lighter than RHS 197D); style arms light grey; F. light brown grey (lighter than 199D), washed brown purple hafts; beards bronze, base purple; ruffled. 8-492: ((Admiralty x Mandolin) x (Pansy Royale x Lux Aeterna)) X Magician's Apprentice. T.B.'s Place 1997.

OZONOVY SLOY (Nina Miroshnichenko, R. 1996). TB, 41" (105 cm), M. White self; beards pink, changing to red in throat; slight sweet fragrance. Parentage unknown. Miroshnichenko 1976.

OZ SKY (Kevin Nilsen, R. 1995). Sdlg. 29-84-1. TB, 38" (98 cm), ML. Sky blue self; beards white, tipped yellow in throat. Prized Possession X Victoria Falls. Iridescence 1995/96.

PACIFIC BEAUTY (Eric Braybrook, R. 1999). Sdlg. 91/2/D. TB, 39" (100 cm), M. Blue to mauve self; beards blue; pronounced fragrance. Titan's Glory X unknown.

PACIFIC BELLE (Larry Lauer, R. 1998). Sdlg. 91-268-1M. TB, 35" (89 cm), EM. S. and style arms pale blue white; F. light lavender purple, rim light blue white; beards yellow, tipped white; ruffled; pronounced sweet fragrance. Acoma X Blue Ballet. Stockton 1998.

PACIFIC BLUE (Eric Braybrook, R. 1999). Sdlg. 91/6/D. TB, 33" (85 cm), M. Dark blue self; beards dark blue; slight fragrance. Midnight Express X Caribbean Dream.

PACIFIC BREEZE (Frederick Held, R. 1996). Sdlg. 001. JI (6 F.), 36" (91 cm), L. White, with few scattered purple veins; style arms amethyst, bordered white, multiple. Parentage unknown; seed from Jelitto Staudensamen, Germany. Nature's Garden 1997.

PACIFIC CLOUD (Larry Lauer, R. 1997). Sdlg. 89-134-4. TB, 33" (84 cm), M. S. white; style arms white, tinted blue; F. light blue, darker blue rim; beards white at end, changing to mustard and yellow; ruffled; slight sweet fragrance. Strictly Ballroom X Alaskan Seas. Stockton 1997.

PACIFIC DARK EYES (Lorena Reid, R. 1998). Sdlg. 92S-8/109-1F. SIB (sino-sib), 36" (91 cm), ML. S. near white, light purple edges and midrib; style arms pale lemon cream; F. palest lemon cream aging near white, faint purple midrib, large dark purple signal with many lash-like lines extending into blade. Lightly Touched X 8S101-1J: (Blue Forty x Mauve Mood). Laurie's Garden 1998.

PACIFIC DESTINY (Larry Lauer, R. 1992). Sdlg. L86-48-2. TB, 34" (86 cm), EM. Heavily ruffled medium sky blue; beards white, tipped blue; slight fragrance. Marine Luster X Up Periscope. Cottage 1993.

PACIFIC FROST (J. T. Aitken, R. 1990). Sdlg. 82PC7. CA, 20" (51 cm), ML. S. white, black line down midrib; F. white, bright blue flash. Parentage unknown. Aitken's Salmon Creek 1990.

PACIFIC MISS (Lois Belardi, R. 1998). Sdlg. ACMM-1. CA, 12" (31 cm), EM. Ruffled medium blue (RHS 97A), F. with deep blue (96A) 3/4" central area. Age of Chivalry X Marine Magic. Bay View 1999.

PACIFIC ORPHAN (B. Charles Jenkins, R. 1992). Sdlg. 85K114B. CA, 18" (46 cm), M. Blue, small F. flash; species appearance. Parentage unknown; from SIGNA seed contributed by Jean Witt as Pacific Coast mix. Portable Acres 1992.

PACIFIC OVERTURES (Donald Denney by James McWhirter, R. 1990). Sdlg. D81-51-1. TB, 38" (97 cm), M. S. dark blue; F. dark purple; beards deep blue purple; pronounced fragrance. (Regents' Row x Winterscape) X D80-23-3: (Hilo Shore x Night Club). Cottage 1991.

PACIFIC RED VELVET (Lorena Reid, R. 1995). Sdlg. cs9-11-1E. SPEC-X (cal-sib), 18" (46 cm), E. S. and style arms very dark red violet; F. velvety very dark red violet, signal of broken white lines rimmed black. Enbee Deeaych X Bubbly. Laurie's Garden 1995.

PACIFIC RIM (Bennett Jones, R. 1990). Sdlg. 86PCN5. CA, 15" (38 cm), M. S. blue, washed white at edge; F. white, veined gold, blending to 1/4" band of deep blue plicata pattern. Inv. long line of sdlgs. hybridized by Lenz, Abell, Cosgrove and Ghio. Aitken's Salmon Creek, Bennett Jones 1991.

PACIFIC SKY (Eric Braybrook, R. 1999). Sdlg. 91/5/B. TB, 30" (77 cm), M. Blue to mauve self; beards grey; pronounced fragrance. Titan's Glory X Caribbean Dream.

PACIFIC SMOOTHIE (Lorena Reid, R. 1993). Sdlg. CS86-27-G4-6. SPEC-X (cal-sib), 30-36" (76-91 cm), M. S. violet, center deeper, edge pale; style arms edged darker, tailored; F. dark violet, large unmarked black violet signal. Enbee Deeaych X Wild Party. Laurie's Garden 1993.

322

PACIFIC SNOWBALL (J. T. Aitken, R. 1998). CA, 12" (31 cm), M. White self, F. with yellow signal; round, overlapped form. Parentage unknown. Aitken's Salmon Creek 1999.

PACIFIC SNOWFLAKE (George Shoop by J. T. Aitken, R. 1995). CA, 12" (31 cm), M. White self. Parentage unknown. Aitken's Salmon Creek 1995.

PACIFIC STARPRINT (Lorena Reid, R. 1992). Sdlg. cs86-27-G12-5. SPEC-X (cal-sib), 20-28" (51-71 cm), ML. S. medium violet, lighter edge, royal purple midrib; style arms with medium violet ruffled crests; F. rich royal purple, black purple signal with white starprint pattern. Enbee Deeaych X Wild Party. Laurie's Garden 1992.

PACIFIER (Ben Hager, R. 1991). Sdlg. IB5008PkPc. IB, 23" (58 cm), M. S. pink; F. apricot cream, pale pink orchid plicata edging, buff on hafts; beards red tangerine. T4603: (Keppel 78-75A: ((Smoke Rings x (Roundup sib x April Melody)) x Peccadillo sib) x Morning Sunshine) X SD4454: (Catani x 4024: ((3393: (2885Y: (Blonde Doll x (Pink Amber x Pink Cushion)) x ((Pink Amber x Pink Cushion) x Buttercup Charm)) x Pet sib) x ((((Pink Cushion x Roberts 65R28) x (Pink Amber x Pink Cushion)) x 2885Pch) x 3393))). Adamgrove 1991.

PAGAN GODDESS (Lynda Miller, R. 1994). Sdlg. 13387C. TB, 32" (81 cm), E & RE. S. pale creamy peach, peach pink midrib flush; style arms creamy peach pink; F. full peach pink, paler edges, small creamy area around beard; beards white base, heavily tipped tangerine; slight musky fragrance. 3176: (Coral Magic x Love Sonnet) X Vanity. Miller's Manor 1995.

PAGAN MIRTH (Barry Blyth, R. 1994). Sdlg. A106-3. TB, 34" (86 cm), VE-M. S. opalescent pastel lavender shot tawny brown; F. velvety red brown; beards light bronze. Y6-5, Imprimis sib, X Chocolate Vanilla. Tempo Two 1994/95.

PAGODA PRINCE (Terrell Taylor, R. 1999). Sdlg. 93-36. TB, 32" (81 cm), M. Burgundy wine (RHS 187A) self; beards burnt orange; sweet fragrance. Faraway Places X Makin' Music.

PAINTED BLUE (Barry Blyth, R. 1991). Sdlg. V84-A. TB, 36" (91 cm), EML. Deep blue violet; beards blue; ruffled S. Swirling Seas X Pledge Allegiance. Tempo Two 1991/92.

PAINTED CANARY (Bennett Jones, R. 1991). Sdlg. 398-1. SDB, 10" (25 cm), E. Lemon yellow, F. with orange brown hafts; beards orange pink. 380: ((Solar Flight x Roberts 65R11) x Pumpkin Center) X unknown. Bennett Jones 1992.

PAINTED PICTURES (Richard Ernst, R. 1992). Sdlg. 84X-61. TB, 42" (107 cm), M. S. blue; style arms blue tipped gold on crests; F. royal purple edged lighter; beards yellow; ruffled. B187-1: ((Bayberry Candle x Hi Top) x Ringo) X Ringo. Cooley 1991.

PAINTED PORCELAIN (Chet Tompkins, R. 1993). Sdlg. 89-120E. TB, 39" (99 cm), M-VL. S. ivory lemon, greenish blue throat; F. deeper ivory lemon with lime and gilt yellow overtones, hafts brushed gold, laced; beards lemon, tipped blue. ((Song of Norway x Gold Ring) x (Grand Waltz x Song of Norway)) X Seeker. Fleur de Lis 1993.

PAINTED SOFTLY (Barry Blyth, R. 1994). Sdlg. A69-1. TB, 38" (97 cm), ML. Rosy orchid, F. with pastel bluish influence; beards tangerine; pronounced sweet fragrance. Taffeta Bow X Rembrandt Magic. Tempo Two 1994/95.

PAINTER'S CHOICE (B. Charles Jenkins, R. 1998). Sdlg. CB03A. SPU, 29-34" (74-86 cm), EM. S. violet, blending to brown inside; style arms violet; F. yellow, violet veined edge, no distinct signal. C1-26U: (Ada Perry x Ping and Pang -- white) X Popped Corn.

PAINTER'S FRENZY (Terrell Taylor, R. 1997). Sdlg. 94-1. TB, 32" (80 cm), EM. S. spanish orange (RHS 26A); F. currant red (46A) brushing on spanish orange; beards bronze; musky fragrance. Thunder Echo X Jitterbug. Bonita Gardens 1997.

PAINT IT BLACK (Schreiner, R. 1994). Sdlg. AA 414-B. TB, 36" (91 cm), ML. S. deep reddish purple (RHS 79A); F. blackish purple (202A); beards black; ruffled. V 94-2: (Black Dragon x R 167-A: ((W 1107-BB: ((Dark Boatman x N 364-1) x Black Swan) x D 232-3, Navy Strut sib) x Storm Flurry)) X N 273-A, Back in Black sib. Schreiner 1994.

PAINT THE SCENE (Barry Blyth, R. 1998). Sdlg. D59-1. TB, 38" (96 cm), VE-M. S. creamy buff; F. smoky rose to old rose, 1/4" blended creamy buff edge; beards bronze at end, bronze tangerine to tangerine in throat; slight sweet fragrance. Sweet Delight X Ace Royale. Tempo Two 1998/99.

PAINT THE TOWN (Donald Sorensen, R. 1993). Sdlg. S-91-15-2. TB, 33" (84 cm), EM. S. cream (RHS 8D), lemon veins and 1/4" band; F. burnt orange (22A), blending to lemon flushed light pink in center; beards red, tipped tangerine; lightly laced; slight sweet fragrance. Beachgirl X Spiced Custard.

PAKI PAKI (Heather Collins, R. 1994). Sdlg. 84-16. IB, 24" (60 cm), M. Very pale blue white, F. with green sheen in center; beards orange. Parentage unknown.

PALACE CHOIR (Hooker Nichols, R. 1991). Sdlg. 9112A. TB, 36" (91 cm), ML. S. lightly laced white; F. blended rose amethyst, amber magenta hafts; beards tangerine. Sweet Musette X Latin Hideaway. Hillcrest 1998.

PALACE LANTERN (Chet Tompkins, R. 1993). Sdlg. 84-58-1A. IB, 27" (69 cm), EML-VL. Heavily ruffled rich golden yellow, F. with snowy white center; beards yellow. (Beautiful Baby x Cat Nap) X Apollodorus. Fleur de Lis 1993.

PALACE PAGODA (Daniel Thruman, R. 1997). JI (6 F.), 35" (89 cm), M. White, large deep lemon gold signal, grey white veining; style arms white; ruffled. Southern Son X Continuing Pleasure.

PALAISGARTEN (Siegmar Goerbitz, R. 1992). Sdlg. 8240A8. TB, 36" (90 cm), ML. S. lightly waved medium blue violet, white midrib; F. medium blue violet, white eye-zone; beards blue, tipped white; slight fragrance. Powder Snow X Rondo. Schoeppinger 1993.

PALATIAL PINK (Donald Delmez, R. 1999). Sdlg. SPR-1. JI (3 F.), 30" (76 cm), E. S. pink, upright and veined; style arms deep pink, crests lighter; F. pink, veined deeper pink, yellow signal. Kaizaiku X Iseji-no-Haru. Delmez Gardens 1999.

PALE MOON RISING (James Harper, MDB, R. 1989). Harper's Garden 1990.

PALE SHADES (Cy Bartlett, R. 1992). Sdlg. ST.SD.C. SDB, 12" (30 cm), EML. S. silvery blue white; F. pale buttery cream; beards very pale blue; light sweet fragrance. ST.SD: (Sarah Taylor x Silverdown) X Capricornia. V. H. Humphrey 1997.

PALIMPSEST (Sharon McAllister, R. 1995). Sdlg. 89-1-7. AB (OGB-), 30" (76 cm), M. S. pewter ground, finely veined gold, gold midrib brushing; style arms golden yellow, violet midrib; F. blended tan, rust and brown, oval area with orange tan veining on ivory around beard, blending outward to red violet flush, red brown signal; beards yellow. Sostenique X Tribe of Judah. McAllister 1995.

PAL JOEY (Mary Dunn by Robert Dunn, R. 1998). Sdlg. M1059A. TB, 36" (91 cm), EM. Ruffled copper rose, F. lighter; beards bright orange; ruffled, faintly laced; slight sweet fragrance. California Classic X Copper Lace. M.A.D. Iris 1999.

PALMETTO PURPLE PLUM (Steve Smart, R. 1997). Sdlg. PGG-93-1a-101. LA, 26" (66 cm), EM. S. purple (RHS 86A); style arms plum purple (79A), yellow mid-line; F. plum purple, indian yellow (17A) signal. Ann Chowning X Evelyn Boon. Pecan Grove Garden 1998.

PALM READER (Joseph Ghio, R. 1998). Sdlg. 93-136P. TB, 36" (91 cm), EM. White ground, overall lining and dotting of rosy blue; beards light tangerine. Cheating Heart X 91-65K, Skipalong sib. Bay View 1999.

PALM SPRINGS (Monty Byers, IB, R. 1989). Moonshine 1990.

PAMELA CAMERON (Heather Pryor, R. 1996). Sdlg. 60/90-9. LA, 40" (102 cm), ML. S. soft lemon washed maroon red, red centerline signal; style arms bright lime green, tips butter yellow; F. red washed yellow under style arms, deeper red veining from yellow splash signal with red veining and lime green steeple center, fine yellow petal rim, pale lemon reverse; lightly ruffled. Gladiator's Gift X Desert Jewel. Iris Haven 1996/97.

PAMELA HART (John C. Taylor, R. 1993). Sdlg. RL 9-4. LA, 55" (140 cm), M. Ruffled and serrate yellow, green yellow signals on all petals. Green Elf X Margaret Lee. Rainbow Ridge 1993/94.

PAMIATI SYNA ANDREYA (Viktor Sheviakov, R. 1995). Sdlg. 21A 14. TB, 30" (77 cm), M. S. smoky light blue; F. sapphire blue; beards smoky light blue. Siva Siva X Arabi Pasha. Sheviakov 1995.

PAMPERED (Polly Black, R. 1991). Sdlg. ESAC7. TB, 36" (91 cm), L. White; beards blue, tipped white; pronounced sweet fragrance. Parentage unknown. Polly Black 1991.

PAMPERED BABY (Ben Hager, R. 1994). Sdlg. BB5611-Pch. BB, 19" (48 cm), M. Peach self; beards tangerine. Sib to Brain Child. Adamgrove 1997.

PAMPLEMOUSSE (Cayeux, R. 1999). Sdlg. 9302 A. IB, 24" (60 cm), EM. S. pure yellow; F. yellow, tinted light olive; beards light orange. Joyful X Jitterbug.

PANACEA (Ben Hager, R. 1991). Sdlg. S965WLv. SPU, 34" (86 cm), M. Deep orchid lavender aging to full medium lavender, F. with small yellow area under crests, narrow deep yellow lance signal; style arms cream white, lavender ridge, deep lavender crests; ruffled. Arts Alive X Clarke Cosgrove. Cordon Bleu 1992.

PANAMA HATTIE (James Begley, R. 1995). Sdlg. F.P.1. TB, 36" (91 cm), EM. S. and style arms light pink; F. plum, narrow light pink edge, conspicuous white lines radiating from tangerine beard. Queen in Calico X Rustic Dance. Stockton 1995.

PANDORA'S PERFECTA (Mary Dunn, R. 1996). Sdlg. M2013AA. TB, 36" (91 cm), M. S. light lavender overlaid deeper rosy lilac; style arms pale lavender; F. light lavender overlaid deeper rosy lilac, darker edge; beards lavender, yellow in throat. Perfecta X Pandora's Purple.

PANHANDLE PRINCESS (Chris Vizvarie, R. 1994). TB, 34" (87 cm), L. Lavender purple self; beards lavender purple; slight sweet fragrance. Rolling Thunder X Pops Concert. Last Scent Farm 1994.

PANI AMBRA (Ladislav Muska, R. 1997). Sdlg. AMLP-07. TB, 39" (99 cm), L. Heavily ruffled, lightly laced deep yellow amber, F. with white near beard; style arms deeper yellow amber; beards light yellow, hairs tipped white, becoming mustard in throat; pronounced fragrance. ((Aphrodisiac x Monte Albano) x (Laced Cotton x Aprhrodisiac)) X Peach Boom. Muska 1997.

PANIC BUTTON (Lynda Miller, R. 1998). Sdlg. 2592. TB, 39" (99 cm), EM. S. purple; style arms purple, base lemon; F. dark plum purple, plum edge, white haft lines; beards dark coral red; slight musky fragrance. 1088, parentage unknown, X 6185B: (Evening in Paris x Far Corners). Miller's Manor 1998.

PAN-PINK (Ladislav Muska, R. 1995). Sdlg. DIGE-01. TB, 39" (99 cm), ML. Ruffled, laced pinkish rose bitone; beards light orange; sweet fragrance. (Discretion x Geniality) X Beverly Sills. Muska 1996.

PANSY GRACE (A. & D. Willott, R. 1995). Sdlg. 90-121. MTB, 24" (61 cm), M. Lightly ruffled light blue violet; beards yellow orange. White Canary X Surprise Blue. Willott 1995.

PAPADAD (Donald Spoon, R. 1995). TB, 35" (89 cm), M. S. white, veined lavender; style arms lavender; F. white, darker lavender veining and border; beards yellow, base white; ruffled. (Pledge Allegiance x self) X Pledge Allegiance.

PAPA LEE (Polly Black, R. 1992). Sdlg. ES5-1B. TB, 34" (86 cm), M. Medium blue, F. veined deep blue; beards orange, tipped white; ruffled; slight fragrance. Parentage unknown. Polly Black 1992.

PAPPY (Allen Harper, SDB, R. 1985). Harper's Gardens 1986.

PAPUNYA (Kevin Nilsen, R. 1995). Sdlg. 46-87-1. TB, 41" (104 cm), EM. Brown self; beards deep yellow. Lady Friend X Burgundy Brown. Iridescence 1995/96.

PARADE BLUES (Edwin Hill, R. 1999). Sdlg. ED 14-15-91B. TB, 30" (76 cm), M. Ruffled medium blue, veined darker blue; style arms light blue blend; beards yellow; slight sweet fragrance. Sky Hooks X Evening Mist.

PARADE IN PINK (Chris Vizvarie, R. 1992). Sdlg. CRV10-10. TB, 33" (84 cm), M. Light pink, F. center deeper pink; beards pink; slight sweet fragrance. Beverly Sills X Elizabeth Marrison. Last Scent Farm 1992.

PARADISE FOUND (Richard Ernst, R. 1993). Sdlg. F159-29. TB, 36" (91 cm), VL. S. honey and lavender blend; F. lavender, honey tan edge; beards yellow, tipped white. Afternoon Delight X Quiet Riot. Cooley 1993.

PARADISE SAVED (George Sutton, R. 1999). Sdlg. F-54. TB, 35" (89 cm), ML. S. and style arms very pale apricot; F. paler creamy apricot; beards tangerine, pale apricot at end; ruffled, laced and fimbriated. Paradise X Peach Bisque.

PARAGRAPH (Sterling Innerst, BB, R. 1987). Innerst 1990.

PARASOL (Ho Shidara, R. 1999). SIB, 30" (76 cm), M. S. absent; style arms white; F. (6) light to medium lavender pink, small yellow green signal, multiple (6). Parentage unknown. Ensata Gardens 1997. Introduced as "Haresugata".

PARDNER (Kenneth Fisher, R. 1992). Sdlg. 91-6. MTB, 20" (51 cm), M. S. honey gold; F. red with honey gold rim; beards yellow. K4: (((Spring Bells x New Idea) x Blue Bisque) x 2HH: ((Elfin Coach x Gold Sovereign) x (Amethyst Sunset x Buenita))) X Consummation. Aitken's Salmon Creek 1993.

PARDON (Lawrence Ransom, R. 1996). Sdlg. 90/232-5. SDB, 11" (28 cm), EM. S. pale purple, fine darker veining overall; F. dark wine purple, lighter edge, white ground showing at haft; beards light violet blue, heavily brushed orange toward throat. Casper's Shadow X Trescols. Iris au Trescols 1996.

PARDON MY GARDEN (Tom Burseen, R. 1990). Sdlg. 6-99A. TB, 33" (84 cm), EM. S. light butterscotch; F. cream ground washed light red purple (RHS 58D); beards tangerine; ruffled; slight fragrance. Lilac Laser sib X Theatre. T.B.'s Place 1991.

PAREMATA (Phyllis Collins, R. 1993). Sdlg. B2-88. SDB, 9" (23 cm), E. S. yellow; F. cherry red, edged yellow; beards pale yellow, tipped gold. Making Eyes X Gingerbread Man. Waimate 1994/95.

PARFUM DE FRANCE (Lawrence Ransom, R. 1999). Sdlg. 89/83-1. TB, 33" (84 cm), M. S.

medium naples yellow, center lighter, midrib infused mauve; style arms deeper naples yellow, midrib mauve; F. cream white center, 3/4" rose red sanded margin, darker red hairline edge; beards yellow ochre; pronounced sweet fragrance. 86/104-12: (Vanity x Needlecraft) X Rosy Cloud.

PARIS BLUES (Mary Dunn, TB, R. 1988). M.A.D. Iris 1990.

PARIS DREAM (Hooker Nichols, TB, R. 1989). Hillcrest 1996.

PARISIAN FLIGHT (George Shoop, R. 1993). Sdlg. 88-17. TB, 36" (91 cm), M. S. white; F. ruffled and flared medium blue; beards tangerine; slight fragrance. 84-3: (American Beauty x 82-12: (French Connection x American Beauty)) X 85-32: (82-12 x French Connection sib). Shoop 1993.

PARISIAN MODEL (Barbara Wight, R. 1995). Sdlg. 90-22-2. TB, 37" (94 cm), EM. S. lavender, aging light pink with lavender cast; F. lavender pink; beards rusty orange; ruffled; sweet fragrance. Hubble Space Telescope X 86-17: (Sky Hooks x Financier). Wight's Iris 1997.

PARISIEN (Jean Cayeux by Richard Cayeux, R. 1995). Sdlg. 87219 A. TB, 37" (95 cm), M. S. chalky white; F. medium blue, paler near red orange beard. Rebecca Perret X tri-colored sib. Cayeux 1994.

PARKRIDGE CHALLENGER (Tom Parkhill, R. 1998). Sdlg. 92-901. TB, 29" (74 cm), EM. Ruffled dark bluish purple self; beards very dark blue; slight fragrance. Dusky Challenger X Winterscape. Parkwood 1999.

PARROT FASHION (Heather Pryor, R. 1997). Sdlg. 29/93-E. LA, 40" (102 cm), ML. Cerise red ground veined darker, lemon rim; raised steeple signal lime green, surrounded by yellow; style arms lemon, blushed cyclamen at base; ruffled. Volcanic Wildfire X Fashion World.

PARTITA (William Maryott, R. 1991). Sdlg. N144A. TB, 38" (97 cm), M. S. poupon yellow (RHS 163B); F. burnt orange (167A), rimmed S. color; beards yellow; ruffled. Speculator X Syncopation. Maryott 1992.

PART PRUDE (Tom Burseen, R. 1997). Sdlg. 93-430A. TB, 34" (86 cm), M. S. pale lavender white; style arms light yellowish white; F. white; beards yellow, base white, ending in large feathered appendage; ruffled; slight fragrance. Neat Pleats X Let's Pretend. T.B.'s Place 1997.

PARTS PLUS (Lynda Miller, R. 1996). Sdlg. 2092C. IB, 24" (61 cm), ML. S. pinkish orchid; style arms flesh pink, edged apricot; F. pinkish orchid, deeper orchid flush near beard; beards tangerine, light violet horn; slight musky fragrance. Sky Hooks X 2986E: ((Inscription x Pixie Pink) x Bright Vision). Miller's Manor 1997.

PARTY LIGHTS (Schreiner, R. 1995). Sdlg. AA 978-2. TB, 38" (97 cm), ML. S. apricot yellow (RHS 17A); F. white center, 3/4" apricot yellow rim; beards tangerine. V 368-2: (S 657-1: ((((((Amethyst Flame x Lavish Lady) x Arctic Flame) x White Taffeta) x Launching Pad) x Joyce Terry) x (Something Else x (((Golden Ice x Celestial Glory) x Flaming Star) x Gold Trimmings))) x Aphrodisiac) X V 322-2: (China Dragon x Spiced Orange). Schreiner 1995.

PARTY PALEFACE (Lorena Reid, R. 1993). Sdlg. cs86-27-G4-3. SPEC-X (cal-sib), 30-36" (76-91 cm), M. S. near-white with some faint blue orchid markings; style arms pale violet, flaring blue violet crests; F. reddish violet, near-white ruffled edge, small gold sunburst line pattern in signal area. Enbee Deeaych X Wild Party. Laurie's Garden 1993.

PARTY QUEEN (Lynda Miller, TB, R. 1988). Miller's Manor 1991.

PARTY TALK (Barry Blyth, R. 1993). Sdlg. A14-6. SDB, 15" (38 cm), M. S. pink, slight violet cast; F. pink with rosy pink radiating ray pattern; beards violet, tangerine in throat. Smoky Imp X Chanted. Tempo Two 1993/94.

PARTY WINE (William Plotner, R. 1992). Sdlg. 85-513. TB, 38-40" (97-102 cm), M. Velvety dark wine purple with smoky purple (RHS 77A) signal on F.; beards dark purple, bronze deep in throat; slight spicy-musky fragrance. 82-64: ((Lilac Wine x Navajo Blanket) x Superstition) X 78-15: (Space Blazer x Superstition). Wildwood Gardens 1992.

PASCOE (R. E. Nichol, R. 1993). Sdlg. L104-4. TB, 47" (119 cm), L. S. pale lavender violet (RHS 85B); F. very dark purple, near-black at center, dark brown (187A) shoulders; beards dull greyed orange (near 163B), insignificant; lightly ruffled, semi-flared. ((Kilt Lilt x Autumn Leaves) x Show Biz) X Doctor Behenna. V. H. Humphrey 1995.

PASSAGE (Jim & Vicki Craig, R. 1996). Sdlg. C22Z18. IB, 24" (60 cm), L. Deep violet self; beards deep violet; ruffled; pronounced sweet fragrance. (Odyssey x Maroon Caper) X 41W38, Blueberry Ice sib. J. & V. Craig 1996.

PASSIONA (Barry Blyth, R. 1999). Sdlg. C247-A. TB, 34" (86 cm), M-VL. S. cream, flushed coral apricot; F. coral apricot, slightly lighter edge; beards vivid saturn red; ruffled, flared; slight sweet fragance. X70-A: (Magharee x Shoop 80-2: (So Rare x (Ringo x Color Bash))) X A153-13, Cafe Risque sib. Tempo Two 1999/2000.

PASSION BLEUE (Jean Peyrard, R. 1994). Sdlg. PN 89/3-8. MDB, 6" (15 cm), M. S. and style arms purple violet; F. darker, with short white streak below beard; beards pale blue violet, base white. Triplicate X Grandma's Hat. Iris au Trescols 1995.

PASSION FLOWER (Monty Byers, TB, R. 1989). Moonshine 1991.

PASS THE SHADES (Tom Burseen, R. 1993). Sdlg. 9-201A. TB, 37" (94 cm), EM. S. bright yellow orange (RHS 21C); F. red (46B) with pronounced yellow rim; beards gold; ruffled, flared; spicy fragrance. Role Model X Indoctrination. T.B.'s Place 1994.

PASTEL BEAU (Barry Blyth, R. 1995). Sdlg. A69-3. TB, 38" (97 cm), M. Blue lilac, F. with silvery sheen; beards mustard yellow; ruffled; slight sweet fragrance. Taffeta Bow X Rembrandt Magic. Tempo Two 1995/96.

PASTEL BLUE (John Durrance, R. 1992). Sdlg. D86-139. TB, 36" (91 cm), M. S. light pink; F. pink and blue; beards orange. Custom Made X Sophistication. Long 1992.

PASTEL RIBBONS (Paul Black, R. 1996). Sdlg. A33A. TB, 33" (84 cm), L. S. buttery buff, heavy orchid infusion up midrib and blending outward; style arms tan; F. orchid, darker at haft; beards red orange; ruffled; slight sweet fragrance. Robusto X Ruth Black. Mid-America 1996.

PASTEL SKY (Connell Marsh, TB, R. 1984). C. Marsh 1990.

PASTEL TRACERY (Lois Rich by James Whitely, R. 1990). Sdlg. R69-165D. AB (OGB+), 21" (53 cm), EM. S. pink orchid, finely veined wine purple; style arms brown to sorrel; F. pink orchid, small halo of heavy pepper dots diminishing into light orchid veins, mulberry wine signal; beards orange yellow. Daughter of Time X Welcome Reward. Aril Patch, Aril Society 1990.

PASTICHE (Janet Hutchinson, R. 1999). Sdlg. PPGL-1. LA, 52" (132 cm), M. S. palest cream, 1/4" pink edge, midrib yellow and tan, paler at base; style arms warm cream touched tan, crests pinkish tan; F. pale raspberry pink, paler line edge, hafts heavily veined, narrow green signal edged tan; pronounced fragrance. Glowlight X unknown.

PATHWAY (Paul Black, R. 1991). Sdlg. 86432C. IB, 23" (58 cm), M. S. white central area with violet plicata markings, 1" brassy tan edge; F. white around beard, blending to orchid violet plicata markings, 1½" orchid violet band; beards mustard, tipped violet at end; slight sweet fragrance. Prediction X Chubby Cheeks sib. Mid-America 1992.

PATIO PARTY (Kirk Strawn, R. 1993). Sdlg. AAA-1985. LA, 37" (93 cm), M. S. light greyed orange (RHS 173D); style arms yellow (4C), brushed light yellow orange; F. darker greyed orange (173C), yellow orange (14B) signal. Deneb X President Hedley. Bois d'Arc 1996.

PATIO ROSE (Louise Bellagamba, R. 1993). Sdlg. PR-91-S. SIB, 29" (74 cm), M. Mauve rose with violet vein in center of F. Augury X unknown. Bella Vista 1993.

PATRICIA BROOKS (Kirk Strawn, R. 1993). Sdlg. 26A-1985. LA, 36" (91 cm), E. S. greyed orange (RHS 167D); style arms light greyed orange (163C); F. darker greyed orange (166C), bright yellow orange (15A) signal. Little Miss Leighley X Valera.

PATRIOTIC BANNER (Dona Fort, R. 1997). Sdlg. 90-452-D. TB, 38" (97 cm), EM. S. white; style arms white, midrib blue; F. medium blue edge fading to white at center; beards tangerine red; ruffled, lightly laced; slight sweet fragrance. 87-47-A: (Grecian Skies x 83-14-A: (Portrait of Larrie x Condottiere)) X 84-152-R: (Pearls and Gold x Blazing Light). Aitken's Salmon Creek 1998.

PATRIOTIC COLORS (O. D. Niswonger, R. 1996). Sdlg. 64-93. TB, 36" (91 cm), M. S. and style arms near-white, touched blue; F. pale blue, lighter rim; beards red. American Beauty X Town Clown. Cape Iris 1998.

PATRIOT'S GEM (Fred Gadd, AB (OGB-), R. 1988). Markham 1993.

PAT ROLLMAN (Chet Tompkins, R. 1992). Sdlg. 84-82. TB, 39" (99 cm), ML. Sea blue, large icy white area around pale lemon beard. Victoria Falls X (((Tinsel Town x Stepping Out) x (Tinsel Town x Dark Town Strutter)) x ((Stepping Out x Tinsel Town) x (Dark Town Strutter x Tinsel Town))). Fleur de Lis 1991.

PAT'S CHOICE (Donovan Albers, SDB, R. 1985). Albers, Borbeleta 1990.

PATTAYA BEACH (Bob Thomason, R. 1992). Sdlg. BT 8931D. TB, 32" (81 cm), M. Medium violet, F. with brown hafts; beards gold; pronounced spicy fragrance. Gypsy Jewels X First Violet. Okie Iris 1994.

PATTERNS (Mary Dunn, TB, R. 1988). M.A.D. Iris 1990.

PATTERNS IN SPACE (Donald Delmez, R. 1995). Sdlg. DDKBVW-1. JI (6 F.), 38" (97 cm), M. Dark blue with fine white lines, signal yellow green; style arms white, sanded blue, tipped dark blue; ruffled. "Sakuraku" X self. Delmez Gardens 1995.

PATTY KAY HALL (Jack Norrick, R. 1997). Sdlg. 91S-1A. SIB, 30" (76 cm), L. S. blue violet; style arms aqua; F. blue violet, small white signal. Grand Junction X unknown. Miller's Manor 1998.

PAULINE HILL (Tom Burseen, R. 1991). Sdlg. 8-479A. TB, 38" (97 cm), VE. S. light peachy orange (RHS 29C); F. slightly lighter; beards white, tipped tangerine; ruffled; sweet fragrance. 6-232: ((Lacy Snowflake x Porta Villa) x Beyond) X Rosecraft. T.B.'s Place 1992.

PAULINE RODERICK (Stephen Stevens, R. 1996). Sdlg. 88-2-2. TB, 36" (91 cm), M. S. lilac (RHS 76B), lighter midrib; style arms lilac; F. lilac, paler near chrome yellow beard; heavily ruffled; slight spicy fragrance. Glory Ballet X 81-7-9: (Kentucky Derby x Ruffled Ballet). Roderick Hillview 1997.

PAUL PAYENS (John C. Taylor, R. 1990). Sdlg. OL 142-2. LA, 47" (120 cm), ML. S. greyed purple (RHS 186A/C), marbled, lighter edge and reverse; F. greyed purple (186A), lighter edge and reverse. M24-4: (C'est Si Bon x Charles Arny III) X Helen Naish. Rainbow Ridge 1992/93.

PAUSBACK SIBTOSA (Tomas Tamberg, R. 1993). SPEC-X (sib-tosa), 36" (90 cm), M. Light blue self. (Cambridge x self) X *I. setosa*. Schoeppinger 1994.

PAVEL TRETIYAKOV (V. & N. Gordodelovy, R. 1995). Sdlg. 153. TB, 37" (95 cm), VE. S. rose brown; F. white, edged rose lilac; beards brown; ruffled. Parentage unknown. Gordodelovy 1990.

PAWNEE PRINCESS (Evelyn Jones, R. 1991). Sdlg. IE87-5. IB, 21" (53 cm), M. Majolica orange, deeper area around burnt orange beard; slight fragrance. 79-20: (Peach Float x (Orange Glory x Shoop sdlg.)) X B. Jones 385: (352: (Solar Flight x (pink IB x *I. pumila* "Blazek")) x Orange Tiger). Bennett Jones 1992.

PAX AMERICANA (David Sindt by Eric Tankesley-Clarke, R. 1994). Sdlg. 681. SDB, 10" (25 cm), M. S. white; F. white, heavily veined blue violet; beards white, tipped tangerine; slight fragrance. 474: (Shaded Pale x 311: (((Happy Birthday x Sun Sparkle) x Roberts 65-R-11) x (Roberts 65-R-11 x Pink Cushion))) X Fire Island. Adamgrove 1994.

PAY THE PRICE (Graeme Grosvenor, R. 1999). Sdlg. V103-X. TB, 34" (86 cm), M. S. white, heavily overlaid light blue; F. white, darker blue rim; beards white, tipped blue. T9-1: (Marriage Vows x Snowbrook) X Zipper Stitch sib. Rainbow Ridge 1999/2000.

PEACE AND HARMONY (Joseph Ghio, R. 1991). Sdlg. 86-34M. TB, 40" (102 cm), EML. True violet; beards white. 82-124ZZ, Inaugural Ball sib, X Silverado. Bay View 1992.

PEACE AND TRANQUILITY (William Plotner, R. 1994). Sdlg. 86-12-1. TB, 34-36" (86-91 cm), ML. S. and style arms cornsilk (RHS 19B); F. white, edged cornsilk; beards chinese orange (30D). 81-3: (Tahiti Sunrise x (Ovation x Royal Gold)) X 80-8: ((Ovation x Royal Gold) x (Maudie Marie x Tinsel Town)). Wildwood Gardens 1994.

PEACE CAPERS (Floyd Dyer, R. 1992). Sdlg. D-37-84-T. BB, 25" (65 cm), M. S. light pink; F. ruffled pale blue violet; beards orange, tipped white; slight musky fragrance. D-12-79-B: (W. F. Brown B-66-168-A x Lilac Flare) X Tulare. Four Cedars 1992.

PEACEFUL MISSION (Richard Ernst, R. 1990). Sdlg. D150-19. TB, 34" (86 cm), ML. S. deep cream, near-white rim, infused yellow; F. white, gold shoulders and highlights, cream reverse; beards gold; fluted, laced. Centennial State X T606-10: ((Countryman x Outreach) x Gold Cadillac). Cooley 1990.

PEACEFUL PERSUASION (Sterling Innerst, R. 1992). Sdlg. 2369-10. TB, 36" (91 cm), M. Light blue with darker highlights; beards blue, tipped lighter; slight fragrance. Seashore X Metallic Blue. Innerst 1993.

PEACEKEEPING FORCE (Sterling Innerst, R. 1992). Sdlg. 1125-11. TB, 36" (91 cm), ML. Light orange apricot self; beards orange beige, tipped lighter; slight fragrance. Summer Love X 332-2: (Silver Shower x Pink Angel). Cooley 1993.

PEACE ON EARTH (Allan Ensminger, R. 1990). Sdlg. 86-73. BB, 26" (66 cm), ML. S. orient pink (HCC 416/2), gold glitter on edge; F. peach (512/3); beards poppy red (16/1); ruffled, laced. 81-30: ((Almost Gladys x Foolish Pleasure) x Almost Gladys) X Christa. Varigay 1990.

PEACE SIGNALS (Francis Rogers, R. 1998). Sdlg. C-139-F. TB, 38" (97 cm), M. S. and style arms lobelia blue (RHS 91C); F. lobelia blue (91B), radiating to darker violet blue (89D) at edge; beards yellow orange, purple horn; sweet fragrance. Conjuration X Kathy's Joy. Meadowbrook 1999.

PEACH BOOM (Ladislav Muska, R. 1996). Sdlg. SLFI-03/B. TB, 36" (91 cm), ML. Heavily laced deep peach self; beards tangerine; sweet fragrance. ("Slahacka": (Buffy x Silver Shower) x Frivolous Idea) X (Lady Madonna x Aphrodisiac). Muska 1996.

PEACH COBBLER (Dana Borglum, R. 1995). TB, 30-32" (76-81 cm), M. S. peach; F. lighter peach; beards tangerine. Parentage unknown.

PEACH COOLER (J. T. Aitken, R. 1993). Sdlg. 88M57. SDB, 12" (30 cm), M. S. peach; F. light peach, deeper spot at orange beard; slight fragrance. (Princess of Love x B. Jones M-334) X Orange Tiger. Aitken's Salmon Creek 1993.

PEACH CURLS (A. & D. Willott, R. 1999). Sdlg. W 95-208. TB, 36" (91 cm), ML. Heavily ruffled peach (RHS 29C), F. blending to near-white in center and hafts overlaid cadmium orange (23C); beards saturn red (30C); slight sweet fragrance. Master Gardener X Anna Belle Babson.

PEACHES IN WINE (Heather Pryor, R. 1997). Sdlg. 7/93-A. LA, 35" (89 cm), E. S. peach, deep red line signal, paler reverse; style arms peach, yellow midrib; F. deep red, fine salmon peach rim, peach reverse, lime yellow steeple signal; ruffled. Bushfire Moon X Lucy Payens. Lone Star 1998.

PEACH FRAPPE (Bernard Hamner by Shepard Iris Garden, R. 1992). Sdlg. 82-216. BB, 27" (69 cm), M. S. white, midrib heavily infused peach; style arms soft peach, laced; F. peach, laced white white edge; beards coral, tipped peach; heavily ruffled. (75-11: (Touch of Envy x (Touche x Misty Dawn)) x 75-225: ((((Fox Charm x Campus Flirt) x Becky Lee) x (Touche x Misty Dawn)) x Peach Sundae)) X Peach Sundae. Hamner Iris, Shepard Iris 1992.

PEACH ICE CREAM (Carol Lankow by J. T. Aitken, R. 1993). Sdlg. 7H106. BB, 26" (66 cm), ML. S. white; F. pale peach; beards white, tipped orange; slight fragrance. Marmalade Skies X ((Spring Bonnet x Wright L85) x Coral Light). Aitken's Salmon Creek 1993.

PEACH NEGLIGEE (Lucille Robinson, R. 1990). Sdlg. 22/1/85. TB, 36" (91 cm), EM. Ruffled smooth peach pink; beards tangerine; laced S.; slight sweet fragrance. Glendale X Christmas Time. Iris Acres 1993.

PEACH PARASOL (Donald Spoon, R. 1995). Sdlg. 93-9. BB, 19" (48 cm), M. Peach (RHS 24D), F. overlaid orchid (75C); beards darker peach (25A); ruffled, flared. Faux Pas X Ozark Evening. Winterberry 1997.

PEACH PARTY (Lynda Miller, R. 1990). Sdlg. 2986C. SDB, 13" (33 cm), ML. S. full peach, straw yellow glow on edge; F. ruffled full peach, light spanish orange shading at hafts and beside beard; beards creamy yellow, tipped orange; slight fragrance. Fruit Salad X Bright Vision. Miller's Manor 1991.

PEACH PETAL PIE (O. D. Niswonger, R. 1992). Sdlg. SDB 35-91. SDB, 11" (28 cm), M. S. ivory with pink infusion; F. ivory, increased pink infusion near white beard. Straw Hat X Ballet Slippers. Cape Iris 1992.

PEACH PICOTEE (Schreiner, R. 1990). Sdlg. S 504-A. TB, 35" (89 cm), M. S. apricot peach (RHS 19C); F. white, 1/4" picoteed rosy rim; beards tangerine; ruffled. M 858-3: (I 524-1: ((Rippling Waters x (Annabel Lee sib x Claudia Rene)) x ((Fairy Rose x Cashmere) x ((R 387 x T 79-F: (Amethyst Flame x Wonderment)) x T 79-2))) x J 288-A: (Miriam Steel sib x Starina)) X N 502-E: ((((C 973-A, Lilac Champagne sdlg., x ((Alpenrose x Whole Cloth) x Cashmere)) x (C 973-A x (((Broadway Star x Giant Rose) x ((Maytime x Opal Beauty) x Whole Cloth)) x Wine and Roses))) x ((Champagne Music x Christmas Time sdlg.) x (Orchid Brocade x (Annabel Lee sib x Emma Cook)))). Schreiner 1990.

PEACH PUNCH (Vernon Wood, R. 1990). Sdlg. 87-4. CA, 10-12" (25-30 cm), E. S. rosy pink (RHS 64C) with few blue lines; F. rosy pink, 1/2" salmon buff edge, slight blue lines at end of center patch. Three Cornered Hat X Wish Fulfillment. Portable Acres 1990.

PEACH ROYALE (LeRoy Meininger, R. 1999). Sdlg. C.P. 90-4. TB, 32" (81 cm), EM. S. light peach pink; style arms peach pink; F. peach pink ground washed and veined rose purple, 1/8" peach pink rim; beards tangerine. Crowd Pleaser X unknown. Monument, Woodland Iris 1999.

PEACH VISION (Jim Hedgecock, R. 1991). Sdlg. 84-71-1. TB, 32" (81 cm), ML. Laced and ruffled peach pink, lighter area around bright red beards; slight sweet fragrance. Carved Cameo X Sunset Sonata. Comanche Acres 1992.

PEACHY SUMMIT (Carl Jorgensen, R. 1996). Sdlg. 85-2-3A. TB, 30" (76 cm), ML. S. carrot red (HCC 612/2), lighter central area giving rimmed effect; style arms carrot red; F. carrot red, central chinese yellow (606/3) area, giving rimmed effect; beards burnt orange (614); ruffled, laced; pronounced sweet fragrance. 74-24-2B: (Merry Miss x Launching Pad) X Ruffles and Lace. Long 1996.

PEACOCK LADY (Norma Barnard, R. 1997). Sdlg. NB 94-2. CA, 14" (36 cm), EM. S. soft gold veined maroon; style arms soft gold, washed maroon; F. maroon, soft gold rim, small gold signal, iridescent blue-washed blaze; lightly ruffled. Lacylady X unknown.

PEACOCK PANACHE (Nora Scopes, R. 1995). Sdlg. PC 37B. CA, 13" (33 cm), M. S. light claret;

F. white, precisely edged deep claret, with round yellow central spot surrounded by fine lines. Spring Daze X unknown.

PEACOCK PAVANE (Nora Scopes, R. 1993). Sdlg. PC 37. CA, 15" (38 cm), M. S. mauve; F. white ground with rich purple markings forming peacock eye pattern. Spring Daze X unknown.

PEACOCK PRIDE (Nora Scopes, R. 1998). Sdlg. PC 103. CA, 10" (25 cm), E. S. purple; style arms lighter purple; F. deep purple, white zone finely striped purple, yellow eye. Parentage unknown -- probably inv. Spring Daze.

PEAK ALONE (Pauline Evans, R. 1997). Sdlg. 92/6. SPU, 42-48" (107-122 cm), E. S. lilac blue, slightly deeper veining; F. creamy white, very faintly veined and edged pale lilac, gold signal spreading over top third. Missouri Blue X Missouri Gal. Tempo Two 1997/98.

PEAK EXPERIENCE (Joseph Hoage, TB, R. 1989). Long 1991.

PEAK OF PINK (Bob Bauer/John Coble, R. 1998). Sdlg. J93-K-3. JI (6 F.), 36" (91 cm), M. Pale pink opening from pink buds, aging cream white; style arms pink. Sakura-No-Sono X Hime Kagami. Ensata Gardens 1999.

PEARL OF LAVENDER (Akihiko Terada, R. 1999). Sdlg. S254-89-21. TB, 37" (94 cm), M. White self, lavender cast; beards yellow, white at end. Chico Maid X Arctic Song. Roris 1999.

PEARLS OF AUTUMN (Ben Hager, R. 1992). Sdlg. RE5079SmkCrBld. TB, 32" (81 cm), M & RE. S. creamy pearl (smoky in cool weather); F. pearl, white deep in hafts; self beards. Mother Earth X Bonus Mama. Melrose 1993.

PEARLS ON ONYX (Lois Rich by Carl Boswell, R. 1990). Sdlg. R77-28B. AB (OB), 6" (15 cm), E. S. deep violet; F. dark purple, black signal; beards very pale cream; slight sweet fragrance. S-5943-B: ((*I. calcarea* x *I. susiana*) x (*I. auranitica* x *I. atropurpurea*)) X Warburton red violet *pumila*.

PEBBLE FRESH (Graeme Grosvenor, R. 1998). Sdlg. V27-10. TB, 35" (89 cm), EM. S. mauve lavender; F. mauve, darker overlay, white lines and spray pattern; beards yellow, tipped white. Mixture X Storyline. Rainbow Ridge 1998/99.

PEDIGREE (Lilly Gartman by Joseph Ghio, R. 1997). Sdlg. G89-20-BO. TB, 34" (86 cm), ML. Bright orange self; beards tangerine. 82-2A: (Preface x Lady Friend) X Guadalajara. Roris 1997.

PEE DEE ENCHANTMENT (Ursula Herz by John Wood, R. 1990). LA, 30" (76 cm), L. Purple violet (RHS 82B). Sweet Accord X unknown. John Wood 1991.

PEEPERS (Lynda Miller, MDB, R. 1989). Miller's Manor 1991.

PEE WEE PETE (D. L. Shepard, R. 1998). Sdlg. 97002-9303. SPU, 38" (97 cm), EM. S. soft yellow, base darker; style arms rich yellow; F. rich yellow, near gold. Megatrend X Baby Chick. Shepard Iris 1998.

PEGASUS BAY (Ron Isles, R. 1996). Sdlg. R10581. SDB, 10" (25 cm), E. Lightly ruffled cobalt blue, F. with darker blue patch under beard, short ray haft patterning; beards light blue. Dear Love X Electric Girl. Waimate 1996/97.

PEGASUS SUNRISE (Ron Isles, R. 1996). Sdlg. R10786. SPU, 45" (114 cm), M. Grey blue, F. with gold signal. GL 8102/3 X GL 8103/7.

PEGGY'S PASSION (Thomas Burch, R. 1994). Sdlg. 91 LWxSS. TB, 40" (102 cm), M. S. yellow (RHS 10B) with violet cast; F. violet (80B) with tan rim; beards yellow, tipped orange; slight sweet fragrance. Lilac Wine X Silver Silence. Burch Fields 1995.

PEGGY'S SONG (G. F. Wilson, R. 1997). Sdlg. 93-91 OZ-B. AB (OGB), 34" (86 cm), E. S. pale violet blue, darker veining; F. blended lemon, violet and rose, darker veining toward edge, slight purple dotting, large dark purple signal; beards grey, tipped mustard, wide; form rounded; slight sweet fragrance. Onlooker X Zerzura.

PEIGNOIR (Lynn Markham, R. 1995). Sdlg. 87-4G2. TB, 34-35" (86-89 cm), ML. S. light pink (RHS 56D base shading to 36D); style arms light pink (56D midrib, 36D edge), crest split, frilled; F. light pink (36D) edges paling to near-white around beard; beards light pink end shading to deep pink (33B) in throat; deeply ruffled. Sib to Florence Fisher. Markham 1996.

PELE (J. T. Aitken, R. 1993). Sdlg. 87M33. SDB, 11" (28 cm), ML. S. orange; F. orange, deep purple spot, orange hafts; beards coral; slight fragrance. (Be Dazzled x B. Jones M-304: (M229-2: (Roberts 65-R-11 x 201) x Melon Honey)) X (Fire One x B. Jones M 334-2: ((Solar Flight x M255: (Melon Honey x M229)) x (L20 x M255))). Aitken's Salmon Creek 1993.

PELLAN (Tony Huber, R. 1992). Sdlg. 89-VWY-01. SPEC (*versicolor*), 27½" (70 cm), EM. S. medium violet; F. violet (RHS 90A), large white center veined darker, yellow signal; slight spicy fragrance. EX-CO-MR-04 X EX-CO-TJ-02, wild collected *versicolor* sdlgs.

330

PELOPONNESUS (Sterling Innerst, R. 1996). Sdlg. 1532-2. JI (6 F.), 36" (91 cm), M. Red purple with blue rays except on 1/4" solid red purple rim; gold signal with blue halo; style arms light red purple, some extra petaloids. Frostbound X Fringed Cloud. Draycott 1997.

PEMCAW (Robert Harding, R. 1991). Sdlg. 87-34. TB, 35" (88 cm), ML. White; beards white. (Mary Frances x Crown Sterling) X Winter Olympics. Tempo Two 1994/95.

PENMATE (John C. Taylor, R. 1998). Sdlg. UL 22-2. LA, 39" (100 cm), M. Ruffled white, yellow spray pattern signal; style arms lemon, edged white. Gladiator's Gift X Dural Dreamtime.

PENNY ANNE (Barry Blyth, R. 1992). Sdlg. X68-1. BB, 26" (66 cm), ML. S. white, faintly flushed pink; F. light cameo pink; beards tangerine. Echo de France X Shoop 80-2: (So Rare x (Ringo x Color Bash)). Tempo Two 1992/93.

PENNY BLACK (Ralph Tubbs, TB, R. 1978). British Iris Society 1989.

PENNY LANE (Larry Lauer, R. 1999). Sdlg. 93-334-1. TB, 34" (86 cm), M. S. and style arms saffron yellow; F. cadmium orange, rim darker; beards tangerine; ruffled, lightly laced; slight sweet fragrance. Voltage X 91-160: (Gratuity x Bogota). Lauer's Flowers 1999.

PENNYROYAL PASSION (James Bingham, R. 1995). Sdlg. 85-9-1. TB, 40" (102 cm), ML. Purple violet (RHS 82A) aging lighter (82B), F. with prominent darker veining; beards orange, tipped purple. Pansy Royale X Louisiana Lace. Pennyroyal Gardens 1996.

PENNY SERENADE (Jean Sanders, R. 1995). TB, 36" (91 cm), M & RE. Medium pink self; style arms pink; beards red orange. Vanity X Coral Charmer.

PENRHYN (Maureen Foster, TB, R. 1987). V. H. Humphrey 1995.

PEPPERONI PIZZA (Roy Bohrer, R. 1992). Sdlg. 88-SW. TB, 32" (81 cm), M. S. blended tan and red violet; F. same, edged tan, violet area around orange beard; laced; slight fragrance. 87-SW: (Shawnee Whisper x Sheer Poetry) X Dazzling Gold.

PEPPER UPPER (Jim Hedgecock, R. 1992). Sdlg. 83-68-1. TB, 32" (81 cm), ML. S. white with wide purple plicata edge, purple midrib; F. white, wide purple plicata edge; beards silver blue, purple horn; ruffled; pronounced sweet fragrance. Going My Way X Mary O. Mahoney. Comanche Acres 1993.

PERFECT DOLL (Ben Hager, TB, R. 1989). Roris 1991.

PERFECT GIFT (Keith Keppel, R. 1995). Sdlg. 89-29B. TB, 34" (86 cm), M. Pale pink (M&P 1-B-1), F. paler (1-A-1) below beard; style arms slightly deeper (1-C-7); beards soft orangish pink (1-I-11/12), deeper in throat; ruffled. Social Event X Femme Fatale. Keppel 1996.

PERFECT HARMONY (Kerryn Turner, R. 1996). Sdlg. KH91-36-1. TB, 34" (86 cm), M. Rich flamingo pink, F. with tannish hafts, bright white area around coral red beard; slight fragrance. Pink Swan X Dance Man. Tempo Two 1996/97.

PERFECT PEARL (Paul Black, R. 1991). Sdlg. 8617A. TB, 30" (76 cm), M. Ruffled icy white with slight blue and lavender tones; beards pale blue grey. Classico X Beautiful Surprise. Mid-America 1991.

PERFECT PITCH (Joseph Gatty, R. 1991). Sdlg. T36-3. TB, 36" (91 cm), ML. S. dark violet (M&P 46-K-12); F. fluorite violet (darker than 46-L-12); beards marine purple (46-G-12) tipped chrome yellow (9-L-7) deep in throat; pronounced sweet fragrance. Q31-1: (Black Dragon x Swirling Seas) X Stormy Night. Keppel 1992.

PERFECT POUT (Tom Burseen, R. 1997). Sdlg. 93-374E. TB, 35" (89 cm), M. S. and style arms light orient pink (RHS 36A); F. light orange, washed light brick red (35D), purple striations on shoulders; beards salmon orange; sweet fragrance. 91-297: ((Edna's Wish x Rosecraft) x (Iris Irene x Classic Capers)) X Orange Blotter. T.B.'s Place 1998.

PERFECT VISION (Cy Bartlett, R. 1996). Sdlg. HHBR 2. SIB (tet.), 34" (86 cm), M. S. medium blue; style arms turquoise blue; F. dark medium blue; lightly waved. Harpswell Happiness X Berlin Ruffles.

PERFUMED LADY (Leslie Donnell, R. 1996). Sdlg. 88-2-4. TB, 31" (79 cm), ML. Blue violet self; beards violet, base orange; pronounced spicy fragrance. Lilac Lustre X Bubbling Over.

PERFUME SHOP (Keith Keppel, R. 1997). Sdlg. 91-51A. IB, 26" (66 cm), EM. S. white ground, near-solid wash of rosy campanula violet (M&P 42-J-9), lighter and bluer (42-G-8) toward edge and base; style arms eventide (42-C-6), midrib darker (42-H-8); F. hyacinth violet (43-K-9), lighter toward center, white ground showing near beard; beards blue white tipped light blue at end, tipped bronze in center, light yellow tipped bronze in throat; ruffled; pronounced sweet fragrance. Faux Pas X Gatty W37-9, Quote sib. Keppel 1998.

PERHAPS LOVE (Barry Blyth, R. 1997). Sdlg. C107-1. TB, 40" (102 cm), M. S. white, faintest pink midrib flush; F. medium pink, lighter creamy white to pink area in center; beards tangerine. Pastel Beau X A113-4, I'm Yours sib. Tempo Two 1997/98.

PERILOUS JOURNEY (Richard Ernst, R. 1993). Sdlg. HS902-1. TB, 36" (91 cm), M. Ruffled dark blue purple, lighter blue zonal area around blue beards. Lavender Luck X Dusky Challenger. Cooley 1993.

PERINBABA (Ladislav Muska, R. 1997). Sdlg. MALS-01. TB, 38" (97 cm), M. Heavily ruffled, lightly laced snow white self; beards light yellow, hairs tipped white; sweet fragrance. (Monte Albano x Laced Cotton) X "Snehulienka". Muska 1997.

PERKY BLUE (B. Charles Jenkins, R. 1995). Sdlg. BB50D. SPU, 32-39" (81-99 cm), M. S. and style arms blue violet; F. yellow signal blending to ivory ground, edged blue violet; ruffled, flared. B3-5B: (Crow Wing x Equality) X A26-28: (Ping and Pang -- white x Protege). Shepard Iris 1998.

PERKY PATRICK (J. Owings Rebert, R. 1999). Sdlg. CB-97-9. SIB, 28" (71 cm), ML. Purple, blending to violet, F. with ivory tan signal. Parentage unknown.

PERLE D'OR (Jean Peyrard, R. 1992). Sdlg. PM89/6a. MDB, 6" (15 cm), M. S. white; F. horizontally flaring, white with large yellow spot; beards white; slight fragrance. Petty Cash X Harry Hite.

PERLE ROSE (Jean Cayeux, R. 1990). Sdlg. 7916 B. TB, 34" (85 cm), EM. Lightly waved bright pink; beards pink. Vanity X (Coral Comments x 69125 B: (Pink Taffeta x Fashion Fling)). Cayeux 1988.

PERRIS GOLD (Bernard Hamner by Shepard Iris Garden, R. 1993). Sdlg. 85-05. TB, 38" (97 cm), E. Gold yellow self, F. edge fluted; beards dark orange. Golden Sparkler X Well Endowed. Hamner Iris, Shepard Iris 1993.

PERSEPHONE (Sterling Innerst, R. 1993). Sdlg. 1555-2. JI (6 F.), 36" (91 cm), M. Brilliant red violet, white area around full yellow signal. Yusho X Banners on Parade. Iris Pond 1994.

PERSIAN ACCENT (Lois Rich by James Whitely, R. 1991). Sdlg. R80-3A. AR (RC), 14-15" (36-38 cm), EM. S. white veined bright violet, violet midrib; style arms tan, orchid at throat; F. gold veined brown, bright violet rose overlay flowing toward edge, large black signal; beards black. Persian Pansy X R75-184B: (((Persian Bronze x (Kerr K55-1 x K55-14)) x (Bagdad Beauty x (*I. gatesii* x *I. hermona*))) x *I. stolonifera* USSR 163). Aril Patch, Aril Society 1991.

PERSIAN FLYER (Graeme Grosvenor, R. 1995). Sdlg. T8-1. BB, 26" (66 cm), M. S. lemon, slight violet dashing; style arms lemon; F. white, edged and dotted methyl violet, hafts olive brown; beards orange yellow; ruffled. Kiss of Gold X Armada. Rainbow Ridge 1995/96.

PERSIAN LANTERN (Mary Louise Dunderman, R. 1990). Sdlg. JJ153. MTB, 23" (58 cm), E. Red purple (RHS 61A), few gold haft veins, wine and cream signal; beards bright orange tipped orange; slight fragrance. DD233 dark red: (Y587 bright rose: (N662 salmon x Carolyn Rose) x unknown) X V122 RED: ((Monarda x E551) x (Daystar x Zingara)). Ohio Gardens 1991.

PERSIAN PEACE (Nathan Rudolph by Loleta Powell, R. 1991). Sdlg. 88-14. TB, 33" (84 cm), ML. Palest pinkish white; beards fire red tipped electric blue; ruffled. Parentage unknown. Powell's Gardens 1992.

PERSIAN WOOD (A. & D. Willott, R. 1996). Sdlg. 93-44. IB, 22" (56 cm), EM. S. light brown, midrib violet; style arms light brown; F. white, edged ecru, hafts brown, few violet dots; beards blue, bronze base and in throat; ruffled. North Coast X Chubby Cheeks. Willott 1996.

PERSIMMON PARASOL (John Durrance, R. 1991). Sdlg. D86-42. TB, 35" (89 cm), M. S. ruffled pinkish orange; style arms orange, laced; F. flaring persimmon orange. Shoot Out X Wild Oats. Long 1991.

PERT (Allan Ensminger, R. 1994). Sdlg. 90-6. SDB, 9" (23 cm), EML. S. flax blue (HCC 42/3); style arms bishops violet (34/2); F. flax blue, 1/8" bishops violet border; beards flax blue. Design X 86-9: (Shazam x Petite Polka). Varigay 1995.

PERTH SKY (T. J. Betts, R. 1995). Sdlg. 718L. LA, 48" (122 cm), ML. S. and F. violet blue (RHS 87A); white burst signals; style arms purple, centered green; petal edges crimped. Mac's Blue Heaven X La Perouse.

PERVY VALS (Liudmila Mironova, R. 1998). Sdlg. 3.13.94. JI (3 F.), 43-45" (110-115 cm), ML. S. purple, stitched white; style arms white, dusted blue; F. white with blue veining, signal yellow. Chayka X Vasili Alfiorov. DVO RAN 1999.

PETER JAMES (A.R.J. Bailey, R. 1996). Sdlg. S-JB-88-17. SDB, 10" (25 cm), ML. Ruffled dark lilac blue, F. with violet veining; beards white and orange; musky fragrance. Sudeley X Jeremy Brian.

PETITE BALLET (Keith Keppel, R. 1991). Sdlg. 83-3A. BB, 25" (64 cm), E. S. pale blue (M&P

42-AB-5) shaded white at base; F. white ground, 3/4" solid campanula (42-J-10) band paling (42-E-8) to narrow outer edge; beards white, tipped pale lemon in throat; pronounced sweet fragrance. 80-130F, Armada sib, X 80-130P, sib. Keppel 1992.

PETITE DOLL (Henry Rowlan, R. 1990). Sdlg. 83 T 11. MTB, 17" (43 cm), M. S. brown; F. brown on yellow ground; beards yellow. Fair Haldis X 81 T 2. Comanche Acres 1991.

PETITE EDITION (Hugh & Mary Thurman, R. 1995). Sdlg. 92-15-1. SDB, 12" (31 cm), M. S. white ground, heavily marked purple, midrib purple; style arms purple; F. white ground, 1/4" purple edge; beards pale lavender; ruffled; slight sweet fragrance. Court Magician X Chubby Cheeks. Kickapoo Gardens 1996.

PETITE LADY (Henry Rowlan, MTB, R. 1989). Comanche Acres 1990.

PETITE MONET (Katharine Steele, MTB, R. 1989). Vine & Branch 1990.

PETITE ONE (Henry Rowlan, MTB, R. 1989). Comanche Acres 1990.

PETITE PLIC (Carl Boswell, R. 1995). Sdlg. 107-85-S. SDB, 10" (25 cm), M. S. buff, dotted pale brown on edge; F. buff, dotted pale brown on hafts and edge; beards tan. Quilting Bee X Tan-a-Maroon. Adamgrove 1996.

PETITE SHADOW (A. & D. Willott, R. 1999). Sdlg. W 91-55. MDB, 5" (13 cm), EM. Dark purple, F. with darker area around purple beard. Jewel Baby X Buttons.

PET NAME (Joseph Ghio, R. 1996). Sdlg. PE-176E. CA, 12" (31 cm), ML. Tawny peach self, F. with yellow halo signal. PG-156-K2: (PI-211J: (Black Eye sib x (Los Padres x (Elberta Peach sib x San Tomas sib))) x PI-MIX-R, unknown) X PG-177-M2: (PI-MIX-A, unknown, x Valet sib). Bay View 1996.

PETRA (Manfred Beer, R. 1991). Sdlg. MB 15/81A. TB, 43" (110 cm), M. Red violet, lighter around yellow beards. Margarita X Alstersegel. Gartencenter Kania 1991.

PETTICOATS AND LACE (Jim Hedgecock, R. 1990). Sdlg. 85-213-1. TB, 34" (86 cm), M. Heavily laced and ruffled pale pink; beards pale tangerine; sweet fragrance. Social Register X Beaux Arts. Comanche Acres 1995.

PEWTER TREASURE (John Durrance, R. 1994). Sdlg. D91W-6. TB, 36" (91 cm), M. Grey blue, F. with green rim. Parentage unknown. Long 1994.

PHAETON (Marky Smith, R. 1992). Sdlg. 89-47 A. TB, 38" (96 cm), M. S. strong yellow; F. more intense yellow (RHS 12A), some white netting around orange (25A) beards; ruffled. Bold Gold X Gold Country. Aitken's Salmon Creek 1997.

PHANTASY IN PINK (Virginia Messick, R. 1999). Sdlg. M89-71. TB, 36" (91 cm), M. S. pink; F. lighter pink, deeper pink rim; beards coral; heavily laced. Romantic Mood X Magic. Messick 1999.

PHANTOM KISS (Ben Hager, R. 1992). Sdlg. SD5184GyBld. SDB, 14" (36 cm), M. Ruffled olive white with faint lavender highlights throughout, tinged and lightly veined olive green on edge of F. and hafts, S. color gradually changing halfway up to gilt glint; self beards softly tipped light bronze. SD4999GrY: (Naiad x SD4449GrSf: ((((Joy Bringer x Ornament) x Spangles sib) x Flirty Mary) x (((((Derring-Do x (Nest Egg x Brassie)) x Zing) x Golden Fair) x April Fool) x Baby Blessed))) X SD4897Gr#1: ((Flirty Mary x Crystal Bubbles) x SD4449GrYSpSh). Adamgrove 1993.

PHANTOM MASQUERADE (Donald Spoon, R. 1997). Sdlg. 87-5A. TB, 45" (114 cm), ML.Lightly ruffled purple black, some white ray patterning around purple black beards. Superstition X Night Owl. Winterberry 1997.

PHANTOM MIST (Jim Hedgecock, R. 1993). Sdlg. 84-1-T. TB, 38" (97 cm), M. Lightly laced and ruffled blue violet, streaked and shaded darker; beards burnt gold; slight sweet fragrance. Sky Hooks X Soul Music. Comanche Acres 1994.

PHARAOH'S SPIRIT (Barry Blyth, R. 1997). Sdlg. D64-2. TB, 38" (97 cm), EM. S. apricot bisque, slight lavender midrib veining; F. blended lilac over cream on outer portion, changing to bright rosy plum in center; beards tangerine, violet at end; slight fragrance. Plume d'Or X A153-5, Cafe Risque sib. Tempo Two 1997/98.

#PHEASANT FEATHERS (Larry Gaulter, TB, R. 1980). Listed as introduced 1981, but entire stock lost prior to distribution. No stock in existence and name released.

PHEASANT FEATHERS (Larry Johnson, R. 1999). Sdlg. JO91-67A. TB, 45" (114 cm), ML. S. tan; F. violet, brown shoulders and rim; beards gold; slight sweet fragrance. Jovial Vagabond sib X Impressionist. Cooley 1999.

PHILANDERER (Barry Blyth, R. 1990). Sdlg. W25-1. IB, 22" (56 cm), VE-M. S. tan, infused red at base of midrib; F. velvety ruby; beards old gold, prominent. Kinetic X T 100-A: (Chinese Treasure x Beachgirl). Tempo Two 1990/91.

PHIL EDINGER (Ben Hager, R. 1991). SPEC-X, 36" (91 cm), E. S. maroon tinge over yellow; F. yellow radially veined brown, prominent brown signal; 30+" glossy deep green foliage. Holden Clough X -- probably self. Melrose 1991.

PHILIPPA MARY (Revie Harvey, R. 1993). Sdlg. 84-RC-C. IB, 22-24" (56-61 cm), E. Pale lavender, F. with pale gold haft infusion, lightly crimped; beards medium lavender. Real Coquette X Commentary.

PHILIP ROWE (Cy Bartlett, R. 1990). Sdlg. CC-JP-JT-P2. TB, 34" (86 cm), EML. Ruffled lemon yellow; beards cream. (Cannington Creamery x (Jeanne Price x Joyce Terry)) X Paradise. Sutton 1996.

PHIL KEEN (Cy Bartlett, R. 1994). Sdlg. C91-55. TB, 37" (94 cm), M. Deep violet purple self; beards purple; sweet fragrance. Cosmic Dance X Pledge Allegiance. Kelways 1998.

PHILOSOPHY (Joseph Ghio, R. 1995). Sdlg. PF-183-1. CA, 16" (41 cm), L. Blue violet, F. with slight turquoise flush. PH-283-O: (National Anthem x ((Solid Citizen x (Lighthouse Point x Mission Santa Cruz)) x Western World)) X Sierra Dell. Bay View 1995.

PHIL'S PICK (Duane Meek, R. 1998). Sdlg. 444-1-5. TB, 36" (91 cm), M. S. and style arms deep orange; F. dark orange, brownish infusion; beards tangerine orange. Marmalade X Orange Star. D & J Gardens 1998.

PHOENIX FIRE (Chet Tompkins, R. 1996). Sdlg. 93-45. TB, 38" (97 cm), M-VL. Bright copper and brass blend; beards copper to brass. ((Hot Pinata x Leo Nyne) x (Syncopation x Masada)) X Air Bubbles. Fleur de Lis 1996.

PHOENIX RED VELVET (Beverly Dopke, LA, R. 1987). Shepard Iris 1990.

PHOTO OP (Paul Black, R. 1999). Sdlg. 91353A. IB, 18" (46 cm), E. Orchid, F. edged paler, style arms with beige sides; beards light violet, gold in throat; slight musky fragrance. Midnight Madness X 8840A: (((Betty Simon x Magic Candle) x (Tequila Sunrise sib x Entourage)) x (Frances Gaulter x Sky Hooks)). Mid-America 1999.

PHYLIS (Sandra Underwood by Louise Smith, R. 1991). Sdlg. 85-100. TB, 39" (99 cm), EM. Ruffled white; beards orange, tipped white; slight sweet fragrance. Tufted Cloud X unknown.

PIANO BAR MELODIES (David Miller, R. 1998). Sdlg. 92-20A. TB, 35" (89 cm), EM. S. violet purple (RHS 88B), midrib highlighted white; style arms light lavender; F. white, 1/4" lavender purple band, shoulders darker and browner; beards white, light yellow in throat; slight musky fragrance. Rumbleseat X 85-1B: (Roundup x Crinoline). Long 1999.

PIANO BAR PIRATE (Chris Vizvarie, R. 1991). Sdlg. IB-BB-1. IB, 18" (45 cm), M. Clear light blue lavender; beards dark blue, tipped blue; slight sweet fragrance. Parentage unknown. Last Scent Farm 1994.

PIBBLING (Sterling Innerst, R. 1993). Sdlg. 3530-5. SDB, 12" (30 cm), ML. White, trimmed mulberry plum; beards blue, tipped bronze. Hee Haw X Chubby Cheeks. Innerst 1994.

PICANTE (Joseph Ghio, R. 1996). Sdlg. 92-98P2. TB, 38" (97 cm), M. Rosy red fuchsia self; beards tangerine. 90-102K: (Quito x (((((Louise Watts x (Ghost Story x Ponderosa)) x 76-37F: (Ballet in Orange x 73-122Z: (Hi Top x ((Ponderosa x Travel On) x Peace Offering)))) x (Blaze of Fire x 76-37F)) x ((((Flareup x 73-122Z) x 76-37F) x (Preface sib x (Old Flame x Pink Angel)))) x (76-110B x Toastmaster))) x Caracas)) X 90-132B: ((((Lady Friend x (Flareup x (Capitation x Coffee House))) x Battle Hymn sib) x ((Homecoming Queen x 76-110B: ((Malaysia x Carolina Honey) x 73-122Z)) x Esmeralda sib)) x ((Romantic Mood sib x 82-16G3, pod parent of Bygone Era) x Lightning Bolt)). Bay View 1997.

PICASSO PRINT (A. & D. Willott, R. 1990). Sdlg. 88-31. SDB, 10" (25 cm), EM. Ruffled cream with red violet splashes intensifying to red violet border; beards orange. Nachos X Pilgrims' Choice. Willott 1991.

PICCO (Barry Blyth, R. 1997). Sdlg. D34-2. SDB, 10-12" (26-30 cm), EM. S. bishops violet; F. bishops violet, hafts deeper violet, small white area near beard; beards white, tipped tangerine. Bee's Knees X A7-1: (Merry Dance x Mini Song). Tempo Two 1997/98.

PICKING TIME (James Bingham, R. 1995). Sdlg. 84-2-6. TB, 34" (86 cm), ML. S. white; F. white, hafts with hint of gold yellow; beards gold yellow, tipped white. Columbia Blue X Playgirl. Pennyroyal Gardens 1996.

PICNIC DAY (John Baldwin, R. 1994). Sdlg. 80-11A. TB, 36" (91 cm), ML. Imperial purple (RHS 78B); beards light red; slight sweet fragrance. Vanity X 77-2A: (Como Queen x Pink Angel).

PICOTEE PRINCESS (Lorena Reid, R. 1991). Sdlg. 87J24 (6 8/9-1). JI (6 F.), 48" (123 cm), M. Ruffled white, sanded violet blue (RHS 91B), heavier at edge, signal greenish yellow; style arms 3-5, making tuft in center. Garnet Royalty X Summer Splash. Laurie's Garden 1992.

PICTURE THIS (Richard Ernst, R. 1993). Sdlg. HR8545-6. TB, 38" (97 cm), M. S. cream with mauve blend; F. medium lavender rose with bluish stripe at end of beard; beards orange yellow, tipped blue white; laced, lightly ruffled; slight sweet fragrance. R8545: (Edith Wolford x Merry Madrigal) X unknown. Cooley 1993.

PIECES OF ICE (Roger Nelson, TB, R. 1985). Iris Country 1990.

PIEDMONT BLUE (John Wood, R. 1992). SIB, 28" (71 cm), M. Velvety violet blue (RHS 93B) self. Big Blue X Tycoon. John Wood 1993.

PIEKNA NIEZNAJOMA (Lech Komarnicki, R. 1999). Sdlg. BIS 94/5-25c set. SPEC (*setosa*), 22" (55 cm), M. Purple, conspicuous yellow median stripe on upper 2/3 of F. Parentage unknown; seed from British Iris Society seed exchange.

PIERO BARGELLINI (Augusto Bianco, R. 1998). Sdlg. 503. TB, 37" (95 cm), EM. S. apricot melon, center peach; style arms apricot; F. oyster white, edge and hafts apricot; beards tangerine, lighter at end; slight spicy fragrance. (Spirit of Memphis x Soap Opera) X Sunny and Warm. Iride 1998.

PIGEON (Ben Hager, SDB, R. 1987). Correction of parentage. Just Dandy X SD3429LvBl: (((Hello x (Sunny Heart x ((Evening Storm x Welch H501) x (Sulina x Melodrama)))) x (Peanuts x Blueberry Muffins)) x Bluetween).

PIGGY BANK (Paul Black, R. 1996). Sdlg. 91312A. SDB, 14" (36 cm), E. S. and style arms coral pink; F. coral pink, lightly blended violet; beards whitish coral, coral pink in throat; pronounced musky fragrance. Broken Halo sib X 88267A: ((Caesura x (Betsey Boo x (Antique Satin x Encanto))) x (Gigglepot x Oriental Blush)). Mid-America 1996.

PIKI (Frances Love, R. 1993). Sdlg. 25/10/3. IB, 19" (48 cm), M. S. white; F. white with touch of yellow deep on hafts; beards white, yellow in throat. Parentage unknown.

PILGRIMS' CHOICE (A. & D. Willott, R. 1990). Sdlg. 84-34. SDB, 12" (31 cm), M. S. blend of grey blue and ecru; F. light violet blue, edged S. color; beards bright violet blue; ruffled. Royal Silk X Michael Paul. Willott 1990.

PILGRIM'S QUEST (Franklin Carr, R. 1990). Sdlg. 87-77. TB, 36" (91 cm), M. S. light bluish violet, darker in throat, violet veining; F. white, bluish violet in throat; beards white, yellow in throat; slight musky fragrance. Edge of Winter X Flair. W. & M. Griner 1999.

PILLOW FIGHT (Duane Meek, R. 1995). Sdlg. R21-1-8. TB, 34" (86 cm), EM. S. soft pink; F. soft pink at edge, merging to ivory below beard; beards melon, lavender blue at end; ruffled, laced. Magic X Sugartime. D & J Gardens 1995.

PINBALL WIZARD (Larry Lauer, R. 1999). Sdlg. 91-184. TB, 35" (89 cm), M. S. bronze yellow; style arms bronze yellow, shaded oxblood red; F. oxblood red; beards mustard yellow, darker tip; ruffled; pronounced musky fragrance. L88-92: ((Howdy Folks x Frances Gaulter) x Tiger Butter) X 88-43-1: (Jazz Echo x Mixed Doubles). Lauer's Flowers 1999.

PINEAPPLE BLUSH (Polly Black, R. 1993). Sdlg. ESAA1. TB, 36" (91 cm), M. S. blushed peach; F. cream, copper veining on shoulder, copper midrib, lighter laced rim on edge; beards orange; slight fragrance. Apricot Blaze X Dawn Delight. Polly Black 1993.

PINES (Eric Tankesley-Clarke, SDB, R. 1988). Adamgrove 1993.

PINEWOOD AMETHYST (R. A. Wise, R. 1991). Sdlg. 2/88. CA, 12" (30 cm), M. Amethyst. San Lorenzo X Banbury Velvet. V. H. Humphrey 1993.

PINEWOOD CHARMER (R. A. Wise, R. 1994). Sdlg. 6/89. CA, 12" (30 cm), M. Yellow and pink blend, F. with yellow center. San Lorenzo X unknown. V. H. Humphrey 1995.

PINEWOOD DAZZLER (R. A. Wise, R. 1996). Sdlg. 8/94. CA, 12" (30 cm), M. S. chrome yellow (RHS 14D); F. buttercup yellow (15B), yellow signal. Pinewood Sunshine X unknown.

PINEWOOD ELEGANCE (R. A. Wise, R. 1996). Sdlg. 11/96. CA, 18" (45 cm), L. S. purple; F. deeper purple, edged lighter, signal yellow. 17/92: (Arnold Sunrise x Pinewood Amethyst) X Idylwild.

PINEWOOD POPPET (R. A. Wise, R. 1994). Sdlg. 4/89. CA, 10" (25 cm), M. S. white, purple mark in center; F. white, yellow signal with purple halo. San Lorenzo X unknown. V. H. Humphrey 1995.

PINEWOOD PRELUDE (R. A. Wise, R. 1996). Sdlg. 1/88. CA, 12" (30 cm), L. Smoky pinkish mauve, F. with yellow signal. San Lorenzo X unknown.

PINEWOOD SUNSHINE (R. A. Wise, R. 1994). Sdlg. 15/89. CA, 12" (30 cm), L. S. yellow; F. deep yellow center shading to cream edge. San Lorenzo X -- probably No Name. V. H. Humphrey 1995.

PINK-ALL-OVER (Kenneth Fisher, R. 1998). Sdlg. 94-3. MTB, 24" (61 cm), M. Medium pink self;

beards reddish pink. TN8: (Abridged Version x TC5: (((Buenita x Amethyst Sunset) x (White Canary x Slim Jim)) x (Puppy Love x Pink Kewpie))) X T. Varner 0-117: (Varner N-101: (Puppy Love x Little Susie) x Hager 3797-2: ((Louise Hopper x ((New Idea x 2271A) x 2271A: ((Seventh Heaven sdlg. x (Frenchi x Pagoda)) x 1242F: (666: (Norah x Thisbe) x sib)))) x (((New Idea x 1242F) x ((666 x Glittering Amber) x Glittering Amber sdlg.)) x ((666 x (Frenchi x Pagoda)) x 1242F)))). Aitken's Salmon Creek 1999.

PINK BLINK (J. T. Aitken, R. 1993). Sdlg. 87M32. MDB, 6" (15 cm), ML. S. pink; F. pink, light lavender veins at pink beard; slight fragrance. (Live Jazz x (80-8A x B. Jones M-304)) X (Wright L56: ((Pink Cushion x Lenna M) x Cotton Blossom) x B. Jones M-271). Aitken's Salmon Creek 1993.

PINK BLOOMER (John Durrance, R. 1992). Sdlg. D86-40. TB, 35" (89 cm), M. Laced pale buff pink, slightly lighter in center of F.; beards two-toned, tipped violet, orange in throat. Love Scene X Hamblen 81-16B. Long 1992.

PINK BLUE GENES (O. D. Niswonger, TB, R. 1989). Cape Iris 1990.

PINK BLUSH (O. D. Niswonger, R. 1999). Sdlg. 43-95. TB, 32" (81 cm), M. S. white, slight pink midrib blush; style arms white; F. white, pink haft blush; beards tangerine, white base and end. Be a Dream X Wish. Cape Iris 1999.

PINK BO PEEP (Marvin Granger, R. 1994). Sdlg. 82-5C. LA, 21" (54 cm), M. S. light pink; style arms greenish yellow; F. pink, greenish yellow signal patch; slight spicy fragrance. *I. brevicaulis* dark purple X BR77-23: (69-1: ((Bramble Queen x pink sdlg.) x Louisiana Sambo) x Charlie's Michele).

PINK BUTTONS (Carol Lankow by J. T. Aitken, R. 1996). Sdlg. 8L96. MTB (tet.), 22" (56 cm), ML. Light pink; beards tipped coral red, base yellow. Ozark Evening X (Abridged Version x Greensleeves). Aitken's Salmon Creek 1996.

PINK CADILLAC (George Sutton, R. 1999). Sdlg. G-78. BB, 26" (66 cm), M-VL & RE. Pale pink (RHS 56D), F. veined darker; style arms slightly deeper (56C); beards pink, hairs tipped coral; heavily laced, ruffled; slight sweet fragrance. F-248: (Pink Bubbles x Lenora Pearl) X 2-14: (Pink Ember x Playgirl).

PINK CANOPY (George Bush, JI, R. 1989). Bush 1990.

PINK CARESSES (Donald Spoon, R. 1997). Sdlg. 90-141C. TB, 28" (71 cm), ML. Ruffled peach pink self; beards darker peach pink; flared. Romantic Mood X Pink Pink.

PINK CAT (Cloyd McCord, R. 1996). Sdlg. 00-93. TB, 40" (102 cm), E. Ruffled and laced rich pink; style arms light pink; beards light orange; sweet fragrance. Quadros' Pride X Pink Swan. McCord 1996.

PINK CHARMING (Joseph Ghio, R. 1992). Sdlg. 88-11D. TB, 36" (91 cm), EM. Light pink with heather plicata markings on F.; beards tangerine. (Romanticist x 82-113G, Chuckles sib) X Storyline. Bay View 1993.

PINK COLCHICUM (Siegmar Goerbitz, R. 1991). Sdlg. 7940 B11. TB, 39" (100 cm), M. Light violet pink; beards light violet red; sweet fragrance. Silver Shower X Rondo. Schoeppinger 1992.

PINK CUPID (Vernon Wood, R. 1993). Sdlg. 9121. CA, 11" (28 cm), EM. S. pink (RHS 56B), red purple (64B) centerline; F. pink (56B) with some red purple (64B) lines nearly solid in center, and halfway down, with small bright yellow spot at tip of center pattern. 89-7: (Roaring Camp x 87-9) X Riva. Portable Acres 1993.

PINK DACE (Jill Copeland, JI, R. 1988). Ensata Gardens 1993.

PINK DAMSEL (Akihiko Terada, R. 1999). Sdlg. 252-11. TB, 34" (86 cm), M. Laced pink self, green haft infusion; beards orange. Vision in Pink X Affluence. Roris 1999.

PINK DANCER (Vernon Wood, R. 1994). Sdlg. 92-48. TB, 35-38" (89-97 cm), M. Neyron rose (RHS 56B) self; beards tangerine pink; ruffled. Bubble Up X 88-84: (((Mais Oui x Carved Pink) x Blushing Pink) x (Pink Belle x ((Pink Attire x Pink Persian) x ((Princess x Pink Taffeta) x Carved Pink)))). Stockton 1995.

PINK DESIGN (Donald Spoon, R. 1997). Sdlg. 90-131C. TB, 34" (86 cm), ML. Ruffled baby ribbon pink self; beards dark pink; flared. Custom Made X Waurine. Winterberry 1997.

PINK ELF (O. D. Niswonger, R. 1994). Sdlg. SDB 8-91. SDB, 10" (25 cm), M. S. pale pink; F. blue pink with dark blue streak below blue beard. Tell Fibs X SDB 3-88: (Peach Bavarian x Peach Eyes). Cape Iris 1994.

PINK EMPRESS (Cleo Palmer, IB, R. 1989). Palmer's Iris 1990.

PINKERTON (Bob Bauer/John Coble, R. 1998). Sdlg. J93-K-4. JI (6 F.), 36" (91 cm), M. Pink, opening from red pink buds; style arms cream, edges and crests pink. Sakura-No-Sono X Hime Kagami. Ensata Gardens 1999.

PINK FANTASY (Pavel Nejedlo, R. 1998). Sdlg. RMFLN-92-3B. TB, 39" (100 cm), ML. Heavily ruffled medium pink; beards coral red; pronounced sweet fragrance. (Romantic Mood x Fantasy Lace) X Natascha N.

PINK FAWN (John Weiler, R. 1993). Sdlg. 87-49-3RE. SDB, 9" (23 cm), ML & RE. Pinkish tan with some slightly darker texture veining on F.; beards blue, tangerine deep in throat. 85-5-1RE: (79-20-1RE: ((70-95-3: (Brighteyes x Grace Note) x Gingerbread Man) x Stockholm) x Leprechaun's Delight) X 84-43-5RE: (((((Yellow Wave x 70-95-2) x 74-3-1: (Cartwheel x 70-95-6)) x Chariots) x 79-20-1RE) x (((Ruby Locket x Little Blackfoot) x ((70-95-3 x Bronze Babe) x 74-3-1)) x Pink Amber)). Rialto 1993.

PINK FLAMINGOS (Paul Black, R. 1993). Sdlg. 879A. TB, 34" (86 cm), E. S. clear pink; F. coral salmon pink blend, slightly darker haft veining; ruffled; slight spicy fragrance. Blazing Sunrise X 8510A: ((Heather Blush x P. Dyer sdlg.: (Peach Spot x Outer Limits)) x Tropical Tempo). Mid-America 1993.

PINK GALA (Vernon Wood, TB, R. 1989). Cottage 1990.

PINK GIGGLES (Terrell Taylor, R. 1996). Sdlg. 93-55. TB, 32" (82 cm), M. Ruffled venetian pink (RHS 49C) with salmon influence; beards tangerine; slight fragrance. Cold Cold Heart X Sweet Musette. Hermosa Gardens 1996.

PINK HEART (Ben Hager by Roris Gardens, R. 1993). Sdlg. T5049-9. TB, 37" (94 cm), M. Ruffled and laced pink self; beards tangerine. T4127: (Paradise x T3557: (Kindness x (Carved Cameo x Vanity))) X (Anna Belle Babson x Muchas Gracias). Roris 1993.

PINK HUGS (Donald Spoon, R. 1997). Sdlg. 92-181. TB, 28" (71 cm), ML. Ruffled baby ribbon pink self; beards dark pink; flared. Femme Fatale X Pink Pink.

PINKIE PAWS (Lynda Miller, R. 1991). Sdlg. 3187C. SDB, 10" (25 cm), M. S. orchid pink; F. pink, cocoa pink spot; beards pale blue, coral in throat. 3184A: ((E. Roberts sdlg. x unknown) x Baby Pink) X 4284A: (Pink Kitten x Inscription). Miller's Manor 1992.

PINK JADE (Joseph Gatty, TB, R. 1988). Correction of parentage. Playgirl X Bonbon.

PINK JUBILEE (Cleo Palmer, R. 1992). Sdlg. 8549. SDB, 12" (30 cm), M. Baby ribbon pink with deeper pink veining on F. hafts; beards pink. 8122: (Miss Oklahoma x (Dove Wings x 7259)) X 8134: (Show Baby x ((Lenna M x Prophecy) x Dove Wings)). Palmer's Iris 1992.

PINK KISSES (Donald Spoon, R. 1995). Sdlg. 90-141A. TB, 30" (76 cm), ML. Baby ribbon pink self; beards pinkish tangerine; heavily ruffled, flared. Romantic Mood X Pink Pink. Winterberry 1998.

PINK LENOX (George Sutton, R. 1995). Sdlg. C-70. TB, 38" (97 cm), M. Porcelain white infused lavender pink (nearest to RHS 62D); beards amethyst (79C); ruffled. Twice Thrilling X Caption. Sutton 1996.

PINK LIPS (George Bush, JI, R. 1989). Bush 1990.

PINK MILLENNIUM (Oscar Schick, R. 1999). Sdlg. 91-25A02. TB, 36-38" (91-97 cm), M. Ruffled medium pink self; beards pinkish orange; slight musky fragrance. McKay X Delicate Balance.

PINK MOON (Donald Spoon, R. 1995). TB, 30" (76 cm), M. Baby ribbon pink self, slight peach F. haft infusion; beards darker baby ribbon pink; ruffled, laced. Parentage unknown.

PINK MYSTERY (Walter Marx by Currier McEwen, JI, R. 1988). Laurie's Garden, Seaways 1990.

PINK NIGHTIE (Paul Black, R. 1991). Sdlg. 85112A. TB, 34" (86 cm), M. S. medium pink; F. slightly paler pink; beards coral tangerine. Love Sonnet X Verbena Moon. Mid-America 1991.

#PINK PARADE (G. Lapham, TB, R. 1938). Not introduced; name released.

PINK PARADE (Pavel Nejedlo, R. 1998). Sdlg. FFRM-92-1. TB, 38" (97 cm), M. S. and style arms light peach; F. lighter creamy peach pink blend; beards deep coral; laced; slight sweet fragrance. Fantasy Lace X Romantic Mood.

PINK PARCHMENT (Cy Bartlett, R. 1995). Sdlg. DD-OS-BF-1. BB, 26" (66 cm), ML. S. pink, midrib flushed violet; F. parchment white, bleeding to pink at edge; beards rusty orange; ruffled; slight sweet fragrance. (Double Dip x Orchidarium sdlg.) X Battle Fury.

PINK PEBBLES (Beryl Pederick, R. 1994). Sdlg. 1. TB, 35" (89 cm), M. Shell pink (HCC 516/3) self; beards red; slight fragrance. Pink Angel X Wish.

PINK PELE (J. T. Aitken, R. 1996). Sdlg. 90M38. IB, 25" (64 cm), ML. Pink (varying to orange at times), F. with purple spot; beards coral red. Pele X Marmalade Skies. Aitken's Salmon Creek 1996.

PINK PINK (Donald Spoon, R. 1995). Sdlg. 88-5. TB, 30" (76 cm), ML. Opalescent baby ribbon pink (RHS 32D) self, slightly paler F. center; beards tangerine pink (32B); lightly ruffled, laced. Custom Made X Waurine. Winterberry 1999.

PINK POTSY (Leo Barnard, R. 1997). Sdlg. L 92-16. SDB, 10-12" (25-31 cm), VL. S. and style arms peppermint pink, darker pink veining; F. peppermint pink, large raspberry signal; beards salmon pink; slight fragrance. Mary's Lamb X Bright Vision. Paradise Iris 1997.

PINK PREVUE (Bennett Jones, R. 1990). Sdlg. 349-1. SDB, 10" (25 cm), M. Peach (HCC 412) with salmon F. spot; beards pink; sweet fragrance. 304: (229-2: (Roberts 65R11 x 201) x Melon Honey) X 271: ((Roberts 65R10 x Roberts 70R32) x 229). Bennett Jones 1991.

PINK PROLIFIC (Leslie Donnell, R. 1997). Sdlg. 90-1-7. TB, 32" (81 cm), M. Pink self; beards red; pronounced spicy fragrace. 88-4-3: ((Pink Petticoat x Rosabelle V.) x Hampton Glory) X 86-12-5: (Rosabelle V. x Pink Petticoat).

PINK PUPPY (Donald Spoon, R. 1997). Sdlg. 93-10C. BB, 24" (61 cm), EM & RE. S. baby ribbon pink, peach pink toward edge; style arms peach pink; F. rose pink, darker veins, peach pink edging; beards tangerine, white base and outer end; ruffled, flared. Roney's Encore X Ozark Evening.

PINK QUARTZ (Vernon Wood, R. 1995). Sdlg. W 93-93. TB, 35-37" (89-94 cm), ML. Pink self (near RHS 56B); beards tangerine; ruffled, lightly laced. Sib to Pink Dancer. Stockton 1996.

PINK REPRISE (Walter Moores, R. 1991). Sdlg. 86-16. BB, 26" (66 cm), EM & RE (Oct./MS). Lightly ruffled peach pink; beards saturn red. Pink Sachet X Peach Reprise. Moores 1991.

PINK REVELRY (O. D. Niswonger, R. 1998). Sdlg. SDB 11-95. SDB, 11" (28 cm), M. Deep pink, F. slightly lighter; beards blue. SDB 24-91: (SDB 27-87: (Oriental Blush x unknown) x Tillie) X Chanted. Cape Iris 1998.

PINK RINGLETS (J. T. Aitken, R. 1995). Sdlg. 90J-11. JI (6 F.), 34" (86 cm), ML. White, flushed pink toward edges; style arms white, edged pink. (Asian Warrior x Ruby Star) X Ruby Star. Aitken's Salmon Creek 1995.

PINK SAPPHIRE (Melba Hamblen, TB, R. 1989). Roris 1992.

PINK SMASH (O. D. Niswonger, R. 1998). Sdlg. SDB 33-93. SDB, 12" (31 cm), ML. Pink self, slight white area near beard; beards pale blue, tangerine in throat. Ballet Lesson X Chanted. Cape Iris 1998.

PINK STARLET (Vernon Wood, R. 1992). Sdlg. 87-41. TB, 35-37" (89-94 cm), M. Ruffled and laced pink (RHS 56B/C); beards tangerine. Pink Belle X 82-38: ((Mais Oui x Carved Pink) x Blushing Pink). Cottage 1993.

PINK TEMPTATION (Stan Dexter by Marie Ingersoll, R. 1994). Sdlg. A16-6-129A. TB, 38" (97 cm), EM. Blush pink, F. with tan haft and center overlay; beards pinkish tangerine. Freda Laura X Today's Fashion. Ingersoll's Iris 1995.

PINK THEME (Flora Brile, R. 1990). Sdlg. 5-89. TB, 33" (84 cm), M. Ruffled pink; beards pink. Entourage X One Desire.

PINK TWILIGHT (O. D. Niswonger, R. 1998). Sdlg. SDB 12-94. SDB, 12" (31 cm), M. Mauve pink self; beards purple. Yat Rock X Chanted. Cape Iris 1998.

PIONEER PINK (Jim & Vicki Craig, R. 1996). Sdlg. C93Z2. MTB (tet.), 23" (58 cm), EM. Clean pale pink self; beards pale yellow. 17W3, Rave Review sib, X 26V6: (4R10: (9N2: ((En Route x Pink Taffeta) x (New Moon x (Sacred Mountain x *aphylla* "Werckmeister"))) x Little Sunrise) x Hager AMT3795WPk: ((AMTPk x Audacious sib) x Puppy Love)). J. & V. Craig 1996.

PIOTR ZABRODIN (Viacheslav Gavrilin, R. 1999). Sdlg. 2-1-1-94. TB, 37" (94 cm), EM. S. light orchid pink, base darker, midrib lilac; style arms orchid pink; F. dark orchid to raspberry pink, light pink pattern around orange red beard; ruffled. Fiesta Time X Starcrest. Gavrilin 1999.

PIPELINE (George Sutton, R. 1998). Sdlg. G-69. TB, 34" (86 cm), ML. Ruffled cerulein blue (RHS 107A) self; beards cerulein blue, 1½" cerulein blue upside down spoon. Dauber's Delight X Busy Being Blue.

PIPIT (Ben Hager, R. 1992). Sdlg. MD5496YRdSp. MDB, 5-7" (13-18 cm), EML. Light yellow, reddish feathered signal; beards darker yellow. Nestling X AMD4972YBrSp#1, Jiffy sib. Adamgrove 1993.

PIQUANT FANCY (Lorena Reid, R. 1996). Sdlg. 8S54-1B3. SIB (sino-sib), 60-66" (152-168 cm), M. S. white, dark purple center with lines fanning out to near edge; style arms dark purple, light tips and slightly pinkish light center ridge; F. pale yellow to white, large gold signal bisected by multiple dark purple dashed lines which pale outside signal; dark purple triangle at lower end of F. Enbee Deeaych X yellow *I. delavayi* hybrid #1. Laurie's Garden 1996.

PIRATE'S PATCH (Paul Black, R. 1994). Sdlg. 91289B. SDB, 12" (30 cm), E. Bishops purple, darker around beards; beards purple, tipped lighter; pronounced spicy fragrance. Sigh X Cheery Delight. Mid-America 1994.

PIRATE'S QUEST (Schreiner, R. 1991). Sdlg. T 1321-1. TB, 36" (91 cm), M. Aureolin yellow (RHS 3A), white signal; self beards. Unknown X Well Endowed. Schreiner 1992.

PITTER PATTER (William Maryott, R. 1994). Sdlg. S235C. SDB, 9" (23 cm), M. S. white; F. white with true blue thumbprint on either side of beard; beards white, yellow deep in throat. Pippi Longstockings X Fingerprints. Maryott 1995.

PIXIE DELIGHT (Keith Fillmore, R. 1993). Sdlg. 8619-1 SDB. SDB, 9" (23 cm), EM. S. violet (RHS 86C) with stitching along edge, lighter toward midrib; F. white ground stitched violet along edge, violet haft markings; beards white, flecked violet; pronounced sweet fragrance. 8305-1: (8007 x self) X self. Bar K Iris 1993.

PIXIE KISSES (A. & D. Willott, R. 1999). Sdlg. W 94-17. MDB, 4" (10 cm), E. White ground, lightly stitched red violet; style arms light violet; beards white; lightly ruffled. Sand Run X Cretica. Willott 1999.

PIXIE PIRATE (A. & D. Willott, R. 1997). Sdlg. W 91-62. MDB, 5" (13 cm), EM. S. and style arms dark violet; F. velvety very dark violet; beards pale blue at end, changing from white to cream in throat. Dark Vader X What Not. Willott 1997.

#PIXIE'S SISTER (A. & D. Willott, SDB, R. 1984). Stock destroyed and name transferred.

PIXIE'S SISTER (A. & D. Willott, R. 1999). Sdlg. W 91-60. MDB, 5" (13 cm), E. White ground, stitched red violet; style arms pale violet, midrib deeper; beards cream; lightly ruffled. Sand Run X Cretica. Willott 1999.

PIXIE TALES (Darlene Pinegar, R. 1991). Sdlg. GS-1-1. BB, 22" (56 cm), EML. S. light lavender blue; F. medium lavender blue, veined and flushed darker, hafts mulberry; beards old gold, tipped lavender blue; lightly ruffled; slight sweet fragrance. Ghost Story X Dusky Evening. Spanish Fork 1992.

PIXIE TIME (Barry Blyth, R. 1993). Sdlg. W149-1. SPU, 24" (61 cm), M. Tan gold, veined deep brown overall. Satinwood X self. Tempo Two 1993/94.

PIXIE TRICKS (Ben Hager, R. 1991). Sdlg. MD5127Pc. MDB, 7" (18 cm), EM. S. pale apricot cream lightly speckled lavender purple; F. pale apricot ground, brown plicata markings on hafts and halfway down; beards cream, tipped tangerine, heavier in throat. Sib to Fairy Lore. Adamgrove 1992.

PIXIE WON (Jill Copeland, R. 1997). Sdlg. PXE-1. SPEC-X, 12-18" (31-46 cm), E. S. spectrum violet (RHS 82B), small and rounded; style arms cream (158C), slight violet at tip; F. spectrum violet, lighter (82C) around sulphur yellow (6B) signal, darker pansy violet (83A) thin line edging signal; foliage yellow green. *I. pseudacorus* white sdlg. X *I. ensata* double purple sdlg. Ensata Gardens 1997.

PIXILATED (Sharon McAllister, R. 1995). Sdlg. 91-36-1. AB (OGB-), 28" (71 cm), EM. S. yellow and soft pink blend, blushed pale pinkish lavender; style arms lemon yellow; F. lemon yellow lightly blushed pinkish violet, burgundy spot surrounding yellow orange beard, burgundy lines extending downward from tip. 86-6-6: (Granted Wish x Sunrise in Glory) X Persian Smoke. McAllister 1996.

PIZZICATO (Donald Spoon, R. 1997). Sdlg. 92-53A. TB, 36" (91 cm), M. Medium blue lavender, F. paling toward edge; beards darker blue lavender, hairs tipped gold; ruffled. G'Day Mate X Honky Tonk Blues. Winterberry 1999.

PLAIN TALK (Henry Rowlan, LA, R. 1989). Comanche Acres 1990.

PLAISIR D'AMOUR (Nora Scopes, R. 1992). Sdlg. 9S81. TB, 36" (91 cm), ML. Ruffled, flared oyster pink; beards dull pink; slight sweet fragrance. 3/179: (5G-220, bright pink bitone, x Entourage) X unknown.

PLAMENIAK (Ladislav Muska by Sergey Loktev, R. 1999). SDB. 13" (33 cm), EML. S. yellow olive, bordeaux base; style arms blended yellow olive; F. yellow olive, brown hafts; beards lilac, yellow in throat. Laced Lemonade X Queen's Pawn. Muska 1993, introduced as "Malibu".

PLANETE MAGIQUE (Pierre Anfosso, R. 1991). Sdlg. P 84 B. SDB, 10" (25 cm), E. S. canary yellow; F. brown, edged yellow; beards light blue mauve. (Petite Fugue x Pulcinella) X Capricornia. Iris en Provence 1991.

PLANTATION BELLE (Mary Dunn, R. 1995). Sdlg. L209-3. LA, 37" (94 cm), M. Iridescent lilac violet self, F. with large light line signal; style arms greenish and lighter lilac. Plantation Beau X Wine Country. Bay View 1996.

PLANTER'S PUNCH (Robert Dunn, R. 1992). Sdlg. B84-858-10. TB, 36" (91 cm), M. S. rose pink;

F. rose pink and buff, deeper rose area at hafts; beards buffy, tipped yellow; ruffled. Pina Colada X Brandy. M.A.D. Iris 1992.

PLATEAU (Graeme Grosvenor, R. 1996). Sdlg. R17-1. TB, 35" (90 cm), EM. Light blue, F. darker in center; beards blue; pronounced spicy fragrance. Scented Nutmeg X Tide Crest. Rainbow Ridge 1996/97.

PLATINUM (Monty Byers by Phyllis Dickey, R. 1994). Sdlg. G39-106. TB, 30" (76 cm), E & RE. Silver white, silvery F. veining; beards white, yellow in throat. Eternal Bliss X Pacific Tide. Misty Hill 1994.

PLAYBOOK (Joseph Ghio, R. 1998). Sdlg. PC-189L3. CA, 13" (33 cm), ML. S. orchid; F. apricot ground washed orchid, precise orchid edge, neon violet signal. Face Value sib. Bay View 1998.

PLAYFUL (Ben Hager, R. 1998). Sdlg. SD5643Y/DpBrFth. SDB, 14" (36 cm), ML. Yellow, F. with deep brown feathered spot. SD4912RndY: (Lemon Rings x SD4024BrtPk: ((3393: (2885: (Blond Doll x (Pink Amber x Pink Cushion)) x ((Pink Amber x Pink Cushion) x Buttercup Charm)) x Pet) x (((2563: (Pink Cushion x Roberts 65-R-28) x (Pink Amber x Pink Cushion)) x 2885) x 3393))) X SD5202WWPk: (4988YSh, Favor sib, x (SD4905PlPkPk: (3393 x ((2563 x (Frosty Lemonade x Pink Cushion)) x Pet Sib)) x (Gigglepot x 4024))). Adamgrove 1998.

PLAYFUL MINX (Heather Pryor, R. 1995). Sdlg. LHP/90. LA, 25" (64 cm), EM. S. soft pastel pink (RHS 62C), darker veining, white rim; style arms butter lemon, speckled pink; F. pink, darker wash at edge, white rim, darker pink veining, green raised signal; slight ruffling. Lucile Holley X unknown. Rainbow Ridge 1996/97.

PLAYING AROUND (Chet Tompkins, R. 1994). Sdlg. 89-47. TB, 38" (97 cm), ML. S. white, flushed and veined violet red; F. white, lined and dotted violet red. Inv. Tinsel Town, Stepping Out, Jet Fire, Starkist, Windwalker X ((April Lost x Masada) x (Masada x (Masada x April Lost))). Fleur de Lis 1994.

PLAY PAL (Ben Hager, R. 1994). Sdlg. BB5611TWh. BB, 18" (46 cm), EM. White self; beards red tangerine. Sib to Brain Child.

PLAY PRETTY (Ben Hager, R. 1993). Sdlg. SD5469WSthPk. SDB, 11" (28 cm), M. Smooth peach pink; beards white, tipped tangerine. SD4979MPk: (Cupid's Cup x ((SD3393Pk: (SD2885: (Blonde Doll x SD2562: (Pink Amber x Pink Cushion)) x (SD2562 x Buttercup Charm)) x ((SD2563-O: (Pink Cushion x Roberts 65-R-28) x (Frosty Lemonade x Pink Cushion)) x Pet)) x ((SD3393DpPch x Pet) x (((SD2563-O x (Pink Amber x Pink Cushion)) x SD2885) x SD3393)))) X SD4986: ((Ceremony x Today's Fashion) x My Sheba). Adamgrove 1994.

PLAY THE FOOL (Pat Otterness, R. 1999). Sdlg. 9697-12X34-102. TB, 31" (79 cm), ML. S. pale sea lavender violet (RHS 85D); F. violet (86C), edged pale sea lavender violet; beards blue, gold in throat; lightly ruffled. Edith Wolford X Silverado.

PLAZA PINK (A. & D. Willott, R. 1993). Sdlg. 91-374. IB, 25" (63 cm), ML. Lightly ruffled bright pink; beards coral. 88-97: ((Apricot Elf x Coral Wings) x Ballet Slippers) X Anna Belle Babson. Willott 1993.

PLEASANT COMPANY (Helen Cochran, R. 1998). Sdlg. 92-02-B. TB, 33" (84 cm), ML. Ruffled and laced pale lavender self; beards violet, dark mustard in throat; slight sweet fragrance. Perils of Pauline X Feeling Blue. Stockton 1999.

PLEASANT EARLYBIRD (Chad Harris, R. 1995). Sdlg. 91JD7. JI (3 F.), 40" (107 cm), VE. S. small, upright, violet (RHS 81C) sanded over white ground, 1/8"-1/4" mulberry violet (81A) edge; style arms white, crests tipped violet blue (92A); F. pastel violet blue (92C), yellow (6A) signal radiating veins through white halo. Enchanted Lake X Sapphire Star. Aitken's Salmon Creek 1996.

PLEASANTLY WARM (Sterling Innerst, R. 1998). Sdlg. 2104-1. TB, 36" (91 cm), M. Laced cream self; beards yellow; slight fragrance. Pure-as-the sib X Laced Cotton. Innerst 1998.

PLEASANT SANDMAN (Chad Harris, R. 1997). Sdlg. 90JC15. JI (6 F.), 44-48" (112-122 cm), L. Lightly sanded violet blue (RHS 90D), heavier at halo, 1" violet (87B) marginal band, bright aureolin yellow (12A) signal; style arms white, edges sanded, crests violet (88B). "Umi Botari" X Dancing Waves. Aitken's Salmon Creek 1998.

PLEASANT STARBURST (Chad Harris, R. 1997). Sdlg. 89JA21. JI (6 F.), 44-48" (112-122 cm), M. Heavily sanded violet blue (RHS 96C) fading out 3/4" from edge, with white ray pattern and violet (87B) shoulders; signals yellow (7A), radiating 1/3 way down F. on veins; style arms white, crests flaring; flared, triangular form. 85JA2, Jaciva sib, X Jaciva. Aitken's Salmon Creek 1998.

PLEASED AS PUNCH (Allan Ensminger, R. 1998). Sdlg. 92-15. IB, 22" (56 cm), ML. S. hyacinth blue (HCC 40/1), white border; style arms white; F. campanula violet (37/3), white luminata pattern around white beard. 89-8: (Hubbub x 86-9: (Shazam x Petite Polka)) X 90-6: (Design x 86-9). Varigay Gardens 1998.

PLEASURE PEACH (Alva Hickerson by Rilla Hickerson, R. 1990). Sdlg. 83-3-1. TB, 34-35" (86-89 cm), E. Ruffled, flared light orange (RHS 24C); beards orange; slight fragrance. Unknown X Gypsy Rings. Rillalva Iris 1991.

PLEASURES OF MAY (Marty Schafer/Jan Sacks, R. 1995). Sdlg. S87-9-5. SIB, 30" (76 cm), EML. S. white, tinted lavender (RHS 69D); style arms white, few light violet flecks; F. light violet (85C), small white signal veined light violet. Lavender Lights X Mad Magenta. Joe Pye Weed 1995.

PLICACUIVRE (Christian Lanthelme, R. 1997). Sdlg. 30B90. TB, 39" (100 cm), L. S. yellow, copper brown at base; style arms yellow; F. yellow ground, brown markings; beards orange. Parentage unknown. Lanthelme 1996.

PLISSEE (Tomas Tamberg, R. 1995). SIB (tet.), 35" (90 cm), M. S. deep blue; F. velvety deep blue, white hairline edge; ruffled. (Lake Niklas x SSTT 183: (Cambridge x SSTT 108)) X Silberkante. Schoeppinger 1995.

PLUM BEAUTY (Ray Lyons, R. 1991). Sdlg. 80-3-4. TB, 34" (86 cm), ML. Laced, heavily ruffled plum; beards rich tangerine. Anon X Pink Sleigh. Long 1993.

PLUME D'OR (Barry Blyth, R. 1994). Sdlg. A63-4. TB, 38" (97 cm), ML. S. lemon, lightening toward precise 1/4" deeper lemon edge; F. creamy white edged lemon, particularly on lower half; beards lemon; pronounced sweet fragrance. Dance Man X Rembrandt Magic. Tempo Two 1994/95.

PLUM JEWEL (A. & D. Willott, R. 1996). Sdlg. 92-119. SDB, 12" (30 cm), M. S. and style arms deep red violet; F. very deep red violet; beards light violet, yellow orange in throat; lightly ruffled. Nachos X Pilgrims' Choice. Willott 1996.

PLUM LUCKY (Carol Lankow by J. T. Aitken, R. 1994). Sdlg. 0F4-2. SDB, 9" (23 cm), ML. S. medium purple; F. velvety deep purple; beards deep purple. Right Honorable X Cherry Pop. Aitken's Salmon Creek 1994.

PLUM LUSCIOUS (A. & D. Willott, SDB, R. 1988). Willott 1990.

PLUM PARASOL (Donald Spoon, R. 1995). Sdlg. 90-50. TB, 30" (76 cm), M. S. white, veined lavender; style arms white, centered plum; F. plum purple; beards plum, hairs tipped yellow, turning to rust and golden yellow in throat; ruffled, flared. Best Bet X Son of Dreams.

PLUM PLEASING (Kirk Strawn, R. 1993). Sdlg. C1985. LA, 39" (99 cm), M. S. purple violet (RHS 82B); style arms purple (77A); F. darker purple violet (82A), yellow (13A) signal. Valera X Neches Royalty. Bois d'Arc 1996.

PLUM RIPPLES (O. D. Niswonger, R. 1994). Sdlg. SDB 41-91. SDB, 14" (36 cm), M. S. light violet; F. white ground, plum plicata markings; beards blue. Chubby Cheeks X Court Magician. Cape Iris 1994.

PLUMS AND CUSTARD (Lynette Black, R. 1996). Sdlg. 89-56-C. SDB, 9" (22 cm), L. Plum red plicata markings on deep golden yellow ground; beards lavender grey; ruffled; pronounced sweet fragrance. Toasty X Muchacha. Netherby Gardens 1996/97.

PLUM TWIZZLER (Opal Wulf, R. 1998). Sdlg. 46-92-1. IB, 18" (46 cm), ML. S. campanula violet (RHS 82C), darker midrib and base; style arms campanula violet; F. purple (79B) rimmed campanula violet, darker purple blaze, white ray pattern beside beard; beards light old gold; ruffled; flowers often with extra parts, up to six F., 4-5 S. and style arms. Hubbub X unknown. Wulf's Backachers 1999.

PLUTOCRAT (Kirk Strawn, R. 1993). Sdlg. LL-1985. LA, 39" (99 cm), M. S. greyed purple (RHS 186A); style arms yellow orange (14B); F. darker greyed purple (187C), signal yellow (8B). Charlie's Ginny X Charles Arny III. Bois d'Arc 1996.

PLYMOUTH HOE (W. & A. Godfrey, R. 1999). Sdlg. HAP3. SDB, 13" (33 cm), M. S. white, navy basal flush, faint green veining; style arms white; F. white, navy blue whiskered thumbprint, white centerline; beards cream, orange in throat; lightly ruffled. HAP2: (Happening x unknown) X self. Hermit Medlars Walk 1999.

POCKETS (Larry Harder, R. 1993). Sdlg. 96-1. SDB, 12" (30 cm), M. S. blue (RHS 94A) with vein pattern; F. blue, darker vein pattern; beards blue, tipped old gold; slight spicy fragrance. Love X Am I Blue.

POCO LOCO (Bob Thomason, SDB, R. 1988). Okie Iris 1994.

POCO TACO (Jayne Ritchie, R. 1995). Sdlg. 89-6-4. SDB, 12" (30 cm), EML. S. uniform medium lemon yellow; style arms lemon yellow; F. smooth oxblood red, yellow wire edge; beards medium yellow. 85-24-12: (Do-Si-Do x (Inscription x (Latin Lover x White Mite))) X Aitken 86M42: ((Sea Urchin x Jones M356: ((Kentucky Bluegrass x Blithe Blue sib) x ((Blithe Blue x (Meadow Moss

341

sdlg. x 218-5: (Gingerbread Man x Meadow Moss))) x (218-bl gr x (Meadow Moss x Kentucky Bluegrass))))) x (Aitken 80-22 x Cherry Tart)). Ritchie 1996.

PODOLCHANKA (Viacheslav Gavrilin, R. 1998). Sdlg. 6-28-3-94. TB, 47" (120 cm), ML. S. and style arms bright yellow; F. light lilac violet, 1/2" yellow brown edge, narrow white centerline; beards yellow, white at end; ruffled, lightly laced; slight fragrance. Fiesta Time X Starcrest. Gavrilin 1999.

PODRUZHKA (Viacheslav Gavrilin, R. 1999). Sdlg. 6-21-2-94. TB, 36" (92 cm), M. S. lemon yellow; style arms light lemon white; F. white, lemon yellow hafts and edge; beards red; ruffled. Wedding Candles X Silver Shower. Gavrilin 1999.

POEM OF ECSTASY (Ben Hager, R. 1995). Sdlg. T5431Pk/DpLv. TB, 36" (91 cm), M. S. clear peach pink; F. smooth deep lavender; beards soft tangerine; fluted, ruffled. T4235CrPk/Lv: (Merry Madrigal x Mother Earth) X Adventuress. Cooley 1997.

POETESS (Barry Blyth, R. 1999). Sdlg. D61-3. TB, 38" (97 cm), ML. S. coffee rose, infused light violet toward midrib; F. coffee rose with tannish overlay deeper toward hafts, lavender flash below tangerine beard; slight sweet fragrance. A63-1, Plume d'Or sib, X Bygone Era. Tempo Two 1999/2000.

POETIC (Joseph Ghio, R. 1991). Sdlg. 86-119N2. TB, 42" (107 cm), L-VL. S. coral orange; F. white, coral orange edge and shoulders; beards tangerine. (Winning Note x Caption) X (Designer Gown x 82-200M: (78-221U: ((Flareup x 73-122Z: (Hi Top x ((Ponderosa x Travel On) x Peace Offering))) x 76-37F: (Ballet in Orange x 73-122Z)) x 80-208: ((Artiste x Tupelo Honey) x ((Malaysia x Carolina Honey) x 73-122Z)))). Bay View 1992.

POETRY IN MOTION (Perry Dyer, R. 1998). Sdlg. 91-174A. TB, 34" (86 cm), ML. Ruffled white ground plicata, heavy medium orchid lilac stitching; style arms lilac orchid; beards coral to shrimp, occasional small horn. Lovebird X Tide Mark. Contemporary 1999.

POINT ARENA (Joseph Ghio, R. 1999). Sdlg. PB-255N3. CA, 13" (33 cm), ML. Caramel gold, maroon signal. Parentage unknown. Bay View 1999.

POINT RICHE (Tony Huber, R. 1999). Sdlg. 94-01. SPEC (*hookeri*), 11" (28 cm), E. S. lavender and white, small, tricuspidate; style arms violet blue (RHS 91B) midrib, pinkish to white edge, hyacinth blue (91A) crests; F. hyacinth blue, haft tinted brown and yellow, cream signal in white spot veined hyacinth blue. *I. hookeri* (collected at Point Riche, Newfoundland) X self.

POINT SANTA CRUZ (Joseph Ghio, R. 1995). Sdlg. PF-148K2. CA, 11" (28 cm), M. Red beige wash over orange base, F. with large maroon half-moon signal centered silver. Villa Montalvo X PH-242R2: (Temblor sib x ((San Gregorio x (Montara sib x Mission Santa Cruz sib)) x Villa Branciforte sib)). Bay View 1995.

POINTS OF LIGHT (Donald Sorensen, R. 1998). Sdlg. S-95-16-3. TB, 34" (86 cm), EM. S. and style arms light blue (RHS 97C); F. dark blue violet (89B), paling near beard with age; beards light blue, hairs tipped yellow in throat; slight sweet fragrance. S-91-6-5: (Polar Seas x Bridal Fashion) X Skylift.

POINT WELL TAKEN (Sharon McAllister, R. 1998). Sdlg. 90-3-19. AB (OGB), 28" (71 cm), M. S. pinkish ivory ground lightly veined golden yellow; style arms soft yellow; F. golden tan ground, heavily stippled rust around mustard brown beard, faint rust wash, brownish black signal. Sandy Dandy X Whirlwind Romance. McAllister 1998.

POLAR QUEEN (Barry Blyth, R. 1994). Sdlg. A115-1. TB, 36-38" (91-97 cm), ML. S. white, slight lemon yellow midrib influence; F. bright yellow, white edging and variable white patterning; beards mustard yellow; slight sweet fragrance. Y7-4, Electrique sib, X X90-2: (Shoop 80-2 x Town Clown). Tempo Two 1994/95.

POLIOT FANTAZII (Galina Shevchenko, R. 1995). MDB, 7½" (19 cm), ML. S. eggyolk yellow; F. reddish brown, bright yellow rim; beards yellow, white base. From *I. pumila* sdlgs. Shevchenko 1995.

POLISHED IMAGE (James Burch, R. 1993). Sdlg. 45-10. TB, 34" (86 cm), EM. S. yellow gold (RHS 12A); F. yellow orange (14A) with yellow gold (12A) hafts, white rays extending from orange (25B) beard. Wonder Struck X Fresno Calypso. Burch Iris 1993.

POLISH PRINCESS (A. & D. Cadd, R. 1999). Sdlg. 82-91-10. TB, 38" (97 cm), EM & RE. S. soft yellow, pale lavender center flush and midrib; style arms soft yellow; F. soft yellow, lavender and peach blend, darker lavender center wash, light brown shoulders marked white; beards yellow; heavily ruffled; slight sweet fragrance. Renoir X Tennison Ridge.

POLNOLUNIYE (Nina Miroshnichenko, R. 1996). TB, 41" (105 cm), M. Ruffled yellow self; beards yellow; pronounced spicy fragrance. Parentage unknown. Miroshnichenko 1988.

POLO KLASSIK (Viacheslav Gavrilin, R. 1998). Sdlg. 6-1-1-94. TB, 33" (85 cm), M. Heavily ruffled lavender lilac; beards lavender lilac, light lilac at end; slight fragrance. Eagle's Flight X unknown. Gavrilin 1999.

POLYNESIAN HONEY (John Wight, R. 1998). Sdlg. J89-5-1. AB (OGB-), 26" (66 cm), M. Lightly ruffled light bronze (RHS 153D), F. with red flush around beard; beards dark orange, cream at end; regelia form. Kentucky Bluegrass X J84-3 yellow amoena: (Holk yellow amoena AB sdlg. x Flanagan AB 77005-5). Aril Society, Wight's Iris 1998.

POMPEII LADY (Barry Blyth, R. 1993). Sdlg. X85-B. TB, 36" (91 cm), ML. S. light apricot, slight smoky cast; F. soft pastel rose, slight smoky cast and some light apricot blending around hafts and vivid tangerine beard. Street Dancer X Mulled Wine. Tempo Two 1993/94.

POM POM GIRL (Lynda Miller, R. 1998). Sdlg. 1792. TB, 33" (84 cm), EM. S. light pink, deeper veining; style arms pink and light coral rose; F. deep coral pink, white center; beards coral, base white; slight musky fragrance. 13487E: (3176: (Coral Magic x Love Sonnet) x Vanity) X Role Model. Miller's Manor 1998.

POND CROWN POINT (C. Greg Speichert, R. 1995). SPEC (*virginica*), 24-32" (60-80 cm), M. S. blue (RHS 99D), barely noticeable veining; F. blue (99C), veining noticeable, bright aureolin yellow (12A) chevron signal. *I. virginica* collected 1990, Crown Point, Indiana. Crystal Palace Perennials 1996.

POND LILAC DREAM (C. Greg Speichert, R. 1995). SPEC (*virginica*), 24-30" (60-75 cm), L. S. white, pale lavender pink (RHS 75D) veining; F. white, slightly deeper (75C) veining, sharp bright lemon yellow (3A) signal; petals rounded, form flared. *I. virginica* collected 1990, Cedar Lake, Indiana. Crystal Palace Perennials 1996.

POND LILY (Evelyn Jones, R. 1994). Sdlg. 88E10-6. TB, 38" (97 cm), M. S. veronica violet (HCC 639/3), flushed deeper (639/2) at midrib; F. veronica violet (639/1) with pink influence; beards tangerine; ruffled. Lullaby of Spring X 85E8-2: (((Heather Blush x So Rare) x (((Lilac Champagne x Sand and Sea) x sib) x Betty Simon) x ((((Beattie 65-36 x (((Spanish Affair x Hamblen H5-35) x (Marilyn C x Shoop 57-35)) x Spanish Gift)) x (Orange Chariot x Bright Butterfly)) x Bright Life) x ((Highland Thistle x Twilight Blush) x ((Rhoda Anne x (Pink Sleigh x (Elizabeth Stuart x Pretty Poise))) x Shoop pink sdlg.)))). Aitken's Salmon Creek 1995.

PO NO MO (Tom Burseen, R. 1997). Sdlg. 93-41B. TB, 36" (91 cm), E. S. lemon yellow; style arms yellow; F. gold, white center flash; beards gold, white at end, darker in throat; ruffled; musky fragrance. 0-101: (Lemon Fever x Bluid) X 1-121: ((Peach Sundae x (Lacy Snowflake x Porta Villa)) x Ample Charm). T.B.'s Place 1997.

PONTYPOOL (Harry Foster, R. 1990). Sdlg. J318/85. SIB (tet.), 42" (107 cm), ML. S. purple blue; style arms azure; F. rich purple blue, fine silver edge, white signal, golden green shoulders. Hubbard X Silver Edge. V. H. Humphrey 1995.

POOGINOOK (Robert Harding, R. 1991). Sdlg. 85-14. TB, 36" (91 cm), M. Medium pink; beards tangerine. Carved Cameo X Starfrost Pink. Tempo Two 1994/95.

POOH BAH (Ben Hager, R. 1999). Sdlg. J100. JI (6 F.), 38-40" (97-102 cm), M. Bright red violet, small white halo and white rays; style arms bright white, crests solid red violet. Mai Ogen X Hozan. Ensata Gardens 1999.

POOKANILLY (Sterling Innerst, R. 1993). Sdlg. 3587-10. IB, 18" (46 cm), M. S. white; F. brown, trimmed white; beards orange; slight fragrance. Cloudless Sunrise X Dash sib. Innerst 1994.

POOL SIDE (Allen Harper, MDB, R. 1989). Harper's Garden 1990.

POOR BUTTERFLY (Keith Keppel, R. 1990). Sdlg. 84-1AA. IB, 24" (61 cm), M. S. burgundy (M&P 56-E-8), faint creamy (9-D-2) haze on midrib base; F. 1/4" lighter (55-H-8) edge and tracery of veins and dotting on cream (9-D-2) to yellow (9-I-2) ground; beards tile red (3-D-12) to terracotta (4-D-12), white base; slight sweet fragrance. Sib to Anagram. Keppel 1991.

POORMAN (Keith Chadwick/Tony DeRose, R. 1999). Sdlg. 98F-8-4. TB, 36" (91 cm), E & RE. S. silvery grey, touched gold; style arms bluish silver, yellow gold edge; F. blended violet and white, hafts striped gold and white; beards tangerine, gold and white at end; slight sweet fragrance. (unknown x Love the Sun) X unknown.

POP (David Sindt by Adamgrove, R. 1992). Sdlg. 760. SDB, 11" (28 cm), ML. Golden brown, F. with mahogany highlights; beards light blue, tipped yellow. 183: (Arrangement x Sun Sparkle) X Monkey. Adamgrove 1992.

POPCORN CITY (William Grise, R. 1999). Sdlg. R-4. TB, 36" (91 cm), EML. White ground, lavender plicata rim, F. with yellow near haft; beards light yellow; slight fragrance. Rondo X unknown. Parkwood 1999.

343

POPINJAY (Nora Scopes, CA, R. 1988). V. H. Humphrey 1992.

POPPA JOHN (Tom Burseen, R. 1999). Sdlg. 95-348A. TB, 36" (91 cm), M. S. golden yellow; F. brownish gold, hafts and edges darker; beards dark gold, large, with dark purplish brown spoon covered with golden hairs or tatters; ruffled; musky fragrance. Sunny Bubbles X Green Streak. T.B.'s Place 1999.

POPPED CORN (B. Charles Jenkins, R. 1992). Sdlg. C17-17J. SPU, 30-36" (76-91 cm), M. S. creamy white; F. deep yellow, precise white edge; ruffled. Highline Honey X self. Shepard Iris 1993.

POP'S BEARD (Polly Black, R. 1995). Sdlg. ST9P1. TB, 36" (91 cm), M. Ruffled bright medium purple self; beards deep yellow, white at end; slight spicy fragrance. Night Canyon X Trident. Polly Black 1995.

POPSIE (Janet Hutchinson, R. 1991). Sdlg. 88SLBM. LA, 47" (146 cm), EM. S. white, veined and lined magenta; F. ruffled medium magenta pink, edged white, pale reverse, yellow signal with green line. Soft Laughter X Buxom. Rainbow Ridge 1995/96.

POPULARITY (Keith Keppel, TB, R. 1989). Roris 1991.

PORCELAIN FRILLS (Ben Hager, R. 1992). Sdlg. RE5080BgRfWh. TB, 31" (79 cm), M & RE. Glazed procelain white, chartreuse yellow deep on hafts; beards white, tipped yellow in throat. Many Happy Returns X Bonus Mama. Melrose 1993.

PORTER'S GOLD (Cyril Field, R. 1992). Sdlg. CF2. TB, 28" (71 cm), M. Lightly laced yellow self; beards orange, yellow flounce. Yellow horned sdlg. X flounced sdlg.

POSEIDON'S REALM (Colin Hill, R. 1999). Sdlg. CH 94-1A. TB, 36" (91 cm), ML. Icy violet white, F. with violet veins bleeding into violet halo at base of beard; beards gold, violet horn. Trick or Treat X Sky Hooks. I. poppin' Irises 1999.

POSH SPICE (Ladislav Muska, R. 1999). Sdlg. 98-DQCG-05. TB, 36" (91 cm), M. S. and style arms light maroon; F. light banana cinnamon ground, 3/4" rich red brown marked edge; beards burnt tangerine; heavily ruffled, crinkled; slight fragrance. ((Date Bait x Queen in Calico) x Calicoball) X (Queen in Calico x Graffiti). Muska 1999.

POSSIBILITIES (Duane Meek, R. 1992). Sdlg. 458-2-4. TB, 35" (89 cm), ML. S. light blue violet; F. ruffled deeper blue violet, lighter area below blue white beard tipped cinnamon; slight fragrance. Carved Crystal X Theatre. D & J Gardens 1992.

POSTMASTER (John C. Taylor, R. 1998). Sdlg. UL 29-3. LA, 47" (120 cm), M. Purple; signals yellow. Louie X Rachel's Request. Rainbow Ridge 1998/99.

POTOMAC FIREWORKS (Donald Spoon, R. 1997). Sdlg. 93-368A. TB, 36" (91 cm), M. S. and style arms near-white, palest lavender blue cast; F. white, blue lavender rim and shadings; beards white-based red, ending in 1" fuzzy lavender blue horn; ruffled. Skyblaze X Stars and Stripes.

POTPOURRI ROSE (Heather Pryor, R. 1995). Sdlg. 60/90-12. LA, 30" (76 cm), ML. S. medium rose (RHS 60D); style arms medium rose, rib centered yellow; F. rose (60C); yellow dagger signal with raised center; ruffled. Gladiator's Gift X Desert Jewel. Lone Star 1997, Iris Haven 1997/98.

POTSELUY (Viacheslav Gavrilin, R. 1999). Sdlg. 7-6-4-94. TB, 33" (85 cm), EM. S. deep lilac lavender, edged darker; style arms and F. lilac lavender; beards light lilac; laced; slight fragrance. Pearl Chiffon X unknown. Gavrilin 1999.

POTSELUY MENIA (Viacheslav Gavrilin, R. 1999). Sdlg. 94-782-1. TB, 35" (88 cm), ML. S. light blue lilac edged lavender; style arms light lavender; F. light lavender, darker edge; beards light lavender. Pearl Chiffon X unknown.

POUNSLEY PURPLE (Jane Hollow, R. 1999). SIB, 28" (70 cm), EM. Very dark violet blue (RHS 89A), F. with pale to deep yellow signal speckled dark violet blue and with silver edge. Parentage unknown; seed from Hardy Plant Society. Pounsley Plants 1999.

POUR IT ON (Paul Black, R. 1996). Sdlg. A114XX. IB, 26" (66 cm), E. S. orchid pink, heavily washed and marked red violet; style arms red violet; F. silvery orchid center wash, wide dark red purple plicata band; beards blackish violet, white base; ruffled; pronounced spicy fragrance. Privileged Character X Polar Seas. Mid-America 1996.

POUZDRANY (Eric & Bob Tankesley-Clarke, R. 1994). SPEC, 14-16" (36-41 cm), L. S. deep yellow; F. light yellow, densely veined black brown coalescing to solid tip blotch; beards yellow. Collected at Pouzdrany, Czechoslovakia; distributed by Randolph prior to 1970 and in commerce as *I. variegata* 61-72.

POVERTY POINT (Patrick O'Connor, R. 1999). LA, 36" (91 cm), M. Medium rose suffused white, aging whiter, F. with large yellow arrowhead signal and darker rose petal rim; style arms medium rose. Ann Chowning X unknown.

POWDER BLUE CADILLAC (George Sutton, R. 1996). Sdlg. G-6-AR. TB, 36" (91 cm), EM. Ruffled cornflower blue (RHS 95D), darker veining; beards white, hairs tipped yellow in throat. Busy Being Blue X Honky Tonk Blues. Sutton 1997.

POWDER BLUE GIANT (Sam Norris by Jan Sacks/Marty Schafer, R. 1997). SPEC (*cristata*), 6" (15 cm), M. Large light blue violet; deep F. crest with white top, yellow beneath, white signal bordered dark blue. Collected in wild, west of Litchfield, Kentucky. Joe Pye Weed 1997.

POWER OF ONE (Barry Blyth, R. 1996). Sdlg. B142-1. TB, 38" (96 cm), ML. S. lemon yellow; F. lemon yellow, white overlay texture veined lemon, 3/8" lemon edge; beards lemon gold; spicy fragrance. Creme d'Or X Romantic Mood. Tempo Two 1996/97.

POWER PLAY (Mary Dunn by Robert Dunn, R. 1999). Sdlg. M2066-A. TB, 36" (91 cm), EM. Ruffled amethyst violet to grape, stained and washed grape; style arms grape; beards old gold, end white; slight sweet fragrance. Oba Oba X Fancy Woman.

POWER STROKE (Glenn Bowers, R. 1998). Sdlg. B45-5. TB, 31" (79 cm), EML. S. and style arms light yellow (Pantone 107C); F. maroon red (1815U), yellow around beards, yellow veining to edges and thin rim; beards yellow (116C), lighter at end, with hairy pale yellow horns; lightly ruffled; pronounced sweet fragrance. Second Act X Juicy Fruit.

POWER SURGE (Joseph Ghio, R. 1990). Sdlg. 87-78F. TB, 40" (102 cm), EML. S. salmon ground overlaid magenta; F. salmon apricot, lined and edged magenta. (Indiscreet sib x 82-236: (Beyond x (Rancho Rose x ((Flareup x Osage Buff) x (Vanity x Anon))))) X Test Pattern sib. Bay View 1991.

POZDNÍ LÉTO (Zdeněk Seidl, R. 1997). Sdlg. 91-ExOS/1. TB, 39" (100 cm), ML. S. and style arms peach (RHS 29D); F. peach, hafts and shoulders tangerine orange (24C); beards saturn red (30B); ruffled, laced; slight spicy fragrance. Extravagant X Orange Star. Seidl 1998.

PRACHTKLEID (Siegmar Goerbitz, R. 1992). Sdlg. 8635B1. TB, 41" (105 cm), M. S. laced red violet; F. waved red violet, center darker; beards orange; slight fragrance. Detmolder Sommer X Visual Arts. Schoeppinger 1993.

PRAETORIAN GUARD (LeRoy Meininger, R. 1998). Sdlg. 91-TwTh-91. TB, 40" (107 cm), M. S. light yellow, edged darker, faint green veining; style arms lemon yellow, edges and midrib deeper; F. lemon yellow, darker border, lavender veining; beards orange yellow, 1/2" lavender horn tipped yellow. Matinee Idol X Twice Thrilling. Monument, Woodland Iris 1998.

PRAIRIE BARON (Floyd Dyer, R. 1989). Sdlg. D-37-84-T. BB, 24" (61 cm), M. S. light peach; F. light lavender, peach hafts; beards bright red orange; lightly ruffled; slight spicy fragrance. D-12-79-B: (W.F. Brown 66-168A x Lilac Flare) X Tulare. Four Cedars 1990.

PRAIRIE BISON (A. & D. Cadd, R. 1999). Sdlg. 39-91-1. TB, 38-42" (97-104 cm), M. S. light chocolate brown; style arms lighter and yellower; F. deep velvety red brown, 1/4" border and centerline light chocolate brown, yellowish shoulders marked white; beards dark yellow; pronounced musky fragrance. Liberty Torch X Inspiration Point.

PRAIRIE BLUFF (Francis Rogers, R. 1990). Sdlg. F-642-A. TB, 35" (89 cm), M. S. greyed orange (RHS 163C); F. greyed orange (164C), violet flash below beard radiating down to greyed orange edge; beards yellow orange; ruffled, crimped; sweet fragrance. Sheer Poetry X FR-80-19A: ((Kilt Lilt x Country Boy) x (Copperopolis x Autumn Leaves)). Meadowbrook 1992.

PRAIRIE DANCER (Floyd Dyer, R. 1991). Sdlg. D-157-85-D. SDB, 13" (33 cm), M. S. pale blue white; F. brown, tip blended yellow; beards blue; slight musky fragrance. D-351-82-D: ((((Green Spot x Knotty Pine) x *I. chamaeiris*) x self) x Gingerbread Man) X D-112-81-D, unknown. Four Cedars 1991.

PRAIRIE DAZZLER (Floyd Dyer, R. 1991). Sdlg. D-87-85-D. SDB, 13½" (34 cm), M. S. white; F. yellow white, lower part white; beards dark blue; slight sweet fragrance. D-50-81-D: (((Knotty Pine x Blue Denim) x self) x White Light) X D-70-82-D: (unknown x Gingerbread Man). Four Cedars 1991.

PRAIRIE DOVE (Floyd Dyer, R. 1994). Sdlg. D71-88B. BB, 27" (68 cm), M. S. light yellow; F. violet to yellow blend, light brown edge, lightly ruffled; beards yellow; slight musky fragrance. Soft Spoken X Brown Lasso. Four Cedars 1994.

PRAIRIE FAIRY (Floyd Dyer, R. 1990). Sdlg. D-129-86D. SDB, 13" (33 cm), M. Ruffled, flared blue violet blend, brown haft markings; beards yellow, tipped blue; slight musky fragrance. Luxurious X Ice Chalet. Four Cedars 1990.

PRAIRIE IN BLOOM (Gene Gaddie, SIB, R. 1989). Gaddies' Gardens 1990.

PRAIRIE REN (Floyd Dyer, R. 1990). Sdlg. D-260-86-D. SDB, 13" (33 cm), M. S. white ground stitched blue; F. white ground lightly stitched blue; beards yellow; ruffled, flared; slight sweet fragrance. Snow Gnome X self. Four Cedars 1990.

PRAIRIE THUNDER (Paul Black, R. 1990). Sdlg. 86407A. AB (OB-), 25" (64 cm), M. S. violet blue; style arms olive tan; F. pale violet shading to tan edge, dark burgundy spot around beard; beards blue white, tipped brown black; slight spicy fragrance. 83158C: (Cindy Mitchell x Silver Finery) X Welcome Reward. Mid-America 1990.

PRALINE FESTIVAL (Dorman Haymon, R. 1992). Sdlg. 12-84-2. LA, 34" (86 cm), M. Cream, heavily veined and dusted rose tan, yellow gold signal streaked green full length of F.; style arms rose tan, edged cream; ruffled. Valera X President Hedley. Deep South Gardens 1992.

PRAWN CRACKER (John Clive Russell, R. 1999). TB, 34" (86 cm), M. Lightly ruffled shrimp pink; F. with white blaze below beard; style arms pink; beards white, tipped pale yellow; slight fragrance. Parentage unknown. Iris Garden 1999.

PRAYER WHEEL (John Marchant, R. 1992). Sdlg. 7887. CA, 10" (25 cm), ML. S. greyed indian yellow (HCC 6/3) flushed light red lavender; F. same, rimmed indian yellow, yellow midrib, diffuse signal. Sdlg. X sdlg.

PRAZDNICHNY (Nina Miroshnichenko, R. 1997). TB, 33" (84 cm), M. S. white, midrib pale lemon; F. light lilac, paling to white center; beards pale lilac white, yellow in throat; slight sweet fragrance. Parentage unknown. Miroshnichenko 1994.

PRECIOUS FIND (Larry Lauer, R. 1999). Sdlg. 92-202-2. SDB, 8½" (21 cm), E. Ruffled light salmon orange, F. with spanish orange wash and cream stripes around beard; beards white, tipped tangerine; slight sweet fragrance. My Sheba X Neon Pixie.

PRECIOUS HARVEST (Donald Spoon, R. 1997). Sdlg. 90-34A. TB, 29" (74 cm), ML & RE. Ruffled, lightly laced yellow self, lighter area below dark yellow beards. Precious Moments X Harvest of Memories. Winterberry 1997.

PRECIOUS HEATHER (Cy Bartlett, R. 1996). Sdlg. C91-56. TB, 34" (86 cm), M. S. white, violet plicata markings; F. white, fewer violet markings; beards greyed white; slight sweet fragrance. Violet Icing X Magic Mountain.

PRECIOUS LITTLE PINK (Monty Byers by Phyllis Dickey, R. 1995). Sdlg. H68-100. IB, 15" (38 cm), E & RE. S. pink, blue cast; F. pale blue pink washed white, deeper pink at hafts; beards orange, tipped blue white; slight sweet fragrance. Northern Flame X Weiler 82-44-3: (Little Bishop x Third Charm). Misty Hill 1995.

PRECISE RIMMED CREAM (Austin Morgan, R. 1990). TB, 36" (91 cm), EML. S. and F. cream with precise yellow edges; beards yellow. Parentage unknown. Iris Test Gardens 1990.

PREPARED (Graeme Grosvenor, R. 1994). Sdlg. L 74-31. JI (3 F.), 54" (137 cm), M. S. white, edged red purple; style arms white, edged red purple; F. red purple, white spray pattern, yellow signal. Geisha Parasol X unknown.

PREPPY (Kevin Vaughn, R. 1999). Sdlg. D92-4. BB, 24" (61 cm), EML & RE. S. white ground stippled lavender blue, slight stitching; style arms lavender blue, some gold on edge and midrib; F. white ground stitched medium lavender blue darker than in S.; beards lavender, hairs tipped gold; ruffled; pronounced spicy fragrance. Stanza X Miss Nellie.

PRESIDENT BARNETTE (Dorman Haymon, R. 1999). Sdlg. 138-92-1. LA, 39" (99 cm), EM. Heavily ruffled green-veined white, green gold signal changing to green veining; style arms dark green, fading to white at tip; slight sweet fragrance. 6-1-88: (Kitty D. x 52-83-5: (Charlie's Angel x Clara Goula)) X Helen Naish.

PRESTIGE ITEM (Ben Hager, R. 1991). Sdlg. T4875Rs. TB, 34" (86 cm), M. Glowing salmon rose; self beards. T3890MvRs: (Entourage x Strawberry Sensation) X T4271BchDpPk: (T3868PkPk: ((Kindness x (Carved Cameo x Vanity)) x ((Ice Sculpture x Liz) x Vanity)) x T3205Frm: (Vanity x Pink Persian)). Melrose 1992.

PRESUMED INNOCENT (Helen Cochran, R. 1995). Sdlg. 83-07-B. TB, 36" (91 cm), M. Ruffled blue white self; beards blue; slight sweet fragrance. Song of Norway X Winterscape. Stockton 1996.

PRETAPORTER (Akihiko Terada, R. 1997). Sdlg. 177-3. TB, 35" (89 cm), M. S. white; F. orchid, white center; beards red orange; slight sweet fragrance. Exotic Melody X Condottiere. Roris 1997.

PRETTY AGAIN (George Sutton, R. 1996). Sdlg. C-92-A. SDB, 10" (25 cm), E & RE. Ruffled greenish yellow (RHS 2C), F. with dark straw yellow (13C) thumbprint; beards white, hairs tipped mustard in throat; slight sweet fragrance. Sno Jo X Twice Blessed. Sutton 1997.

346

PRETTY BEGINNING (Evelyn Jones, R. 1990). Sdlg. 87E-7-1. TB, 38" (96 cm), M. S. phlox purple (HCC 623/3); F. full orchid purple (31/2); beards geranium; ruffled; sweet fragrance. 81-36: ((Highland Thistle x Twilight Blush) x (Elizabeth Stuart x Point Clear)) X 82-8: ((Rhoda Anne x Shoop pink sdlg.) x (Elizabeth Stuart x Point Clear)). Bennett Jones 1991.

PRETTY BUTTERFLY (Sass Brothers by Philip Edinger, R. 1999). BB, 24" (61 cm), M. S. and style arms icy lilac (RHS 76D); F. icy lilac with network of violet (82A) veining; beards yellow, end white with hairs tipped yellow. Parentage unknown, diploid. In circulation prior to 1965.

PRETTY CUTE (Ben Hager, R. 1992). Sdlg. SD5464ClrPk. SDB, 13" (33 cm), M. Smooth clear pink; beards white, tangerine in throat. SD5131PkBlBds: ((((3393Pk: (2885Y: (Blonde Doll x 2562B: (Pink Amber x Pink Cushion)) x 2888DpY: (2562A x Buttercup Charm)) x (2919Pch: (2563-O: (Pink Cushion x Roberts 65-R-28) x (Frosty Lemonade x Pink Cushion)) x Pet)) x 4024PkPc: ((3393DpPch x Pet sib) x (3420 x 3393Pk))) x (Gigglepot x 4024PkPc)) x (((2919Pch x 2920Apr: (2563-O x (Pink Amber x Pink Cushion))) x 3420: (2920Apr x 2885Pch)) x My Sheba sib)) X Kandi Moon. Adamgrove 1993.

PRETTY IS (Ron Mullin, R. 1994). Sdlg. 84-455M. TB, 35" (89 cm), EM. Sunny yellow, F. with white area around yellow gold beard extending to near petal edge. Speculator X Precious Moments. M.A.D. Iris 1995.

PRETTY JAZZY (Riley Probst, R. 1997). Sdlg. 91PQX28RJ1. MTB, 25" (63 cm), M. S. bright golden yellow (RHS 7A); F. mahogany purple (187A), hafts white with purple lines, rim yellow (162A); beards marigold; flared; slight fragrance. Pretty Quirky X Real Jazzy.

PRETTY QUIRKY (Ann Probst, R. 1991). Sdlg. 9-27-49. MTB, 24" (61 cm), ML. S. yellow (RHS 7C); F. violet (84D) veined darker around hafts; beards yellow, tipped white; slight fragrance. Quirk X --- probably Amethyst Sunset. Manchester Garden 1992.

PRETTY REWARD (Riley Probst, R. 1998). Sdlg. 92PQX18WR2. MTB, 22" (56 cm), M. S. gold; F. raspberry purple rimmed gold, veined mahogany and cream from haft into blade; beards cream yellow; S. open, F. flared. Pretty Quirky X Welch's Reward.

PRETTY WOMAN (William Maryott, R. 1991). Sdlg. M129A. TB, 35" (89 cm), M. Ruffled light lavender blue; beards deep purple, tipped bronze; ruffled. Touch of Bronze X Good Morning America. Maryott 1992.

PREYEMNITSA (Viacheslav Gavrilin, R. 1999). Sdlg. 96-209-1. TB, 37" (95 cm), M. S. white; style arms light yellow; F light yellow edged darker, white in center, hafts yellow; beards yellow, white at end, tangerine in throat; ruffled, laced. Wedding Candles X Mistie's Audience.

PRIDE AND GLORY (Cleo Palmer, R. 1990). Sdlg. 8565. IB, 24" (61 cm), E. S. pale smoky blue white, hint of pink at base; F. medium blue violet, amber hafts and shoulders; beards red. Flamingo Blues X 8134: (Show Baby x 7319: (Lenna M x (Prophecy x Dove Wings))). Palmer's Iris 1992.

PRIDE IN BLUE (Currier McEwen, R. 1995). Sdlg. T(6)83/94. SIB. (tet.), 28" (70 cm), EML. S. light blue (RHS 100D), midrib darker blue (100A); style arms light blue (101D); F. light blue (100D), few veins (100C), darker shoulder markings (96C), white signal. T(5)78/103: (((Sally Kerlin x Cambridge) x Silver Edge) x Signals Blue sib) X T(4)78/51(2): (Signals Blue sib x Harpswell Haze). Eartheart 1998.

PRIMA BEAUTY (Akihiko Terada, R. 1998). Sdlg. 239-2. TB, 37" (94 cm), ML. S. pale pink; F. red purple, white edge; beards orange; ruffled; slight musky fragrance. Con Amore X Ringo. Roris 1998.

PRIM AND PROPER (Sharon McAllister, R. 1994). Sdlg. 87-1-13. AB (OGB+), 28" (72 cm), EM. S. white; F. primrose yellow with arrowhead-shaped reddish near-black signal patch at tip of yellow beard. Wished For Child X *I. kirkwoodii*. McAllister 1994.

PRIMORIYE (Liudmila Mironova, R. 1997). Sdlg. 2-87. JI (6 F.), 34" (85 cm), M. White ground, purple violet veining, dark purple violet band around yellow signal. Patrocle X unknown -- seed treated with gamma rays. DVO RAN 1996.

PRIMROSE CREAM (Primrose Upward by Jennifer Hewitt, R. 1995). Sdlg. PU/1. SIB, 18" (46 cm), M. Small tailored white, F. with deep primrose yellow hafts and central veins. Parentage unknown. Cotswold Garden Flowers 1993.

PRIMROSE PROMISE (Gary Middleton, R. 1999). Sdlg. 96/FREP 1. TB, 38" (97 cm), M. S. pale primrose yellow; style arms pale yellow; F. pale primrose yellow blended white, deeper yellow gold hafts veined gold; beards yellow; ruffled; slight sweet fragrance. Elizabeth Poldark X Fort Regent.

PRINCE GEORGE (George Shoop by Keith Keppel, R. 1996). Sdlg. 90-7-1. TB, 37" (94 cm), M.

S. cool white (M&P 41-A-4) fading white (41-A-2); style arms cool white, amber white (11-B-1) crest flush; F. perilla purple (42-K-12), paling (42-J-11) toward edge and between veins, pallid lavender blue (42-A-2) wire rim, conspicuous circular pattern from hafts to below beard of perilla purple to greenish tan (14-H-4) veins on white; beards bittersweet orange (3-B-12), base white; ruffled. Parisian Flight X Condottiere. Keppel 1997.

PRINCE JURI (G. F. Wilson, R. 1997). Sdlg. 91-91BLO-B. AB (OGB), 29" (74 cm), E. S. pure white; F. white, slight lemon cast, slight wine dotting, large wine signal; beards yellow, wide; recurved form. Blond Bearded Lady X Onlooker.

PRINCE OF BURGUNDY (O. D. Niswonger, R. 1992). Sdlg. IB 37-90. IB, 22" (56 cm), M. S. dark burgundy, center touched white; F. white, burgundy plicata edge; beards white, very slightly tipped yellow. Goddess X Chubby Cheeks. Cape Iris 1993.

PRINCE OF THIEVES (A. & D. Willott, R. 1999). Sdlg. W 99-26. SDB, 10" (25 cm), M. S. white ground washed light blue and ecru; style arms light violet; F. white ground heavily marked full purple; beards blue violet; lightly ruffled. Sib to Mystic Plum.

PRINCE OF TIDES (James McWhirter, R. 1992). Sdlg. J88-18-3. TB, 38" (97 cm), EM. Heavily ruffled clear sky blue; beards white, tipped blue; slight fragrance. J81-74: (Winterscape x Sky Gem) X Busy Being Blue. Stockton 1994.

PRINCE SOLMS (J. R. Allen, R. 1994). Sdlg. W 3 B. TB, 38" (97 cm), EM. S. and style arms grape; F. grape, deepening to grape purple; beards light blue, light gold in throat; heavily ruffled; slight sweet fragrance. Adam Conerly X S 11 G: (Victoria Falls x Rebecca Anne). Allen Iris 1997.

PRINCESS BLUEBEARD (A. & D. Willott, R. 1990). Sdlg. 88-26. SDB, 11" (28 cm), EM. S. pink with slight blue cast; F. pink, hafts apricot; beards bright deep blue. Pink Panther X Poet Laureate. Willott 1991.

PRINCESS BLUE EYES (George Sutton, R. 1995). Sdlg. C-83. SDB, 10" (25 cm), M & RE. S. and style arms canary yellow (RHS 9A); F. yellow (11A), greenish (near 1B) thumbprint; beards bright blue violet (104C); ruffled; slight sweet fragrance. Amazon Princess X Manchu Coffee. Sutton 1996.

PRINCESS BRIDE (George Sutton, R. 1999). Sdlg. H-220 C. BB, 25" (64 cm), ML-VL. S. white, midrib cream yellow; style arms creamy white; F. white, hafts yellow; beards bright yellow orange, creamy white at end; fluted; slight spicy fragrance. Elizabeth Poldark X F-3: (Bubble Up x Elizabeth Poldark).

PRINCESSE CAROLINE DE MONACO (Richard Cayeux, R. 1997). Sdlg. 90132 A. TB, 34" (85 cm), EM. Pure light blue self; beards orange red. 8439 A: (Alizes x 8164: ((Condottierre x Metropolitan) x sib)) X Skyblaze. Cayeux 1998.

PRINCESS ELEXIS (Donald Spoon, R. 1995). Sdlg. 90-141-87. TB, 32" (81 cm), M. Baby ribbon pink self, F. lighter near tangerine beard; ruffled, lightly laced. Romantic Mood X (Waurine x Loveboat). Winterberry 1997.

PRINCESS GOWN (Donald Spoon, R. 1995). Sdlg. 89-115B. TB, 33" (84 cm), M. Ruffled and laced pale pink self; beards white at end, changing to pink, tangerine in throat. Femme Fatale X Sweet Musette.

PRINCESS KISS (Richard Ernst, R. 1991). Sdlg. D150-21. TB, 36" (91 cm), M. Ruffled very pale lavender; beards yellow, tipped white; pronounced sweet fragrance. Eastertime X A107-1: ((Millrace x Christmas Time) x Cherry Smoke). Cooley 1991.

PRINCESS LEIA (Heather Pryor, R. 1997). Sdlg. 60/90-16. LA, 45" (114 cm), M. S. and F. cyclamen purple (RHS 74B), white rim and reverse, raised lime yellow steeple signal with crimson veining; style arms white, pale pink blush when fresh; ruffled. Gladiator's Gift X Desert Jewel. Iris Haven 1997/98.

PRINCESS MAXINE (Cloyd McCord, R. 1991). Sdlg. 82-1. TB, 38" (97 cm), M. S. dark blue; F. dark blue, blue signal; beards dark blue; sweet fragrance. Pledge Allegiance X 83-5: (Evening Mist x (Beauty Crown x Homecoming Queen)). McCord 1991.

PRINCESS OF PINK (Akihiko Terada, R. 1994). Sdlg. S-009-89-3. TB, 37" (94 cm), M. S. pink; F. white, edged pink; beards apricot pink, white at tip. Beverly Sills X Dance Away. Roris 1995.

PRINCESS PITTYPAT (Chet Tompkins, R. 1995). Sdlg. 92-3. TB, 37" (94 cm), M & RE. S. ivory, smoky heliotrope edge; style arms smoky brown, tinged blue; F. dark ivory, bordered and peppered smoky heliotrope; beards smoky bronze, tinted blue. (Daredevil x Busy Butterfly) X (Apollodorus sib x Purple Pepper). Fleur de Lis 1995.

PRINCESS SABRA (Cy Bartlett, R. 1995). Sdlg. CSP-C. TB, 38" (97 cm), L. S. bright hot pink;

F. intense burgundy wine; beards red orange; ruffled. Cannington Sweet Puff X ((Carnaby x In Tempo) x (Carnaby x Evening Frolic)).

PRINCESS SHARMA (John C. Taylor, R. 1994). Sdlg. RL 41-2. LA, 52" (132 cm), ML. Pink, veined lemon yellow, signals yellow. N 61-A: (red sdlg., unknown parentage, x Koorawatha) X Margaret Lee. Rainbow Ridge 1994/95.

PRINCIPLES (Sterling Innerst, R. 1992). Sdlg. 3322-1. TB, 32" (81 cm), M. Silvery white; beards cream white, tipped yellowish; slight fragrance. Twice Delightful X 1851-2: ((Appalachian Spring x Navy Strut) x ((Captain Jack x Warm Laughter) x sib)). Innerst 1993.

PRINTSESSA KAVKAZA (V. & N. Gordodelovy, R. 1995). Sdlg. 40. TB, 32" (80 cm), E. Heavily ruffled lilac, tinted pink; beards cream at end, changing to creamy orange, red in throat. Parentage unknown. Gordodelovy 1986.

PRINZESSIN ZUR LIPPE (Siegmar Goerbitz, R. 1991). Sdlg. 8351A8. TB, 39" (100 cm), M. Frilled, lightly ruffled medium blue; beards blue, orange base. (Shipshape x Rondo) X St. Louis Blues. Schoeppinger 1990.

PRISCILLA OF CORINTH (Bernice Miller, R. 1996). TB, 37" (94 cm), E & RE (Sept.-Nov./AL). Laced and ruffled light pinkish peach; beards coral. Playgirl X Coral Charmer. Garden of the Enchanted Rainbow 1994.

PRISM (Marky Smith, R. 1994). Sdlg. 89-27C. IB, 24" (61 cm), EM. S. solid greyed violet (RHS 90B); F. blended violet (89D to 86A) with faint lavender luminata pattern merging to grey halo around beard; beards lilac grey, yellow in throat; ruffled; pronounced sweet fragrance. Chubby Cheeks X Snowbrook. Aitken's Salmon Creek 1995.

PRISM VIEW (Richard Ernst, R. 1993). Sdlg. F147A. TB, 34" (86 cm), ML. Cool lavender violet blend with brown veining, F. with pastel brown rim; beards yellow, tipped white; ruffled; slight sweet fragrance. Afternoon Delight X B106: ((Millrace x San Leandro) x Ringo). Cooley 1992.

PRISTINE ELEGANCE (Hugh Knight by John Wood, R. 1992). Sdlg. K-104-86. JI (6 F.), 36" (91 cm), M. White (RHS 155D) with yellow green (150A) signal; style arms white (155B). Parentage unknown. John Wood 1993.

PRIVATE RESERVE (J. T. Aitken, R. 1993). Sdlg. 86T50. TB, 36" (91 cm), M. Ruffled wine red; beards violet, tipped white; slight fragrance. Warrior King X Gyro. Aitken's Salmon Creek 1993.

PRIVATE STOCK (Melba Hamblen, TB, R. 1989). Roris 1991.

PRIVATE TREASURE (George Shoop, R. 1993). Sdlg. 87-23. TB, 36" (91 cm), M. S. orange; F. ruffled and flared yellow; beards tangerine. Blazing Light X Edna's Wish. Shoop 1993.

PRIVILEGED CHARACTER (Paul Black, R. 1990). Sdlg. 86269B. SDB, 14" (36 cm), M. S. silvery orchid white ground, bright rose purple plicata markings and band; F. silvery orchid white ground, bright rose purple plicata markings inside matching band; beards orchid white, tipped old gold; pronounced spicy fragrance. Gentle Air X Chubby Cheeks. Mid-America 1990.

PRIX D'AMOUR (John C. Taylor, R. 1994). Sdlg. RL 64-1. LA, 44" (110 cm), ML. Ruffled and laced light pink veined rose pink, lighter rims, green line signal surrounded by yellow. OL 121-1: ((Edith Fear x Valera) x Limited Edition) X Margaret Lee. Rainbow Ridge 1996/97.

PRIX D'ELEGANCE (Heather Pryor, R. 1995). Sdlg. 38/91-F. LA, 35" (89 cm), EM. S. and F. soft rose pink, green signal ribbed deep rose, cream rim and reverse; style arms lemon, flushed rose pink; ruffled. Dazzling Star X Jazz Ballet. Lone Star 1997, Iris Haven 1997/98.

PROFESSOR BARBARA (Joseph Mertzweiller, R. 1990). Sdlg. T-63-79A. LA (tet.), 32-34" (81-86 cm), M. S. medium yellow, pale bluish cast; style arms greenish; F. medium yellow, greenish orange signal; musky fragrance. C-76-4: (Professor Ike X Wheelhorse colchicine-treated chimera) X C-76-88E: (66-G-Z, colchicine chimera, x Professor Ike). Cordon Bleu 1992.

PROFESSOR CHAYANOV (Viktor Sheviakov, R. 1995). Sdlg. 495 IU. TB, 34" (87 cm), ML. S. and F. white ground, dotted violet blue edges; beards light yellow; ruffled. Dancers Veil X Rococo. Sheviakov 1991.

PROFESSOR FRITCHIE (Joseph Mertzweiller, R. 1993). Sdlg. T-85-41A. LA (tet.), 40-44" (102-112 cm), E. S. medium yellow, slight blue cast; F. medium yellow, inconspicuous greenish yellow signal; slight musky fragrance. C-77-33: (Professor Ike x President Hedley, colchicine chimera) X Professor Barbara. Cordon Bleu, Lone Star 1995.

PROFESSOR JOHN PEARN (Allan Llewellyn, R. 1990). Sdlg. AL-1. TB, 30" (76 cm), M. S. pale gold, tip lighter; F. purple mauve (RHS 76C) veined deep purple; beards light yellow; lightly ruffled. Parentage unknown.

PROFESSOR MARTA MARIE (Joseph Mertzweiller, R. 1990). Sdlg. C-76-4C. LA (tet.), 30-32" (76-81 cm), EM. Rose pink, signals medium greenish yellow; musky fragrance. Professor Ike X Wheelhorse, colchicine treated chimera. Cordon Bleu 1992.

PROFESSOR NEIL (Joseph Mertzweiller, R. 1990). Sdlg. T-63-79B. LA (tet.), 30" (75 cm), M. S. dark red; F. velvety dark red, large brilliant yellow signal; musky fragrance. Sib to Professor Barbara. Cordon Bleu 1992.

PROGRESSIVE ATTITUDE (Sterling Innerst, R. 1991). Sdlg. 3093-1. TB, 36" (91 cm), EM. S. white; F. white, narrow stitched blue edge; beards lemon, tipped white; slight musky fragrance. Instructor X 2237-15: (Burgundy Brown x (Osage Buff x Spinning Wheel)). Innerst 1992.

PROMISE OF LOVE (Eugene Hunt by Sharon McAllister, AB (OGB), R. 1986). Aril Society, McAllister 1991.

PROMISES PROMISES (William Maryott, R. 1997). Sdlg. XM262REA. IB, 23" (58 cm), EML & RE. Slightly ruffled bright lemon yellow (RHS 13A), F. with slight darker yellow veining near yellow orange beard; slight fragrance. Wake Up X Pure as Gold. Maryott 1997.

PROPER LADY (Lynda Miller, R. 1995). Sdlg. 6187A. TB, 34" (86 cm), ML. S. pale creamy peach, edge deeper; style arms cream to pale orange; F. light orange; beards tangerine, base cream; slight musky fragrance. 5484B: (Odyssey x Roundup) X Wedding Candles. Miller's Manor 1996.

PROPOSAL (Barry Blyth, R. 1999). Sdlg. D87-C. TB, 36" (91 cm), ML. Metallic electric blue lilac, shot tan brown, F. with tan hafts; beards blue, lemon in throat; sweet fragrance. Vanda Song X Plume d'Or. Tempo Two 1999/2000.

PROSPECTOR'S GOLD (Barbara Wight, R. 1996). Sdlg. 92-3. TB, 32" (81 cm), ML. S. and style arms lemon yellow (RHS 13B); F. lemon yellow ground, lined and dotted tan border; beards gold, tipped purple, ending in horn; slight spicy fragrance. Space Shuttle Light X Come To Me. Wight's Iris 1997.

PROSPERO'S ISLE (Nora Scopes, R. 1993). Sdlg. 95137A. TB, 38" (97 cm), M. S. pale blue mauve; F. rich blue mauve; beards maraschino red; sweet fragrance. China Seas X Street Dancer.

PROSPEROUS VOYAGE (Ben Hager, R. 1996). Sdlg. T5399YOrBds. TB, 32" (81 cm), EM. S. yellow; F. slightly deeper yellow; beards orange. Gratuity X Quasar. Cooley 1997.

PROTOCOL (Keith Keppel, R. 1994). Sdlg. 90-6M. IB, 23" (58 cm), EM. S. white (M&P 9-A-1), flushed pinard yellow (9-J-2) in center; style arms white; F. darker than dandelion yellow (9-L-4), paling slightly at edge; beards white at end, deep chrome yellow (9-L-7) midsection, cadmium yellow (9-L-8) in throat; slight fragrance. Over Easy X Amber Snow. Keppel 1996.

PROTON (Barry Blyth, R. 1996). Sdlg. D34-23. SDB, 12" (30 cm), ML. S. soft pastel pink; F. white, 1/8" pastel pink outer edge, 1/8" dotted and blended pastel lavender inner edge; beards red, lavender at end. Bee's Knees X A7-1: (Merry Dance x Mini Song). Tempo Two 1996/97.

PROUDLY MINE (Margaret Summerill, R. 1993). Sdlg. E119-5. TB, 43" (109 cm), EM. S. creamy white, strongly infused smoky violet; F. creamy white blended cream, solid border and dotting of smoky violet (RHS 87D); beards burnt gold; ruffled. Lawrence Welk X Smoke Rings.

PROUD MARY (Lois O'Brien, R. 1993). Sdlg. 92101-A. TB, 40" (102 cm), M. S. sky blue, hint of periwinkle at midrib; F. slightly darker with lavender overtones; beards honey, tipped cream; slight sweet fragrance. Mary D X Fort Bragg. O'Brien Iris 1995.

PROUD MOMENT (B. Charles Jenkins, R. 1992). Sdlg. BD43E. SPU, 30-38" (76-97 cm), ML. S. white; F. yellow, crimped white edge. B4-0A: (Dawn Candle x unknown) x B5-3CC: (Equality x Crow Wing). Shepard Iris 1993.

PROUD PAPA (Sharon McAllister, R. 1992). Sdlg. PP-HS-2. AB (OGB+), 28" (72 cm), EM. S. white, veined pale pinkish violet; F. pink and yellow blend formed by soft yellow ground faintly washed violet, few burgundy veins radiating from beard; beards gold, tipped burgundy. Persian Pansy X Heart Stealer. McAllister 1992.

PROUD PRINCESS (A. & D. Willott, R. 1999). Sdlg. W 92-167. SDB, 11" (28 cm), ML. Lightly ruffled pale pink, F. with rose haft lines; beards white. W 83-66: (W 78-133: (Peach Bavarian x (Blueberry Muffins x (Roberts 65R27A, Lenna M sib, x Dove Wings))) x Coral Wings) X W 88-38: (W 83-66 x Pink Crystal).

PROUD SPIRIT (A. & D. Willott, R. 1995). Sdlg. 89-100. SDB, 12" (30 cm), ML. S. pale yellow; F. cream, tinted blue, red brown spot; beards gold. Star Search X 76-44: (Carousel Belle x Royal Bee). Willott 1995.

PROUD TRADITION (Schreiner, R. 1990). Sdlg. W 164-A. TB, 36" (91 cm), EM. S. light blue (RHS

91C); F. ruffled medium blue (93A); beards blue, tipped yellow. J 50-G: (D 241-1: ((First Violet x King's Choice) x (Allegiance x ((Pierre Menard x Blue Ensign) x Harbor Blue)) x ((First Violet x Arabi Pasha) x (Salem x Bluebird Blue))) x Navy Strut) X Royal Crusader. Schreiner 1990.

PROVEN STOCK (Kenneth Fisher, R. 1996). Sdlg. 93-4. MTB, 20" (51 cm), M. S. brass to wheat; F. medium plum purple, brass to wheat 1/16" rim; beards orange, aging yellow. H8: (G17: (Carolyn Rose x Chickee) x Consummation) X Consummation. Aitken's Salmon Creek 1997.

PROWL (Barry Blyth, R. 1998). Sdlg. F103-1. IB, 22" (56 cm), EM. S. lemon yellow, deepening at base to brown; F. mustard, deeper haft veining to brown at throat, small white venation around beard; beards mustard yellow, bright lavender at end. Touch and Go X Cast a Spell. Tempo Two 1998/99.

PRUDY (R. E. Nichol by Jean Nichol, R. 1998). Sdlg. S 278-4. BB, 27" (70 cm), M. S. and style arms pale blue; F. rich purple; beards yellow, pale blue tip; lightly ruffled; slight fragrance. N 195: (Pascoe x Warleggan) X N 185-2: (K 84-6: (Cardew x Warleggan) x Bluebird Wine).

PRUSSIAN BLUE (Tomas Tamberg, R. 1993). SIB (tet.), 33½" (85 cm), M. S. deep blue; F. ruffled velvety blue. Germantet One X Blue Burgee. Schoeppinger, Tamberg 1993.

PRUSSIAN MAGIC (Barry Blyth, R. 1993). Sdlg. EQ-3. SPU, 48" (122 cm), ML. S. pastel lavender blue; F. muted gold upper half, pastel lavender lower half. Equality X self. Tempo Two 1993/94.

PSEUDO LEWDO (Tom Burseen, R. 1990). Sdlg. 6-185A. TB, 36" (91 cm), M. S. laced creamy yellow ground sprayed with maroon red dots and streaks; F. ruffled and laced maroon red, fine yellow edge, white and yellow streaks on hafts and halfway down F.; beards gold; spicy fragrance. Villa Splendor X 4-231A: (Fiji Dancer x Wings of Dreams). T.B.'s Place 1993.

PSHAW (Tom Burseen, R. 1993). Sdlg. 9-215B. TB, 35" (89 cm), M. S. grape red purple (RHS 59C); F. creamy apricot ground, dotted slightly darker grape red purple, more concentrated toward edge; beards bronze; ruffled. Point Made X 6-146: (Rio de Oro x Noon Siesta). T.B.'s Place 1994.

PSSST (Mitch Jameson, R. 1997). Sdlg. 7-93. TB, 32" (81 cm), M. S. and style arms soft yellow; F. satiny lavender; beards yellow and lavender. Emanations X Mavis Waves.

PSY (Lawrence Ransom, R. 1994). Sdlg. 90/322. MTB, 16" (41 cm), ML. S. medium yellow, frosted gold; style arms medium yellow; F. white, faintly edged pale yellow, very fine maroon violet veining or stitching, yellow hafts veined maroon violet; beards orange, whiter at end, tipped light maroon violet, occasional very short hairy horn; heavily ribbed foliage. *I. astrachanica* sdlg. (SIGNA seed) X Welch's Reward. Iris au Trescols 1995.

PTÁK OHNIVÁK (Zdeněk Seidl, R. 1997). Sdlg. 91-ExOS/5. BB, 27" (70 cm), L. Orange (RHS 29C), F. with red blaze; beards saturn red (30B); slight sweet fragrance. Extravagant X Orange Star.

PTITSA SCHASTIYA (Viacheslav Gavrilin, R. 1999). Sdlg. 96-210-1. TB, 30" (76 cm), EM. S. white; style arms light yellow; F. yellow-tinted white, yellower hafts, thin yellow rim; beards yellow; ruffled. Wedding Candles X Starlight Express.

PU ABI (Ladislav Muska, R. 1995). Sdlg. GERI-03. TB, 38" (97 cm), M. S. light pink; F. light red, edged pink; beards tangerine; ruffled, laced. (Geniality x Ringo) X (Paradise x "Rarete"). Muska 1996.

PUCCINI (Joseph Ghio, R. 1998). Sdlg. 94-26D3. TB, 36" (91 cm), EML. S. white; F. white, purple lines radiating from red beard, light purple marginal dotting, shoulders gold. 92-42: (90-45B: (((Tomorrow's Child x (Caption x (Dream Affair x (Artiste x Tupelo Honey)))) x Costa Rica) x (Costa Rica sib x London Lord)) x 88-180P, pod parent of Snowed In) X 92-75D4: (90-86V2: (((83-80: ((Handiwork x (Gay Parasol x Mystique)) x Goddess) x (Gem of Sierra x ((((Ponderosa x Honey Rae) x ((((Commentary x Claudia Rene) x Claudia Rene) x Ponderosa) x (Ponderosa x New Moon))) x Osage Buff) x 76-11: (Vanity x Anon))) x Gigolo) x (Indiscreet x Columbia the Gem)) x ((Indiscreet sib x (Goddess x (Rancho Rose x ((Flareup x Osage Buff) x 76-11)))) x (Indiscreet x 83-80))) x 88-180P). Bay View 1999.

PUFFLET (Marion Ball, R. 1998). Sdlg. MB 93. SPEC (evansia), 33-35" (85-90 cm), EML. S. pale lavender; style arms medium lavender; F. medium lavender, bright yellow crest edged with deep lavender markings, surrounded by distinct white area; slight fragrance. Question Mark X Chengdu.

PUG (Eugene Kalkwarf, R. 1999). Sdlg. EK 95-00. MTB, 24" (61 cm), M. S. gold, some brown flecking; F. white with brown stripes, gold edging; beards yellow. Sand Princess X unknown.

PUGET MOON (Stan Dexter by Marie Ingersoll, R. 1990). Sdlg. 83-231AA. TB, 34" (86 cm), M.

S. cream yellow; F. cream yellow edged yellow, darker rib and hash markings; beards gold. Parentage unknown. Ingersoll's Iris 1990.

PULSE RATE DATE (Tom Burseen, R. 1990). Sdlg. 6-80J. TB, 36" (91 cm), E. S. creamy pink washed light maroon purple; F. creamy yellow, fancy maroon purple wash and streaks; beards mustard; heavily ruffled; slight fragrance. Lilac Laser sib X Queen in Calico. T.B.'s Place 1992.

PUMPIN' IRON (Paul Black, R. 1990). Sdlg. 86323A. SDB, 14" (36 cm), M. S. dark sooty red black; F. dark black cherry spot shading to red purple margin; beards purple; pronounced spicy fragrance. P. Dyer G-6: (Demon x (Cherry Garden x Bloodspot)) X Forte. Mid-America 1990.

PUMPKIN CHEESECAKE (O. D. Niswonger, R. 1995). Sdlg. 25-92. TB, 30" (76 cm), M. S. white; F. orange; beards tangerine orange. Apricot Frosty X sib to 26-85: (Ambrosia Delight x 16-80: (Coral Beauty x pink amoena Marmalade Skies sib)). Cape Iris 1995.

PUMPKIN CHIFFON (D. L. Shepard, R. 1999). Sdlg. 88004-8603. LA, 36" (91 cm), M. S. pumpkin orange, darker centerline; style arms creamy pumpkin, edged darker; F. pumpkin orange, lime line signal surrounded by large dark pumpkin blush; flat form. Bobbie Lou X Creole Flame.

PUMPKINFEST (Jim Hedgecock, R. 1997). Sdlg. 84-6-K. TB, 30" (76 cm), EM. Ruffled and laced medium orange, F. with white ray pattern near wide red orange beard; pronounced sweet fragrance. Sun Fire X Mandolin. Comanche Acres 1998.

PUMPKIN MUNCHKIN (Perry Dyer, R. 1999). Sdlg. 94-24B. SDB, 9" (22 cm), ML. S. light apricot; style arms apricot pumpkin; F. deeper apricot pumpkin; beards medium orange, light orange base; ruffled. Tweety Bird X Bright Chic.

PUN (Keith Keppel, R. 1990). Sdlg. 84-5A. IB, 19" (48 cm), EM. S. deep chrome lemon (M&P 9-L-2) ground, strongly shaded rosy brown (6-H-9) on outer two-thirds; F. deep chrome lemon, chalet red (6-K-10) hafts, very faint dot edge matching tan yellow effect of S.; beards white base, pale violet mid-layer, light yellow top; slight sweet fragrance. 82-12A: (Gigolo x 79-78A: (((Roundup x Artwork sib) x Osage Buff) x (Anon x Prediction sib))) X Pepper Mill. Keppel 1991.

PUNK (Lawrence Ransom, R. 1997). Sdlg. 90/247-3. MDB, 7" (18 cm), ML. S. dark cobalt violet, center lighter; F. medium cobalt violet, dark red violet spot; beards light violet ending in fat, hairy horn. Clay's Caper X Peyrard PB 88/1: (Planet Iris x *pumila*). Iris au Trescols 1998.

PUPP (Ladislav Muska, R. 1995). Sdlg. TGMH-05A. TB, 41" (104 cm), ML. Ruffled dark purple blue self; beards blue. Titan's Glory X Morning Hymn. Muska 1992.

PUPPET MASTER (Bryce Williamson, R. 1993). Sdlg. 289-A. BB, 25" (64 cm), M. Dark gold tan, F. with henna rust brown plicata haft pencilling; beards gold; slight fragrance. Dazzling Gold X Carnival Magic. Pacific Coast Hybridizers 1993.

PURE AS GOLD (William Maryott, TB, R. 1989). Maryott 1993.

PURE AT HEART (Sharon McAllister, R. 1994). Sdlg. 89-33-1. AB (OGB), 28" (72 cm), EM. S. white, violet stitching intensifying around edge; style arms yellow, rust crest veining; F. yellowish ivory, heavy burgundy dotting and veining underlying beard, finer veining extending over blade; beards layered mustard and maroon. Sunrise in Glory X 85-3-17: (Boaz x Jean Ralls). McAllister 1994.

PURE REASON (Akihiko Terada, R. 1999). Sdlg. S133-89-6. TB, 36" (91 cm), M. White self; beards red. Romantic Mood X Beautiful Dreamer. Roris 1999.

PURGA (Nina Miroshnichenko, R. 1996). TB, 39" (98 cm), M. Ruffled milky white self; beards light yellow; slight sweet fragrance. Parentage unknown. Miroshnichenko 1976.

PURIST'S DELIGHT (Les Fort, R. 1990). Sdlg. 88-373-C. TB, 36" (91 cm), M. Heavily ruffled pastel pink, orange and vanilla blend; beards delicate salmon; pronounced sweet fragrance. First Endeavor sib X (Custom Made x Song of Norway).

PURPLE CONCERTO (B. Charles Jenkins, R. 1992). Sdlg. BD28B. SPU, 35-40" (89-102 cm), M. Blended purple and ivory. C12-7A: (Far Out x Crow Wing) X B3-5B: (Crow Wing x Equality). Shepard Iris 1993.

PURPLE DREAM (Nora Scopes, CA, R. 1983). V. H. Humphrey 1992.

PURPLE EYE (Akihiko Terada, R. 1997). Sdlg. S-158-89-1. BB, 26" (66 cm), M. Light lavender, purple in center; beards orange, tipped light purple. Olympiad X Batik. Roris 1997.

PURPLE HEART IMPRESSION (Luella Danielson, R. 1996). Sdlg. 76-7-L. AB (OGB+), 19" (48 cm), ML. S. light lavender veined darker, lighter lavender midrib tinged green; style arms light lavender, deep violet near anthers; F. light lavender, white hairline edge, sparse dark violet veining, violet signal; beards slate effect, hairs green, yellow and white tipped violet; pronounced sweet fragrance. ((Tul Kerem x Kalifa Gulnare) x (A 86-2 LD, parentage unknown, x Sand and

Snow)) X ((Tul Kerem x (*I. camillae* x Judean Pixie)) x (Shah Abbas x Fairy Fantasy)). Aril Society, Pleasure Iris 1997.

PURPLE HEART THROB (Leslie Donnell, R. 1991). CA, 10" (26 cm), E. S. yellow (RHS 161C); F. same, purple (80A) throat, faint blue lines running downward. Parentage unknown.

PURPLE LASSIE (Kirk Strawn, R. 1996). Sdlg. X-1985. LA, 28" (71 cm), M. S. and F. violet purple (darker than RHS 77A); signals yellow green (151A/B); style arms beetroot (71A). #1, unknown, X Black Gamecock. Bois d'Arc 1996.

PURPLE MAGIC (Donald Spoon, R. 1995). Sdlg. 90-6-2. TB, 32" (81 cm), EM & RE. Ruffled purple self; beards purple, hairs tipped yellow; flared. Lilla's Gloves X Orbiter. Winterberry 1997.

PURPLE MOUNTAIN MAJESTY (W. H. Clough, R. 1993). Sdlg. RWB-87. TB, 36" (91 cm), M. S. deep purple at base blending to lighter at edge; style arms light purple; F. pale lavender fading to white; beards yellow; lightly ruffled. Edge of Winter X SSRWB-84: (SS-78 x Secret Society). Clough 1994.

PURPLE PAGODA (John Baldwin, R. 1994). Sdlg. 82-35D. TB, 30" (76 cm), ML. Deep purple (RHS 80A), cream area around tangerine beards; slight fragrance. 76-60A: (((Skywatch x 69-21C) x (Irish Lullaby x 66-100F)) x (((63-65E x Rippling Waters) x Sunset Snows) x (Irish Lullaby x 62-37A))) X Entourage.

PURPLE PALLAS (John C. Taylor, LA, R. 1989). Rainbow Ridge 1991/92.

PURPLE PEPPER (D. C. Nearpass, TB, R. 1986). Correction of parentage. J-69-22: (Dancers Veil x 4-66-3: ((New Adventure x (Captured Heart x Melodrama)) x Ribbon Round)) X Easy Street.

PURPLE PLEASER (Everette Lineberger, R. 1994). Sdlg. QHT 131. TB, 40" (102 cm), ML. S. purple; F. velvety red purple, white reverse, white triangle with prominent purple lines around beard; beards gold, tipped white; ruffled; slight fragrance. Rose Shiner X Pops Concert. Quail Hill 1995.

PURPLE PLUS (Currier McEwen, R. 1993). Sdlg. 68/7B. JI (9+ F. dip.), 32" (81 cm), EML-VL & RE. Rich velvety blue purple (RHS 86A), signal yellow; styles tufted. Payne sdlg. X Blue Butterfly. Eartheart, Seaways 1993.

PURPLE POLKA (Monique Dumas-Quesnel, R. 1992). Sdlg. 89-X-versata-05. SPEC-X (versata), 40½" (105 cm), M. S. dark violet blue (RHS 89C); F. dark violet (86A), bright yellow signal; slight sweet fragrance. EX-86-1-45, *versicolor* sdlg., X purple *ensata* sdlg.

PURPLE PUMA (Brad Kasperek, R. 1997). Sdlg. 92M-24P. MDB, 7" (18 cm), M. Dark violet purple (RHS 88A) self; beards wistaria blue (92A); lightly ruffled; slight fragrance. Snowy River X Quicken. Miller's Manor 1998.

PURPLE SAND (Anna Mae Miller, R. 1990). Sdlg. 85-49-4. SIB, 36" (91 cm), M & RE. S. light violet (RHS 85B); style arms pale violet blue; F. light violet veined darker. Esther C.D.M. X Almost a Melody. Old Douglas Perennials 1991.

PURPLE SEQUIN (Howard Shockey, R. 1992). Sdlg. 85-40-4A. AR (OG), 9" (23 cm), M. Milky white, dark violet purple (near RHS 83A) signal; beards violet purple (88B). 77-47-5A: (Shah Azul x 60-96: (Judean Bonnet x CGW W-157)) X 82-22-5A: (77-68-9A: (62-31-G: (*I. urmiensis* x (Austin 157-2 x *I. iberica*)) x 73-44-1: ((*I. gatesii* x *I. mariae*) x (Judean Bonnet x CGW W-157))) x 74-5-1B: ((Judean Bonnet x CGW W-157) x ((*I. susiana* x Andromache) x Judean Charmer))). Arilian Acres, Aril Society 1992.

PURPLE SMOKE (B. Charles Jenkins, R. 1995). Sdlg. BJ27D. SPU, 42-51" (107-130 cm), M. S. purple; F. purple washed over yellow, yellower at signal area. Lively One X Now This. Shepard Iris 1995.

PURPLET CHA-CHA (Monique Dumas-Quesnel, R. 1992). Sdlg. 90-X-versata-06. SPEC-X (versata), 47½" (120 cm), M. S. violet (RHS 83C); F. darker violet (83A), creamy white line below dull yellow signal; slight sweet fragrance. EX-DW-13, *versicolor* sdlg., X purple *ensata* sdlg.

PURPLE TRINITY (Marion Ball, R. 1998). SPEC (*unguicularis*), 7-8" (18-20 cm), ML. S. and style arms medium violet; F. dark violet, pronounced darker velvety violet flush surrounding gold signal which fades to white in throat, hafts unveined; slight fragrance. Parentage unknown -- probably inv. Mary Barnard.

PURPUROVA MANTIYA (Oleg Amekhin, R. 1996). Sdlg. JC-1. JI (3 F.), 47" (120 cm), E. Reddish purple self. Oyodo X Vasili Alfiorov. Amekhin 1996.

PURSUIT OF DREAMS (Evelyn Kegerise, TB R. 1989). Evelyn Kegerise 1991.

PUST VSEGDA SOLNTSE (V. & N. Gordodelovy, R. 1996). Sdlg. 37. TB, 39" (100 cm), M. Golden yellow self; beards orange; slight fragrance. Parentage unknown. Gordodelovy 1985.

PUTSCH (Lawrence Ransom, R. 1996). Sdlg. 90/330-15. SDB, 10" (25 cm), EM. S. medium dark violet; F. lustrous black violet center, lighter toward edge and on shoulders; beards violet-tinted white. Khaki Print X Trescols. Iris au Trescols 1996.

PUZZLE (Joseph Ghio, R. 1991). Sdlg. PL-MIX-E. CA, 15" (38 cm), EM. Mustard gold, textured deeper, neon violet signal. Parentage unknown. Bay View 1992.

PYSHKA (Viktor Sheviakov, R. 1996). Sdlg. 20d7b. TB, 33" (85 cm), ML. S. creamy yellow, tinged orange; F. creamy yellow orange, brown violet striations near creamy yellow orange beard; ruffled, lightly laced; spicy fragrance. Radiant Apogee X Pink Taffeta. Sheviakov 1996.

QUADROS' DELIGHT (Cloyd McCord, R. 1993). Sdlg. 13-0-3. TB, 36" (91 cm), M. Ruffled, laced dark rich orange; beards red; sweet fragrance. 79-10: (Beauty Crown x Homecoming Queen) X Homecoming Queen. McCord 1993.

QUADROS' JOY (Cloyd McCord, R. 1993). Sdlg. 85-3-A. TB, 36" (91 cm), M. S. pale rose lavender; F. white ground, 1¼" lavender trimmed edge, lavender shoulders, pale yellow around red beard; ruffled, laced; sweet fragrance. Homecoming Queen X 73-13: (Angie Quadros x Homecoming Queen). McCord 1993.

QUADROS' PRIDE (Cloyd McCord, R. 1993). Sdlg. 84-6-B. TB, 36" (91 cm), M. Pale lavender blended pink, pale lavender area around bright orange beards; ruffled, laced; sweet fragrance. Homecoming Queen X 76-13: (Song of Erin x (Irish Delight x Singing Pines)). McCord 1993.

QUADROS' QUEEN (Cloyd McCord, R. 1992). Sdlg. 82-2-A. TB, 36" (91 cm), E. S. pale rose lavender; F. white ground, 1/4" lavender trimmed edge, lavender on upper portion, pale yellow around red beard; laced, ruffled; sweet fragrance. Homecoming Queen X 76-13: (Beauty Crown x Homecoming Queen).

QUADROS' WISH (Cloyd McCord, R. 1992). Sdlg. 82-64. TB, 36" (91 cm), M. S. light orange; F. red, trimmed light orange around edge; beards yellow; ruffled; sweet fragrance. Entourage X 73-13: (Angie Quadros x Homecoming Queen).

QUAIL HOLLOW (A. & D. Willott, R. 1999). Sdlg. W 95-125. SDB, 9" (23 cm), L. S. blended pale blue and yellow; style arms pale blue; F. golden brown; beards full blue, yellow in throat; lightly ruffled. Taffy Touch X Harlem Nocturne.

QUAINT LADY (Ray Lyons, TB, R. 1988). Long 1991.

QUALIFIED (Graeme Grosvenor, R. 1999). Sdlg. V23-2. TB, 32" (81 cm), ML. Apricot peach pink self; beards tangerine; sweet fragrance. Larcenist X Bogota. Rainbow Ridge 1999/2000.

QUANAH PARKER (Hyram Ames, R. 1996). Sdlg. A884. TB, 28" (71 cm), M. S. red black; style arms red black, lighter midrib; F. darker red black, hafts chocolate; beards maroon, hairs tipped bronze; ruffled, laced; slight spicy fragrance. A853: ((A7211: (((Black Taffeta x Archibald sdlg.: (Blue Gown x All Eternity)) x (Dark Fury x Orchid Jewel)) x Laced Tapestry) x Study in Black) x (A7710: (A7211 x Dusky Dancer) x Superstition)) X A845: (((A656: ((Party Dress x Black Hills) x (Sugarplum x Violet Hills)) x Wonderful One) x (A656 x Laced Tapestry)) x ((A7211 x Wonderful One) x A7710)). Comanche Acres 1998.

QUANDIALLA (Kevin Nilsen, R. 1992). Sdlg. 70-85-1. TB, 30" (76 cm), M. S. blended amber and yellow; F. light violet center over white ground, rose tan blended edge, glowing yellow hafts; beards deep orange yellow; heavily ruffled. Parentage unknown. Iridescence 1992/93.

QUARTA CARAVELLA (Augusto Bianco, R. 1999). Sdlg. 431. TB, 33" (85 cm), L. S. rose to peach; style arms rose and violet; F. violet, lighter near beard; beards tangerine, base cream; slight spicy fragrance. Lovely Glow X Planned Treasure. Iride 1999.

QUEBELLE (Tony Huber, R. 1998). Sdlg. 95-132 (91-881). SPEC-X (biversata), 43" (110 cm), ML. S. violet blue (RHS 90C), some darker veining; style arms violet blue, bordered wistaria blue (92C); F. violet (86A/B), bright golden yellow signal surrounded by white veins, reverse side wistaria blue (92C) with white center; slight musky fragrance. 89-747-06: (89-MR03-14 *versicolor* x 3-F. purple *ensata* sdlg.) X MR03-13 *versicolor*: (MR03-555 x MR03-04).

QUEEN ANNE'S LACE (William Maryott, R. 1998). Sdlg. W115T. TB, 38" (97 cm), EM. White, faint shading of lavender; style arms white; beards orange, wide; heavily laced; slight fragrance. Birthday Greetings X Divinity. Maryott 1998.

QUEEN BEE (Mary Dunn, R. 1993). Sdlg. M83-817AA. BB, 22" (56 cm), M. Light violet, stained and netted violet overall, with lighter area at end of beard; beards light violet, tipped white. Ghio 77-70: ((Premonition sib x Mystique) x Barletta) X Fancy Face. M.A.D. Iris 1994.

QUEEN CHARLOTTE (B. J. Brown, R. 1992). Sdlg. 2288. TB, 32" (81 cm), E. Pale pink self; beards pale pink, tipped white; slight fragrance. Vanity X 1384: (Nefertiti x Scintillation). B. J. Brown 1993.

QUEEN NECHES (Albert Faggard, LA, R. 1988). Faggard 1994.

QUEEN OF ANGELS (Schreiner, R. 1995). Sdlg. BB 1188-1. TB, 36" (91 cm), L. Heavily laced white self, tinted lavender (RHS 155B); beards white, tipped yellow. W 630-1: ((Last Hurrah sib x Laced Cotton) x Lady Madonna) X V 495-A: (Visual Arts x (G 525-6: (((Crinkled Beauty x P 309-1) x Lilac Supreme) x ((Amethyst Flame x Silvertone) x Lilac Supreme)) x Fond Wish)). Schreiner 1995.

QUEEN OF BALLET (Cloyd McCord, R. 1997). Sdlg. 706. TB, 36" (91 cm), M. S. and style arms cream; F. white, 1/4" lavender marginal band; beards orange, white at end; sweet fragrance. Ballet Dreamer X Princess Maxine. McCord 1997.

QUEEN OF ELEGANCE (Barry Blyth, R. 1997). Sdlg. C124-A. TB, 40" (102 cm), EM. S. pale silvery blue, deeper midrib flush; F. paler silver blue, deeper blended line below beard; beards silvery blue, tipped white; slight fragrance. A77-4, All Silent sib, X Maybe an Angel. Tempo Two 1997/98.

QUEEN OF LOVE (Cloyd McCord, R. 1991). Sdlg. 3-R. TB, 36" (91 cm), M. S. light lavender; F. light yellow, light lavender edge; beards yellow; sweet fragrance. 82-1: (Chorus Girl x Custom Made) X 84-1: (Last Call x American Sweetheart). McCord 1991.

QUEEN OF SPADES (Hyram Ames, TB, R. 1989). Comanche Acres 1992.

QUEEN'S CIRCLE (Frederick Kerr, R. 1999). Sdlg. 930401. TB, 32" (81 cm), ML. S. white; F. white, dark blue edge; beards orange red, pale yellow at end. Victoria Circle X Christiana Baker.

QUEEN SHEBA (Howard Shockey, R. 1993). Sdlg. 88-177-A. AB (OGB), 28" (71 cm), M. S. very pale orchid violet, aging near-white; F. very pale buff, aging near-white, large dark burgundy chevron signal; beards yellow bronze; slight fragrance. 86-138-R: ((79-105-C: (Stars Over Chicago x Welcome Reward) x Desert Princess) x 83-107-A: (Heart Stealer x 80-108-A: (Heart Stealer x Kalifa Gulnare))) X 86-140-T: (((79-105-H x Syrian Moon) x (Heart Stealer x 79-105-C)) x Onlooker). Arilian Acres 1993.

QUEEN'S IVORY (Thelma Naylor, SDB, R. 1988). David Austin Roses 1991.

QUEEN'S PRIZE (George Shoop, R. 1993). Sdlg. 89-47. SDB, 10" (25 cm), M. White self; beards tangerine; lightly ruffled, flared. Spring Dancer X Pink Caper. Shoop 1993.

QUEEN'S VIOLET (Howard Shockey, R. 1993). Sdlg. 88-239-A. TB, 37" (94 cm), M. Violet (RHS 88B) self; beards blue violet; slight sweet fragrance. Sea of Joy X 85-220-7B: (El Morado x High Flight). Arilian Acres 1994.

QUEEN TOPPER (Cloyd McCord, R. 1997). Sdlg. 206-6. TB, 35" (89 cm), M. S. and style arms white; F. yellow, white in center; beards yellow; slight fragrance. Lovely Spring X White Snow. McCord 1997.

QUEST FOR FIRE (Marlene Schaller, R. 1999). Sdlg. 94.3.1. TB, 38" (97 cm), EM. S. medium red, veined darker; style arms medium gold, crests medium red; F. deep red, narrowly edged medium red; beards gold, some hairs tipped red; lightly ruffled; slight sweet fragrance. Copper Capers X Brimstone.

QUICK CHANGE ARTIST (Sharon McAllister, R. 1995). Sdlg. 90-29-1. AB (OGB-), 28" (71 cm), M. S. white, veined and dotted lilac (near RHS 80C); style arms white, flushed yellow, midrib and crests lilac; F. white, veined lilac, center veining aging to leave plicata-like edging; beards golden yellow and violet mixture. Unknown blue violet and white TB plicata X Whither Thou Goest. McAllister 1995.

QUICKEN (J. T. Aitken, R. 1991). Sdlg. 86M41A. SDB, 10" (25 cm), EM. White, edges stitched dark purple; beards frost white, tipped violet; slight fragrance. Chubby Cheeks X Peso. Aitken's Salmon Creek 1991.

QUICK PICK (Lilly Gartman, R. 1990). Sdlg. 86-9A. TB, 36" (91 cm), E. S. spanish orange (HCC 010/2); F. white, edged spanish orange; beards orange. 83-34B: (Piping Hot x 180-10B: (Soap Opera x Ghio 76-63C: (Joyce Terry x Entourage))) X Alluring. Roris 1992.

QUICK THINKING (Richard Ernst, R. 1991). Sdlg. D139-1. TB, 38" (97 cm), ML. S. deep amber gold; F. crimson maroon; beards gold; ruffled. Show Biz X Taco Supreme. Cooley 1991.

QUIET ELEGANCE (J. T. Aitken, R. 1994). Sdlg. 88T5. TB, 38" (97 cm), M. Soft yellow, F. blending to white around lavender beard. Advanced generations from intercrossing (Lemon Lyric x Song of Erin) sdlgs. Aitken's Salmon Creek 1994.

QUIET FLIRT (Francis Rogers, R. 1993). Sdlg. F-941-C. TB, 32" (81 cm), M. S. orange (RHS 29C); F. red purple (65C), lighter area below beard; beards red orange, tipped yellow orange; lightly ruffled; sweet fragrance. (Bonbon x Coral Beauty) X Apricot Flush. Meadowbrook 1994.

QUIET FRIENDSHIP (Larry Gaulter by Cooley's Gardens, R. 1990). Sdlg. 79-11. TB, 36" (91 cm),

M. Fluted pastel lavender infused darker; beards near-white to orange. Inv. sdlgs. from Persian Berry lines. Cooley 1990.

QUIET HARBOUR (John C. Taylor, R. 1991). Sdlg. OL 131-1. LA, 39" (100 cm), EM. Blue (RHS 100C) edged lighter blue, signal greenish yellow; style arms white, lined and tipped blue. Poseidon's Pool X Helen Naish. Rainbow Ridge 1991/92.

QUIET INTENTIONS (Franklin Carr, R. 1990). Sdlg. 84-17VW. TB, 30" (76 cm), M. S. reddish brown violet, subdued white infusion turning light violet yellow in throat; style arms brownish yellow infused light violet; F. reddish brown violet, light brown halo, yellow red shoulders, white radiating from yellow beard; slight sweet fragrance. 81-33A: (Daylight Splendor x Royal Trumpeter) X Broadway.

QUIET THOUGHT (Nora Scopes, TB, R. 1980). V. H. Humphrey 1992.

QUINALT (Jim & Vicki Craig, R. 1999). Sdlg. 43Z68. BB, 27" (68 cm), E. S. and style arms rosy beige; F. rich magenta, lighter haft marking; beards old gold; ruffled. 9V35: ((22L8, Little Sunrise sib, x (Starchild x 6H1: (Sacred Mountain x *I. aphylla* "Werckmeister"))) x ((Odyssey x *I. aphylla* "Werckmeister") x (Chapeau x 6H1))) X 37X10, Sailing Free sib. J. & V. Craig 1999.

QUINCINERA (Sharon McAllister, R. 1998). Sdlg. 90-19-4. AB (OGB+), 24" (61 cm), EM. S. white ground, few thin yellow veins; style arms greenish ivory; F. greenish ivory, veins changing from thick chocolate at beard to faint rust at edge; beards mustard, hairs tipped burgundy. Werckmeister's Beauty X Whirlwind Tour. McAllister 1998.

QUINTESSENCE (Bernard Hamner, R. 1990). Sdlg. 85-776. TB, 36" (91 cm), EML. Ruffled violet blue (RHS 91B); self beards; slight sweet fragrance. Bubbling Over X Classic Profile. Hamner Iris 1990.

QUITE QUAINT (Tom Burseen, R. 1990). Sdlg. 5-66A. TB, 37" (94 cm), EM. S. light grey; F. lighter grey; beards mustard, tipped burnt orange; ruffled; slight fragrance. Admiralty X New Moon. T.B.'s Place 1990.

QUITE THE REVERSE (William Maryott, R. 1998). Sdlg. S252REVBLAM. TB, 37" (94 cm), ML. S. and style arms medium blue violet (RHS 94A); F. lighter violet (97B fading to 97C); beards blue, hairs tipped white, slight yellow in throat; leaf base purple; slight sweet fragrance. Yankee Pride X Honky Tonk Blues. Maryott 1998.

QUITO (Joseph Ghio, R. 1992). Sdlg. 88-164K2. TB, 40" (102 cm), EML. Copper orange, F. with violet flash; beards brick. (Esmeralda sib x Stratagem sib) X Bogota. Bay View 1993.

QUIVER (Barry Blyth, R. 1994). Sdlg. Z34-2. IB, 24" (61 cm), ML. S. pink flushed lavender, giving blue-pink effect; F. paler, light tan on hafts, lavender lines below beard; beards lavender, tipped tangerine. Tiffany Time X Chanted. Tempo Two 1994/95.

QUMRAN CANARY (Luella Danielson, R. 1998). Sdlg. 87-4LD. AB (OGB+), 28" (71 cm), M. S. yellow, midrib darker, sparse purple flecking; style arms bright orange yellow; F. maroon brown, heavily veined maroon and white on hafts and central area, becoming more solid maroon brown on lower portion, yellow brown 1/4" marginal band, sparse purple flecking; beards yellow brown; slight musky fragrance. Passing Fancy X Angel's Star.

QUOTE (Joseph Gatty by Keith Keppel, R. 1992). Sdlg. W37-13. SDB, 12" (30 cm), ML. S. between marguerite and reed yellow (M&P 10-D-1 to 10-D-3), 3/8" edge of beech (15-E-4) to mouse brown (15-C-6); F. oyster white (10-B-1) to marguerite (10-C-1), 3/8" honey (12-J-6) to khaki (13-J-7) edge; beards pale blue at end, orange ochre (near 11-L-10) in throat; slight sweet fragrance. Chubby Cheeks X S48-4, Toy Clown sib. D & J Gardens 1993.

RABBLE ROUSER (Suz Winspear, R. 1997). Sdlg. 90B2. SDB, 10" (25 cm), E. S. clear bluish mauve; F. dark purplish red, shading to butterscotch at rim; beards white and yellow; sweet fragrance. Scribe X Fantasy Isle.

RACHEL DRUMM (Ron Mullin, R. 1999). Sdlg. 189A. TB, 37" (94 cm), M. S. bright yellow; style arms yellow; F. yellow, cream white center; beards yellow orange. Cup Race X Speculator.

RACHELLE'S STAR (Shirley Sylvia, R. 1997). Sdlg. 2. SPU, 28" (71 cm), ML. S. bright yellow; style arms yellow; F. bright yellow gold. Sdlg., parentage unknown, X unknown.

RACHEL ROSE (Dana Borglum, R. 1992). Sdlg. C-2-20-A. TB, 33" (84 cm), M. S. red purple with yellowish cast (near RHS 64B); F. slightly darker; beards light tangerine; lightly ruffled; slight sweet fragrance. Strawberry Sensation X Lady Friend. Borglum's Iris 1995.

RACHEL'S REQUEST (John C. Taylor, R. 1993). Sdlg. OL 114-P (PL1). LA, 47" (120 cm), M. Heavily ruffled cream, yellow-veined signal with green influence. Koorawatha X Helen Naish. Rainbow Ridge 1993/94.

RADIANT BURST (A. & D. Willott, R. 1993). Sdlg. 91-322. IB, 24" (61 cm), M. S. white ground, heavily marked and bordered royal purple; F. white ground, bordered and striped royal purple; beards purple and bronze; ruffled. Radiant Flair X Chubby Cheeks. Willott 1994.

RADIANT EMBER (Donald Spoon, R. 1995). Sdlg. 90-205. TB, 33" (84 cm), M. Lightly ruffled orange red self; beards red, hairs tipped orange. Warrior King X Time Lord.

RADIANT GLEAM (Stan Dexter by Marie Ingersoll, R. 1993). Sdlg. 21-84-59B. TB, 38" (97 cm), ML. Orange gold overlaid rusty red, F. edged slightly darker; beards orange. 80-123: (Pink Taffeta x Crandall sdlg.) X Candy Counter. Ingersoll's Iris 1994.

RADIANT WHITE (Kevin Nilsen, R. 1996). Sdlg. 24-90-1. TB, 35½" (90 cm), VE-E. Heavily ruffled, laced pure white, slight greenish veining; style arms white; beards orange red, white base. Radiant Energy X Melissa Sue.

RADIOACTIVE (Perry Dyer, R. 1998). Sdlg. 91-309B. SDB, 12" (30 cm), ML. S. and style arms medium yellow; F. cherry to mahogany red, 1/8" yellow edge; beards bright yellow. Spot of Tea X Jazzamatazz. Contemporary 1999.

RADIOLAND (David Spence, R. 1996). Sdlg. S83-336-1. TB, 39" (99 cm), EM. S. pale gold, 1/4" slightly deeper marginal halo; style arms pale gold; F. white, 1/4" dotted pale rose border; beards old gold; ruffled. Spyglass Hill X DSIT-2: (Odyssey x Smoky Jo). Master Creations 1997.

RAFA (Donald Spoon, R. 1997). Sdlg. 90-54A. TB, 32" (81 cm), M. Ruffled lavender blue, deeper area in center of all petals, short white rays around beards; beards white, hairs tipped yellow. Honky Tonk Blues X Queen Dorothy. Winterberry 1997.

RAFFLES (Colin Rigby, R. 1999). Sdlg. 88-12-97. CA, 16" (41 cm), M. Deep bright golden yellow, F. signal with lighter edge, deeper heavy gold veining. Poppy X Meek 167.

RAGAMUFFIN (Nora Scopes, R. 1993). Sdlg. 9S32. SDB, 12" (30 cm), E. Copper red, red spot in F. center; beards brown. Sdlg. X Darkover.

RAGING TIGER (Chet Tompkins, R. 1992). Sdlg. 87-5A. TB, 37" (94 cm), EML. Fiery orange gold, F. heavily striped, washed and dotted bright oxblood red; beards mustard; fluted, lightly ruffled. Fun and Games X Laredo. Fleur de Lis 1992.

RAGTIME DANCE (Robert Hollingworth, R. 1992). Sdlg. 88T2D1. SIB, 29" (74 cm), M. Heavily ruffled medium red purple self. 85B1B10, Sweet Surrender sib, X 85C3A2: ((Pink Haze x Fairy Dawn) x (Super Ego x Anniversary)). Windwood Gardens 1997.

RAH (Adolf Volfovich-Moler, R. 1999). Sdlg. B133. TB, 39" (100 cm), L. Ruffled and lightly laced pale orange, F. with brighter pencil rim; beards bright orange, white at end; pronounced sweet fragrance. Aelita X Fresno Calypso.

RAH RAH BOYS (Adolf Volfovich-Moler, R. 1997). Sdlg. V-147. TB, 45" (115 cm), E. S. light lilac, base greenish orange; style arms light lilac, edged yellow orange; F. light lilac center, surrounded by cream with orange stripes, orange edge; beards bright yellow, creamy white at end; ruffled, laced; slight fragrance. Pink Sleigh X Vdokhnoveniye. Volfovich-Moler 1999.

RAIDER PRIDE (Harry Wolford, R. 1994). Sdlg. P01 + 101-A92. TB, 38" (97 cm), M. Magenta self; beards magenta, tipped deep old gold; slight sweet fragrance. Pagan X Inferno.

RAIDER SPIRIT (Harry Wolford, R. 1994). Sdlg. G09 + F03-A92. TB, 36" (91 cm), M. Old gold self; beards gold; slight musky fragrance. Gold Cadillac X Flaming Light.

RAINBOW CENTER (Anna Rettig, R. 1995). Sdlg. AR-077. JI (3 F.), 36" (91 cm), M. S. magenta, small, incurved and held nearly vertical; style arms white to pale violet, edged violet (RHS 87A); F. white ground, violet allover wash heavier near edge, some purplish veining in white channel; nearly-horizontal falls with center channel creating pointed form. Numazu X unknown. A & M Perennials 1995.

RAINBOW CONNECTION (Joseph Ghio, R. 1993). Sdlg. PG-145C. CA, 12" (30 cm), EM. Apricot ground infused rusty wine, deep wine signal. PI-201J, Villa Montalvo sib, X PI-209V2, Santa Clarita sib. Bay View 1994.

RAINBOW ETUDE (Frederick Kerr, R. 1993). Sdlg. 87-39-3. TB, 32" (81 cm), EM. Ruffled medium violet blue, white area around blue white beards. Ruffled Ballet X Titan's Glory. Rainbow Acres 1993.

RAINBOW GODDESS (Richard Ernst, R. 1994). Sdlg. F169-23. TB, 34" (86 cm), ML. S. medium purple violet; F. creamy white with pale violet wash, blended light yellow orange edge, darker on shoulders; beards tangerine; ruffled; slight sweet fragrance. Afternoon Delight X C142-7, Tracy Tyrene sib. Cooley 1994.

RAINBOW HUES (Richard Ernst, R. 1993). Sdlg. AFD-88. TB, 34" (86 cm), ML. S. violet pink

357

infused amber, warm brown inner rim; F. pale lavender, darkening toward warm brown rim; beards white, thin; ruffled. Afternoon Delight X self. Cooley 1992.

RAINBOW MAKER (Richard Ernst, R. 1994). Sdlg. F120-14. TB, 36" (91 cm), M. S. medium blue violet; F. lighter blue violet with darker rim; beards blue violet, tipped white; lightly ruffled; slight sweet fragrance. Afternoon Delight X Gaulter 81-17, inv. Irene Nelson. Cooley 1994.

RAINBOW MOUNTAIN (Duane Meek, R. 1994). Sdlg. 723-2-1. TB, 32-34" (81-86 cm), M. S. red violet; F. deep red violet, dark blue violet blaze extending from beard to edge, golden tan hafts; beards violet, tipped mustard; ruffled. Deep Fire X Cherry Smoke. D & J Gardens 1994.

RAINBOW PRELUDE (Frederick Kerr, R. 1993). Sdlg. 87-39-2. TB, 39" (99 cm), EML. Ruffled violet mauve with darker F. veining; beards mauve violet; slight fragrance. Ruffled Ballet X Titan's Glory. Rainbow Acres 1992.

RAINBOWS (Lynda Miller, MDB, R. 1989). Miller's Manor 1990.

#RAINBOW'S END (Clint McDade, TB, R. 1943). Not introduced, name released.

RAINBOW'S END (Gerald Richardson, R. 1991). Sdlg. 73-12-1. TB, 36" (91 cm), M. S. medium yellow gold (RHS 7B); F. slightly deeper (7A); beards gold orange; slight fragrance. Marshmallow X Kingdom. Fort Iris 1992.

RAINBOW SKY (Duane Meek, R. 1995). Sdlg. 246-1-1. TB, 36" (91 cm), ML. S. oyster white; F. white with red violet shading deeper in center, white area near beard with dark veins raying to petal rim; beards white lightly tipped yellow; ruffled. Love Magic X Premonition. D & J Gardens 1995.

RAINBOW TOUR (Paul Black, R. 1990). Sdlg. 86103G. TB, 38" (97 cm), M. S. medium pink, ruffled; F. bright fuchsia purple, pink hafts, pinkish white spray pattern around orange beard, smoky orchid pink edge; slight sweet fragrance. Sorceress X Planned Treasure. Mid-America 1990.

RAIN CHECK (Harold Stahly, R. 1993). Sdlg. 87-25. TB, 36" (91 cm), M. Ruffled pallid blue; beards medium deep blue. On the Road X High Five. Stahly 1993.

RAINDANCE KID (J. T. Aitken, R. 1990). Sdlg. 81M2. IB, 25" (64 cm), M. Medium blue; beards medium blue; slight fragrance. Rain Dance X -- probably Blue Luster. Aitken's Salmon Creek 1990.

RAINER VON DER SCHULENBURG (George Gessert, R. 1998). Sdlg. 83-7D. CA, 7½" (19 cm), M. S. white, center veined purple; style arms white, infused yellow and violet; F. white, gold signal surrounded by magenta blaze. Western Queen X Emigrant.

RAIN MAN (Joyce Meek, R. 1994). Sdlg. 442-1-3. TB, 36" (91 cm), M. S. white ground, wide red violet plicata edge; F. white ground, 1/4" red violet edge and dotting under beards, 1/4" arrow at beard tip, hafts dotted brown; beards white, lightly tipped yellow, violet at end; ruffled, flared; slight sweet fragrance. Lingering Love X B70-1-7: (Keppel 68-39D: (((Irma Melrose x Tea Apron) x ((Full Circle x Rococo) x Tea Apron)) x April Melody) x B13-1-4: (Circle Step x Smoke Rings)). D & J Gardens 1994.

RAIN PATTERN (Yuri Pirogov, R. 1997). Sdlg. 92-2A. TB, 36" (91 cm), EM. White ground plicata, washed and dotted medium violet at edge, paler in center; style arms white, edged violet; beards white; slight fragrance. Spinning Wheel X "Depeche Mode": (Rancho Rose x Sketch Me). Pirogov 1997.

RAINY FALLS (William Maryott, TB, R. 1983). Correction of parentage. Scented Nutmeg X Victoria Falls.

RAISON D'ETRE (Mary Dunn, LA, R. 1989). Bay View 1990.

RAKON (Josef Dudek, R. 1997). Sdlg. 91-PAVA-2. TB, 36" (91 cm), M. Ruffled dark blue lavender (RHS 88A) self, hafts veined; beards light blue, yellow orange with blue base in throat; pronounced spicy fragrance. Pledge Allegiance X Visual Arts. Josef Dudek 1998.

RAKU (Nora Scopes, R. 1991). Sdlg. P.C. 19. CA, 12" (30 cm), M. S. purple; F. violet purple with magenta glow, gold signal. Banbury Velvet sdlg. X Popinjay.

RAKU BLAZE (J. T. Aitken, R. 1996). Sdlg. 88T9D. TB, 34" (86 cm), ML. S. amber yellow; F. light lavender, deep lavender blaze, copper brown hafts and rim; beards gold. Warrior King X Walking Tall. Aitken's Salmon Creek 1996.

RAMBLIN' ROSE (Schreiner, R. 1993). Sdlg. Z 494-B. TB, 37" (94 cm), ML. Lightly crinkle-laced raspberry rose (RHS 70B); beards tangerine. T 1771-1: (L 512-3: (((Fairy Rose x Cashmere) x B 887-1) x Meghan) x Lovely Jan) X Mulled Wine. Schreiner 1993.

RAMONA HOWARD (James McWhirter, TB, R. 1989). Cottage 1990.

RAM RUHEE (Ladislav Muska, R. 1996). Sdlg. SLFI-02/A. TB, 40" (102 cm), ML. Ruffled pinkish rose self; beards tangerine; sweet fragrance. ("Slahacka": (Buffy x Silver Shower) x Frivolous Idea) X Beverly Sills. Muska 1996.

RANCHO GOLD (Tom Burseen, R. 1991). Sdlg. 5-266A. TB, 36" (91 cm), ML. S. dark bronzy gold with orange infusion (near RHS 169D) over gold; F. dark mahogany brown (165A), gold streaks concentrated in center to finely laced gold edge; beards orange; musky fragrance. Rio de Oro X Fiji Dancer. T.B.'s Place 1990.

RANDY LEE (Mary Miller, R. 1997). Sdlg. M61-3. TB, 30" (76 cm), M. S. apricot (Nickerson 7.5 YR 8/8) shaded pink (2.5 R 8/5); style arms apricot; F. apricot, shaded pink; beards strong red orange (10 R 6/12); slight spicy fragrance. Carmela X Top Flight.

RANMAN (Ho Shidara, R. 1999). SIB, 30" (76 cm), M. S. absent; F. multiple (6-9), light lavender pink with darker speckles, small white signal; style arms and stamens forming petaloid rosebud center. Parentage unknown. Ensata Gardens 1997.

RANPO (Shuichi Hirao by Society for Japanese Irises, R. 1994). JI (6 F.), 36" (90 cm), EM. Blue violet self. Parentage unknown. Hirao 1966.

RAPPORT (Mary Dunn, R. 1990). Sdlg. L107-1. LA, 37" (94 cm), M. Blue, lime green line signal; self styles edged light violet. Monument X Handmaiden. Bay View 1991.

RAPSCALLION (Lynda Miller, R. 1994). Sdlg. 100291B. SDB, 11" (28 cm), E. Dark purple violet self; beards medium blue; slight sweet fragrance. Dark Vader X Bantam. Miller's Manor 1995.

RAPT (Barry Blyth, R. 1999). Sdlg. F21-1. SDB, 14" (36 cm), ML. S. citrus lemon; style arms lemon, base shaded pastel blue; F. white, outer 1/8" edge blended lemon, inner citrus lemon crescent; beards orange, lavender blue at end. D6-YY, Blissed Out sib, X D21-6, Baci sib. Tempo Two 1999/2000.

RAPTURE IN BLUE (Schreiner, R. 1990). Sdlg. W 440-A. TB, 36" (91 cm), M. Heavily ruffled light blue (RHS 100D); beards white. N 57-A: ((Sailor's Dance x G 30-A: ((Pacific Panorama x Parisian Blue) x Sapphire Hills)) x (Sapphire Hills x D 136-G: (Parisian Blue x ((Blue Linen sib x (J 274-A x Violet Harmony)) x (Swan Ballet x Snowy Heron))))) X Tide's In. Schreiner 1990.

RAQUELLE ANNE (Darlene Pinegar, R. 1997). Sdlg. DS-4A. TB, 28" (71 cm), M. S. and style arms bright yellow; F. medium orchid veined darker, shaded white, 1/4" yellow gold edge, hafts dark yellow marked gold; beards dark yellow orange; ruffled; slight sweet fragrance. Double Scoop X Havana Revels. Spanish Fork 1998.

RARE LUCK (Henry Rowlan, R. 1991). Sdlg. 82-SA-28. BB, 25" (64 cm), ML. Currant red (RHS 46A); beards orange brown, red horn. Jewel Tone X 72-G-1: (Spooned Premiere x Donnybrook).

RARE OCCASION (Joseph Gatty by Keith Keppel, R. 1992). Sdlg. T23-6. TB, 36" (91 cm), M. S. peach (M&P 9-A-5); F. slightly paler (9-AB-4), hafts suffused capucine buff (9-E-5); beards grenadine red (1-D-11) to carnelian red (2-E-1), ibis pink (1-B-10) at end; pronounced sweet fragrance. 019-1: (Pretty Lady x K55-1: (Nefertiti x Playgirl)) X Presence. Keppel 1994.

RARE QUALITY (Schreiner, R. 1999). Sdlg. DD 137-1. TB, 36" (91 cm), M. White (RHS 155D) ground plicata, deep plum purple edge; beards blue, yellow hair tips and in throat. 1987 #5, unknown, X Honky Tonk Blues. Schreiner 1999.

RARE SONG (George Sutton, R. 1998). Sdlg. E-92. IB, 25" (64 cm), EM. S. white ground, 1" plum purple to violet purple edge, midline and speckles; style arms violet purple; F. white, 5/8" plum purple to violet purple edge and veining around beard; beards yellow to bronze, base white blended lavender; ruffled; slight sweet fragrance. Rare Edition X Jesse's Song.

RARE STAR (Floyd Dyer, R. 1995). Sdlg. D-11-92-D. SDB, 13½" (34 cm), M. S. dark blue, base blended violet; F. blue, red violet overlay; beards orange, blue at end; ruffled; slight musky fragrance. Cindy Mitchell X Rangerette. Dyer's Garden 1995.

RARING TO GO (Sharon McAllister, R. 1998). Sdlg. 90-37-8. AB (OGB-), 32" (81 cm), ML. S. iridescent spectrum violet; style arms violet; F. reddish violet rimmed spectrum violet, near-black stippled signal; beards bright yellow. Soul Kiss X Whirlwind Romance.

RASPBERRY CANDY (Bob Bauer/John Coble, R. 1999). Sdlg. J86E-3. JI (6 F.), 34" (86 cm), EM. White with large dark red violet halo, dark red violet veins branching at petal edge, wide dark yellow signal. Geisha Gown X Iapetus. Ensata Gardens 1999.

RASPBERRY CHEESECAKE (Phyllis Dickey, R. 1997). Sdlg. P 106-1. TB, 30" (76 cm), E. S. cream; F. white ground, red raspberry plicata edge; beards yellow, white at end; slight sweet fragrance. Blatant X Eagle's Flight. Misty Hill 1997.

RASPBERRY DAZZLER (Vernon Wood, R. 1995). Sdlg. 93-83. CA, 15-16" (38-41 cm), ML. S. raspberry, lined darker, center lighter; style arms raspberry, short; F. raspberry, veined and centered darker; ruffled. Distant Nebula X 89-7: (Roaring Camp x 87-9, from sdlgs. of unknown parentage). Stockton 1996.

RASPBERRY GLOW (J. T. Aitken, R. 1992). Sdlg. 86J-1. JI (6 F.), 46" (117 cm), ML. Raspberry with blue rays, 1" violet edge. Hue and Cry X Electic Rays sib. Aitken's Salmon Creek 1992.

RASPBERRY LACE (Darlene Pinegar, R. 1990). Sdlg. RR-1-1. BB, 27" (68 cm), EML. S. medium red purple, lightening after opening; F. medium red purple, lighter center, orchid haft markings; beards deep gold, tipped light lavender; heavily laced, lightly ruffled; slight sweet fragrance. Raspberry Ripples X Petite Posy. Spanish Fork 1991.

RASPBERRY RAINBOW (Chandler Fulton, R. 1995). Sdlg. 7GT-5. SIB, 29" (73 cm), ML. S. light lilac red (near RHS 77C) veined blue; style arms lilac red, aqua rib; F. outer third raspberry pink (81B) blending to sky blue (97A) center, with bright yellow (7A) signal narrowly rimmed white; buds deep violet (89A); ruffled. 84G-4: (Butter and Sugar x Sparkling Rosé) X self. Pope's Perennials 1996.

RASPBERRY RASCAL (Clarence Protzmann, BB, R. 1988). Protzmann 1990.

RASPBERRY SNOW (George Sutton, TB, R. 1989). Sutton 1991.

RASPBERRY SPLASH (Polly Black, R. 1991). Sdlg. GR14-3. TB, 34" (86 cm), M. S. white tinted orchid; F. raspberry, orchid tinted edge; beards orange; ruffled; slight fragrance. Parentage unknown. Polly Black 1991.

RASPBERRY SPLENDOR (O. D. Niswonger, R. 1992). Sdlg. 66-89. TB, 36" (91 cm), M. Raspberry self; beards pinkish tangerine. Matinee Idol X Pink Ballerina. Cape Iris 1993.

RASPBERRY YUM YUM (Carl Boswell, R. 1991). Sdlg. 153-85-1B. TB, 31" (79 cm), M. Lightly laced and ruffled raspberry; beards tangerine; slight musky sweet fragrance. Frosty Pastel X Autumn Blush. Adamgrove 1992.

RASSVET (Viktor Koroliov, R. 1999). Sdlg. S123-96K. TB, 37" (95 cm), ML. S. rose lilac; style arms cream, lilac cests; F. rose lilac, hafts marked yellow; beards yellow, lighter at end, tangerine in throat; lightly ruffled; pronounced sweet fragrance. May Magic X Frost and Flame. Koroliov 1999.

RATAPAT-PAN (Nora Scopes, R. 1994). Sdlg. 9S50. IB, 22" (56 cm), E. S. yellow, sanded copper; F. white, edged yellow and copper; beards red brown; flaring. Torchlight Tattoo X Muchacha.

RAVE (George Shoop, R. 1992). Sdlg. 82-21. TB, 36" (91 cm), M. Ruffled and laced bright peachy pink; beards pink; slight fragrance. Fantasy Lace X 79-1: ((Dutch Magic x Hula Girl) x Gypsy Girl). Shoop 1992.

RAVEN'S QUOTE (Richard Ernst, R. 1994). Sdlg. HS902-3. TB, 35" (89 cm), M. Ruffled dark violet blue, slightly lighter around beard; beards violet blue, tipped light blue; ruffled; slight sweet fragrance. Lavender Luck X Dusky Challenger. Cooley 1994.

RAVEN'S RETURN (John Weiler, R. 1995). Sdlg. 82-183-1RE. TB, 37" (94 cm), EML & RE. S. very dark violet; style arms dark violet; F. blackish violet; beards dark violet; ruffled; slight sweet fragrance. Ravenwood X Satan Satin sib. Friendship 1997.

RAVE ON (Schreiner, R. 1990). Sdlg. V 401-3. TB, 36" (91 cm), ML. Ruffled orange (RHS 23A), creamy white signal; beards tangerine. M 748-C: (K 905-D, Skyfire sib, x J 571-B: (G 121-A: ((Golden Ice x Celestial Glory) x Flaming Star) x Gold Trimmings)) X China Dragon. Schreiner 1990.

RAVE REVIEW (Jim & Vicki Craig, R. 1991). Sdlg. C17W4. MTB, 23" (58 cm), E & RE. Ruffled, flared light lavender, faint white haft marks; beards light pinkish red; slight sweet fragrance. Gumdrops sib X C20T2: (((En Route x Pink Taffeta) x (New Moon x (Sacred Mountain x *I. aphylla* "Werckmeister"))) x Puppy Love). J. & V. Craig 1992.

RAVING BEAUTY (Mary Dunn, R. 1995). Sdlg. L208-1. LA, 36" (91 cm), ML. S. smooth purple grape; style arms light grape; F. smooth purple grape, large green spear signal, green heart; flat form. Plantation Beau X Valera. Bay View 1996.

RAVISHING (Lynda Miller, R. 1993). Sdlg. 4489. TB, 29" (74 cm), ML. S. orange, midrib with pink cast; F. orange, pink cast around tangerine beard; laced; slight musky fragrance. Can't Elope X Copper Classic. Miller's Manor 1995.

RAW TIMBER (Tom Burseen, R. 1990). Sdlg. 4-55A. TB, 36" (91 cm), ML. S. golden yellow ground, heavy burgundy red wash; F. golden yellow ground, bright burgundy red streaks down to solid burgundy red edge; beards orange; ruffled; spicy fragrance. Rio de Oro X Piute Pass. T.B.'s Place 1990.

RAYTHEON (Virginia Messick, R. 1990). Sdlg. M86-52. SDB, 14" (36 cm), M. White, blue spray radiating over F. Short Distance X Azure Gem.

RAZOO (Barry Blyth, R. 1993). Sdlg. A44-19. SDB, 12" (31 cm), M. S. light violet; F. white, 1/8" light violet edge and few dots and lines overall; beards tangerine, violet on end; slight fragrance. (Cupid's Cup x Yipee sib) X Chanted. Tempo Two 1993/94.

RAZOR EDGE (Kevin Vaughn, R. 1998). Sdlg. F-17-1. LA, 25" (64 cm), EM. S. amber, narrow rose edging; style arms amber, lined and tipped rose; F. amber, 1/4" bright rose rim, amber gold signal outlined rose; lightly ruffled. Heavenly Glow X Kelley's Choice.

RAZZBERRY RITA (Mary Dunn, R. 1996). Sdlg. M2010-1. TB, 36" (91 cm), M. S. bright raspberry fuchsia; style arms raspberry; F. bright raspberry fuchsia, bluish area at tip of red orange beard. Delirious X Kamora. M.A.D. Iris 1998.

RAZZLEBERRY (Roger Nelson, R. 1995). Sdlg. RN 90-51 EX. TB, 37" (94 cm), ML. Deep rosy pink orchid self; beards deep shrimp rose; pronounced sweet fragrance. Indulge X Enchanted World. Iris Country 1995.

RAZZLEBERRY LADY (Norma Barnard, R. 1997). Sdlg. NB 91-90. CA, 12-14" (31-37 cm), ML. S. and style arms raspberry, veined brown; F. raspberry red, black raspberry signal with lighter veins below; lightly ruffled. Parentage unknown; seed from Shepard Iris Garden.

REAL CHALLENGER (Austin Morgan, R. 1990). TB, 37" (94 cm), EM. S. light tan; F. rose violet upper, tan lower; beards tangerine. Parentage unknown. Iris Test Garden 1983.

REAL EASY (John C. Taylor, R. 1998). Sdlg. UL 22-4. LA, 39" (100 cm), ML. S. white; style arms light yellow; F. light yellow, yellow orange signal; heavily fluted, recurved. Gladiator's Gift X Dural Dreamtime. Rainbow Ridge 1999/2000.

REALITY (Joseph Ghio, R. 1994). Sdlg. 88-100-H2. TB, 36" (91 cm), ML. S. deep mauvewood; F. metallic rosy mauvewood, electric violet blaze; beards burnt orange. 85-161-T2: (Fortunata x 82-135-G3, Romantic Mood sib) X 85-155: (Newlywed x Electrabrite). Bay View 1995.

REALLY MINE (Joyce Meek, R. 1995). Sdlg. 261-1-3. TB, 34" (86 cm), ML. S. pale apricot pink; F. light red violet; beards melon; laced, fluted. Candace X Janie Meek. D & J Gardens 1995.

REAL SWEETHEART (A. & D. Willott, R. 1994). Sdlg. 91-301. SDB, 12" (30 cm), ML. Ruffled light bluish pink, amber vein pattern over light area around beards; beards red orange, tipped violet. Barney's Delight X 84-140: (Apricot Elf x Coral Wings). Willott 1996.

REAL TREASURE (John C. Taylor, R. 1993). Sdlg. OL 119-P (PL2). LA, 51" (130 cm), ML. Purple, strong yellow signal on all petals. (Freddie Boy blue sdlg. x Grace Scott) X Pintharuka. Rainbow Ridge 1993/94.

REAP THE REWARDS (Graeme Grosvenor, R. 1999). Sdlg. V110-1. TB, 38" (97 cm), M. S. light blue; F. blue purple; beards light blue violet; pronounced fragrance. T18-1: (Silverado x Honky Tonk Blues) X T18-2, sib.

REBECCA JOHNS (John Carter, R. 1999). JI (3 F.), 36" (91 cm), ML. S. very pale pink with slightly whiter center, large and floppy; style arms cream white, yellow rib and base, pink tips; F. sugar pink, slightly darker veining, very narrow near-white edge, small deep yellow signal; slightly ruffled. Parentage unknown.

REBECCA PERRET (Jean Cayeux, R. 1993). Sdlg. 84109K. TB, 39" (100 cm), EM. S. pure white; F. white, edged light blue lavender; beards tangerine. (Condottiere x Delphi) X (Alizes x (Condottiere x Lunar Rainbow)). Cayeux 1992.

REBECCA RUTH (Myrtle Wolff, BB, R. 1988). Hildenbrandt's Iris 1990.

REBECCA'S CHOICE (Currier McEwen, R. 1998). Sdlg. 89/41(2). JI (3 F.), 36" (91 cm), ML. S. phlox purple (RHS 75C); style arms white, rose purple (75A) edges and tufts; F. rose purple (75B) appearance, with phlox purple base color and darker (75A) veining; ruffled, arched form. Hime Kagami X Celestial Pink sib. Eartheart 1999.

REBEL YELL (Barry Blyth, R. 1990). Sdlg. X47-1. IB, 25" (64 cm), EM. Antique tan gold, deepening at hafts to antique brown; beards electric purple. (Inca Queen x Beachgirl) X (Peach Eyes x Kandi Moon). Tempo Two 1990/91.

REBIA (Raymond Smith, R. 1991). Sdlg. 8622CF. BB, 18" (46 cm), M & RE. S. brownish orange (Nickerson 2.5 YR 5/9); F. brown, light golden yellow area around yellow beard. 7711KR, Remarkable sib, X 7711NR, sib.

REBOUND (Betty Wilkerson, R. 1996). Sdlg. F31-1Re. TB, 34" (86 cm), E & RE (Oct./KY). S. and style arms greyed red (RHS 181B); F. cream ground overlaid greyed red; beards old gold. Highland Chief X Earl of Essex. Bridge in Time 1996.

REBUS (Joseph Gatty by Keith Keppel, R. 1995). Sdlg. Y2-3. SDB, 11" (28 cm), EM. S. pontiff violet (M&P 41-K-10), center shaded white; style arms pontiff violet; F. cream white ground, 3/16"-1/4" sanded pontiff violet edge; beards sunflower (9-L-4), white base; lightly ruffled; pronounced sweet fragrance. Motto X Nimble Toes. Keppel 1996.

RECALLED TO LIFE (George Slade, R. 1990). Sdlg. 83-15-2. TB, 36" (91 cm), EM & RE. S. dark berry purple infused white; F. white ground stitched berry purple; beards burnt orange, tipped violet; pronounced sweet fragrance. Frivolity X Wild Berry. Wyle Wynde 1990.

RECIPE FOR SUCCESS (Sharon McAllister, R. 1998). Sdlg. 83-5-3. AB (OGB), 28" (71 cm), M. S. pinkish violet; style arms yellow ivory; F. yellowish ivory ground blushed burgundy, burgundy stippling on ivory around yellow beard. Boaz X Sunrise in Glory. McAllister 1998.

RECKLESS (John C. Taylor, R. 1998). Sdlg. UL 5-X. LA, 39" (100 cm), M. S. blue violet; style arms white, edged violet; F. blue violet, reverse lighter, yellow signal stronger in center; fluted. 'Bout Midnight X Rachel's Request.

RECONSIDERED (Libby Cross, R. 1997). Sdlg. 90-A-3. TB, 30" (76 cm), M & RE. S. pale yellow; style arms yellow; F. white, edged yellow; beards yellow, base white; slight sweet fragrance. Immortality X unknown. Crosspatch 1998.

RECURRENT EVENT (Larry Lauer, R. 1998). Sdlg. 92-204-2. SDB, 10" (25 cm), E & RE. S. light yellow ground, violet blue marginal markings lighter at top; style arms violet blue, crest yellow; F. light yellow, light violet blue plicata markings, yellow edge; beards violet at end, yellow and white midsection, orange in throat; slight sweet fragrance. Chubby Cheeks X Bountiful Harvest. Lauer's Flowers 1998.

RECURRING DELIGHT (Larry Lauer, R. 1998). Sdlg. 91-143-1R. TB, 35" (89 cm), L. S. greyed yellow, lavender midrib flush; style arms lavender flush on yellow grey; F. lavender, rim lighter, hafts brown; beards yellow, tipped lavender; heavily ruffled; pronounced sweet fragrance. 87-48-3: (Edith Wolford x Breakers) X Mother Earth. Stockton 1998.

RECURRING DREAM (Ben Hager, R. 1992). Sdlg. RE5174HgV. TB, 32" (81 cm), M & RE. Medium purple self; beards blue white. Winds of Change X RE5058RV: (Mother Earth x Feed Back). Melrose 1993.

RECURRING FANTASY (Larry Lauer, R. 1999). Sdlg. 543-1R. TB, 34" (86 cm), EM & RE. Ruffled aster violet, S. with lighter midrib, F. with white markings around beard; beards blue, hairs tipped white at end, merging to dark yellow in throat; pronounced sweet fragrance. Speeding Again X Waterworld.

RECURRING GLORY (George Sutton, R. 1996). Sdlg. G-46RE. TB, 36" (91 cm), M & RE. Pansy violet (RHS 83A) self; beards bluebird blue (94B), hairs tipped light lavender. Titan's Glory X Earl of Essex.

RECURRING RUFFLES (Ben Hager, TB, R. 1989). Melrose 1990.

RED ABUNDANCE (Kirk Strawn, R. 1993). Sdlg. 0-1985. LA, 35" (89 cm), M. S. currant red (RHS 46A); style arms cardinal red (53A); F. slightly darker currant red, yellow orange (17A) signal. Deneb X President Hedley. Bois d'Arc 1996.

RED AT NIGHT (Richard Ernst, R. 1993). Sdlg. F102-1. TB, 38" (97 cm), EM. S. dark red, base slightly lighter; F. velvety dark red; beards yellow, tipped red; ruffled. Danger X Chief Hematite. Cooley 1992.

RED EARTH (Eugene Hunt by Sharon McAllister, R. 1992). Sdlg. ORB 88-5. AB (OGB), 28" (72 cm), EM. S. pale greyed yellow orange (RHS 106C to 165D); F. greyed yellow (near 162C) ground showing as clear 3/8" rim, solid red orange (173A) overlay blending to brownish black signal; beards mustard and brown. Muhlestein 599C: (Sojourn x Almost) X Welcome Reward. McAllister 1992.

REDEFINE SHINE (Tom Burseen, TB, R. 1988). T.B.'s Place 1992.

REDELTA (Raymond Smith, R. 1991). Sdlg. 8806DR. TB, 37" (94 cm), M & RE. S. washed purple (Nickerson 5P 4/9); F. white ground, purple vein lines parallel with blue beard and around edge, faint centerline. 7434DR: (Stepping Out x 5872A) X Earl of Essex. R. G. Smith 1994.

RED EPAULETS (Richard Sparling, R. 1991). SDB, 12" (30 cm), M. S. rosy brown; F. washed rosy brown, red (RHS 53C) lines around yellow beard. Parentage unknown. Green Box 1992.

RED EYELASHES (Lloyd Zurbrigg, R. 1994). Sdlg. KK 25B. SDB, 10" (25 cm), EE. Bright yellow, F. with red eyelash pattern; beards yellow. Sunstrip X Marita. Friendship 1995.

RED FLURRY (Roy Fielding by Philip Edinger, R. 1999). TB, 40" (102 cm), ML. Ruffled oxblood red, F. with prominent haft marking and patterning. Snow Flurry X diploid Sass plicata sdlg. Combsie's Garden 1956.

RED FRINGE (Stephen Stevens, R. 1992). Sdlg. 83-12-23. TB, 35" (89 cm), M. S. maroon red (RHS 59B), purple midrib infusion; F. maroon red, purple mark extending from marigold beard;

ruffled, laced; slight spicy fragrance. 79-23-16: (Pink Sleigh x (After All x sdlg.)) X 79-21-5: (76-12-23: (Red Raven x Post Time) x Heat Pump). Hahn's Rainbow 1993.

RED GROUSE (B.L.C. Dodsworth, R. 1995). Sdlg. EB 92A. TB, 34" (86 cm), M. Ruffled red self; beards rust. Red Kite X Danger.

RED HAWK (Schreiner, R. 1995). Sdlg. BB 891-1. TB, 36" (91 cm), L. Heavily ruffled deep red (RHS 60A), base of S. midrib yellow; beards red, yellow in throat; pronounced sweet fragrance. Play With Fire X Garnet Velvet. Schreiner 1995.

RED HEAT (Jim Hedgecock, R. 1992). Sdlg. 84-100-2. TB, 32" (81 cm), M. S. butterscotch, veined pale maroon; F. wine red, edged butterscotch, large white haft marks; beards golden yellow; ruffled, laced. Caramba X unknown. Comanche Acres 1993.

RED KITE (B.L.C. Dodsworth, TB, R. 1989). British Iris Society, Iris Garden 1993.

RED LIPS (Cloyd McCord, R. 1997). Sdlg. 684. TB, 35" (89 cm), M. S. and style arms orange; F. black, yellow around beards; beards orange, yellow in throat; spicy fragrance. Sexton's Black Swan X Goblin Dancer. McCord 1997.

RED MANTLE (H. Valmar Slamova by Philip Edinger, R. 1999). TB, 35" (89 cm), EM & RE. Dark carmine red, F. veined blackish carmine; beards yellow. Joseph's Mantle X (Tea Rose x Yuma). Rainbow Hybridizing Gardens 1961.

RED MYSTIQUE (Stephen Stevens, R. 1992). Sdlg. 84-13-4. TB, 33" (84 cm), M. Ruffled ruby (RHS 59A) self; beards ruby, tipped orange; slight fragrance. 81-41-1: (76-12-19: (Red Raven x Post Time) x Deep Fire) X unknown.

RED NECK HAVEN (Tom Burseen, R. 1990). Sdlg. 4-204D. TB, 34" (86 cm), M. S. heavily ruffled sandy red; F. cream, reddish maroon plicata corrugated edge; beards mustard. Medieval X Joy Ride. T.B.'s Place 1990.

RED PEARL (Udo & Rudolf Wilkeneit, R. 1996). SDB, 10" (25 cm), L. S. velvety dark red, black center; F. velvety black red; beards blue; slight fragrance. Parentage unknown.

RED PIPER (A. Theodore Mueller, R. 1994). Sdlg. 86-54. IB, 20" (51 cm), EM. S. light lavender blended yellow toward edge, reddish blaze; style arms light lavender, tipped yellow; F. light lavender, red violet center blaze blending to yellow shoulders; beards yellow; slight fragrance. Piper's Tune X Seductress. Mueller's Garden 1994.

RED RASPA (Monique Dumas-Quesnel, R. 1992). Sdlg. 90-PY-117. SPEC-X, 40½" (105 cm), E. S. purple violet (RHS 82A); F. dark purple (77A), darker zones around dark yellow signal. EX-CO-MR-05, *I. versicolor* sdlg., X unknown *I. ensata* sdlg.

RED RIDER (Larry Lauer, R. 1998). Sdlg. 91-240-2. TB, 34" (86 cm), E. S. light plum; style arms light plum, midrib purple; F. dark reddish plum; beards mustard; slight sweet fragrance. 86-76-1: (Sinister x Role Model) X Sheba's Queen. Stockton 1998.

RED RINGLETS (J. T. Aitken, R. 1994). Sdlg. 87J28. JI (6 F.), 30" (76 cm), M. White, raspberry rim. (Midsummer Reverie x Freckled Geisha) X sib. Aitken's Salmon Creek 1994.

RED ROOSTER (John Durrance, R. 1990). Sdlg. D80-16A. BB, 26" (66 cm), EM. Ruffled, flared deep red brown. Hamblen H74-88: (Pagan x Red Jade) X Maroon Bells. Long 1990.

RED ROYALE (Hugh Pearson, R. 1991). Sdlg. 7797-1. SIB, 18" (45 cm), M. Dark red purple (RHS 71A) with bluish F. blaze; style arms red purple (72A); slight fragrance. 72-P-3 X Royal Ensign. Whitehouse Perennials 1998.

RED SANDS (Howard Shockey, R. 1993). Sdlg. 88-164-BA. AB (OGB), 28" (71 cm), M. S. rose orchid; F. light buff ground with rose overlay, brown black signal; beards bronze. 86-138-R: ((79-105-C: (Stars Over Chicago x Welcome Reward) x Desert Princess) x Syrian Moon) X 86-140-T: (((79-105H x Syrian Moon) x (Heart Stealer x 79-105C)) x Onlooker). Arilian Acres 1993.

RED SHOCKER (William Ginter, R. 1995). Sdlg. TRT-4. TB, 36" (91 cm), L. Ruffled dark red, hafts marked; self beards; slight sweet fragrance. Thriller X Red Tornado. Parkwood 1998.

RED SHOES (Connell Marsh, TB, R. 1987). C. Marsh 1990.

RED THUMBPRINTS (A. & D. Cadd, R. 1999). Sdlg. 16-93-1. BB, 25" (64 cm), E. S. light chocolate brown, slightly lighter border; style arms lighter and yellower; F. light chocolate brown, reddish wash to within 1/2" of edge, lighter center touched violet, faint yellow lines on lower half of petal, dark red brown shoulder spots with yellow lines; beards light orange; pronounced sweet fragrance. Beyond X 18-91-1: (Feminine Charm x Tan Sun).

RED VELVET ELVIS (Kevin Vaughn, R. 1996). Sdlg. C-12-5. LA, 34-38" (86-97 cm), EML. S. dark red black; style arms near black, slight red shading near tip; F. velvety dark red black, orange yellow spear signal partially hidden by styles; lightly ruffled; slight fragrance. Jeri X Cajun Cookery. Contemporary 1997.

REDWOOD GROVE (Lilly Gartman by Joseph Ghio, R. 1995). Sdlg. 86-20. TB, 36" (91 cm), M. Maroon self; beards yellow. (Lady Friend x (Woodwine x Entourage)) X Marauder. Roris 1996.

REDWOOD MIST (John Marchant, R. 1990). Sdlg. 7187. CA, 12" (30 cm), M. Cream white infused violet blue, F. with creamy white edge, diffused yellow signal. Sdlg. X sdlg. Portable Acres 1990.

REFEREE (Joseph Ghio, R. 1998). Sdlg. PC-208H. CA, 10" (25 cm), EM. Gold, signal veined tan. PE-207S: (PG-188J2, Osocales sib, x PG-154, Spanish Don sib) X Osocales. Bay View 1998.

REFLECT (John C. Taylor, R. 1998). Sdlg. UL 22-9. LA, 39" (100 cm), M. Violet blue, signals yellow; style arms brushed light violet blue. Gladiator's Gift X Dural Dreamtime. Rainbow Ridge 1999/2000.

REFLECTED SUNSET (A. & D. Willott, R. 1999). Sdlg. W 92-231. TB, 32" (81 cm), ML. Ruffled light orange (RHS 28D), F. with white area around saturn red (30C) beard, deeper orange hafts; ruffled. Beverly Sills X Master Gardener.

REFLETS SAFRAN (Richard Cayeux, R. 1998). Sdlg. 89131B. TB, 33" (85 cm), ML. S. golden yellow; F. yellow, lightly bronzed, intensifying around bronze beard. Supreme Sultan X Gold Galore. Cayeux 1999.

REGAL AMBROSIA (Sara Doonan, R. 1990). Sdlg. 83-22-11. TB, 39" (99 cm), EML. Sunfast regal purple with hint of red violet; self beards; pronounced sweet fragrance. Master Touch X Super Indiglow. Sunset Iris 1990.

REGAL BARON (Agnes Frech, R. 1997). Sdlg. 2893. TB, 39" (99 cm), M. S. reddish purple; style arms purple and yellow; F. reddish purple, purple-veined blue wash below beard, blue centerline, red shoulders; beards blue and mustard; ruffled; slight fragrance. Star Wars X Edna's Wish.

REGAL CLASSIC (Vernon Wood, R. 1995). Sdlg. 92-24. CA, 16-18" (41-46 cm), EM. S. white, lined violet; style arms near-white; F. white, lined violet, with 1" violet rim, 1/8" pale rim edge. Invincible X Ego Trip. Stockton 1996.

REGAL SURPRISE (J. Ellis, SPEC-X, R. 1988). British Iris Society 1990.

REGIMEN (Joseph Ghio, R. 1999). Sdlg. 94-15L3. TB, 31" (79 cm), L. S. red chocolate; F. smooth red chocolate, muted blue blaze; beards burnt tangerine. 92-21: (((Stratagem x Bygone Era) x (Caracas x (Fortunata x ((78-221J: ((Flareup x 73-122Z) x (Ballet in Orange x 73-122Z)) x (Preface sib x (Old Flame x Pink Angel))) x (76-181J: ((Ponderosa x Honey Rae) x ((((Commentary x Claudia Rene) x Claudia Rene) x Ponderosa) x (Ponderosa x New Moon))) x Homecoming Queen) x Orangerie))))) x ((((Lady Friend x (Flareup x (Capitation x Coffee House))) x Battle Hymn sib) x (((Praline x Lady Friend) x (76-181J x (Entourage x Homecoming Queen))) x (((Creme de Creme x Financier) x ((Ballet in Orange x Coffee House) x Cinnamon sib)) x Cafe Society))) x Quito) X 92-71F2: (Enhancement x ((Romantic Mood sib x (Designer Gown x (78-221U x ((Artiste x Tupelo Honey) x ((Malaysia x Carolina Honey) x 73-122Z: (Hi Top x ((Ponderosa x Travel On) x Peace Offering sib))))))) x Winning Smile)).

REG WALL (Barry Emmerson, R. 1999). Sdlg. BE 95/8/22. TB, 37" (94 cm), M. Lightly ruffled deep violet; beards light blue, orange in throat; sweet fragrance. Wensleydale X Bartlett C95/23: (Midnight Fire x (Midnight Fire x Cosmic Dance)).

REHASH (George Sutton, R. 1997). Sdlg. H-85. SDB, 13" (33 cm), VE-E & RE. S. naples yellow (RHS 11A); style arms empire yellow (11D); F. white, naples yellow haft and 3/8" edge, violet flush at beard tip; beards bright violet blue (97), orpiment orange (25) in throat; ruffled; slight fragrance. Sigh X Chanted. Sutton 1998.

REI MOMO (Ladislav Muska, R. 1995). Sdlg. FAQC-01. TB, 40" (102 cm), M. Heavily ruffled red lilac plicata; beards honey; sweet fragrance. (Don Epifano x ("Cipkovana Krinolina": (After All x Grand Waltz) x Krimhilde)) X Queen in Calico. Muska 1996.

REISYUN (Hiroshi Shimizu by Clarence Mahan, R. 1994). JI (3 F.), 36" (91 cm), EM. S. and style arms clear pink; F. lighter clear pink veined darker pink, yellow signal with green overtones. "Ano-Otome" X "Togen". Iris Pond 1996.

RELINQUISH (John C. Taylor, R. 1998). Sdlg. UL 9-1. LA, 39" (100 cm), M. S. violet, midrib darker; style arms yellow green tipped violet; F. violet, darker on midrib and surrounding yellow signal; ruffled. C'est La Mote X Helen Naish. Rainbow Ridge 1998/99.

REMARKABLE (Raymond Smith, R. 1991). Sdlg. 7711JR. TB, 30" (76 cm), ML & RE. Golden tan (Nickerson 2.5Y 6/8) blend, lighter (2.5Y 8/12) around orange beard. 7316B: ((Memphis Lass x

D19AF) x ((Fall Majesty x Rainbow Gold) x Laced Duet)) X 2571DR: (((Hall sdlg. x Gibson Girl) x Pin Up Girl) x Leora Kate). R. G. Smith 1994.

REMBRANDT MAGIC (Barry Blyth, R. 1992). Sdlg. X79-A. TB, 36" (91 cm), EM. Coffee brown, F. deeper; beards dull mustard; slight fragrance. Light Beam X (Edna's Wish x Orangerie). Tempo Two 1992/93.

REMEMBERING ELVIE (Bruce Clark, R. 1999). Sdlg. 93-78. BB, 27" (68 cm), ML. S. pale purple; style arms pale purple, lower half edged yellow; F. pale purple, upper part veined burgundy purple, white haft markings extending beyond beard; beards yellow, base white. Pacific Tide X Pagan Dance.

REMEMBRANCE DAY (Pauline Evans, R. 1997). Sdlg. 94/1. SPU, 45" (114 cm), EML. S. and F. light yellow, completely overlaid purple, giving taupe to khaki effect, F. with small yellow signal. Missouri Blue X "Grey Lady", parentage unknown.

REMINGTON PARK (Perry Dyer, R. 1998). Sdlg. 90-166A. TB, 36" (91 cm), ML. Lightly ruffled and laced deep maroon wine; beards bronze, base deep brown. Clearfire X Burgundy Bubbles.

REMINISCENCE (Clarence Mahan, R. 1992). Sdlg. MTB90-2. MTB, 18" (46 cm), M. S. ruffled mineral violet; style arms pallid lavender; F. velvety plum purple, edged mauve, prominent white haft reticulation; beards gold. Consummation X Rosemary's Dream. Iris Pond 1994.

RENASCENT (Ben Hager, R. 1998). Sdlg. RE5316BlVW. TB, 36" (91 cm), M & RE. Ruffled blue violet self; beards pale blue white, hairs tipped yellow in throat. RE4839BlWh, Autumn Grandeur sib, X Twice Delightful.

RENATE (Manfred Beer, R. 1991). Sdlg. MB16/85C. TB, 41" (105 cm), M. S. pink; F. violet red, edged pink; beards orange. Metropolitan X Gypsy Caravan. Gartencenter Kania 1991.

RENEÉ LYNN (Jim Hedgecock, R. 1992). Sdlg. C-82-1-G. TB, 32" (81 cm), M. S. creamy yellow, pink midrib flush; F. pale yellow, white blaze; beards tangerine; ruffled, laced; pronounced sweet fragrance. Angie Quadros X Homecoming Queen. Comanche Acres 1993.

RENE SERVRANCKX (Alphonse Van Mulders, R. 1990). Sdlg. 170-16/86. TB, 38" (97 cm), M. S. rose violet; F. mahogany red; ruffled. Suave X Caramba. Jardinart-Van Mulders 1989.

RENJO-NO-TAMA (Society for Japanese Irises, R. 1992). JI (6 F.), 31½" (80 cm), ML. Lilac, white center and veining, yellow signals. Parentage unknown. 19th Century historic cultivar believed hybridized by Matsudaira Shoo. Incorrectly marked as obsolete in 1939 Check List.

RENOWN (Lloyd Zurbrigg, R. 1992). Sdlg. JJ 93-4-4. TB, 36" (91 cm), EE & RE. Oyster white self; beards light yellow. Matrix X Suky. Avonbank 1992.

REPINK (Virginia Keyser, R. 1999). Sdlg. 93-51. TB, 33" (84 cm), EM & RE. Light pink self; beards tangerine; slight sweet fragrance. Pinkness X Nordica.

RE-PLEAT (John Weiler, R. 1995). Sdlg. 90-10-6RE. SDB, 10" (25 cm), ML & RE. S. off-white, suffused and stippled light blue violet; F. off-white, light blue violet plicata border; beards light blue, tangerine orange in throat; slight sweet fragrance. Pink Fawn X 88-13-5RE: (Rainbow Sherbet x ((((Ruby Contrast x Little Blackfoot) x ((70-95: (Brighteyes x Grace Note) x Bronze Babe) x (Cartwheel x 70-95))) x Pink Amber) x (Melon Honey x ((Bloodspot x 70-95-1) x Satin Lustre)))).

REPUTATION (Mary Dunn, R. 1991). Sdlg. L158-6. LA, 34" (86 cm), M. French lilac, pale yellow signal. C'est Magnifique X L79-3: ((Queen o' Queens x Mrs. Ira Nelson) x Dark Tide). Bay View 1992.

REREWHA (Frances Love, R. 1998). SPEC (*laevigata*), 20" (51 cm), M. S. white, washed lavender; style arms lavender; F. white, washed lavender, spotted central streak. Parentage unknown; seed from Japan.

RESPONSE (Glenn Corlew, SPU, R. 1988). Bay View 1989.

RESTLESS REBEL (Chet Tompkins, R. 1997). Sdlg. 91-19B. TB, 36" (91 cm), EML. S. custard ground, overall maroon red markings; style arms amber, blended red; F. custard ground, heavily marked maroon red; beards mustard gold. Fancy Wrappings sib. Fleur de Lis 1997.

RETOLD TALE (Ben Hager, R. 1998). Sdlg. RE5596LtBl. TB, 36" (91 cm), E & RE. Light blue self; beards blue white. T4657IcBl, Winds of Change sib, X Tinted Crystal.

RETRO-STIL (Viktor Koroliov, R. 1997). Sdlg. S21-86K. TB, 43" (110 cm), M. S. light lilac, streaked brown; style arms light lilac; F. rose violet, whitish hafts heavily streaked brown; beards yellow, white at end; slight spicy fragrance. Hypnos X New Snow. Koroliov 1993.

RETTA ELIZABETH (J. Owings Rebert, R. 1996). Sdlg. AHB-1. SIB, 30" (76 cm), M. S. light red; F. fuchsia pink, gold hafts, signal white. Parentage unknown.

RETURN ADDRESS (Joseph Ghio, R. 1999). Sdlg. 93-98J3. TB, 38" (97 cm), L & RE. S. orange;

F. white, banded orange; beards orange tangerine. 90-21Y, pod parent of Blonde Bombshell, X 91-121D2: (88-105X, pod parent of Heaven, x 88-100U, Reality sib).

RETURNING CHAMELEON (Betty Wilkerson, R. 1995). Sdlg. C54-1 RE. TB, 32" (81 cm), M & RE. S. and style arms greyed white to pale lavender (RHS 91C), occasionally palest pink; F. grey white to pale pink; beards white, tipped pale orange in throat; ruffled; slight musky fragrance. Pink Sleigh X Immortality. Bridge in Time 1995.

RETURNING ROSE (William Maryott, R. 1998). Sdlg. W182ARE. TB, 37" (94 cm), M & RE. S. pinkish orchid (RHS 186B), slight cream midrib; style arms pinkish orchid; F. light yellow to cream ground, pinkish orchid plicata banding, shoulder veining and slight mid-stripe; beards brick orange; pronounced spicy fragrance. Storyline X Lingering Love. Maryott 1998.

RETURN MAIL (John C. Taylor, R. 1998). Sdlg. UL 16-2. LA, 39" (100 cm), L. S. buff, veined purple violet; style arms reddish tan; F. purple violet, edge lighter, darker around yellow signal. Dancing Vogue X Noble Planet.

REVEL IN RED (Donald Spoon, R. 1998). Sdlg. 90-206. BB, 25" (64 cm), ML. Velvety deep rich red self; style arms deep red; beards deep red, hairs tipped bronze; ruffled, flared. Warrior King X Time Lord. Winterberry 1998.

REVIVAL MEETING (Chet Tompkins, R. 1990). Sdlg. 83-63A. TB, 36" (91 cm), EML. S. smoky gold infused lilac, pink and cream; F. deeper shades of lilac, rose and lavender blue with pink overtones; beards rich ruby and chocolate blended with electric blue and violet; slight spicy fragrance. ((Nile Flower x dark sib) x (Song of Norway x Nile Flower)) X ((dark Nile Flower sib x Cosmic Dawn) x (Elegant Era x Nile Flower)). Fleur de Lis 1990.

REZEDA (Viacheslav Gavrilin, R. 1998). Sdlg. 1-16-1-94. TB, 35" (90 cm), M. S. and style arms dull pink, yellow flush; F. wine red to violet, narrow dull pink rim, white patterning near beard; beards brown, violet at end; lightly ruffled; slight fragrance. Latin Lover X unknown. Gavrilin 1999.

RHAPSODY IN BLOOM (Richard Ernst, R. 1993). Sdlg. F120-8. TB, 35" (89 cm), ML. Ruffled orchid, cream orchid area around beards, honey shoulders; beards yellow orange, tipped white; slight sweet fragrance. Afternoon Delight X Gaulter 81-17: (Irene Nelson x Glendale sdlg.). Cooley 1993.

RHEA PEERZ (Brad Kasperek, R. 1998). Sdlg. 92R-42A. IB, 23" (58 cm), EM & RE. S. creamy light chartreuse yellow (RHS 2D); style arms yellow (3A); F. lemon yellow (3D), deeper (3A) shoulders; beards yellow (3A); ruffled. Grace Thomas X Ditto. Zebra 1999.

RHIANNON (Nora Scopes, R. 1996). Sdlg. 00/122. TB, 37" (94 cm), M. S. white; F. white, faint cream glow in heart; beards pale yellow; ruffled; sweet fragrance. Designer's Choice X 4/74: (1/147: (Launching Pad x (Cambodia x Western Wind)) x 2/178: ((Fiametta x unknown) x Dachstein)).

RHINEMAIDENS (Tom Magee, BB, R. 1988). Long 1990.

RHINESTONE COWGIRL (Sharon McAllister, R. 1992). Sdlg. 87-4-9. AB (OGB), 28" (72 cm), EM. S. sparkling soft magenta rose (near RHS 186D); F. similar but slightly more yellow, signal area veined burgundy; beards gold and maroon. Heart Stealer X Whither Thou Goest. McAllister 1993.

RHONDA FLEMING (Ron Mullin, R. 1992). Sdlg. 84-7X. TB, 34-35" (86-89 cm), M. S. white center blending to lilac; style arms darker lilac; F. white, narrow solid lilac band; beards white, ruffled, lightly laced; slight spicy fragrance. Go Around X Laced Cotton. M.A.D. Iris 1993.

RHONE VALLEY (Eric & Bob Tankesley-Clarke, R. 1994). SPEC, 8-10" (20-25 cm), E. S. chartreuse yellow; F. chartreuse to light green; beards yellow; pronounced sweet fragrance. Collected, Rhone Valley, Switzerland; distributed prior to 1980 and in commerce as *I. lutescens virescens* U51.

RHYME OR REASON (Mary Dunn, R. 1995). Sdlg. L181-1. LA, 36" (91 cm), M. S. smooth smoky plum; style arms pinkish plum; F. smooth smoky plum, bright golden signal, golden reverse; ruffled. L119-3: (Clara Goula x (Charlie's Michele x Carmen)) X L155-3: (Southerner x (Charlie's Michele x Rhett)). Bay View 1996.

RHYME TIME (William Simon, TB, R. 1986). Stahly 1993.

RHYTHM KING (Harold Stahly, R. 1992). Sdlg. 86-8. TB, 35" (89 cm), M. Heavily ruffled deep blue violet (RHS 86A); beards deep blue; slight sweet fragrance. Deep Pacific X 81-9: ((Ivy League x River Patrol) x Navy Strut). Stahly 1992.

RHYTHM MASTER (William Simon, TB, R. 1986). Stahly 1991.

RIBANDS (Graeme Grosvenor, R. 1993). Sdlg. R27-1. TB, 38" (97 cm), EM. S. pink; F. pink, lighter center, apricot hafts; beards red; ruffled. Snow Cream X First Movement. Rainbow Ridge 1993/94.

RICH AND FAMOUS (Mary Dunn, R. 1993). Sdlg. L156-4. LA, 32" (81 cm), ML. S. burgundy wine red; F. ruffled deep wine red, yellow line signal. Easter Tide X L79-3: ((Queen o' Queens x Mrs. Ira Nelson) x Dark Tide). Bay View 1993.

RICHARD B. HARRIS (Gary Anderson, TB, R. 1989). Pacific Coast Hybridizers 1992.

RICHARD GREANEY (John Carter, R. 1991). SPEC (*laevigata*), 24" (61 cm), M. Pale blue.Parentage unknown. Rowden Gardens 1991.

RICHARD'S PINK (Janet Hutchinson, R. 1995). Sdlg. SL/RP. LA, 49" (125 cm), ML. S. bright mallow pink, paler buff pink linear edge, narrow salmon buff centerline; style arms mallow pink over white; F. slightly darker than S., signal rich gold over white, green at throat; lightly ruffled; slight sweet fragrance. Soft Laughter X unknown. Iris Haven 1997/98.

RICH BOY (Joseph Ghio, CA, R. 1989). Bay View 1990.

RICH IN SPIRIT (O. D. Niswonger, R. 1997). Sdlg. 28-92. TB, 30" (76 cm), M. S. and style arms apricot; F. red violet, apricot rim; beards tangerine. Halo in Pink X unknown. Cape Iris 1997.

RICH JEWEL (Richard Morgan, R. 1994). Sdlg. L709-D. LA, 32" (81 cm), EM. Dark violet, large yellow steeple signal; style arms pale red. Tanako X Charles Arny III. Redbud Lane 1995.

RICHLIE BLESSED (Wayne Richlie, R. 1999). TB, 26-34" (66-86 cm), E. S. lavender blue; F. rosy lavender, lavender blue border; beards yellow, white tip; slight sweet fragrance. Petite Posy X Cabaret Royale. Missoula Gardens 1999.

RICH MAN (Everette Lineberger, R. 1994). Sdlg. QHT 133. TB, 37" (94 cm), ML. S. violet purple; F. velvety dark violet purple, white area at hafts; beards gold, tipped lavender; ruffled, semi-flared; slight fragrance. Rose Shiner X Pops Concert. Quail Hill 1995.

RICHMOND WHITE (Lucy Delaney by Hilmary Catton, R. 1996). SDB, 9" (24 cm), M & RE. S. white, faint lime green midrib; F. white, pale lime green veining around white beard. Parentage unknown.

*RICH RELATIONS (James McWhirter, TB, R. 1989). Cottage 1990.

RICH TRADITION (John C. Taylor, R. 1990). Sdlg. OL 142-3. LA, 47" (120 cm), EM. Heavily ruffled violet (RHS 88B), lighter edge and reverse, yellow signal on all petals. M24-4: (C'est Si Bon x Charles Arny III) X Helen Naish. Rainbow Ridge 1990/91.

RICK (Betty Wyss, R. 1996). Sdlg. 881-15. MTB, 22" (56 cm), ML. S. white ground splattered blue lavender, lavender midrib and edge; F. white ground, haft and edge line blue lavender; beards lilac, hairs tipped yellow bronze. Sand Princess X unknown. Stockton 1996.

RICKLINGER BURGUNDER (Harald Moos, R. 1993). Sdlg. 86/6007B. TB, 31½" (80 cm), M. Wavy fuchsia pink; beards orange. Matinee Idol X Mulled Wine. Schoeppinger 1993.

RICKLINGER YELLOW (Harald Moos, R. 1989). Sdlg. 84/55A. SIB, 23½" (60 cm), M. S. white; F. light yellow, dark yellow signal. Gelbe Moeve X Creme Chantilly. Moos 1991.

RIDDLE (Keith Keppel, R. 1991). Sdlg. 84-1A. IB, 20" (51 cm), EM & RE. S. marguerite (M&P 10-C-1) to ivory (10-B-2), flushed cornsilk (10-G-3); F. marguerite, eventide (42-C-6) line-flush below beard; beards white, tipped flame (1-C-12). Sib to Anagram. Keppel 1992.

RIDE THE WIND (Schreiner, R. 1991). Sdlg. W 450-2. TB, 38" (97 cm), M. S. white (RHS 155D); F. blue (95A), slightly ruffled white edge; beards lemon, tipped white. Pledge Allegiance X N 39-B: (H 201-T: ((inv. Harbor Blue, Blue Sapphire, Celestial Snow, First Violet, King's Choice, Allegiance) x (Rococo x Prince Indigo)) x H 173-B: (Margarita sdlg. x ((Salem x Cahokia sdlg.) x ((Broadway Star x Whole Cloth) x Blue Mountains)))). Schreiner 1991.

RIELLE (Donald Spoon, R. 1997). Sdlg. 89-112. BB, 24" (61 cm), M & RE. S. white, brushed and overlaid light sulphur yellow (RHS 6D); style arms white and sulphur yellow; F. white, bordered darker sulphur yellow (6C), lighter streaks at hafts; beards sulphur yellow (6C), white base; ruffled, lightly laced. I Do X Other Mary. Winterberry 1999.

RIFF-RAFF (A. Farrington, MDB, R. 1986). British Iris Society 1987.

RIGATTI ROSE (Mary Tubbs, R. 1992). Sdlg. RR-1. TB, 34" (86 cm), M. Raspberry pink self; beards pale orange. Raspberry Ripples X Paradise Bird.

RIGATTIERE (Augusto Bianco, R. 1999). Sdlg. 679. TB, 34" (86 cm), M. White self; beards yellow with cream base, yellow in throat; foliage variegated green and cream; slight sweet fragrance. Ensminger variegated-foliage sdlg. X (Immortality x Murrah Memorial).

RIGHT ALREADY (John Durrance, R. 1992). D82-3. TB, 35" (89 cm), ML. S. red; F. velvety darker red; beards burnt red. Anon X Taco Belle. Long 1992.

RIGHT STUFF (Ken Mohr, R. 1993). Sdlg. P-27-C. TB, 36" (91 cm), M. S. light to medium chicory blue tinted lavender; F. medium to dark chicory blue, paling to S. color at edge; beards cream, tipped yellow; ruffled; slight fragrance. Romantic Voyage X (J-88 x Light Fantastic). Pacific Coast Hybridizers 1993.

RILL (Louise Bellagamba, R. 1991). Sdlg. S1-89. SIB, 18" (46 cm), M. Medium blue, small white ray pattern; style arms pale blue white. Parentage unknown. Bella Vista 1992.

RINGER (Keith Keppel, R. 1996). Sdlg. 92-11A. SDB, 10" (25 cm), EM. S. dark plum brown (M&P 56-J-10), faint yellow (9-J-2) center shading; style arms mauve brown (56-J-3) flushed castilian brown (7-J-9); F. cadmium lemon (9-L-1), solid 1/4" dark plum brown border; beards dull brass (11-L-6); ruffled. Firestorm X Quote. Keppel 1997.

RINGLETS (David Sindt by Adamgrove, R. 1992). Sdlg. 717. SDB, 9" (23 cm), EML. S. white, edged blue violet; F. same with blue violet rays extending from beard area; beards blue violet. Lime Rhapsody X 518: (401: (Quip x Mini-Plic) x Velvet Trim). Adamgrove 1992.

RINGOLETTO (Ladislav Muska, R. 1997). Sdlg. GERI-02. TB, 36" (91 cm), EM. S. light vanilla; style arms blended vanilla and caramel; F. light lilac, wide smoky cream edge; beards bright orange; heavily ruffled, lightly laced; pronounced fragrance. (Geniality x Ringo) X Carrara Lace. Muska 1997.

RING O' ROSES (Nora Scopes, R. 1991). Sdlg. PC 22. CA, 12" (30 cm), M. Pale rose pink, F. lighter in heart. Parentage unknown.

RINGS AND THINGS (Lyle Fort by Dona Fort, R. 1997). Sdlg. 89-420-Q. BB, 25" (64 cm), M. S. white, coral pink edge, slight pink flush; style arms coral pink, deep pink midrib flush; F. white, coral pink edge; beards tangerine; ruffled, heavily laced; slight sweet fragrance. Lady Madonna X 84-152-Z: (Pearls and Gold x Blazing Light).

RINGS OF SATURN (George Sutton, R. 1997). Sdlg. G-27. TB, 36" (91 cm), ML. Heavily ruffled cool white, 1/8" sky blue edging on S. and F.; beards blue white, tipped yellow, 2" cool white spoon edged sky blue; slight sweet fragrance. Sky Hooks X Winterscape. Sutton 1998.

RING TOSS (David Sindt by Eric Tankesley-Clarke, R. 1995). Sdlg. 798. SDB, 12" (30 cm), M. S. and F. white, 1/4" violet edge; beards blue; slight sweet fragrance. 590: ((Clap Hands x Quip) x Velvet Trim) X Royal Magician. Adamgrove 1995.

RINKY-DINK (Keith Keppel, R. 1992). Sdlg. 82-13N. BB, 25" (64 cm), ML. S. flesh blond (M&P 4-A-9) suffused pale greyed orchid (52-B-3) in center; F. vanilla (10-C-3), with fine-dot wash and almost solid edge near coronation purple (45-L-8); beards tile red (3-D-12) faintly shaded coronation purple; slight sweet fragrance. Gigolo X 79-83A, Change of Heart sib. D & J Gardens 1993.

RIOPELLE (Tony Huber, R. 1992). Sdlg. 1DM-Bar-01. SPEC (*versicolor*), 27½" (70 cm), VE. S. light rosy mauve; F. rosy mauve, large white central area veined deep mauve; slight sweet fragrance. Collected, Magdalen Islands, Quebec, Canada.

RIP CITY (Schreiner, R. 1999). Sdlg. EE 280-1. TB, 39" (99 cm), ML. Bright red (RHS 59A); beards yellow. War Chief X Mulberry Punch. Schreiner 1999.

RIPPLETTE (Jayne Ritchie, R. 1990). Sdlg. 84-3-2. SDB, 12" (33 cm), E. Ruffled medium blue (near RHS 98D); beards blue and white, hairs tipped gold in throat, outer end medium blue. 80-8-5: ((Spring Salute x Pale Suede) x (Blue Pools x Pale Suede)) X Baron's Delight. Ritchie 1990.

RIPPLING RIVER (Schreiner, R. 1995). Sdlg. BB 155-1. TB, 36" (91 cm), M. Heavily ruffled medium navy blue self; beards blue. W 138-4: (R 33-B: (((Shipshape x Sailor's Dance) x St. Louis Blues sib) x Land o'Lakes) x R 40-1: ((Sailor's Dance x ((Pacific Panorama x Parisian Blue) x Sapphire Hills)) x ((G 1517-B x Neptune's Pool) x Royal Regency))) X Jean Hoffmeister. Schreiner 1995.

RIP SNORTER (Chet Tompkins, R. 1990). Sdlg. 84-159A. TB, 38-40" (97-102 cm), ML. Marigold orange; beards red orange. (Grand Manner x (Lovely Light x Orange Parade)) X ((Beau Bright x Dawn Forecast) x Twilight Torch). Fleur de Lis 1990.

RI-SAMPEI (Ladislav Muska, R. 1996). Sdlg. QCCA-09. TB, 37" (94 cm), EM. Nut brown plicata; beards orange; ruffled, heavily laced; spicy fragrance. ((Queen in Calico x "Fialovy Kvet": (Windsor Rose x Laced Cotton)) x Calicoball) X Moonlight Sketch. Muska 1996.

RISEN STAR (William Maryott, R. 1991). Sdlg. N135B. TB, 38" (97 cm), M. Ruffled medium lemon yellow (RHS 14B), F. with white flash; beards yellow; leaf bases purple. Radiant Energy X Sound of Gold. Maryott 1991.

RISKY VENTURE (William Grise, R. 1999). Sdlg. BRX. TB, 36" (91 cm), ML. S. bright medium yellow; style arms yellow, streaked red; F. red; beards red; ruffled; slight fragrance. Gay Parasol X Ringo. Parkwood 1999.

RITE OF SPRING (Ben Hager, R. 1995). Sdlg. T4840#1. TB, 36" (91 cm), M. S. blended violet; F. violet center blot fading toward edge; beards violet. Tinted Crystal X T3702: (Silver Flow x Ruffled Ballet). Cooley 1996.

RITUAL (Joseph Ghio, R. 1998). Sdlg. 93-44V3. TB, 36" (91 cm), EM. S. red mahogany; F. electric violet, blended red mahogany band, shoulders deeper; beards yellow. Engaging X 90-129I: (87-101V: ((84-133-C3: (Lady Friend x (Flareup x (Capitation x Coffee House))) x Battle Hymn sib) x Court Martial) x (84-133-C3 x (((Praline x Lady Friend) x ((((Ponderosa x Honey Rae) x ((((Commentary x Claudia Rene) x Claudia Rene) x Ponderosa) x (Ponderosa x New Moon))) x Homecoming Queen) x (Entourage x Homecoming Queen))) x ((((Creme de Creme x Financier) x ((Ballet in Orange x Coffee House) x Cinnamon sib)) x Cafe Society))))). Bay View 1999.

RIVER AVON (George Sutton, R. 1995). Sdlg. F-106-A. TB, 39" (99 cm), EML. Ruffled light blue (RHS 108D) self; beards butterfly blue (near 106B). Demi et Demi X Chico Maid. Sutton 1996.

RIVERBOAT BLUES (Schreiner, R. 1991). Sdlg. W 472-C. TB, 38" (97 cm), ML. Ruffled medium blue (RHS 96D); beards white. Memphis Blues X P 81-A: ((G 11-1, St. Louis Blues sib, x (G 1517-B x Neptune's Pool)) x L 93-5: ((Navy Strut x E 1313-A) x (Fuji's Mantle x Matinata))). Schreiner 1991.

RIVERDANCE (Marty Schafer/Jan Sacks, R. 1997). Sdlg. S90-13-1. SIB, 40-45" (102-114 cm), M. S. cornflower blue (RHS 95A/B); style arms cornflower blue, white wire edge; F. brighter cornflower blue, shoulders flecked white, white wire edge, white signal yellow in center and veined cornflower blue; rolled ruffling. Forrest McCord X Jaybird. Joe Pye Weed 1997.

RIVER JORDAN (Hooker Nichols, TB, R. 1989). Hillcrest 1996.

RIVER MIST (John Marchant, R. 1990). Sdlg. 1187. CA, 10" (25 cm), M. S. naples yellow (HCC 403/3) with violet blue midrib infusion; F. naples yellow, large light violet blue wash fading to edge, diffuse yellow signal. Sdlg. X sdlg.

RIVER OF DREAMS (Keith Chadwick/Tony DeRose, R. 1999). Sdlg. 95-K.I.T.01. IB, 18" (46 cm), L. S. dark violet base blending to light violet toward tip; style arms light violet; F. sky blue, bronze veining on shoulders; beards white, tangerine red toward throat. Zounds X unknown. Riverview 1999.

RIVER PEARL (Cy Bartlett, R. 1998). Sdlg. PC-TOB.1. TB, 34" (86 cm), EM. Lightly ruffled pale milky blue white, F. flushed cerise near beard; style arms pale milky blue white touched cerise; beards very dark blue bronze; slight fragrance. (Pledge Allegiance x Chico Maid) X Touch of Bronze. Sutton 1999.

RIVER ROAD (Patrick O'Connor, R. 1992). Sdlg. 83-3. LA, 36" (91 cm), M. Medium blue, yellow line signal on white ground; style arms medium blue, marked cream. Southdowns X Clyde Redmond. Bois d'Arc 1993.

RIVER RUNNER (Richard Ernst, R. 1999). Sdlg. 9-2L. TB, 38" (97 cm), M. Ruffled medium blue self; beards whitish blue. Probably -- F116-10, Blue It Up sib, X F116-2, sib. Cooley 1999.

RIVER'S EDGE (Larry Lauer, R. 1995). Sdlg. L89-58-1. TB, 35" (89 cm), M. S. dark blue, thin white edge; style arms dark blue; F. dark blue, white on shoulders around beard, slight white edge; beards white. America's Cup X Larry Gaulter. Stockton 1996.

RIVER'S END (George Sutton, R. 1999). Sdlg. H-124 A. TB, 37" (94 cm), ML. S. light violet blue (RHS 97C); style arms and F. slightly lighter (97D); beards violet blue (97A), bronzy gold base, medium violet blue (97A) horn; ruffled; slight sweet fragrance. G-15A: (Winterscape x Sky Hooks) X G-15B, sib.

RIVER SIREN (Robert Dunn, R. 1997). Sdlg. B1034A. TB, 37" (94 cm), M. ruffled royal purple self; beards purple. Skyship X M931-Z: ((((Pagan sib x Royal Heritage) x Manuel) x Plum Dazzle) x (Intuition x Cranberry Ice)). M.A.D. Iris 1998.

RIVERSONG (William Maryott, R. 1998). Sdlg. U136U. TB, 36" (91 cm), M. Medium blue violet self; beards light blue; slight sweet fragrance. Blue sdlg., parentage unknown, X Breakers. Maryott 1999.

RIVIERA STOP (Pierre Anfosso, R. 1990). Sdlg. P 82 20D. TB, 33½" (85 cm), EM. Heavily ruffled soft pink. Carmen X X Beverly Sills. Iris en Provence 1990.

RIVULETS OF PINK (O. D. Niswonger, R. 1995). Sdlg. Sp 10-94. SPU, 42" (107 cm), M. Pinkish mauve, F. overlaid yellow in center. Sp 8-88: (Sp 6-80: (Far Out x Redwood Supreme) x unknown) X Firemist. Cape Iris 1996.

RIVULETS OF WINE (J. T. Aitken, R. 1999). Sdlg. 91J5C. JI (6 F.), 40" (102 cm), M. White ground overlaid with intense wine red veins, blending to solid wine around yellow signal; style arms wine red, edges lighter. Flashing Koi X unknown. Aitken's Salmon Creek 1999.

ROAD SONG (Barry Blyth, R. 1993). Sdlg. Z63-2. TB, 36-38" (91-97 cm), VE-M. S. white; F. glowing honey with outpouring of deeper honey; beards orange. W117-1: ((Alpine Journey x Beachgirl) x (Beachgirl x ((Tranquil Star x Coral Strand) x (Persian Smoke x Chimbolam)))) X Chocolate Vanilla. Tempo Two 1993/94.

ROAR (Tom Burseen, R. 1997). Sdlg. 1-155D. TB, 36" (91 cm), EM. S. and style arms orange gold; F. yellow, central area streaked yellow; beards golden orange; ruffled. 9-168: (Salmon Band x Gigolo) X First Fuss. T.B.'s Place 1997.

ROARING FORTIES (John Baldwin, R. 1994). Sdlg. 82-22D. TB, 32" (81 cm), EM. Heavily ruffled white; beards very pale yellow, tipped white; slight spicy fragrance. Wedding Vow X 78-26A: (Rock-n-Roll x 74-34C: (((Satin Ripples x Winter Olympics) x Regal Rhythm) x (Satin Ripples x Winter Olympics))).

ROARING JELLY (Marty Schafer/Jan Sacks, R. 1992). Sdlg. 86-36-1. SIB, 36" (91 cm), M. S. lavender grey (RHS 85D) with diffused red purple veining; style arms same, flushed blue aqua; F. shaded and dappled throughout giving red purple maroon overall effect, signal white with dark veining and dark blue flush. Warburton ARV82-31: ((Atoll x Ruffled Velvet) x Ruffled Velvet) X Springs Brook. Joe Pye Weed 1992.

ROASTED PECAN (Kevin Vaughn, R. 1998). Sdlg. F-17-8. LA, 25" (64 cm), ML. Bright copper, dark rose veining overall, F. with gold signal edged rose; style arms bright copper. Heavenly Glow X Kelley's Choice.

ROBE D'ÉTÉ (Richard Cayeux, R. 1998). TB, 33" (85 cm), EM. S. light lemon yellow; F. amethyst pink with narrow light lemon yellow edge; beards bright yellow. Tracy Tyrene X Sweet Musette. Cayeux 1999.

ROBE OF ROYALTY (Jim Hedgecock, R. 1990). Sdlg. 84-55-1. TB, 33" (84 cm), M. S. royal maroon red; F. darker velvety maroon red; beards maroon red. Sky Hooks X Superstition. Comanche Acres 1991.

ROBERT M. PINTO (Louise Smith, R. 1992). Sdlg. 84-109(1). BB, 26½" (67 cm), M. S. bright yellow; F. soft brown flush, soft yellow edge, red brown haft lines; beards orange yellow, tipped yellow; pronounced sweet fragrance. Spirit of Memphis X Chocolate Daddy.

ROBIN GOODFELLOW (Clarence Mahan, R. 1993). Sdlg. 788-3(MTB). MTB, 19" (48 cm), ML. White self; style arms white; beards yellow. White Canary X Table Queen. Iris Pond 1994.

ROBIN OF LOXLEY (Donald Spoon, R. 1997). Sdlg. 93-7A. TB, 36" (91 cm), M. S. light plum lavender, deeper midrib; style arms light plum lavender; F. darker plum, edged plum lavender, white rays around beard; beards white base and end, tangerine midsection deepening in throat; ruffled, laced; slight sweet fragrance. (Femme Fatale x Sweet Musette) X Champagne Elegance.

ROBIN'S EGG (David Sindt, MDB, R. 1986). Adamgrove 1993.

ROBINZON (Viacheslav Gavrilin, R. 1999). Sdlg. 94-621. TB, 36" (92 cm), M. S. chocolate brown to orange, yellow base; style arms yellow; F. chocolate orange, violet stripe below yellow beard, narrow yellow rim; lightly laced. Fiesta Time X Starcrest.

ROCCAPINA (Tomas Tamberg, R. 1993). SPEC (*pseudacorus*), 49" (120 cm), L. Yellow, faint darker signal. Collected, Roccapina, southern Corsica. Schoeppinger 1994.

ROCCO BOY (Alphonse Van Mulders, R. 1990). Sdlg. 89-22/86. TB, 33" (76 cm), M. Ruffled white ground plicata stitched red violet. Provencal X Crinoline. Jardinart-Van Mulders 1989.

ROCKABYE (Barry Blyth, R. 1993). Sdlg. Z10-C. SDB, 10" (25 cm), M. Rosy tan, F. with deeper rosy brown pumila spot; beards bright lavender, burnt tangerine in throat; sweet fragrance. Camarilla X Chanted. Tempo Two 1993/94.

ROCKEN WITH BLONDIE (Glenn Stoneking-Jones, R. 1999). Sdlg. CIR6-5357-06-02-1999. TB, 28" (71 cm), EM. S. mustard yellow; style arms dark burgundy; F. burgundy; beards bronze; slight musky fragrance. (Vigilante x Supreme Sultan) X (Dusky Challenger x Vigilante).

ROCKET LAUNCH (T. J. Betts, R. 1997). Sdlg. 902E. LA, 28" (71 cm), ML. Red (RHS 42D) becoming brown (171D), F. with long yellow steeple signal; style arms brown. Sun Fury X Shrimp Creole.

ROCKET MASTER (Barry Blyth, R. 1990). Sdlg. V119-2. TB, 36" (91 cm), EML. S. burgundy wine; F. white ground, 3/4" burgundy plicata band with some veining into white area; beards cream white; heavily ruffled. (Sapharine x Flamenco) X (Fancy Dancer x Broadway). Tempo Two 1990/91.

ROCKET SMOKE (Terrell Taylor, R. 1994). Sdlg. 93-67. TB, 31½" (80 cm), ML. Ruffled blue white, violet blue (HS 92C) highlights; beards tangerine, tipped white. Cold Cold Heart X Sweet Musette. Bonita Gardens 1995.

ROCK STAR (Monty Byers, R. 1990). Sdlg. F16-1. TB, 30" (86 cm), EM. S. apricot orange, almost completely overlaid with red violet mottling; F. apricot orange, medium red violet stitched edge, deeper stitching over hafts; beards red orange, light orange horn speckled red violet; heavily ruffled; slight sweet fragrance. Lovebird X Gigolo. Moonshine 1991.

ROCKY MOUNTAIN MUSIC (Frank Foster, R. 1995). Sdlg. 8750 BL. TB, 35" (89 cm), M. Medium blue self; beards cream yellow; lightly ruffled. Bodega Bay X Alabama Bound.

ROCKY MOUNTAIN PARK (Glenn Stoneking-Jones, R. 1999). Sdlg. CSPU6-41-03-30-1994. SPU, 40" (107 cm), M. White, F. with large yellow signal. *I. ochroleuca* X Ochroleuca Gigantea.

ROCOCO ECHO (Kevin Nilsen, R. 1992). Sdlg. 44-87-1. BB, 23" (59 cm), EM. S. medium violet blue plicata markings on white ground; F. white ground, edges stitched medium violet; beards white, yellow in throat; ruffled; foliage with deep purple base. Gentle Rain X 9-84: (Rococo Valley x Burgundy Brown).

RODEO BLUE (B. Charles Jenkins, R. 1994). Sdlg. BF21K. SPU, 38-45" (97-114 cm), E. S. sky blue; style arms blue; F. blue, blending to white radiating from yellow signal. Bali Bali X Lenkoran. Shepard Iris 1994.

RODEO CLOWN (Hooker Nichols, IB, R. 1989). Hillcrest 1991.

RODEO DRIVE (James McWhirter, R. 1993). Sdlg. J87-771-1. TB, 36" (91 cm), M. Ruffled rich cranberry purple; self beards; pronounced fragrance. Winterscape X Larry Gaulter. Stockton 1994.

RODEO PRINCESS (A. & D. Willott, R. 1993). Sdlg. 89-27. SDB, 13" (33 cm), EM. S. light apricot pink; F. pale apricot pink, apricot spot either side of beard; beards light orange, red orange in throat; ruffled. Barney's Delight X 84-140: (Apricot Elf x Coral Wings). Willott 1994.

RODEO STAR (Hooker Nichols, TB, R. 1988). Hillcrest 1995.

RODNIK (Nina Miroshnichenko, R. 1996). TB, 43" (110 cm), EM. Ruffled white, tinted blue, F. with brown haft patterning; beards yellow orange; slight sweet fragrance. Parentage unknown. Miroshnichenko 1977.

ROEMER JENER (Hilmary Catton, R. 1996). Sdlg. C 8922. MDB, 7" (18 cm), E. S. lemon yellow; F. cream, edges and haft lemon; beards lemon. Eyebright X Bibury. Richmond Iris 1998/99.

ROGER LUCE (Currier McEwen, R. 1999). Sdlg. ST(10)94/88(R2-2). SIB (tet.), 30" (76 cm), VE. S. light violet blue (RHS 89D) tinged red; style arms dark violet blue (91B) midrib, edged lighter; F. blue (93B), white signal. ST(9)92/1: (T(8)88/1(1): (White Prelude x Lucky Lilac) x sib) X unknown.

ROGUE (Joseph Ghio, R. 1994). Sdlg. 88-60-O. TB, 38" (97 cm), ML. Brick red self, shoulders deeper; beards brick tangerine. Caracas X 85-209-V2: ((((Cream Taffeta x (Ponderosa x New Moon)) x 76-37F: (Ballet in Orange x 73-122Z)) x (Blaze of Fire x 76-37F)) x ((((Flareup x 73-122Z: (Hi Top x ((Ponderosa x Travel On) x Peace Offering))) x 76-37F) x (Preface sib x (Old Flame x Pink Angel))) x (((Malaysia x Carolina Honey) x 73-122Z) x Toastmaster))). Roris 1996.

ROISIN (Jennifer Hewitt, R. 1996). Sdlg. P 8414/16. SIB, 36" (91 cm), M. S. pale lavender pink (RHS 76C) flushed deeper (77C), upright, edges crimped; style arms off-white speckled lavender; F. lavender pink (84A), signal of few small white lines, semi-flared. Pink Haze X Lavender Bounty.

ROKKI ROCKWELL (Dorman Haymon, R. 1992). Sdlg. 12-84-17. LA, 38" (97 cm), M. S. medium yellow, streaked gold; style arms medium yellow tipped dark yellow, green deep in heart; F. medium yellow, streaked gold, slight brown overlay, gold line signal; ruffled; slight fragrance. Valera X President Hedley. Deep South Gardens 1992.

ROLLING SEAS (J. T. Aitken, R. 1994). Sdlg. 88J7. JI (6 F.), 48" (122 cm), ML. Soft medium blue self. 85J4, unknown, X 86J14: (T. Hill 81-J-10 x Izu-no-Umi). Aitken's Salmon Creek 1994.

ROMAN AUTUMN (Chet Tompkins, R. 1999). Sdlg. 94-117. TB, 35" (89 cm), EML. S. and style arms molten orange brass; F. wine red; beards orange brown. Megabucks X Up and Coming. Fleur de Lis 1999.

ROMAN CARNIVAL (D. C. Nearpass, R. 1996). Sdlg. 88-20. TB, 36" (91 cm), M. S. pale violet (Munsell 7.5 PB 6/9); style arms flushed purple; F. white ground, overall stippling and dotting of medium dark purple; beards rusty orange; ruffled. Purple Pepper X Rose Tattoo. Friendship 1997.

ROMANCE IN DURANGO (Barry Emmerson, R. 1998). Sdlg. BE 95-26-4. TB, 38" (97 cm), M. S. chestnut brown, midrib suffused yellow; style arms chestnut brown; F. yellow ground, near-solid stippled chestnut brown edge and midstripe, yellow wire rim; beards dark orange; lightly ruffled; slight fragrance. Dodsworth 86KK: ((Royal Trumpeter x Fireball) x (Royal Trumpeter x Post Time)) X Battle Hymn.

ROMANETO (Zdeněk Seidl, R. 1997). Sdlg. 90-GBx/7. SPU, 47" (120 cm), M. Yellow, F. veined green. "Gold Brunner" X unknown.

ROMAN FESTIVAL (Vernon Wood, R. 1994). Sdlg. 92-57. CA, 12-14" (30-36 cm), M. S. yellow orange with dark red lines; F. yellow orange, heavily lined dark red (RHS 46A) to lighter (46D) near edge, 1/4" yellow orange rim; ruffled. Mimsey X Riva. Stockton 1996.

ROMANITA (Barry Blyth, R. 1993). Sdlg. Z13-6. SDB, 12" (31 cm), VE-M. Greenish creamy apricot, F. with slight lavender flash; beards soft lavender. Cupfull X Minisong. Tempo Two 1993/94.

ROMAN NOIR (Lawrence Ransom, R. 1996). Sdlg. 90/330-13. SDB, 14" (36 cm), M. S. dark violet blue; F. black; beards lavender blue, brushed yellow in throat. Khaki Print X Trescols. Iris au Trescols 1996.

ROMAN SOLDIER (Ed Matheny III, R. 1995). Sdlg. 06-01-91. TB, 39" (99 cm), M. S. and style arms violet (RHS 83D); F. dark reddish violet (83A); beards mustard yellow, purple horn. Roman Lover X Trick or Treat. Ed's Iris 1996.

ROMAN SONG (Barry Blyth, R. 1993). Sdlg. Z72-1. TB, 36" (91 cm), EM. S. pastel pink; F. white ground, rosy lavender plicata stitching and rose centerline; beards pastel apricot; ruffled. Just Delicious sib X Shiralee. Tempo Two 1993/94.

ROMANTIC DREAM (Daniel Thruman, R. 1997). SIB, 28" (71 cm), E. S. lavender pink (RHS 76B); style arms white, feathered; F. deeper lavender pink (76A), white signal veined lavender pink, white edge, golden brown haft veining. Summer Sky X Lavender Bounty.

ROMANTIC EVENING (Joseph Ghio, R. 1994). Sdlg. 90-56W. TB, 36" (91 cm), ML. S. lilac blue; F. smooth blackish red purple; beards deep brick. 88-14: ((83-73-J2: (Success Story x (Fancy Tales x Alpine Castle)) x ((Persian Smoke x Entourage) x ((Strawberry Sensation x (Artiste x Tupelo Honey)) x Borderline sib))) x Costa Rica) X 88-215: (Witch's Wand x 86-3, Costa Rica sib). Roris 1996.

ROMANTIC GLOW (Mary Dunn by Joseph Ghio, R. 1998). Sdlg. 175-2. LA, 36" (91 cm), M. S. and style arms rose red; F. rose red, with yellow sunburst pattern, chartreuse signal tipped red. Cassiopee X Bonaparte. Bay View 1998.

ROMANTIC INTERLUDE (W. Terry Varner, R. 1996). Sdlg. S-162. BB, 20" (51 cm), ML. S. medium yellow; style arms yellow; F. medium yellow, white central spot, stronger yellow hafts; beards deep yellow; ruffled. Brown Lasso X P-108 light pink: (Abridged Version x Hager 3796: ((Ringbearer x 2275: (666: (Norah x Thisbe) x (Frenchi x Pagoda)) x 1242F: (666D x 666E))) x (((New Idea x 1242F) x ((666 x Glittering Amber) x (pink TB x Glittering Amber))) x 2275A))). Markham, Ohio Gardens 1997.

ROMAN WARRIOR (John C. Taylor, R. 1996). Sdlg. UL 23-2. LA, 39" (100 cm), ML. S. rose, reverse lighter; style arms rose, edges highlighted white; F. magenta, edged white, reverse lighter, signal yellow; ruffled; slight fragrance. Gladiator's Gift X Rachel's Request. Rainbow Ridge 1997/98.

ROMIE STEWART (Tom Burseen, R. 1991). Sdlg. 7-133A. TB, 39" (99 cm), VE-M. S. red brown, lavender and tan blend; F. creamy tan overlaid S. color in lighter tones, hafts and edge red brown, violet blue outpouring at golden yellow beard; ruffled, laced; pronounced fragrance. Persian Berry X Polished Amber. T.B.'s Place 1992.

RONDA THOMASON (Bob Thomason, R. 1992). Sdlg. BT 8946K. TB, 32" (81 cm), EM. Medium greyed cranberry, F. with yellow hafts; beards gold; lightly ruffled; slight spicy fragrance. Art Shades X Cranberry Ice. Okie Iris 1999.

RONEY'S ENCORE (Donald Spoon by Merrick Shawe, R. 1994). Sdlg. 89-17. TB, 33" (84 cm), EM & RE. Light peachy yellow self; beards tangerine orange to yellow. Delia's Child X Samurai Warrior. Winterberry 1997.

RONNIE'S CHARM (William Phillips by Francis Scott Key Iris Society, R. 1992). Sdlg. 90-20. TB, 34" (86 cm), M. S. light yellow; F. white, yellow edge and haft markings; beards deep yellow. Hindenburg X Mary Frances. Francis Scott Key Iris Society 1993.

ROSA ADELL (Dana Borglum, R. 1990). Sdlg. C-2-20. TB, 33" (84 cm), M. Ruffled dark red purple

(RHS 59A), lighter around orange beard. Strawberry Sensation X Lady Friend. Borglum Iris 1992.

ROSA-DI-SERA (Valeria Romoli, R. 1999). Sdlg. F-20-90. TB, 36" (92 cm), ML. S. light silvery pink, midrib darker; style arms lilac pink; F. lilac pink overlaid silver; beards coral red, paler base and in throat; laced; slight sweet fragrance. 10-F-85 lilac X Electrabrite.

ROSALIE FIGGE (Jane McKnew, R. 1991). Sdlg. 1-2. TB, 39" (99 cm), M & RE. S. violet (RHS 86B); style arms violet (85C) streaked darker (86A) on midline; F. dark violet (86A), white spray pattern around beard; beards white, tipped violet (86C), yellow in throat; pronounced sweet fragrance. Titan's Glory X Violet Miracle. Rialto 1993.

ROSALIE M (Carol Lankow by J. T. Aitken, R. 1991). Sdlg. 2F28-5. SDB, 12" (30 cm), M. Pastel peach pink; beards white, tipped orange. Lucky Duck X Broad Grin. Aitken's Salmon Creek 1991.

ROSA NOVA (Schreiner, R. 1991). Sdlg. S 569-1. TB, 35" (89 cm), M. Heavily laced raspberry rose (RHS 74D), white signal; beards tangerine. M 472-A: (Princess x J 416-O: (Pink Taffeta x (Pink Horizon x (Valimar x (May Hall x Pink Enchantment))))) X Blushing Pink. Schreiner 1991.

ROSA VANITOSA (Augusto Bianco, R. 1999). Sdlg. 300. TB, 32" (82 cm), ML. Mallow rose with violet spots; style arms mallow and violet; beards carrot red; slight sweet fragrance. Probably -- Maria Tormena X Far Corners.

ROSE ADAGIO (W. A. Payne, JI, R. 1968). Correction of typographical error (ROSE ADGIO) in 1969 Check List.

ROSE AND READY (Austin Morgan, R. 1990). TB, 36" (91 cm), EM. S. rose; F. red, edged rose; beards rose. Parentage unknown. Iris Test Garden 1990.

ROSEBUD MELODY (Anna Mae Miller, R. 1994). Sdlg. 85.7.2. SIB, 28" (71 cm), M. Velvety purple (RHS 96A) self; rosebud shape. Almost a Melody X Fattaneh. Ensata Gardens 1994.

ROSE CAPER (Dorothy Guild, MTB, R. 1989). Guild 1990.

ROSE COLORED GLASSES (Sharon McAllister, R. 1994). Sdlg. 87-4-2. AB (OGB), 29" (73 cm), EM. S. white with medium violet veining, heavier around edge; F. yellowish ivory (near RHS 19D), finely veined deep burgundy (near 187D), burgundy dotting in triangular area around near-black beards. Heart Stealer X Whither Thou Goest. McAllister 1995.

ROSE COOPER (William Simon, TB, R. 1987). Stahly 1990.

ROSE D'MAI (Hyram Ames, R. 1998). Sdlg. A907. TB, 30" (76 cm), M. Ruffled dusty rose, F. lighter around rose beard; style arms rose, midrib lighter; slight spicy fragrance. Rosecraft X Fara Morgana. Zebra 1999.

ROSE ON PRIMROSE (Donna Aldridge, R. 1998). SPEC (*pseudacorus*), 39" (98 cm), M. Primrose (RHS 2C), F. with soft burgundy (51B) stipples and markings giving effect of old-rose to pink signal. Parentage unknown; seed from SIGNA.

ROSEPLIC (Jean Cayeux, R. 1990). Sdlg. 7342 E. TB, 34" (85 cm), ML. S. pure light pink; F. white, pure light pink border, deeper pink around dark beard; waved. Pink Taffeta X Schiaparelli. Cayeux 1982.

ROSE POLENTZ (Mercedes Olsen, R. 1994). Sdlg. 1AA-88-2. BB, 27" (69 cm), M. Ruffled medium pink; beards coral. Pink Pleasure X Paradise. Celebrity Iris 1995.

ROSE TEALL (Herbert Holk, R. 1995). Sdlg. 2813A. TB, 32" (81 cm), M & RE (Nov./CA). S. light greyed magenta rose (RHS 186C); F. darker magenta rose (64A), light area around orange beard; slight sweet fragrance. Mulled Wine X 2905: (Eva J x Startler). Cal-Dixie 1995.

ROSEWATER (Bob Bauer/John Coble, R. 1995). Sdlg. J89J-2. JI (6 F.), 38" (96 cm), L. Rose violet with darker veins radiating from blue violet halo, signal yellow; style arms dark violet, midribs sanded lighter. Gayety X Jocasta. Ensata Gardens 1996.

ROSIE GIRL (Barbara Wight, R. 1996). Sdlg. 90-17. TB, 28" (71 cm), ML. S. light rose (RHS 182D); style arms greyed orange (173D); F. light chrysanthemum crimson (185C), light rose border, light rose and greyed orange hafts; beards tangerine; slight sweet fragrance. Entrancement X Horny Lorri. Wight's Iris 1996.

ROSSANDEL (Jennifer Hewitt, R. 1995). Sdlg. RQ 2. SIB, 35" (88 cm), M. S. old rose pink (near RHS 78B); style arms rose pink, edged paler, midrib violet; F. deeper old rose pink (78A), small white signal. Rose Quest unknown. British Iris Society 1997.

ROSSELLINE (Jennifer Hewitt, R. 1996). Sdlg. P 8619/9. SIB, 26" (62 cm), ML. S. medium violet pink (RHS 82B/84A), flared; style arms light blue violet pink; F. rich red violet (82A/78A), white signal veined violet, arched; slight sweet fragrance. P 796: (Dreaming Yellow x MA 2/2: (Sparkling Rosé x Polly Dodge)) X Pink Haze. British Iris Society 1997.

ROSSETTO (Augusto Bianco, R. 1994). Sdlg. 315. TB, 36" (90 cm), ML. Silky full oxblood red self; beards deep brown, tipped bronze; lightly waved; pronounced spicy fragrance. Red Rose X (Natchez Trace x Post Time). Contemporary 1996.

ROSY AMOENA (Austin Morgan, R. 1990). TB, 36" (91 cm), EML. S. white; F. red, edged white; beards rose. Parentage unknown. Iris Test Garden 1990.

ROSY FINCH (Jean Witt, R. 1997). Sdlg. 92-10. MTB, 22" (56 cm), M. Slightly greyed rose red; style arms blended rose; beards yellow; slight fragrance. Parentage unknown.

ROSY FORECAST (Bryce Williamson, R. 1993). Sdlg. 4785-A. TB, 36" (91 cm), M. S. cream pink, heavily sanded and dotted rose pink; F. cream pink, wide rose pink plicata border, deeper shoulders; beards tangerine red; lightly laced, ruffled; slight fragrance. Queen in Calico X Poet.

ROSY IMAGE (Lynn Bausch, R. 1991). Sdlg. K-50. MTB, 24" (61 cm), M. Greyed red brown (RHS 178A), medium yellow hafts; style arms gold; beards bright gold. Butternut X Carolyn Rose. Garden of the East Wind 1993.

ROSY LADY (Ray Lyons, R. 1998). Sdlg. LY-84-50-1. TB, 36" (91 cm), M. Ruffled and laced rose pink; beards coral pink. Haviland X Mattie Silks. Long 1998.

ROSY OUTLOOK (Calvin Helsley, R. 1993). Sdlg. 88-6. SIB, 28" (71 cm), EM. S. rosy red (RHS 78B); style arms rosy red (78B), violet (88B) midrib; F. rosy red (77A), blue violet (88A) flush around signal; signal pale yellow (13D), darker (13B) in throat. Parentage unknown. Helsley 1997.

ROSY SCENARIO (Virginia Messick, R. 1999). Sdlg. M91-1. TB, 33" (84 cm), ML. S. smoky rose pink; F. rose pink infused blue violet, hafts bronze, bronze wire edge; beards pale pink at end, bronze pink midsection, bronze in throat; heavily laced, ruffled; slight fragrance. Art Nouveau X Romantic Mood.

ROSY SUNRISE (Adolph Vogt, JI, R. 1989). Ensata Gardens 1992.

ROTE LATERNE (Lothar Denkewitz, SDB, R. 1986). Schoeppinger 1990.

ROTER FALTER (Harald Moos, R. 1990). Sdlg. 86/624B. TB, 33½" (85 cm), M. Ruffled bright dark red brown; beards golden yellow. Samurai Warrior X 82/362B. Schoeppinger 1993.

ROTUNDA (Monty Byers, R. 1990). Sdlg. D77-100. TB, 38" (97 cm), M & RE. Medium deep violet, blended with reddish violet in F.; beards blue; ruffled. Leda's Lover X Violet Classic. Moonshine 1991.

ROUGE ROYANS (Christian Lanthelme, R. 1997). Sdlg. 15B91. TB, 35" (90 cm), M. S. and style arms orange red; F. velvety blood red; beards gold. Parentage unknown. Lanthelme 1997.

ROUND TUIT (Tom Burseen, R. 1997). Sdlg. 93-416A. TB, 35" (89 cm), EM. S. yellow ground, solid rusty red (181B) wash; style arms light orange red; F. yellow ground, heavy rust (178C) wash; beards tan; pronounced spicy fragrance. Maybe Baby X 90-38: (Hubba Hubba Hubba x 7-66: ((Silver Shower x Rancho Rose) x Villa Splendor)). T.B.'s Place 1998.

ROVNINY (Zdeněk Seidl, R. 1997). Sdlg. 88-MRx/1. SIB, 27" (70 cm), M. S. pale pinkish lilac; F. light lilac. Mrs. Rowe X unknown.

ROWDEN (John Carter, R. 1991). SPEC (*ensata*), (3 F.), 36" (91 cm), L. S. purple; F. white. Parentage unknown. Rowden Gardens 1991.

ROWDEN ALLEGRO (John Carter, R. 1999). SPEC (*versicolor*), 30" (75 cm), M. S. white, overlaid and feathered wine; style arms white, dark pink rib and tips; F. deep purple to wine red, slightly feathered toward edge, large white signal, very small deep yellow area at throat; F. rounded. Parentage unknown.

ROWDEN AUTOCRAT (John Carter, R. 1999). JI (6 F.), 36" (91 cm), ML. White to very pale mauve, heavily veined and overlaid dark purple, yellow signal with slight purple halo; style arms bright violet purple, white tips and edges, upright, broad. Parentage unknown.

ROWDEN BEGUM (John Carter, R. 1999). JI (3 F.), 36" (91 cm), M. S. pinkish parma violet, small; style arms deep violet; F. pale pure violet, darker veining, small primrose yellow signal; flared. Parentage unknown.

ROWDEN EMPEROR (John Carter, R. 1999). JI (3 F.), 36" (91 cm), M. S. magenta purple, tall and broad, large; style arms dark magenta purple, whitish edges; F. drooping, deep magenta purple, paling slightly at edges, darker veining overall, small signal clear yellow with slight blue halo. Parentage unknown.

ROWDEN KING (John Carter, R. 1999). JI (3 F.), 36" (91 cm), M. S. deep red purple, tall; style arms white; F. washed pinkish mauve purple paling toward edge, darker veining, small dark yellow signal. Parentage unknown; selected unnamed cv. from Stapeley Water Gardens.

ROWDEN MAZURKA (John Carter, R. 1999). SPEC (*versicolor*), 30" (75 cm), M. S. white, veined pink; style arms white, pink center rib and tip, long; F. white, heavily overlaid and veined cerise plum, tawny yellow throat, white signal blending into cerise feathering; flowers smallish, F. elongate. Parentage unknown.

ROWDEN MIKADO (John Carter, R. 1999). JI (3 F.), 36" (91 cm), EML. S. and style arms dark feathered purple or similar to F., style arms also with whitish center; F. white, overlaid purple, blue and mauve giving shot silk effect, small dark yellow signal. Parentage unknown; selected unnamed cv. from Coleton Fishacre.

ROWDEN PALADIN (John Carter, R. 1999). JI (3 F.), 36" (91 cm), M. S. very pale grey pink, very short; style arms violet, very short; F. whitish grey, veined blue, primrose yellow signal, flared and flat. Parentage unknown.

ROWDEN PRINCE (John Carter, R. 1999). JI (6 F.), 36" (91 cm), M. Purple with allover grey and mauve splashing, signal deep yellow with blue halo; style arms deep purple, whiter center rib. Parentage unknown.

ROWDEN SCHERZO (John Carter, R. 1999). SPEC (*versicolor*), 30" (75 cm), M. S. white, strongly veined and feathered pink; style arms white, deep lilac center; F. white, strongly veined deep lilac pink becoming near-solid at distal end. Parentage unknown.

ROWDEN SULTANA (John Carter, R. 1999). JI (3 F.), 36" (91 cm), M. S. deep rosy red; style arms grey white, dark rosy red edge; F. rosy red aging plum red, long. Parentage unknown.

ROWDEN SYMPHONY (John Carter, R. 1999). SPEC (*versicolor*), 30" (75 cm), M. S. pale violet purple, heavily veined darker purple; style arms white, tinged lilac, pink lilac rib, pale blue tip; F. dark violet, white signal veined medium purple with pronounced white centerline, gamboge yellow at throat; F. shield-shaped. Parentage unknown.

ROWELLA (R. E. Nichol, TB, R. 1985). British Iris Society 1987.

ROYAL BLAZE (Nancy Bartlett, R. 1995). Sdlg. 88C3. TB, 38" (97 cm), M. Dark purple, F. with white streaks around beard; beards white, purple horn. Batman X Lavender Queen. Nancy Bartlett, Rancho de Los Flores 1996.

ROYAL CADET (B. Charles Jenkins, R. 1992). Sdlg. C16-36J. SPU, 38-48" (97-122 cm), M. Mauve blue, large gold signal on F. Happy Choice X Terra Nova. Shepard Iris 1992.

ROYAL DANA (Lois O'Brien, R. 1994). Sdlg. 86-42. TB, 37" (93 cm), M. Ruffled silvery blue (RHS 100D) self; style arms slightly deeper blue (100C); beards frosted lemon (4C); slight sweet fragrance. Silent Patriot X Columbia Blue. O'Brien Iris 1995.

ROYAL DANDY (Henry Rowlan, R. 1990). Sdlg. 84-LA-21. LA, 34" (86 cm), ML. S. solferino purple (HCC 26/3); F. amaranth rose (530), narrow light pink edge, red dagger signal edged green. Bryce Leigh X unknown. Comanche Acres 1991.

ROYAL DEBUTANTE (Hugh Thurman, R. 1998). Sdlg. 92-18-2. MTB, 22" (56 cm), L. S. and style arms aureolin yellow (RHS 12A); F. medium violet purple (77A), lighter at edge and rimmed yellow, white area around yellow orange (14A) beard; slight fragrance. Bumblebee Deelite X unknown.

ROYAL DECREE (Hooker Nichols, SDB, R. 1988). Hillcrest 1991.

ROYAL DESIGN (Mary Dunn, R. 1996). Sdlg. M885-S. TB, 36" (91 cm), ML. S. white ground, lilac lavender plicata edge, deeper lilac midrib; style arms lilac; F. white, tiny violet edge, deep violet haft lined around beard; beards yellow, deep violet at end. M75-531: (Going My Way x Midway) X Momentum. M.A.D. Iris 1997.

ROYAL DOLLY (Lorena Reid, R. 1995). Sdlg. St9-8-5J. SPEC-X (sibtosa), 18-24" (46-61 cm), M. S. light pinkish violet; style arms pale lavender; F. dark maroon, gold signal in throat edged white, closely lined very dark red violet; spatulate falls. Polly Dodge X *I. setosa alba*. Laurie's Garden 1995.

ROYAL DUX (Ladislav Muska, R. 1996). Sdlg. DESM-03. TB, 38" (97 cm), EM. Ruffled smoked salmon self; beards orange; slight fragrance. Don Epifano X (Don Epifano x Sweet Musette). Muska 1996.

ROYAL EMBLEM (Leonard Brummitt, SDB, R. 1978). British Iris Society 1990.

ROYAL FAMILY (Akihiko Terada, R. 1998). Sdlg. S073-89-11. TB, 36" (91 cm), M. Blackish deep wine, F. slightly lighter, velvet finish; beards sienna rust; pronounced musky fragrance. Grand Old Opry X Harlem Hussy. Roris 1998.

ROYAL FLIRT (George Shoop, R. 1994). Sdlg. 89-49. IB, 16" (41 cm), M. Deep pink self; beards pink to red; lightly ruffled; slight fragrance. Keppel 1995.

ROYAL GORGE (John Durrance, R. 1994). Sdlg. JRD91W-9. TB, 36" (91 cm), M. Violet blue, F. edged darker. Parentage unknown. Long 1994.

ROYAL GOSSIP (Hooker Nichols, IB, R. 1988). Hillcrest 1993.

ROYAL HONEY (Barry Blyth, R. 1991). Sdlg. Y2-4. TB, 38" (96 cm), EML. S. cream, edged lemon, pinkish midrib blush; F. mango blended golden mango; beards tangerine orange; pronounced fragrance. Tango Bravo X ((Alpine Journey x Beachgirl) x ((Beachgirl x (Tranquil Star x Coral Strand)) x (Persian Smoke x Chimbolam))). Tempo Two 1992/93.

ROYAL IMP (Henry Rowlan, R. 1991). Sdlg. 11-LA-26. LA, 37" (94 cm), ML. Campanula violet (RHS 82C), creamy yellow steeple signal. 85-LA-24 X unknown.

ROYAL INTRIGUE (Schreiner, R. 1991). Sdlg. 1984 #161. TB, 38" (97 cm), EM. Velvety dark purple (RHS 86A); self beard. Parentage unknown; mixed seed. Schreiner 1991.

ROYAL MADAME (Valera Chenoweth, LA, R. 1987). Blossom Valley 1990.

ROYAL MONARCH (Ed Matheny III, R. 1996). Sdlg. 03-01-91. TB, 36" (91 cm), EM. S. banana yellow (RHS 13C); F. greyed purple (77A); beards burnt orange; slight fragrance. Best Bet X Boy Friend. Ed's Iris 1997.

ROYAL ONE (William Ackerman, JI, R. 1989). Nicholls Gardens 1990.

ROYAL PERFORMANCE (Elvan Roderick, R. 1996). Sdlg. 9301. TB, 36" (91 cm), ML. S. purple; F. fuchsia; beards tipped white. Silverado X Glory Ballet. Roderick Hillview Garden 1997.

ROYAL PINK (O. D. Niswonger, R. 1992). Sdlg. 81-89. TB, 33" (84 cm), ML. S. white, lightly infused pink; F. pink; beards pink. 3-86: (Love Chant x Ambrosia Delight) X 12-79: (Coral Strand x Peach Spot). Cape Iris 1992.

ROYAL RAGE (Chet Tompkins, R. 1992). Sdlg. 85-89. TB, 38" (97 cm), ML. Smooth dark red with vivid scarlet undertone; beards bronze. Involved red sdlg. lines. Fleur de Lis 1991.

ROYAL SHORTS (Betty Wilkerson, R. 1996). Sdlg. E15-WIDE. BB, 26" (66 cm), EM. Royal purple (RHS 95A) self; beards white, hairs tipped pale lavender. Feedback X Titan's Glory.

ROYAL WARRANT (Frederick Kerr, R. 1998). Sdlg. 913501. TB, 38" (97 cm), M. S. and style arms white, tinted violet; F. medium red purple with large violet-tinted white area around beard, edges lighter; beards yellow, violet-tinted white at end; ruffled. Cranberry Crush X Rosette Wine. Rainbow Acres 1998.

ROY'S CHOICE (Hugh & Mary Thurman, R. 1995). Sdlg. SDB 92-1-1. SDB, 12" (31 cm), ML. S. white, purple midrib and 1/4" rim; F. white, purple veins and 1/4" rim; beards violet, base white; slight sweet fragrance. Court Magician X Chubby Cheeks. Kickapoo 1996.

ROZ (Sterling Innerst, R. 1995). Sdlg. 4169-1. IB, 19" (48 cm), M. S. gold; style arms yellow gold; F. gold, red spot; beards orange. Mariachi Music X Smart. Innerst 1996.

ROZOVAYA MECHTA (Viktor Sheviakov, R. 1996). Sdlg. 7d5a. TB, 32" (80 cm), ML. Ruffled white ground plicata marked rose red; style arms orange brown; beards yellow brown; slight spicy fragrance. Dancers Veil X Radiant Apogee. Sheviakov 1996.

ROZOVOYE OBLAKO (Liudmila Mironova, R. 1998). Sdlg. 8.7.94. JI (6 F.), 35-39" (90-100 cm), M. Pink, signal yellow; style arms lilac, crests darker. 4-80: (unknown sdlg. x Vasili Alfiorov) X Chayka. DVO RAN 1999.

ROZOVY BORDIURNY (Irina Driagina, R. 1995). Sdlg. 75-23. BB, 22" (55 cm), ML. Cream pink self; beards orange. K Yubileyu Iliyicha X Craithie. Driagina 1989.

ROZOVY GNOM (Galina Shevchenko, R. 1995). MDB, 5" (13 cm), M. S. light pink, lilac haze; F. lilac pink, raspberry bronze rim; beards light blue, yellow in throat; ruffled; pronounced spicy fragrance. From *I. pumila* sdlgs. Shevchenko 1992.

ROZOVY VETER (Viktor Sheviakov, R. 1995). Sdlg. 20V 4A. TB, 30" (77 cm), M. S. white ground, dotted light purple; F. large white spot, edges dotted light purple; beards pinkish red; ruffled. Latin Lover X Limelight. Sheviakov 1997.

ROZOVY VOSKHOD (V. & N. Gordodelovy, R. 1995). Sdlg. 51. TB, 30" (75 cm), E. Ruffled pink, light brown hafts; beards red, pink on end. Parentage unknown. Gordodelovy 1991.

RUBACUORI (Augusto Bianco, R. 1999). Sdlg. 688. TB, 32" (80 cm), ML. S. mahogany red; style arms mahogany to plum; F. garnet, few lemon lines; beards mimosa yellow; waved; slight musky fragrance. Queen in Calico X Battle Hymn. Iride 1999.

RUBAN BLEU (Jean Cayeux by Richard Cayeux, R. 1997). Sdlg. 8461 F. TB, 33" (85 cm), ML. S. white; F. blue, large white heart; beards orange. 8245 A: (7706 A, Alizes sib, x Love Bandit) X 8109 A: (Condottiere x Delphi). Cayeux 1997.

RUBIES IN GOLD (Tom Magee, R. 1999). Sdlg. 904A. SDB, 14" (36 cm), E. S. and style arms gold; F. gold, with two ruby blazes; beards gold, orange in throat; slight sweet fragrance. Stintfang X 8630B: (8013: (Treasure Room x 7734: (Colorado Sunshine x White Lightning)) x Baby Tiger).

RUBY CORDON (Kevin Nilsen, R. 1990). Sdlg. 3-84-1. TB, 30" (76 cm), M. Ruffled red purple blend, violet area in center of F.; beards bronze yellow. Caramba X Plum Gleam. Iridescence 1990/91.

RUBY DELIGHT (Elyse Hill, R. 1998). Sdlg. EJ 26-22-93. TB, 34" (86 cm), L. S. lavender purple (RHS 75A); style arms lavender violet; F. violet to purplish wine (80A), 1/4" lavender rim, shoulders striped white; beards orange; slight sweet fragrance. EJ 3-7-89: (Liaison x Lightning Ridge) X Ringo. O'Brien Iris 1999.

RUBY ERUPTION (Chuck Chapman, R. 1997). Sdlg. 92-100-1. SDB, 12" (31 cm), ML. S. bright yellow ground heavily marked dark ruby red; F. yellow ground lighter near beard, dark ruby red plicata edge, narrow yellow outer rim; beards cream, hairs tipped dark orange red; ruffled. Rusty Dusty X Chubby Cheeks. Chapman Iris 1997.

RUBY EYES (Elyse Hill, R. 1998). Sdlg. EJ-15-7. CA, 6" (15 cm), E. S. rose, veined darker; style arms light yellow, blended rose; F. rose, darker veining, light yellow edges and central blaze with deep blackish wine signal; ruffled cartwheel form. Reflecting Pool X unknown.

RUBY RIBANDS (Donna Aldridge, R. 1998). Sdlg. 132B. SPEC (*pseudacorus*), 40" (101 cm), ML. Rich yellow, F. with strong dark ruby signal-mark bands curving unusually low on blade, surrounding large chrome yellow signal inlay. Parentage unknown; seed from SIGNA.

RUBY RUBY (Jack Worel, R. 1999). Sdlg. RR1. SIB, 34" (86 cm), M & RE. Dark ruby red (RHS 59A), F. with small yellow signal lined ruby red. Ruby Wine X unknown. Holly Lane 1999.

RUBY STAR (J. T. Aitken, R. 1991). Sdlg. 86J-1-2. JI (6 F.), 36" (91 cm), ML. Raspberry red, white flash around yellow signal. Stranger in Paradise X King's Court. Aitken's Salmon Creek 1991.

RUBY TUESDAY (William Maryott, R. 1992). Sdlg. P138P. SDB, 10" (25 cm), M. S. brown; F. velvety deep red mahogany, precise brown edge; beards red mahogany. Jazzamatazz X Logo. Maryott 1993.

RUDDY RED (Tom Burseen, R. 1995). Sdlg. 1-292A. TB, 35" (89 cm), ML. S. and style arms gold, heavily flushed rusty red (44A); F. golden maize, flushed rusty red (44B), lighter near gold beard; ruffled, laced; sweet fragrance. Afternoon Delight X Caliph. T.B.'s Place 1996.

RUÉE VERS L'OR (Jean Segui, R. 1998). TB, 32" (80 cm), M. Indian yellow (RHS 17B), F. with brown (178B) rays; beards darker indian yellow (17A); ruffled, laced. Broadway X "Catalan": (Limerick x Orange Chiffon). Iris de Thau 1992.

RUFFLED COPPER SUNSET (James Gibson, TB, R. 1988). Cooley 1993.

RUFFLED FEATHERS (Sterling Innerst, TB, R. 1989). Innerst 1990.

RUFFLED FLORETTE (George Shoop, R. 1992). Sdlg. 82-27. TB, 36" (91 cm), M. Ruffled light to medium blue; beards red tangerine; slight fragrance. Vivien X Sea Gypsy. Shoop 1992.

RUFFLED GARNET (Donald Spoon, R. 1995). TB, 31" (79 cm), ML. Ruffled red garnet self; style arms red garnet and deep yellow; beards rose to red garnet; flared. Parentage unknown.

RUFFLED GODDESS (Richard Tasco, R. 1992). Sdlg. 86-26. TB, 32" (81 cm), M. Heavily ruffled pink lavender (Pantone 14-3207); beards yellow, tipped pink lavender; slight fragrance. Entourage X Mary Frances. Superstition 1993.

RUFFLED HONEY (Kirk Strawn, R. 1993). Sdlg. 24-1985. LA, 32" (81 cm), M. S. mimosa yellow (RHS 8D); dresden yellow (5B) styles with purple blush; F. yellow orange (20C), bright yellow orange (14A) signal. Freddie Boy X President Hedley. Bois d'Arc 1996.

RUFFLED ROUND (Currier McEwen, R. 1994). Sdlg. T(8)84/104(1). SIB (tet.), 28" (70 cm), M. S. dark violet blue (RHS 93B); F. darker (93A), small white signal; velvety; ruffled. Regency Belle sib X T(7)81/111(8): (Marshmallow Frosting x (Dear Dianne x Happy Event sib)). Eartheart, Seaways 1994.

RUFFLED SKIRTS (Hooker Nichols, TB, R. 1988). Hillcrest 1992.

RUFFLED SUNSHINE (Jim Hedgecock, R. 1990). Sdlg. C-83-10-1. TB, 34" (86 cm), M. Medium yellow; beards bright yellow; heavily ruffled, laced; sweet fragrance. Temple Gold X Madeira Belle. Comanche Acres 1991.

RUFFLED TIGER (H. Fothergill by P. McCormick, IB, R. 1975). British Iris Society 1995.

RUFFLES (Clarence Mahan, R. 1995). SIB, 26" (66 cm), M. S. campanula violet (RHS 86B/C); style arms with deep blue purple midrib; F. campanula violet, signal yellow green in center, turning to white; F. with flared twist. Laughing Brook X unknown. Iris Pond 1996.

RUMBLESEAT (Sterling Innerst, R. 1990). Sdlg. 2397-3. TB, 36" (91 cm), ML. White ground trimmed raspberry; beards yellow. 1980-1: (Colortrak sib x Burgundy Brown) X 1666-10: ((April Melody x Wedding Vow) x Flamenco). Innerst 1991.

RUMOURS (Barry Blyth, R. 1996). Sdlg. D29-2. IB, 20" (51 cm), VE-M. S. soft pink, near white;

F. deeper mushroom pink; beards tangerine; slight fragrance. Scion X A44-2, Gosh sib. Tempo Two 1996/97.

RUPAUL (Mary Dunn, R. 1995). Sdlg. M1085C. TB, 37" (94 cm), L. S. light tan-blond; style arms tan, edged lilac; F. lilac, edged light tan-blond, light area at tip of lilac beard; ruffled. Mary D. X Silver Flow. M.A.D. Iris 1996.

RURI OGI (Shuichi Hirao by Society for Japanese Irises, R. 1992). JI (6 F.), 36" (90 cm), ML. Deep blue with violet highlights, white central area feathering out to edge, signal yellow. Parentage unknown. Hirao 1958.

RUSALKA (V. & N. Gordodelovy, R. 1995). Sdlg. 38. TB, 39" (100 cm), E. S. light green, tinted gold; style arms creamy lettuce green, white center stripe; F. light green tinted gold; beards greenish cream, orange in throat; ruffled. Parentage unknown. Gordodelovy 1987.

RUSH CREEK (Jack Worel, R. 1999). Sdlg. DR3. TB, 32" (81 cm). M. S. rose, midrib and very thin edge yellow gold; style arms lighter rose, edge brownish yellow; F. rust red, 1/8" yellow gold edge, slight white area marked rust red around gold beard; slight sweet fragrance. Gentle Dragon X Rustler. Holly Lane 1999.

RUSH HOUR (Larry Lauer, R. 1999). Sdlg. 444-2. TB, 36" (91 cm), M. Ruffled aureolin yellow, S. with thin darker rim, F. darker overall; beards dark aureolin yellow, light orange to orange in throat; pronounced spicy sweet fragrance. 91-262: (L86-20: (Nancy Glazier x Brandy) x Hager T4717: ((Crystal Cathedral x Mother Earth sib) x (Birthstone x Sky Hooks))) X Hager T5399: (Gratuity x Quasar).

RUSTIC RUFFLES (Barbara Wight, R. 1996). Sdlg. 91-17. TB, 28" (71 cm), M. S. brown (RHS 176C); F. reddish brown (182B); beards tangerine; slight spicy fragrance. 86-30: (82-7: (Honey Mocha x Good Earth) x Happy Trails) X 86-31: (82-4-1: (Gala Madrid x Rustic Dance) x self).

RUSTLE OF SPRING (Graeme Grosvenor, R. 1998). Sdlg. V53-3. TB, 34" (86 cm), EML. Rose tan; beards tangerine. Rustler X Bogota. Rainbow Ridge 1999/2000.

RUSTLING DEVIL (Brian Farrington by Oz Reyna, R. 1996). Sdlg. BF9301. TB, 42" (107 cm), E. S. oxblood red (redder than RHS 183B); F. darker (redder than 187B); beards golden orange; ruffled; slight sweet fragrance. Rustler X Reyna sdlg.: (Latin Lover x Sable Night).

RUSTY MAGNIFICENCE (O. D. Niswonger, R. 1995). Sdlg. 55-89. TB, 34" (86 cm), M. Deep brown self; style arms brown; beards yellow; ruffled. Parentage unknown -- probably Minted Halo X Kabaka. Cape Iris 1995.

RUSTY NAIL (Virginia Messick, R. 1993). Sdlg. M89-16. SDB, 11" (28 cm), EM. S. gold; F. rusty brown; "pie crust" ruffling. Sherlock X Inflamed. Messick 1993.

RUSTY O (Charles Arny, R. 1991). Sdlg. BitR-2-89. LA, 42" (107 cm), M. S. claret rose (HCC 021/2); F. claret rose (021), large deep yellow radial signal extending beyond tip of short narrow light rose style arm. Charles Arny III X Charlie's Ginny. Bois d'Arc 1992.

RUSTY ROAD (Steve Moldovan, R. 1996). Sdlg. 1-71. IB, 16" (41 cm), M. S. amber brown; F. creamy amber, deeper spot; beards bluish. Rising Fawn X Dove Wings. Moldovan 1982.

RUTH BLACK (Paul Black, R. 1996). Sdlg. 8632AA. TB, 32" (81 cm), L. S. orchid violet center blending to buff pink, salmon buff edge; style arms salmon, orchid center; F. pearly violet center, blending to orchid violet, edges salmon buff; beards red orange; heavily laced and ruffled; slight spicy fragrance. Extravagant X Geniality. Mid-America 1996.

RUTHIE GIRL (James Ennenga, R. 1993). Sdlg. E-85-16-1. TB, 30" (76 cm), E. S. white ground with wide edge, midrib and heavy stippling of amethyst violet (RHS 87A); style arms yellow, amethyst violet midrib and crest; F. white ground, blended darker amethyst violet on edge, with lighter center, heavy dark amethyst violet markings on hafts; beards white, violet at end, yellow in throat; pronounced sweet fragrance. Warburton 34-V-1: (Singing Rain x Keppel 64-45G: ((Full Circle x Rococo) x Tea Apron)) X Pandora's Purple. Ennenga Iris 1993.

RUTHIE'S SNOWDRIFT (William Phillips by Francis Scott Key Iris Society, R. 1992). Sdlg. 87-10. TB, 40" (102 cm), M. White self; beards white. 82-1 X Mary Frances. Francis Scott Key Iris Society 1993.

RUTH KAC (George Gessert, R. 1999). Sdlg. 91-39B. CA, 13" (33 cm), L. S. white, few purple veins broken into dots and dashes; style arms white, brushed lavender and purple; F. white, signal yellow with gold center, surrounded by fringe of purple veins broken into dots and dashes. Olaf Stapledon: (All Around x collected "Valley Banner type") X 86-54A: (Western Queen x C84-18, collected *tenax-chrysophylla* hybrid).

RUTH KEITH (Sharon McAllister, R. 1995). Sdlg. 91-1-47. AB (OGB-), 16" (41 cm), E. S. soft blue, soft willow green midrib flush; style arms willow green; F. soft willow green, soft blue center wash; beards blue white to white, yellow in throat. Hunt sdlg.: (Lilli-Bright x unknown) X Ginger's Girl. McAllister 1995.

RUTH KNOWLES (Ivor Knowles by Mary Tubbs, R. 1992). Sdlg. RK-11. SDB, 10½" (26 cm), M. Violet purple; beards pale blue. Parentage unknown. British Iris Society 1993.

RUTH LOUISE (Francis Rogers, R. 1996). Sdlg. F-738-G. TB, 32" (81 cm), M. Ruffled and crinkled azalea pink (RHS 38C); style arms deeper (38B); beards brick red (35B); spicy fragrance. F-215-L: (Bonbon X Rancho Rose) X Triple Crown. Meadowbrook 1997.

RUTH MARILYN (Beryl Pederick, R. 1994). Sdlg. 1. TB, 30" (76 cm), EM. S. pansy violet (HCC 033/2); F. violet purple (733), edged lighter; beards light purple; slight fragrance. Child of Fortune X Wish.

RUTH SIMMONS (Ron Mullin, R. 1999). Sdlg. 441S. TB, 38" (97 cm), M. S. and style arms cream yellow; F. white, blending to soft gold border; beards golden yellow. Speculator X Laced Cotton.

RUTH WALKER (Donald Spoon, R. 1999). TB, 36" (91 cm), M. Ruffled peach pink self; beards pinkish tangerine; foliage purple-based. Orien X Jennifer Rebecca. Winterberry 1999.

RUTH WERLINE ALDRIDGE (Donna Aldridge, R. 1998). Sdlg. PS-41 Ivory. SPEC (*pseudacorus*), 36" (90 cm), EML. Ivory, F. with taupe violet markings on ivory signal area. Parentage unknown.

RYAN JAMES (R. E. Nichol by Jean Nichol, R. 1998). Sdlg. R 256-6. TB, 38" (97 cm), M. S. bright tan gold (RHS 167D), overall dark tan veining; style arms pale gold; F. deep tan (172A), faint purple central flush; beards bright tan; lightly ruffled; slight fragrance. Carnaby X M 145-9: ((((Kilt Lilt x Autumn Leaves) x Show Biz) x (Port Lisbon x Show Biz)) x ((Sketch Me x Show Biz) x ((Kilt Lilt x Autumn Leaves) x Show Biz))).

RYOSEKI (Mototeru Kamo by Society for Japanese Irises, R. 1995). JI (6 F.), 30" (76 cm), M. White, lightly brushed blue (RHS 92C/D), signals yellow (12A/B); style arms tufted. Parentage unknown. Introduced in Japan, 1965.

RYUKO HIRAO (Shuichi Hirao by Society for Japanese Irises, R. 1991). Sdlg. SH-8. JI (3 F.), 39" (99 cm), M. S. white, cupped; style arms creamy, ribbed; F. white with diamond dusting, crepe texture, yellow signal with greenish cast, conspicuous center ridge bleeding into F.; slight fragrance. Parentage unknown. Society for Japanese Irises 1992.

SABBATH SUNSET (Ruth Goebel, TB, R. 1989). Long 1993.

SABLE D'ARGENT (Igor Fedoroff by Sylvain Ruaud, R. 1997). Sdlg. S88. TB, 36" (90 cm), ML. S. light apricot; style arms apricot; F. apricot, traces of mauve pink around orange beard; waved; slight sweet fragrance. Sumptuous X Entourage.

SABRINA'S KISS (A. & D. Willott, R. 1997). Sdlg. 94-117. SDB, 12" (30 cm), M. S. pale pink, dotted and edged light red violet; style arms light red violet; F. pale pink, narrowly edged and dotted light red violet, markings heavier at haft; beards deep orange; ruffled. Pink Caper X W 88-39: ((Apricot Tart x Coral Wings) x ((Mister Roberts x Fresh Face) x Coral Wings)). Willott 1997.

SACIA ROSE (Darlene Pinegar, R. 1998). Sdlg. TTE-93-115D. TB, 34" (86 cm), ML. S. pinkish tan, yellow at base, darker pinkish tan veining; style arms blended gold and mauve; F. dark fuchsia, light centerline, narrow pinkish tan edges, hafts white, yellow at edge, with dark fuchsia marking; beards dark lemon, long smooth orchid horn; moderately ruffled, laced. Tracy Tyrene X Anne Boleyn. Spanish Fork 1999.

SA-COMA (Ladislav Muska, R. 1996). Sdlg. VACA-10. TB, 39" (99 cm), M. S. vanilla cream; F. light blue lavender, light vanilla cream rim; beards orange; ruffled, laced; sweet fragrance. ((Vanilla Lace x ((French Gown x Geniality) x Bab Babbili)) x "Charmante") X Lavender Petticoats. Muska 1996.

SACRED WATERS (Koen Engelen, R. 1997). Sdlg. 91-012. TB, 32-34" (80-85 cm), EM. S. cobalt blue, edged lighter; F. ice white; beards white; slight fragrance. (Edge of Winter x Faraway Blue) X (Enthralling Pink x Undersea Adventure). Engelen 1998.

SAFARI DAWN (Revie Harvey, IB, R. 1983). Catton 1991.

SAFFORD JAZZ (Terrell Taylor, R. 1999). Sdlg. 93-3. TB, 31" (79 cm), EM. S. and style arms bright maize yellow (RHS 21B); F. yellow ground heavily overlaid cardinal red (53A) dotting, nearly solid toward narrow yellow edge; beards bronze; musky fragrance. Jitterbug X Fanfaron.

SAGE (Joseph Ghio, SPU, R. 1989). Bay View 1990.

SAGER CEDRIC (A. J. Trinder, R. 1995). Sdlg. 91035. TB, 28" (70 cm), L. S. light purple; F. white ground, edge stippled light purple, matching centerline; beards yellow. 8718, carmine purple plicata, X 8806, purple plicata. David Austin Roses 1995.

SAHARAN SUN (Brad Kasperek, R. 1994). Sdlg. 91B-7A. TB, 30" (76 cm), EM. Ruffled brilliant sunshine yellow (RHS 12B) lightly streaked silver white (155C); beards golden yellow. Hot Streak X Tiger Honey. Zebra 1995.

SAIGYOZAKURA (Yoshio Mitsuda by Society for Japanese Irises, R. 1999). JI (6 F.), 36" (91 cm), EM. Bright pink, deep pink veins radiating from signal; style arms bright pink, crests fringed and frilled. Parentage unknown. Introduced in Japan, 1986.

SAILING FREE (Jim & Vicki Craig, R. 1993). Sdlg. C37X6. IB, 23" (58 cm), E. S. pale blue; F. medium blue; beards yellow, tipped light blue; lightly ruffled; slight sweet fragrance. Payoff X C31T6, Takeoff sib. J. & V. Craig 1993.

SAILING THE BLUE (Francis Rogers, R. 1999). Sdlg. C-210-X. TB, 39" (99 cm), L. Ruffled white, F. with 3/8" pale lavender blue rim, flared; beards yellow orange, white base and at end, orange in throat; slight spicy fragrance. Conjuration X Spinning Wheel.

SAILOR (Marky Smith, R. 1995). Sdlg. 89-27D. IB, 23" (58 cm), E. S. greyed blue violet (RHS 97C), midrib dark violet blue, faint dotting in paler center; style arms greyed blue violet, dark violet blue rib; F. white, 1/2" solid dark violet blue (darker than 94A) rim, 1/4" lighter (94A) stitched and dotted inner band; dark stitching surrounding and star point below beard; beards dark blue violet, tipped brown, changing to brown gold to gold in throat; ruffled. Chubby Cheeks X Snowbrook. Aitken's Salmon Creek 1996.

SAILOR HAT (Isabelle Bowen Henderson by Philip Edinger, R. 1999). Sdlg. 49-8. TB, 39" (99 cm), EM. S. light cream; F. white, narrow ruffled yellow border, reverse solid yellow, flared. Parentage unknown. Fairmount 1955.

SAILOR'S FANCY (Marty Schafer/Jan Sacks, R. 1991). Sdlg. S86-13-1. SIB, 33" (84 cm), M. S. light blue violet (RHS 97C), darker (93C/B) veins and shading; style arms light blue violet; F. medium blue violet (93D), darker (93A/B) veins and shading, paler edge; yellow signal veined dark blue on S. and F.; ruffled. Springs Brook X Butter and Sugar. Joe Pye Weed 1991.

SAINT LAWRENCE (Myrtle Holden by Glenn Stoneking-Jones, R. 1999). Sdlg. CIR6-5253-09-18-1998. TB, 30" (76 cm), EM. Blackish violet, style arms veined bronze; beards purple, hairs tipped bronze; slight sweet fragrance. *I. pallida dalmatica* sdlg. X Maplecrest.

SAINT LOUIS WOMAN (Louise Bellagamba, R. 1991). Sdlg. PA 1-88. TB, 34" (86 cm), M. Ruffled white ground plicata with tiny orchid pink dots, heaviest on F. edge; beards red, tipped white. An-Jan X Rudolph pink sdlgs. Bella Vista 1992.

SAKAE MURASAKI (Zensaku Makino by Society for Japanese Irises, R. 1993). JI (3 F.), 36" (90 cm), E. Bright violet, F. with yellow signal; style arms light violet, feathered. Parentage unknown. Makino 1966.

SAKAKO (Elaine Hulbert, R. 1990). Sdlg. 83SKJ3. JI (6 F.), 36" (91 cm), ML. White center with white rays running into wide pink border, signal yellowish green; style arms and crests white, edged pink. Sakurajishi X self. Cooper's Garden 1990.

SAKES ALIVE (Bob Thomason, SDB, R. 1988). Okie Iris 1994.

SAKURAGAI (Society for Japanese Irises, R. 1992). JI (3 F.), 26" (66 cm), ML & RE. S. light pink (lighter than RHS 65D); style arms light pink (65D); F. pink (69D), darker (77C) veins and blush (77D), signal yellow. Parentage unknown. Introduced by M. Kamo, date unknown.

SAKURAJISHI (Koji Tomino by Society for Japanese Irises, R. 1992). JI (6+ F.), 36" (90 cm), EM. Heavily ruffled light pink, signal yellow. "Otome" X self. Tomino 1952.

SAKURA KOMACHI (Toyokazu Ichie by Society for Japanese Irises, R. 1995). JI (3 F.), 23" (58 cm), EM. S. and style arms pink (RHS 75D), edges and tips darker (75B/C); F. pale pink (75D) ground with darker (75B) veins giving overall effect (75C/D), signal rich yellow (12A). Miyoshino X "Kyokusui-no-Uta". Introduced in Japan ca. 1982.

SAKURA-NO-HARU (Shuichi Hirao by Society for Japanese Irises, R. 1993). JI (6 F.), 34" (86 cm), EM. Pink with prominent white center, yellow signal; style arms white edged and tipped pink; ruffled. Parentage unknown. Hirao prior to 1980.

SAKURA-NO-MIYA (Society for Japanese Irises, R. 1992). JI (3 F.), 31½" (80 cm), M. Lilac pink self, signal yellow. Hybridizer and parentage unknown. Introduced in Japan prior to 1984.

SAKURA-NO-SONO (Toyokazu Ichie by Society for Japanese Irises, R. 1993). JI (6 F.), 32" (81 cm), M. Very pale pink with darker pink veining, yellow signal; style arms deep pink. Parentage unknown. Ichie prior to 1980.

SALAMANDER CROSSING (Marty Schafer/Jan Sacks, R. 1999). Sdlg. S92-65-15. SIB, 42" (107 cm), EML. S. palest lavender ground, heavy lavender (90C/D) speckling; style arms speckled lavender, buff tips; F. pale yellow heavily speckled lavender, less at edge, gold to yellow signal with deep lavender veining. S89-9-2: (Isabelle x Silver Illusion) X Snow Prince. Joe Pye Weed 1999.

SALLIE JONES KEITH (Albert Faggard, R. 1994). Sdlg. F-LAV-PK-1-86. LA, 38" (97 cm), E. S. light lavender pink; style arms green yellow, crests tipped lavender pink; F. lavender pink, large yellow crest. Mistis X Deneb.

SALLY JANE (A. J. Trinder, R. 1991). Sdlg. 85.06.11. BB, 26" (66 cm), M. S. deep ochre, flecked light purple; F. creamy yellow ground, deep ochre to brown veining ending toward edge, violet line and stippling; beards yellow; ruffled. Brownish bitone sdlg. X ochre bitone sdlg. David Austin Roses 1995.

SALSA (Chet Tompkins, R. 1994). Sdlg. 87-9. TB, 38" (97 cm), ML. S. pale brown to tan; F. dark medium brown heavily edged cream; beards brown. Sdlgs. inv. Trudy and Camelot Rose. Fleur de Lis 1994.

SALUTE TO DAVE (Siegmar Goerbitz, R. 1991). Sdlg. 8204 A 38. TB, 48" (120 cm), M. S. light blue; F. blue violet edged lighter; beards yellow; slight fragrance. Full Tide X Spinning Wheel. Schoeppinger 1992.

SAMANTA SMIT (Viktor Sheviakov, R. 1995). Sdlg. 210-1. TB, 32" (80 cm), ML. Ruffled white, greenish reverse on F.; beards light yellow, light blue at end. Swan Ballet X Starshine. Sheviakov 1993.

SAMANTHA ROSE (Allan Ensminger, R. 1999). Sdlg. 96-1. IB, 24" (61 cm), ML. S. gentian blue (HCC 42/2); style arms white; F. gentian blue (42/3), white edge and splash by white beard, luminata pattern; slight fragrance. Pert X unknown.

SAMANTHA'S SONG (Nancy Burrows, TB, R. 1989). Stornoway Gardens 1990.

SAM CARNE (R. E. Nichol, TB, R. 1985). British Iris Society 1990.

SAM MARSHALL (Barry Emmerson, R. 1998). Sdlg. BE 93-10-28. TB, 38" (97 cm), M. S. lemon, midrib flushed pink; style arms lemon; F. deep lemon shoulders and edge, paling toward center, white area under tangerine beard; lightly ruffled; slight fragrance. Frost and Flame X Scopes sdlg. inv. Early Light.

SAMSARA (Lawrence Ransom, R. 1996). Sdlg. 90/230-1. TB, 37" (94 cm), M. Ruffled soft cream yellow, center of F. paler; style arms light yellow, crests medium yellow; beards orange yellow, base white. Caroline Penvenon X Catalyst. Iris au Trescols 1997.

SAMSON (J. T. Aitken, R. 1994). Sdlg. 88M9. SDB, 10" (25 cm), EM. Honey yellow, deeper gold hafts; beards deep gold. Sam X 86M6: (82M95-5 plicata, unknown, x Chubby Cheeks). Aitken's Salmon Creek 1994.

SAMTPFOETCHEN (Lothar Denkewitz, R. 1990). Sdlg. M-83-schw-1. BB, 16" (42 cm), M. S. deep red violet; F. velvety blackish red violet; beards bright blue violet; slight spicy fragrance. (Wee Lad x (Adrienne Taylor x Snow Elf)) X Gingerbread Man. Schoeppinger 1989.

SAMUEL JACK (A.R.J. Bailey, R. 1994). Sdlg. CS/S4. SDB, 10" (25 cm), M. S. chrome yellow; F. chrome yellow with deeper thumbprint, white and purple striations around beard; beards white, tipped orange; spicy fragrance. Sudeley X Church Stoke.

SAMURAI CREST (William Ackerman, R. 1995). Sdlg. 94-1. JI (3 F.), 44" (112 cm), M. S. purple (RHS 77A/B); F. purple (77B/C) ground with broad white veins radiating from pale yellow (3C) signal to within 1 cm of margin. Yayoi Kagami X D4-14-91: (D5-6-1 double cream x Gosho-Asobi). Nicholls Gardens 1996.

SAMURAI SHIELD (Ed Matheny III, R. 1994). Sdlg. J:00-03-93. JI (6 F.), 40" (102 cm), EM. Violet, lightly etched cream areas throughout, royal blue (RHS 100A) area around yellow signal; style arms violet sky (90C). Geisha Gown X Glitter and Glamour. Ed's Iris 1995.

SANAE-NO-MAI (Kamo Nursery by Society for Japanese Irises, R. 1999). JI (3 F.), 36" (91 cm), E. S. red violet; style arms white, crests tinged violet; F. white, veined and sanded red violet. Kyomai X unknown. Kamo Nursery 1984.

SAN ANDREAS (Joseph Ghio, R. 1990). Sdlg. PJ-164-O. CA, 12" (30 cm), VE. S. velvety purple; F. purple, deeper in center. Western World X Idylwild. Bay View 1991.

SANDER (Erhard Woerfel, R. 1990). Sdlg. 26/86. TB, 32½" (80 cm), L. S. dark red brown; F. dark brown; beards yellow brown. Thanatos X Garnet Velvet. Hochheimer 1991.

SAND ETCHING (Lois Rich by James Whitely, R. 1991). Sdlg. R76-81A. AB (OGB+), 27" (69 cm), M. S. rose ground heavily veined bright violet, ruffled; style arms golden yellow rose; F. light rose veined violet, black lines on dark mahogany signal; beards bright yellow orange. R74-88A:

(R79-109C: ((Bagdad Beauty x Pink Formal) x Welcome Reward) x R70-209F: ((((*I. lortetii* x *I. auranitica*) x W83-0) x (Kerr K55-1 x K55-14))) X R73-176K: (R71-109C x (Welcome Reward x RR61-23A)). Aril Patch, Aril Society 1991.

SANDHILL CRANE (Daniel Thruman, R. 1997). JI (3 F.), 36" (91 cm), EM. S. violet (RHS 83B), distinct white marginal line; style arms purplish violet (80B), feathered and tufted; F. purplish violet with yellow signal, greenish lines in center, white toward outside. Oriental Classic X Japanese Pinwheel.

SANDRA BERNSCHEIN (Manfred Beer, R. 1995). Sdlg. MB 10/87 A. TB, 36" (90 cm), M. S. and style arms yellow (RHS 7A); F. yellow (8A), shoulders darker (12A), with paler (11D) area below beard; beards orange (24A) to yellow orange (23A), tipped yellow (12A). Tut's Gold X Gold Trimmings. Beer 1996.

SANDSATION (J. T. Aitken, R. 1997). Sdlg. 88J33. JI (6 F.), 36" (91 cm), ML. White ground, sanded violet, 1/8" more densely shaded edge, signal yellow; style arms (6) white, edged violet. Parentage unknown. Aitken's Salmon Creek 1997.

SANDSTONE ROSE (Sharon McAllister, R. 1996). Sdlg. 90-65-9. AB (OGB-), 16" (41 cm), E. S. and style arms greyed rose; F. greyed rose, brighter rose spot, burgundy veining on yellow haft; beards yellow. Wished For Child X Hunt sdlg.: (Lilli-Bright x unknown). McAllister 1996.

SANDWASHED SILK (Jeanne Holley, R. 1999). Sdlg. 100-95. TB, 33" (84 cm), M. S. and style arms white; F. white with lavender wash, lighter very narrow lavender edge; beards gold, tipped light yellow. Catalyst X Chiffon Ruffles.

SANDY BEACH (Larry Lauer, R. 1998). Sdlg. 91-144-21. TB, 36" (91 cm), ML. S. and style arms creamy light yellow; F. iridescent light lavender; beards yellow, light lavender at end; ruffled; pronounced sweet fragrance. 86-24: (Last Dance x Lady Chatterly) X L88-111: (Gaugin x Speakeasy). Lauer's Flowers 1998.

SANDY DARLENE (J. Owings Rebert, R. 1997). SIB, 30" (76 cm), M. S. blue violet, very erect; style arms slightly lighter; F. blue violet, gold and cream signal. Super Ego X unknown.

SAN FELIPE (Joseph Ghio, CA, R. 1969). Bay View 1990.

SAN FRANCISCO BOUND (Glenn Stoneking-Jones, R. 1999). Sdlg. CIR6-53810-06-02-1999). TB, 36" (91 cm), M. Ruffled mulberry pink; beards red orange; slight sweet fragrance. Extravagant X Fragrant Lilac.

SANGONE (Augusto Bianco, R. 1999). Sdlg. 682. IB, 18" (46 cm), E. Plicata, violet on ice white ground; style arms icy lilac; beards cream, hairs tipped mustard; slight musky fragrance. Farfui X (Chubby Cheeks x Earl of Essex). Iride 1999.

SAN JUAN SILVER (David Miller, R. 1996). Sdlg. 85-9B. TB, 34" (86 cm), M. Silvery white self; beards silvery blue white; slight musky fragrance. Song of Norway X Wedding Vow. Long 1998.

SAN LORENZO VALLEY (Joseph Ghio, R. 1992). Sdlg. PH-308L3. CA, 14" (36 cm), ML. S. white; F. white, large blue purple watercolor signal. Idylwild X Fault Zone sib. Bay View 1993.

SAN MIGUEL (William Maryott, R. 1995). Sdlg. U161C. TB, 38" (97 cm), M. S. tan (RHS 199D), infused violet; F. violet (83B), lighter flash by bright orange beard. Cherry Glen X Ghio 88-5: (Costa Rica x 86-29F, Tempting sib). Maryott 1996.

SANTA (George Shoop by Keith Keppel, R. 1997). Sdlg. 89-26. TB, 34" (86 cm), M. S. blended cream (M&P 9-D-1) strongly flushed peach buff (9-B-5) in center; style arms deeper orange buff (9-E-6); F. warm white (9-AB-1), shoulders with large thumbprint overlay of pinkish salmon buff (10-F-9), petal reverse cream buff (9-E-2/3); beards poppy red (1-J-12); ruffled; slight sweet fragrance. Tropical Magic X sib. Keppel 1998.

SANTA CLARITA (Joseph Ghio, R. 1991). Sdlg. PI-209D. CA, 12" (30 cm), ML. Heliotrope over metallic base, violet signal. Las Lomas X PK-303M2: ((Roaring Camp sib x (San Vicente x Emigrant)) x Wildman). Bay View 1992.

SANTAFAIR (Opal Brown, R. 1991). Sdlg. 79-2A1. TB, 36" (91 cm), M. Ruffled white, F. fluted; beards coral. 70-8B16: (((Dawn Flight x Winter Olympics) x sib) x Salmon River sib) X 76-2A33: (Spring Bride x Royal Coachman). Brown's Sunnyhill 1991.

SANTA FE STYLE (Labriano Anaya/Julian Wells, R. 1991). Sdlg. LW84A. TB, 38" (97 cm), EM. S. laced deep copper brown; F. golden brown, washed deeper copper brown with faint violet infusion; beards bronze; pronounced fragrance. (Angie Quadros x Homecoming Queen) X Samurai Warrior. Rancho de la Flor de Lis 1991.

SANTA FE TILE (Kirk Strawn, R. 1993). Sdlg. 39-1984. LA, 40" (102 cm), L. S. and style arms greyed red (RHS 182D); F. darker greyed red (181B), yellow orange (17A) signal. Sun Fury X Shrimp Louis. Bois d'Arc 1996.

SANTA ROSALITA (Joseph Ghio, R. 1996). Sdlg. PD-264K2. CA, 13" (33 cm), EM. Apricot ground, washed and lined rose overall, rose halo on all petals, rose F. signal. PF-188-O: (Eagle Eyes x (Las Lomas x Aftershock sib)) X PG-172A, Charter Member sib. Bay View 1997.

SANTA'S HELPER (Carol Lankow by J. T. Aitken, R. 1997). Sdlg. 4J34. IB, 24" (61 cm), ML. White self; beards orange. Hutchings 85-3A X ((Cheers x Fresno Calypso) x Dixie Pixie). Aitken's Salmon Creek 1997.

SANTIAGO (Joseph Ghio, TB, R. 1989). Bay View 1990.

SANTIAM SNOW (E. D. Zimmerly, R. 1992). CA, 16-23" (41-58 cm), M. White, pale yellow signal on F.; ruffled, fluted; spicy-sweet fragrance. Selection of *I. douglasiana* from seed gathered in Santiam Canyon, OR.

SANTOLERIA (Tom Burseen, R. 1999). Sdlg. 94-265X. TB, 35" (89 cm), M. S. gold, darker edge; F. gold, washed brown, edge light tan; beards gold, hairs tipped tangerine; ruffled; slight fragrance. Citoyen X Roar. T.B.'s Place 1999.

SAPPHIRE CROWN (Bob Bauer/John Coble, R. 1996). Sdlg. J88H-1. JI (6 F.), 38" (95 cm), M. White ground, small blue violet (RHS 93A) sanded halo and veins out to 1/4" edge of heavy red violet (83B) veining, white wire rim; style arms multiple, dark purple (83A) with large flared crests. Iapetus sib X unknown. Ensata Gardens 1996.

SAPPHIRE ROYALE (Hugh Pearson, R. 1991). Sdlg. 7777-13. SIB, 17½" (45 cm), M. S. dark violet blue (RHS 94A); style arms light purple (76B); F. darker violet blue (93A). Caesar's Brother X White Swirl. Chapman Iris 1999.

SAPPHIRES IN SNOW (Nora Scopes, R. 1992). Sdlg. 9S128A. TB, 38-40" (97-102 cm), ML. S. white, deepening to blue in heart; F. ice blue, fading white at edge; beards deep sapphire; ruffled, flared; sweet fragrance. Icelandic Moon X sib.

SARA E. BRYAN (Robert Fabel-Ward, R. 1990). LA, 35" (89 cm), EM. Red brown, large yellow signal. Freddie Boy X Little Miss Sims.

SARAFAN (Yuri Pirogov, R. 1998). Sdlg. 92-2E. TB, 35" (90 cm), M. S. apricot flushed cardinal red; style arms apricot; F. apricot with white at center, covered by cardinal red plicata wash, narrow yellow rim; beards dark yellow; ruffled, lightly laced. Spinning Wheel X "Depeche Mode": (Rancho Rose x Sketch Me).

SARAH JANE (Wilford James, R. 1998). Sdlg. 88-6. TB, 30" (76 cm), M. S. white, pale blue infusion; style arms white, midrib blue; F. light blue; beards white, orange in throat; ruffled; pronounced sweet fragrance. Gypsy Woman X Swirling Seas. Cuyahoga Valley 1998.

SARAH LAUREN (Rosa Belle Van Valkenburgh, R. 1992). Sdlg. VV4-86. TB, 32" (81 cm), EM. S. dark blue purple; F. velvety dark blue purple, white patch below white beard. Victoria Falls X Titan's Glory. Maple Tree Garden 1995.

SARAH O'CONNOR (Patrick O'Connor, LA, R. 1987). Bois d'Arc 1996.

SARAH'S WINDMILL (Polly Black, R. 1993). Sdlg. NRWB19-8. TB, 28" (71 cm), M. Deep golden yellow, shoulders lightly flushed brown; self beards; slight fragrance. Gold Galore X unknown. Polly Black 1993.

SARAH TIFFNEY (Marty Schafer/Jan Sacks, R. 1999). Sdlg. S92-65-14. SIB, 36" (91 cm), EML. S. whitish pale lavender (paler than RHS 84D) with very light lavender rose (83C/D) speckling; style arms buff yellow, tips deepest; F. lavender rose (83A/D, 84A) wash and speckling over yellow base, 1/8" yellow orange (16C/D) rim, gold to pale yellow signal, violet (83B) veining; slight fragrance. S89-9-2: (Isabelle x Silver Illusion) X Snow Prince. Joe Pye Weed 1999.

SARAMOHR (Philip Loomis by Catherine Gates, R. 1990). AB, 36" (91 cm), ML. S. blend of chartreuse, uranium yellow and grey; F. same with amethyst overlay, copper haft markings; beards yellow; musky fragrance. William Mohr X unknown. Long 1961.

SARA'S BEAUTY (Darlene Pinegar, R. 1995). Sdlg. EF-1-1. TB, 31" (79 cm), EML. S. white ground, 1/2" medium violet stitched edge, plus sanding and dotting; style arms white; F. white ground, medium light violet dotting and stitched edge; beards burnt orange, hairs tipped lavender violet; ruffled; slight sweet fragrance. Eagle's Flight X Daredevil. Spanish Fork 1996.

SARA'S LOVE (W. Terry Varner, R. 1994). Sdlg. 5-160-DG. MTB, 22" (56 cm), M. Lightly ruffled white; beards light lemon. Baby Bibs X (82-DG-123: (Emmie Lou x inv. Jana White, Frenchi) x 79-DG-85: (74-DG-130 x Pagoda)). Ohio Gardens 1994.

SARU ODORI (Society for Japanese Irises, R. 1993). JI (3 F.), 32" (80 cm), E. S. rosy violet with white veins; style arms and crests white, edged rosy violet; F. rosy violet, very pale edge, small white veins, yellow signal. Parentage unknown. Introduced in Japan prior to 1920. (Incorrectly shown as obsolete in 1939 Check List.)

SASAME YUKI (Yoshio Mitsuda by Society for Japanese Irises, R. 1994). JI (6 F.), 31½" (80 cm), ML. Clear medium blue with white stippling; style arms blue, centers white. Parentage unknown. Mitsuda 1957.

SASSY GIRL (Francis Rogers, R. 1993). Sdlg. F-215-D. TB, 36" (91 cm), M. S. greyed purple (RHS 186C); F. red purple (71A), edged greyed purple, light area around orange beard; ruffled, lightly laced; slight sweet fragrance. Bonbon X Rancho Rose. Meadowbrook 1995.

SASSY KOOMA (Currier McEwen, R. 1993). Sdlg. M84/100. SIB, 18" (46 cm), M. S. white, midrib light yellow; F. creamy white (RHS 10D), slightly darker (10C) crimped edge and veins, bright yellow signal; ruffled. Baby Sister X Ruffled Velvet. Eartheart, Seaways 1993.

SASSY LASSIE (Lynda Miller, R. 1994). Sdlg. 22289. SDB, 12" (31 cm), ML. S. light canary yellow; F. bright deep canary yellow, tinted green; beards light blue, tipped yellow; slight musky fragrance. Dark Vader X Jewel Baby. Miller's Manor 1995.

SASSY MISS (Francis Rogers, R. 1993). Sdlg. F-941-B. TB, 31" (79 cm), M. S. purple (RHS 78C); F. darker purple (78A), edged lighter (78C) and veined purple (80A), white area around orange red beard; ruffled, lightly laced; slight fragrance. F-651-N: (Bonbon x Coral Beauty) X Apricot Flush. Meadowbrook 1994.

SATAN'S MISTRESS (Gus Seligmann, TB, R. 1982). Correction of hybridizer's name as shown in 1989 Check List.

SATIN KNIGHT (Bryce Williamson, R. 1992). Sdlg. 92-270. TB, 36" (91 cm), EM. S. satiny cream white, midrib shaded yellow cream; F. satiny cream white, yellow cream shading at ruffled edge, pronounced chartreuse gold shoulders; beards lemon; slight musky fragrance. Irish Spring X Dream Affair. Pacific Coast Hybridizers 1991.

SATIN SASHES (Lynn Markham, R. 1992). Sdlg. 85-3C3. BB, 27" (68 cm), ML. S. cold near-greenish white, pronounced green midrib; F. same, with greenish texture veining; beards bluish white, 1/4" end section pale blue, hairs strongly tipped bright gold in throat; ruffled, satin finish; slight sweet fragrance. 7783-2A: (Angel Feathers x (Sheaff 60-3: (Hall pink sdlg. x Celestial Snow) x Arctic Flame)) X 7783-1A: (Angel Feathers x Warburton 20KL-3: ((Buttrick blue sdlg. x (Progenitor x Serene Valley)) x (Sunfrost x (Summit x *I. aphylla* "Polonica")))).

SATURABICO (Ladislav Muska, R. 1997). Sdlg. INBN-05. TB, 40" (107 cm), M. S. light lavender blue; style arms deeper lavender blue; F. deep blackish blue, bright lavender blue rim; beards tangerine; heavily ruffled, lightly laced; spicy fragrance. (Into the Night x "Bila Neha": (Lavender Petticoat x Silver Shower)) X Cardinale C. Muska 1996.

SATURDAY NIGHT LIVE (Schreiner, R. 1996). Sdlg. DD 607-1. TB, 37" (94 cm), EML. Burgundy wine (RHS 59A) self; beards bronze yellow; slight fragrance. Crimson Fire X Y 682-2: (Thriller sib x T 449-A: ((Master Touch x J 483-4, sib to pod parent of Spellbreaker) x ((Sailor's Dance x F 142-1) x ((G 1517-B x Neptune's Pool) x Royal Regency sib)))). Schreiner 1996.

SATURDAY NIGHT SPECIAL (Keith Fillmore, R. 1991). Sdlg. 8605-3-SDB. SDB, 13" (33 cm), L. Black; beards dark iridescent blue. Drummer Boy X unknown. Bar K Iris Garden 1990.

SATURN FIRE (Cleo Palmer, R. 1994). Sdlg. 8952. SDB, 12" (30 cm), M. S. orange; F. orange, large red violet spot, 1/4" orange edge; beards tangerine. 8610: ((7607 x (Dove Wings x 7416)) x (Lenna M x unknown)) X 8548: (Delicate Pink x (7607: (Dove Wings x ((Wilma V. x unknown) x Little Titan)) x Dove Wings)). Palmer's Iris 1994.

SATURN SWIRL (Heather Pryor, R. 1995). Sdlg. 57/90-4. LA, 38" (97 cm), ML. Pale lemon, washed soft rose at end and edges, white rim, darker rose veining; raised bright lime green line signal on all petals; style arms bright lime green. Desert Jewel X Noble Planet. Iris Haven 1996/97.

SATYRE (Lawrence Ransom, R. 1999). Sdlg. 90/247-15. SDB, 9" (23 cm), M. S. chrome yellow; style arms chrome yellow, pale mauve stigma; F. cadmium yellow upper center and hafts, diffuse intermediate cream yellow halo, chrome yellow edge; beards yellow, grey white base, hairy mauve grey horn; pronounced sweet fragrance. Clay's Caper X Peyrard PB 88/1-1: (Planet Iris x *pumila*). Iris au Trescols 1999.

SAUCY (Jim & Vicki Craig, R. 1998). Sdlg. AH28C17. IB, 25" (63 cm), EM. S. white ground heavily washed light purple, wide purple rim; style arms deep purple; F. white ground, dark purple hafts and edge thinning to wire rim at end, remainder washed lighter purple, sparsely dotted purple; beards pale blue; ruffled; pronounced sweet fragrance. Classic Image X 8Z13: (*I. aphylla* 61-56A x (Gentle Rain x (((High Above x Lhasa) x Deborah Suzanne) x Stepping Out))). J. & V. Craig 1998.

SAUCY SPRITE (A. & D. Willott, R. 1997). Sdlg. 91-46. MDB, 6" (15 cm), EM. Creamy white, F. with yellow shoulders; beards white. Daisy Fresh X Creamette. Willott 1997.

SAVAGE QUEEN (Ben Hager, TB, R. 1960). Melrose 1961.

SAVANNAH (William Maryott, R. 1994). Sdlg. S124A. TB, 38-39" (97-99 cm), M. Medium orange self; beards bright orange; slight fragrance. Good Show X (Radiant Energy x Oktoberfest). Iris Garden (IN) 1994.

SAXON (Monty Byers, TB, R. 1989). Moonshine 1990.

SAXON PRINCESS (C. Bird, TB, R. 1985). V. H. Humphrey 1992.

SAY CHEESE (Tom Burseen, R. 1993). Sdlg. 7-287A. TB, 36" (91 cm), ML. S. apricot pink (RHS 38B); F. lighter (38D) with some orange infusion; beards orange; ruffled, laced; sweet fragrance. Exhilaration X Salmon Song. T.B.'s Place 1994.

SAY HELLO (Barry Blyth, R. 1995). Sdlg. B34-5. SDB, 15" (38 cm), VE-M. S. apricot ochre; F. apricot ochre, bright lavender chevron below beard, slight white area around chevron; beards lavender, tangerine in throat; ruffled, waved. Z15-4, Fairy Favours sib, X Z24-1, Volts sib. Tempo Two 1995/96.

SAY OKAY (Tom Burseen, R. 1990). Sdlg. 5-58A. TB, 36" (91 cm), E. S. creamy white ground washed violet blue (RHS 94B); F. creamy white ground, precise violet blue (94A) stitched band; beards yellow, tipped white; ruffled; sweet fragrance. Burgundy Brown X Decolletage. T.B.'s Place 1991.

SAYO-NO-TSUKI (Toyokazu Ichie by Society for Japanese Irises, R. 1994). SPEC-X, 30" (76 cm), EM. S. creamy white; style arms white, midrib creamy pale yellow; F. creamy white, blue violet halo surrounding light yellow signal, short blue violet lines extending from halo. *I. pseudacorus* X *I. ensata*. Introduced in Japan ca. 1990.

SCAN (Graeme Grosvenor, R. 1998). Sdlg. V79-Q. TB, 38" (96 cm), EM. S. pale blue; F. white ground, irregularly patterned blue violet; beards white, tangerine in throat; slight fragrance. Work Ethic X S86-3: (Momentum x Snowbrook). Rainbow Ridge 1998/99.

SCARABEUS LUX (Ladislav Muska, R. 1996). Sdlg. FPBB-05. TB, 40" (102 cm), M. S. rich amber; F. light lilac lavender, narrow light brown edge; beards yellow; heavily ruffled; pronounced fragrance. ((French Gown x Paradise) x Bab Babbili) X Discretion. Muska 1995.

SCARBOROUGH AFFAIRE (Tom Burseen, R. 1995). Sdlg. 1-268A. TB, 35" (89 cm), ML. S. mulberry red (RHS 53C); style arms mulberry brown; F. dark mulberry brown (185A); beards bronze (34B), bushy; ruffled; spicy fragrance. Caliph X 7-239C: (Witches' Sabbath x Touch of Bronze). T.B.'s Place 1995.

SCARLET EMBERS (James Begley, R. 1995). Sdlg. G.1.SS. TB, 36" (91 cm), ML. S. rose; F. wine burgundy, rose rim, burgundy-lined white spot near beard; beards gold, white at tip. G.1: (Latin Lover x Splash o' Wine) X Sooner Serenade. Stockton 1995.

SCARLETT (Mary Dunn by Joseph Ghio, R. 1998). Sdlg. 220-3. LA, 36" (91 cm), M. Red self, signal yellow. (Billy x self) X Midnight Drama. Bay View 1999.

SCARLETT IN GOLD (Ladislav Muska, R. 1996). Sdlg. LFIV-08/A. TB, 40" (102 cm), M. S. light lemon yellow; F. white, banded lemon yellow; beards canary yellow, white at end; ruffled, laced; sweet fragrance. (Sunshine Express x White Window) X (Lemon Fire x "Vernisage": (Glory Bound x Silver Shower)). Muska 1995.

SCARLET WHISPER (Jim Hedgecock, R. 1995). Sdlg. 83-76-2. TB, 31" (79 cm), M. White self; beards white, tipped tangerine red; ruffled, laced; pronounced sweet fragrance. Lady Marie X Brilliant Star. Comanche Acres 1995.

SCAT (Barry Blyth, R. 1992). Sdlg. X2-A. SDB, 14" (36 cm), VE. S. tan, flushed light violet deepening toward outer edge; F. tan with violet cast, violet flash, brown area one-third way down; beards mustard and tan. Anjaya X Camarilla. Tempo Two 1992/93.

SCATTERED DOTS (Ladislav Muska, R. 1998). Sdlg. CGQC-05. TB, 37" (94 cm), M. S. light lilac rose, light mahogany rim; style arms mustard; F. white ground widely striped and stitched rose maroon, darkening at rim; beards mustard; sweet fragrance. ((Calicoball x Queen in Calico) x Casbah) X Graffiti. Muska 1998.

SCENE STEALER (Hooker Nichols, R. 1990). Sdlg. 8897C. TB, 36" (91 cm), ML. S. laced white, violet midrib and base; F. purple, edged white, large white zonal area; beards orange yellow and white; ruffled; pronounced fragrance. Diddler X Song of Spring. Hillcrest 1998.

SCENIC WONDER (Tom Burseen, R. 1991). Sdlg. 6-266A. TB, 36" (91 cm), M. Heavily ruffled and waved light violet (RHS 85C); beards white, tipped lemon; slight fragrance. Local Motion X Ruffled Ballet. T.B.'s Place 1992.

SCHMOO (Lucy Burton, R. 1998). Sdlg. L93-D-14. SDB, 12" (30 cm), L. S. off-white, light yellow midrib and basal shading on reverse; style arms off-white, sides shaded gold; F. off-white, gold veining on hafts and beside beard; beards cream, hairs tipped gold; flared. Peach Eyes X Cotton Blossom.

SCHNEEWITTCHEN (Eberhard Fischer, R. 1999). Sdlg. 10. TB, 39" (100 cm), M. Waved pure white self; beards white, pale yellow in throat. Azucena X Leda's Lover.

SCHOKOLADEN-JONNY (Lothar Denkewitz, R. 1995). Sdlg. N-94-pl 1. SDB, 12½" (32 cm), M. S. yellow ground, few brown dots, 1/3" clear chocolate brown edge; style arms yellow; F. yellow, dotted brown, heavier at edge; beards brownish yellow, base bluish; slight spicy fragrance. (Bodderlecker sib x Dunlin) X Auburn Valley. Von Zeppelin 1997.

SCHOOL BOY (Joseph Ghio, R. 1992). Sdlg. PH-268L2. CA, 14" (36 cm), EM. Golden yellow self. Las Lomas X ((San Gregorio x (Montara sib x Mission Santa Cruz sib)) x Villa Branciforte). Bay View 1993.

SCHOOL DAYS (Lynda Miller, R. 1999). Sdlg. 2093. SDB, 11" (28 cm), ML. Rich cream, F. with slate violet to grey spot; beards cream, tipped orange except at end. Cosmos X Cream Cake. Miller's Manor 1999.

SCHUBERTIAD (Mitch Jameson, R. 1996). Sdlg. 1-87. TB, 34" (86 cm), EM. S. and style arms apricot; F. lavender violet, slight blue flash, hafts apricot; beards red orange; slight fragrance. 1-84: (Cabaret Royale x Son of Star) X Song of Spring. Knee-Deep in June 1997.

SCHWANENLIEBE (Frank Kathe, R. 1998). Sdlg. 100/1-91. SDB, 15" (39 cm), M. White self; beards white, yellow in throat; pronounced fragrance. ((Magic Dot x Irish Sea) x Lenna M) X ((Magic Dot x Irish Sea) x Lenna M). Kathe 1999.

SCHWANENWYK (Lothar Denkewitz, R. 1995). Sdlg. N-88-w 1. SDB, 13½" (35 cm), L. Warm white self, F. with clear yellow throat; beards white; pronounced spicy fragrance. Baroque Prelude X Sonnentrude. Von Zeppelin 1997.

SCHWANENZUG (Eberhard Fischer, R. 1999). Sdlg. 13. TB, 41" (105 cm), M. Waved pure white, F. with pale yellow hafts; beards yellow, white at end. Azucena X Leda's Lover.

SCHWEFELBLUETE (Tomas Tamberg, R. 1995). Sdlg. SSTT 278. SIB (tet.), 43" (110 cm), M. S. white; F. sulphur yellow. 8378 yellow tet: (white tet SSTT 177: (McEwen white tet x Tamberg white tet) x converted yellow sdlg.: (Dreaming Yellow x self)) X Dreaming Orange. Schoeppinger 1996.

SCIGHERA (Ladislav Muska, R. 1999). Sdlg. 98-SDSE-08. TB, 36" (91 cm), M. S. bright orchid; style arms orchid; F. deep blackish burgundy red, narrow orchid rim; beards light pink; slight fragrance. ((Soissons x Nejedlo DERRSM-89-2, Spacelight Sketch sib) x (Sweeter Than Wine x Ringo)) X "Erebuni": (Thriller x ((Vandal Spirit x Okavango) x (Simple Pleasures x Tropicana Doll))). Muska 1999.

SCION (Barry Blyth, R. 1994). Sdlg. A27-1. SDB, 14-15" (36-38 cm), EML. S. apricot; F. slightly deeper apricot, small white area around beard; beards white, tangerine in throat; slight fragrance. Wanderer X Chanted. Tempo Two 1994/95.

SCOONCHEE (Peter DeSantis, R. 1996). Sdlg. 85-26. TB, 42" (107 cm), E. S. dark plum violet (RHS 82A); style arms white, centerline and edge plum violet; F. velvety dark plum violet, brown blush and markings on haft; beards violet blue; slight fragrance. 1979-2A: ((Valhalla x Turbulence) x Top Executive) X B-78-651-2: (Midnight Special x Tarde). Stockton 1997.

SCOOP (Barry Blyth, R. 1997). Sdlg. D34-18. SDB, 12" (30 cm), L. S. pink, heavily infused violet, some white at midrib; style arms pink; F. white ground, 3/8" pinkish violet edge, few deeper violet veins; beards tangerine, violet at end. Bee's Knees X A7-1: (Merry Dance x Mini Song). Tempo Two 1997/98.

SCORCH (Tom Burseen, R. 1993). Sdlg. 6-72C. TB, 34" (84 cm), M. S. yellow (RHS 19A), reverse creamy white with yellow rim and veining; style arms white, rimmed yellow; F. buttercup yellow (15B), darker toward edge; spicy fragrance. Gigolo X Street Walker. T.B.'s Place 1994.

SCORPIO (Monty Byers, TB, R. 1989). Moonshine 1990.

SCORPIO SNOW (Walter Moores, R. 1994). Sdlg. 88-47. TB, 34" (86 cm), EM & RE (Oct.-Nov./MS). White, yellow hafts; beards yellow. Stellar Lights X Retreat.

SCORPIO STAR (Walter Moores, R. 1994). Sdlg. 87-15RE. TB, 34" (86 cm), M & RE (Oct.-Nov./MS). Lightly ruffled medium violet purple, white spot surrounding white to yellow beards; pronounced sweet fragrance. Victoria Falls X Fall Spotlight. Moores 1996.

386

SCOTCH (Mary Dunn, R. 1991). Sdlg. M84-901-4. TB, 36" (91 cm), L. Ruffled golden butterscotch; self beards. California Classic X Copper Classic. M.A.D. Iris 1992.

SCOTCH-HOPPER (Sterling Innerst, R. 1994). Sdlg. 4139-1. SDB, 12" (30 cm), M. Mustard yellow, green F. spot; beards orange, tipped white; slight fragrance. Assignment X Jeepers sib. Innerst 1995.

SCOTLAND YARD (James Begley, R. 1996). Sdlg. 88-A-22. TB, 36" (91 cm), ML. S. tan, edges infused lilac, midrib green; style arms infused lilac; F. whitish cream ground, lilac purple plicata markings; beards light lilac; slight sweet fragrance. Laced Cotton X Tennison Ridge. Stockton 1996.

SCRAMBLED EGGS (Richard Sparling, R. 1991). SDB, 12" (30 cm), M. S. dirty white infused yellow; F. white with brown and yellow specks, solid yellow (7A) partway down edge; beards white, bluish tip. Parentage unknown. Green Box 1992.

SCREEN PLAY (Keith Keppel, R. 1995). Sdlg. 89-148A. TB, 38" (97 cm), E. S. greyed rose orchid (M&P 52-C-7 to 52-D-8) near-solid suffusion on warm grey (12-A-2) ground; style arms rosy lavender; F. pinkish ivory (10-AB-3) ground, raisin purple (54-B-12) 1" plicata edge, hafts and partial centerline; beards soft pumpkin (10-I-10), white base; ruffled. Film Festival X Storyline. Keppel 1996.

SCRUPLES (Lynda Miller, MDB, R. 1989). Miller's Manor 1993.

SCULPTURED WILD (Barry Blyth, R. 1996). Sdlg. D37-1. IB, 25" (64 cm), ML. S. lemon chartreuse outer 3/8", blending to violet toward midrib; style arms violet and chartreuse; F. plum burgundy, 1/8" lavender grey edge, heavy white venation on upper half; beards old gold, lavender blue at end; pronounced sweet fragrance. Wild Vision X A28-1: (Impish x Chanted). Tempo Two 1997/98.

SEA ADMIRAL (Vernon Wood, R. 1995). Sdlg. 93-51. CA, 14-16" (41-46 cm), ML. S. white, lined violet, veining lighter in center; style arms white, slightly veined violet; F. nearly solid heavy violet veins, 1/4" near-white edge; ruffled. Idylwild X Star Symphony. Stockton 1995.

SEA BABY (Henry Rowlan, R. 1990). Sdlg. 86-5-1. MTB, 21" (53 cm), ML. Hyacinth blue (HCC 40/2), 1/8" paler blue edge; beards yellow. Peewee X self. Comanche Acres 1991.

SEABRIGHT COVE (Joseph Ghio, R. 1992). Sdlg. PH-300C3. CA, 16" (41 cm), EM. Deep blue, purple shading at hairline white edge, small yellow signal. Idylwild X San Andreas. Bay View 1993.

SEA CADET (J. T. Aitken, R. 1993). Sdlg. 87T115. BB, 27" (69 cm), ML. Deep navy violet, lighter by beards; beards violet, lighter tips; slight fragrance. (Stellar Lights x sib) X Maui Magic. Aitken's Salmon Creek 1993.

SEA CONSUL (John C. Taylor, R. 1990). Sdlg. OL 140-1. LA, 47" (120 cm), EM. Lightly ruffled blue (RHS 101B), lighter reverse and serrated edge. M28-2: (Koorawatha sib x Lucile Holley) X Helen Naish. Rainbow Ridge 1990/91.

SEAFIRE (Marky Smith, R. 1999). Sdlg. 95-03A. SDB, 12" (31 cm), M. Medium light blue (RHS 97A), F. with bronze green shoulders; beards cream at end, red in throat; ruffled; slight musky fragrance. 93-05T: (Tweety Bird x Flaming Rhythm) X sib 93-05L.

SEA FLUFF (Raymond Smith, R. 1991). Sdlg. 8805LR. TB, 33" (84 cm), M & RE. Light blue (Nickerson 5PB 7/7); beards yellow, tipped white. Olive Reflection X 8606JR: (7602A x Victoria Falls). R. G. Smith 1994.

SEAFORTH (Nancy Burrows, R. 1992). TB, 33" (84 cm), EM. S. white; F. lavender blue, blue white center; beards orange, tipped white; ruffled, laced; pronounced sweet fragrance. Mystique X Simple Pleasures.

SEA GAL (Lois Belardi, R. 1993). Sdlg. PDI-2. CA, 18" (46 cm), M. S. medium true blue; F. white ground washed medium true blue, small yellow signal; ruffled. PHD-8: (Pacific High x Del Rey) X Idylwild. Bay View 1994.

SEAKIST (Schreiner, R. 1997). Sdlg. CC 1334-C. TB, 38" (97 cm), ML. S. and style arms creamy white (RHS 155A); F. white, with bluebird blue (94B) streaks and paler (94C) wash; beards yellow, white base; slight fragrance. Edith Wolford X W 410-A: (S 311-1: (((Breaking Dawn x (Amethyst Flame x ((Lavanesque x Opal Beauty) x Wonderment))) x Navajo Blanket sib) x (G 1519-A x Distant Chimes)) x N 502-FF, sib to pollen parent of Peach Picotee). Schreiner 1997.

SEA LORD (John C. Taylor, LA, R. 1989). Rainbow Ridge 1990/91.

SEA MONSTER (Lynda Miller, R. 1992). Sdlg. 2287. SDB, 10" (25 cm), EM. S. sky blue; F. olive green, paling at edge; beards baby blue; slight sweet fragrance. 3584: (Lemon Puff x Flirty Mary) X 3684: (Daisy x Indian Jewel). Miller's Manor 1993.

SEA POWER (Keith Keppel, R. 1998). Sdlg. 93-89B. TB, 38" (97 cm), M. S. cornflower to campanula blue (M&P 42-10-E), paling to light chicory blue (42-B-7) toward edge; style arms cornflower to campanula blue; F. commodore blue (43-F-12), paling slightly toward edge, slight tan haft suffusion; beards blue white at end, light lemon in throat; heavily ruffled; pronounced sweet fragrance. Yaquina Blue X Jazz Me Blue. Keppel 1999.

SEA QUEST (George Shoop, TB, R. 1989). Roris 1990.

SEARCH (Loleta Powell, R. 1998). TB, 38" (97 cm), EML. S. light blue, base deeper; F. light blue, center streak violet; beards yellow, tipped blue; sweet fragrance. (Timescape x Pacific Mist) X unknown. Powell's Gardens 1998.

SEARIOUS SITUATION (Tom Burseen, R. 1991). Sdlg. 6-72B. TB, 36" (91 cm), EM. Ruffled, lightly laced bright lemon yellow (RHS 14B), edge faintly seared red brown, F. center washed white; beards golden yellow; musky fragrance. Gigolo X Street Walker. T.B.'s Place 1993.

SEA SHADOWS (Marjorie Brummitt, SIB, R. 1964). Correction of introductory data: Orpington 1966.

SEA SIREN (Chet Tompkins, R. 1998). Sdlg. 95-68A. TB, 39" (99 cm), EML-VL. Deepwater sea blue self; beards pale blue, tipped lemon. Sheer Bliss X Honky Tonk Blues. Fleur de Lis 1998.

SEASON JOY (Loleta Powell, R. 1999). TB, 34" (86 cm), EML-VL. S. light salmon pink; F. lavender salmon; beards tangerine; sweet fragrance. Berry Blush X Heavenly Rapture. Powell's Gardens 1999.

SEASONS (John Weiler, R. 1992). Sdlg. 84-152-2RE. TB, 36" (91 cm), EML & RE. S. pale peachy yellow; F. medium peachy orange, some haft lines; beards orange red; slight sweet fragrance. 82-178-1RE: (79-133-2: ((((Ultrapoise x Travel On) x Orange Chiffon) x ((Moon River x Orange Crush) x Ole)) x 75-1: (Fresno Fiesta x Fresno Calypso)) x Peach Sundae) X 82-149-2: (Peach Sundae x Vernal Falls). Rialto 1992.

SEASON TICKET (Joseph Gatty by Keith Keppel, R. 1994). Sdlg. Y9-1. IB, 26" (66 cm), EM & RE. S. and style arms yellow (M&P 10-J-6) with pinkish (10-E-3) midrib cast; F. slightly deeper yellow (10-J-7) with apricot cast; beards fire red (1-F-12); ruffled, often with extra petals; slight spicy-sweet fragrance. Florida Orange X Orange Tiger. Keppel 1995.

SEA SPLASH (George Shoop, R. 1994). Sdlg. 89-15. TB, 36" (91 cm), M. S. medium light blue; F. blue white; beards tangerine; lightly ruffled; slight fragrance. Ruffled Florette X 87-38, blue amoena. Shoop 1994.

SEASTONE (George Sutton, R. 1999). Sdlg. G-85 J. SDB, 12" (31 cm), VE-EM & RE. S. and style arms pale wistaria blue (RHS 92D) to near grey blue; F. battleship grey veined darker, pale greyed yellow edge; beards dark violet blue; ruffled; slight sweet fragrance. Sigh X Chanted.

SEA STORM (Frederick Kerr, R. 1999). Sdlg. 901904. TB, 30" (76 cm), M. S. blue white, blue basal infusion; F. dark blue; beards blue, tipped gold; ruffled, flared; slight sweet fragrance. Best Bet X Satin Satan.

SEA SWELLS (Joseph Ghio, R. 1997). Sdlg. 91-40B. TB, 38" (97 cm), ML. S. medium blue, midrib flushed white; F. medium blue, white area radiating from white beard. Water Ballet X Quintessence. Bay View 1998.

SEA SWEPT (Duane Meek, R. 1999). Sdlg. 74-1-1. TB, 34" (86 cm), ML. S. pale blue; style arms blue white; F. pale blue, ivory area below beard with darker veining, hafts dotted; beards pale violet blue, hairs tipped yellow in throat; ruffled. Sib to Expertise. D & J Gardens 1999.

SEA VOYAGE (Calvin Helsley, R. 1990). Sdlg. 87-26. SIB, 30" (76 cm), M. S. medium blue, veined violet; style arms light red violet, veined blue; F. medium violet, bright gold signal; ruffled. Ruffled Velvet X unknown. Helsley 1997.

SEAWAYS OUTSET (Currier McEwen, R. 1997). Sdlg. 89/2(2). JI (3 F.), 26" (65 cm), VE. Ruffled pure white, F. with yellow (RHS 7B) signal with unobtrusive greenish (2C) veins. Springtime Snow X self. Eartheart 1998.

SEA WORLD (Monty Byers, TB, R. 1989). Moonshine 1990.

SEBASTIAN (William Plotner, R. 1992). Sdlg. 84-162-1. TB, 38-40" (97-102 cm), EM. S. popcorn yellow (RHS 15C/D); F. velvety deep red; beards dark orange red. (Cimbay x Latin Lover) X ((Camelot Rose x Wine and Roses) x (Camelot Rose x Stunning)). Wildwood Gardens 1992.

SECOND ACT (Monty Byers, R. 1990). Sdlg. D157-107. TB, 36" (91 cm), EML & RE. S. medium lemon yellow; F. same, paling to cream in center and sometimes with icy blue undertoning; beards blue white, tipped bright yellow; heavily ruffled; slight sweet fragrance. I Do X B-8-2: (Cease-Fire x Sky Hooks). Moonshine 1991.

SECOND CHANCE (Dorothy Guild, MTB, R. 1989). Ohio Gardens 1991.

SECOND FIDDLE (William Maryott, R. 1998). Sdlg. W110ARE. TB, 36" (91 cm), E & RE. S. and style arms light lavender (RHS 85B), slight maroon midrib flush; F. deep velvety maroon (77A), 1/8" light lavender rim; beards tangerine. Double Agent X S248A: (Tomorrow's Child x Double Agent). Maryott 1998.

SECOND OPTION (Graeme Grosvenor, R. 1999). Sdlg. V20-2. TB, 34" (86 cm), ML. S. blue; F. light blue white, darker around beard; beards yellow, tipped blue. Silverado X Timescape. Rainbow Ridge 1999/2000.

SECOND SUNRISE (Ian Barry, R. 1998). Sdlg. H36-1. TB, 41" (104 cm), E. S. light yellow; style arms lemon; F. light yellow, white area around light orange beard. E7-6: (Joan McClemens x ((Lemon Mist x Charmaine) x Solano)) X unknown.

SECRET GLANCE (Ladislav Muska, R. 1999). Sdlg. QGCR-04. TB, 36" (91 cm), M. S. cream ground, burgundy red veining; style arms deep cream; F. pure white, 1 cm red plicata border; beards orange; slight fragrance. Queen in Calico X ((Graffiti x Zuzana) x (Calicoball x Rei Momo)). Muska 1998.

SECRET MISSION (Eugene Hunt by Sharon McAllister, R. 1990). Sdlg. ORB 89-5. AB (OGB), 29" (74 cm), EM. S. violet; F. reddish violet, purple black V-shaped signal; beards tangerine in heart, brownish violet at end. Esther the Queen X Rare Form. Aril Society 1990.

SECRET PLAN (Richard Ernst, R. 1990). Sdlg. B105-2. TB, 35" (89 cm), M. S. watermelon blend; style arms and crests with yellow highlights; F. deeper watermelon blend, white center stripe; beards deep yellow. Autumn Leaves X Haviland. Cooley 1990.

SECRET WEAPON (Lynn Markham, R. 1992). Sdlg. 85-2A3. BB, 26" (66 cm), EM. S. pale violet blue (Munsell 10PB 8/4), slight greenish midrib, deeper violet blue stain inside base; style arms pale violet, light violet blue midrib; F. lighter shade of S. color with slight bluish texture veining; beards pale blue violet. Angel Feathers X 7783-1A: (Angel Feathers x Warburton 20KL-3: ((Buttrick blue sdlg. x (Progenitor x Serene Valley)) x (Sunfrost x (Summit x *I. aphylla* "Polonica")))). Markham 1994.

SEDMOYE NEBO (Nina Miroshnichenko, R. 1996). TB, 33" (85 cm), M. White self, tinted light blue; beards yellow; slight sweet fragrance. Parentage unknown. Miroshnichenko 1977.

SEEING ORCHID (Carl Boswell, R. 1995). Sdlg. 121-85-5. SDB, 9" (23 cm), E. S. pale blue violet, base deeper; F. pale blue with orchid cast, edges paler, blue centerline; beards very pale blue. Raspberry Jam X Leprechaun's Eyelash. Adamgrove 1995.

SEEING YOU (Nora Scopes, R. 1996). Sdlg. PC 107. CA, 13" (33 cm), M. Blue lavender, F. with round white central spot. Parentage unknown.

SEEKING (Loleta Powell, R. 1998). TB, 36" (91 cm), EML. Violet blue, all petals widely edged light blue; beards yellow, tipped violet; sweet fragrance. (Timescape x Pacific Mist) X unknown. Powell's Gardens 1998.

SEESAW (Schreiner, R. 1995). Sdlg. AA 2248-B. SDB, 13" (33 cm), M. Yellow (RHS 7A) self; beards blue. K 1334-1: (Int. #2, unknown, x Gingerbread Man) X Canary Isle. Schreiner 1995.

SEE THE LIGHT (Joseph Ghio, R. 1991). Sdlg. PI-201G3. CA, 18" (46 cm), ML. Deep rich golden yellow. PK-321A: (((Banbury Candy x Simply Wild) x (Native State sib x Emigrant)) x (Elberta Peach sib x (Going West x Mission Santa Cruz))) X PK-331D3: (Cup of Tea x Wildman). Bay View 1992.

SEIRAN (Clarence Mahan, R. 1993). SPEC (*laevigata*) (3 F.), 27" (69 cm), M. S. medium wistaria blue, violet stripe extending from base halfway up center; style arms violet, crests wistaria blue; F. medium wistaria blue, pale yellow ridges extending from pale yellow signal. Parentage and origin unknown. Introduced in Japan prior to 1987.

SEI SHONAGON (Shuichi Hirao by Society for Japanese Irises, R. 1992). JI (3 F.), 36" (90 cm), EM. Wistaria blue violet, F. with yellow signal. Parentage unknown. Hirao 1969.

SEIZE THE SIZZLE (J. T. Aitken, R. 1997). Sdlg. 87F49B. TB, 36" (91 cm), L-VL. Light red violet, F. with white around bright red beard; lightly ruffled. unknown X Persian Gown. Aitken's Salmon Creek 1997.

SELECT CIRCLE (Joseph Ghio, R. 1996). Sdlg. 92-44T2. TB, 38" (97 cm), EML. S. blackish plum dotting and stitching on white; F. white, edges dotted and stitched blackish plum; beards brick, purple at end. 90-52L2, Epicenter sib, X 90-65 tall, Somersault sib. Bay View 1997.

SELENA (John C. Taylor, LA, R. 1989). Rainbow Ridge 1990/91.

SELF EVIDENT (Ben Hager, R. 1996). Sdlg. MD5491 Clean. MDB, 6" (15 cm), EML. S. clean white; style arms white; F. dark blue violet narrowly edged clean white; beards white, pale yellow in throat. AMD5161YSp: ((Little You x (Inca Toy x (BU68 *pumila* x Atomic Blue))) x Ditto sib) X MD4972Var, Jiffy sib. Adamgrove 1997.

SEMINOLE SECRET (Jim Hedgecock, R. 1995). Sdlg. 85-201-1. TB, 33" (84 cm), EM. S. pale reddish brown, darker veins; F. white ground, edged pale reddish brown, darker brown hafts; beards golden orange; ruffled. Beyond X Desert Mist. Comanche Acres 1995.

SEMINOLE SPRING (Roger Nelson, R. 1992). Sdlg. RN86-37BL. TB, 38" (97 cm), M. S. light lilac lavender with blue influence (RHS 91C) aging to blue white; F. lighter lavender blue (near 91D) aging to pale blue white; beards lavender white, golden orange in throat; ruffled; pronounced sweet fragrance. Neil Diamond X Lorilee. Iris Country 1993.

SENECA BLUE ROSE (Dana Borglum, R. 1993). Sdlg. D-4-33-2. SIB, 31" (79 cm), M. Wide blue purple. Gulls Way X Violet Swirl. Borglum's Iris 1995.

SENECA BRIDE (Dana Borglum, R. 1995). Sdlg. C-1-29. TB, 35" (89 cm), M. Ruffled, laced white, gold wire edge on all petals, slight yellow haft marks on F.; beards orange, tipped white. Yellow Tapestry X Piping Hot. Borglum's Iris 1995.

SENECA CLOUD PUFFS (Dana Borglum, R. 1993). Sdlg. D-4-33 or 36. SIB, 32" (81 cm), M. Wide white. Gulls Way X Outer Loop or Violet Swirl. Borglum's Iris 1995.

SENECA EGRET COVE (Dana Borglum, R. 1993). Sdlg. D-4-36-3. SIB 33" (84 cm), M. White; style crests feathered. Gulls Way X Outer Loop. Borglum's Iris 1999.

SENECA FEATHER DANCER (Dana Borglum, R. 1993). Sdlg. D-4-36-2. SIB, 28" (71 cm), M. S. feathery light blue, veined darker; style arms aqua; F. light sky blue, dark veining at hafts; lightly ruffled. Gulls Way X Outer Loop. Borglum's Iris 1995.

SENECA GLACIER FLOW (Dana Borglum, R. 1999). Sdlg. LKNS-4. SIB, 33" (84 cm), EM. S. bluebird blue (RHS 94B); style arms lighter gentian blue (94D); F. deeper gentian blue (94C), 1/4" darker bluebird blue (94A) edging on hafts and sides; lightly ruffled, F. recurved. Lake Keuka X Seneca Night Sky.

SENECA MOODSTONE (Dana Borglum, R. 1999). Sdlg. LK 01. SIB, 31" (79 cm), M. S. light wistaria blue (RHS 92B) fading paler (92C/D); style arms pale wistaria blue (94D), fimbriated; F. deeper wistaria blue (92A) on upper third, remainder lighter (92B) fading paler (92D) to give multicolor effect, white spray signal; ruffled, rounded. Lake Keuka X Seneca Feather Dancer.

SENECA NIGHT SKY (Dana Borglum, R. 1993). Sdlg. D-4-33-1. SIB, 32" (81 cm), M. S. blue purple; style arms aqua; F. dark blue purple, white haft markings. Gulls Way X Violet Swirl. Borglum's Iris 1999.

SENECA NORMA JEAN (Dana Borglum, R. 1993). Sdlg. E29-1. TB, 32" (81 cm), M. S. light pink; F. light pink, slightly lighter around tangerine red beard; ruffled, laced. Anna Belle Babson X self. Borglum's Iris 1995.

SENECA PROM GOWN (Dana Borglum, R. 1999). Sdlg. EM 00-1. SIB, 32" (81 cm), M. White, lime yellow signal; ruffled; flared, open form. Esther C.D.M. X unknown.

SENECA QUEEN (Dana Borglum, R. 1995). Sdlg. B 121. TB, 35" (89 cm), M. White, F. with light gold shoulders; beards white, tipped tangerine; ruffled. Money X Yellow Tapestry. Borglum's Iris 1995.

SENECA REBOUND (Dana Borglum, R. 1995). SDB, 11" (28 cm), M & RE. S. white, pale yellow cast; F. white, light yellow haft markings; beards yellow, bluish at end. (Mary's Lamb -- probably) X Baby Blessed. Hermit Medlars Walk 1999.

SENECA RED STARBURST (Dana Borglum, R. 1993). Sdlg. 87-J-051. SIB, 31" (79 cm), M. S. red maroon; F. same, with gold hafts turning to white, then pinkish, pronounced purple veining. Seed from SIGNA. Dutch X unknown.

SENECA SKYLITES (Dana Borglum, R. 1993). Sdlg. D-4-36-4. SIB, 32" (81 cm), M. S. light hazy sky blue; style arms light aqua; F. light hazy sky blue with darker center. Gulls Way X Outer Loop. Borglum's Iris 1997.

SENECA SNOWDRIFT (Dana Borglum, R. 1995). Sdlg. C-1-16. TB, 37" (94 cm), M. Ruffled white self; beards white, yellow in throat. A-1-2: (Coral Magic x unknown) X Skiers' Delight. Borglum's Iris 1995.

SENECA SPRING SONG (Dana Borglum, R. 1995). SDB, 11" (28 cm), ML. S. creamy white, center infused yellow; F. creamy white, bright golden yellow thumbprint; beards yellow, white at end; ruffled. Parentage unknown. Hermit Medlars Walk 1999.

SENECA STORM CLOUDS (Dana Borglum, R. 1995). Sdlg. D-4-33-3. SIB, 28" (71 cm), M. Dark blue purple self. Gulls Way X Violet Swirl.

SENECA SUNNYSIDE UP (Dana Borglum, R. 1993). Sdlg. F48. TB, 30½" (77 cm), M. S. golden yellow, whitening at top edge; F. pure white, gold shoulders; beards yellow. B104: (Radiant Summer x Ming Dynasty) X C-1-25: (Chartreuse Ruffles x Fire Goddess).

SEN HIME (Yoshio Mitsuda by Society for Japanese Irises, R. 1995). JI (3 F.), 30" (76 cm), M. S. light violet (RHS 87D), darker (87B) at tip; style arms off-white, light violet stigma and tip; F. light violet ground (75D), veined (87B); ruffled. Parentage unknown. Introduced in Japan ca. 1975.

SENIOR PROM (Myrtle Wolff, R. 1990). Sdlg. 1984-2-2. BB, 24" (61 cm), ML. Ruffled and laced doge purple (HCC 732/3), lighter in center of F.; beards tangerine; slight sweet fragrance. Angela X Jane Ann. Hildenbrandt's Iris 1991.

SENNYO-NO-HORA (Society for Japanese Irises, R. 1994). JI (6 F.), 27½" (70 cm), EM. Red violet marbled with white splashes; style arms red violet, near-white center; old Edo type. Correction of entry for Senjo-No-Hora in 1939 Check List. Parentage unknown. Introduced in Japan prior to 1910.

SENORITA JUANITA (Ladislav Muska, R. 1995). Sdlg. TCCK-03-1. TB, 39" (99 cm), ML. S. pinkish vanilla; F. pinkish vanilla, washed lavender; beards tangerine; ruffled; sweet fragrance. Tomorrow's Child X (Lady Madonna x "Cipkovana Krinolina": (After All x Grand Waltz)). Muska 1995.

SENSATIONAL (Cleo Palmer, SDB, R. 1989). Palmer's Iris 1990.

SENSUALITY (Roger Nelson, TB, R. 1987). Iris Country 1991.

SENSUELLE (Lawrence Ransom, R. 1999). Sdlg. 90/109-3. TB, 40" (102 cm), M. S. flesh pink, edges shaded orange; style arms soft orange pink; F. cream white center, edges soft cream pink, hafts orange pink, flesh pink reverse; beards light cadmium orange; strong sweet fragrance. Desiris X Halo in Pink.

SENTRA (Glenn Corlew, SPU, R. 1988). Bay View 1993.

SEPTEMBER FROST (George Sutton, R. 1997). Sdlg. G-39-A. TB, 38" (97 cm), EML & RE. Ruffled white self tinged lavender, diamond dusted; beards yellow, white tinged lavender at end; slight sweet fragrance. Recurring Ruffles X Best Bet. Sutton 1998.

SEPTEMBER REPLAY (Frank Jones by Mike Lowe, R. 1992). Sdlg. J82-35. TB, 30" (76 cm), E & RE. S. lightly frilled golden tan; F. white ground with darker cinnamon overlay and golden tan markings, brown midline below orange beard; pronounced spicy fragrance. J74-13 X Autumn Echo. Nicholls Gardens 1992.

SERAPH'S JEWEL (Howard Shockey, R. 1991). Sdlg. 88-165-A. AB (OGB), 27" (69 cm), M. S. white; F. white, recurved, sharply defined greyed maroon signal; beards yellow; slight sweet fragrance. 86-143-B: (84-120-6A: ((79-105-C: (Stars Over Chicago x Welcome Reward) x Desert Princess) x (Heart Stealer x 79-105-C)) x Onlooker) X Turkish Heart. Arilian Acres 1992.

SERENDIPITY ELF (O. D. Niswonger, R. 1992). Sdlg. SDB 26-90. SDB, 12" (30 cm), M. S. old rose with slight olive rim; F. light fuchsia, deep fuchsia halo around beard, gold haft markings and near-gold edge; beards light blue, tipped tangerine. SDB 20-87: (C. Palmer 7259: ((Wilma V. x unknown) x Little Titan) x Nichols 8109A: (April Anthem x Passport)) X Adoring Glances. Cape Iris 1993.

SERENE MOMENT (Schreiner, R. 1998). Sdlg. DD 977-2. TB, 38" (97 cm), M. Ruffled orchid lavender (RHS 87B), F. with deeper mulberry rim, large white area around yellow beard. Grape Ice X Mulberry Punch. Schreiner 1998.

SERENE PRESENCE (Craig Carroll, R. 1995). Sdlg. 91-C-C. LA, 41" (104 cm), M. S. and F. pink, veined light brown; signals yellow, tipped pink. Opening Presence X Andy Dandy.

SERENE SEA (Barry Blyth, R. 1992). Sdlg. V84-A. TB, 34" (86 cm), EM. Medium blue violet; beards violet blue. Swirling Seas X Pledge Allegiance. Tempo Two 1992/93.

SERENE SUMMIT (Carl Jorgensen, R. 1996). Sdlg. 87-P-8R. TB, 34" (86 cm), ML. S. and style arms veronica violet (HCC 639/2); F. lighter veronica violet (639/3); beards capsicum red (715), hairs tipped violet; ruffled, laced; pronounced sweet fragrance. 85-P-6J: (Colorado Winter Morning x 75-2-2: (Summit Lady x Flaming Star)) X So Rare. Long 1996.

SERENE VIEW (Terrell Taylor, R. 1995). Sdlg. 93-52. TB, 34" (87 cm), EM. S. pale lavender (RHS 76C); F. lavender (78C); beards yellow, tipped white; sweet fragrance. Designing Woman X World Class. Bonita Gardens 1995.

SERENGETI (Barry Blyth, R. 1991). Sdlg. V101-4. TB, 34" (86 cm), ML. S. light biscuit, rosy midrib infusion; F. mulberry rose to burgundy, flared; beards tangerine orange; musky fragrance. Street Dancer X London Lord. Tempo Two 1991/92.

SERENGETI SPAGHETTI (Brad Kasperek, R. 1998). Sdlg. 94B-25A. TB, 32" (81 cm), M. S. dawn pink (RHS 49A), streaked white (155C); style arms greyed orange, lightly laced; F. dawn pink with muted white stripes, overlaying netted pattern of spiraea red (63D) to beetroot purple (71A); beards orange; broken color pattern; slight fragrance. Bewilderbeast X Tanzanian Tangerine. Zebra 1999.

SERENITY COVE (Jim Hummel, R. 1990). Sdlg. JH 83-15K. TB, 34" (86 cm), ML. S. salmon (RHS 27C), light pink midrib flush; style arms indian yellow (19C); F. egyptian buff (HCC 407/3), edged deeper; beards lemon yellow (13B). Paradise X JH 81-62H: (Summer Haze x Carved Pink). Bumble Bee 1991.

SEREN WIB (Harry Foster, R. 1991). Sdlg. R55/87. SIB (tet.), 32" (81 cm), L. S. medium blue (RHS 90A); style arms rose purple (87A); F. rich purple blue (94A) stitched white, wide edge stitched silver. Dear Dianne X Harpswell Happiness.

SERIOZHENKA (Nataliya Khimina, R. 1997). Sdlg. 12. SDB, 13" (32 cm), M. S. straw yellow, dotted brown; style arms yellow; F. straw yellow, heavily dotted brown edge; beards white; slight spicy fragrance. Sheldon Butt X unknown. Khimina 1998.

SERPANTIN (Viacheslav Gavrilin, R. 1998). Sdlg. 4-2-54-94. TB, 39" (100 cm), M. Heavily ruffled lilac violet, F. lighter below light lilac beard; slight fragrance. Ruffled Ballet X Breakers. Gavrilin 1999.

SE-SEQUE (Ladislav Muska, R. 1996). Sdlg. PIPT-12. TB, 39" (99 cm), EM. S. brown red; F. deep burgundy red, washed maroon; beards medium orange red; heavily ruffled; slight fragrance. (Play With Fire x (Inferno x Red Tornado)) X Thriller. Muska 1996.

SESSIONS (Larry Cowdery by William Maryott, R. 1991). Sdlg. G9. TB, 37" (94 cm), M. Ruffled very pale lavender; beards red. Smooth Talk X Peppermint Crush. Maryott 1992.

SESSYU (Mototeru Kamo by Currier McEwen, R. 1995). JI (3 F.), 34" (85 cm), M. S. white, edged reddish violet (RHS 83D); style arms white, tufted; F. white, brushed soft violet blue (91B), fading with age, signal yellow (7B). Parentage unknown. Introduced in Japan, 1979.

SETA (Barry Blyth, R. 1990). Sdlg. W12-2. SDB, 12" (31 cm), ML. S. lavender grey; F. same, with bluish flash below beard, rosy brown to rosy tan hafts; beards pale lavender, tangerine in throat. Oladi X Kandi Moon. Tempo Two 1990/91.

SET SAIL (Lloyd Zurbrigg, R. 1999). Sdlg. OO 33C-6-1 'Superba'. TB, 36" (91 cm), M. S. light violet; style arms and F. deeper violet; beards pale yellow, ending in flounce. Renown X Mesmerizer. Friendship 1999.

SETSU-NO-HAMA (Society for Japanese Irises, R. 1994). JI (6 F.), 40" (102 cm), M. Dark rose violet, white halo and rays, signal yellow; style arms white. Parentage unknown. Imported from Japan, hybridizer unknown. George Bush ca. 1980.

SET THE TONE (James Burch, R. 1993). Sdlg. 48-16. TB, 34" (86 cm), M. Maroon black (RHS 187A) self; beards yellow orange (16A). Superstition X Elizabeth Carol. Burch Iris, Comanche Acres 1994.

SETTIMO CIELO (Valeria Romoli, R. 1999). Sdlg. 3C-91. TB, 37" (94 cm), EML. Lightly laced solid blue violet; beards sea blue violet, base paler, yellow orange in throat; silk to velvet sheen; pronounced fragrance. 7P-88: (unknown blue x Titan's Glory) X Skyblaze.

SEUVER FOURSES (J. R. Ellis by Anne Blanco White, R. 1995). SPEC-X, 48" (120 cm), M. S. very deep violet; F. very deep violet, no white ground visible. *I. pseudacorus* X *I. versicolor*.

SEUVER PUNCH (J. R. Ellis by Anne Blanco White, R. 1995). SPEC-X, 48" (120 cm), M. S. dark violet; F. heavy dark veining on white, edge white. *I. pseudacorus* X *I. versicolor*.

SEUVER SYLLABUB (J. R. Ellis by Anne Blanco White, R. 1995). SPEC-X, 48" (120 cm), M. S. medium blue violet; F. ground white, medium blue veining. *I. pseudacorus* X *I. versicolor*.

SEUVER THRUMENTY (J. R. Ellis by Anne Blanco White, R. 1995). SPEC-X, 48" (120 cm), M. S. pale grey blue; F. white ground, dominant pale grey blue veining. *I. pseudacorus* X *I. versicolor*.

SEVENTY-SEVEN (Allan Ensminger, R. 1994). Sdlg. 91-12. SDB, 9" (23 cm), ML. Saffron yellow (HCC 7/3) self; beards marigold orange (11/2). Orange Tiger X Tiny Cherub. Varigay 1995.

SEVERNAYA ORKHIDEYA (Viacheslav Gavrilin, R. 1999). Sdlg. 6-23-1-94. TB, 43" (110 cm), ML. Ruffled white; beards orange red; slight fragrance. Silver Shower X Christmas Time. Gavrilin 1999.

SEVERN SIDE (Cy Bartlett, R. 1996). Sdlg. C91-64. TB, 36" (91 cm), EM. S. chartreuse; F. slate blue; beards brown; ruffled, very flared; slight sweet fragrance. (greenish sdlg. inv. Emerald Fountain, Benton Olive, and Pride of Ireland x Intuition) X (Cherished Memory x Wensleydale).

SEWING CIRCLE (Robert Harding, TB, R. 1983). Iris Acres 1993/94.

SEW IT UP (Jim Hedgecock, R. 1997). Sdlg. 83-20-4. TB, 30" (76 cm), M. White ground, S. and F.

with dark purple stitched border; beards dark purple; lightly ruffled; slight sweet fragrance. Going My Way X Hey Looky. Comanche Acres 1998.

SEXTON'S BLACK SWAN (Cloyd McCord, R. 1994). Sdlg. 82-3-BB. TB, 36" (91 cm), M. Ruffled near-black; beards golden brown; slight spicy fragrance. American Sweetheart X Raven's Roost. McCord 1994.

SEXTON'S BLUE (Cloyd McCord, R. 1994). Sdlg. 85-22-B. TB, 34" (86 cm), M. Ruffled pale light blue; style arms light blue; beards yellow, pale blue at end; slight sweet fragrance. Princess Maxine X 76-13: (Beauty Crown x Homecoming Queen). McCord 1994.

SEXTON'S GIRL (Cloyd McCord, R. 1994). Sdlg. 86-1-CC. TB, 35" (89 cm), M. Ruffled violet blue; style arms light violet blue; beards yellow; pronounced sweet fragrance. Princess Maxine X 76-13: (Beauty Crown x Homecoming Queen). McCord 1994.

SEZITSO (Tom Burseen, R. 1997). Sdlg. 93-468A. TB, 36" (91 cm), M. S. violet mauve (RHS 88D); style arms brownish violet; F. dark purple (79D), white spray pattern near light lemon beard; ruffled; slight spicy fragrance. City Lights X Searious Situation. T.B.'s Place 1998.

SHABANA (Bob Thomason, R. 1992). Sdlg. BT 8813A. SDB, 9" (23 cm), EM. S. medium violet; F. deep red violet, heavily veined, slight white haft markings; beards yellow, tipped lavender; slight musky fragrance. Ruckus X Velvet Caper. Okie Iris 1999.

SHADES OF EASTER (John Wight, R. 1996). Sdlg. J86-6-1. AB (OGB), 20" (51 cm), M. S. pale cream; F. champagne, light maroon markings beside beard, rosy blush at beard tip; beards yellow, hair tips dotted brown. Dawn Caress X Big Black Bumblebee. Aril Society, Wight's Iris 1996.

SHADOW BOX (Paul Black, R. 1995). Sdlg. 91289A. SDB, 14" (36 cm), M. S. and style arms dark sooty purple; F. red purple with dark sooty purple blended band; beards dark violet, tipped old gold; ruffled; slight musky fragrance. Sigh X Cheery Delight. Mid-America 1995.

SHADOWED EYES (Calvin Helsley, R. 1992). Sdlg. 91-1. SIB, 27" (70 cm), M. S. light violet blue (RHS 98D) with darker (89D) flush at base; style arms light blue (100D) with darker (100B) ribs; F. blue (98C) with darker blue shoulders on either side of large white signal; ruffled. Mabel Coday X S. Varner S060: (Marlya x Steve). Helsley 1995.

SHADOWMAN (Monty Byers by Phyllis Dickey, R. 1996). Sdlg. F42-1. TB, 30" (76 cm), M. S. dark blue purple; F. very dark velvety blue purple; beards dark purple, large dark purple horn. D191-1: (Villain x B25-4) X Titan's Glory. Misty Hill 1996.

SHADOW RIDER (Fred Crandall by Marie Ingersoll, R. 1990). TB, 36" (91 cm), M. S. violet blue; F. white ground stitched blue violet; beards orange. 42-72-3C X Smoke Rings. Ingersoll's Iris 1990.

SHADOW TIME (Darlene Pinegar, R. 1997). Sdlg. FN-4A. TB, 36" (91 cm), ML. S. smoky maroon; style arms blended maroon and brown; F. smoky maroon and fuchsia blend, hafts yellow at edge, white near beard, with heavy maroon markings; beards dark gold; lightly ruffled; slight sweet fragrance. FN-4: (Friday Night x War Lord) X Ever After. Spanish Fork 1997.

SHAH KEBIR (Howard Shockey, R. 1992). Sdlg. 80-21-3J. AR (OH), 12" (30 cm), L. S. white, slight yellow flush on lower midrib; F. yellow (near RHS 11B), red (near 46A) signal; beards orange yellow. 77-28-9A: (Shah Abbas x ((CGW W-157 x *I. lortetii*) x (Judean Bonnet x W-157))) X 73-35-9B: ((Judean Bonnet x W-157) x Babylonian Brass). Arilian Acres, Aril Society 1992.

SHAKE AND BAKE (Tom Burseen, R. 1997). Sdlg. 9-262A. TB, 36" (91 cm), ML. S. light red purple, edges washed tan orange; style arms tan; F. maize, washed golden tan edge, tan brown hafts; beards brick red, base purple; ruffled; spicy fragrance. Bishop's Cloak X Role Model. T.B.'s Place 1997.

SHAKEDOWN (Roger Duncan, R. 1995). Sdlg. 0-B-2. TB, 33" (84 cm), EM. S. golden yellow; F. golden yellow, widely banded burgundy red, with burgundy center stripe; beards gold; lightly ruffled. Parentage unknown. Superstition 1996.

SHAKER (Joseph Ghio, R. 1990). Sdlg. PJ-193E. CA, 8" (20 cm), E. Yellow orange, cream hairline edge. (Villa Branciforte sib x San Gregorio) X (San Gregorio x (Montara sib x Mission Santa Cruz sib)). Bay View 1991.

SHAKER'S PRAYER (Carol Warner, SIB, R. 1989). Iris Pond 1990.

SHAKKYO (Yoshiteru Yoshida by Society for Japanese Irises, R. 1997). JI (6 F.), 32" (80 cm), EM. Red violet, greenish yellow signals; style arms red violet; drooping form. Parentage unknown. Introduced in Japan prior to 1901.

SHALL WE DANCE (Robert Hollingworth, R. 1992). Sdlg. 87N4C1. SIB, 31" (79 cm), L. S. very light blue; F. medium light blue violet, veined deeper; ruffled. Harpswell Hallelujah X 85D3B1:

(((Super Ego x Anniversary) x Windwood Spring sib) x (Pink Haze x Wing on Wing)). Windwood Gardens 1992.

SHALUNIYA (Viacheslav Gavrilin, R. 1998). Sdlg. 2-1-1-94. TB, 39" (100 cm), M. S. pink, midrib tinted blue; style arms pink; F. raspberry beet, narrow pink rim, small pink median line, white pattern around red beard; ruffled; slight fragrance. Fiesta Time X Starcrest. Gavrilin 1999.

SHAMAYIM (Robert Fabel-Ward, R. 1992). CA, 20" (51 cm), E. White, blue thumbprint on F. Chimes X white sdlg.

SHAMELESS (Barry Blyth, R. 1998). Sdlg. E52-1. IB, 24" (61 cm), ML. Mushroom to beige pink, lavender flush at base of S.; beards powder blue, tangerine in throat. B15-1: (Impish x Z24-1, Volts sib) X Cafe Ole. Tempo Two 1998/99.

SHAMROCK BAY (Vernon Wood, R. 1990). Sdlg. 88-55. CA, 12-14" (30-36 cm), E. S. yellow green (RHS 160B) with few darker veins; F. yellow green, gold (162A) center with green gold rays. Long Shot X Mimsey. Portable Acres 1990.

SHANA (Stan Cherniss, R. 1991). Sdlg. 89-A12. SDB, 9" (23 cm), M. Blue violet, dark violet on hafts to edge; beards lighter blue violet, 1/8" yellow base; slight fragrance. Blue Denim X Velvet Capers.

SHANS UDACHI (Viacheslav Gavrilin, R. 1999). Sdlg. 94-473-2. TB, 38" (97 cm), M. S. and style arms yellow; F. light lilac lighter below yellow beard, narrow yellow rim; ruffled. Fiesta Time X Starcrest.

SHARE THE SPIRIT (Graeme Grosvenor, R. 1998). Sdlg. V60-9. TB, 35" (89 cm), L. Heavily ruffled blue violet, F. with lighter edge; beards pale blue; slight fragrance. Silverado X Timescape. Rainbow Ridge 1998/99.

SHARIKA (Helen Cochran, R. 1999). Sdlg. 94-02-B. TB, 36" (91 cm), M. Ruffled white self; beards yellow, blue at end; slight spicy fragrance. Bubble Up X Modern Times.

SHARON JULIETTE (Patrick O'Connor, R. 1999). Sdlg. 96-9. LA, 30-32" (76-81 cm), EM. S. light red, suffused white; style arms cream yellow; F. medium red, deep yellow spear signal on yellow field veined red. False River X High Rank.

SHARON MARIE (Donald Spoon, R. 1999). Sdlg. 89-54A. TB, 35" (89 cm), ML. Lightly ruffled clear golden yellow; beards darker yellow. Magic Memories X Yukon Fever. Winterberry 1999.

SHARP IMAGE (Tom Burseen, TB, R. 1989). T.B.'s Place 1990.

SHARRE (Bryce Williamson, R. 1998). Sdlg. 291. TB, 35" (89 cm), M. S. and style arms cool white; F. pallid blue white, fading white, lime yellow hafts; beards lemon; deeply ruffled; slight musky fragrance. Best Bet X Winterscape. Stockton 1999.

SHASHOO (Ed Matheny III, R. 1996). Sdlg. J:00-04-92. JI (6 F.), 38" (97 cm), M. White, brushed victorian violet (RHS 90B), signals yellow; style arms cream with lavender (85C) sheen. Snowy Hills X Flashing Koi. Ed's Iris 1997.

SHATYR-KURGAN (Galina Shevchenko, R. 1995). MDB, 6" (16 cm), M. S. blended purplish brown, tinted ginger; F. dark purplish brown; beards purplish brown, hairs tipped dark orange; pronounced musky fragrance. From *I. pumila* sdlgs. Shevchenko 1992.

SHEBANG (Bob Bauer/John Coble, R. 1999). Sdlg. S93-E7. SIB, 30" (76 cm), M. S. (6-12) rose violet; style arms absent; F. (6) rose violet, large white blaze, yellow in throat; multipetal hose-in-hose form: 3 F. and 3-6 S., then additional 3 F., 3-6 S. S89A-2: (Shirley Pope x (Sultan's Ruby x Hollingworth sdlg.)) X Ranman. Ensata Gardens 1999.

SHEBA'S JEWEL (Howard Shockey, R. 1994). Sdlg. 90-112-D. AB (OGB) 28" (71 cm), M. S. white, slight maroon basal flush; F. white, large sharp crescent-shaped maroon purple signal; beards light bronze; rounded form; slight sweet fragrance. Seraph's Jewel X Queen Sheba. Arilian Acres 1994.

SHE DEVIL (Paul Black, R. 1996). Sdlg. 85348A. AB (OB-), 14" (36 cm), E. S. beetroot; style arms amber to beetroot; F. velvety dark red, veined black; beards brown, gold at base. Lollipop X Welcome Reward. Mid-America 1996.

SHEER ECSTASY (Schreiner, R. 1996). Sdlg. AA 549-A. TB, 36" (91 cm), EM. Lightly ruffled raspberry rose (RHS 71B) self; beards tangerine; slight fragrance. S 366-A: (Enchanted World x Lorilee) X Mulled Wine. Schreiner 1996.

SHEER ROYALTY (W. Terry Varner, R. 1992). Sdlg. P-355. MTB, 18" (46 cm), ML. S. medium purple, sanding in rib area; F. purple overlaid white, 1/2" purple band and sanding toward white center, purple signal; beards golden orange; slight fragrance. N330: ((La Bohemienne x Greenlee yellow sdlg. #2) x (Brewing Storm x *I. attica* yellow)) X N300: (((First Call x Colonial Lady) x P-297, Carolyn Rose sib) x Welch T-201, amoena sdlg.). Ohio Gardens 1992.

SHEILA LEE (Marie Murdy, R. 1992). Sdlg. D-1-6-90. TB, 28" (71 cm), ML. Lightly ruffled butter yellow; beards bright yellow. Danielle's Twin X Betty Simon.

SHELDON BUTT (O. D. Niswonger, R. 1995). Sdlg. SDB 16-92. SDB, 14" (36 cm), M. Citron yellow, slight greenish cast; style arms yellow; beards purple. 2-89: (Chubby Cheeks x unknown) X unknown -- probably self. Cape Iris 1995.

SHELLEY SPANGLER (J. R . Allen, TB, R. 1987). Allen Iris 1997.

SHEPCHINOK (Viacheslav Gavrilin, R. 1997). Sdlg. 94-88-1. TB, 35" (88 cm), M. S. bright orange; style arms light orange; F. dark red, 1/2" dull orange edging, shaded whitish spot under orange beard, claret veining from beard to edge; ruffled; slight fragrance. Fiesta Time X Starcrest. Gavrilin 1999.

SHERBET LEMON (Cy Bartlett, R. 1991). Sdlg. MNR/SW. IB, 20" (51 cm), E. S. bright light lemon yellow; F. shade darker; beards lemon; ruffled. Mrs. Nate Rudolph X Sunny and Warm. David Austin Roses, Sutton 1995.

SHERMAN (John J. Taylor, R. 1994). Sdlg. AA-24-5. SPEC-X, 14-16" (35-44 cm), EM. Full yellow (near RHS 15A) self; beards orange. P-17: (*I. imbricata* x M-3: (*I. timofejewii* x *I. reichenbachii* "Van Nes")) X M-3.

SHERRYL RENEÉ (Tom Burseen, R. 1992). Sdlg. 7-22A. TB, 34" (86 cm), EM. S. light creamy pink (RHS 49D); F. purple violet (80B) washed lighter; beards shrimp pink orange; sweet fragrance. Local Motion sib X Child of Fortune. T.B.'s Place 1993.

SHERWOOD DAWN (B.L.C. Dodsworth, R. 1999). Sdlg. EB 90A. TB, 34" (86 cm), M. Tailored pink self; beards pink; slight fragrance. Paradise X Vanity.

SHERWOOD GLACIER (Walter Marx by Dorothy Rogers, R. 1991). JI (6 F.), 38-40" (97-102 cm), ML. White ground with random blue splashes, lemon yellow signal; style arms white. Parentage unknown. Caprice Farm 1991.

SHERWOOD PINK (B.L.C. Dodsworth, R. 1996). Sdlg. EB 908. TB, 44" (112 cm), L. Ruffled pale pink; beards pink. EB 140 pale yellow: (Edale x Nanga Parbat) X Early Light.

SHERWOOD PRIMROSE (B.L.C. Dodsworth, R. 1996). Sdlg. EB 91R. TB, 42" (107 cm), M. Ruffled primrose yellow self; beards yellow. Buckden Pike X Sanderling.

SHIELD (Austin Morgan, R. 1990). TB, 35" (89 cm), EM. S. dark purple; F. white shield design in center, edge stitched dark purple; beards purple. Parentage unknown. Iris Test Garden 1990.

SHIHODEN (Shuichi Hirao by Society for Japanese Irises, R. 1992). JI (6+), 35½" (90 cm), M. Double or multipetal deep red purple, signal yellow. Parentage unknown. Hirao 1956.

SHII-NO-HOMARE (Toyokazu Ichie by Society for Japanese Irises, R. 1993). JI (3 F.), 31" (80 cm), M. Deep blue violet, F. with yellow signal; style arms deep blue violet. Parentage unknown. Ichie prior to 1989.

SHII-NO-SODE (Kamo Nursery by Society for Japanese Irises, R. 1999). JI (3 F.), 36" (91 cm), M. S. and F. deep violet, white rim; style arms deep violet. Parentage unknown. Kamo Nursery 1983.

SHIKI-NO-HAJIME (Shuichi Hirao by Society for Japanese Irises, R. 1993). JI (3 F.), 36" (91 cm), VE. S. light red violet; style arms white, crests blue violet; F. blue violet, turning red violet toward edge, white center and rays, yellow signal. Parentage unknown. Hirao prior to 1980.

SHILLY-SHALLY (Allan Ensminger, R. 1998). Sdlg. 793-1. SDB, 16" (41 cm), ML. S. mimosa yellow (HCC 602/1); style arms sulphur yellow (1/3); F. sulphur yellow, brown spot around beard; beards sulphur yellow (1/2); many flowers 4-falled. Zing Me X 91-4: (85-3: (Do-Si-Do x 83-6: (Eye Shadow x Reath 6-64)) x Chubby Cheeks). Varigay 1998.

SHINASAHI-NO-YUKI (Shuichi Hirao by Society for Japanese Irises, R. 1993). JI (7-9 F.), 38" (97 cm), EML. Rosy red violet, shading deeper at center and lighter toward edge, white halo and veins, yellow signal. Parentage unknown. Hirao prior to 1980.

SHINDIG (Barry Blyth, R. 1999). Sdlg. F9-4. SDB, 12" (30 cm), VE. S. beige pink, violet midrib infusion; style arms beige pink, violet center infusion; F. beige pink, stronger 3/16" beige pink edge, broad plum spot, peach haft veining; beards lavender, tipped bronze. In Jest X Celsius. Tempo Two 1999/2000.

SHINE (Kevin Nilsen, R. 1996). Sdlg. 35-90-1. TB, 35½" (90 cm), VE-E. S. deep golden yellow; style arms golden yellow; F. yellow ground paler toward deep yellow beard, with red brown edge, peppering and centerline. 15-84: (Bicentennial x San Jose) X Gigolo.

SHINGO (Anna Mae Miller, R. 1994). Sdlg. 80.16.16. JI (3 F.), 35" (89 cm), ML. S. red violet (RHS 81A), white wire rim; style arms dark red violet, lighter rib area, white wire rim around crests; F.

white to pale lavender, red purple veining out from purple halo, yellow signal. 78.28 X Kyokko. Ensata Gardens 1994.

SHINING DEBUT (Jim & Vicki Craig, R. 1990). Sdlg. 37V5. IB, 24" (61 cm), M. S. pale blue; F. light blue, veined medium blue; beards mustard, tipped medium blue; ruffled. 2R13, Little Stylist sib, X 11R4, Reformation sib. J. & V. Craig 1990.

SHINING PRINCE (Shuichi Hirao by Society for Japanese Irises, R. 1991). Sdlg. SH-24. JI (6 F.), 37" (94 cm), M. Deep violet (RHS 86A), blue halo and white veins washed blue, yellow signal; style arms white. Parentage unknown. Society for Japanese Irises 1992.

SHINKAI-NO-IRO (Shuichi Hirao by Society for Japanese Irises, R. 1993). JI (6 F.), 30" (76 cm), ML. Deep blue violet with short white rays, yellow signal; style arms off-white, sanded, edged and tipped blue violet. Parentage unknown. Hirao prior to 1980.

SHINONOME (Society for Japanese Irises, R. 1993). JI (6 F.), 36" (90 cm), EM. Very pale blue violet, yellow signal; ruffled. Parentage unknown. Correction of 1939 Check List entry shown as Shino-no-Me. Introduced in Japan prior to 1887.

SHINSEI (Ed Matheny III, R. 1997). Sdlg. J:03-04-93. JI (6 F.), 36" (91 cm), EM. Violet, signal yellow with blue halo; style arms cream sanded violet, crests purple. Cascade Spice X Midsummer Reverie. Ed's Iris 1998.

SHINSHIHODEN (Shuichi Hirao by Society for Japanese Irises, R. 1999). JI (6 F.), 36" (91 cm), L. Deep violet, near navy; style arms white with violet edges and crests. Parentage unknown. Introduced in Japan prior to 1965.

SHIPS ARE SAILING (Marty Schafer/Jan Sacks, R. 1998). Sdlg. S92-19-1. SIB, 35" (89 cm), M. S. light blue (RHS 97C) ground, darker bluebird blue (94B/C) shading and veining, light blue (97D) 1/8" edge; style arms pearly pale blue, darker midrib; F. darker bluebird blue (94A/B), deeper (93A) veining, light blue (97D) 1/8" edge; signal small, yellow gold with heavy deep blue violet veining; lightly ruffled. S86-8-1: (Forrest McCord x Springs Brook) X S89-23-4: (S85-6-6: (Star Cluster x Ruffled Velvet) x Isabelle). Joe Pye Weed 1998.

SHIRASAGI (Clarence Mahan, R. 1992). SPEC (*laevigata*), 28" (71 cm), M. F. (6) white with pale yellow ridges; style arms white, pronounced violet center; anthers white with violet spot just below filament; very slight fragrance. In commerce and widely grown in Japan; very similar (if not identical) to YAGURUMA, which was introduced ca. 1910. Iris Pond 1993.

SHIRE OF WARRNAMBOOL (Bruce Clark, R. 1999). Sdlg. 96-201. TB, 33" (85 cm), ML. S. light blue, midrib veined purple; style arms light blue, midrib light violet; F. dark red purple, edges lighter blue, white haft markings extending length of beard; beards yellow, pale at end and deeper in throat, hairs with brown midlayer and white base. Tomorrow's Child X Silverado.

SHIRLEY DUGAL (Clyde Hahn, R. 1993). Sdlg. 85-4-1. TB, 30" (76 cm), M. Medium brown, F. with lighter central area and lavender flush at tip of yellow beard. D. Palmer 2179B: ((((Sorcerer's Apprentice x Sea of Stars) x Mystical Aura) x sib) x ((sdlg. x Meghan) x Ponderosa)) X Sheer Poetry. Hahn's Rainbow 1993.

SHIRLEY M (Evelyn Kegerise, R. 1992). Sdlg. 87-862-P. TB, 35-36" (89-91 cm), ML. Lightly ruffled pale true pink; beards light blue. 83-445-1: ((Pearl Chiffon x Portrait of Amy) x Movie Queen) X Sophistication. Evelyn Kegerise 1995.

SHIRLEY'S DELIGHT (Richard Kindermann, R. 1992). Sdlg. K1018. TB, 37" (94 cm), M. S. ruffled lavender, tan highlights; F. burgundy red, 1/4" gold edge; beards gold; spicy fragrance. Triple Play X (Wild Apache x Wild Jasmine).

SHIRLEY TRIO (James McWhirter, R. 1995). Sdlg. J86-41. TB, 34" (86 cm), ML. S. white, narrow gold trim; F. blended magenta, ruby red and brown, deepening toward edge; beards yellow, tipped white. Bristo Magic X Frances Gaulter. Stockton 1995.

SHIRO-NIHONKAI (Shuichi Hirao by Society for Japanese Irises, R. 1993). JI (6 F.), 33" (85 cm), M. White ground tinted lavender with variable violet (RHS 87A) splashes and iridescent sparkle overall; style arms white with blue violet midrib. Parentage unknown. Hirao prior to 1985.

SHIROTAE (Mototeru Kamo by Society for Japanese Irises, R. 1993). JI (6 F.), 36" (90 cm), M. White, signal yellow with greenish cast. Parentage unknown. Kamo 1976.

SHMEL (Sergey Loktev, R. 1999). Sdlg. 92-L13-8A. SDB, 13" (33 cm), M. S. and style arms yellow; F. bordeaux brown, indistinct olive rim, haft marked white to yellow; beards yellow. Unknown blue SDB X Whiz Bang. Loktev 1999.

SHOKO (Koji Tomino by Society for Japanese Irises, R. 1992). JI (3 F.), 33" (85 cm), EM. Light pink, signal yellow. Akashi X self. Tomino 1956.

SHOKOLADNY BATON (Viacheslav Gavrilin, R. 1998). Sdlg. 6-29-2-94. TB, 41" (105 cm),

ML. S. lilac chocolate, lighter yellowish base; style arms lilac chocolate; F. light lilac chocolate edged darker, hafts yellowish, small white median line; beards yellow; ruffled, lightly laced; slight fragrance. Fiesta Time X Starcrest. Gavrilin 1999.

SHOOTING STARS (Richard Ernst, R. 1993). Sdlg. F125-5. TB, 36" (91 cm), M. Ruffled bright golden yellow, F. with golden brown spatter spray pattern, white flush around deep yellow beard; slight spicy fragrance. Edna's Wish X Wild Jasmine. Cooley 1992.

SHOPTALK (Merle Roberts, R. 1997). Sdlg. E-131B. TB, 36" (91 cm), M. Ruffled cerise purple self; style arms cerise; beards purple, lighter in throat; slight fragrance. Darkside X Wide Hips. Roberts Backyard 1997.

SHORAI (Koji Tomino by Society for Japanese Irises, R. 1995). JI (3 F.), 32" (80 cm), EM. S. pale lilac violet; style arms white, lavender edge and crests; F. lavender, veined darker. Parentage unknown. Introduced in Japan, 1958.

SHORELAND (Thelma Naylor, SDB, R. 1988). British Iris Society 1995.

SHORTBREAD CREME (Barry Blyth, R. 1997). Sdlg. D62-1. TB, 38" (97 cm), M. S. peachy cream, pinkish midrib flush; F. peach cream, blended pinkish to light tan overlay deepening toward haft; beards lemon tangerine, whitish at end; pronounced spicy fragrance. Chestnut Avenue X B136-2: (Lover's Lane x Z63-4, Aztec Burst sib). Tempo Two 1997/98.

SHORT CUT (Chet Tompkins, R. 1996). Sdlg. 93-55A. TB, 39" (99 cm), ML. Vivid metallic red self; beards reddish brown. ((Royal Rage x Homer Unn) x Sound and Fury) X Foundation. Fleur de Lis 1996.

SHORT POEM (Ron Mullin, R. 1999). Sdlg. 91-43F. SDB, 12" (31 cm), E. Pale peach pink, F. with tiny bright pink edge at bottom; beards peach pink. Pink Crystal X Broad Grin.

SHOSHONE MOON (Jim Hedgecock, TB, R. 1989). Comanche Acres 1990.

SHOUT (A. & D. Willott, R. 1999). Sdlg. W 96-21. SDB, 11" (28 cm), E & RE. Ruffled blue white, F. with large violet spot; beards white, yellow in throat. Ice and Indigo X Silk and Velvet.

SHOW ME YELLOW (Dorothy Anderson, SDB, R. 1988). Adamgrove 1990.

SHOWY WHEEL (Ladislav Muska, R. 1999). Sdlg. 98-QQGC-04. TB, 34" (86 cm), M. S. mellifluous amber blend tinted lilac; style arms amber tan; F. vanilla yellow ground, 1" wide mahogany plicata edge; beards cerise orange; heavily ruffled, laced; slight fragrance. ((Queen in Calico x Spacelight Sketch) x (Queen in Calico x Graffiti)) X Colortart. Muska 1999.

SHRAWLEY (Jennifer Hewitt, R. 1999). SIB, 30" (75 cm), M. S. deep violet (redder than RHS 89A); style arms deep reddish violet; F. white ground veined deep violet blue (89B), more densely at sides, with near-solid color at tip; signal white, veined deep violet. Parentage and raiser unknown. Found at Shrawley, England, by Glazeley Gardens and introduced prior to 1973.

SHRIMP BOAT (Joseph Gatty, R. 1991). Sdlg. P41-2. BB, 26" (66 cm), M. S. peach (M&P 9-A-5 to 1-A-9) blended vanilla (10-C-3) toward edge; F. creamier peach (9-B-5) to vanilla; beards cream, tipped chinese orange (9-D-12); slight sweet fragrance. Quiet Moment X L92-4: (Paradise x (Valentina x (Pink Sleigh x Liz))). Keppel 1992.

SHTANDART UKRAINY (Oleg Amekhin, R. 1996). SPEC-X, 35" (90 cm), M. Blue self, bright yellow signal. *I. ensata* X (*I. versicolor* x *I. virginica*). Amekhin 1996.

SHTURMAN RIABOVA (Irina Driagina, R. 1996). Sdlg. 6-54. TB, 44" (112 cm), EM. White, S. tinted light blue; beards light yellow. Parentage unknown. Driagina 1974.

SHUGAR (Barry Blyth, R. 1990). Sdlg. W33-1. IB, 20" (51 cm), ML. Salmon pink, faint white area below coral tangerine beard. (Cupid's Cup x Capricornia) X Erleen Richeson. Tempo Two 1990/91.

SHUICHI HIRAO (Shuichi Hirao by Society for Japanese Irises, R. 1990). Sdlg. SH-30. JI (3 F.), 35" (89 cm), M. White, F. with yellow signal veined green; style arms cream, tipped white. Parentage unknown. Society for Japanese Irises 1991.

SHUMMIN (Koji Tomino by Society for Japanese Irises, R. 1993). JI (3 F.), 27" (70 cm), M. White, F. with yellow signal; style arms white; Ise type. Akashi X self. Tomino 1953.

SHURTON INN (Cy Bartlett, R. 1994). Sdlg. BA.1. TB, 34" (86 cm), ML. S. near-white; F. olive brown blend; beards grey to yellow; ruffled. ((((Chimbolam x Walter Bruce) x (Chimbolam x inv. Tracey)) x (Champagne Braise x (Alpine Sunshine x Sun King))) x Echo de France) X Fritillary Flight. Sutton 1994.

SHUSHAN WARRIOR (Stan Dexter by Marie Ingersoll, R. 1992). Sdlg. 7-231-A. TB, 40" (102 cm), EM. S. gold yellow; F. smoky brown overlaid purple, lighter haft markings with lines extending full length; beards gold. Elegant Addition X Sunshine Song. Ingersoll's Iris 1993.

SHY GLANCE (Barry Blyth, R. 1999). Sdlg. E134-3. TB, 34" (86 cm), EM. Lilac pink overlaying creamy white, F. with blended creamy area below tangerine beard; foliage very dark-based. Stylist X A71-1: (Liqueur Creme x unknown). Tempo Two 1999-2000.

SHY MISS (D. Steve Varner, R. 1990). Sdlg. 9030. SDB, 12" (30 cm), ML. Light lavender blue paler near edge, blended deeper toward center, 1/16"-3/16" milk white line below beard; beards pale lavender blue, tipped white; slight fragrance. Golly Molly X Bantam. Illini Iris 1990.

SHY ROYAL (John C. Taylor, R. 1994). Sdlg. RL 74-1. LA, 38" (97 cm), M. S. pale pink, veined darker pink; F. magenta pink, edged pale pink, pale pink reverse, green line signal surrounded by yellow; ruffled, fluted. OL 142-3: ((C'est Si Bon x Charles Arny III) x Helen Naish) X Margaret Lee. Rainbow Ridge 1994/95.

SHY STAR (Tom Burseen, R. 1995). Sdlg. 9-274A. TB, 36" (91 cm), EM. S. and style arms pink (RHS 37C); F. creamy white, pink rim; beards red orange, tipped white; ruffled, laced; sweet fragrance. 5-68: (Old Flame x Joy of Springtime) X Romantic Mood. T.B.'s Place 1995.

SIBCAL BEAUTY (Tomas Tamberg, R. 1995). SPEC-X (tet.), 24" (60 cm), M. S. medium red violet; F. velvety deep red violet. 84-24 dark violet: (Starting Calsibe x converted near-black calsibe sdlg.) X converted tet sino-sib sdlg. Schoeppinger 1995.

SIBLING RIVALRY (Bryce Williamson, R. 1993). Sdlg. 2285-B. TB, 36" (91 cm), EM. S. cream white; F. lightly ruffled cream white with greenish shoulders and wash; beards yellow; slight fragrance. Irish Spring X Dream Affair. Pacific Coast Hybridizers 1993.

SIBTOSA PRINCESS (Tomas Tamberg, R. 1998). SPEC-X (sibtosa) tet., 36" (91 cm), M. S. light lavender pink; F. lavender pink. Converted lavender sibtosa: (Pink Haze x lavender *I. setosa*) X Fourfold Lavender. Joe Pye Weed 1998.

SIDE BY SIDE (Nancy Burrows, IB, R. 1989). Stornoway Gardens 1990. Change of height and classification from original registration: IB, 27" (69 cm).

SIDESTITCH (Gary Sides, R. 1992). Sdlg. B38-D8. TB, 28" (71 cm), M. S. white ground, medium violet dotted midrib and stitched edge; F. white ground, medium violet vertical lines and stitched edged, medium violet signal; beards white, tipped yellow orange. Needlecraft X Spinning Wheel. Miller's Manor 1992.

#SIDONIE (Caparne, DB, R. 1902). Marked as obsolete in 1939 Check List, name released.

SIDONIE (Pauline Evans, R. 1997). Sdlg. 93/4. SPU, 60" (153 cm), M. S. deep violet overlay on paler ground, shading to yellow base; F. light violet veined deeper, signal yellow. Missouri Blue X Airy Fancy. Tempo Two 1997/98.

SIERRA AZUL (Joseph Ghio, R. 1997). Sdlg. PD-194F5. CA, 11" (28 cm), EM. Light azure blue self, small cream signal. PF-142ltbl: (Deep Blue Sea x Sierra Dell) X PF-191T3: ((Los Californio x San Andreas) x Sierra Dell). Bay View 1997.

SIERRA GRANDE (Schreiner, R. 1992). Sdlg. Y 71-B. TB, 38" (97 cm), M. S. white (RHS 155C); F. blue (96B); beards light yellow, tipped white; ruffled. Pledge Allegiance X Glistening Icicle. Schreiner 1992.

SIERRA RIM (A. & D. Willott, R. 1997). Sdlg. W 93-45. IB, 24" (61 cm), EM. S. white ground, edged and stippled greyed violet; style arms light greyed violet; F. white, edged greyed violet; beards blue; ruffled. North Coast X Chubby Cheeks. Willott 1997.

SIERRA SHADOW (Agnes Frech, R. 1997). Sdlg. 491. TB, 36" (91 cm), M. S. grey, slight silver edge; style arms gold; F. medium blue in center, grey blue toward edge, shoulders gold; beards orange; ruffled; slight sweet fragrance. Azure Luster X Speculator.

SIERRA SPRITE (Nancy Bartlett, R. 1995). Sdlg. 6BX4. TB, 37" (94 cm), EM. S. and F. white to pale lavender; style arms light lavender; beards red orange, with prominent lavender horn or flounce; ruffled. Bubbling Over X Lavender Queen.

SIGH OF COLOURS (Barry Blyth, R. 1997). Sdlg. C236-A. TB, 32" (81 cm), VE-M. S. lemon cream; F. white ground, 3/4" soft lavender pink plicata edge; beards white, heavily tipped gold; pronounced sweet fragrance. Z79-2, Copatonic sib, X Z62-4, Harmonics sib. Tempo Two 1997/98.

SIGHS AND WHISPERS (Paul Black, TB, R. 1989). Mid-America 1990.

SIGNET RING (Tom Magee, R. 1995). Sdlg. LSX. IB, 18" (46 cm), M. S. light purple with buff shadow around purple midrib; style arms light purple shadowed buff; F. dark rich purple with buff blaze around purple center streak; beards capucine red; slight spicy fragrance. Parentage unknown -- probably sport of Logo.

SIGNIFICANT OTHER (Richard Ernst, R. 1994). Sdlg. HA141-2. TB, 38" (97 cm), M. S. white, pale blue cast; F. medium blue with violet tones; beards yellow; ruffled. R8545: (Edith Wolford x Merry Madrigal) X (Edith Wolford x self). Cooley 1994.

SIGN OF VIRGO (Lloyd Zurbrigg, R. 1990). Sdlg. R 106 A. TB, 37" (94 cm), EM & RE (Sept./VA). S. white, occasionally touched violet at tip; F. white, stitched violet on edge; beards yellow; sweet fragrance. O 180-4: (H 89 AM: ((Goliath's Mate x (Grand Baroque x (Crinkled Ivory x Autumn Sensation))) x Dawn Violet) x Skiers' Paradise) X Earl of Essex. Avonbank 1991.

SIGNPOST (Joseph Ghio, R. 1990). Sdlg. 85-24G4. TB, 40" (102 cm), L-VL. S. orange; F. white, edged orange; beards tangerine. 83-37: ((((Artiste x Tupelo Honey) x ((Malaysia x Carolina Honey) x (73-122Z: (Hi Top x ((Ponderosa x Travel On) x Peace Offering sib)) x 73-17G: (Louise Watts sib x ((((Commentary x Claudia Rene) x Claudia Rene) x Ponderosa) x (Ponderosa x New Moon)))))) x Crystal Dawn) x (Preface sib x Crystal Dawn)) X 82-198F3: (((Cream Taffeta x (Show Time x (Ponderosa x New Moon))) x (Ballet in Orange x 73-122Z)) x Caption). Bay View 1991.

SILBERKANTE (Tomas Tamberg, R. 1993). Sdlg. 8414-1. SIB (tet.), 29" (75 cm), L. S. dark blue; F. dark blue, wide white edge. Dear Dianne X SSTT183: (Cambridge x ((Tycoon x Limeheart) x Limeheart)). Schoeppinger 1994.

SILENCIO (John C. Taylor, R. 1993). Sdlg. RL 68-2. LA, 47" (120 cm), ML. Heavily ruffled violet, rims and reverse lighter, yellow signal on all petals. OL 137-4, Margaret Lee sib, X Margaret Lee. Rainbow Ridge 1994/95.

SILENT CIRCLE (Chet Tompkins, R. 1999). Sdlg. 93-85B. TB, 37" (94 cm), ML. Cornflower blue, F. with blue white area on upper portion, paler frosty blue edge; beards blue white. (Sterling Silver x Radiant Bride) X (Frostalot x (Cascade Waters x (Ave x Sheer Bliss))). Fleur de Lis 1999.

SILENT DREAMS (O. D. Niswonger, R. 1997). Sdlg. 2-94. SPEC-X, 32" (81 cm), M. Pale yellow self, F. with gold signal veined brown. Seed from Tomas Tamberg. Starting Calsibe X converted yellowish cal-sib, parentage unknown. Cape Iris 1997.

SILENT FORCE (Ed Roberts, R. 1993). Sdlg. 927. TB, 34" (86 cm), M. Heavily laced mulberry pink, touch of brown on either side of yellow beards; slight fragrance. Visual Arts X Blushing Pink. Ed Roberts 1994.

SILENT JAZZ (John Marchant, R. 1990). Sdlg. 487. CA, 10" (25 cm), ML. Indian yellow (HCC 6/2), magenta purple halo on F. with blue eye spot fading into slate blue overlay. Sdlg. X sdlg.

SILENT ONE (Barry Blyth, R. 1995). Sdlg. A60-1. TB, 38" (97 cm), ML. S. lemon, overlaid cream; F. creamy white, lemon veining, lemon gold hafts; beards white, tipped gold; slight sweet fragrance. Dance Man X Elegant Blue. Tempo Two 1995/96.

SILENT RAIN (Tom Burseen, R. 1997). Sdlg. 92-288A. TB, 36" (91 cm), M. S. pinkish grey; style arms tan grey; F. light grey, yellow hafts; beards yellow; ruffled; sweet fragrance. 9-311: (Sharlee x Big Duke) X Fifth Dimension. T.B.'s Place 1997.

SILENT SHADOW (Barry Blyth, R. 1995). Sdlg. B95-3. IB, 22" (56 cm), ML. S. violet, heavily flushed medium brown; F. burgundy with shot-silk effect; beards white, heavily tipped brown; slight sweet fragrance. Buzz Me X Electrique. Tempo Two 1995/96.

SILENT STAR (Floyd Dyer, R. 1994). Sdlg. D231-85D. SDB, 13" (33 cm), M. S. white; F. lightly ruffled violet; beards yellow, tipped blue; slight musky fragrance. Blue Drifter X self. Four Cedars 1994.

SILENT TEARS (Les Peterson by Ardi Kary, R. 1991). Sdlg. PR100-LP. AB (OGB-), 27" (69 cm), M. Light violet blue with purple violet splashes; beards pale yellow, tipped violet blue. ((Amanda Sings x Jealous Lover) x Stitched Beauty) X Heart Stealer. Kary Iris 1991.

SILENT THUNDER (Bob Bauer/John Coble, R. 1996). Sdlg. J88E-5. JI (9+ F.), 40" (102 cm), L. Medium rose violet, veined darker; multiple style arms light violet, large crests dark violet. Jocasta X Hagoromo. Ensata Gardens 1996.

SILENT WISH (Lin Flanagan, AB (OGB), R. 1989). Aril Society 1991.

SILETZ BAY (Richard Ernst, R. 1996). Sdlg. KF168-1F. TB, 45" (114 cm), M. Medium blue, violet cast, F. blended lighter blue at end of beard; beards medium blue; ruffled; pronounced sweet fragrance. Fair Dinkum X F168-1: ((Irene Nelson x Honest Pleasure) x Gaulter 81-17, inv. Irene Nelson). Cooley 1996.

SILICON PRAIRIE (Tim Stanek, R. 1991). Sdlg. 85-1. TB, 34" (86 cm), EM. S. light lobelia blue (RHS 97D), pronounced golden edge; F. light yellow ochre (160C) over green; self beards; laced; pronounced fragrance. 83-2A: (Laced Cotton x Storm Center) X Chartreuse Ruffles. Eight Mile Grove 1991.

SILIQUE (Barry Blyth, R. 1998). Sdlg. E49-4. IB, 25" (64 cm), ML. S. lavender blue, small white area; F. white, 1/4" solid deeper lavender blue edge, 1/4" inner band of blue dots, hafts brown; beards lavender at end, old gold to bronze in throat; sweet fragrance. C29-4: (A30-5, Imbue sib, x A14-8, Noble Toff sib) X C146-2: (A113-3, I'm Yours sib, x A80-2: (Y2-1, Royal Honey sib, x Chocolate Vanilla)). Tempo Two 1998/99.

SILK (Lynn Markham, R. 1992). Sdlg. 85-2D3. BB, 21½" (55 cm), ML. S. crystalline blue-white (Munsell 7.5PB 9/1) with greenish midrib; F. same, very faint greenish texture veining; beards blue white, heavily tipped bright gold (2.5Y 8/12) in throat; lightly ruffled. Sib to Secret Weapon.

SILK AND VELVET (A. & D. Willott, R. 1992). Sdlg. 89-75. SDB, 10" (25 cm), ML & RE. S. very dark violet; F. darker; beards dark violet; lightly ruffled. Nachos X Pilgrims' Choice. Willott 1992.

SILK BROCADE (Keith Keppel, R. 1998) Sdlg. 91-88B. TB, 35" (89 cm), EM. S. pinkish bishops violet (M&P 44-J-5), rayed grey white toward center; style arms pinkish lilac (44-I-2), salmon buff (10-C-5) margins; F. white ground tinted cream to pale peach, slightly redder and greyer bishops violet (44-K-6) 1" edging applied in near-solid strips of fine dots; beards indian orange (1-D-12), end hairs based white; ruffled, faintly laced; pronounced sweet fragrance. 88-63A: ((Highland Haze x 79-83D, Change of Heart sib) x (Ever After x Lorilee)) X Dawn Sky. Keppel 1999.

SILK DEGREES (Barry Blyth, R. 1996). Sdlg. A110-3. TB, 36" (91 cm), VE. S. icy lavender; F. lavender, pink and tan blend giving shot silk effect, white spray pattern around beard, 1/4" faint blended icy lavender edge; beards burnt tangerine lilac; slight fragrance. Y6-11, Imprimis sib, X Electrique. Tempo Two 1996/97.

SILKEN SHADOWS (William Maryott, R. 1992). Sdlg. L192A. TB, 37" (94 cm), M. S. light blue violet; F. deep velvety blue black, fine rim of light blue violet; beards bronze; slight sweet fragrance. J65: (((Dusky Dancer x Pink Angel) x By Night) x Twist of Fate) X Witches' Sabbath. Maryott 1993.

SILK LINGERIE (A. & D. Willott, R. 1990). Sdlg. 88-32. SDB, 10" (25 cm), EM. Lightly ruffled light apricot pink; beards light blue. 84-88: (Oh Katz x Coral Wings) X Poet Laureate. Willott 1991.

SILK ROMANCE (Barry Blyth, R. 1999). Sdlg. E148-2. TB, 42" (107 cm), EM. Laced and ruffled orchid lilac, F. slightly lighter and more silvery around bright tangerine beard; slight sweet fragrance. Cloud Berry X About Town. Tempo Two 1999/2000.

SILK SILHOUETTE (Lilly Gartman, TB, R. 1989). Roris 1992.

SILK STOCKINGS (Perry Dyer, R. 1999). Sdlg. 92-10A. SDB, 12" (30 cm), M. Creamy cameo pink self; beards tangerine, light pink base; ruffled, satin finish. My Sheba X Delicate Pink.

SILLA (Erhard Woerfel, R. 1990). Sdlg. 9/84. TB, 45" (115 cm), M. Apricot orange; beards orange. Papagena X Rosé. Hochheimer 1991.

SILVER BOWL (Joseph Ghio, R. 1998). Sdlg. PL-222P. CA, 12" (31 cm), EM. Silvery lilac blue, F. with precise violet signal. Local Girl X PE-182K2: (PG-172A, Charter Member sib, x Rainbow Connection). Bay View 1998.

SILVER CIRCLE (B. Charles Jenkins, R. 1992). Sdlg. B30-5K. CA, 16" (41 cm), M. S. ivory, midrib veined purple; F. purple, yellow blaze, edged ivory. Santa Rita X Campaigner. Portable Acres 1992.

SILVER COEUR (Udo & Rudolf Wilkeneit, R. 1996). Sdlg. 174/5/94. SPEC (*pseudacorus*), 37" (95 cm), E. Silvery white, F. with blackish violet patterning; slight fragrance. Parentage unknown.

SILVER COVE (Graeme Grosvenor, R. 1993). Sdlg. R2-1. TB, 36" (91 cm), M. Ruffled blue violet; beards yellow. Silverado X Skyblaze. Rainbow Ridge 1995/96.

SILVER DIVIDENDS (Lloyd Zurbrigg, TB, R. 1989). Avonbank 1991.

SILVER DRAGON (Leo Barnard, R. 1997). Sdlg. L 91-77 WH. TB, 36" (91 cm), ML. Heavily ruffled glittering white, F. with yellow shoulders and pale green line below beard; beards white, hairs tipped gold, ending in silvery white spoon or horn; slight fragrance. Borderline X Twice Thrilling. Paradise Iris 1997.

SILVER FIZZ (Ben Hager, R. 1991). Sdlg. T4861PlOcLc. TB, 36" (91 cm), ML. S. pale silver lavender; F. near-white around white beard to silver at edge; heavily laced. T4222: (Silver Flow sib x T3953: ((Sea Venture x 2797:(DuBose 46-27 x 2097A: ((Mixed Emotions x Diehl reverse amoena sdlg.) x sib))) x (3172, reverse sib of Silver Flow, x Surf Rider))) X Blythe Dean. Melrose 1991.

SILVER FOX (Vernon Wood, TB, R. 1988). Cottage 1990.

SILVER GHOST (Eric Tankesley-Clarke, R. 1996). SDB, 13" (33 cm), M. Oyster grey to blue white, F. with brass hafts; beards blue white; slight sweet fragrance. Frosty Atom X Dixie Pixie. Adamgrove 1996.

SILVER GLACIER (Mark Grumbine, R. 1999). Sdlg. 96-33-2. TB, 33" (84 cm), ML. S. white, lightly tinted silver blue; F. white, pale blue violet tint, hafts with violet veins in yellow; beards white tipped pale blue on end, yellow in throat; heavily ruffled, laced. Alexander's Ragtime Band X Winter Panorama.

SILVER PLATE (Joseph Ghio, R. 1998). Sdlg. PD-241V5. CA, 12" (31 cm), ML. Lavender pink, F. with mauve signal shading to ochre center. Local Girl X Charter Member. Bay View 1998.

SILVER PRIZE (Lucille Robinson, R. 1990). Sdlg. 5/E/85. TB, 34" (86 cm), ML. S. blue white; F. pale blue white; beards white; ruffled; slight spicy fragrance. Lemon Mist X Mystique. Iris Acres 1993.

SILVER RINGS (Jennifer Hewitt, R. 1995). Sdlg. T872/3. SIB (tet.), 36" (91 cm), M. Medium violet blue (RHS 93B), edged white, F. with white plicata markings, white sunburst signal extending over half of blade. Hoar Edge X Reddy Maid.

SILVER SKATES (Ed Roberts, R. 1998). Sdlg. 961. TB, 36" (91 cm), M. S. pale silvery blue; style arms silver; F. white, touch of blue below white beard, aging white; sweet fragrance. Sky Search X Honky Tonk Blues.

SILVER WOLF (Geoff Austin, R. 1998). Sdlg. EWS-795. TB, 37" (95 cm), M. S. and style arms light blue; F. medium blue violet; beards yellow; ruffled; slight sweet fragrance. Edith Wolford X Silverado. Austland 1998/99.

SILVINGTON (Jennifer Hewitt, R. 1994). Sdlg. VER/82/1. SPEC (*versicolor*), 30-36" (75-91 cm), ML. Light blue violet, veined darker; signal white, pale yellow center streak. Parentage unknown. British Iris Society 1995.

SIMFONIYA (Adolf Volfovich-Moler, R. 1995). Sdlg. V-35. TB, 47" (120 cm), L. S. light blue lilac; F. purple lilac; beards orange; ruffled, laced. Pipes of Pan X Rippling Waters. Volfovich-Moler 1992.

SIMMER (Lynn Markham, R. 1998). Sdlg. 92-10B. BB, 26" (66 cm), EM. S. smoky reddish blend (near Munsell 5RP 3/9), slightly lighter edges with faint gold infusion; F. slightly darker, hafts blended bronze; beards antique gold (near 10YR 7/10); ruffled, flared; slight spicy fragrance. Fiddler X 90-13A: (Secret Weapon x Ignition). Markham 1999.

SIMPATICHNAYA OSA (Viacheslav Gavrilin, R. 1998). Sdlg. 7-14-1-94. TB, 35" (90 cm), M. S. and style arms pink; F. dark pinkish raspberry, narrow white edge, white patterning on upper half; beards orange; ruffled, laced; slight fragrance. Secret Melody X Color Splash. Gavrilin 1999.

SIMPLE ENOUGH (Ben Hager, R. 1998). Sdlg. MD6060Cr/GrY. MDB, 5½" (14 cm), ML. S. and style arms cream; F. greenish yellow; beards white, hairs tipped yellow. Ivory Buttons X MD4475Am: (Ditto sib x 3409BlAm: ((((Orange Caper x Puppet sib) x 1997: (Rickshaw x Lilli-Var)) x Wink) x ((1997 x Bongo) x (Russet Dot x 1997)))). Adamgrove 1998.

SIMPLE GIFTS (Robert Hollingworth, R. 1992). Sdlg. 87N2A12. SIB, 30" (76 cm), M. Tailored extremely pale lavender blue, small white signal; style arms white. 84V1A9: (Steve Varner x Windwood Serenade sib) X 84V1A12, sib. Windwood Gardens 1994.

SIMPLE SIMON (Robert Banghart, R. 1994). Sdlg. 2-90. TB, 28-30" (71-76 cm), ML. Tailored white self; beards intense yellow; slight fragrance. Ice Sculpture X Condottiere.

SIMPLY IRRESISTIBLE (Heather Pryor, R. 1998). Sdlg. 56/90-A. LA, 45" (115 cm), M. S. cherry red (RHS 185C), lemon rim and reverse; style arms cherry red; F. deeper cherry red (185B), lemon rim and reverse, raised lime steeple signal; ruffled. Designer's Dream X Gladiator's Gift. Iris Haven 1999/2000.

SIMPLY LUSCIOUS (Sharon McAllister, R. 1994). Sdlg. 89-12-7. AB (OGB-), 28" (72 cm), EM. S. cocoa with pinkish undertone; F. cocoa with yellowish undertone, chocolate veining and stippling around chocolate brown beard. Casa Vicente X Joint Venture. McAllister 1994.

SIMPLY MAJESTIC (Ken Mohr, R. 1990). TB, 36" (91 cm), M. Deeply ruffled satiny deep blue violet; beards blue violet. ((Cup Race x Babbling Brook) x Navy Strut) X (Deep Pacific x His Lordship). Pacific Coast Hybridizers 1990.

SIMPLY STUNNING (Darlene Pinegar, R. 1997). Sdlg. SKK-1-1A1. TB, 33" (84 cm), M. S. light peach pink; style arms medium peach pink; F. cream white ground, hafts peach, with brownish markings, light tan dotted edge, medium brown centerline; beards coral orange; heavily ruffled and laced; pronounced sweet fragrance. Grandma's Bloomers X PNS-2-3: (Earlirose x Queen in Calico). Spanish Fork 1998.

SINCERELY YOURS (Betty Wilkerson, R. 1996). Sdlg. G3-3Bl. TB, 36" (91 cm), EM. Ruffled blue (RHS 98A) self; beards blue; slight sweet fragrance. Bridge in Time X E15-5: (Feedback x Titan's Glory).

SINDY (Manfred Beer, R. 1992). Sdlg. MB 83/75 A. TB, 39" (100 cm), E. S. violet white; F. same, violet stitched edge; beards cream white; sweet fragrance. (Stepping Out x Out Yonder) X Stepping Out. Beer 1994.

#SING (Calvin Helsley, TB, R. 1979). Stock destroyed and name transferred.

SING (Calvin Helsely, R. 1998). Sdlg. 96-4. SIB, 37" (94 cm), M. S. light blue violet (RHS 96D), lightly mottled darker (96B/C); style arms light violet blue (98D), midrib darker (98B); F. light blue violet (96D), darker (96B) edge, still darker (96A) area on shoulders and either side of white signal; flat, flared form. Mabel Coday X D. S. Varner S060: (Marlya x Steve).

SINGING BIRD (Sharon McAllister, R. 1990). Sdlg. 81-1-2. AB (OGB), 29½" (75 cm), EM. S. pinkish purple (RHS 76A to 73C); F. blend of yellow, apricot and dusty rose, yellow ground (10D) showing at heart, rosy violet (182D) overlay blending through apricot to dusty rose at edge, signal burgundy (darker than 187A); beards burgundy. Heart Stealer X Mary of Magdala. Aril Society 1990.

SING OUT (James Gibson by Cooley's Gardens, R. 1994). Sdlg. 1-5P. TB, 35" (89 cm), EM. S. yellow cream ground evenly sanded rosy berry; F. yellow cream ground, berry plicata markings becoming more intense toward edge, pencil-line cream rim; beards reddish orange; ruffled. Gigolo X Osage Buff. Cooley 1994.

SINGS SO SOFTLY (Allan Ensminger, R. 1995). Sdlg. 90-45. TB, 34" (86 cm), M. S. peach (HCC 512/3); F. amethyst violet (35/3); beards carmine (021/1); slight sweet fragrance. 86-74: (Tiny Bubbles x Christa) X Evelyn Kegerise 85-453-1: ((Ice Sculpture x Trill) x Rosabelle V.). Varigay 1997.

SING THE BLUES (Lorena Reid, R. 1997). Sdlg. 9J55-16D. JI (6 F.), 36-42" (91-107 cm), ML. Smooth blue violet giving very blue effect; 1/3"-1/2" ruffled and turned up white edge; signals green gold, yellowish white halo; style arms yellowish white, light blue crests. Warai-Hotei X D579-2: (A112-1: (striped sdlg. x Royal Crown) x Midnight Whisper). Laurie's Garden 1997.

SINI SINI INEY (Viktor Sheviakov, R. 1995). Sdlg. 22A 6. TB, 32" (80 cm), ML. Blue, tinted light violet; F. with darker hafts, light blue to straw striations; beards light blue at end, yellow to orange in throat. Rippling Waters X Matinata. Sheviakov 1997.

SINISTER (Don Denney by James McWhirter, TB, R. 1989). Cottage 1990.

SINISTER DESIRE (Paul Black, R. 1998). Sdlg. C100A. IB, 25" (63 cm), L. S. and style arms dark black cherry; F. velvety red black, edge slightly lighter; beards bronzed sienna; slight spicy fragrance. Red Zinger X Tom Johnson. Mid-America 1998.

SIOBHAN (Jennifer Hewitt, R. 1998). Sdlg. JPW89/2. SIB, 30" (75 cm), EM. S. rich lavender pink (near RHS 80B); style arms turquoise, edges and crests lavender pink; F. deep red violet (nearest 80A), near-violet center, with small, diffuse cream white signal; short, flared S., semi-flaring and slightly ruffled F.; slight sweet fragrance. Reprise X Springs Brook.

SIOUX ANN (Clarence Dybvig, R. 1996). SDB, 13" (33 cm), M. S. and style arms light blue; F. darker lavender blue; beards blue; slight spicy fragrance. Az Ap X unknown. Dybvig 1998.

SIOUX UPRISING (Jim Hedgecock, R. 1997). Sdlg. 83-118-2. TB, 32" (81 cm), M. S. medium red; F. dark glowing red; beards burnt golden orange, 3/4" red horn; ruffled, lightly laced. Curtain Call X Moon Mistress. Comanche Acres 1998.

SIRENEVAYA DYMKA (Liudmila Mironova, R. 1998). Sdlg. 7.4.94. JI (6 F.), 47" (120 cm), VE. Light lilac, yellow signal surrounded by dark lilac rim; style arms dark lilac. Chayka X 4-80: (unknown sdlg. x Vasili Alfiorov). DVO RAN 1999.

SIRENEVAYA SLAVA (V. & N. Gordodelovy, R. 1995). Sdlg. 400. TB, 35" (90 cm), M. Lilac, brown haft striations on F.; beards red. Parentage unknown. Gordodelovy 1986.

SIRENEVY TOPAZ (Nina Miroshnichenko, R. 1998). TB, 28" (71 cm), EM. S. lilac; style arms pale lilac, darker midrib and crests; F. lilac, near-white area around beard; beards yellow, lilac at end and orange in throat. Parentage unknown. Miroshnichenko 1994.

SIRENEVY TUMAN (Galina Shevchenko, R. 1995). SDB, 9" (22 cm), VE. S. smoky lilac; F. light blue, tinted purple; beards smoky blue, lilac in throat; lightly ruffled; slight sweet fragrance. From *I. pumila* sdlgs. Shevchenko 1994.

SISTER ACT (Evelyn Robarts, R. 1994). Sdlg. 615-2. TB, 36-40" (91-102 cm), M. Pink peach self; beards bright tangerine pink, tipped pink, slightly horned; slight sweet fragrance. 71-pink horned sdlg.: ((Pink Taffeta x Schiaparelli) x (#40 horned sdlg. x Pink Sleigh)) X 22-B: (Holiday House x Far Corners). Stahly 1994.

SISTER MIRIAM SINGS (Bernice Miller, R. 1996). TB, 36" (91 cm), EM & RE. Lemon yellow self, hafts slightly deeper, white spot below yellow beard; ruffled, laced. Radiant Angel X Sarah's Laughter. Garden of the Enchanted Rainbow 1994.

SISTERS THREE (Jim Hedgecock, R. 1998). Sdlg. F-26-3. TB, 30" (76 cm), M. Icy blue; beards icy blue, yellow in throat; ruffled, lightly laced; pronounced sweet fragrance. Lucille Em X Pink Diablo. Comanche Acres 1999.

SIT IN (John C. Taylor, R. 1998). Sdlg. UL 16-4. LA, 43" (110 cm), M. Light red purple, midribs darker, lighter edges, F. with yellow signal; style arms lemon. Dancing Vogue X Noble Planet. Rainbow Ridge 1999/2000.

SITTING BULL (Jim Hedgecock, R. 1993). Sdlg. C-84-14-1. TB, 36" (91 cm), M. Ruffled dark maroon red veined lighter around orange beards; sweet fragrance. Quadros 82-1: (Angie Quadros x Homecoming Queen) X Lady Friend. Comanche Acres 1994.

SIX BITS (John J. Taylor, R. 1992). SPEC-X, 4½-6" (12-15 cm), M. Full bright yellow (RHS 13B), F. with brownish haft veining; beards gold. *I. bloudowii* X *I. humilis.*

SIXTINE C. (Richard Cayeux, R. 1995). Sdlg. 86106 A. TB, 41" (105 cm), M. S. pure white; F. white, 4/5" bright violet blue veins along edge; beards orange red. Condottiere X 8109 B: (Condottiere x Delphi). Cayeux 1994.

SKAZOCHNY PRINTS (V. & N. Gordodelovy, R. 1996). Sdlg. 233. TB, 32" (80 cm), E. S. red violet on white ground, base shaded brown; F. white ground, red violet sanding, hafts sanded brown; beards orange; pronounced fragrance. Parentage unknown. Gordodelovy 1993.

SKIDDLE (Sterling Innerst, R. 1993). Sdlg. 2825-1. SDB, 12" (30 cm), M. Medium blue, F. with darker spot and light blue stripe from beard tip to edge; beards blue, tipped bronze. Pippi Longstockings X Do-Si-Do. Innerst 1994.

SKID MARKS (Dagon Gillespey, R. 1990). Sdlg. D-86-11-20-48. TB, 32" (81 cm), E & RE. S. muted gold, edged deeper; F. muted gold flushed cream, edged deeper, light brown haft veining, chocolate brown streak from beard to edge; beards muted gold, slightly darker tip; slight fragrance. Grenadine Pacesetter X Summer Olympics.

SKIES ALWAYS BLUE (Sharon McAllister, R. 1998). Sdlg. 89-18-15. AB (OGB+), 24" (61 cm), EM. S. sky blue; style arms soft blue, yellow on midrib, crests yellow; F. pale blue heavily veined rust on inner portion, large black signal with violet wash below, yellow hairline rim; beards yellow and mustard blending to blue violet at tip. Werckmeister's Beauty X Child of God.

SKIES OVER YORK (George C. Bush, R. 1999). Sdlg. 98-1-20. SIB, 34" (86 cm), M. S. clear light blue; style arms pale blue; F. clear medium blue, signal hidden; slight fragrance. Spirit of York X unknown.

SKIF (Galina Shevchenko, R. 1995). MDB, 7½" (19 cm), E. S. dark violet; F. darker violet, near black; beards orange brown, violet base; slight musky fragrance. From *I. pumila* sdlgs. Shevchenko 1992.

SKI-HI-FORTY (George C. Bush, R. 1999). Sdlg. 40-60-34. SIB (sino-sib), 60" (152 cm), E. Light violet blue, F. with slight white signal; slight fragrance. Seed from SIGNA. Cleeton Fancy X unknown.

SKINSOME (Tom Burseen, R. 1997). Sdlg. 0-135D. TB, 35" (89 cm), L. Ruffled and laced light pink, F. with slightly darker edge and light red purple haft; beards red orange; sweet fragrance. Newlywed X Matinee Idol. T.B.'s Place 1997.

SKIPALONG (Joseph Ghio, R. 1995). Sdlg. 91-65L. TB, 33" (84 cm), EM. S. marbled rose heliotrope; F. white ground, lined dark heliotrope, center speckled; beards white, shading to tangerine in throat. 88-161K: ((82-113AA, Chuckles sib, x 81-50V: ((Handiwork x (Gay Parasol x Mystique)) x Goddess)) x (Desert Fox x Shenanigan)) X Filibuster. Bay View 1996.

SKI SEASON (Peter Jackson, R. 1999). Sdlg. LWM2. LA, 39" (100 cm), EM. Lightly ruffled white, gold spear signals; style arms green, tips white. Watch Out X Malibu Magic. Iris Acres 1999/2000.

SKOAL (Nancy Bartlett, R. 1993). Sdlg. 4E1. TB, 40" (102 cm), ML. Golden tan with brown haft markings; beards golden, prominent tan horn. Tawny Wings X Solano. Rancho del los Flores 1994.

SKOMOROKH (Viacheslav Gavrilin, R. 1999). Sdlg. 6-28-2-94. TB, 31" (78 cm), M. S. and style arms yellow; F. yellow ground, heavy vertical red striping, bright yellow spot below red beard, 1/5" yellow edge; ruffled; slight fragrance. Fiesta Time X Starcrest. Gavrilin 1999.

SKY ADVENTURE (William Simon by Elizabeth Simon, R. 1993). Sdlg. 51-67-49. TB, 36" (91 cm), M. Lavender self; beards red, tipped white. Enchanted World X (Rondetta x Glory Bound). Stahly 1994.

SKY AND SUN (Donald Spoon, R. 1997). Sdlg. 92-30. TB, 32" (81 cm), M. Ruffled sky blue self; beards golden yellow, large; flared. Navajo Jewel X Clear Day. Winterberry 1999.

403

SKY BEAUTY (Mary Louise Dunderman, R. 1994). Sdlg. EE28. MTB, 23" (58 cm), M. Lightly ruffled white ground plicata, light blue markings; beards white to yellow; slight fragrance. Y370 White: (Tid-Bit x 123R71: (Pixakeet x M19, white plicata)) X AA504 White. Ohio Gardens 1994.

SKY BLUE PINK (O. D. Niswonger, R. 1994). Sdlg. 95-91. TB, 34" (86 cm), M. S. pink; F. light pink; beards pink, tipped blue. Pink Blue Genes X 58-88: (Matinee Idol x Pink Ballerina). Cape Iris 1994.

SKYBO (Tom Magee, R. 1999). Sdlg. 8815 G. BB, 25" (64 cm), L. S. purple, white midrib; style arms light purple; F. white ground, purple plicata halo and streaks from beard area; beards gold, light blue at end; slight musky fragrance. Mirror Image X Acoma.

SKY BRITE (Jean Witt, R. 1992). Sdlg. 83-03-RA. MTB, 20" (51 cm), M. Light blue; beards yellow; leaf bases purple. Pale Wings X 70-13-JU blue, Shady Sands sib.

SKY CAVALIER (William Simon, TB, R. 1986). Stahly 1991.

SKY COVER (Vernon Wood, R. 1995). Sdlg. 93-14. CA, 18" (46 cm), EM. S. white, dotted violet, partial yellow midrib; style arms white, yellow rib; F. white, heavily lined and spotted violet plicata pattern, small yellow heart; ruffled. Ego Trip X 89-43: (Fort Point x Encircle). Stockton 1996.

SKYDANCER (Sylvia Chapman, R. 1996). Sdlg. 92-357-6. SDB, 13" (33 cm), M. S. cool white; style arms white; F. cool white, bright yellow spot; beards light violet; slight fragrance. C. Chapman 90-103-7: (87-03-1: (Crown Princess x Joyful) x Loveshine) X C. Chapman 90-57-17: (Chubby Cheeks x 87-1-2: (Crown Princess x Real Coquette)). Chapman Iris 1997.

SKY DANCING (Barry Blyth, R. 1995). Sdlg. A144-2. TB, 40" (102 cm), EM. S. icy blue white, deeper blue midrib infusion; F. pure icy white; beards white, tipped lemon in throat. Just Magic X Honky Tonk Blues. Tempo Two 1995/96.

SKYE BLUE (B.L.C. Dodsworth, R. 1996). Sdlg. EB 91V. TB, 40" (102 cm), M. Ruffled pale blue self; beards white. Sullom Voe X Morwenna.

SKYETOUCH (Don Nebeker, R. 1999). Sdlg. N-92-1100-7. TB, 36" (91 cm), M. S. white; style arms white, touched violet; F. white, 3/4" veronica violet margin solid at edge and shading to white; beards tangerine, whitish hair tips; slight sweet fragrance. N 994-3: (Classic Treasure x Planned Treasure) X Delightsum. Zebra 1999.

SKY FALLS (Ladislav Muska, R. 1995). Sdlg. SHVF-01. TB, 38" (97 cm), ML. Ruffled aquamarine blue self; beards yellow, deep blue horn. Sky Hooks X Victoria Falls. Muska 1993.

SKY FIESTA (Tom Magee, R. 1999). Sdlg. 8815 E. TB, 34" (86 cm), L. S. white ground, wide dark violet plicata edge; style arms violet, base white; F. white ground, violet plicata halo; beards violet, gold in throat; ruffled. Mirror Image X Acoma.

SKY KNOCKER (Terrell Taylor, R. 1998). Sdlg. 96-7. TB, 37" (94 cm), EM. Lightly ruffled amethyst (RHS 79C) self; beards burnt orange; sweet fragrance. Twilight Blaze X (Daredevil x Allstar). Bonita Gardens 1998.

SKYLARK'S SONG (Schreiner, R. 1996). Sdlg. CC 126-A. TB, 36" (91 cm), ML. S. and style arms snow white (RHS 155C); F. light blue (97B); beards white, hairs tipped light yellow; ruffled; slight fragrance. Overnight Sensation X Oregon Skies. Schreiner 1996.

SKYLASH (Lois Belardi, R. 1993). Sdlg. PDI-1. CA, 18" (46 cm), M. Heavily ruffled pure white with 3/8" medium blue eyelash around small yellow signal. PHD-8: (Pacific High x Del Rey) X Idylwild. Bay View 1994.

SKY LIFT (Jim Browne, TB, R. 1989). Cottage 1993.

SKYLINE SONG (G. F. Wilson, R. 1994). Sdlg. 62-90AT-A. AB (OGB), 28" (71 cm), EM. S. pale blue, lightly veined; F. pale blue blended light cream, violet line signal; beards brown tipped cream, wide; slight fragrance. Aril Skyline X (Tuesday Song x Holden Ho5 arilbred). Pleasure Iris 1995.

SKY PIE (Tom Burseen, R. 1990). Sdlg. 5-62B. TB, 36" (91 cm), E. S. creamy yellow blended butterscotch, some lavender shading; F. white, light blue purple shading more pronounced toward edge, faint yellow blended into color; beards tan; ruffled, waved. Apache Rose X Barletta. T.B.'s Place 1990.

SKY RAIN (Tom Magee, R. 1999). Sdlg. 8815 F. TB, 39" (99 cm), L. S. sky blue; style arms blue; F. ivory ground, purple streaks and wide plicata border; beards gold, purple at end. Mirror Image X Acoma.

SKYRAY (Richard Tasco, R. 1995). Sdlg. 91-65-04. SDB, 14" (36 cm), M. S. and style arms light lavender blue; F. white, lined and stippled darker lavender blue; beards white, tangerine red in throat. Nimble Toes X Hanky. Superstition 1996.

SKY ROAD (Chet Tompkins, R. 1997). Sdlg. 92-1. TB, 36" (91 cm), ML. S. and style arms milky blue, S. flushed deeper at base; F. light kings blue, forget-me-not blue haft brushing and stripe from beard to tip; beards mustard green tinted blue, lemon base. Beijing X (((Nile Flower x Hamblen 63-38L) x Beijing) x Cosmic Dawn). Fleur de Lis 1997.

SKY SEARCH (Larry Gaulter by Cooley's Gardens, R. 1993). Sdlg. 81-179. TB, 38" (97 cm), EM. Lightly ruffled medium light sky blue, near-white zonal area around beard; beards blue white, tipped white; pronounced sweet fragrance. Inv. Portrait of Larrie sdlgs. Cooley 1992.

SKYWALKER (Schreiner, R. 1996). Sdlg. AA 88-B. TB, 36" (91 cm), M. S. azure blue (RHS 97D), streaked creamy white; style arms azure blue wash; F. medium blue (96D) streaked azure blue, with creamy white band; beards light blue, yellow in throat, base yellow; heavily ruffled; slight fragrance. Altruist X Honky Tonk Blues. Schreiner 1996.

SLAM DUNK (O. D. Niswonger, R. 1995). Sdlg. IB 29-87. IB, 20" (51 cm), M. S. and style arms pale yellow; F. near-white, pale yellow at hafts; beards pale yellow. Lemon Mist X Captured Spirit. Cape Iris 1995.

SLAP BANG (O. D. Niswonger, SDB, R. 1989). Cape Iris 1990.

SLAPSTICK (Duane Meek, R. 1998). Sdlg. 319-1-7. TB, 34" (86 cm), EM & RE. S. peach, upper midrib flushed rosy violet; F. light violet with deeper violet fine streaks, narrow peach rim, upper haft area ivory with minute red violet dotting; beards white, hairs tipped brick orange. Lingering Love X Shenanigan. D & J Gardens 1998.

SLATE 'N GOLD (Richard Sparling, SDB, R. 1988). Green Box 1990.

SLAVA VSEVYSHNEMU (Viktor Sheviakov, R. 1995). Sdlg. 2V 11. TB, 37" (95 cm), ML. Heavily ruffled blackish violet self; beards blue violet. Matinata X Pink Taffeta. Sheviakov 1995.

SLAVEGIRL (Barry Blyth, R. 1994). Sdlg. A44-14. SDB, 12" (30 cm), ML. S. light pink flushed light rose, gold-glittered wire edge; F. bright white, 1/8" plicata edge stitched light pink, fine lavender dotting inside stitching; beards white, tipped tangerine. V7-5, Gigolette sib, X Chanted. Tempo Two 1994/95.

SLAVIANSKI BAZAR (Nina Miroshnichenko, R. 1996). TB, 37" (95 cm), ML. S. bordeaux violet, base lighter; style arms greenish yellow, crests violet; F. white, wide bordeaux brown edge; beards bronze, light violet at end; ruffled; slight sweet fragrance. Parentage unknown. Miroshnichenko 1989.

SLAVNY KHLOPCHINA (Borys Pravdyvy, R. 1999). Sdlg. 4D20-7. SDB, 13" (33 cm), ML. S. pale greenish yellow, slightly lighter edge, base violet; style arms pale greenish yellow; F. pale greenish beige, greenish lemon spot; beards light blue lavender, yellow in throat, hairs at end tipped cream white. 2D2-2: (Beau x unknown) X *I. pumila*. Pravdyvy 1999.

SLEEPWALK (Roger Nelson, R. 1991). Sdlg. 84-101P. TB, 34" (86 cm), ML. S. deep violet (near RHS 86A); F. deep violet (near 90A) at hafts becoming brighter dark violet (near 88A) at edge, deep blue highlights throughout; beards deep violet blue (89B); sweet fragrance. Royal Regency X Azure Lights. Iris Country 1992.

SLEEPYHEAD (Schreiner, R. 1994). Sdlg. AA 2337-A. SDB, 10" (25 cm), E. Pure light baby blue (RHS 98C); beards white. Jeremy Brian X Rain Dance. Schreiner 1994.

SLICK TRICK (Jim & Vicki Craig, R. 1997). Sdlg. 20V14. SDB, 12" (31 cm), ML-VL & RE. Medium blue self; beards pale blue, white base and in throat. Hager AMT3790BstBl: (Ting-a-Ling sib x Dinky) X ((Light Fantastic x *I. aphylla* "Van Nes") x ((En Route x Maroon Caper) x Whole Cloth)). J. & V. Craig 1997.

SLICK WILLIE (Robert Fabel-Ward, R. 1992). LA, 32" (81 cm), EM. Red tan with cream spray overcast. *I. fulva* (light tan) X Bayou Goula.

SLIGHT ACCENT (William Plotner, R. 1994). Sdlg. 86-60-4. TB, 40-42" (102-107 cm), ML. S. popcorn (RHS 11B); style arms jonquil yellow (19B); F. white, slightly veined purple (79), blending by small darker purple (79C) dots to purple (79C/D) edge; beards bronze yellow. 83-161: (Butterscotch Swirl x Windwalker) X Tompkins 83-1B, Fun and Games sib. Wildwood Gardens 1994.

SLIGHTLY ENVIOUS (Anna Mae Miller, R. 1995). Sdlg. 85-17-2. SIB, 32" (81 cm), ML & RE. S. and style arms creamy white, green lines; F. creamy white, yellow sides and haft area, definite greenish cast. 79.16.1: ((67.8.U: (Mountain Lake x unknown) x Jimmy's Gem) x Wing on Wing) X Butter and Sugar. Abbey Gardens 1995.

SLOW BLOW (Tom Burseen, R. 1999). Sdlg. 95-270A. TB, 36" (91 cm), M. S. light creamy pink, edge yellow; F. white, edge yellow; beards yellow, hairs tipped tangerine; heavily ruffled, scalloped; slight fragrance. Sunny Bubbles X Air Up There. T.B.'s Place 1999.

SLOWPOKE (James Ennenga, R. 1993). SPEC (*brevicaulis*), 14" (36 cm), L. Violet blue (RHS

93B), white signal with yellow and green infusion at midrib; zigzag stems with flowers at nodes; slight sweet fragrance. Collected near New Hope, AL. Ennenga's Iris 1993.

SLUMBERING DRAGON (Bob Bauer/John Coble, R. 1998). Sdlg. J86MM-11. JI (6 F.), 30" (76 cm), M. Ruffled dark wine red with lighter edges, yellow signal; style arms red violet, crests darker. Capaneus X Innerst 1555-1: (Yusho x Banners on Parade). Ensata Gardens 1997.

SLY FOX (Vernon Wood, R. 1996). Sdlg. 92-20. TB, 32-34" (81-86 cm), E. Ruffled white self; beards red. Bubble Up X 88-84: (82-38: ((Mais Oui x Carved Pink) x Blushing Pink) x 85-13: (Pink Belle x ((Pink Attire x Pink Persian) x ((Princess x Pink Taffeta) x Carved Pink)))). Stockton 1997.

SMALL BLESSINGS (A. & D. Willott, R. 1999). Sdlg. W 91-81. MDB, 6" (15 cm), M. Pale blue self; beards pale blue; cupped S., flared F. Brass Shoppe X W 79-13: (Greenlee GX-2 x Buttons). Willott 1999.

SMALL REWARD (George Shoop, R. 1994). Sdlg. 89-59-4. SDB, 9" (23 cm), M. Ruffled white, pink spot on F.; beards tangerine; slight fragrance. Miss Sunshine X 86-52: (pink IB x Pink Caper). Shoop 1994.

SMALL THING (Ben Hager, R. 1998). Sdlg. MD5967Y/DpMr. MDB, 5¼" (13 cm), ML. S. and style arms yellow; F. deep maroon; beards yellow. MSD5495Var: (Jiffy x Nestling) X Input.

SMART (Sterling Innerst, R. 1990). Sdlg. 2815-3. SDB, 13" (33 cm), M. Red violet, purple spot on F.; beards blue; slight fragrance. Little Episode X Pippi Longstockings. Innerst 1991.

SMART CARD (John C. Taylor, R. 1998). Sdlg. UL 29-4. LA, 47" (120 cm), M. S. and style arms purple; F. purple, deeper in center, signal yellow. Louie X Rachel's Request. Rainbow Ridge 1998/99.

SMART MOVE (Keith Keppel, R. 1994). Sdlg. 88-157A. TB, 38" (97 cm), L. S. rattan (M&P 11-K-5/6); F. blended tan-rose effect: monterey (5-J-12) with amber brown (13-K-12) hafts and narrow rim, rosy violet (44-L-6/7) flush strongest in center; beards light brown, base lavender; lightly ruffled; slight fragrance. Burgermeister X Enchanting. Keppel 1995.

SMASH HIT (Chet Tompkins, R. 1996). Sdlg. 93-16A. TB, 36" (91 cm), EML-VL. Heavily ruffled medium butter yellow self; beards yellow. (Pagoda Goddess x (Lux Aeterna x (Bonbon x Deft Touch))) X (Genesis x self). Fleur de Lis 1996.

SMELL ME (Leo Barnard, R. 1996). Sdlg. L 91-13-A1. IB, 18" (46 cm), VE. S. lavender (RHS 92B), deeper midrib and flecking; style arms lavender blue (92D), midrib darker (97A); F. lavender with purple (87A) central wash and shoulder veining; beards brass, lavender base; pronounced sweet fragrance. Jesse's Song X Ritz. Paradise Iris 1996.

SMILE A MILE (Lynn Bausch, R. 1995). Sdlg. R 20-1. SDB, 10½" (26 cm), EM. S. full yellow (RHS 21C), light green midrib base; style arms full yellow, laced; F. full yellow, darker tan yellow hafts and beside beard; beards full yellow, ruffled; slight sweet fragrance. J 4-2: (Moonspinner x Lilaclil) X Flirty Mary. Garden of the East Wind 1996.

SMILEY (Janet Hutchinson, R. 1995). Sdlg. MSDWB/HS. LA, 43" (110 cm), EM. S. clear light yellow, deeper edge, light olive buff center veining; style arms light yellow, deeper tips; F. light yellow, deeper edge, narrow deep gold signal; ruffled, edges serrate; slight sweet fragrance. Marsha Sue X Dural White Butterfly.

SMILING ANGEL (Schreiner, R. 1994). Sdlg. AA 2011-1. TB, 37" (94 cm), ML. Laced pure white (RHS 155D); beards yellow, tipped white. V 515-2: (Visual Arts x R 687-2: ((Fabulous Frills x ((Citron Creme x Tinsel Town) x Cindy Ellen)) x (G 510-A x Fabulous Frills sib))) X Song of Angels. Schreiner 1994.

SMILING FACES (Keith Keppel, R. 1997). Sdlg. 92-59E. TB, 30" (76 cm), M. S. warm white, faint lemon (M&P 9-C-1) center flush; style arms white; F. warm white overlaid light lemon, deepening toward edge to form blended lemon (9-J-1 to 10-K-1) band, warm white outer wire rim; beards cream at end, light yellow midsection, tipped chrome yellow in throat; heavily ruffled; pronounced musky sweet fragrance. Lucky Lemon X Overjoyed. Keppel 1998.

SMILING GOLD (Richard Ernst, R. 1991). Sdlg. F169-9. TB, 36" (91 cm), ML. S. deep golden yellow; F. white ground, veined yellow, 1/4" deep golden edge; beards golden yellow. Afternoon Delight X C142-7: (Ringo x (Cranberry Ice x Grand Waltz)). Cooley 1991.

SMILING SKIES (A. & D. Willott, R. 1993). Sdlg. 89-26. SDB, 11" (28 cm), EM. Lightly ruffled light blue, slightly deeper around cream beards. Sapphire Gem X Pilgrims' Choice. Willott 1994.

SMITTEN (Barry Blyth, R. 1997). Sdlg. D8-5. SDB, 15" (38 cm), ML. S. pastel pink, slight lavender blue midrib flush; F. pastel pink, white central area; beards lavender, tangerine in throat, bushy. Smoky Trail X A44-2, Slavegirl sib. Tempo Two 1997/98.

406

SMITTEN KITTEN (J. T. Aitken, R. 1991). Sdlg. 85M2-1. IB, 22" (56 cm), M. S. white; F. pink, ruffled; beards white, tipped orange. Lucky Duck X Marmalade Skies. Aitken's Salmon Creek 1991.

SMOKED PEARL REVISITED (O. D. Niswonger, R. 1995). Sdlg. 44-88. TB, 34" (86 cm), L. Smoky mauve self, slightly lighter F. center; beards dark tangerine. Matinee Idol X Pink Ballerina. Cape Iris 1995.

SMOKEY BABE (Lynette Black, R. 1996). Sdlg. 89-54-H. SDB, 10" (26 cm), ML. Smoky lavender plicata markings on cream white ground; beards blue lavender; ruffled; pronounced sweet fragrance. Muchacha X Court Magician. Netherby Gardens 1996/97.

SMOKEY JOE CONRAD (Marge Powell, R. 1993). Sdlg. PIP8805. LA, 38" (97 cm), M. S. violet blue (RHS 90C) with darker violet veins, giving smoky effect; F. same, yellow green (1C) signals with darker green veins and yellow orange line, yellow green (151C) reverse with darker green veins. Parentage unknown. Powell's Iris Patch 1993.

SMOKETTE (Robert Strohman, R. 1994). Sdlg. 90-1-5. SDB, 9" (23 cm), M. S. smoky pale tan lavender blend, flushed medium lavender at base; style arms pale lavender; F. greenish brass with smoky shadings, white line bisecting F. below lavender beard; slight sweet fragrance. Hafnium X Limeline. Gardens Ltd. 1995.

SMOKY IMP (Barry Blyth, R. 1990). Sdlg. X15-1. SDB, 15-16" (38-41 cm), ML. S. smoky pink; F. smoky pink overlaid smoky lavender; beards deep tangerine, bright violet outer 1/4". V7-4, Gigolette sib, X V17-5, Camarilla sib. Tempo Two 1990/91.

SMOKY PIECES (Barry Blyth, R. 1991). Sdlg. X31-4. SDB, 12-13" (30-33 cm), VE. Smoky lavender slate, lavender flash below beard; beards tangerine, outer 1/2" lavender. Yipee X Camarilla. Tempo Two 1991/92.

SMOKY RIDGE (Stan Dexter by Marie Ingersoll, R. 1993). Sdlg. 3-84-18A. TB, 34" (86 cm), EM. S. smoky gold; F. maroon; beards yellow bronze. 81-23-A: (69-26 x Flamenco) X Glowing Garnet. Ingersoll's Iris 1995.

SMOKY TRAIL (Barry Blyth, R. 1993). Sdlg. A14-2. SDB, 14-15" (36-38 cm), M. Smoky lilac pink, F. with few deeper pink veins around beard; beards tangerine, outer 1/2" lavender blue; slight fragrance. Smoky Imp X Chanted. Tempo Two 1993/94.

SMOOTH FLOW (Chet Tompkins, R. 1992). Sdlg. 84-58A. TB, 37" (94 cm), ML. S. blended cream and peach pink; F. strawberry rose, picoteed peach buff edge; beards light red. (((Cimbay x Latin Lover) x (Cimbay x Treasure Key)) x ((Cimbay x Latin Lover) x (Starburst x Cimbay))) X Apollodorus sib. Fleur de Lis 1991.

SMOOTHIE (Joseph Ghio, R. 1999). Sdlg. PB-276F3. CA, 15" (38 cm), ML. Lavender self, yellow line signal. PD-229-Z2: (PF-167-Z2: ((Earthquake x (Santa Cruz Beach x (Refugio x ((Simply Wild x Camp Capitola sib) x (Big Wheel x California Mystique)))))) x (Las Lomas x ((Running Wild x Moraga sib) x (Roaring Camp sib x (Montara sib x Mission Santa Cruz sib))))) x PF-153W3, Bat Boy sib) X PE-187Y, Easter Egg Hunt sib. Bay View 1999.

SMOOTH MOVE (Lynda Miller, R. 1995). Sdlg. 11591A. TB, 32" (81 cm), M. S. and style arms lilac; F. deep orchid, edges paler; beards orange; slight musky fragrance. Everything Plus X Sienna Waltz. Miller's Manor 1998.

SMOOTH OPERATOR (John Knudtson, R. 1994). Sdlg. 84-14-RP. TB, 35" (89 cm), M. Mulberry red violet, F. with lighter area around orange beard, white hafts; slight sweet fragrance. Rancho Rose X Lady Friend.

SMOOTH TRANSITION (Tony Huber, R. 1999). Sdlg. 95-168-96-033. SPEC-X (versata), 37" (94 cm), EML. S. violet blue (RHS 90D); style arms violet blue (90C) bordered white and lilac; F. darker violet blue (90A/B), creamy yellow signal surrounded by white veins. *I. versicolor* 449 violet X *I. ensata* (6 F.) white.

S'MORE (J. T. Aitken, R. 1992). Sdlg. 85M71. MDB, 6" (15 cm), L. S. deep violet; F. red brown; beards frosty light violet. Abracadabra X Cherry Garden. Aitken's Salmon Creek 1992.

SMUDGER'S GIFT (T. Burge by Ian Smith, R. 1996). Sdlg. T101/86. SIB (tet.), 26" (66 cm), ML. Light blue, faint mauve influence, F. with white signal veined light blue; lightly ruffled. T31/84: (Dear Dianne x Happy Event) X T34/84, sib.

SMUG (Barry Blyth, R. 1998). Sdlg. E47-1. IB, 18" (46 cm), VE-M & RE. S. pink, smoky cast; F. pinkish violet, deeper violet around darker violet spot, line signal; beards apricot tangerine, base white; sweet fragrance. Z27-1: (Gigolette x Armada) X unknown. Tempo Two 1998/99.

SMUTJE (Lothar Denkewitz, R. 1990). Sdlg. N-85-w-2. SDB, 12" (30 cm), E. S. greenish white blue, pale lavender edge; F. white blue, hafts pale olive; beards blue, tipped yellow; pronounced sweet fragrance. Sdlgs. inv. Sky and Snow, Snow Elf, Bodderlecker. Von Zeppelin 1992.

SNEEZY (Keith Keppel, R. 1995). Sdlg. 89-126C. TB, 29" (74 cm), M. S. apricot buff (M&P 10-H-5); style arms buff orange (10-I-6); F. lemon apricot (9-G-2), allover fine dot-wash of rose violet (7-A-6), heaviest toward hafts; beards solid red orange (2-F-12); ruffled; pronounced musky fragrance. Light Show X 86-4E: (((Morocco x Broadway) x (Theatre x (Anon x Prediction sib))) x ((Flamenco sib x (Roundup sib x April Melody)) x Broadway sib)). Keppel 1996.

SNEZHNAYA KOROLEVA (Viktor Sheviakov, R. 1996). Sdlg. 10a1. TB, 32" (80 cm), ML. Milky white, slight greenish cast below beard; beards yellow orange, white at end; slight fragrance. Southern Comfort X Winter Olympics. Sheviakov 1996.

SNEZHNY BARS (Viacheslav Gavrilin, R. 1999). Sdlg. 94-623-3. TB, 36" (90 cm), EM. Ruffled light yellowish cream; beards tangerine orange. Parentage unknown.

SNICKERDOODLE (Opal Wulf, R. 1993). Sdlg. STGO-C-88. MTB, 17-19" (43-48 cm), EML. S. golden yellow with light dusting of cinnamon brown on edge and midrib; F. white, edged yellow; beards bright yellow; foliage purple-based. Striking Gold X unknown. Wulf's Backachers 1993.

SNICKERS (Keith Keppel, R. 1998). Sdlg. 91-57Z. SDB, 14" (35 cm), M. S. lime yellow (M&P 11-L-5) blended honey (12-J-6), citrine (14-L-6) to old bronze (14-L-7) base; style arms brass (11-L-6) to tennis (12-L-6), shaded honey; F. blended brass 3/8" to 1/2" band, breaking into fine dotting, small aureolin yellow (10-L-2) blaze; beards burnished gold (12-L-7) to buckthorn (13-L-8); pronounced sweet fragrance. Rusty Dusty X Quote. Keppel 1999.

SNIFF-SNIFF (John Durrance, R. 1993). Sdlg. 90-92. TB, 34" (86 cm), ML. Lightly ruffled light blue; self beards; sweet fragrance. Shoop 79-44-1: ((Hula Girl sib x Dutch Magic) x sib) X Monarch's Robe. Long 1993.

SNIPS (Lynda Miller, R. 1995). Sdlg. 192. MDB, 4½-5" (12-14 cm), E. Red violet, F. with deep ruby red spot; beards light blue, orange in throat. 987: (684, unknown, x Copper Chief) X Copper Chief. Miller's Manor 1996.

SNOB APPEAL (Ben Hager, R. 1997). Sdlg. AMT5624Pk. MTB, 22" (56 cm), EM. Clear medium pink; beards tangerine. Sib to Devotee. Adamgrove 1997.

SNOOPY (Carol Lankow by J. T. Aitken, R. 1996). Sdlg. 7K45. BB, 25" (64 cm), M. White self; beards white, hairs tipped red. Paris Kiss X Cool Treat. Aitken's Salmon Creek 1996.

SNOWBELT (Keith Keppel, R. 1991). Sdlg. 83-10G. TB, 35" (89 cm), EM. S. blue white (M&P 41-A-1); F. white, 3/8" solid blue (41-E-10) edge, hafts and small dart below beard; beards blue white, lemon in throat; pronounced sweet fragrance. 80-131H, Snowbrook sib, X Snowbrook. Keppel 1992.

SNOW BLANKET (Richard Ernst, R. 1991). Sdlg. F123-4. TB, 38" (97 cm), EM. Heavily ruffled white, pale lavender infusion at lower midrib of S.; beards tangerine, tipped yellow white; slight sweet fragrance. Afternoon Delight X Edna's Wish. Cooley 1991.

SNOW BLINK (Leo Barnard, R. 1995). Sdlg. 91L-13. IB, 16" (41 cm), EM. S. white, short violet blue (RHS 93A) rays at base; style arms white; F. white, violet blue rays and spot; beards white, tipped gold; ruffled; slight sweet fragrance. Jesse's Song X Starry Eyed. Paradise Iris 1995.

SNOW BUNNY (Opal Brown, R. 1991). Sdlg. 82-18B2. BB, 25" (64 cm), M. White with dainty ecru pink ruffled edge on S. & F., ecru pink shoulders; beards orange red. 77-1A5: (Baroque x (Saber Dance x Silver Shower)) X 78-3B5: (Old Flame x ((Grandiflora x Arctic Flame) x Buffy)). Brown's Sunnyhill 1991.

SNOW BURST (Bernard Hamner, R. 1991). Sdlg. 83-6. TB, 38" (97 cm), M. Ruffled white, F. edged violet blue (RHS 97B/C); beards white, tipped pale yellow. Dutch Girl X Glistening Icicle. Shepard Iris 1991.

SNOW COUNTRY (Jack Worel, R. 1995). Sdlg. W83-93. TB, 34" (86 cm), M. Ruffled white self; beards yellow, tipped white; slight sweet fragrance. (Grandma's Bluegown x Laced Cotton) X (Good Morning America x Song of Norway). Holly Lane 1995.

SNOW CROWN (George Shoop, R. 1991). Sdlg. 84-13. TB, 36" (91 cm), M. S. white; F. deep pink, edged white; beards tangerine; ruffled. 80-2: (American Beauty x Friday Surprise) X 82-38: (80-3: (Ringo x Color Bash) x 79-32, inv. pink amoena sdlgs.). Shoop 1991.

#SNOW DANCER (Calvin Helsley, TB, R. 1976). Stock destroyed and name released.

SNOW DANCER (Calvin Helsley, R. 1993). Sdlg. 6-85. JI (6 F.), 32" (81 cm), M. Ruffled white, olive green signal. Parentage unknown. Helsley 1997.

SNOW D'OR (Barry Blyth, R. 1991). Sdlg. X130-1. TB, 34" (86 cm), EM. S. white, faint lemon at midrib; F. mustard yellow, 1/4" white edge on sides; beards orange. (Alpine Journey x Beachgirl)

X (Tomorrow's Child x ((Champagne Snow x Chimbolam) x Chinese Treasure)). Tempo Two 1991/92.

SNOWED IN (Joseph Ghio, R. 1998). Sdlg. 93-90L3. TB, 34" (86 cm), EML. S. light blue, thin tan edge; F. violet black, white sunburst pattern around red beard. 88-180P: (Notorious x ((Success Story x (Fancy Tales x Alpine Castle)) x ((Persian Smoke x Entourage) x ((Strawberry Sundae x (Artiste x Tupelo Honey)) x Borderline sib)))) X Romantic Evening. Bay View 1999.

SNOW GIANT (B. Charles Jenkins, R. 1993). Sdlg. C17-6F. SPU, 35-42" (89-107 cm), M. White, small pointed yellow signal. Highline Honey X Clarke Cosgrove. Shepard Iris 1993.

SNOW-IN-SUMMER (Libby Cross, R. 1993). Sdlg. 90-A-2. TB, 30" (76 cm), M & RE. Fluted white self; beards gold; slight sweet fragrance. Immortality X unknown. Crosspatch 1994.

SNOW JOB (Paul Black, R. 1998). Sdlg. B123A. TB, 34" (86 cm), M. White self, S. with slight crystalline edge; beards orange; slight sweet fragrance. Victorian Frills X Robusto. Mid-America 1998.

SNOW LEOPARD (Connell Marsh, TB, R. 1981). C. Marsh 1990.

SNOW MOON (Howard Shockey, TB, R. 1989). Arilian Acres 1990.

SNOW PARASOL (Donald Spoon, R. 1997). Sdlg. 93-33B. TB, 30" (76 cm), M & RE. Ruffled white self; beards white, yellow in throat; flared. Lucie Andry X Chaste White. Winterberry 1999.

SNOW PLUM (George Shoop, R. 1994). Sdlg. 89-50-1. IB, 16" (41 cm), M. S. white; F. peach pink; beards tangerine; slight fragrance. Lankow 2A28-3: (Spring Bonnet x M. Wright L85: (Blue Trinket x Cotton Blossom)) X Snow Crown. Shoop 1994.

SNOW PRINCE (Sarah Tiffney, SIB, R. 1988). Pope's Perennials 1990.

SNOW SEASON (Evelyn Jones, R. 1992). Sdlg. I89-24-4. SDB, 14" (36 cm), M. White self; pale lilac pink beards. Lankow 7B45-3-2: ((Andi x (pink TB sdlg. x Yellow Dresden)) x Miss Nellie) X Blue Line sib. Bennett Jones 1993.

SNOW SHOES (Manley Osborne by Maryott's Gardens, R. 1995). Sdlg. 891. TB, 31" (79 cm), M. S. white, blue (RHS 91B) center glow; style arms blue white, light blue lip; F. white, white petaloid at end of wide blue white beard; slight sweet fragrance. Bubbly Mood X Special Feature. Maryott 1995.

SNOW TREE (Robert Sobek, R. 1990). Sdlg. 82S81. SDB, 11" (28 cm), EM. White, with pronounced dark brownish purple veining over 3/4 of F.; beards white, tipped orange. Soft Air X 79S5: (Flapjack x Baby Toes). Joe Pye Weed 1990.

SNOW WHITE DOVE (Donald Spoon, R. 1997). Sdlg. 89-122B. TB, 28" (71 cm), M. Ruffled, lightly laced white, slight yellow haft area; beards white, yellow in throat; flared. Romantic Mood X I Do.

SNOWY CHANGE (Barry Clark by Albert Faggard, R. 1994). Sdlg. 87-5. LA (tet.), 31" (79 cm), E. S. cream white veined green, slight blue infusion when fresh; style arms lime green, tipped cream; F. cream white veined green, long lime green signal; slight spicy fragrance. Professor Paul X self. Albert Faggard 1994.

SNOWY SHAMROCKS (Cleo Palmer, R. 1993). Sdlg. 9031. SDB, 15" (38 cm), L. S. white, slight yellow midrib flush; F. white with light grass green flush, light yellow haft veining; beards yellow, tipped white; pronounced sweet fragrance. (Fluffy x 8225: (Crescent Moon x unknown)) X unknown. Palmer's Iris 1993.

SNOWY TRIO (George Bush, JI, R. 1983). Bush 1990.

SNUGGLEBUG (Schreiner, R. 1993). Sdlg. AA 2252-1. SDB, 10" (25 cm), E. S. red maroon (RHS 60A); F. velvety maroon black (60A) with darker thumbprint (187A); beards red maroon. R 1007-B, Li'l Red Devil sib, X Lady in Red. Schreiner 1993.

SOARING (Barry Blyth, R. 1991). Sdlg. U108-A. TB, 40" (102 cm), ML. S. lemon cream; F. pastel blue; beards bright gold; slight sweet fragrance. Fly to Vegas X Dutch Girl. Tempo Two 1991/92.

SOARING SPIRIT (Chet Tompkins, R. 1992). Sdlg. 83-56D. TB, 38" (97 cm), ML-VL. Clean brown self; beards brown. ((Copperclad x Perique) x (Honeyflow x (Hermit Thrush x Argus Pheasant))) X (((Allaglow x Olympic Torch) x (Starburst x Post Time)) x (Starburst x Velvet Brass)). Fleur de Lis 1992.

SOARING WINGS (Terrell Taylor, R. 1998). Sdlg. 96-15. TB, 36" (91 cm), M. Ruffled medium blue (RHS 90A); beards orange; sweet fragrance. Twilight Blaze X (Daredevil x Allstar). Bonita Gardens 1998.

SOAR WITH EAGLES (Ben Hager, R. 1994). Sdlg. T5430TIPk/Pr. TB, 50" (127 cm), L. S. and style arms peach pink; F. purple, edged lighter; beards tangerine; ruffled; edges serrate. T4235BchPk: (Merry Madrigal x Mother Earth) X Melba Hamblen.

SO CALLED (Akihiko Terada, R. 1999). Sdlg. 107-89-7. TB, 37" (94 cm), ML. S. pink; F. brown; beards light orange. Romanticist X Romantic Mood. Roris 1999.

SO CHARMING (Stan Dexter by Marie Ingersoll, R. 1995). Sdlg. A96-129B. TB, 36" (91 cm), ML. S. soft light pink; F. soft light pink, pinkish orange hash marks; beards pinkish orange. Freda Laura X Today's Fashion. Ingersoll's Iris 1996.

SOCIAL EVENT (Keith Keppel, R. 1990). Sdlg. 84-175A. TB, 36" (91 cm), M. Buff peach (M&P 9-AB-4); beards flame (1-C-12); pronounced musky fragrance. 78-25D: (73-17C, Maraschino sib, x Thelma Rudolph) X Gatty M8-2A, Satin Siren sib. Keppel 1991.

SOCIAL GESTURE (Evelyn Kegerise, R. 1991). Sdlg. 85-630-4. TB, 35" (89 cm), EML. Ruffled and fluted medium violet blue (RHS 92A); beards pale blue, tipped white, yellow in throat; pronounced sweet fragrance. Silent Morn X Swirling Seas. Evelyn Kegerise 1991.

SOCIETY PAGE (Joseph Ghio, R. 1999). Sdlg. 95-39-I2. TB, 32" (81 cm), EML. S. pale pink, deeper pink midrib; F. pale pink, edges and shoulders deeper pink; beards tangerine, tipped white. Haute Couture X Boudoir.

SO FINE (Schreiner, R. 1996). Sdlg. AA 1630-A. TB, 37" (94 cm), ML. S. and style arms lavender orchid (RHS 76A); F. royal purple (79A) with 1/4" lavender orchid rim; beards bright tangerine; pronounced sweet fragrance. W 325-12: (Latin Lady x Bristo Magic) X Sweeter Than Wine. Schreiner 1996.

SO FRESH (Chet Tompkins, R. 1996). Sdlg. 93-73. TB, 38" (97 cm), ML. S. icy white, faint hazy gilt and pink midrib flush; style arms icy white, tinted pink; F. deep raspberry pink, wide paler blended edge; beards lemon pink on white. (Intermission x Angel's Touch) X (Ming Porcelain x (Angel's Touch x Adventuress)). Fleur de Lis 1997.

SOFT APPROACH (William Plotner, R. 1992). Sdlg. 86-607-7. TB, 34" (86 cm), ML. Soft wistaria violet; beards light blue. (Mysterious x Untamed) X (Mary Frances x Master Mariner). Wildwood Gardens 1991.

SOFT AS SILK (William Maryott, R. 1994). Sdlg. R114A. TB, 37" (84 cm), EM. S. light yellow pink (RHS 27A); F. smooth red violet (55C) wash on light pink (27A) ground; beards tangerine; ruffled. Sweet Musette X Natural Beauty. Maryott 1995.

SOFT CARESS (Joseph Gatty, R. 1990). Sdlg. Q19-1. TB, 35" (89 cm), ML. Polar bear (M&P 9-B-2); beards mikado orange (9-J-9); slight spicy sweet fragrance. Quiet Moment X Simply Pretty. Keppel 1991.

SOFT COVER (Paul Black, R. 1998). Sdlg. A52C. TB, 30" (76 cm), M. S. ecru cream overlaid gilt, violet midrib line; style arms gold, midrib violet; F. blended medium violet, rim paler, white haft with olive to brick veins; beards violet at end, grey gold to orange gold in throat; ruffled. Touch of Bronze X 88115A: (Bubble Bath x Titan's Glory). Mid-America 1998.

SOFT HEARTED (Mary Dunn by Joseph Ghio, R. 1999). Sdlg. L247-5. LA, 36" (91 cm), ML. Medium blue self, white hairline edge, slight yellow signal; style arms white. (Plantation Beau x Easter Tide) X Sea Consul.

SOFT SINGER (Chet Tompkins, R. 1992). Sdlg. 87-52. TB, 34" (86 cm), EML. S. champagne buff flushed lilac, pink and apricot; F. slightly deeper; beards vivid red. (Revival Meeting x Air Bubbles) X (Nile Flower x Cosmic Dawn). Fleur de Lis 1991.

SOFTWARE (Ben Hager, SDB, R. 1989). Melrose 1990.

SOFT WINDS (Robert Hollingworth, R. 1998). Sdlg. 85C3A2. SIB, 27" (69 cm), M. Ruffled light blue violet, F. with green hafts, small white blaze; style arms shaded blue. 83M3B8: (Pink Haze x Fairy Dawn) X 80X1C2: (Super Ego x Anniversary). Greystone 1998.

SO I SEE (Lloyd Zurbrigg, R. 1990). Sdlg. V 85. TB, 35" (89 cm), EM & RE. S. white, very lightly plicata-marked violet; F. white lightly marked violet; beards light yellow, tipped white. R 768 Wide: ((Halt x Earl of Essex) x I Do) X Earl of Essex.

SOISSONS (Ladislav Muska, R. 1995). Sdlg. SHBR-02. TB, 38" (97 cm), M. Ruffled pale blue self; beards tangerine, long lavender horn. (Sky Hooks x Monte Albano) X Sky Hooks. Muska 1996.

SOJOURNER (Elyse Hill, R. 1998). Sdlg. EJ 17-3. CA, 6" (15 cm), E. S. orange, lined red; style arms orange; F. orange, red lines radiating from 3/4" deep red signal; ruffled cartwheel form. Reflecting Pool X unknown.

SOKA-NO-KAORI (Ginan Goda by Society for Japanese Irises, R. 1995). JI (6 F.), 35" (90 cm), M.

Light blue violet, white halo around signal; style arms light blue violet, white center. Parentage unknown. Introduced in Japan prior to 1990.

SOLAN GOOSE (B.L.C. Dodsworth, TB, R. 1984). British Iris Society 1997.

SOLAR IMPACT (David Haveman, R. 1994). Sdlg. 9-85-14. TB, 34" (87 cm), E. Bright lemon yellow (RHS 6B) self; beards deeper yellow; slight sweet fragrance. Aztec Sun X (Sky Hooks x Gold Galore). Stockton 1995.

SOLAR PRISM (Luella Danielson, R. 1995). Sdlg. 4-30. SPU, 38-40" (97-102 cm), M. S. blue violet, pink veining from midrib changing to blue violet toward outer edge; style arms blue violet; F. lemon yellow hafts, 1" darker yellow signal surrounded by white halo, 1/4" blue violet edge. Ila Crawford X unknown. Pleasure Iris 1996.

SOLAR RADIANCE (J. D. Stadler, R. 1992). Sdlg. J21/1. TB, 30" (76 cm), M. Lightly laced and ruffled medium orange; beards deep orange; slight fragrance. Orange Punch X Marmalade.

SOLAR SCREAMER (Jared Harris, R. 1997). BB, 24-27" (61-70 cm), ML. Intense deep sunfast yellow gold self; beards deep red orange; slight spicy fragrance. Coral Satin X Sunset Sonata.

SOLAR SPRINKLES (Darlene Pinegar, R. 1998). Sdlg. GM-1A. TB, 34" (86 cm), ML-VL. S. dark rust brown; style arms medium yellow gold; F. upper third dark yellow, some dark rust brown marking, remainder blended yellow brown shaded rust brown, small irregular yellow dots randomly scattered; beards dark yellow orange, lighter yellow orange at end, long fuzzy dark yellow orange horn; moderately ruffled and laced; slight sweet fragrance. Golden Mistress X Fringe Benefits. Spanish Fork 1999.

SOLAR SYSTEM SPECIAL (Darlene Pinegar, R. 1999). Sdlg. HR-95-32A. TB, 33" (84 cm), M. S. white; style arms yellow, lip orchid; F. lavender blue shaded darker, edge lighter, hafts white with gold marks; beards light yellow orange, darker in throat, fuzzy lavender blue horn; lightly ruffled; slight sweet fragrance. Havana Revels X Stingray.

SOLAR WIND (G. F. Wilson, R. 1994). Sdlg. 64-91TFO-C. AB (OGB), 32" (81 cm), EM. S. pale rose veined yellow, yellow midrib; F. golden yellow amber blend, large circular maroon black signal surrounded by light maroon dotting; beards brown, tipped yellow; slight sweet fragrance. Turkish Fez X Onlooker. Pleasure Iris 1995.

SOLFRIANE (O. D. Niswonger, R. 1993). Sdlg. 46-88. TB, 33" (84 cm), M. Lilac pink, blue line extending downward from beard; beards white, tipped pink. Brandy X Pink Ballerina. Cape Iris 1994.

SOLIGO (Augusto Bianco, R. 1999). Sdlg. 569. MDB, 8" (20 cm), E. S. and style arms lavender; F. blended lilac and hazel; beards lavender; slight spicy fragrance. ((Leprechaun's Gold x Baja) x Chubby Cheeks) X (Zounds x (Stockholm x Baja)). Iride 1999.

SOLNECHNY TASHKENT (V. & N. Gordodelovy, R. 1995). Sdlg. 44. BB, 26" (65 cm), E. S. golden yellow; style arms orange yellow; F. white, golden yellow rim; beards orange yellow; heavily ruffled. Parentage unknown. Gordodelovy 1981.

SOLNECHNY VETER (Nina Miroshnichenko, R. 1997). TB, 32" (82 cm), ML. S. lemon yellow; F. white, narrow lemon rim, yellow hafts; beards yellow; pronounced sweet fragrance. Parentage unknown. Miroshnichenko 1995.

SOLNECHNY ZAYCHIK (Adolf Volfovich-Moler, R. 1995). Sdlg. V-14. BB, 24" (60 cm), L. S. bright yellow; F. bright yellow with white spot, hafts dotted brownish violet; beards yellow; ruffled. Buttercup Bower X unknown. Volfovich-Moler 1992.

SOLNYSHKO MOYO (Nataliya Khimina, R. 1998). Sdlg. 96-12. IB, 22" (55 cm), E. S. and style arms yellow; F. bright yellow, darker median line; beards yellow; slight fragrance. Impulse X John.

SOLOIST (Richard Ernst, R. 1994). Sdlg. G102-2. TB, 35" (89 cm), M. S. honey tan, midrib infused violet; F. cream blending to yellow honey edge, gold shoulders; beards yellow orange, tipped gold; ruffled. St. Helens' Wake X Hula Dancer. Cooley 1994.

SOLOMON'S SEAL (Allan Ensminger, R. 1998). Sdlg. 95-43. TB, 35" (89 cm), ML. S. very pallid blue to white; style arms and F. white; beards dauphins violet (HCC 039), long and pointed; slight fragrance. Electric Surge X 92-77: (189-53: (86-21: (Peach Jam x ((75-18 x (71-33: (68-26: ((Snow Goddess x (May Hall x unknown)) x (63-5 x Rippling Waters)) x 68-21) x 71-31)) x Vivien)) x Special Feature) x sib). Varigay 1999.

SOLOMON'S WISDOM (Lois Rich by James Whitely, R. 1994). Sdlg. R62-RC3. AR (RC), 5" (13 cm), EM. S. white, distinctly veined fuchsia mahogany, darker at midrib; F. white with dark chocolate veins from chocolate signal to edge; beards dark chocolate. *I. korolkowii* "Brown and

Green" X K54-4B: (*I. gatesii* x ((*I. susiana* x *I. atropurpurea*) x (*I. gatesii* x *I. gatesii*))). Aril Patch 1994.

SO LONG (Lois Rich by James Whitely, R. 1994). Sdlg. R84-96B. AB (OGB), 17" (43 cm), ML. Bright yellow self, large brown mahogany signal; beards yellow. R77-112U: (R71-117G: ((K55-33-0 x ((*I. korolkowii concolor* x Judean Charmer) x (*I. atrofusca* x *I. nazarena*))) x Clark 67-C6-A: (63-C22 x ((Hel-W118 x K5344 LF) x 640-OY))) x White Lightning) X R80-118F: (Sand Etching x (((CR64-12C: (inv. Iman Onco), *I. lortetii*, *I. auranitica*, MX7-0) x (Judean Charmer x Judean Cream)) x Garden Gold) x ((K55-9A x ((*I. lortetii* x *I. auranitica*) x (W83-0 x *I. barnumae*))) x Mishawaka))). Aril Patch 1994.

SO LOYAL (John C. Taylor, R. 1995). Sdlg. RL 67-2. LA, 35" (89 cm), M. S. white, with variable purple veining; style arms yellow green blushed purple at tips; F. purple (RHS 78B), edged lighter, signal yellow. OL 136-1: (M 19-1: (C'est Si Bon x Koorawatha sib) x Helen Naish) X Margaret Lee. Rainbow Ridge 1995/96.

SOLSTICE (John Weiler, R. 1992). Sdlg. 84-77-3RE. TB, 37" (94 cm), EML & RE. Heavily ruffled medium blue; beards soft cream; pronounced sweet fragrance. 78-32-2: (74-120: ((((Glittering Gold x Orange Crush) x (Ballerina x Orange Crush)) x New Moon) x (White King x New Moon)) x White Lightning) X Avalon Bay. Rialto 1992.

SOMBRERO WAY (Schreiner, R. 1996). Sdlg. BB 885-1. TB, 39" (99 cm), ML. S. gold yellow (RHS 163C); style arms yellow, red near lip; F. red (178A); beards rusty brown, hairs tipped golden yellow; ruffled; slight fragrance. Warrior King X Vigilante. Schreiner 1996.

SOME ARE ANGELS (Barry Blyth, R. 1996). Sdlg. Z62-A. TB, 36" (91 cm), M. Pure crystalline white; beards lemon yellow. W56-1: (Lipstick Lies x Light Beam) X Snowbrook. Tempo Two 1996/97.

SOMEBODY LOVES ME (Robert Hollingworth, R. 1998). Sdlg. 92J3B20. SIB (tet.), 32" (81 cm), EM. Ruffled medium blue violet, F. with very large white blaze; style arms light blue. 88U2D4: (((Wizardry x Wildwood Springs sib) x (78F1, induced tet. from Dreaming Spires, x 78G2, induced tet. from Cambridge)) x (Happy Event x 82J2C7, Jewelled Crown sib)) X Coronation Anthem. Windwood Gardens 1998.

SOMEONE CARES (Darlene Pinegar, R. 1990). Sdlg. BH-1-3. TB, 28" (71 cm), M. Heavily ruffled and laced white, yellow shoulders blending down to beard tip, faint yellow edge on F.; beards yellow orange; slight sweet fragrance. Bride's Halo X Moon Mistress. Spanish Fork 1991.

SOMERSAULT (Joseph Ghio, R. 1994). Sdlg. 90-65K3. TB, 42" (107 cm), ML. S. deep plum over salmon ground; F. light salmon ground, wide edge of plum lines and dots, heart and shoulders heavily dotted deep plum; beards sienna. ((82-113D, Chuckles sib, x Keppel 80-103A: (Gigolo x Anon)) x (Hot Streak x (((Handiwork x (Gay Parasol x Mystique)) x Goddess) x (Gem of Sierra x (((Ponderosa x Honey Rae) x (((Commentary x Claudia Rene) x Claudia Rene) x (Ponderosa x New Moon))) x Osage Buff) x (Vanity x Anon))))) X Power Surge. Bay View 1995.

SOMERSET BLUE (Cy Bartlett, R. 1997). Sdlg. C95-47. TB, 37" (94 cm), M. Medium blue, F. slightly darker; beards blue white, lemon in throat; slight sweet fragrance. Pledge Allegiance X Breakers. Sutton 1997.

SOMETHING WONDERFUL (Terrell Taylor, R. 1994). Sdlg. 93-49. TB, 33" (84 cm), ML. S. pink (RHS 62D) with lavender highlights; F. pink (186D) with lavender highlights, more pronounced around outer 1/2"; beards tangerine; ruffled, lightly laced; sweet fragrance. Designing Woman X Sweet Musette. Bonita Gardens 1995.

SOMEWHAT QUIRKY (Riley Probst, R. 1997). Sdlg. 91PQX28RJ3. MTB, 21" (53 cm), M. S. creamy yellow; F. white, lined and veined light lavender; beards golden orange; slight fragrance. Pretty Quirky X Real Jazzy.

SOMEWHERE IN TIME (Darlene Pinegar, R. 1999). Sdlg. TTE-93-115A. TB, 34" (86 cm), ML. S. and style arms creamy yellow; F. white center blending to medium dark orchid, narrow lighter rim, hafts white marked orange yellow; beards white, dark yellow in throat, long light orchid horn sometimes ending with yellow and orchid flounce; lightly ruffled and laced; pronounced sweet fragrance. Tracy Tyrene X Anne Boleyn.

SOMSEE SOMSIGH (Tom Burseen, R. 1990). Sdlg. 4-178C. TB, 36" (91 cm), EM. Ruffled and laced creamy apricot (RHS 19B); beards orange, tipped white; slight fragrance. Vanity Skirt X Mandolin. T.B.'s Place 1991.

#SOMSUBIN (Bob Thomason, SDB, R. 1988). Stock destroyed, name released.

SOMSUBIN (Bob Thomason, R. 1991). Sdlg. BT 8811C. SDB, 10" (25 cm), EM. S. medium violet;

F. deep red violet, medium violet rim; beards light violet; slight fragrance. Dove Wings X Tortuga. Okie Iris 1999.

SONAM (Jean Peyrard, R. 1997). CA, 12" (30 cm), M. S. golden cream, veined purple; style arms golden cream, medium purple midrib; F. violet, wide cream gold margin, large yellow signal. Sdlgs. from Ghio seed.

SON AND SNO (George Sutton, R. 1995). Sdlg. C-76. SDB, 11" (28 cm), EM. S. yellow (RHS 2B) edged white; style arms yellow and white; F. pale yellow (3D); beards white, hairs tipped gold; ruffled. Sno Jo X Pied Pretty. Sutton 1996.

SONATA IN BLUE (Raymond Smith, R. 1991). Sdlg. 8621BR. TB, 31" (78 cm), M & RE. Ruffled brilliant violet (Nickerson 10PB 5/9); beards yellow, tipped white; slight fragrance. F. Wampler sdlg. X Victoria Falls. R. G. Smith 1994.

SONG OF ANGELS (Schreiner, R. 1991). Sdlg. T 1017-1. TB, 36" (91 cm), L. White (RHS 155C), heavily laced borders gently tinted soft lavender (76D); beards white. Visual Arts X Cloud Cocktail. Schreiner 1991.

SONG OF BABYLON (Sharon McAllister, R. 1992). Sdlg. 81-47-1. AB (OGB), 28" (72 cm), EM. S. pale lilac (near RHS 76D); F. tuscan yellow (near 162C) covered with heavy network of rust veining; beards mustard. Sheik X Esther the Queen. McAllister 1992.

SONG OF GRACE (Tom Parkhill, R. 1998). Sdlg. 91-1605. TB, 34" (86 cm), M. Heavily ruffled blue white; style arms white; beards bright sky blue; slight fragrance. 87-1205: (Pacific Mist x Song of Norway) X Winterscape. Parkhill 1999.

SONG OF JOY (Beryl Pederick, R. 1994). Sdlg. 2. TB, 38" (97 cm), E. S. white with lemon blaze and border; F. apricot (HCC 609/2-3) with faint pink markings; beards orange; slight fragrance. Mandolin X Beachgirl.

SONG OF LOVE (Cloyd McCord, R. 1997). Sdlg. 444. TB, 36" (91 cm), M. S. peach; F. pale lavender, peach blaze; beards orange; slight fragrance. Queen of Love X Lovely Spring. McCord 1997.

SONG OF SOLITUDE (Jim Hummel, TB, R. 1987). Bumble Bee 1991.

SONIA ROXANNE (Pauline Evans, R. 1997). Sdlg. 94/2. SPU, 45" (114 cm), ML. S. wistaria blue, overlaid deeper blue; style arms tipped deep lavender; F. light yellow overlaid wistaria, yellow signal; ruffled. Missouri Blue X "Grey Lady", parentage unknown.

SONNENFALTER (Vera Matthe, R. 1990). Sdlg. VM 80-63-1. TB, 39" (100 cm), M. S. yellow (RHS 12B); style arms yellow (12B); F. white (155D), edged yellow (12A), few white haft marks; beards yellow orange (19A). Starring Role X Warm Gold.

SONNENGOLD (Siegmar Goerbitz, R. 1991). Sdlg. 8604A3. TB, 36" (90 cm), M. Golden yellow; beards orange. ((Outreach x Gold Trimmings) x Tut's Gold) X Orange Empire. Schoeppinger 1991.

SONNTAGSKIND (Frank Kathe, R. 1993). Sdlg. 24/6-88. SDB, 12" (32 cm), M. S. butter yellow; F. velvety brown yellow to ochre; blue grey lavender beards. Gingerbread Man X Dale Dennis. Kathe 1993.

SON OF BOAZ (Sharon McAllister, R. 1998). Sdlg. 85-3-12. AB (OGB), 28" (71 cm), M. S. white veined and stippled red violet, heavier at edge; style arms yellow; F. ground paling from yellow in center to near-white at edge, finely dotted and veined orange brown to reddish violet; beards mixed mustard and maroon. Boaz X Jean Ralls. McAllister 1998.

SON OF DRACULA (Jim Hedgecock, R. 1990). Sdlg. 83-40-2. TB, 32" (81 cm), M. Black; beards blue black, gold in throat. Superstition X Soul Music. Comanche Acres 1991.

SON OF DREAMS (Donald Spoon, TB, R. 1989). Winterberry 1995.

SON OF SATAN (Paul Wickersham by Roger Nelson, R. 1999). TB, 36" (91 cm), M. Dark plum to deep maroon with black overcast; beards deep bronze brown. Parentage unknown. Cooley 1962.

SONOMA DANCER (Cleo Palmer, R. 1994). Sdlg. 8956. SDB, 11" (28 cm), M. Pale bluish pink self; beards tangerine, tipped blue. Dorothy Howard X 8614: ((Miss Oklahoma x 7607: (Dove Wings x ((Wilma V. x unknown) x Little Titan))) x (Show Baby x ((Lenna M x Prophecy) x Dove Wings))). Palmer's Iris 1994.

SONORAN CARNIVAL (Floyd Wickenkamp, R. 1995). Sdlg. SP-89-14. SPU, 40" (102 cm), L. S. violet, yellow center stripe, reverse violet; style arms white, tipped violet; F. orange yellow, heavily striped brown, narrow violet edge, reverse violet. Headway X SP-83-2: (Burnished Brass x SP-79-9: (Burnished Brass x Proverb)). Shepard Iris 1996.

SONORAN CUTIE (Floyd Wickenkamp, R. 1997). Sdlg. SP-90-1. SPU, 28" (71 cm), M. S. medium yellow; style arms yellow, edged white; F. medium yellow, lightly veined darker yellow; ruffled, laced; falls horizontal. First Fruits X Sonoran Senorita. Shepard Iris 1998.

SONORAN SANDS (Richard Tasco, R. 1995). Sdlg. 91-10-07. IB, 24" (61 cm), M. S. golden yellow; style arms yellow; F. lighter yellow, rusty brown sanded wash heaviest on shoulders and near beard, lighter sanding on lower F.; beards orange; lightly ruffled. Panocha X Sam. Superstition 1996.

SONORAN SKIES (Floyd Wickenkamp, R. 1992). Sdlg. SP-88-6. SPU, 43½" (110 cm), M. S. sky blue; F. sky blue, large yellow blaze, lightly lined brownish yellow. Cobalt Mesa X Betty My Love. Shepard Iris 1993.

SONORAN SUNSET (Floyd Wickenkamp, R. 1992). Sdlg. SP-89-5. SPU, 41½" (105 cm), M. S. full red brown; F. ruffled and waved full red brown, yellow blaze extending in rays into base color. Destination X Border Town. Shepard Iris 1993.

SOOTHING (James Burch, R. 1990). Sdlg. 40-19. TB, 36" (91 cm), M. Light lavender (RHS 77C); beards red (43B). 74-14-1: (Winona H x Kimberlina) X Frosty Jewels. Burch Iris 1991.

SOPERNIK (Viacheslav Gavrilin, R. 1998). Sdlg. 7-10-1-94. TB, 32" (82 cm), ML. S. and style arms pink; F. raspberry wine, narrow pink edge; beards red, pinkish lilac hair tips; ruffled. Color Splash X unknown. Gavrilin 1999.

SOPHISTIKITTY (Darlene Pinegar, R. 1997). Sdlg. ME-93-16A. SDB, 11" (28 cm), EM. S. and style arms white; F. violet veined darker, white edge, white hafts marked gold; beards white, dark yellow in throat; lightly ruffled; pronounced sweet fragrance. Making Eyes X Starlight Waltz. Spanish Fork 1998.

SOPRA IL VULCANO (Augusto Bianco, R. 1998). Sdlg. 390-A. BB, 27" (69 cm), M. S. and style arms blended rose, buff and copper; F. velvety red wine, border slightly lighter, distinct white striations on shoulders and around smoky carrot beard; ruffled; slight spicy fragrance. Love Chant X (Sunrise Sunset x Shenanigan). Contemporary, Iride 1998.

SORAK BLUE (Jean Witt, R. 1997). SPEC (*sanguinea*), 24-30" (61-76 cm), M. S. and style arms medium blue; F. slightly deeper medium blue, inconspicuous white signal, hafts veined brown; spathes green. Collected 1982 near Sorak National Park, Korea. Unnamed but in commerce since 1985, Northwest Hybridizers.

SORBET (Mary Dunn, R. 1991). Sdlg. L125-1. LA, 34" (85 cm), M. S. lemon cream; style arms ivory; F. lemony cream, large green center area, lime green line signal. Fantastic X Delta Dawn. Bay View 1992.

SORCERER'S STONE (Robert Dunn, R. 1999). Sdlg. B1069-A. TB, 36" (91 cm), EM. Ruffled cordovan red self; beards bronze; slight spicy fragrance. M786-C, California Classic sib, X M931: (M747: (((((Bang x Edenite) x Martel) x Royal Heritage) x Manuel) x Plum Dazzle) x M699: (Intuition x Cranberry Ice)).

SOROCCO (Donald Spoon, JI, R. 1989). Nicholls Gardens 1990.

SORRENTO CHIARO (Ladislav Muska, R. 1996). Sdlg. SSPL-01. TB, 38" (97 cm), ML. Ruffled mustard gold self; beards yellow; slight fragrance. Silver Shower X Paris Lights. Muska 1993.

SORRENTO MOON (Heather Pryor, R. 1997). Sdlg. 4/91-B. LA, 40" (102 cm), E. S. and F. soft creamy white, veined beige, lime yellow line signal; style arms soft lime green tipped beige; heavily ruffled. Koorawatha X Fat Tuesday.

SOUEICH (Jean Peyrard, R. 1991). Sdlg. 1253. MDB, 4" (10 cm), E. S. yellow; F. greenish yellow, large brown spot; beards yellow white; pronounced sweet fragrance. Parentage unknown -- BIS seed exchange.

SOUL SISTER (Robert Dunn, R. 1995). Sdlg. 2000-4. TB, 37" (94 cm), E. Deep blue violet self; beards blue violet, old gold at end. Skyship X Sea Wolf. M.A.D. Iris 1997.

SOUL SOUND (Barry Blyth, R. 1995). Sdlg. B112-1. BB, 20" (51 cm), EM. S. lilac; F. lilac, heavily overlaid lavender, deepening toward tan hafts, 1/4" to 1/8" honey brown signal spot; beards deep bronze; slight sweet fragrance. Zing Me X Y6-2, Imprimis sib. Tempo Two 1995/96.

SOUPÇON (Lawrence Ransom, R. 1997). Sdlg. 90/434-5. SDB, 10" (25 cm), M. Apricot orange, F. undertoned pink; style arms orange, midrib pink; beards tangerine, cream base. Tiny Cherub X Tabita. Iris au Trescols 1998.

SOUTHDOWNS (Patrick O'Connor, R. 1992). Sdlg. 80-6. LA, 38" (97 cm), EM. Light blue purple with pronounced white underlay, giving pale blue effect, signal orange; style arms white. Cajun Caper X unknown. Bois d'Arc 1993.

SOUTHERN AUTUMN (Ron Busch, R. 1991). Sdlg. 8355/4. TB, 40" (102 cm), M. S. rose white flushed cream; F. brick red, light cream edge; beards golden brown. Parentage unknown. Busch 1992.

SOUTHERN DAWN (Lin Flanagan, R. 1993). Sdlg. 83056-1. AB (OGB), 26" (66 cm), E. S. pale violet blended buff; F. rosy amber, dark red signal; beards brown; ruffled; slight fragrance. 77005-5: (Dune Shadows x Desert Dove) X Springscape. Aril Society 1994.

SOUTHERN OCEAN (Bruce Clark, R. 1997). Sdlg. 94-139. TB, 31" (79 cm), EM. S. and style arms medium blue; F. purplish blue, lighter toward edge; beards light blue, yellow with white base in throat; ruffled. Am I Blue X Pledge Allegiance.

SOUTHERN SON (Currier McEwen, JI, R. 1989). Pope's Perennials, Seaways 1990.

SOUTHERN SONG (Lin Flanagan, R. 1993). Sdlg. 86001-1. AB (OGB), 26" (66 cm), M. S. pale violet; F. dusky amber, slight brown markings around dark violet beard; ruffled, wide recurved form; slight fragrance. Mainstream X Open House. Aril Society 1994.

SOUTHWEST COWGIRL (Alton Pyburn, R. 1999). Sdlg. 97-7A. TB, 28" (71 cm), M. S. white, pallid grape edge; style arms white; F. white ground, narrow deep grape plicata border; beards white; sweet fragrance. Sdlg. X sdlg.

SOUTHWEST LOVE (Alton Pyburn, R. 1999). Sdlg. 206. TB, 28" (71 cm), M. S. blue violet; style arms light blue violet; F. white center, shading to blue violet; beards orange red; sweet fragrance. Irene Nelson X Ah Ça Ira.

SOUTHWEST MARIA (Alton Pyburn, R. 1997). Sdlg. 93-64A. TB, 28½" (72 cm), M. Gold, lightly overlaid brown; beards gold; pronounced sweet fragrance. From sdlgs., parentage unknown.

SOUTHWEST SILVER (Alton Pyburn, R. 1997). Sdlg. 93-241B. TB, 33½" (85 cm), M. Light silver self; beards blue and light gold; pronounced sweet fragrance. Silverado X unknown.

SOUTHWEST TATTOOED LADY (Alton Pyburn, R. 1997). Sdlg. 93-82A. TB, 28½" (72 cm), M. S. soft grape; F. white, striped burgundy; beards orange; pronounced sweet fragrance. Colortart X unknown.

SOUTHWEST VADA LIKES (Alton Pyburn, R. 1997). Sdlg. 93-104V. BB, 26" (66 cm), M. S. white, brushed yellow; F. cadmium yellow edged white; beards orange gold; ruffled; pronounced sweet fragrance. Borderline X unknown.

SOUTH YARRA DARLING (Heather Pryor, R. 1999). Sdlg. 20/94-A. LA, 43" (109 cm), ML. Red brown (RHS 173A), pale lemon rim and reverse, raised yellow steeple signal on all petals; style arms lime green base, yellow midrib, brown tip. 35/92-A: (Volcanic Wildfire x Spanish Ballet) X Hot and Spicy. Iris Haven 1999/2000.

SPACE DANCER (George Sutton, R. 1998). Sdlg. G-27. TB, 36" (91 cm), EM. Heavily ruffled pale lavender (RHS 91D); beards lavender, hairs tipped yellow at end, continuing as lobelia blue (91C) horn. Sky Hooks X Winterscape.

SPACE FILLED (Tomas Tamberg, R. 1997). Sdlg. SSTT279. SIB (tet.), 32" (81 cm), M. S. light blue; style arms medium blue; F. light to medium blue; flowers large, standards upright. Blue Reverie X 8421 medium blue: (Zweites Hundert x Dear Dianne). Joe Pye Weed 1997.

SPACELIGHT SKETCH (Pavel Nejedlo, R. 1998). Sdlg. DERRSM-89-1. TB, 38" (97 cm), M. S. light brown, dotted, lightly veined cocoa brown; style arms brown; F. yellow brown, heavily dotted lavender around mustard beard, heavily washed dark brown, edged lighter; ruffled; pronounced spicy fragrance. Desert Echo X (Rancho Rose x Sketch Me). Lukon 1998.

SPACE MIST (Cy Bartlett, R. 1996). Sdlg. HD-IQ 2. TB, 36" (91 cm), M. S. blended blue and yellow; F. greyed blue, edged yellow; beards blue, horned; ruffled. Howdy Do X Inca Queen. Kelways 1998.

SPACE MOON (Barbara Wight, R. 1995). Sdlg. 90-26-1. BB, 21" (53 cm), E. S. bright yellow; F. white, bright lemon yellow rim, yellow hafts; beards yellow, 1" purple horn; pronounced sweet fragrance. 86-17: (Sky Hooks x Financier) X Sky Hooks. Wight's Iris 1997.

SPACE PIRATE (Monty Byers by Phyllis Dickey, R. 1995). Sdlg. G 54-1. TB, 36" (91 cm), ML & RE. S. deep gold; F. deep gold with deep electric violet overall wash, gold ruffled edge; beards bright yellow ending in electric violet flounce tipped gold; slight sweet fragrance. Syncopation X Fire Within. Misty Hill 1995.

SPACE PSALMS (Hooker Nichols, IB, R. 1988). Hillcrest 1990.

SPACE SHUTTLE CHARMER (Barbara Wight, TB, R. 1989). Wight's Iris 1990.

SPACE SHUTTLE SNOWBALL (Barbara Wight, TB, R. 1989). Wight's Iris 1991.

SPACE STATION (Darlene Pinegar, R. 1997). Sdlg. CL-93-113C. TB, 35" (89 cm), EML. Lightly ruffled light lavender, F. shaded darker in center and with dark gold haft marks; beards bright blue purple, dark brown in throat, with 1-1½" medium purple horn; slight musky fragrance. Codicil X Anne Boleyn. Spanish Fork 1998.

SPANISH BALLET (John C. Taylor, R. 1991). Sdlg. OL 138-1. LA, 36" (91 cm), M. Ruffled cream, (RHS 11D) veined greenish yellow. Dazzling Star X Watch Out. Rainbow Ridge 1992/93.

SPANISH BAY (Lois Belardi, CA, R. 1989). Bay View 1990.

SPANISH BOLERO (Francis Rogers, R. 1997). Sdlg. C-106-J. TB, 42" (107 cm), M. S. and style arms greyed yellow (RHS 162A): F. greyed purple (187A), 1/4" buff (164C) marginal band; beards yellow ochre (22A); spicy fragrance. Chippewa Brave X Gallant Rogue. Meadowbrook 1997.

SPANISH DON (Joseph Ghio, R. 1993) Sdlg. PG-154K. CA, 13" (33 cm), EM. Bright gold with green throat. PI-211J: (Black Eye sib x (Napa Valley x Western World)) X PI-MIX-W2, unknown. Bay View 1994.

SPANISH EMPIRE (Cleo Palmer, SDB, R. 1989). Palmer's Iris 1990.

SPANISH FIESTA (Kirk Strawn, R. 1993). Sdlg. JJJ-1985. LA, 41" (104 cm), M. S. greyed orange (RHS 172C); style arms same with some yellow; F. darker greyed orange (172B), yellow orange (14A) signal. Kirk Strawn X Count Pulaski. Bois d'Arc 1996.

SPANISH FIREBALL (Bennett Jones, R. 1994). Sdlg. 88-5. TB, 38" (97 cm), M. S. cadmium orange (HCC 8); F. lemon yellow (4); beards deep carrot red; slight fragrance. 85-5: (((Orange Chiffon x (((Shoop 59-6-2 x (591-1 x Dream Fashion)) x Gypsy Rings sib) x (918: (591: (Spanish Affair x Marilyn C) x (Spanish Affair x Shoop 58-18)) x Shoop 64-5))) x (((Bright Butterfly x Dream Fashion) x (Bright Butterfly x Spanish Gift)) x ((((Marilyn C x Bright Magic) x 591-1) x Shoop 62-5) x 918-3))) x Early Surprise) X Fame. Aitken's Salmon Creek 1995.

SPANISH ICE (Darlene Pinegar, R. 1991). Sdlg. VF-1-1. TB, 32" (81 cm), M. Ruffled blue white, aging white; beards deep yellow, tipped light blue; moderate sweet fragrance. Victoria Falls X Cloud Fire. Spanish Fork 1992.

SPANISH LIME (Eleanor McCown, R. 1991). Sdlg. 88-10. SPU, 36" (91 cm), L. S. lime yellow tinted tan; F. ruffled deep lime yellow, tiny gold line signal. *I. halophila* sdlg. X Pieces of Eight. Cordon Bleu 1991.

SPANISH SKIES (Darlene Pinegar, R. 1993). Sdlg. VF-1-3. TB, 36" (91 cm), EM. Ruffled medium blue, lighter around beard; beards deep yellow, tipped white. Victoria Falls X Cloud Fire. Spanish Fork 1994.

SPANISH SPIRIT (Kirk Strawn, R. 1993). Sdlg. FFF-1985. LA, 46" (117 cm), M. S. and style arms greyed orange (RHS 178C); F. greyed orange (172B), yellow orange (14A) signal. Kirk Strawn X Count Pulaski. Bois d'Arc 1996.

SPANISH SUNRISE (Henry Rowlan, R. 1990). Sdlg. 89-LA-10. LA, 30" (76 cm), ML. S. mars orange (HCC 013/2); style arms and crests greenish orange; F. burnt orange (014), maroon signal edged orange. Missey Reveley X Dixie Deb. Comanche Acres 1991.

SPARKLE BERRY (Bernard Hamner, R. 1991). Sdlg. 8-535. TB, 32" (81 cm), M. S. white, edged berry red (RHS 180D); F. white, berry red hafts, edge and light crescent lines from tangerine beard; ruffled. Gem of Sierra X Wild Berry. Shepard Iris 1991.

SPARKLETTS (Paul Black, R. 1998). Sdlg. B323A. MDB, 7" (18 cm), M. Ruffled translucent white, S. with greenish midrib, F. with fine greenish haft veining; beards tangerine, white base; pronounced spicy fragrance. 90-303A: (85-368B, Wake Up sib, x Broken Halo sib) X 91-311A: (Broken Halo x 89-235A: ((Apricot Elf x (Melon Honey x unknown)) x ((Melon Honey x unknown) x (Oriental Blush x Sniffs 'n' Sneezes)))). Mid-America 1998.

SPARKLING DEW (Schreiner, R. 1992). Sdlg. S 460-1. TB, 36" (91 cm), L. Laced white (RHS 155C) softly tinted pale lavender; beards yellow, tipped white. Visual Arts X Laced Cotton. Schreiner 1992.

SPARKLING GRAPE (D. L. Shepard, R. 1996). Sdlg. 91001-8912. TB, 31" (79 cm), M. S. violet purple, slight white midrib flush; style arms grape; F. white ground, 1/2" grape purple rim and centerline; beards mustard gold. Dotted Dove X Carnival Magic. Shepard Iris 1996.

SPARKLING SAPPHIRE (Adolph Vogt, JI, R. 1985). Ensata Gardens 1990.

SPARKLING SKY (Cleo Palmer, SDB, R. 1989). Palmer's Iris 1990.

SPATTERPAINT (Donald Sorensen, R. 1995). Sdlg. S-91-11-5. TB, 36" (91 cm), EM. S. white ground, shaded and dotted rose burgundy (RHS 70A); style arms cream, washed burgundy; F. white ground, dotted and splashed purple burgundy (77A); beards rust to red; slight sweet fragrance. Highland Haze X Colortrak.

SPEAKEASY (Donald Denney by James McWhirter, R. 1990). Sdlg. 79-7-2. TB, 36" (91 cm), ML.

Maroon brown blend with deep violet F. blaze; beards brown, tipped mustard; slight fragrance. Bay Rum X Spectacular Bid. Cooley 1990.

SPEAK TO ME (Luella Danielson, R. 1991). Sdlg. D 66. AR (OH), 10" (25 cm), E. S. bluish white, heavily veined blue, dark purple flash inside at midrib; F. bluish white, veined dark purple, central area flushed violet around big violet black signal. (Jewel of Galilee x 59-9) X (Shah Abbas x Fairy Fantasy). Pleasure Iris 1992.

SPECIAL CLASS (Eric Tankesley-Clarke, R. 1995). Sdlg. 392C. IB, 12-18" (31-46 cm), EM. S. soft peach pink (near RHS 36A); F. soft peach pink with prominent light to medium red violet (near 82B) spot; beards tangerine (32C); slight sweet fragrance. Strange Child X Puppy Love. Adamgrove 1995.

SPECIAL EVENT (Lin Flanagan, R. 1997). Sdlg. 89019-2. AB (OGB-), 30" (76 cm), E. S. light yellow; style arms light violet; F. light yellow, rosy center flush; beards greyed orange; ruffled, semi-recurved; slight fragrance. New Moon X 85002-1: (Dunshanbe x Desert Dove). Aril Society 1998.

SPECIAL FRIEND (William Maryott, R. 1992). Sdlg. M137C. TB, 36" (91 cm), M. S. greyed red (RHS 182B) over yellow; F. deep yellow orange (162A) with precise purple (187C) plicata markings on hafts, slight stripe of purple under orange beard. Gigolo X H114A: (Rustic Dance X Beyond). Maryott 1993.

SPECIAL GUEST (Eugene Hunt by Sharon McAllister, R. 1992). Sdlg. ORB 82-2. AB (OGB), 28" (72 cm), EM. S. yellow buff ground overlaid with burgundy flush, giving brick red appearance; F. slightly darker brick red, 1" dark burgundy signal; beards mustard. Probably -- Fourteen for Rachel X Jean Ralls. McAllister 1992.

SPECIAL MOZART (Pierre Anfosso, R. 1991). Sdlg. P 83 13 B. TB, 31½" (80 cm), M. S. bright silver blue, deeper in heart; F. almost white; beards near-white. (Mystique x Flair) X Sea Venture. Iris en Provence 1991.

SPECKLED HEN (Heather Pryor, R. 1994). Sdlg. 31/90-3. LA, 31" (78 cm), E. S. soft peach tan (RHS 179D) veined slightly darker; style arms yellow green, crests bright yellow; F. soft tan (162B) base with rose pink veining and speckling, fine yellow border, yellow signal veined green; lightly ruffled. Myra Arny X Lucy Payens. Iris Haven 1996/97.

SPECK SO (Opal Wulff, R. 1996). Sdlg. 5593. MTB, 20" (51 cm), M. S. and style arms greyed yellow (RHS 162B): F. white ground, violet (86A) heavily-veined edge and mid-petal speckling; beards yellow orange, hairs tipped white. Lisette X Snickerdoodle.

SPECTRAL CHALLENGE (Richard Ernst, R. 1996). Sdlg. KD150-19-2. TB, 37" (94 cm), L. Ruffled yellow (RHS 7B), F. lighter near beard, blended deeper at edge; beards yellow (near 14A). D150-19, Princess Kiss sib, X F125-20: (Edna's Wish x Wild Jasmine). Cooley 1997.

SPEEDING AGAIN (Larry Lauer, R. 1998). Sdlg. 91-247-1R. TB, 38" (97 cm), M & RE. S. light purple, midrib flushed white; style arms light purple; F. light purple, white central flash; beards white, yellow in throat; ruffled; pronounced sweet fragrance. Stellar Lights X Speed Limit. Lauer's Flowers 1998.

SPEED LIMIT (Larry Lauer, R. 1991). Sdlg. L88-48-1. TB, 38" (97 cm), EM & RE. S. medium blue, white spot; F. medium blue, white spot below white beard; ruffled, flared; slight fragrance. Up Periscope X Marine Luster. Cottage 1992.

SPELLBREAKER (Schreiner, R. 1991). Sdlg. T 983-2. TB, 36" (91 cm), ML. Ruffled cranberry violet (RHS 77A); beards white, bushy. J 483-1: (E 575-1: (Y 1735-AA: ((Alpenrose x Anthem) x (Amethyst Flame x Melodrama)) x Y 1734-1: ((Alpenrose x Brigadoon) x (Amethyst Flame x Melodrama))) x Rondo) X Raspberry Frills. Schreiner 1991.

SPELL FIRE (Frederick Kerr, R. 1999). Sdlg. 902410. TB, 37" (94 cm), M. White, S. and hafts lightly tinted blue; beards salmon red; foliage purple-based. Bubble Up X Renoir.

SPENCER FREDERICK (J. Owings Rebert, R. 1999). Sdlg. CB-97-2. SIB, 24" (61 cm), M. Ivory white, F. with gold signal. Parentage unknown.

SPICE ATTACK (John C. Taylor, R. 1998). Sdlg. UL 29-5. LA, 47" (120 cm), L. S. and F. purple violet, midrib darker, buff edge and reverse, yellow signal; style arms buff, brushed purple violet; fluted. Louie X Rachel's Request. Rainbow Ridge 1999/2000.

SPICED GINGER (Bernard Hamner by Shepard Iris Garden, R. 1992). Sdlg. 84-59. TB, 34" (86 cm), EM. S. mustard yellow; F. white ground stitched gingersnap brown, edged brown. (Sketch Me x Shaft of Gold) X (Flamenco x Broadway). Hamner Iris, Shepard Iris 1992.

SPICED TIGER (Brad Kasperek, R. 1994). Sdlg. 91B-7E. TB, 31" (79 cm), E. S. light brown sugar (RHS 165B), butter yellow (2B) at base, lightly splashed with silver white (155C); F. mahogany

(178A) with silver white streaking, shoulders butter yellow overlaid mahogany; beards golden brown; pronounced spicy fragrance; ruffled, crinkled edges. Hot Streak X Tiger Honey. Zebra 1996.

SPICE IS NICE (A. & D. Willott, R. 1992). Sdlg. 89-21. SDB, 12" (30 cm), EM. S. ruffled khaki; F. flaring bright red brown; beards orange and blue. Nachos X Pilgrims' Choice. Willott 1992.

SPICE WORLD (Mary Dunn by Joseph Ghio, R. 1999). Sdlg. L248-8. LA, 34" (86 cm), EM. Mocha tan self, gold fan signal; style arms yellow. ((Charlie's Michele x Rhett) x (Clara Goula x Southerner)) X Rich Tradition.

SPICY RASCAL (Francis Rogers, R. 1993). Sdlg. F-638-Q. TB, 31" (79 cm), M. S. greyed red (RHS 182B); F. greyed yellow (160B) ground, 3/8" edge stitched greyed red (178B), greyed red line below yellow orange beard; ruffled; sweet fragrance. Rancho Rose X unknown. Meadowbrook 1994.

SPICY TWIST (Joy Flint, R. 1995). Sdlg. FL89C14. TB, 28" (71 cm), M & RE. S. medium copper (Pantone 472U), light red orange (1365U) lace; style arms light orange (157U); F. dark copper (1805U) to light copper (473U) at edge, haft markings gold (116U) to white; beards red orange (1655), white tip. Anon X Copper Classic. Monashee Perennials 1997.

SPIFFY (Polly Black, R. 1991). Sdlg. SWC2N1. AB (OGB), 24" (61 cm), E. S. porcelain white, greenish yellow vein accent; F. greenish yellow, deeper toward beard, small black lines in signal area; beards yellow orange, tipped lighter. Kalifa Hirfa X Bangladesh. Polly Black 1991.

SPIN AGAIN (Paul Black, R. 1995). Sdlg. 91216A. SDB, 11" (28 cm), E. S. light yellow; style arms cream; F. white, light yellow rim and reverse; beards yellow orange, lavender white at end; ruffled; slight spicy fragrance. Patacake X 86363A: (Mary's Lamb x Azure Gem). Mid-America 1995.

#SPIN AROUND (Maryott, TB, R. 1986). Stock destroyed, name released.

SPIN DOCTOR (Marvin Davis, R. 1994). Sdlg. 87-165X. TB, 32" (81 cm), E. S. soft mustard yellow; F. creamy yellow ground veined and heavily dotted full dahlia purple, narrow brown purple edge; beards cream, tipped yellow orange; slight spicy fragrance. Rancho Rose X Spinning Wheel. Miller's Manor 1995.

SPINNING SONG (Robert Hollingworth, R. 1996). Sdlg. 88V3B3. SIB, 34" (86 cm), EM. S. red violet; style arms lighter red violet, feathered; F. deep red violet, small white blaze bordered blue; slightly ruffled. 85D4A2: (81D2A37: ((White Swirl x Polly Dodge) x (Polly Dodge x Anniversary)) x Sultan's Ruby) X 85G2A3: (81F3A10: ((Starsteps x New Wine) x (Polly Dodge x Anniversary)) x Lady Vanessa). Greystone 1997.

SPIRIT DANCER (Cleo Palmer, R. 1990). Sdlg. 89110. SDB, 13" (33 cm), L. S. pale lavender blue to ice white; F. very pale lavender blue, large pale lavender spot with turquoise hues and hint of olive green and reddish brown; beards pale yellow, tipped pale blue; slight sweet fragrance. 7259: ((Wilma V x unknown) x Little Titan) X unknown. Palmer's Iris 1991.

SPIRIT OF SOUTHEAST (O. D. Niswonger, R. 1992). Sdlg. 79-89. TB, 36" (91 cm), M. S. gold; F. maroon, very light streak below gold beard, very slight pale edge. All That Jazz X Gatty K41-1: (Show Biz x Villain). Cape Iris 1994.

SPIRITUAL TALE (Ladislav Muska, R. 1996). TB, 38" (97 cm), M. Heavily ruffled and laced light orchid, F. rimmed light brown; beards orange; slight fragrance. Don Epifano X (Don Epifano x "Cipkovana Krinolina": (After All x Grand Waltz)). Muska 1996.

SPIRIT WORLD (Keith Keppel, R. 1992). Sdlg. 86-18D. TB, 36" (91 cm), EM. S. 1/8" to 3/8" irregular marguerite yellow (M&P 10-C-1) edge blending to thistle (42-J-7), deepening in center to english violet (44-K-9); F. 1/8" marguerite edge, blended coronation (46-L-8) to velvety cyclamen (47-L-9) with paler veining, small white area by beards; beards golden poppy (9-L-12) to mikado (2-B-12), paler tip; pronounced sweet fragrance. 84-15A: ((((68-39F: (66-35C: ((Irma Melrose x Tea Apron) x ((Full Circle x Rococo) x Tea Apron)) x April Melody) x 68-39D) x ((Joy Ride x Roundup) x (April Melody x 68-40B: (66-35B x April Melody)))) x (Mistress x 75-98B, Peccadillo sib) x (77-111Q, Gigolo sib, x Rosy Cloud sib)) X 84-15B, sib. Keppel 1994.

#SPITFIRE (H. Groff, TB, R. 1941). Not distributed. Name released 1991.

SPITFIRE (Ben Hager, R. 1991). Sdlg. BB4338FlrTWhRe. BB, 27" (69 cm), E & RE. Ruffled white; beards tangerine red. T3676TWh: (Beverly Sills x Wings of Dreams) X T3848SmRfTWh: (T3301: (Risque x (T2435: Babson M131-4 x Morning Breeze) x Crystal Flame)) x Bride's Lace). Adamgrove 1992.

SPLASHACATA (Richard Tasco, R. 1997). Sdlg. 93-41-15. TB, 35" (89 cm), M. S. pallid violet; style arms same, midrib deeper; F. white ground, allover peppering of purple dots more concentrated at edge; beards white, pale violet cast at end, remainder with hairs tipped golden yellow; lightly ruffled. Purple Pepper X 91-04: (Snowbrook x Jesse's Song). Superstition 1998.

SPLASH OF PURPLE (Floyd Dyer, R. 1991). Sdlg. D158-85-D. SDB, 12½" (30 cm), M. S. white tinted blue; F. buff tinted yellow; beards dark blue; slight musky fragrance. D105-81-D: (Forty Winks x ((Orange Bantam x Knick-Knack) x Gingerbread Man)) X D-112-81-D, unknown. Four Cedars 1991.

SPLASH OF RASPBERRY (Joseph Hoage, R. 1993). Sdlg. H85-14. TB, 36" (91 cm), ML. Raspberry red; beards red. Far Corners X Mulled Wine. Long 1995.

SPLENDID COMPANION (Tony Huber, R. 1998). Sdlg. 92-247 (sel. 95-206). SPEC-X, 43" (110 cm), ML. S. violet (86C); style arms violet, border white; F. deeper violet (86A), bright golden yellow signal with darker halo; slight sweet fragrance. 92-247: (Dom F/3 044: (Belle Promesse x self) x Riopelle) X Belle Promesse.

SPLENDID TOUCH (Chet Tompkins, R. 1998). Sdlg. 94-44C. TB, 38" (97 cm), ML-VL. Moonlight chamois, blended biscuit pink; beards matching. Gossamer Gown sib. Fleur de Lis 1998.

SPLISH SPLASH (Tom Burseen, R. 1993). Sdlg. 9-272F. TB, 37" (94 cm), ML. S. white, light purple (RHS 75C) midrib; F. darker purple (75A), white wash around golden yellow beard; lightly ruffled, fluted; sweet fragrance. Lullaby of Spring X Full Swing. T.B.'s Place 1994.

SPOKEN SOFTLY (Calvin Helsley, R. 1999). Sdlg. 98-2. TB, 32" (81 cm), M. S. white, faint blue tint; style arms and F. pale blue (RHS 97C); beards cadmium orange (23A); ruffled, flared; slight sweet fragrance. Parentage unknown.

SPOONED FANTOM (Lloyd Austin, TB, R. 1959). Incorrectly listed in 1959 Check List as SPOOKED FANTOM.

SPOT IT (Carl Boswell, R. 1995). Sdlg. 65-85-M. MDB, 7" (17 cm), M. S. smoky orchid; F. pale lilac, red maroon spot; beards light lavender. Ace of Clubs X (Gingerbread Man x *I. balkana*). Adamgrove 1997.

SPRAY MATE (Tom Burseen, R. 1993). Sdlg. 8-465A. TB, 30" (76 cm), M. S. violet blue (RHS 89D), lighter center and style arms; F. dark violet blue (89B), vivid white spray below orange beard; laced; sweet fragrance. 6-51: ((Glory Bound x Latin Lover) x Street Walker) X Lace Jabot. T.B.'s Place 1995.

SPREADSHEET (Joseph Ghio, R. 1999). Sdlg. PB-285-O3. CA, 15" (38 cm), EM. Dark blackish crimson. Common Sense X PD-265Z: (Cozumel x PF-159E: (PI-MIX-B2, unknown, x ((Bubbly x (Solid Citizen x (Lighthouse Point x Mission Santa Cruz))) x National Anthem))). Bay View 1999.

SPREE (Keith Keppel, R. 1998). Sdlg. 91-25L. SDB, 15" (39 cm), M. S. and style arms cyclamen (M&P 47-L-8/9); F. coronation purple (46-L-8), center flushed cotinga purple (45-L-10), deeper texture veining; beards blue violet (43-J-10), paler and tipped bronze in throat. Jade Jewels X Chanted. Keppel 1997.

SPRING (Orville Fay, TB, R. 1965). Fay Gardens 1968.

SPRINGBURST (William Ackerman, R. 1998). Sdlg. B3-8. JI (6 F.), 42" (107 cm), M. F. near white ground with fine dusting, mottling and veining of imperial purple (RHS 78A), chartreuse green (154A) signal; style arms white, margins purple, large purple lips. Beni Tsubaki X A4-1-119: (A3-6-177: (D4-6-195 x D4-13-129) x self). Nicholls Gardens 1999.

SPRING CHILD (Barry Blyth, R. 1991). Sdlg. V71-A. TB, 36" (91 cm), EM. Light sky blue; beards white, lemon in throat. Perfect Couple X Pledge Allegiance. Tempo Two 1991/92.

SPRING CONCERTO (Melba Hamblen, R. 1991). Sdlg. 85-19D. TB, 34" (86 cm), ML. S. pink purple (RHS 75A), deepening toward hafts; F. violet (82B), deeper lacy wire edge; beards burnt sienna, tipped violet. Dance Away X Nancy Glazier. Mission Bell 1992.

SPRING FAIR (Opal Brown, R. 1990). Sdlg. 82-20B2. TB, 34" (86 cm), M. Ruffled, flared lavender pink, center of F. lighter; beards henna orange. 78-10C1: (Mystic Vision x Neon Magic) X 79-3J1: (Old Flame x (Spring Bride x Royal Coachman)). Brown's Sunnyhill 1990.

SPRING FRESH (Keith Keppel, R. 1996). Sdlg. 91-25T. SDB, 11" (28 cm), M. Ruffled bright lemon yellow (M&P 10-L-3) self; beards wistaria blue (41-C-8), yellow in throat. Jade Jewels X Chanted. Keppel 1997.

SPRINGHOUSE (Sterling Innerst, R. 1990). Sdlg. 2632-1. TB, 36" (91 cm), EM. Butterscotch, large blue waterfall blaze under beard; beards bronze, tipped gold; slight fragrance. 2152-1: (World News x Show Biz) X 2150-1: (Show Biz x Warmed bythe Sun). Innerst 1991.

SPRING JADE (Edwin Hill, R. 1999). Sdlg. ED 14-15-91G. TB, 30" (76 cm), M. S. cream geen blend; style arms green; F. lavender blue, green hafts and rim; beards gold; laced; pronounced sweet fragrance. Sky Hooks X Evening Mist.

SPRING NUPTIALS (Revie Harvey by Marion Ball, R. 1999). Sdlg. 81/7/11/85. TB, 43-47" (110-120 cm), ML. S. strong coral pink; style arms coral pink; F. coral pink, infused white toward center; beards white, tipped deep coral pink; slight fragrance. (Flamingo Fling x (Saffron Robe x Angel Unawares)) X Beverly Sills.

SPRING PARASOL (Richard Ernst, R. 1993). Sdlg. F119A. TB, 38" (97 cm), ML. Ruffled, laced bright lavender pink, deeper veining, paler area at tip of light orange beard, slight tan shoulder infusion. Afternoon Delight X Gaulter 81-099, inv. Glendale. Cooley 1992.

SPRING PASTEL (Joyce Ragle, R. 1996). Sdlg. 88-14L. BB, 24" (61 cm), M. Ruffled pastel lavender (HCC 440/2), base of S. and F. center lighter; beards poppy red (16/1), end pastel lavender with hairs tipped poppy red; slight fragrance. Pink Bubbles X (Lilac Treat x Pink Sleigh). Lauer's Flowers 1999.

SPRING RHAPSODY (William Maryott, R. 1994). Sdlg. L156A. TB, 38" (97 cm), M. S. light muted lavender to greyed orchid, F. same, paling with age, slight brown hints at shoulders; beards light yellow; sweet fragrance. Sib to Temperence. Maryott 1994.

SPRING SERENADE (Opal Brown, R. 1992). Sdlg. 831A10. TB, 31½" (80 cm), M. Heavily ruffled neyron rose (RHS 55D); beards orange red (33B). ((Schiaparelli x Instant Charm) x Electrabrite) X Cozy and Warm. Brown's Sunnyhill 1992.

SPRING SHADOWS (Marvin Granger, R. 1991). Sdlg. 88-18. LA, 19-20" (48-51 cm), EM. S. light chartreuse yellow; F. medium chartreuse yellow, smoky tan edge, small greenish yellow signal; slight fragrance. Parentage unknown.

SPRING SHOWER (Keith Keppel, R. 1993). Sdlg. 87-97C. TB, 36" (91 cm), EM. S. palest blue (M&P 42-A-1/2) tip, deepening to chicory blue (42-B-7) in center, gentian blue (43-D-10) base; F. blue white (41-A-1) with faint cream sheen; beards white, tipped dandelion (9-L-4), to chrome yellow (9-L-7); ruffled. 82-84D: (Vivien x Battle Fury) X 84-147C: (Skyblaze x Swirling Seas). Keppel 1994.

SPRING SONATA (Franklin Carr, TB, R. 1989). Carr 1991.

SPRING SPLENDOR (Richard Ernst, R. 1991). Sdlg. F169-90. TB, 38" (97 cm), M. S. ruffled lavender infused lemon yellow, yellow highlights on edge; F. pale lavender, yellow laced edge and reverse; beards yellow; ruffled. Afternoon Delight X C142-7: (Ringo x (Cranberry Ice x Grand Waltz)). Cooley 1991.

SPRING SUNSATION (Franklin Carr, R. 1990). Sdlg. 84-3Y. TB, 33" (84 cm), M. S. medium yellow; F. white ground, light yellow margin, light brown plicata shoulder markings; beards yellow; ruffled; slight musky fragrance. Daylight Splendor X Broadway.

SPRING SURPRISE (Tony Huber, R. 1998). Sdlg. 94-69. SPEC-X, 24" (60 cm), M. S. pink to lilac; style arms small, narrow; F. pink to lilac blue; foliage white, cream and variegated before bloom, then turning olive green. From Cobalt-60 irradiated seed -- *I. virginica* var. *shrevei* 90-VTF-90 X *virginica-versicolor* sdlg.

SPRING TAPESTRY (Heather Pryor, R. 1997). Sdlg. 20/92-B. LA, 38" (97 cm), EM. Lightly ruffled cream self with fine golden veining, lime green signal surrounded by golden yellow; style arms lime green, tipped lemon. Koorawatha X 27/90-1: (Rosebery x Old South). Iris Haven 1997/98.

SPRINGTIME BANNER (John Wight, R. 1995). Sdlg. J84-18A. AB (OGB), 19" (48 cm), EM. S. light lavender finely veined purple red, giving violet red effect; F. light cream, rose red haft striations and overlay, black maroon dime-size signal; beards dark bronze brown. Sheik X Dorcas. Aril Society 1995.

SPRINGTIME FIESTA (John Wight, R. 1998). Sdlg. J93-47-3. AB (OGB), 23" (58 cm), M. S. light greyed lavender, veined violet red; F. light greyed lavender, overlaid iridescent fuchsia red, dark violet red thumbprint signal; beard narrow and tapered, orange with dark bronze hair tips. Turkish Tracery X Judean Rouge. Aril Society, Wight's Iris 1998.

SPRINGTIME MELODY (Lorena Reid, R. 1994). Sdlg. 87J19-3. JI (3 F.), 24-36" (76-91 cm), VE. S. pale mauve, deeper mauve veining; style arms deep mauve edged lighter; F. white ground with mauve veins nearly to edge, mauve halo, lemon signal veined deep gold; edges serrate. Springtime Showers X Springtime Snow. Laurie's Garden 1994.

SPRINGTIME PRAYER (Lorena Reid, R. 1994). Sdlg. 87J19-5. JI (3 F.), 30-36" (76-91 cm), VE. Maroon and mauve heavily splashed and veined on light ground, F. with gold signal serrate at edge; style arms deep purple. Springtime Showers X Springtime Snow. Laurie's Garden 1994.

SPRING TWILIGHT (Joseph Gatty by Keith Keppel, R. 1997). Sdlg. X63-4. BB, 26" (66 cm),

ML. Greyed mulberry purple (M&P 45-J-9 to 45-K-10), F. with paler (42-F-5) central overlay, shoulders infused pale flesh (4-E-9) to ivory, veined mulberry; beards amethyst (45-J-8) at end, cacao brown (5-B-11) to brick orange (5-B-12) midsection and throat; ruffled, lightly laced; pronounced musky sweet fragrance. T-1-2: ((Nefertiti x Playgirl) x Presence) X Rare Occasion. Keppel 1998.

SPRING WELCOME (Heather Pryor, R. 1996). Sdlg. 26/90-2. LA, 38" (97 cm), VE-E. Soft lemon veined mauve, F. with bright green to golden yellow blush signal between mauve veining; lightly ruffled. Dazzling Star X Old South.

SPRINKLED SPICE (Polly Black, R. 1995). Sdlg. PAT3-3. TB, 36" (91 cm), M. S. light tan, overall purplish veining; F. tan, purplish veining, unmarked tan marginal band, orange yellow haft markings, plum lines around orange beard; musky fragrance. Afternoon Delight X Tarlatin. Polly Black 1995.

SPRINKLES (Bob Bauer/John Coble, R. 1993). Sdlg. S85B-4. SIB, 32" (82 cm), M. S. lavender (85C) with distinct peppering around edge; style arms pale lavender edged darker, turquoise midrib, crests peppered dark lavender (88B); F. lavender ground (85C) evenly sprinkled violet lavender (88B), lighter toward edge. S82F-21: (Temper Tantrum x unknown) X Esther C.D.M. Ensata Gardens 1994.

SPY (Jim & Vicki Craig, R. 1999). Sdlg. AH28C4. BB, 24" (60 cm), M. S. white ground, solid blue violet band, lighter central wash; style arms deep violet; F. white, deep violet shoulders and sides thinning to narrow stitching at end, central area shaded violet; beards blue, based white in central section, yellow in throat; slight sweet fragrance. Sib to Saucy. J. & V. Craig 1999.

SQUIDDLER (Sterling Innerst, R. 1994). Sdlg. 4140-1. SDB, 12" (30 cm), L. S. moss green, aqua blue midrib; F. aqua blue; beards orange, tipped blue. 3531-10: (Hee Haw x Jeepers) X Assignment. Innerst 1995.

SQUIGGLES (Lynda Miller, R. 1994). Sdlg. 100391. MDB, 5½" (14 cm), EM. Bright canary yellow, F. with few brown rays; beards cream; slight spicy fragrance. 987: (Daring Eyes x Copper Chief) X 2187: (Candy Fluff x Bright Vision). Miller's Manor 1995.

STACY LESTER (Alice Kronebusch, TB, R. 1986). Holly Lane 1990.

STACY RUTH (Marle Smith, R. 1997). TB, 30" (76 cm), L. S. blue orchid; style ams white, tinged blue; F. silvery blue orchid; beards gold, light blue tip; heavily ruffled, lightly laced. (Fragrant Lilac x Winterscape) X Honky Tonk Blues.

STAGE LIGHTS (Joseph Ghio by Maryott's Gardens, R. 1998). Sdlg. 94-170-O2. TB, 38" (97 cm), M. S. light peach, midrib flushed maroon; style arms light peach; F. medium maroon luminata wash, light peach veining and halo around peach beard, shoulders flushed orange. New Leaf X 92-159-I2: (Spirit World x 90-54-I: (Chatter sib x (((((Handiwork x (Gay Parasol x Mystique)) x Goddess) x (Gem of Sierra x ((((Ponderosa x Honey Rae) x ((((Commentary x Claudia Rene) x Claudia Rene) x Ponderosa) x (Ponderosa x New Moon))) x Osage Buff) x (Vanity x Anon)))) x Gigolo) x (Desert Fox x Shenanigan)))). Maryott 1999.

STAGE SHY (John C. Taylor, R. 1993). Sdlg. RL 42-1A. LA, 55" (140 cm), EM. S. light yellow, magenta midline and flush; F. magenta pink, rimmed yellow, yellow signal with light green line. Dawn Planet X OL 113-1: (Koorawatha x Dazzling Star). Rainbow Ridge 1993/94.

STAIRWAY TO HEAVEN (Larry Lauer, R. 1992). Sdlg. L87-48-3. TB, 40" (102 cm), EM. S. creamy off-white; F. medium blue undertoned lavender; beards white; slight fragrance. Edith Wolford X Breakers. Cottage 1993.

STAND BY ME (Margie Robinson, R. 1995). Sdlg. 88-44. BB, 25" (64 cm), M. Light orange (RHS 24D) self; style arms and crests flushed pink; beards solid red orange (33B); finely laced; pronounced sweet fragrance. (Bright Spirit x Something Special) X Florentine Fable.

STANDING OVATION (John Nelson by Bryce Williamson, R. 1995). TB, 34" (86 cm), M. Lightly ruffled deep watermelon pink self; beards coral red. Inv. Wenatchee Valley, Glacier Sunset, Buffy, Coral Comments, Pink Sleigh and Pink Taffeta. Pacific Coast Hybridizers 1990.

STAN'S DREAM (Stan Dexter by Marie Ingersoll, R. 1995). Sdlg. 7-66A. TB, 36" (91 cm), M. S. white; F. tan pink, hafts more tan; beards orange, white tip. Beachgirl X 1980-99C: (Coral Magic x unknown). Ingersoll's Iris 1996.

STANZA (Monty Byers, R. 1990). Sdlg. E77-100. BB, 24" (61 cm), EM & RE. S. white, heavily overlaid with spray of light red violet mottling; F. white, stippled cinnamon over hafts, light red violet around edge; beards yellow orange; heavily ruffled; slight sweet fragrance. (Re-Treat x Sky Hooks) X sib. Moonshine 1991.

STARBABY (Marky Smith, R. 1992). Sdlg. 88-02A. SDB, 13½" (35 cm), E. S. white ground, heavily dotted and washed dark violet (RHS 83A), 3/8" solid dark violet edge; F. white, 1/8" solid dark violet edge widening to 3/8" on chestnut-toned shoulders, random dark stitching inside rim; beards white, tipped medium dark blue violet; ruffled; slight sweet fragrance. Peso X Chubby Cheeks. Aitken's Salmon Creek 1993.

STARBLAZE (J. D. Stadler, R. 1992). Sdlg. J29/9. TB, 30" (76 cm), M. Golden yellow, F. hafts with dark brown markings; beards deep yellow; heavily ruffled; slight fragrance. Veneer X Flamenco.

STARBOUND (Janet Hutchinson, R. 1995). Sdlg. GLB2. LA, 39" (100 cm), ML. S. white, veined olive buff, centerline pinkish mauve; style arms white, washed cream, mauve to buff; F. deep mauve pink, white linear edge, small signal yellow green over white; ruffled; petals serrate; slight sweet fragrance. Glowlight X -- probably Buxom.

STARDUST MEMORIES (Schreiner, R. 1990). Sdlg. W 208-1. TB, 36" (91 cm), EM. White ground plicata stitched lavender pink (RHS 80B); beards yellow, tipped lavender. R 183-1: (Master Touch x J 483-4, sib to pod parent of Spellbreaker) X T 1982-B, unknown. Schreiner 1990.

STARDUST ROAD (Ed Roberts, R. 1991). Sdlg. 912. TB, 38" (97 cm), M. S. chartreuse; F. greyish lilac, deep chartreuse hafts, chartreuse edge; beards gold. Plum Gleam X Chartreuse Ruffles. Ed Roberts 1994.

STARE STEALER (Tom Burseen, R. 1993). Sdlg. 7-195C. TB, 35" (89 cm), ML. S. purple pink (RHS 70C), toasted edge; F. golden amber (31B) washed cream pink in center, toasted edge; beards orange; heavily laced; musky fragrance. Lace Jabot X Feminine Wiles. T.B.'s Place 1994.

STAR FLEET (Keith Keppel, R. 1992). Sdlg. 86-32A. TB, 38" (97 cm), ML. S. near mulberry purple (M&P 45-J-10); F. near canterbury purple (43-J-12), slightly redder on margins, dark rosy brown (47-E-3) haft suffusion; beards tomato red (3-I-12) to orange vermilion (2-G-12), tipped lavender. 81-54A: (((((Arctic Flame x (Rippling Waters x Gypsy Lullaby)) x Touche) x (65-32A: (Marquesan Skies x Babbling Brook) x Touche)) x Firewater) x (Firewater x (((B. Jones 743 x 65-32A) x ((Morning Breeze x Babbling Brook) x B. Jones 730-1)) x Intuition))) X 83-39B: (Orangerie x Lady Friend). D & J Gardens 1993.

STAR GLORY (Graeme Grosvenor, R. 1993). Sdlg. Q9-1. TB, 40" (102 cm), EM. Ruffled purple self; beards blue; pronounced sweet fragrance. Scented Nutmeg X (Titan's Glory x Star Wars). Rainbow Ridge 1996/97.

STAR IMAGE (Cleo Palmer, R. 1993). Sdlg. 8976. SDB, 12" (30 cm), L. S. lavender, base deeper; F. lilac lavender, dark red violet spot; beards yellow, tipped lavender. Parentage unknown. Palmer's Iris 1993.

STARKER'S PINK (Philip Edinger, R. 1999). SPEC (*unguicularis*), 6-9" (15-23 cm), ML (winter). Light orchid pink. Parentage and origin unknown; distributed ca. 1950 by Carl Starker, Jennings Lodge, OR.

STARLETTE ROSE (Richard Cayeux, R. 1995). Sdlg. 8847 A. TB, 32" (80 cm), EM. Bright shrimp pink; beards red. 8344 A ((Ovation x Premier Bal) x (Pink Angel x Playgirl)) X 8503: ((Metropolitan x Loudoun Lassie) x ((Condottiere x Metropolitan) x sib)). Cayeux 1996.

STARLIGHT EXPRESS (Schreiner, R. 1994). Sdlg. W 757-3. TB, 34" (86 cm), EM. S. bright canary yellow; F. white, bright canary yellow hafts and 1/4" edge; beards yellow; ruffled, flared. 1979 Greenie, unknown, X S 659-1, Outrageous Fortune sib. Schreiner 1994.

STARLIT VELVET (Harold Stahly, R. 1990). Sdlg. 86-6. TB, 36" (91 cm), M. Ruffled velvety deep black purple (deeper than RHS 79A), small white spray pattern around beard; beards purple, tipped deep bronze. Night Lady X Spinning Wheel. Stahly 1991.

STAR OF AFRICA (Perry Dyer, R. 1998). Sdlg. 89-21A. SDB, 14" (36 cm), EM. Light chicory blue self; beards medium sapphire blue. Blue Line X Serenity Prayer. Contemporary 1999.

STAR OF SPRING (Lin Flanagan, R. 1999). Sdlg. 83045-4. AB (OGB), 26" (66 cm), M. S. and style arms light tan red blend; F. red brown blend, red brown blaze around dark red black beard; ruffled, F. recurved; slight fragrance. Springscape X Warrior's Mantle.

STAROYE TANGO (Sergey Loktev, R. 1997). Sdlg. L-III-7A. TB, 35" (88 cm), M. Lilac self, bottom of F. slightly darker; beards yellow, near-white at end; slight fragrance. Marina Raskova X Stepping Out. Loktev 1997.

STARPLE (Tom Burseen, R. 1993). Sdlg. 9-215M. TB, 34" (86 cm), M. S. straw yellow (RHS 168D); F. bright lemon ground with red purple (71B) plicata wash; beards gold; ruffled, lightly laced; spicy fragrance. Point Made X 6-146: (Rio de Oro x Noon Siesta). T.B.'s Place 1994.

STAR POWER (Mary Dunn, R. 1993). Sdlg. L122-3. LA, 36" (91 cm), M. Ruffled velvety plum purple, medium-size spear-shaped gold signal. L78-1: (Bajazzo x Full Eclipse) X Clara Goula. Bay View 1993.

STAR QUALITY (Joseph Ghio, R. 1995). Sdlg. 91-132-J2. TB, 35" (89 cm), ML. Rosy garnet self; beards red. 88-129-R2: ((82-135-T4, Romantic Mood sib, x 82-16G: ((Paris Original sib x ((Princess x (Pink Sleigh x (Opening Round x Champagne Music))) x (Louise Watts x (Ghost Story x Ponderosa)))) x (((Louise Watts sib x ((((Commentary x Claudia Rene) x Claudia Rene) x Ponderosa) x (Ponderosa x New Moon))) x Crystal Dawn) x (Preface sib x Crystal Dawn)))) x Lightning Bolt) X 88-95-I2: ((Caption x (Classico x ((Preface sib x Crystal Dawn) x ((Datebook x (Ponderosa x (Ponderosa x New Moon))) x Actress)))) x Lightning Bolt). Bay View 1996.

STARQUEST (A. & D. Willott, R. 1994). Sdlg. 93-5. SDB, 11" (28 cm), EM. S. creamy white; F. medium yellow, edge slightly lighter; beards white, orange in throat; ruffled. Coral Light X 79-13: (Greenlee GX-2: ((White Mite x self) x (*I. pumila alba* x Hanselmayer)) x Buttons). Willott 1995.

STARRING (Joseph Ghio, R. 1999). Sdlg. U92-5R. TB, 33" (84 cm), ML. S. white; style arms white, gold-fringed crests; F. purple black; beards brick red. Probably -- Romantic Evening sdlg.

STAR SAILOR (Schreiner, R. 1994). Sdlg. BB 169-2. TB, 36" (91 cm), EML. Ruffled light blue (RHS 100C) self; beards yellow, tipped white. W 90-D: S 26-2: (Land o'Lakes x (G 11-1, St. Louis Blues sib, x (D 39-F: (Tufted Cloud sib x ((Sparkling Waters x Sierra Skies) x Music Maker)) x Sailor's Dance))) x S 20-3: (M 21-1, Tide's In sib, x unknown)) X Jean Hoffmeister. Schreiner 1995.

STARS AND STRIPES (Monty Byers by Phyllis Dickey, R. 1992). Sdlg. F54-1. TB, 36" (91 cm), ML. S. smooth very pale violet; F. violet; beards white, tipped bright red, violet horn. Vanity X ((Sky Hooks x Condottiere) x Conjuration). Moonshine 1992.

STARS AT NIGHT (Ben Hager, R. 1995). Sdlg. S897DpVBrtSp. SPU, 37" (94 cm), EM. Dark maroon violet (near black), F. with smallish bright deep yellow signal spot. Crow Wing X Far Out. Adamgrove 1997.

STARSHIP ENTERPRISE (Schreiner, R. 1999). Sdlg. CC 758-B. TB, 36" (91 cm), ML. S. crystalline white (RHS 155D), midrib golden yellow; F. light creamy yellow (10A) to white, yellow shoulders, 2" rosy magenta (71B) marginal band; beards golden yellow. AA 1324-G: (Gypsy Woman x N 502-FF: (I 335-5: ((C 973-A: (Lilac Champagne x (Toll Gate x After Dark)) x ((Alpenrose x Whole Cloth) x Cashmere)) x (C 973-A x (((Broadway Star x Giant Rose) x ((Maytime x Opal Beauty) x Whole Cloth)) x Wine and Roses))) x H 238-A: ((Champagne Music x (R 1052-2 x Christmas Time)) x (Orchid Brocade x (Annabel Lee sib x Emma Cook))))) X AA 1374-A: ((Sailmaster x ((Mysterious x (Matinata x (Agatine x Tompkins 50-82) x Edenite))) x (Shoreline sib x Brook Flower))) x Ragtime). Schreiner 1999.

STARSTRUCK (James Burch, R. 1990). Sdlg. 44-6. TB, 34" (86 cm), M. S. ruffled light orange (RHS 24A), almost coral at midrib; F. yellow orange (22A); beards orange red (32A). Mandolin X Fresno Calypso. Burch Iris 1990.

STAR SURGE (George Sutton, R. 1999). Sdlg. H-254. TB, 36" (91 cm), ML. S. and style arms imperial purple (RHS 77B); F. imperial purple (78A) speckled white, lower third dark plum purple (79) with thin white to violet edge; beards bronze; ruffled; slight spicy fragrance. Power Surge X Rock Star.

STAR SYMPHONY (Vernon Wood, R. 1991). Sdlg. 91-1. CA, 12" (30 cm), E. S. white, heavily lined purple violet (RHS 80A), 1/4" white edge; F. lined and flushed purple violet deepening to near solid violet (83A) in center, 3/16" white edge. Solid Citizen X Different Drummer.

STARTING VERSI-LAEV (Tomas Tamberg, R. 1993). SPEC-X (tet.), 24" (60 cm), ML. S. blue purple; F. deep blue purple, yellowish signal. 8356AC (converted): (wine red *I. versicolor* x Regal) X self. Schoeppinger 1994.

STAR TRACKS (Loleta Powell, R. 1996). Sdlg. 93-2. TB, 39" (99 cm), EML. S. pale blue, royal violet toward center; style arms pale blue; F. pale blue, sprayed royal violet in center; beards yellow, pale blue tip; ruffled; pronounced sweet fragrance. Timescape X Pacific Mist.

STAR TRIP (Barbara Wight, R. 1993). Sdlg. 86-25. BB, 26" (66 cm), M. Ruffled greyed red mauve (RHS 186C); beards yellow, tipped mauve, short mauve horn; ruffled; slight sweet fragrance. Battle Star X 82-50: (Jack R. Dee x 79-150). Wight's Iris 1993.

STARWARD (Chet Tompkins, R. 1994). Sdlg. R81-22. TB, 44" (112 cm), M-VL. S. white, edged blackish violet; F. white, edged blackish purple; beards bronze. 8-4-17: (sib x Flickering Firelight) X 8-14-17: (Flickering Firelight x sib). Fleur de Lis 1994.

STAR WISH (Barbara Wight, R. 1998). Sdlg. 94-1. TB, 35" (89 cm), E. Light peach self; beards tangerine, long lavender horn; slight sweet fragrance. Beverly Sills X 90-22: (Hubble Space Telescope x 86-17: (Sky Hooks x Financier)). Wight's Iris 1998.

STAR WITNESS (Joseph Ghio, R. 1997). Sdlg. PD-205C. CA, 12" (31 cm), EM. Creamy yellow self, white signal. PF-154U: (PI-MIX-R, unknown, x Eagle Eyes) X PH-266H: (Las Lomas x Aftershock sib). Bay View 1997.

STARWOMAN (Marky Smith, R. 1997). Sdlg. 90-26E. IB, 25" (64 cm), M. S. blackish royal purple (blacker than RHS 86A), faint lavender grey marks at deep purple midrib; style arms strong mauve violet, edges greyer; F. pearl (lighter than 156D) ground, 1/2" darkest black violet (darker than 86A) rim and center stripe, dark violet dashing and stitching within rim; beards blue violet at end, gold-tipped blue violet central area, yellow in throat; ruffled; slight sweet fragrance. Chubby Cheeks X Keppel 83-8A: (Snowbrook x sib). Aitken's Salmon Creek 1998.

STARY SAMOVAR (Viktor Koroliov, R. 1995). Sdlg. S-2 86K. TB, 39" (100 cm), M. Dark yellow, F. shaded brown; beards yellow; pronounced spicy fragrance. "Zhiolty Velikan" X Siegfried. Koroliov 1991.

STATELY ART (J. T. Aitken, R. 1997). Sdlg. 91T14. TB, 44" (112 cm), ML. Medium blue self; beards bright coral red. (Vivien x Irene Nelson) X (Secret Cove x Irene Nelson). Aitken's Salmon Creek 1997.

STATELY FLAMINGO (Adolph Vogt, JI, R. 1987). Ensata Gardens 1990.

STATIC (Paul Black, R. 1996). Sdlg. 91306B. SDB, 14" (36 cm), E. S. pale buff pink, wide violet plicata band; style arms pale buff pink; F. warm pinkish white, violet plicata markings; beards whitish violet to violet, tangerine in throat; slight spicy fragrance. 87132CC: (Chubby Cheeks x Catani) X Wake Up sib. Mid-America 1996.

STATUS (Barry Blyth, R. 1996). Sdlg. C27-A. SDB, 12-14" (30-36 cm), ML. Rich orange; beards orange tangerine; slight fragrance. Scion X Carats. Tempo Two 1996/97.

STATUS SEEKER (Lilly Gartman, TB, R. 1988). Roris 1990.

STAVROPOLSKI (Galina Shevchenko, R. 1995). MDB, 7" (17-18 cm), E. Ruffled dark purple violet; beards orange, base brown; pronounced spicy fragrance. From *I. pumila* sdlgs. Shevchenko 1992.

STAVROPOLSKIYE STEPI (Galina Shevchenko, R. 1995). MDB, 7" (17-18 cm), E. Light yellow, few brown strokes; beards white at end, light yellow middle, dark yellow in throat; pronounced spicy fragrance. From *I. pumila* sdlgs. Shevchenko 1992.

STAY TUNED (Tom Burseen, R. 1991). Sdlg. 7-302A. TB, 34" (86 cm), EM. S.orange tan (RHS 34D); F. gold ground heavily streaked rusty maroon red (175B), hairline cream yellow edge; beards yellow; ruffled; musky fragrance. Oh Babe X 4-94: (Wild Berry x Medieval). T.B.'s Place 1992.

STEADFAST LOVE (Franklin Carr by Margaret Carr, R. 1994). Sdlg. 87-96FL. TB, 37" (94 cm), M. S. light blue, darker at base; F. pale to light blue, white infusion around beard; beards light blue white, yellow in throat. Edge of Winter X Chico Maid.

STEALING HOME (Louise Bellagamba, SDB, R. 1988). Bella Vista 1990.

STEEL CITY (Graeme Grosvenor, R. 1998). Sdlg. U115-1. TB, 36" (91 cm), M. S. light blue, midrib flushed darker; F. dark blue; beards blue, yellow in throat. Nordic Seas X Best Bet. Rainbow Ridge 1998/99.

STEFFIE (Kenneth Fisher, R. 1992). Sdlg. 89-1. MTB, 20" (51 cm), M. S. white; F. white with violet spray pattern; beards cream. 2M: (unknown sdlg. x 79-2: (Amethyst Sunset x Buenita)) X TC4: (Pink Kewpie x Puppy Love). Aitken's Salmon Creek 1993.

STEFFIE ANN (Everette Lineberger, R. 1999). Sdlg. QHT 134. TB, 40" (107 cm), EM. Ruffled white; beards red orange, lavender horn. Ann X Twice Thrilling.

STEFFI SCHADE (Manfred Beer, R. 1991). Sdlg. MB 30/84. TB, 41" (105 cm), M. S. white ground stitched light blue violet; F. white, stitched light blue violet edge; beards yellow. On the Go X Rondo. Gartencenter Kania 1991.

STEINBECK COUNTRY (Joseph Ghio, R. 1997). Sdlg. PD-196H2. CA, 12" (31 cm), ML. Buckskin self, mahogany signal. PF-148M2, Point Santa Cruz sib, X Osocales. Bay View 1997.

STEINHUDER MEER (Harald Moos, R. 1995). Sdlg. 91/A 42 y. TB, 36" (91 cm), M. Dark blue self; beards blackish blue; waved. Dusky Challenger X Five Star Admiral. Schoeppinger 1996.

STELLA IRENE (B. Charles Jenkins, R. 1995). Sdlg. BD29A. SPU, 38-47" (97-119 cm), M. S. dark purple; F. black purple, narrow yellow signal. B3-5B: (Crow Wing x Equality) X Purple Reign. Shepard Iris 1995.

STELLA NIAGARA (Anna Rettig, R. 1995). Sdlg. AR-039. JI (3 F.), 35" (89 cm), M. S. white, edged violet (RHS 87A); style arms white, edged violet (88A); F. blue violet (87A) with prominent white veining, very small yellow signal obscured by style arms. Parentage unknown; seed from Dr. Nigishi, Japan. A & M Perennials 1995.

STELLA PELISSOT (John C. Taylor, R. 1993). Sdlg. RL 40-1. LA, 55" (140 cm), ML. S. light purple ground, darker feathering; F. purple, yellow signal; ruffled. Heliostat X Margaret Lee. Rainbow Ridge 1993/94.

STEPANYCH (Viacheslav Gavrilin, R. 1998). Sdlg. 4-8-3-94. TB, 35" (90 cm), EM. S. and style arms whitish light brown; F. violet, lighter below beard, brown hafts and indistinct rim; beards lilac to violet, hairs tipped brown; slight fragrance. Darkside X unknown. Gavrilin 1999.

STEP ASIDE (Luella Danielson, R. 1990). Sdlg. A86-L1. AB (OGB), 30" (76 cm), M. S. medium to dark lavender (RHS 82D), darker veining; style arms with gold crests infused F. color; F. bright red (187B) edged tan gold, brown red (183A) signal, black markings around brown red beard. Bionic Burst X Bionic Flash. Pleasure Iris 1991.

STEP BEYOND Tom Burseen, R. 1991). Sdlg. 8-499A. TB, 36" (91 cm), EM. S. blended light grape (RHS 85A to 88D); F. cream ground, heavily stippled, washed and streaked grape (86A); beards gold; ruffled; spicy fragrance. 4-85B: (Pencil Sketch x Barletta) X 6-107A: ((Pencil Sketch x Pinwheel) x (Theatre x Dazzling Gold)). T.B.'s Place 1992.

STERLING FLURRY (Sterling Innerst, R. 1991). Sdlg. 3344-2. TB, 32" (81 cm), ML. White, edged medium blue; beards blue, tipped yellow; slight sweet fragrance. Rain Flurry X Sterling Stitch. Innerst 1992.

STERLING PRINCE (Sterling Innerst, R. 1983). Correction of parentage. 720-1: (Pencil Sketch x Hankins 69-1: (High Life x Wild Ginger)) X Flamenco.

STEVIE C (C. & R. Schulz, TB, R. 1989). Wild Mountain Thyme 1990.

STEWARDESS (Adolf Volfovich-Moler, R. 1998). Sdlg. V-154. TB, 43" (110 cm), M. Ruffled light blue violet self; beards yellow, pale purple at end; slight fragrance. Victoria Falls X Mary Frances. Volfovich-Moler 1999.

STILLNESS (Barry Blyth, R. 1995). Sdlg. A63-B. TB, 36-38" (91-97 cm), ML. S. creamy apricot; F. creamy white, deepening to creamy apricot toward edge, deeper fall reverse; beards apricot orange, base white; slight musky fragrance. Dance Man X Rembrandt Magic. Tempo Two 1995/96.

STINGER (Monty Byers, R. 1991). Sdlg. G18-2. SDB, 13" (33 cm), M. S. maize yellow, faint light violet center speckling; F. maize yellow hafts, white center, half-halo of violet stitching, blended outer rim; beards burnt yellow orange, deep purple horn. Muchacha X Egyptian. Misty Hill 1994.

STINTFANG (Lothar Denkewitz, R. 1990). Sdlg. N-80-var-1. SDB, 9" (23 cm), M. S. clear yellow; F. yellow, mahogany spot; beards light blue, tipped yellow; slight sweet fragrance. (Paricutin x Watercolor) X Tiger Blaze. Adamgrove 1989.

STIPPLED LADY (Jack Norrick, R. 1995). Sdlg. 91-2. MTB, 18" (46 cm), ML. S. white, peppered violet; F. white, heavier violet haft peppering; beards yellow. White Canary X Jubie. Miller's Manor 1996.

STITCHED NETS (Ladislav Muska, R. 1999). Sdlg. FGQF-04. TB, 37" (94 cm), M. S. light maroon, deep cream rim; style arms mustard; F. white and yellow ground, wide heavily stitched light maroon edge; beards mustard; heavily ruffled, laced. (((Funny Bird x Graffiti) x Date Bait) x (Queen in Calico x French Gown)) X Ri-Sampei. Muska 1998.

STOCK EXCHANGE (Graeme Grosvenor, R. 1996). Sdlg. R3-3. TB, 35" (88 cm), EM. Medium blue self; beards blue, hairs tipped yellow. Skyblaze X Silverado. Rainbow Ridge 1996/97.

STOLEN DREAMS (Ben Hager, TB, R. 1989). Roris 1990.

STONEWASHED (Dana Borglum, R. 1993). Sdlg. C-2-15. TB, 30" (76 cm) E & RE. S. light blue with white and dark blue streaks; F. light blue, heavier streaking; beards yellow, tipped white. Doodle Strudel X Earl of Essex. Borglum's Iris 1995.

STOP AND GO (Mary Dunn, R. 1995) Sdlg. L159-11. LA, 35" (89 cm), M. Rosy shrimp red, F. with large yellow signal; style arms pale yellow. Southerner X L96-15: (Charlie's Michele x Rhett). Bay View 1996.

STOP THE NATION (John C. Taylor, R. 1995). Sdlg. RL 25-5. LA, 43" (110 cm), ML. S. white; style arms cream, blushed pink; F. mauve-toned pink (RHS 65C) heavily veined darker violet pink, white around yellow to green signal, lighter fall rim. Margaret Lee X Dancing Vogue. Rainbow Ridge 1995/96.

STORM BLUE (Pauline Evans, R. 1997). Sdlg. 92/3. SPU, 60" (153 cm), ML. Ruffled smoky deep lavender purple, F. with small gold signal. Missouri Blue X Missouri Gal. Tempo Two 1997/98.

STORM WATCH (Jim Hedgecock, R. 1990). Sdlg. 83-96-5. TB, 33" (84 cm), M. Ruffled royal blue, slight silver area by silver beards; pronounced fragrance. Navy Strut X Victoria Falls. Comanche Acres 1991.

STORMY CINDY (D. L. Shepard, R. 1998). Sdlg. 89007-8649. TB, 38" (97 cm), M. S. sandy mauve; F. grape purple, edged soft grape; beards yellow, orange in throat; heavily ruffled. Wedding Vow X Rustic Dance. Shepard Iris 1998.

STORMY CIRCLE (Barry Blyth, R. 1995). Sdlg. C30-3. SDB, 14" (36 cm), EM. S. solid bishops purple to purple violet; F. white, 1/2" plicata edge matching S. color; beards white, tipped violet on outer 1/2", tangerine in throat; slight sweet fragrance. A30-5, Imbue sib, X A21-20: (X20-A: (Camarilla x Yipee) x Chanted). Tempo Two 1995/96.

STORMY LIZ (Wanda Dow, R. 1992). Sdlg. LBB-IR-1. IB, 24" (61 cm), M. Greyed purple (RHS 187A), slight haft markings on F.; beards blue, tipped yellow; slight fragrance. Little Black Belt X Ida Red.

#STORMY WEATHER (Chet Tompkins, TB, R. 1942). Not introduced, name released 1982.

STORMY WEATHER (Chet Tompkins, R. 1995). Sdlg. 80-20. TB, 39" (99 cm), EML. S. amber buff blend; F. violet, blended red copper and fuchsia, copper edge; beards smoky red, base blue. (((Cosmopolitan x Gypsy Prince) x Star Spangled) x Stately Mansions) X (Hamblen sdlg. x Air Bubbles). North Cascade Gardens 1982.

STORYLAND (Duane Meek, R. 1995). Sdlg. G9-2-8. TB, 33" (84 cm), M. Intense pink, F. with lighter area below coral red beard; ruffled, lightly laced, style crests fringed. (Blond Goddess x Chanteuse) X Blushing Pink. D & J Gardens 1995.

STORYLINE (Joseph Ghio, TB, R. 1989). Bay View 1990.

STORYTELLER (Joseph Ghio, R. 1993). Sdlg. 88-26A. TB, 40" (102 cm), EM. S. fuchsia, apricot at base; F. light salmon ground edged fuchsia, dotted inside band; beards burnt orange. (Chuckles x Romanticist) X Storyline. Bay View 1994.

ST. PETERSBURG (Monty Byers, R. 1989). Moonshine 1990.

STRAIGHT BURGUNDY (Cy Bartlett, R. 1995). Sdlg. T.BF. IB, 20" (51 cm), M. S. wine purple; F. deeper wine purple; beards wine purple; lightly waved. Tease X Black Flag. Sutton 1996.

STRANGE BUTTERFLY (Tony Huber, R. 1998). Sdlg. 95-146 (91-545). SPEC-X (versata), 30" (75 cm), EML. S. violet (RHS 86B); style arms violet blue (96A), bordered mauve and white; F. dark blue violet (89B), light yellow signal surrounded by white-veined or -striped zone. MR 03-14 *versicolor*. (MR03-555 x ex MR-03) X white 6-F. *ensata* sdlg.

STRANGE FANTASY (Tony Huber, R. 1998). Sdlg. 94-30. SPEC-X (biversata), 26" (65 cm), EM. S. purple (RHS 79C); style arms purple center bordered pink, crest lilac; F. deeper purple (79B) changing to purplish violet (82A), haft and signal brown, veined yellow and white. Dom 031: (Belle Promesse x Nouvel Age) X Dom 031.

STRATHMORE (Cedric Morris, TB, R. 1948). R. Wallace & Co. 1949.

STRATO CUMULUS (Tom Burseen, R. 1991). Sdlg. 6-312B. TB, 38" (97 cm), ML. S. creamy lemon (RHS 158B); F. light violet (85B), washed somewhat darker; beard grey, tipped tan; heavily ruffled, flared. Merry Madrigal X Local Motion sib. T.B.'s Place 1997.

STRAWBERRY APRICOT (Donald Spoon, R. 1995). Sdlg. 93-10A. BB, 27" (69 cm), EM & RE (Oct./VA). S. light pink (RHS 36D); F. and style arms apricot (23D); beards darker orange pink (30B). Roney's Encore X Ozark Evening. Winterberry 1999.

STRAWBERRY FAIR (Robert Hollingworth, R. 1992). Sdlg. 87Q6C5. SIB (tet.), 29" (74 cm), L. Heavily ruffled crushed strawberry pink, small white signal; style arms light blue. 81C2C5(T): (Pink Haze x Wing on Wing) X Jewelled Crown. Windwood Gardens 1994.

STRAWBERRY PLAINS (William Grise, R. 1999). Sdlg. BRX-2. TB, 35" (89 cm), ML. S. light yellow; style arms dark gold edges, pale center; F. strawberry lavender, faint white streaking, narrow light yellow rim; beards golden yellow; slight musky fragrance. Gay Parasol X Ringo.

STRAWBERRY SWIRL (Chet Tompkins, R. 1993). Sdlg. 89-183A. TB, 38" (97 cm), ML. S. creamy white; F. rich strawberry pink tinted lilac, ruffled creamy white edge; beards rose pink. Sdlg. lines inv. Camelot Rose, Clarion Call, Blushing Butterfly, Armageddon and Heavenly Body. Fleur de Lis 1993.

STREETCAR NAMED DESIRE (John Durrance, R. 1990). Sdlg. D86-32. TB, 34" (86 cm), M. S. pink; F. white, edged pink; beards pink, tipped light blue. Hamblen 81-16B X Love Scene. Long 1990.

STREET OF DREAMS (Frank Foster, R. 1995). Sdlg. 89-506 PKS. TB, 34" (86 cm), M. Rosy pink self; beards pinkish red; lightly ruffled. Paradise X (Pink Sleigh x (Sunday Chimes x Christmas Time)).

STREET TALK (Barry Blyth, R. 1999). Sdlg. E159-2. TB, 34" (86 cm), VE. S. creamy lemon, slightly deeper edge; F. citrus yellow, tiny white chevron below golden yellow beard; ruffled. B202-1: (Affaire x Z55-3: (X108-2, Chocolate Vanilla sib, x X108-10, sib)) X Yes. Tempo Two 1999/2000.

STREET VENDOR (Paul Black, R. 1993). Sdlg. 89U20. TB, 34" (86 cm), M. S. dark plum; F. blue flash at end of gold beard, blending to medium red purple with edges darker, hafts brick brown; ruffled; slight spicy fragrance. Probably -- Syncopation X Glitz 'n Glitter. Mid-America 1993.

STRICTLY BALLROOM (Larry Lauer, R. 1994). Sdlg. 87-48-4. TB, 34" (86 cm), M. S. white; F. medium blue, undertoned lavender; beards white, tipped lavender; slight fragrance. Edith Wolford X Breakers. Stockton 1994.

STRICTLY JAZZ (Barry Blyth, R. 1999). Sdlg. E88-12. TB, 36" (91 cm), EM. S. lavender blue, slightly deeper midrib; F. navy blue violet, 1/8" lavender blue band, heavy white striations halfway down petal; beards tangerine orange, base white; slight sweet fragrance. Crazy For You X About Town. Tempo Two 1999/2000.

STRIKE IT RICH (Richard Ernst, R. 1993). Sdlg. HD175-5. TB, 35" (89 cm), M. Ruffled and lightly laced yellow self; beards yellow orange, tipped yellow; slight spicy fragrance. D175-5: (A141-3: (Cheesecake x (Sumptuous x Sandberry)) x Piping Hot) X self. Cooley 1993.

STRIKING (Joyce Meek, R. 1991). Sdlg. 55-1-6. TB, 34" (86 cm), ML. S. white, heavily stitched orchid; F. white; beards white, tipped coral; lightly ruffled. 473-1-3: (Deanna Darcy x Candace) X Lingering Love. D & J Gardens 1991.

STRIPED MOONBEAM (D. L. Shepard, R. 1990). Sdlg. 88056. AB (OGB-), 18" (46 cm), M. Lemon yellow with pencil line cream white striping; beards lemon yellow; foliage grey green, variegated white; slight fragrance. Afghanistan X Lemon Custard. Shepard Iris 1990.

STRIPED RED NEGLECTA (Austin Morgan, R. 1990). TB, 36" (91 cm), EML. S. lime; F. red with full length stripe, lime rim; beards yellow. Parentage unknown. Iris Test Garden 1990.

STRIZHAMENT (V. & N. Gordodelovy, R. 1995). Sdlg. 316. TB, 39" (100 cm), E. Laced, lightly ruffled white self; beards orange. Parentage unknown. Gordodelovy 1986.

STROZZAPRETI (Augusto Bianco, R. 1999). Sdlg. 702. TB, 32" (82 cm), ML. S. garnet red; style arms mahogany and hazel; F. velvety near-black, garnet edge; beards bronze; slight spicy fragrance. (Red Rose x Cherry Smoke) X (Jolt x Beachgirl).

STRUTTING EGRET (Brad Kasperek, R. 1996). Sdlg. 92P-37A. SDB, 10" (25 cm), EM. Ruffled clean white ground, 1/8" blue violet plicata edge; beards white, hairs tipped blue. Shooting Sparks X Flea Circus. Zebra 1997.

STRUTTIN' HIGH (Bernard Hamner, R. 1991). Sdlg. 84-91. TB, 36" (91 cm), M. Ruffled greyed orange; beards tangerine. Good Earth X Homecoming Queen. Shepard Iris 1991.

STUDY IN AMETHYST (Eugene Hunt by Sharon McAllister, R. 1990). Sdlg. ORB 89-4. AB (OGB), 28" (72 cm), EM. S. amethyst violet (near RHS 85A); F. amethyst pink (near 78C), deep purple lines radiating from grey brown (near 199A) beard. Dorcas X Mary of Magdala. Aril Society 1990.

STUNNING SERENADE (Hugh & Mary Thurman, R. 1995). Sdlg. 92-1-4. TB, 37" (94 cm), M. S. and style arms yellow tan; F. black cherry, narrow yellow tan rim; beards yellow; ruffled. Sooner Serenade X Most Stunning. Kickapoo Gardens 1997.

STURMVOGEL (Uwe Knoepnadel, R. 1990). JI (dip.), 47" (120 cm), EM. White, signals yellow. Sdlg. X unknown. Friesland Staudengarten 1990.

STYLED MODESTY (Tony Huber, R. 1998). Sdlg. 94-032 (91-629). SPEC-X (versata), 30" (75 cm), ML. S. aster violet (RHS 87C); style arms darker (87A), bordered amethyst violet (84B), crest aster violet (87B); F. aster violet (87B), yellow signal with extended line surrounded by darker halo; slight sweet fragrance. 89-402 white *versicolor* X white 6-F. *ensata* sdlg.

STYLE MODEL (Ben Hager, R. 1999). Sdlg. AMT6104WWhBld. MTB (tet.), 21" (53 cm), E. Off-white blend, F. slightly lighter; beards yellow, cream base; flared. AMT5209BI: (Spring Crest x Little Me) X Tit Willow. Adamgrove 1999.

STYLETIME (Henry Rowlan, R. 1990). Sdlg. 83-LA-11. LA, 32" (81 cm), EM. S. magenta rose (HCC 027/2), 3-point red line from throat halfway to edge; style arms magenta rose (027); F. magenta rose (027), yellow lancehead signal edged green; ruffled. Miss Arkansas X Roll Call. Comanche Acres 1991.

STYLISH LADY (Kirk Strawn, R. 1993). Sdlg. R2-1985. LA, 36" (91 cm), M. S. greyed orange (RHS 177D); style arms yellow (8D), hint of greyed orange (177D) on end; F. greyed orange (174B), yellow (12A) signal. Valera X Charles Arny III.

STYLISH SOCIALITE (Heather Pryor, R. 1994). Sdlg. 40/90-9. LA, 35" (89 cm), E. S. cerise mauve (RHS 78B) bordered white; style arms cerise mauve, fringed white, yellow center rib; F. darker cerise mauve (78A) bordered white, yellow raised steeple signal. Alluvial Gold X Gladiator's Gift. Lone Star 1998.

STYLIST (Barry Blyth, R. 1996). Sdlg. A70-2. TB, 32" (81 cm), M. S. bright lilac; F. bright silvery lilac; beards bright lemon yellow. Liqueur Creme X Taffeta Bow. Tempo Two 1996/97.

SUBASTRAL (Graeme Grosvenor, R. 1995). Sdlg. T5-1. BB, 26" (66 cm), M. S. pale blue, base violet; style arms pale blue, flushed violet; F. pale blue; beards very dark blue (near black); ruffled. Codicil X Snowbrook. Rainbow Ridge 1995/96.

SUBLIME (Lois O'Brien, TB, R. 1977). O'Brien Iris 1995.

SUBTLE HINT (Richard Ernst, R. 1991). Sdlg. D134-8. TB, 37" (94 cm), ML. S. amber yellow; F. golden brown with maroon overtones; beards orange. Equestrian X Tiger Butter. Cooley 1991.

SUCCESSFUL BID (John C. Taylor, R. 1994). Sdlg. RL 7-3. LA, 26" (65 cm), EM. Ruffled cream, green line signal surrounded by yellow; style arms lemon green. Dazzling Star X Margaret Lee. Rainbow Ridge 1996/97.

SUDDEN ARRIVAL (C. R. King, R. 1994). Sdlg. 1 CRK 93. TB, 48" (122 cm), E. Very pale mauve self, near white; beards yellow; ruffled. Parentage unknown.

SUDDEN IMPACT (Richard Tasco, R. 1996). Sdlg. 91-01-03. TB, 39" (99 cm), ML. Heavily ruffled medium blue self, aging paler silvery blue; beards light blue. Dusky Challenger X Ruffled Goddess. Superstition 1997.

SUDS (Tom Burseen, R. 1995). Sdlg. 1-298E. TB, 33" (84 cm), M. S. and style arms clean white; F., clean chalky white, texture veined, some golden maize haft coloration; beards yellow, red orange in throat; ruffled, heavily laced; spicy fragrance. Say Cheese X Lavish Lace. T.B.'s Place 1996.

SUE KEEFE (Mary Newton, R. 1997). Sdlg. 88-BO+C6. TB, 38" (97 cm), M. S. pale blue aging near white, with pale blue violet veining remaining on inside; style arms near white, blue violet (NEGS BV#4) midrib; F. blue violet (BV#3), lighter oval around beard, darker veins to end of beard, slightly darker central blaze; beards white, yellow in throat; ruffled, flared; slight sweet fragrance. Bubbling Over X Congratulations.

SUE'S A JEWEL (Wilford James, R. 1999). Sdlg. 92-1. TB, 31" (79 cm), M. Ruffled white ground plicata with light purple stitching, heaviest at haft; style arms white; beards light yellow at end, orange toward throat; slight fragrance. Snowbrook X Anna Belle Babson. Willott 1999.

SUE ZEE (Sterling Innerst, R. 1995). Sdlg. 4163-1. IB, 18" (46 cm), M. Medium green; style arms green; beards medium blue. Lesson X Best Bet. Innerst 1996.

SUGAR CANDY (Marjorie Brummitt, CA, R. 1966). Bay View 1974.

SUGAR MAGNOLIA (Schreiner, R. 1998). Sdlg. DD 1247-1. TB, 35" (89 cm), EM. S. white (RHS 155D); style arms pink; F. bright venetian pink (49B); beards tangerine red. 1987 #15, unknown, X AA 1493-2: (T 820-A: (Flamingo Way x ((A 1287-AA x Sunset Snows) x ((Champagne Music x (R1052-2 x Christmas Time)) x (Orchid Brocade x (Annabel Lee sib x Emma Cook))))) x Beachgirl). Schreiner 1998.

SUGAR SNAPS (Darlene Pinegar, R. 1998). Sdlg. CC-94-55A. IB, 19" (48 cm), E. S. light pinkish orange; style arms light orange; F. light yellow orange; beards dark tangerine; lightly ruffled; slight sweet fragrance. Carrot Curls X Jungle Cat. Spanish Fork 1999.

SUGI IRI (John Wood, R. 1992). SIB (dip.), 21" (53 cm), ML. Lavender (RHS 76B), veined darker (76A); style arms lavender (76D). Parentage and hybridizer unknown -- probably a Japanese import. Cook's Gardens ca. 1980.

SUITEN ISSHOKU (Nobutsone Nishida by Society for Japanese Irises, R. 1992). JI (3 F.), 39" (100 cm), M. Clear deep blue, yellow signal. Parentage unknown. Introduced in Japan prior to 1939.

SUKY (Clarence Mahan, TB, R. 1988). Iris Pond 1991.

SULEIMAN (Nora Scopes, R. 1999). Sdlg. 06/78. TB, 37" (94 cm), ML. S. deep greenish gold; F. deep crimson with blackish sheen intensifying in center, lighter crimson centerline, orange in throat; beards deep yellow; ruffled; sweet fragrance. 03/150B, Wolf Whistle sib, X 9S126B, Down Under sib.

SULLOM VOE (B.L.C. Dodsworth, TB, R. 1989). V. H. Humphrey 1992.

SULTAN'S DAUGHTER (Barry Blyth, R. 1995). Sdlg. A166-4. TB, 36" (91 cm), M. S. biscuit to beige, flushed rose; F. plush ruby, lighter edge; beards old gold; slight musky fragrance. Town Gossip X Supreme Sultan. Tempo Two 1995/96.

SULTAN'S HONEY (Chuck Chapman, R. 1999). Sdlg. 89-329-2. TB, 39" (99 cm), ML. S. yellow cream; F. amber honey upper half, yellow cream lower half; beards amber honey. Supreme Sultan X Coral Beauty. Chapman Iris 1999.

SULTAN'S SASH (O. D. Niswonger, SPU, R. 1989). Cape Iris 1990.

SULTRY PINK (Cleo Palmer, R. 1992). Sdlg. 9035. SDB, 11" (28 cm), L. S. white, midrib light yellow; F. light tannish orange, slight pink infusion; beards red orange, tipped paler. 8546: (Gigglepot x 8211: ((Dove Wings x ((Wilma V. x unknown) x Little Titan)) x (Dove Wings x 7416: (Baria x -- probably Carpathia)))) X unknown. Palmer's Iris 1992.

SUMMER BUTTER (John Marchant, R. 1992). Sdlg. 1287. CA, 12" (30 cm), M. Clear aureolin yellow (HCC 3/2), F. faintly veined darker yellow. Sdlg. X sdlg.

SUMMER CAMP (Paul Black, R. 1999). Sdlg. C109D. IB, 18" (46 cm), M. S. palest yellow, near-complete rose wine overblending; style arms light brown, sides gold; F. light yellow ground, hafts marked burgundy, wide rose wine plicata band and centerline; beards dull grey gold, gold in throat; slight spicy fragrance. 91304A: (87130H: (Chubby Cheeks x (Gentle Air x Chubby Cheeks)) x Privileged Character) X 91109B: (Sorceress x 88105C, Dream of Gold sib). Mid-America 1999.

SUMMER CARNIVAL (Akihiko Terada, R. 1999). Sdlg. 263-3. TB, 39" (99 cm), ML. S. yellow; F. white, edged yellow; beards yellow. Bicentennial X Silverado. Roris 1999.

SUMMER ECLIPSE (William Ackerman, R. 1997). Sdlg. VI-1-13. JI (3 F.), 46" (117 cm), M. S. violet (RHS 83A), upright and cupped; style arms violet (83A), large, broad-lipped; F. violet (88A) with pansy violet (83A) veining and around aureolin yellow (12A) signal. Husky Hero X Dark Enchantment. Nicholls Gardens 1997.

SUMMER FRUIT (O. D. Niswonger, R. 1994). Sdlg. SDB 2-91. SDB, 12" (30 cm), M. S. buff; F. apricot orange; beards tangerine, tipped blue. Live Jazz X SDB 16-87: (Peach Bavarian x Peach Eyes). Cape Iris 1994.

SUMMER JOY (Darlene Pinegar, R. 1990). Sdlg. P-2-3. TB, 30" (76 cm), M. S. cranberry grape, midrib light apricot; F. cranberry grape with apricot and bluish tints; beards orange; lightly ruffled; slight sweet fragrance. Palladium X Moon Mistress. Spanish Fork 1991.

SUMMER MOON (Lois Rich by Ensata Gardens, R. 1993). Sdlg. K79-2E. JI (6 F.), 36" (92 cm), M. Ruffled white, large yellow signal veining out over F.; style arms cream, crests white. Parentage unknown. Ensata Gardens 1994.

SUMMER OF FORTY-TWO (Joseph Hoage, TB, R. 1989). Long 1990.

SUMMER PROMISE (Charles Rhodes, R. 1989). Classification and height changed to TB, 31" (79 cm). Bowood Farms 1991.

SUMMER RADIANCE (Betty Wilkerson, R. 1996). Sdlg. E31-1Re. TB, 36" (91 cm), E & VL.S. bright chrome yellow (RHS 14B); F. chrome yellow (14A); beards yellow; slight spicy fragrance. Lemon Reflection X Hindenburg. Bridge in Time 1996.

SUMMER REVELS (Marty Schafer/Jan Sacks, R. 1999). Sdlg. S92-80-10. SIB, 28" (71 cm), M & RE. S. and style arms cream to light canary yellow (RHS 9D), green midrib in style arms; F. yellow base, warm yellow central flush and shoulders, deeper yellow signal flowing outward, bright green hafts. S89-23-1: (S85-6-6: (Star Cluster x Ruffled Velvet) x Isabelle) X S90-35-1: (S86-3-2: (Butter and Sugar x Percheron) x S86-2-1: (Creme Chantilly x Warburton 84-26-4: (Butter and Sugar x (Atoll x Ruffled Velvet)))). Joe Pye Weed 1999.

SUMMER REVIEW (Tony Huber, R. 1999). Sdlg. 94-027. SPEC-X (versata), 37" (95 cm), ML. S. violet blue (RHS 90) aging aster violet (87C); style arms violet (83) edged lilac (76D); F. violet (83A), paling (82B/C) at edge; signal bright yellow surrounded by purple-veined white area. *I. versicolor* 92-112: (PRK-068 x MR 03-04) X white and violet veined *ensata* sdlg.

SUMMER SOLSTICE (David Miller, R. 1999). Sdlg. 93-7A. TB, 38" (97 cm), EM. Gold, F. with small white spot at tip of orange gold beard; slight musky fragrance. 85-4B: (Gold Galore x Copper Classic) X Glazed Gold.

SUMMER SONATA (Jim Hedgecock, R. 1997). Sdlg. 84-25-11. TB, 36" (91 cm), EM. Ruffled and heavily laced medium yellow, F. with large white ray pattern radiating from dark gold beards. Sunset Sonata X Sky Hooks. Comanche Acres 1998.

SUMMER SPLASH (Lorena Reid, R. 1991). Sdlg. D558-2. JI (3 F.), 42-48" (107-122 cm), E. S. white, rimmed violet (RHS 87B); style arms white, edged violet (87B); F. white, marked violet

(87B/C), heavier at shoulders and edge, white around greenish yellow signal. Mystic Buddha X Frilled Enchantment. Laurie's Garden 1991.

SUMMER'S SMILE (Richard Ernst, R. 1991). Sdlg. D130-3. TB, 35" (89 cm), L. S. amber gold; F. bright maroon, 1/4" smoky amber rim; beards yellow. A138-1: (Flash Fire x Taco Belle) X Tiger Butter. Cooley 1991.

SUMMER STAR (Gordon Nicholson, R. 1999). TB, 32" (81 cm), M & RE. S. and style arms soft violet; F. velvety deep violet black, soft violet center stripe and 1/4" edge; beards pumpkin orange; tailored; slight sweet fragrance. Cosmic Storm X unknown.

SUMMER SURF (Walter Moores, R. 1990). Sdlg. 82-23-B. TB, 36" (91 cm), EM & RE (June, Nov./MS,TX) S. pale lavender; F. darker lavender violet; beards pale yellow, tipped white; lightly ruffled. Summer Holidays X Hawaiian Surf. Moores 1991.

SUMMER SYMPHONY (Heather Pryor, R. 1997). Sdlg. 41/93-D. LA, 35" (89 cm), EM. S. soft lemon, burnt red blush at edge; style arms apricot lemon; F. yellow base, terra cotta blush at edge, lemon rim, raised lime green signal surrounded by yellow; ruffled. 62/90-1: (Frank Chowning x Desert Jewel) X Heather Pryor. Iris Haven 1999/2000.

SUMMERTIME BLUES (George Sutton, R. 1997). Sdlg. H-186. TB, 37" (94 cm), M & RE. S. pale wistaria blue (RHS 92D), midrib slightly deeper; style arms pale wistaria blue; F. paler wistaria blue; beards orange, wistaria blue at end; heavily ruffled, diamond dusted; pronounced sweet fragrance. G-74: (Busy Being Blue x Deity) X Star Master.

SUMMIT ANGEL (Carl Jorgensen, R. 1994). Sdlg. 84-01-2D. TB, 30" (76 cm), ML. Heavily ruffled white self; style arms with white crests; beards white; slight sweet fragrance. 82-01-3: (78-24-5A x 76-01-1A: (73-24-5A x Christmas Time)) X 78-24-5B: (73-24-5C: (Merry Miss x Dream Spinner) x 74-24-7A: (Merry Miss x Symphonette)). Long 1994.

SUMMIT AVALANCHE (Carl Jorgensen, R. 1998). Sdlg. 92-01-1G. TB, 32" (81 cm), ML-VL. Ruffled very pale french blue; beards french blue, pale bronze in throat; pronounced sweet fragrance. Bride's Halo X unknown. Long 1998.

SUMMIT FLURRY (Carl Jorgensen, TB, R. 1989). Long 1990.

SUMMIT QUEEN (Carl Jorgensen, TB, R. 1989). Long 1990.

SUMMIT SUNDAE (Carl Jorgensen, R. 1994). Sdlg. 85-P-6B. TB, 28-30" (71-76 cm), EML. S. orange (HCC 12/3); style arms fringed; F. edged orange (12/2), lighter area below orange (12) beard; ruffled, laced; pronounced sweet fragrance. Colorado Winter Morning X 75-2-2: (0-21-4B: (Summit Lady x Flaming Star) x Piping Hot). Long 1994.

SUMMIT SUNRISE (Carl Jorgensen, R. 1998). Sdlg. 85-P-1G. TB, 30" (76 cm), ML. S. majolica yellow (HCC 09/1) deepening to egyptian buff (407); style arms majolica yellow, phlox purple lip; F. phlox purple (632/2), chrome yellow (605/1) hafts, amber yellow rim deepening to egyptian buff and majolica yellow; beards saffron yellow (7/1). Colorado Winter Morning X 75-2-2: (Summit Lady x Flaming Star).

SUN BELT (George Slade, R. 1990). Sdlg. 85-12-1. TB, 38" (97 cm), M. S. pale orange; F. white, 3/8" orange edge; beards bright tangerine; ruffled, laced; pronounced sweet fragrance. Exuberant X Lois Hill. Wyle Wynde 1990.

SUNBONNET SUE (Mary Louise Dunderman, R. 1991). Sdlg. HH341 Pink. MTB, 21" (54 cm), M. Light pink (RHS 62D), lighter toward blossom center; beards light yellow. DD656 coral pink X EE55 ruffled white. Ohio Gardens 1992.

SUNBURN (Colin Rigby, R. 1999). Sdlg. 9104. CA, 12" (31 cm), M. Cherry red blushed gold, thin cream edge, F. with gold signal with fine darker gold veining; style arms cherry red blushed gold. Red Bluff X Gold Dusted.

SUNBURNT COUNTRY (Janet Hutchinson, R. 1995). Sdlg. DDSL3. LA, 33" (85 cm), EML. S. pale apricot to terracotta, strong pinkish brown centerline; style arms blended apricot yellow, green center; F. pale apricot to terracotta over cream, tips tinged mauve pink, centerline brown, olive veining, small rich yellow signal; slightly ruffled; slight sweet fragrance. Delta Dawn X Soft Laughter.

SUN CASCADE (Tony Huber, R. 1992). Sdlg. Pseud. 89-050. SPEC (*pseudacorus*), 47" (120 cm), M. Yellow (RHS 9A) with dark brown markings on center of F.; flowers double, 6-9 F. Sdlg., double: (single x unknown) X sdlg., single. W. H. Perron 1993.

SUNCATCHER (Allan Ensminger, R. 1991). Sdlg. 87-32. TB, 30" (76 cm), ML. S. sulphur yellow (HCC 1/0); F. mimosa yellow (601/3), widely banded sulphur yellow (1/1); beards chrome yellow; heavily ruffled; slight fragrance. 82-27: (Ruffled Surprise x Morning Sunshine) X Idol's Dream. Varigay 1992.

SUNCHIME (Barry Blyth, R. 1998). Sdlg. E12-2. SDB, 10" (25 cm), ML. S. cream, erect; style arms creamy white; F. creamy white, 1/8" lemon edge, bright mustard splash on either side of beard; beards white, lemon in throat. Moustache X Little Bev. Tempo Two 1998/99.

SUNDAY MORNING (George Slade, R. 1991). Sdlg. 85-10-1. TB, 36" (91 cm), M. Bright yellow, white area around yellow orange beards; pronounced sweet fragrance. Laced Cotton X Orange Game.

SUNDOWN SABER (LeRoy Meininger, R. 1999). Sdlg. 89-3. TB, 32" (81 cm), M. S. lemon yellow; style arms lemon yellow, lavender midrib; F. medium lavender in center blending to 1/4" golden lavender edge, gold veining extending from golden hafts; beards gold, 1" lavender horn. Smooth Talk X Gladys Austin. Monument, Woodland Iris 1999.

SUNDRAGON (Nora Scopes, R. 1992). Sdlg. 8/182B. TB, 36-38" (91-97 cm), M. Brilliant golden yellow, hafts deeper yellow, lighter patch below yellow ochre beards; ruffled, flared. 1/189B: (Dark Rosaleen x Superstition) X Dansellon.

SUN EAGLE BAY (Bob Thomason, R. 1991). Sdlg. 8621A. IB, 18" (46 cm), EM. S. medium purple; F. velvety deep purple; beards lavender. Evening Event X Toy Parade. Okie Iris 1994.

SUN FLARE (Dorman Haymon, LA, R. 1989). Deep South Garden 1990.

SUN HALO (B. Charles Jenkins, R. 1998). Sdlg. AW04F. SPU, 38-44" (97-112 cm), M. S. brown, blended yellow at base; style arms brown; F. yellow, with fringe of brown and brown veining converging at signal area. Janice Chesnik X A1-0A: (Ada Perry x unknown). Shepard Iris 1998.

SUN IN SPLENDOUR (Jennifer Hewitt, R. 1997). Sdlg. 94/RS. SPEC-X, 60" (153 cm), ML. S. barium yellow (RHS 10B), horizontal, minute; style arms blended aureolin (12A/C), prominent crests; F. rich yellow (14A), yellow signal edged with small brown veins; slight sweet fragrance. "Rising Sun" (putative *pseudacorus-ensata* hybrid) X unknown.

SUNKISS (Lilly Gartman by Joseph Ghio, R. 1993). Sdlg. 86-9G. TB, 34" (86 cm), ML. S. deep yellow; F. white, edged yellow; beards gold. 83-34B: (Piping Hot x (Soap Opera x (Joyce Terry x Entourage))) X Alluring. Roris 1994.

SUNKIST DELIGHT (O. D. Niswonger, R. 1995). Sdlg. 92-91. TB, 36" (91 cm), ML. S. light yellow, flecked deeper; style arms light yellow, crest deeper; F. white ground, wide deep golden yellow rim, yellow flecks; beards deep yellow. Sunkist Frills X 38-88: (Halo in Yellow x Peach Band). Cape Iris 1995.

SUNKIST MEADOWS (O. D. Niswonger, R. 1996). Sdlg. 63-92. TB, 34" (86 cm), M. S. and style arms light yellow; F. light yellow, white center blush; beards marigold orange. Sib to Sunkist Delight. Cape Iris 1998.

SUNLIGHT SKETCH (Pavel Nejedlo, R. 1998). Sdlg. DERRSM-90-2. TB, 34" (86 cm), M. S. cream, veined yellow; style arms deep orange yellow; F. medium yellow heavily dotted and washed cinnamon brown, edges silvery yellow; beards brown orange; ruffled; slight spicy fragrance. Desert Echo X (Rancho Rose x Sketch Me). Lukon 1998.

SUNLIT FRINGES (Ben Hager by Roris Gardens, R. 1993). Sdlg. T5041. TB, 36" (91 cm), M. S. white, midrib suffused yellow, yellow highlights on edge; F. white, yellow highlights on edge and shoulders; beards yellow; ruffled, laced. Amazon Bride X Joy of Springtime. Roris 1993.

SUNMASTER (William Maryott, R. 1994). Sdlg. S163A. TB, 27-32" (69-81 cm), E & RE. S. lemon yellow (RHS 9C); F. white, 3/8" lemon yellow rim; beards deep yellow; sweet fragrance. Lemon Fever X Temperence. Maryott 1995.

SUNNY ANGEL (Henry Rowlan, LA, R. 1989). Comanche Acres 1990.

SUNNY BUBBLES (William Maryott, R. 1992). Sdlg. P132BST. TB, 38" (97 cm), M. Medium bright yellow, F. with slightly lighter center; beards yellow; heavily ruffled; pronounced sweet fragrance. Radiant Energy X Blowtorch. Maryott 1993.

SUNNY CINNAMON (Bennett Jones, R. 1991). Sdlg. IN85-3-2. IB, 22" (56 cm), M. S. white infused orange at base; F. cinnamon; beards red orange. Color Bash X Orange Tiger. Bennett Jones 1992.

SUNNY DISPOSITION (Lloyd Zurbrigg, TB, R. 1989). Avonbank 1991.

SUNNY GLOW (J. T. Aitken, R. 1994). Sdlg. 88M7. BB, 26" (66 cm), ML. Medium orange, intensified haft flush; beards coral orange. ((Tangerine Sunset x Something Special) x Maid of Orange) X Blazing Light. Aitken's Salmon Creek 1994.

SUNNY LACE (Adolf Volfovich-Moler, R. 1998). Sdlg. V-123. TB, 30" (75 cm), L. S. pale yellow, brighter edge; style arms light yellow; F. mustard yellow, indistinct white central area; beards bright yellow; heavily ruffled, laced; pronounced musky fragrance. Pink Sleigh X Chartreuse Ruffles.

SUNNY MOOD (Henry Rowlan, R. 1990). Sdlg. 86-LA-5. LA, 36" (91 cm), ML. Ruffled canary yellow (HCC 2/2), raised green line signal. 80LA13 yellow sdlg. X Winter's Snow. Comanche Acres 1991.

SUNNY PEACH (Paul Black, R. 1998). Sdlg. A59A. TB, 32" (81 cm), L. S. pinkish peach, rim darker; style arms pinkish peach; F. salmon peach; beards orange; ruffled; slight musky fragrance. Victorian Frills X Good Show. Mid-America 1998.

SUNNY RED WINE (Tomas Tamberg, R. 1998). Sdlg. SSTT363. SPEC-X (cal-sib, tct.), 14" (36 cm), M. S. light wine red; F. wine red, golden yellow signal. Red/yellow tet. cal-sib sdlg.: (Starting Calsibe x converted yellow cal-sib sdlg.) X converted dark violet cal-sib sdlg.: (sino-siberian sdlg. x Miramar). Schoeppinger 1998.

SUNNY REFLECTION (Kirk Strawn, R. 1996). Sdlg. AA 1985. LA, 36" (91 cm), M. S. canary yellow (RHS 9B); style arms barium yellow (10C); F. sulphur yellow (6C), signal aureolin (12B) with deeper (12A) center. Sun Fury X Charjoy's Anne.

SUNNY SACRAMENTO (Akihiko Terada, R. 1994). Sdlg. S-219-89-6. TB, 36" (91 cm), M. Yellow self; beards deep orange, white at tip. Good Show X Flaming Victory. Roris 1995.

SUNNY SAIL (Francis Rogers, R. 1993). Sdlg. F-656-G. TB, 32" (81 cm), VL. S. white; F. white (RHS 157C) edged blue violet (92D); beards yellow, tipped white; ruffled, laced; pronounced fragrance. (Song of Norway x Lady Marie) X (Lacy Snowflake x (Jakarta x Stepping Out)). Meadowbrook 1994.

SUNNY SHOULDERS (Ben Hager, TB, R. 1989). Melrose 1990.

SUNNY SONNY (Bob Thomason, R. 1991). Sdlg. BT 8630A. SDB, 11" (28 cm), EM. Bright gold, brown plum print around beard; beards dark orange, tipped light orange, bushy; slight fragrance. Small Favor X Solar Flight. Okie Iris 1999.

SUNNY TYKE (Lynda Miller, R. 1991). Sdlg. 285A. MDB, 4" (10 cm), E. S. ivory, cream yellow midrib; F. ivory, gold halo; beards ivory. Baby Smile X unknown. Miller's Manor 1991.

SUNPOLKA (Tom Magee, TB, R. 1988). Long 1991.

SUNPRINT (Calvin Helsley, R. 1993). Sdlg. 93-13. SPEC (*pseudacorus*), 36" (91 cm), M. Deep yellow, F. with spray pattern of brown lines from throat forming 1/2" signal. From sdlgs. Helsley 1995.

SUNRAY REFLECTION (Richard Ernst, R. 1993). Sdlg. F112-7. TB, 38" (97 cm), ML. S. lemon yellow; F. white with 1/4" lemon yellow rim and shoulders; beards yellow; ruffled, lightly laced; slight sweet fragrance. Afternoon Delight X Gaulter 81-74, inv. Glendale. Cooley 1992.

SUNRISE IN EDEN (Bernice Miller, R. 1992). Sdlg. SIE93. TB, 34" (86 cm), EM & RE (Nov./AL). Laced and widely ruffled apricot pink; beards coral red; slight fragrance. Sunrise Sunset X Pink Sachet. Comanche Acres, Garden of the Enchanted Rainbow 1993.

SUNRISE IN MISSOURI (O. D. Niswonger, R. 1995). Sdlg. Sp 5-88. SPU, 40" (102 cm), M. Lightly ruffled deep golden yellow self. Sp 6-80: (Far Out x Redwood Supreme) X unknown -- probably self. Cape Iris 1995.

SUNRISE IN SONORA (Floyd Wickenkamp, R. 1993). Sdlg. SP-89-7. SPU, 44" (112 cm), M. Dark maroon violet; F. with large bright gold blaze;, lightly veined red violet; style arms tipped red violet, bright blue ridge. Headway X SP-83-2: (Burnished Brass x (Burnished Brass x Proverb)). Shepard Iris 1994.

SUNRISE SALUTE (Jim Hummel, R. 1990). Sdlg. JH 82-73T. BB, 25½" (64 cm), L. S. naples yellow (RHS 11B); F. empire yellow (11D) edged lighter yellow (11A); beards cadmium orange (23A). Dream Affair X 78-36D: (Warm Gold x (Sleeping Beauty x Summer Dawn)). Bumble Bee 1991.

SUNRISE SEDUCTION (David Miller, R. 1996). Sdlg. 88-13B. TB, 28" (71 cm), M. Deep aureolin yellow (RHS 12A), F. with large white spot surrounding bushy orange red beard; slight musky fragrance. Flaming Victory X Glazed Gold. Long 1998

SUNSBLOOD (Nora Scopes, R. 1992). Sdlg. 8/182A. TB, 36" (91 cm), M. Flaring deep mustard yellow; beards brownish ochre. 1/189B: (Dark Rosaleen x Superstition) X Dansellon.

SUNSET BOULEVARD (Frank Foster, R. 1990). Sdlg. 84BP-1. TB, 33" (84 cm), M. Ruffled apricot peach; beards red orange. 81-80-PEACH: (Pink Taffeta x (New Moon x Pink Taffeta)) X (New Moon x Hamblen pink sdlg.).

SUNSET COLORS (B. Charles Jenkins, R. 1994). Sdlg. C18-31E. SPU, 45-56" (114-142 cm), M.

Pastel mauve and lavender blend on yellow ground, with yellow more prominent at signal area. Ila Crawford X Sierra Nevada. Shepard Iris 1994.

SUNSET DUNES (Lois Rich by James Whitely, R. 1990). Sdlg. R75-135G. AB (OGB+), 21" (53 cm), M. S. pink orchid over creamy ground, finely veined orchid; style arms veined cream orchid; F. pink orchid over creamy ground, narrow halo of pepper dots extending from brown wine signal area; beards yellow brown. R73-176L: ((R69-108A: (Bagdad Beauty x Pink Formal) x Welcome Reward) x (Welcome Reward x RR64-23A: (R62-OB-1D x Kalifa Hirfa))) X Hf17A. Aril Patch, Aril Society 1990.

SUNSET FOG (Darlene Pinegar, R. 1998). Sdlg. AC-94-140C. TB, 36" (91 cm), M. S. light yellow, pinkish center infusion and veining; style arms light yellow; F. medium apricot veined darker, hafts cream with medium apricot marking; beards tangerine, yellow at end; slight sweet fragrance. Aphrodisiac X Blazing Sunrise. Spanish Fork 1999.

SUNSET MUSIC (Mercedes Olsen, R. 1994). Sdlg 91-1A-0. TB, 36" (91 cm), M. Deep orange self; beards orange. (Mandolin x Honeysuckle) X Fresno Flash. Celebrity Iris 1995.

SUNSET ROYALE (Sara Doonan, TB, R. 1989). Sunset Iris 1989.

SUNSET TRAIL (G. F. Wilson, R. 1991). Sdlg. 16-89TTWM-A. AB (OGB), 25½" (65 cm), E. S. bright rose crimson veined darker, deep rose midrib; F. bright brick red, brown black lines radiating from chestnut brown beard, diffuse brown black signal; sweet fragrance. Turkish Tangent X Warrior's Mantle. Pleasure Iris 1993.

SUNSET WARRIOR (Vernon Wood by James Whitely, R. 1991). Sdlg. WW86-100-6. AB (OGB), 32" (81 cm), M. S. pale mahogany, veined violet; F. dark blood red aging oxblood with tan edge, bright red around large black signal to edge; beards brown. W83-3: ((Habibi x Grecian Form) x Welcome Reward) X Dawn Cascade. Aril Patch, Aril Society 1991.

SUNSHINE GOLD (Akihiko Terada, R. 1997). Sdlg. 251-4. TB, 35" (89 cm), ML. Ruffled clear light yellow, F. with white center; beards yellow; slight sweet fragrance. Anna Belle Babson X Speculator. Roris 1997.

SUNSHINE ISLE (Richard Brook, R. 1992). Sdlg. A20/1. SDB, 9" (23 cm), E. Cream, F. with intense sandy greenish yellow spot; beards blue. Music Box X Joyous Isle. Zephyrwude Irises 1992.

SUNSHINE SALLY (Bennett Jones, R. 1992). Sdlg. 458-8. SDB, 11" (28 cm), EM. S. light lemon yellow; F. chrome, edged light lemon yellow; beards white; ruffled; slight fragrance. 428: (396: ((Miss Oklahoma x (Blue Pools x Wink)) x Oregold) x Loveshine) X 426: (396 x sib). Bennett Jones 1993.

SUNSHINE SHOWOFF (William Plotner, R. 1992). Sdlg. 84-115-1. TB, 32" (81 cm), EML. S. chartreuse yellow; F. amber white, chartreuse yellow hafts and wide edge; beards inca gold; ruffled; slight spicy fragrance. (Pretty Please x Stately Mansions) X ((Cosmopolitan x Allegany Moon) x (Stately Mansions x Genesis)). Wildwood Gardens 1991.

SUNSHINE STATUS (Graeme Grosvenor, R. 1999). Sdlg. U40-2. TB, 38" (97 cm), M. Golden yellow, F. with lighter area around golden yellow beard; slight fragrance. Dance Man X Bogota. Rainbow Ridge 1999/2000.

SUN SINGER (Ben Hager, R. 1991). Sdlg. S882RfY. SPU, 38" (97 cm), M. Ruffled bright yellow. Ila Crawford X Elan Vital. Cordon Bleu 1991.

SUNSO (Barry Blyth, R. 1995). Sdlg. B95-2. IB, 20" (51 cm), EM. S. lemon yellow; F. lemon gold; beards white, tipped gold; ruffled. Buzz Me X Electrique. Tempo Two 1995/96.

SUNSPINNER (Lynn Markham, R. 1990). Sdlg. 66-18A. BB, 26" (66 cm), EM. Ruffled bright yellow (RHS 6A), paler area around beard; beards deep yellow orange (17B) tipped deeper (17A); slight sweet fragrance. Sheaff 62-21X, BB sib to Pearl Kemp, X Tulare. Markham, Wild Mountain Thyme 1991.

SUN SPLASH (B. Charles Jenkins, R. 1995). Sdlg. BA63A. SPU, 38-43" (97-109 cm), EM. S. creamy white; F. creamy white margin blending to prominent canary yellow signal; heavily ruffled. Candle Lace X Elan Vital. Shepard Iris 1997.

SUN SPRITE (Lucy Burton, R. 1992). Sdlg. L87-CR-1. SDB, 12-14" (30-36 cm), E. Soft yellow (near RHS 10C), F. with intense yellow (11A) wash changing to yellow veining on white ground around beards and at hafts; beards blue white, yellow in throat; lightly ruffled. April Anthem X Bibury. Burton 1993.

SUNSTRUCK (E. D. Zimmerly, R. 1992). CA, 9" (23 cm), E. S. pale gold; F. ruffled clear yellow, creamy yellow signal. *I. douglasiana* X open pollination.

SUN SUN LIGHT (Udo & Rudolf Wilkeneit, R. 1996). Sdlg. EW 14/1/94. SDB, 12" (30 cm), L. Dark yellow; beards yellow, white at end; slight fragrance. Parentage unknown.

SUN'S UP (Lynda Miller, R. 1991). Sdlg. 3085. BB, 22" (56 cm), EM. S. cream yellow, deeper edge; F. deep lemon yellow, yellow spot; beards yellow. Lemon Punch X Queen in Calico. Miller's Manor 1992.

SUN THEME (Loleta Powell, R. 1997). Sdlg. 94-1. TB, 35" (89 cm), EML. Clear yellow self; beards yellow; sweet fragrance. Preferred Stock X Bohemian. Powell's Gardens 1997.

SUPERACT (Barry Blyth, R. 1994). Sdlg. 4. SIB, 30" (76 cm), ML. Iridescent violet, F. with 1" blue lavender central area blended green and white. Parentage unknown -- from McEwen seed. Tempo Two 1994/95.

SUPERNATURAL (Barry Blyth, R. 1994). Sdlg. 2. SIB, 32" (81 cm), ML. Light magenta red wine, F. with white and blue lines radiating from very faint blue violet central area. Parentage unknown -- from McEwen seed. Tempo Two 1994/95.

SUPREME DREAM (Lamoyne Hedgecock, R. 1999). Sdlg. E-27-1. TB, 35" (89 cm), M. Heavily laced and ruffled bright yellow, F. with tiny near-white blaze at end of golden orange beard; slight sweet fragrance. Harvest Queen X Breakers.

SUPREME LADY (J. D. Stadler, TB, R. 1989). Celestial Gardens 1990.

SUPREME QUEEN (Donald Spoon, R. 1997). Sdlg. 92-255. TB, 36" (91 cm), M. S. and style arms yellow; F. deep red, edges paler; beards red orange; lightly ruffled, laced. Clearfire X Latin Rock.

SUR DEUX NOTES (Jean Segui, R. 1998). TB, 32" (80 cm), E. S. white; style arms white, lightly edged yellow; F. yellow (RHS 14B), shoulders darker; beards indian yellow (17A). Fairy Magic X Sunset Snows. Iris de Thau 1981.

SURE BET (Mary Dunn, R. 1994). Sdlg. 139-3. LA, 34" (86 cm), M. Velvety red purple, tiny lime yellow line signal; waved, ruffled. Full Eclipse X Gold Reserve. Bay View 1994.

SURELY WHITE (Larry Lauer, R. 1999). Sdlg. 443-2. TB, 37" (94 cm), EM. Laced white, F. with brown shoulders; beards tangerine, small horn; slight sweet fragrance. Sib to April Jewel.

SURF AND SAND (Frederick Held, R. 1998). Sdlg. X. JI (3 F.), 36" (91 cm), M. S. white; style arms ivory; F. white, yellow signal. Parentage unknown -- seed from Jelitto Staudensamen, Germany.

SURF COAST (Barry Blyth, R. 1998). Sdlg. F85-1. IB, 22" (56 cm), EM. Sunny bright yellow, F. lighter toward creamy center; beards bright lemon yellow, 1/8" white end; pronounced sweet fragrance. Say Hello X C225-2, Gala Greetings sib. Tempo Two 1998/99.

SURFIE GIRL (Barry Blyth, R. 1993). Sdlg. Z69-3. TB, 38" (97 cm), EML. S. light tannish beige; F. white with 1/2" stitched edge of bishops violet, deepening at hafts to reddish tan; beards light mustard. Lark About X Snowbrook. Tempo Two 1993/94.

SURPRISE DARK (Willy Hublau, R. 1996). JI (6 F.), 28" (70 cm), M. Beetroot purple (RHS 71A) stripes and dots on greyed white (156D), signal dark yellow; style arms beetroot purple. Sdlg. X sdlg.

SURPRISE ENDING (Ben Hager, R. 1992). Sdlg. T4859DpOcLc. TB, 34" (86 cm), VL. Heavily laced deep orchid; beards orange yellow. T4387SthMOc: (T3324: (((Babson M131-4 x Morning Breeze) x Dream Time) x Grand Waltz) x T3708: (Pleasure Dome x Monaco)) X Blythe Dean. Melrose 1992.

SURPRISE LIGHT (Willy Hublau, R. 1996). JI (6 F.), 24-28" (60-70 cm), M. Greyed white (RHS 156D) striping and dotting on beetroot purple (71A), signal dark yellow; style arms greyed white. Sdlg. X unknown.

SURPRISE OFFER (John C. Taylor, R. 1991). Sdlg. OL 137-7. LA, 43" (110 cm), M. Ruffled mauve (RHS 70C), lighter mauve rim; sometimes double. Dazzling Star X Helen Naish. Rainbow Ridge 1994/95.

SURPRISING WIT (James Gibson by Cooley's Gardens, R. 1999). Sdlg. 10-2D. TB, 35" (89 cm), E. S. tan, veined purple; F. white ground, raspberry plicata markings; beards mustard brown. 28-4I, Inspiration Point sib, X Broadway. Cooley 1999.

SURREAL (Monty Byers by Phyllis Dickey, R. 1996). Sdlg. G59-2. TB, 29" (74 cm), M. S. golden yellow, veined and dotted purple; F. white ground, purple stitched edge and hafts; beards golden brown, purple horn. Everything Plus X Egyptian. Misty Hill 1996.

SURSKIYE ZORI (Viktor Sheviakov, R. 1995). Sdlg. 20D 17. TB, 28" (72 cm), ML. S. light brick red; F. dark brick red, rim light red brown, hafts shaded yellow to tan; beards brown; ruffled. Heather Hawk X Latin Lover. Sheviakov 1995.

SUSAN GILLESPIE (Cy Bartlett, R. 1995). Sdlg. C91-50. IB, 22" (56 cm), M. S. pale lemon; F. chrome yellow; beards lemon; lightly ruffled. (Mrs. Nate Rudolph x Pamela Ahn) X Sunny and Warm.

SUSANNA SURPRISED (Nora Scopes, TB, R. 1986). British Iris Society 1989.

SUSAN'S GOLDEN SUN (William Phillips by Francis Scott Key Iris Society, R. 1992). Sdlg. 81-4. TB, 30" (76 cm), M. Deep gold self; beards orange. Parentage unknown. Francis Scott Key Iris Society 1993.

SUSAN VARNER (D. Steve Varner, R. 1993). Sdlg. 9074. TB, 33" (84 cm), EM. Heavily ruffled deep light blue with lavender tint; self beards; slight sweet fragrance. Cup Race X 4137: (Leda's Lover x Quiet Kingdom). Illini Iris 1993.

SUSLIK (John Burton II, R. 1995). Sdlg. CP4. SPEC (*pumila*), 4½" (11 cm), E. Dark red violet, deeper around beard; style arms red violet; beards blue violet to blue, gold in throat, bushy. SIGNA seed (87-A-372), collected by Rodionenko, North Caucasus. Burton 1996.

SUSPICION (Keith Keppel, R. 1998). Sdlg. 93-83H. TB, 38" (97 cm), M. S. greyed greenish yellow (M&P 19-DE-1), central area blended aster violet (45-F-7); style arms greenish yellow (19-C-1), lavender lip; F. light greenish yellow (19-B-1), slightly darker margins (19-C-1) and shoulders (20-K-1), giving russet green to oil yellow (12-L-1) effect; beards yellow (10-L-6); pronounced sweet fragrance. Wishful Thinking X Spring Shower. Keppel 1999.

SUSQUEHANNA (Ed Roberts, R. 1993). Sdlg. RV-15-93. TB, 32" (81 cm), M. S. blue violet; F. off-white with dark blue violet blotch; beards dark blue violet; pronounced fragrance. Olympiad X Honky Tonk Blues. Ed Roberts 1995.

SUVENIR KAVKAZA (V. & N. Gordodelovy, R. 1995). Sdlg. 39. TB, 32" (80 cm), E. S. light cream, brown at base; F. creamy lettuce green, white haft striations; beards cream, red in throat; ruffled. Parentage unknown. Gordodelovy 1988.

SUWAGORYO (Kiyoro Yoshie by Society for Japanese Irises, R. 1995). JI (3 F.), 35" (90 cm), VE. S. and style arms deep blue violet; F. deep blue violet with darker veining. Parentage unknown. Introduced in Japan, 1980.

SUZI PAYNE (Mary Tubbs, R. 1994). Sdlg. SMM-2. TB, 28" (71 cm), M. Brilliant deep violet self; beards pale violet; tailored; sweet fragrance. Superstition X Kernewek.

SUZUKI CHIC (Ladislav Muska, R. 1996). Sdlg. EWTE-05. TB, 39" (99 cm), EM. S. light yellow; F. medium lavender blue, light caramel band; beards orange; heavily ruffled and laced; sweet fragrance. Edith Wolford X (Tut's Gold x Edith Wolford). Muska 1996.

SVADEBNYYE SVECHI (Viktor Sheviakov, R. 1999). Sdlg. 10B6. TB, 33" (85 cm), ML. S. and style arms bright yellow; F. dark tan yellow, light tan yellow rim; beards light tan yellow; ruffled. Radiant Apogee X Fairy Fable.

SVETLANA (Viktor Sheviakov, R. 1995). Sdlg. 519-U. TB, 32" (82 cm), M. Porcelain white, shaded light cream; beards greenish brown. Winter Olympics X Samanta Smit. Sheviakov 1992.

SVETLIACHOK (Galina Shevchenko, R. 1995). MDB, 7" (18 cm), M. S. white, tinted light cream; F. light yellow cream; beards white at end, changing to cream, dark yellow in throat; slight sweet fragrance. From *I. pumila* sdlgs. Shevchenko 1992.

SVETLONOS (Ladislav Muska, R. 1996). Sdlg. GEMV-02/B. TB, 39" (99 cm), ML. S. orchid, flushed pink; F. light lavender blue, narrow orchid rim; beards tangerine; heavily ruffled and laced; slight fragrance. ((Geniality x Invocazione) x (Beverly Sills x Sweet Musette)) X Da Lus. Muska 1996.

SVIATNIF (Irina Driagina, R. 1995). Sdlg. 78-02. BB, 26" (65 cm), L. S. light yellow; F. white, light yellow rim; beards yellow. Olimpiyski X Stepping Out. Driagina 1987.

SVITANOK (Nina Miroshnichenko, R. 1997). TB, 34" (87 cm), M. Creamy pink self; beards tangerine; slight fragrance. Parentage unknown. Miroshnichenko 1996.

SWAGGER MATTER (Tom Burseen, R. 1995). Sdlg. 1-293A. TB, 35" (89 cm), M. S. lemon cream (RHS 19B); style arms slightly darker lemon; F. darker, brighter lemon (22B), center washed white; beards tangerine; ruffled; pronounced spicy fragrance. 9-212: (Fine China x Bluid) X 8-66: (Radiant Energy x Sunny and Warm). T.B.'s Place 1996.

SWAGMAN (Heidi Blyth, R. 1990). Sdlg. 8H-6-B. SDB, 8" (20 cm), EM. Lemon yellow, bright ruby thumbprint 3/4 way down F.; beards creamy white, gold in throat. Jazzamatazz X unknown. Tempo Two 1990/91.

SWALEDALE (B.L.C. Dodsworth, TB, R. 1988). British Iris Society 1990.

SWAMP MONSTER (Ken Durio, R. 1992). Sdlg. CAN-PAT #11. LA (tet.), 36-48" (91-122 cm), ML. S. full violet, pale violet edge, full yellow signal; style arms and appendages pale violet; F.

435

very dark violet, full yellow signal; slight spicy fragrance. (Professor Ike x Professor Claude) X Godzilla.

SWAMP PIONEERS (Albert Faggard, R. 1994). Sdlg. FPP-3-87. LA, 36" (91 cm), E. S. light peach, yellow midline; style arms yellow; F. light peach, yellow signal crest radiating over white ground; slight sweet fragrance. Parentage unknown. Faggard 1994.

SWAN BALLET (Tell Muhlestein, TB, R. 1953). Correction of parentage. Spanish Peaks X 49-17: (Azure Skies x 45-45: (Easter Morn x Stella Polaris)).

SWANN'S WAY (Clarence Mahan, R. 1994). Sdlg. 1388-1. TB, 36" (91 cm), ML. Laced, lightly ruffled white self; beards violet; slight fragrance. Lady Bird Johnson X Betty Frances. Stockton 1998.

SWANSEA (Harry Foster, R. 1990). Sdlg. J310/85. SIB (tet.), 36" (91 cm), L. Rich purple blue, F. with strong silver edge, white netted signal, gold shoulders and green hafts. Reddy Maid X Silver Edge.

SWAZI DAME (Henry Danielson by Luella Danielson, R. 1991). Sdlg. DM 84-4. AB (OGB), 28" (71 cm), M. S. cream white, blending to light pink; style crests light lemon; F. light rose burgundy, large maroon black signal; beards reddish brown. (Morning Radiance x 72-41) X (Bionic Flash x Dee Mouse). Aril Society, Pleasure Iris 1992.

SWEDISH DELIGHT (Elyse Hill, R. 1998). Sdlg. EJ 28-16-91. TB, 36" (91 cm), M. S. yellow (RHS 7B); style arms maize yellow (21B); F. violet blue (90A), shoulders orange; beards gold; slight fragrance. Swedish Modern X Edith Wolford. O'Brien Iris 1999.

SWEET ALEDA (Helen Monroe, TB, R. 1983). Pacific Coast Hybridizers 1992.

SWEET AMBROSIA (Joyce Ragle, R. 1996). Sdlg. 90-5895-SCCB. TB, 33" (84 cm), ML. S. white, midrib peach (HCC 512/3), maize yellow (607/2) base; style arms white, edged maize yellow; F. spanish orange (010/3) shading to majolica yellow (09/1) at hafts, 1/8" white edge diminishing at bottom; beards capsicum red (715), tip slightly lighter; lightly ruffled; slight sweet fragrance. Spiced Custard X Coral Beauty.

SWEET BALLERINA (Richard Ernst, R. 1996). Sdlg. JF169-11-13. TB, 34" (86 cm), M. S. light violet (near RHS 85A/B); F. light violet, much paler near beard, darker violet (85A) rim; beards orange, blue white at end, orange yellow in throat; slight sweet fragrance. Different World X F123-2: (Afternoon Delight x Edna's Wish). Cooley 1997.

SWEET BITE (Paul Black, R. 1995). Sdlg. 91316C. SDB, 14" (36 cm), M. S. buff, midrib infused pink; style arms white; F. diamond-dusted warm white, blushed pale tan pink around beard; beards white, tipped orange; slight musky fragrance. Broken Halo sib X Earliglo. Mid-America 1995.

SWEET CHARM (Graeme Grosvenor, R. 1997). Sdlg. T2-2. TB, 46" (117 cm), ML. S. yellow; F. mauve, magenta and tan blend; beards honey tan; ruffled; pronounced sweet fragrance. Rancho Grande X Sweet Musette. Rainbow Ridge 1997/98.

SWEET COSETTE (John C. Taylor, R. 1997). Sdlg. UL 17-3. LA, 39" (100 cm), ML. Pink tan, blending to buff at edge; signal yellow green, darker pinkish tan halo; style arms cream and buff. Dancing Vogue X Dural White Butterfly. Rainbow Ridge 1997/98.

SWEET DELIGHT (Barry Blyth, R. 1995). Sdlg. A62-1. TB, 38" (97 cm), M. S. peachy pink to apricot, midrib blended slightly deeper; F. creamy with peach apricot outpouring; beards rich apricot; ruffled, laced; pronounced sweet fragrance. Dance Man X Neo Classic. Tempo Two 1995/96.

SWEETER DREAM (Daniel Thruman, R. 1997). TB, 37" (94 cm) ML. S. creamy light caramel; style arms caramel; F. darker caramel, purplish centerline, hafts with bold veining on white; beards gold, purple-tipped horn with white hairs; sweet fragrance. Sky Hooks X Supreme Sultan.

SWEET FORTUNE (Graeme Grosvenor, R. 1996). Sdlg. T1-C. TB, 37" (95 cm), M. Peach pink self; beards coral pink; slight fragrance. Fortunata X Sweet Musette. Rainbow Ridge 1997/98.

SWEET FREIDA (Clyde Hahn, R. 1995). Sdlg. 91-14-C. TB, 38" (97 cm), M. Bright chrome yellow self; matching beards. Sunkist Frills X Piping Hot. Hahn's Rainbow 1995.

SWEETHEART KISS (Loleta Powell, R. 1994). Sdlg. 91-36. TB, 35" (89 cm), ML. S. and style arms cream, tinged blue; F. bluish mulberry, edged white; beards very bright red; pronounced sweet fragrance. American Sweetheart X Magic Kiss. Powell's Gardens 1996.

SWEETHEART RING (Donald Spoon, R. 1995). TB, 31" (79 cm), M & RE. S. creamy yellow, infused darker yellow; style arms light yellow; F. white, narrow bright yellow border; beards yellow, white base and end; ruffled, lightly laced. I Do X Romantic Mood. Winterberry 1997.

SWEETIE GIRL (Tom Magee, BB, R. 1988). Long 1991.

SWEET JESS (Francis Rogers, TB, R. 1989). Meadowbrook 1990.

SWEET KATE (Nora Scopes, SDB, R. 1985). British Iris Society 1987.

SWEET LEMONADE (Akihiko Terada, R. 1995). Sdlg. 192-3. TB, 36" (91 cm), M. S. lemon; F. deep lemon; beards yellow; ruffled, laced. Moon Journey X Tiger Shark. Roris 1996.

SWEET LENA (Martin Holland, R. 1992). TB, 28" (71 cm), ML. Light blue, narrowly edged white, white throat; beards yellow; pronounced sweet fragrance. Parentage unknown. Holland Gardens 1993.

SWEET MEI (Chun Fan, R. 1999). Sdlg. F93-1043. TB, 30" (76 cm), ML. Ruffled, lightly laced dark violet blue (RHS 90A), F. with ruby red (59A) shoulders; beards gold; flared; slight sweet fragrance. Twilight Blaze X Honky Tonk Blues.

SWEET MIRIAM (Janet Hutchinson, R. 1998). Sdlg. MA/AD/1. LA, 37-45" (94-114 cm), M. S. pale pink over white, tip darker, pale line edge, salmon brown midline; style arms cream; F. light old rose pink, darker toward edge, pale line edge, salmon brown midline, lime green and white signal; lightly ruffled, slight picotee edge; slight fragrance. (Myra Arny x Andy Dandy) X Dural White Butterfly.

SWEETNESS AND LIGHT (Sharon McAllister, R. 1990). Sdlg. 84-7A-1. AB (OGB-), 28" (72 cm), EM. Smooth amethyst violet (near RHS 85A); style arms yellow, violet midrib; F. ashes of roses (greyer than 186C/D), oxblood red signal; beards layered pale violet, brown purple and mustard; pronounced sweet fragrance. Paisano X El Coronel. McAllister 1992.

SWEET ORANGE SPICE (George Sutton, R. 1993). Sdlg. B-432A. TB, 34" (86 cm), EM. Light orange self; beards light orange; pronounced spicy fragrance. Show Biz X 2-20: (Dazzling Gold x Taco Belle). Sutton 1993.

SWEET PEACH (Francis Rogers, R. 1999). Sdlg. C-216-W. TB, 30" (76 cm), E. S. and style arms peach (RHS 29C); F. majolica yellow (168D); beards saturn red (30C); ruffled; sweet fragrance. Ellie Lou X Apricot Flush.

SWEET REMEMBRANCE (Chet Tompkins, R. 1994). Sdlg. 88-19M. TB, 38" (97 cm), ML. S. vivid azure blue; F. deep blue violet; beards pale yellow. Sib to Total Obsession. Fleur de Lis 1994.

SWEET REVENGE (Duane Meek, R. 1992). Sdlg. 834-1-6. TB, 35" (89 cm), M. Baby ribbon pink, F. with lighter area below melon beard; ruffled, laced. Sue Ellen X Vision in Pink. D & J Gardens 1992.

SWEET ROMANCE (Donald Spoon, R. 1995). Sdlg. 92-101A. TB, 35" (89 cm), ML. S. pearl pink; style arms darker pearl pink; F. rosy pink, pearl pink edge; beards tangerine, white base; ruffled, lightly laced, flared. Sweetheart Ring X Jennifer Rebecca.

SWEET SAVANNAH (Darlene Pinegar, R. 1999). Sdlg. FT-1-1. TB, 29" (74 cm), M. S. and style arms salmon; F. salmon, red purple haft marks and striping becoming near-solid on lower half, narrow salmon edge; beards deep orange; lightly ruffled, laced; slight musky fragrance. Fancy Tales X Queen in Calico.

SWEET SCENT OF (David Miller, R. 1999). Sdlg. 92-2B. SDB, 11" (28 cm), L. S. and style arms golden yellow (RHS 11A); F. darker golden yellow, veined reddish brown; beards silvery white; pronounced sweet fragrance. Sass with Class X Toy Clown.

SWEET SENSATION (Margie Robinson, R. 1994). Sdlg. 85-36. BB, 27" (69 cm), M. Heavily ruffled icy blue (RHS 112D) self; beards icy blue, yellow in throat; slight sweet fragrance. Pink Bubbles X unknown. Robinson 1994.

SWEET SOLITUDE (D. C. Nearpass, R. 1996). Sdlg. 91-102. TB, 33" (84 cm), M & RE (late). S. white; F. white, 3/16" blue (Munsell 7.5PB 5/11) rim (Emma Cook pattern); beards tangerine (2.5YR 8/6). My Katie X Entourage.

SWEET STUFF (Terrell Taylor, R. 1998). Sdlg. 94-38D. TB, 37" (93 cm), M. S. aster mauve (RHS 78C) on sulphur yellow (6D) to white ground; F. imperial purple (78A), cadmium yellow central area marked sienna to fuchsia; beards bronze; pronounced musky sweet fragrance. Lingering Love X Theatre. Bonita Gardens 1998.

SWEET SUCCESS (D. Steve Varner, R. 1993). Sdlg. 3150. SIB, 22" (56 cm), ML. Royal purple; signal area veined gold. Belfast X Foretell. Illini Iris 1994.

SWEET SURRENDER (Robert Hollingworth, R. 1992). Sdlg. 85A1B27. SIB, 34" (86 cm), E. Medium wine red, white blaze; style arms light blue, red rim. 81A5C3: (7712: (Varner 062: (Dreaming Spires x Tealwood) x unknown) x Augury) X 83M3B8: (Pink Haze x Fairy Dawn). Windwood Gardens 1992.

SWEET TANGO (Monique Dumas-Quesnel, R. 1992). Sdlg. 90-X-versata-0. SPEC-X, 36" (90 cm),

M. S. dark violet blue (RHS 90A); F. slightly lighter violet blue (89C), pointed bright yellow signal; slight sweet fragrance. EX-DW-13, *versicolor* sdlg., X purple *ensata* sdlg.

SWEET THING (Lynda Miller, R. 1995). Sdlg. 2191. SDB, 14" (36 cm), M. S. cream ground, light plum plicata markings, solid 3/16" golden tan edge; F. white ground, orchid plicata border, 1/8" golden tan band; beards baby blue; slight musky sweet fragrance. 3587B: (Smidget x Sniffs 'n' Sneezes) X Chubby Cheeks. Miller's Manor 1996.

SWEET TOOTH (Ben Hager, R. 1999). Sdlg. MD6155Pk. MDB, 4-5" (10-13 cm), EML. True pink, S. lighter; style arms pink; beards white, tangerine in throat. MD5486BBfPk: (AMD4971BrtY, sib to Wee Me pod parent, x MD4938Pch: (((((((Evening Storm x Welch H501) x (Sulina x Melodrama)) x ((Nest Egg x Progenitor) x (Brassie x Brownie))) x (Idol's Eye x (Scale Model x Brownett))) x Buttercup Charm) x (Pet sib x Tiny Apricot)) x (((Buttercup Charm 2562: (Pink Amber x Pink Cushion)) x 2888: (2562 x Buttercup Charm)) x (2888 x (Buttercup Charm x (Pink Cushion x Roberts 65R28)))))) X MD5146Pch: (((3739LtYel: (Pet sib x Tiny Apricot) x ((2562 x (Frosty Lemonade x Pink Cushion)) x 2888)) x (3739CrY x (Pet sib x Tiny Apricot))) x Pet sib). Adamgrove 1999.

SWEET VANILLA PEACH (Barbara Wight, R. 1996). Sdlg. 90-29. TB, 29" (74 cm), ML. S. and style arms light peach (RHS 27B); F. light pastel yellow (8D), fading to white; beards orange, lemon at end; slight sweet fragrance. Peach Everglow X Horny Lorri. Wight's Iris 1996.

SWING (Barry Blyth, R. 1997). Sdlg. D34-10. SDB, 12" (30 cm), EM. S. pastel lavender pink; F. white, 1/4" soft pastel lavender edge; beards lavender blue at end, white in middle, tangerine in throat. Bee's Knees X A7-1: (Merry Dance x Mini Song). Tempo Two 1997/98.

SWING AND SWAY (Virginia Messick, R. 1994). Sdlg. 87-7. TB, 37" (94 cm), M. Near-white with blue violet highlights; self beards, tipped blue; ruffled, flared. (Ron x Winterscape) X (Pacific Mist sdlg. x Bubbling Over). Messick 1994.

SWING DANCING (Virginia Messick, R. 1999). Sdlg. M88-28. TB, 37" (94 cm), M. Ruffled clear medium blue self; beards blue; slight fragrance. (Ron x Winterscape) X Breakers. Messick 1999.

SWINGTOWN (Schreiner, R. 1996). Sdlg. CC 333-A. TB, 36" (91 cm), L. Heavily ruffled mulberry claret (RHS 77A) self; beards blue purple; pronounced sweet fragrance. Sultry Mood X V 489-2: (1981 #26, unknown, x K400-1: (Cranberry Ice x H 301-B: ((Dream Time sib x Mulberry Wine) x (Skywatch x (Amethyst Flame x Silvertone))))). Schreiner 1996.

SWIRLED FRECKLES (Ladislav Muska, R. 1999). Sdlg. 98-DQSZ-02. TB, 35" (89 cm), M. S. cream, light brown rim; style arms golden brown; F. vanilla yellow ground covered by mahogany plicata markings; beards mustard; heavily ruffled, lightly laced; slight fragrance. (((Spacelight Sketch x Calicoball) x (Queen in Calico x Scattered Dots)) x Zuzana) X Mezzotinto. Muska 1999.

SWIRLING PETALS (Agnes Frech, R. 1999). Sdlg. 193. TB, 34" (86 cm), M. S. taupe, light and dark purple swirls; style arms gold; F. taupe, purple and plum swirls; beards mustard; variable pattern. Batik X Be My Love.

SWISH (Barry Blyth, R. 1995). Sdlg. B75-1. SDB, 10" (25 cm), VE. S. mustard; F. gold, lighter than S., with brownish plicata stitching; beards mustard gold; slight sweet fragrance. X44-B, Acid Print sib, X Ashanti. Tempo Two 1995/96.

SWITCHCROZZLE (Lawrence Ransom, R. 1993). Sdlg. 87/8-5. IB, 21" (53 cm), M. S. warm white, wide border stitched raspberry; F. white, edged raspberry, cream yellow hafts heavily dotted and stitched raspberry and maroon; beards bushy white brushed light orange, hairs lightly tipped orchid; lightly ruffled, flared. Swizzle X Cross Stitch. Iris au Trescols 1994.

SWITCHED ON (John C. Taylor, R. 1996). Sdlg. UL 20-5. LA, 39" (100 cm), ML. S. cream, rose marbling and midrib; style arms green, blended cream and rose; F. yellow, sprayed rose edge, green signal surrounded by yellow; slight fragrance. Desert Jewel X Margaret Lee. Rainbow Ridge 1998/99.

SWITCHEROO (Graeme Grosvenor, R. 1999). Sdlg. V53-7A. TB, 36" (91 cm), EM. S. rosy brown; F. dark rosy brown, center lighter; beards tangerine. Rustler X Bogota.

SWOON (Barry Blyth, R. 1999). Sdlg. E14-2. SDB, 12" (30 cm), VE. S. blue pink to grey smoke, deeper blue midrib; F. same, large tan blue pink pumila spot; beards deep navy blue; slight fragrance. Celsius X B25-1: (Z7-2, Toy Kingdom sib, x Z24-1, Volts sib). Tempo Two 1999/2000.

SYDNEY (Graeme Grosvenor, R. 1998). Sdlg. V0-1. TB, 35" (90 cm), ML. Blue self; beards blue; pronounced sweet fragrance. Breakers X Quintessence.

SYLVAN (Monty Byers, TB, R. 1989). Moonshine 1990.

SYLVANSHINE (Clarence Mahan/Carol Warner, R. 1997). Sdlg. MW10. SPEC (*setosa*), 30" (76 cm), M. White self; 3- to 4-branched, up to 10 buds, flowers largish; foliage with slight violet basal tinge. Seed from SIGNA. Parentage unknown. Draycott 1997.

SYLVAN SMILING (Tom Burseen, R. 1999). Sdlg. 94-253C. TB, 34" (86 cm), M. S. peach pink; F. peach ground, heavily streaked and washed dark purple, fine peach rim; beards mustard; ruffled. Light Show X Filibuster. T.B.'s Place 1999.

SYRIAN ROSE (G. F. Wilson, R. 1996). Sdlg. 66-91BFO-A. AB (OGB+), 29" (74 cm), E. S. bright orchid rose, slightly darker veining; F. rose, very large round sharp black signal surrounded by cream, slight maroon dotting; beards bright deep yellow. Bionic Flash X Onlooker. Pleasure Iris 1997.

TABLE TIME (Tom Burseen, R. 1995). Sdlg. 1-314C. TB, 36" (91 cm), M. S. purple (RHS 79C), brown at base; style arms tan, washed purple; F. purple, white haft stitches; beards gold, bushy; ruffled; musky fragrance. 9-153: ((Afternoon Delight x Sooner Serenade) x Burnt Crisp) X 9-358: ((Bubble Bath x Titan's Glory) x Bluid). T.B.'s Place 1995.

TACEY (Melba Hamblen, TB, R. 1989). Roris 1991.

TACHYON (Barry Blyth, R. 1997). Sdlg. D34-20. SDB, 14" (36 cm), ML. S. light to medium violet, some white at midrib; F. bright white ground, 1/4" light to medium violet edge; beards white, lavender at end, tangerine in throat. Bee's Knees X A7-1: (Merry Dance x Mini Song). Tempo Two 1997/98.

TACT (Keith Keppel, R. 1994). Sdlg. 90-6K. IB, 24" (61 cm), EM. S. warm white (M&P 9-AB-1); style arms white; F. aureolin yellow (10-L-2); beards white at end, sunflower (9-L-4) and golden glow (9-L-6) in throat; slight fragrance. Over Easy X Amber Snow. Keppel 1995.

TADZHIKI BANDIT (Lawrence Ransom, R. 1996). Sdlg. 88/25-1. AR (RC), 20" (51 cm), EM. S. beige brown, overall darker veining more violet over paler center; style arms lilac violet, crests red brown; F. dark red brown, cream white ground showing on sides and hafts, diffuse brownish black signal; beards medium blue violet, hairs tipped bronze. Vera X Sam Norris T-N85G: ((*I. camillae* x (T-N78R: (C-N73B: ((((*I. susiana* x Andromache) x (*I. susiana* x *I. gatesii*)) x *I. sari*) x C-N73A: ((Bagdad Beauty x (*I. susiana* x Andromache)) x *I. sari*)) x *I. sari*)) x ((C-N73A x (B66T x *I. sari*)) x T-N78R)). Iris au Trescols 1997.

TADZHIKI ECLIPSE (Lawrence Ransom, R. 1996). Sdlg. 88/25-2. AR (RC), 22" (56 cm), EM. S. blended medium violet brown, darker overall veining, paler center with midrib flushed violet; style arms light violet, red brown veined crests; F. white ground heavily veined and sanded dark violet brown, large circular black signal; beards medium blue, hairs tipped bronze. Sib to Tadzhiki Bandit. Iris au Trescols 1997.

TAFFETA AND VELVET (William Ackerman, JI, R. 1984). Nicholls Gardens 1990.

TAFFETA TUTU (Chet Tompkins, R. 1992). Sdlg. 86-102. TB, 39" (99 cm), ML. Mulberry cerise, blended rich violet; beards lilac; ruffled. (Lilac Breeze x (Mary Frances x Pretty Please)) X ((Ad Vantage x Mulled Wine) x (Night Lightning x Matinee Idol)). Fleur de Lis 1992.

TAFFY SURPRISE (Sharol Longaker, 1991). TB, 36" (91 cm), M. S. creamy honey gold; F. honey gold, lavender hafts, white spot below creamy yellow beard; ruffled, flared; sweet fragrance. Laced Cotton X Post Time. Anderson Iris 1991.

TAFFY TOUCH (A. & D. Willott, R. 1992). Sdlg. 88-89. SDB, 12½" (32 cm), M. S. light gold; F. full gold; beards violet; ruffled. Nachos X Pilgrims' Choice. Willott 1992.

TAGA SODE (Shuichi Hirao by Society for Japanese Irises, R. 1992). JI (6 F.), 36" (91 cm), EM. Red purple boldly veined white, signal yellow; style arms white, edged red purple. Parentage unknown. Hirao 1957.

TAHITIAN NIGHT (John C. Taylor, R. 1993). Sdlg. RL 18-7. LA, 47" (120 cm), M. Purple, yellow signal on all petals, pale reverse. Louisiana Derby X Margaret Lee. Rainbow Ridge 1993/94.

TAHITIAN SKIES (Allen Harper, R. 1991). Sdlg. M38-1. TB, 34" (86 cm), M. Lavender (RHS 92D); beards yellow; slight fragrance. Song of Norway X Victoria Falls.

TAIKO (Shuichi Hirao by Society for Japanese Irises, R. 1992). JI (6 F.), 27½" (70 cm), L. Ruffled red purple, bold white center and veins, signal yellow; style arms white, edged red purple. Parentage unknown. Hirao 1960.

TAILEM BEND (Leslie Donnell, R. 1997). Sdlg. 94-4-5. TB, 37" (94 cm), M. Apricot, F. with white patch; beards red; slight sweet fragrance. ((Speculator x Tintinara) x Hampton Glory sib) X Coomandook.

TAJA (Barry Blyth, R. 1990). Sdlg. X28-4. SDB, 15" (38 cm), VE. S. bishops violet with iridescence, faint white at midrib; F. white, heavy bishops violet plicata markings around edge and running into white center; beards bishops violet. Yipee X Royal Magician. Tempo Two 1990/91.

TAKEOFF (Jim & Vicki Craig, R. 1991). Sdlg. 31T15. IB, 27" (68 cm), E. S. pale blue violet, base deeper; F. warm medium violet, hafts darker; beards dark yellow, tipped blue; ruffled, flared. 10R23, Step Ahead sib, X 6R10: ((Odyssey x Maroon Caper) x (Chapeau x (Sacred Mountain x *aphylla* "Werckmeister"))). J. & V. Craig 1991.

TAKE TIME (John C. Taylor, R. 1997). Sdlg. UL 13-2. LA, 43" (110 cm), ML. S. and style arms light purple; F. dark purple, fine edge and reverse lighter purple, yellow dagger signal surrounded by cream. Dancing Vogue X First Favourite. Rainbow Ridge 1997/98.

TALBINGO SKY (Graeme Grosvenor, R. 1996). Sdlg. T7-6. TB, 36" (92 cm), EM. S. white, dotted and edged light blue; F. white, edged sky blue; beards orange yellow; slight fragrance. Daredevil X Snowbrook. Rainbow Ridge 1999/2000.

TALDRA (Harry Foster, R. 1991). Sdlg. R60/87. SIB (tet.), 48" (122 cm), ML. S. dark lilac (RHS 89); style arms purple blue (89D); F. rich purple blue (89A) edged silver. Harpswell Happiness X Dear Dianne.

TALK (Barry Blyth, R. 1994). Sdlg. A1-5. SDB, 14" (36 cm), VE-M. Ashes of roses to rose beige, F. with outpouring of rich burgundy half-way down; beards bright tangerine, outer few hairs tipped lavender. Scat X X32-B: (Tricks x Yipee). Tempo Two 1994/95.

TALK MAGIC (Barry Blyth, R. 1992). Sdlg. X47-A. IB, 24" (61 cm), EML. S. smoky pink; F. deeper smoky pink with smoky rose overlay; beards electric navy tipped bronze, tangerine in throat. (Inca Queen x Beachgirl) X (Peach Eyes x Kandi Moon). Tempo Two 1992/93.

TALK THAT TALK (Tom Burseen, R. 1999). Sdlg. 95-351A. TB, 35" (89 cm), M. Pale lilac white (RHS 69D); beards tan with large uplifted flounce; ruffled, strongly flared; musky fragrance. All Aflutter X Air Up There.

TALK TO ME (Richard Ernst, R. 1994). Sdlg. HR 8545-4. TB, 37" (94 cm), M. S. dark mustard yellow, midrib infused violet; style arms mustard; F. dark blue violet; beards mustard; ruffled; slight sweet fragrance. From sdlgs. inv. Edith Wolford and Merry Madrigal. Cooley 1995.

TALL ORDER (Graeme Grosvenor, R. 1998). Sdlg. V60-7. TB, 38" (96 cm), ML. Blue violet, F. with lighter edge; beards orange yellow; pronounced sweet fragrance. Silverado X Timescape. Rainbow Ridge 1999/2000.

TALL SHIPS (J. T. Aitken, R. 1993). Sdlg. 84T19. TB, 38" (97 cm), ML. S. medium blue with white flush, blue line down midrib; F. medium blue, white flush below light violet beard; slight fragrance. Victoria Falls X Sea Wolf. Aitken's Salmon Creek 1993.

TAL-Y-BONT (Harry Foster, SIB, R. 1989). British Iris Society 1999.

TAMARAU BEAUTY (Eric Braybrook, R. 1999). Sdlg. 91/2/B. TB, 39" (99 cm), M. Pale blue self; beards grey; slight fragrance. Titan's Glory X unknown.

TAMATSUSHIMA (Shuichi Hirao by Society for Japanese Irises, R. 1992). JI (3 F.), 31" (80 cm), M. S. white, edged red violet; style arms white; F. white, blushed red violet, signal yellow. Parentage unknown. Hirao 1957.

TAMMY JEAN DOLAN (Bob Thomason, R. 1991). Sdlg. BT 8809A. TB, 30" (76 cm), M. S. plum; style arms plum, yellow at base; F. medium violet, white hafts veined brown; beards dark orange; slight fragrance. Jamari X Mary Randall. Okie Iris 1994.

TAMMY SUE (Jim Hedgecock, R. 1990). Sdlg. C-84-241. TB, 31" (79 cm), M. S. pale blue, midrib green; F. pale blue, pronounced green highlights; beards medium blue; slight fragrance. Ron X Quadros 76-13. Comanche Acres 1992.

TAMZIN (Hilmary Catton, R. 1996). Sdlg. C 8941. SDB, 12" (30 cm), EM. S. pale blue, midrib green; style arms blue; F. pale blue, green hafts, blue green wash; beards cream, tipped yellow. Chubby Cheeks X Rainmaker. Richmond Iris 1998/99.

TANAKO (Richard Morgan, R. 1992). Sdlg. L246-R. LA, 33" (84 cm), M. Red, large orange yellow signal on F., sometimes line signal on S. L4-A: (Trail of Tears x Bayou Comas) X Chowning 77-6: (Mockers Song x Ann Chowning). Redbud Lane 1993.

TAN CHEEKS (John Durrance, R. 1993). Sdlg. D89-17. MTB, 26" (66 cm), EM. Tawny apricot; beards henna. Eastertime X Speculator. Long 1993.

TANGERINE FAIRY (Daniel Thruman, R. 1997). TB, 38" (97 cm), M. Heavily ruffled light pink self, F. slightly lighter; beards tangerine orange; slight sweet fragrance. Gypsy Woman X Outrageous Fortune.

TANGERINE SUNRISE (B.L.C. Dodsworth, TB, R. 1979). British Iris Society 1981.

TANGERINE TANGENT (Paul Black, R. 1990). Sdlg. 86281A. SDB, 14½" (37 cm), ML. S. medium purple; F. medium red purple, darker red purple spot, white haft markings; beards lavender, tipped fluorescent orange; pronounced spicy fragrance. Reluctant Dragin X 84207A: (Gigglepot x Oriental Blush). Mid-America 1990.

TANG FIZZ (Robert Annand, R. 1993). Sdlg. 85-100B. TB, 36" (91 cm), M & RE. S. white, midrib blended apricot; F. apricot orange, ruffled 3/16" white edge; beards tangerine. 77-4: (peach sdlg. x Snowline) X Peach Spot. Milwood Nursery 1993.

TANGFU (Barry Blyth, R. 1995). Sdlg. B91-1. IB, 18" (46 cm), VE-M. S. smoky tan pink, violet flush at base; F. smoky tan pink, bluish flush below beards; beards lavender blue, tipped burnt tangerine; slight musky fragrance. Z7-3, Toy Kingdom sib, X Electrique. Tempo Two 1995/96.

TANGLED WEB (Keith Keppel, R. 1998). Sdlg. 91-118C. TB, 37" (94 cm), ML. S. prune (M&P 47-J-8) to cyclamen (47-L-9), slight apricot beige (11-B-4) suffusion in center; style arms greyed mauve (46-H-5), banana (11-K-5) toward base; F. eggplant (45-H-12) edge, lightening to prune, rattan (11-J-6) central blaze partially obscured by radiating markings; beards orange and dark violet, pumpkin (10-H-11) in throat; ruffled. 87-26A: (Rosarita x ((Rancho Rose x (71-12C, Flamenco sib, x (68-17A, Roundup sib, x April Melody))) x Gigolo) X 87-44A: (Foreign Accent x (Change of Heart x Queen in Calico)). Keppel 1999.

TANGO DANCER (Stan Dexter by Marie Ingersoll, R. 1990). Sdlg. 1983/153. TB, 32" (81 cm), M. Ruffled, heavily crinkled purple pink dusted gold, orange hash marks; beards pink orange; pronounced sweet fragrance. Hombre X 1980/97A: (Beverly Sills x Koala). Ingersoll's Iris 1991.

TANGUERAY (Mary Dunn, R. 1991). Sdlg. M87-1026. TB, 38" (97 cm), M. S. ivory cream; style arms golden; F. off-white, chartreuse hafts and edge, giving green effect; beards mustard; ruffled. Crystalyn X Precious Moments. M.A.D. Iris 1993.

TANIMA-NO-HIKARI (Society for Japanese Irises, R. 1992). JI (3 F.), 36" (90 cm), M. S. and style arms white edged red violet; F. red violet, veined white, large white halo. Gosho Asobi X "Isui-no-Hama". Introduced in Japan, 1956

TAN MAN (J. T. Aitken, R. 1996). Sdlg. 87T49. TB, 39" (99 cm), VL. Tan pink; style arms peach; beards purple, hairs tipped bright red. unknown X Persian Gown. Aitken's Salmon Creek 1996.

TANNER (Darlene Pinegar, R. 1995). Sdlg. SW-5-4. TB, 36" (91 cm), ML. S. and style arms deep bright yellow; F. white ground around beard, blending to cream, 1/4"-1/2" stitched brownish red purple marginal band with 1/4" yellow gold outer rim; beards dark yellow orange; ruffled; pronounced sweet fragrance. Spinning Wheel X Broadway. Spanish Fork 1996.

TANNISH ANNA (Cloyd McCord, R. 1992). Sdlg. 83-46. TB, 36" (91 cm), M. S. tannish light lavender blend over pale yellow ground; F. light yellow, 1/4" light tannish lavender edge; beards yellow; ruffled, laced; sweet fragrance. Angie Quadros X 82-3B: (Beauty Crown x Homecoming Queen). McCord 1992.

TANTALIZING TIDBIT (Libby Cross, R. 1996). SDB, 9" (23 cm), EM & RE. S. wistaria blue (RHS 92C) washed green gold, midrib deeper wistaria blue (92B); style arms wistaria blue, yellow tip; F. paler wistaria blue (92), darker midrib, wide golden brown haft markings, pale antique gold rim; beards blue violet. Blue Pools X unknown. Crosspatch 1998.

TANTRA (Mary Dunn by Joseph Ghio, R. 1998). Sdlg. 239-7. LA, 38" (97 cm), EM. S. light orchid; style arms orchid; F. muted grape. Midnight Drama X self. Bay View 1998.

TANTRUM (Keith Keppel, R. 1996). Sdlg. 91-68A. IB, 24" (61 cm), EM. S. light chrome yellow (M&P 10-L-4), faint greyed rosy brown (6-C-3) center flush; style arms aureolin (10-L-2); F. cadmium lemon (9-L-1), solid 1/2" oxblood (7-L-9) border, oxblood dart at tip of light chrome yellow (10-L-4) beard; ruffled; slight sweet fragrance. 88-28A: (Jitterbug x Hot Streak) X Gatty W37-19, Quote sib. Keppel 1997.

TANTSUYUSCHI SHIVA (Viktor Sheviakov, R. 1996). Sdlg. 7c7. TB, 33" (85 cm), ML. S. golden red; F. porcelain white, wide red brown plicata edge, narrow red brown center stripe; beards light golden brown; ruffled; slight sweet fragrance. Siva Siva X Radiant Apogee. Sheviakov 1996.

TANYA LYNN (Jim Hedgecock, TB, R. 1989). Comanche Acres 1990.

TANZANIAN TANGERINE (Brad Kasperek, R. 1994). Sdlg. 91P-1C. TB, 38" (97 cm), EM. S. radiant deep tangerine; F. tannish orange (RHS 164D) ground with stippled red wine (168D) overlay; beards light orange; ruffled, flared. Tiger Honey X Jitterbug. Zebra 1995.

TARA PAIGE (J. Owings Rebert, R. 1997). Sdlg. NP-E1. SIB, 24" (61 cm), M. Blue violet self, brown haft markings and ivory signal. Parentage unknown.

TARNHELM (Bob Bauer/John Coble, R. 1998). Sdlg. J89U-3. JI (9 F.), 36" (90 cm), M. White self, yellow signal; style arms white; layered dome form. Frosted Pyramid X Frilled Enchantment. Ensata Gardens 1997.

TARNISHED ANGEL (Carl Boswell, R. 1990). Sdlg. 84-85S. SDB, 10" (25 cm), EM. Pale cream, F. with light greyish lime wing pattern; beards pale cream; slight spicy fragrance. Maya Mama X (Three Smokes x Plum Spot). Adamgrove, Aril Patch 1991.

TART (Ben Hager by Monty Byers, R. 1990). Sdlg. SD5126OrRE. SDB, 12" (30 cm), EML-VL & RE. S. orange; F. tannish orange; beards tangerine orange; slight sweet fragrance. (Bright Vision x SD4299BrtOr: (((Blond Doll x 2562B: (Pink Amber x Pink Cushion)) x Solar Flight) x (2888TY: (2562A x Buttercup Charm) x Solar Flight))) X (SD4299DpAp x ((((Buttercup Charm x 2562D) x 2888TY) x Hammered Copper) x ((2562Pinkest x (Frosty Lemonade x Pink Cushion)) x 2888SmY))). Moonshine 1991.

TASHA (A. J. Farrington, SDB, R. 1988). British Iris Society 1989.

TASHKENT (Adolf Volfovich-Moler, R. 1995). Sdlg. V-52. TB, 35" (90 cm), ML. S. bright yellow; F. orange red, edged bright yellow; beards yellow; ruffled, laced. Rippling Waters X Broadway Star. Volfovich-Moler 1992.

TASSAL OF HORNS (Ladislav Muska, R. 1999). Sdlg. 99-SHFC-01. TB, 34" (86 cm), L. S. and style arms light lavender; F. deep lavender; beards light red orange, lavender horn; ruffled, crinkled; sweet fragrance. (("Svitanie": ((Don Epifano x "Bozenka": (Pink Angel x (Buffy x Silver Shower))) x La Dentelle) x Hellada) x Fontanone) X (Conjuration x Fontana di Trevi).

TATANKASK (L. J. Duffy, R. 1992). Sdlg. WI-13-72. SPEC (*setosa*), 30-36" (76-91 cm), E. White with yellow streaking or veining at base of ruffled F.; style arms white; cream buds turning white before opening. Selection of *I. setosa interior* collected 1972 near Fairbanks, Alaska.

TATIANA (Evelyn Kegerise, R. 1990). Sdlg. 83-462-2. TB, 35-36" (89-91 cm), ML. S. light yellow; F. medium yellow; beards yellow, tipped orange; ruffled. Idol's Dream X Catalyst. Evelyn Kegerise 1991.

TATSUTA GAWA (Matsudaira Shoo by Society for Japanese Irises, R. 1994). JI (3 F.), 36" (90 cm), M. S. white, edged red violet; style arms white, red violet crests; F. red violet, large white center and radiating veins. Parentage unknown. Old Edo variety hybridized prior to 1856.

TATTLER (Keith Keppel, R. 1995). Sdlg. 91-26A. SDB, 13" (33 cm), EML. S. chartreuse (M&P 11-L-1) to oil yellow (12-L-1); style arms olive yellow (12-L-2); F. oil yellow and pyrethrum yellow (11-L-2) blend, small elongated cornflower blue (42-C-10) spot at end of beard; beards white, lightly tipped yellow and bronze, end section solid cornflower blue; lightly ruffled; slight sweet fragrance. Hafnium X Chanted. Keppel 1996.

TATTLETALE (Sharon McAllister, R. 1998). Sdlg. 86-7-1. AB (OGB), 28" (71 cm), M. S. soft violet, smoky overlay; style arms greyed violet, smoky overlay, large near-black tongue-shaped signal; beards brownish mustard. Edith Seligmann X Seligmann MM-MD-14-1: (Martha Mia x Moon Dust). McAllister 1998.

TATTYARA (Geoff Austin, R. 1998). Sdlg. EPS-196. TB, 29" (75 cm), M. S. blue purple; style arms and F. purple; beards blue, white in throat; ruffled; slight sweet fragrance. Everything Plus X Silverado. Austland 1998/99.

TAURIS (Lawrence Ransom, R. 1996). Sdlg. 89/165-1. AB (OGB+), 30" (76 cm), M. S. blue white; style arms cream white, bluish upper rib, yellower lower rib and stigmatic lip; F. blue white, small diffuse V-shaped grey purple signal below beard; beards golden yellow, tapered, beard tipped bronze; sweet fragrance. *I. hoogiana* X Tabriz. Iris au Trescols 1997.

TAURUS (H. Valmar Slamova by Philip Edinger, R. 1999). TB, 30" (76 cm), ML & RE. S. light crimson red; F. deep velvety red; beards with 1" horn. Joseph's Mantle X Hit Parade. Rainbow Hybridizing Gardens 1961.

TAUSENDSCHOEN (Walter & Anne-Ruth Brehm, R. 1992). Sdlg. S 3-426. TB, 27½" (70 cm), M. S. medium yellow; F. creamy white edged yellow; beards dark yellow; lightly waved; pronounced sweet fragrance. Probably -- (Antique Ivory x Soft Moonbeam) X unknown. Fachgruppe Iris 1992.

TAWNY WINGS (Nancy Bartlett, TB, R. 1984). Bartlett 1990.

TAXI (Paul Black, R. 1997). Sdlg. A142A. SDB, 11" (28 cm), M. Dark gold self; beards dark old gold; pronounced spicy fragrance. Transcribe X (84207A: (Gigglepot x Oriental Blush) x 86384A: ((Oriental Blush x Gigglepot) x (Gigglepot x Chubby Cheeks sib))). Mid-America 1997.

TAX TIME (Robert Strohman, R. 1994). Sdlg. 90-1-1. SDB, 12" (31 cm), EML. S. and style arms light violet; F. bronze, blending to light violet at edge; beards violet; flared; slight sweet fragrance. Hafnium X Limeline. Gardens Ltd. 1995.

TAYNA (Galina Shevchenko, R. 1995). MDB, 7½" (19 cm), VE. S. rich blue; F. very dark blue; beards white, orange in throat; pronounced sweet fragrance. From *I. pumila* sdlgs. Shevchenko 1992.

TAYNY LIUBOVNIK (Viktor Sheviakov, R. 1997). Sdlg. 22b22a. TB, 30" (75 cm), M. S. and style arms light pinkish orange; F. dark red orange, narrow light pinkish orange edge; beards bright orange; ruffled; slight sweet fragrance. 18c21: (Latin Lover x Rippling Waters) X Beaux Arts.

TEA CEREMONY (George Bush, JI, R. 1986). George Bush 1990.

TEACUP CHATTER (Heather Pryor, R. 1997). Sdlg. 51/93-J. LA, 40" (102 cm), ML. S. soft lavender, veined coffee, paler reverse; style arms soft rose, blushed green, yellow center rib and tip; F. milk coffee, veined burnt terracotta, rim lemon, raised yellow steeple signal; ruffled. Joie de Vivre X Stylish Socialite. Iris Haven 1999/2000.

TÈ ALLA PESCA (Augusto Bianco, R. 1999). Sdlg. 425. TB, 33" (85 cm), ML. S. chrome yellow, rose center; style arms cream to peach; F. primrose yellow; beards golden orange; pronounced sweet fragrance. Classico X (Gold Trimmings x Laced Daisy). Iride 1999.

TEAPOT TEMPEST (Lynn Markham, R. 1998). Sdlg. 92-17B. BB, 27" (69 cm), ML. Bright raspberry orchid self (Munsell 10P, 4/10 to 3/9); style arms white, raspberry orchid ribs and crests; beards soft light blue blending to soft gold in throat; crystalline finish; flared, lightly frilled; purple leaf base; very slight sweet fragrance. Angel Feathers X Pops Concert. Markham 1999.

TE AROHA (Heather Pryor, R. 1997). Sdlg. 56/90-5. LA, 35" (89 cm), ML. Soft lemon white (RHS 13D) with green veining, F. with lime green raised steeple signal veined lime green; style arms soft butter lemon; ruffled. Designer's Dream X Gladiator's Gift. Lone Star 1998.

TEBERDA (V. & N. Gordodelovy, R. 1996). Sdlg. 238. TB, 32" (80 cm), EM. White, tinted light blue, brown haft shading; beards lilac at end, changing to yellow, orange in throat. Parentage unknown. Gordodelovy 1991.

TEE LOU (Udo & Rudolf Wilkeneit, R. 1996). Sdlg. 18/1/94. MDB, 7" (18 cm), L. S. creamy brown, blue flash, violet red heart, blue border; F. creamy brown, blue flash; beards yellow grey; slight fragrance. Parentage unknown.

TEENSIE VIOLET (J. & L. Fry, R. 1990). Sdlg. 78-F-2. MDB, 1½-2" (4-5 cm), M. S. full violet; F. black, edged full violet; beards violet; fragrant. Sun Sparkle X Tiny Teardrop. J. & L. Iris 1991.

TEESDALE (B.L.C. Dodsworth, R. 1999). Sdlg. EB 94K. TB, 34" (85 cm), M. S. magenta; style arms and F. deep magenta; beards brown; ruffled; slight fragrance. Paradise Bird X Mulled Wine.

TEIGNBELLE (A.R.J. Bailey, R. 1996). Sdlg. NZ 90-2. SPEC (*unguicularis*), 7" (18 cm), ML. Pale rose pink, F. with small yellow median stripe; slight sweet fragrance. Starker's Pink X unknown.

TEIGNGRACE (A.R.J. Bailey, R. 1995). Sdlg. NZ 90-1. SPEC (*unguicularis*), 8" (20 cm), EML. S. rose pink, erect; F. rose pink, yellow median stripe surrounded by very pale pink area; foliage short, narrow. Starker's Pink X *I. unguicularis*, seed from New Zealand.

TELEGRAPH HILL (James McWhirter, R. 1993). Sdlg. J87-5-A. TB, 38" (97 cm), M. Sky blue, F. edged silver; beards white; heavily ruffled; slight fragrance. Winterscape X Bridal Fashion. Stockton 1994.

TELEMAX (Harald Moos, R. 1994). Sdlg. 90/77G. TB, 31" (80 cm), M. S. pinkish red; F. red brown, edged pinkish red; beards yellow; waved. 83/350A: (100/79: (Glendale x Vanity) x Lady Friend) X Buchholzer Glut. Moos 1995.

TELL FIBS (Barry Blyth, SDB, R. 1986). Correction of parentage: (Cupid's Cup x Tiger Rouge) X Capricornia.

TEMBLOR (Joseph Ghio, R. 1990). Sdlg. PJ-178D. CA, 12" (31 cm), M. Vivid orange bronze, deep bronze signal. (Peanut Gallery x Villa Branciforte sib) X (San Gregorio x (Montara sib x Mission Santa Cruz sib)). Bay View 1991.

TEMPERENCE (William Maryott, R. 1991). Sdlg. L156B. TB, 35" (89 cm), M & RE. S. tan rimmed honey (RHS 163C); F. violet (91B), 1/2" tan band; beards pale yellow, tipped white; heavily ruffled. (Soap Opera x Armistice) X H26LAV: ((Carved Cameo x Wings of Dreams) x Ghio 76-257X: (Entourage x Homecoming Queen)). Maryott 1991.

TEMPEST TOWN (Mary Dunn by Robert Dunn, R. 1999). Sdlg. M2048-E. TB, 36" (91 cm), EM. S. and style arms wistaria blue; F. violet blue; beards near-white, slight blue end; slight sweet fragrance. Royalist X Honky Tonk Blues.

TEMPLE BROCADE (John Gass, R. 1997). Sdlg. G-85-80. TB, 38" (97 cm), M. Ruffled and laced medium yellow, F. with pale center; style arms light yellow; beards dark yellow; musky fragrance. Temple Gold X Lemon Brocade. Rainbow Chasers 1998.

TEMPLECLOUD (Cy Bartlett, R. 1991). Sdlg. LA/F. IB, 24" (61 cm), EML. S. very pale silvery blue (near-white); F. deep violet, hafts with brown overtones; beards cream, tinted brown violet in throat; lightly waved and ruffled. Little Admiral X Faraway. Sutton 1994.

TEMPLECOMBE (Cy Bartlett, TB, R. 1989). Sutton 1994.

TEMPLE MEADS (Cy Bartlett, R. 1992). Sdlg. G-S.1. IB, 25" (64 cm), M. S. pale greyed blue; F. deep violet; beards cream to yellow in throat. Gossip X Snowbrook. David Austin Roses 1995.

TEMPLE TALK (J. Owings Rebert, R. 1995). Sdlg. FY-12. SIB, 45" (114 cm), M. S. pale blue, light blue veining; F. medium violet blue veined darker, shoulders yellow and tan, beige to light tan signal veined light violet. Parentage unknown. Draycott 1998.

TEMPLE TAPESTRY (J. Owings Rebert, R. 1995). Sdlg. P-123. SIB, 40" (107 cm), M. Deep violet blue, F. with yellow and tan shoulder markings, white signal lines. Vi Luihn X unknown. Draycott 1998.

TEMPTING (Joseph Ghio, R. 1991). Sdlg. 86-29D. TB, 36" (91 cm), EM. S. pink, deeper at midrib; F. red purple, narrow pink edge; beards red. 87-73K: (Success Story x (Fancy Tales x Alpine Castle)) X (Liaison x Ecstatic Echo). Bay View 1992.

TEMPTING FATE (Duane Meek, R. 1993). Sdlg. 327-1-5. TB, 34" (86 cm), ML. S. blue white, flushed deeper at midrib; F. very dark blue purple with small ray pattern at tip of beards; beards lavender, tipped bronze. 450-1-1: (Premonition x Pacific Shores) X Graduation. D & J Gardens 1993.

TEMPTONE (Graeme Grosvenor, R. 1993). Sdlg. R5-1. TB, 38" (97 cm), M. Ruffled purple self; beards purple. Silverado X Dusky Challenger. Rainbow Ridge 1993/94.

TENDER FRILLS (Bernard Hamner, R. 1990). Sdlg. 85-402. TB, 34" (86 cm), EML. Baby pink (RHS 49D), F. lighter in center; beards tangerine red. Valentine Roses X Melissa Sue. Hamner Iris 1990.

TENDER GENDER (Tom Burseen, R. 1997). Sdlg. 93-130A. TB, 36" (91 cm), M. S. and style arms light coral pink (RHS 38D); F. very light venetian pink (49C), purple shoulder striations; beards orange; ruffled; sweet fragrance. Orange Blotter X 90-21A: (Pulse Rate Date x (Tangerine Dream x Copper Lace)). T.B.'s Place 1998.

TENDER MERCY (Frederick Kerr, R. 1999). Sdlg. 9369.102. TB, 35" (89 cm), ML. S. and style arms light pink; F. paler pink, light pink hafts; beards salmon, end lighter; heavily ruffled; slight sweet fragrance. Elizabeth Poldark X Sweet Musette.

TENDER TUNE (Tom Burseen, R. 1995). Sdlg. 1-287A. TB, 36" (91 cm), M. S. creamy lemon (RHS 27B), base touched purple; style arms creamy lemon; F. red violet (bluer than 70A); beards tangerine, hairs tipped cream; ruffled. 9-415: (((Condottiere x Night Edition) x Local Motion) x Bluid) X Mariachi Music. T.B.'s Place 1996.

TENGCHONG LACE (Craig Carroll, R. 1996). Sdlg. 1-92. SPEC-X (evansia), 24" (60 cm), E. Palest icy blue, fading white, F. with yellow gold crests surrounded by mauve dotting; style arms mauve, icy blue edge, fimbriated; ruffled, frilled; slight fragrance. Fairyland X *I. wattii*, Tengchong form.

TENGCHONG PRINCESS (Craig Carroll, R. 1996). Sdlg. 2-92. SPEC-X (evansia), 18" (46 cm), E. White, F. with gold crest surrounded by mauve dotting; style arms mauve, edged white, fimbriated; ruffled, frilled; slight fragrance. Fairyland X *I. wattii*, Tengchong form.

TENNESSEE BICENTENNIAL (John Pierce, R. 1994). TB, 32" (81 cm), M. S. light blue; F. medium blue; beards white. Royal Crusader X unknown. Memphis Botanic Garden 1996.

TENNESSEE GENTLEMAN (Sterling Innerst, TB, R. 1989). Innerst 1991.

TENNESSEE STAR (George Slade, R. 1991). Sdlg. 87-31-1. TB, 35" (89 cm), M. Bright orange, F. with white spot at end of tangerine beard. Mint Condition X Orange Gem.

TENNESSEE VOL (O. D. Niswonger, R. 1993). Sdlg. 71-89. TB, 33" (84 cm), M. Tailored brilliant orange with yellow background glimmer; beards brighter orange. Fresno Flash X 5-79: (Countdown x Marmalade Skies). Cape Iris 1993.

TENNESSEE WOMAN (Sterling Innerst, TB, R. 1989). Innerst 1990.

TENUE ROYALE (Tony Huber, R. 1998). Sdlg. 95-090 (90-934). SPEC-X, 28" (70 cm), EM. S. lilac purple (RHS 70A); style arms beetroot purple (71A) center bordered lilac purple (70B) and white; F. beetroot purple (71A/B), greenish yellow haft and signal mixed with purple, surrounded by yellow and white veined zone. Dom F3 084: (Belle Promesse x Nouvel Age) X Dom F3 066: (Nouvel Age x Belle Promesse).

TERESSA (Colin Rigby, R. 1998). Sdlg. UNG-12. SPEC (*unguicularis*), 10" (25 cm), M. S. smooth medium purple, midrib darker; style arms lighter purple; F. medium purple, darker area below small bright yellow signal, haft with some thin white lines. *I. unguicularis* X Mary Barnard. Iris Gallery 1998.

TERRA ROSA (Schreiner, R. 1998). Sdlg. AA 768-1. TB, 39" (99 cm), M. Reddish brown (RHS 165B) self; beards reddish brown, hairs tipped yellow. Danger X T 1488-1: (M 912-AA: (((October Ale x Credit Card) x (Calypso Bay sib x ((Olympic Torch x Brass Accents sib) x ((Casa Morena sdlg. x Inca Chief) x Dark Chocolate)))) x Copper Nugget) x San Jose). Schreiner 1998.

TERRA VERDE (Allan Ensminger, R. 1993). Sdlg. 488-4. SDB, 12" (30 cm), E. Sulphur yellow with green spot; beards yellow. 285-3: (Do-Si-Do x 83-6) X 85-8: (Small Flash x Sweet 'n Neat). Varigay 1994.

TERRE DE FEU (Richard Cayeux, R. 1997). Sdlg. 89131 A. TB, 33" (85 cm), EM. S. bright copper red; F. copper red, large metallic violet heart; beards bronze. Supreme Sultan X Gold Galore. Cayeux 1997.

TERRYTON (Hyram Ames, R. 1996). Sdlg. A921. TB, 35" (89 cm), M. S. and style arms yellow; F. white, slight violet shading, 1/4" brown rim, hafts washed yellow; beards yellow orange; slight sweet fragrance. Joyce Terry X Nebeker 994-1: (Classic Treasure x Planned Treasure). Zebra 1997.

TERYN LEIGH (Myrtle Wolff, R. 1993). Sdlg. 84-1-6. BB, 19" (48 cm), M. S. canary yellow (HCC 2); F. buttercup yellow (5/1); beards tangerine orange; ruffled, laced. Dwight John X Jane Ann. Hildenbrandt's Iris 1994.

TESSA DARK EYES (J. T. Aitken, R. 1995). Sdlg. 88J6. JI (6 F.), 48" (122 cm), VL. Light lavender, washed and veined darker, pencil-line light rim; style arms deep purple. Dancing Waves X Knight in Armor. Aitken's Salmon Creek 1995.

TEST PATTERN (Joseph Ghio, TB, R. 1989). Bay View 1990.

TETON VALLEY (Cleo Palmer, R. 1992). Sdlg. 89124. IB, 22" (56 cm), L. Golden yellow, F. with brassy gold spot, hafts and shoulders, and with white area around beard; beards orange yellow, paler tip; sweet fragrance. Gold Galore X Sunny Hills. Palmer's Iris 1992.

TEUFELSBRATEN (Lothar Denkewitz, R. 1990). Sdlg. N-83-4-2. SDB, 9" (23 cm), E. Dark wine red, F. slightly darker; beards red violet. Karen Denkewitz X ((Wee Lad x Cherry Garden) x (Adrienne Taylor x Snow Elf)). Von Zeppelin 1992.

TEVERLAE (J. R. Ellis, R. 1991). SPEC-X, 33" (84 cm), L. Medium purple, yellow signal patch edged white. Induced tetraploid *I. versicolor* X induced tetraploid *I. laevigata*.

TEXAS GLORY (Hooker Nichols, TB, R. 1989). Hillcrest 1994.

TEXAS LONGHORN (Leo Barnard, R. 1996). Sdlg. L-91-77C. TB, 36" (91 cm), ML. S. and style arms blended ivory to butter; F. ivory base, gold shoulders and rim, shadowy blue center wash; beards gold, ending in fuzzy blended blue brown horn; ruffled; slight sweet fragrance. Borderline X Twice Thrilling. Paradise Iris 1996.

TEXAS NIGHT (Elmer Williams, R. 1997). Sdlg. A-24-90. TB, 34" (86 cm), M & RE. S. light purple; style arms and F. purple; beards purple; slight fragrance. Titan's Glory X unknown. Permian Basin Iris Society 1998.

TEXAS STYLE (William Simon, TB, R. 1986). Stahly 1990.

TEXTRONICS (Tom Burseen, R. 1997). Sdlg. 94-12A. TB, 36" (91 cm), E. Heavily ruffled imperial purple (RHS 78A); beards white, hairs tipped orange; sweet fragrance. Halogram X 90-21A: (Pulse Rate Date x (Tangerine Dream x Copper Lace)). T.B.'s Place 1998.

THABOR (John Holden by Jean Peyrard, AB (OGB+), R. 1989) Correction of parentage as printed in 1989 Check List to show Welcome Reward (rather than Welcome Return). Aril Society 1991.

THAI ORANGE (Richard Ernst, R. 1996). Sdlg. JF169-11-8. TB, 37" (94 cm), M. S. apricot orange, slight pink cast deepest at midrib; style arms apricot orange; F. apricot orange, pale violet shoulder cast; beards bright orange; lightly ruffled, laced; slight spicy sweet fragrance. Sib to Sweet Ballerina. Cooley 1996.

THALASSO (Lawrence Ransom, R. 1999). Sdlg. 90/211-7. TB, 39" (100 cm), ML. S. pale lavender blue, base veined and blended light olive ochre; F. medium lavender blue, edge lighter, hafts olive ochre, reverse light olive ochre; beards dark blue, brushed bronze. Blackbeard X 88/13-1: (Soap Opera x Opera Bouffe).

THANKSGIVING FEST (Mary Dunn by Joseph Ghio, R. 1998). Sdlg. 237-6. LA, 38" (97 cm), M. Cranberry self. Rich and Famous X Natural Wonder. Bay View 1998.

THAT'S MY BABY (Robert Hollingworth, R. 1993). Sdlg. 84U2B18. SIB, 21" (53 cm), M. Heavily ruffled deep red violet, inconspicuous white dashes in signal area. Lady Vanessa X 82K4B1, sib. Windwood Gardens 1995.

THAT'S PINK (O. D. Niswonger, R. 1996). Sdlg. SDB 4-93. SDB, 12" (31 cm), M. Pink, slight white area at tip of beard; beard tangerine pink, base white. SDB 2-90: (Ballet Slippers x Tillie) X Chanted. Cape Iris 1997.

THAT'S RED (Kenneth Fisher, R. 1999). Sdlg. 97-1. MTB, 21" (53 cm), EM. Deep red; beards red. TZZ8: (New Idea x New Wave) X TS8: (TC4: (Puppy Love x Pink Kewpie) x New Idea).

THAVY (Bob Thomason, R. 1991). Sdlg. BT 8614B. SDB, 12" (30 cm), EM. Light yellow, deep yellow hafts and markings around beard; beards orange, tipped yellow. Stockholm X (Angel Baby x Sno-Jo). Okie Iris 1993.

THEO D'OR (Christian Lanthelme, R. 1997). Sdlg. 8A94. MDB, 6" (15 cm), M. S. cream yellow; style arms light yellow; F. mustard yellow; beards medium yellow; sweet fragrance. Demon X unknown. Lanthelme 1998.

THEODOSIA (Mary Jeanselme, R. 1993). Sdlg. 91B-2. TB, 36" (91 cm), EM. S. yellowish amber (RHS 12A); F. intense yellowish amber blended darker; beards dark yellow; slight musky fragrance. Crimson Fire X Skating Party.

THEOTMALLI (Siegmar Goerbitz, R. 1991). Sdlg. 8622B14. TB, 29" (100 cm), M. S. dark red violet; F. velvety black red; beards brown, tipped gold yellow. (Superstition x Swazi Princess) X (Silver Shower x Rondo). Schoeppinger 1991.

THERAPY (W. Terry Varner, R. 1993). Sdlg. S-340. MTB, 18" (46 cm), EM. Medium lavender, white area around yellow beards; slight fragrance. Jill Welch X O-352: (M-315A: ((E-303 x Dunderman O-195) x Dunderman O-195: (Jana White x unknown)) x Opal Imp). Ohio Gardens 1993.

THERESA LYNN (Joseph Hoage, R. 1993). Sdlg. H86-10C. TB, 34" (86 cm), ML. Pale lavender white blend; beards red. Gibson 47-7CF: (Starfrost Pink x ((Lorna Lee x (Tahiti Sunrise x (Tahiti Sunrise x Lorna Lee))) x ((Lorna Lee x Tahiti Sunrise) x (Tahiti Sunrise x Lorna Lee)))) X O. Brown 78-3B4: (Old Flame x ((Grandiflora x Arctic Flame) x Buffy)). Long 1995.

THESSALONIKI (Ladislav Muska, R. 1997). Sdlg. DESA-01. TB, 38" (97 cm), EM. S. light creamy brown, style arms deeper; F. medium lavender, wide light creamy brown band; beards orange; ruffled; heavily laced; sweet fragrance. (Don Epifano x Extravagant) X Sa-Coma. Muska 1996.

THIMBLEBERRY (Dana Borglum, R. 1995). Sdlg. F76-1. BB, 24" (61 cm), ML. Rose purple with purplish variegation; beards rose purple. Pink Bubbles X pink sdlg., unknown parentage.

THIN BLUE LINE (George Sutton, R. 1998). Sdlg. F-214-A. TB, 35" (89 cm), EM. S. white, union jack blue (RHS 99A) dots, lines and 2" edge; style arms white mottled blue; F. white, blue 1/4" stippled edge, broken veins; beards white, dotted blue, hairs tipped yellow in throat; ruffled; slight sweet fragrance. C-24-A: (Momentum x 4-33: ((Heavenly Harmony x Petite Posy) x French Gown)) X C-24-B, sib. Sutton 1999.

THINGS TO COME (Sharon McAllister, R. 1993). Sdlg. 89-16-1. AB (OGB+), 22" (56 cm), M. S. amethyst ground with faint gold veins converging to gold filigree around rim; style arms amethyst, crests gold; F. golden ground, center completely covered deep ruby red; beards yellow orange, tipped violet. Ballalaika Music X Thunderstorm. McAllister 1993.

THINKING OUT LOUD (Richard Ernst, R. 1994). Sdlg. HD 175A-1BB. TB, 38" (97 cm), EM. S. pale lemon yellow, deeper yellow highlights especially on midrib, violet cast on inside, pale yellow inner rim; style arms pale yellow, gold highlights; F. bright berry plum with mulberry shoulders, reddish inner rim, honey tan outer edge, bluish stripe below beard; beards yellow, tipped white; heavily laced. D143: ((Kentucky Derby x Blue Luster) x Hula Girl) X Shoop 73-4. Cooley 1994.

THIRSTY OASIS (Tom Burseen, R. 1997). Sdlg. 93-351Y. TB, 36" (91 cm), M. Heavily ruffled, laced wistaria blue (RHS 92D), F. texture veined; style arms violet blue; beards lemon, hairs tipped white; musky fragrance. Crystal Springs X Yaquina Blue. T.B.'s Place 1998.

THIS AND THAT (Paul Black, R. 1998). Sdlg. A114J. IB, 27" (69 cm), E. S. dark purple, pinkish orchid midrib; style arms medium purple; F. silvery orchid, heavily washed medium red purple, narrow dark purple edge; beards medium purple; ruffled; pronounced sweet fragrance. Privileged Character X Polar Seas. Mid-America 1998.

THOAS (Erhard Woerfel, R. 1990). Sdlg. 11/86. TB, 35½" (90 cm), L. S. bright pink; F. light pink, throat nearly white; beards tangerine. Priamos X ((Miss Dolly Dollars x Peach Frost) x Piping Hot). Hochheimer 1991.

THOROUGHBRED (Currier McEwen, R. 1997). Sdlg. T(6)90/23(1). JI (3 F.) tet., 38" (95 cm), EM & RE. S. dark purple (RHS 79B), deeper veining, 1/8" white edge; style arms off-white, tufts brushed methyl violet (85C); F. white, vivid dark blue violet (89A) halo around aureolin yellow (12A) signal, vivid dark blue violet veining extending 2/3 way to edge; ruffled. Japanese Harmony X T(1)84/28: ((Fairy Carillon x unknown) x sib). Eartheart 1999.

THOR'S LIGHTNING BOLT (Walt Dean, R. 1996). TB, 30-32" (76-81 cm), M. S. purple; style arms white, purple tip and midrib; F. purple; beards orange, forked at tip and confined to throat area, continuing as white membranous F. attachment, spear-shaped and extending 2/3 length of F., ending in small purple horn at spear tip; slight musky fragrance. Trick or Treat X Too Many Flounces. Sutton 1998.

THOUSAND LAKES (Richard Brook, R. 1995). Sdlg. A 20/2. SDB, 15" (38 cm), M. S. pastel creamy blue, creamy green midrib flush; F. flushed creamy green, hafts deeper honey green (RHS 153B), pastel creamy blue rim; beards deep blue, bushy. Music Box X Joyous Isle. Zephyrwude 1996.

THREE QUARTERS (Tomas Tamberg, R. 1993). SPEC-X (sib-tosa, tet.), 39" (100 cm), M. Medium blue self. Lake Niklas X Starting Sibtosa. Schoeppinger 1995.

THREE SEASONS (George Sutton, R. 1996). Sdlg. G-54RE. TB, 35" (89 cm), EM & RE. Ruffled white, F. veined verdigris (RHS 129D); beards white. Waltz Across Texas X Orange Popsicle. Sutton 1997.

THREE STRIKES (Robert Annand, R. 1998). Sdlg. 88-72A. TB, 36" (91 cm), M. S. yellow gold, midrib violet; style arms yellow gold; F. yellow gold, dark violet purple stripe from beard to tip; beards yellow, hairs tipped bronze. (Fly to Vegas x Marsh Light) X (Marsh Light x Brown Lasso). Forest Ranch 1998.

THREE TOKENS (George Shoop, R. 1993). Sdlg. 89-58-1. SDB, 10" (25 cm), EM. Peach, F. with darker peach spot; beards tangerine. Dancin' X 86-57: ((Pink Caper x cream dwarf sdlg.) x Pink Caper). Shoop 1993.

THRILLING EXPERIENCE (Jim Hedgecock, R. 1994). Sdlg. 84-76-A. TB, 37" (94 cm), M. Pale yellow, F. with darker edges and hafts; beards yellow orange, large yellow white spoon at end; ruffled, laced; slight sweet fragrance. Spooned Blaze X Eastertime. Comanche Acres 1995.

THRILLSEEKER (Richard Ernst, R. 1993). Sdlg. HR8545-17. TB, 36" (91 cm), M. S. bright yellow gold; F. medium blue violet; beards yellow, tipped blue; ruffled. (Edith Wolford x Merry Madrigal) X unknown. Cooley 1993.

THROB (John Weiler, R. 1990). Sdlg. 85-175-1. TB, 37" (94 cm), ML. Lightly laced dark cadmium yellow; beards dark gold, tipped orange; slight sweet fragrance. 78-18-8: (Temple Gold x Flaming Victory) X Fame. Rialto 1991.

THUMKIN (Glenn Corlew, R. 1995). Sdlg. 1325-1A. BB, 17" (43 cm), M. S. medium violet, deeper base and midrib; style arms violet; F. pale to medium violet, blended yellow in upper area, shading to brown at hafts; beards violet. Abracadabra X Olympiad. Cooley 1996.

THUMPER SNOOK (Jim Hedgecock, R. 1995). Sdlg. 83-96-6. TB, 37" (94 cm), M. Medium blue, F. with white area below beard; beards white, yellow in throat; ruffled. Navy Strut X Victoria Falls. Comanche Acres 1995.

THUNDERBALL (George Sutton, R. 1997). Sdlg. G-92, TB, 38" (97 cm), M. S. and style arms sea lavender violet (RHS 85D); F. iridescent amethyst (79C), 1/8" sea lavender violet edge; beards burnt orange, 1½" red violet horn; ruffled. Tomorrow's Child X Sky Hooks. Sutton 1998.

THUNDERBIRD SONG (Chet Tompkins, R. 1993). Sdlg. 89-8. TB, 40" (102 cm), ML-VL. S. deep sky blue; F. black purple, white onco-like signal patch with grainy medium blue overlay and blackish veins; beards violet. (((Out Yonder x Silver Peak) x (Whole Cloth x black oncobred sdlg.)) x ((Amigo x Louise Blake) x black oncobred sdlg.)) X (Night Hawk x Lowell Storm). Fleur de Lis 1993.

THUNDERCAT (Barry Blyth, R. 1993). Sdlg. X16-B. SDB, 12" (31 cm), ML. Metallic burgundy, F. with deeper black burgundy spot; beards burnt tangerine. (Cupid's Cup x Yipee sib) X Camarilla sib. Tempo Two 1994/95.

THUNDERING HILLS (Nora Scopes, R. 1995). Sdlg. 9S 109. TB, 36-38" (91-97 cm), ML. S. deep violet; F. velvety violet; beards deep purple; ruffled; strong sweet fragrance. 7/3: (Sea Music x Cobweb Morning) X Dusky Challenger.

THUNDERING WATERS (Cleo Palmer, SDB, R. 1989). Palmer's Iris 1990.

THUNDER SPIRIT (Schreiner, R. 1996). Sdlg. AA 447-A. TB, 39" (99 cm), M. S. and F. deep indigo (RHS 89A); style arms dark purple; beards dark purple; heavily ruffled; slight sweet fragrance. Darkside X T 315-A: (K 398-1: (((R 100-A x Blue Mountains) x (Toll Gate x After Dark)) x H 296-A) x P 273-B: (Morning Hymn x Louisiana Lace)). Schreiner 1996.

TIANANMEN SQUARE (Bob Thomason, R. 1992). Sdlg. BT 8940H. TB, 28" (71 cm), M. Satiny red violet, F. with lighter rim; beards bronze, tipped blue; slight sweet fragrance. Mary Randall X Jamari.

TICKFAW (Patrick O'Connor, R. 1992). Sdlg. 83-17. LA, 32" (81 cm), M. Lightly ruffled red, some yellow streaking radiating from yellow signal; style arms red. Glad You Came X Ann Chowning.

TICKLED PEACH (Carol Lankow by J. T. Aitken, R. 1994). Sdlg. 2H27-1. SDB, 10" (25 cm), ML. Peach self; beards white to yellow, tipped carrot orange. Spring Dancer X Aitken 82M18-10: (80-22, unknown, x Dixie Pixie). Aitken's Salmon Creek 1994.

TICKLE ME (Chuck Chapman, R. 1998). Sdlg. 92-82-1. MDB, 5" (13 cm), L. Coral-toned pink; beards intense coral red. Tiny Cherub X Candy Fluff. Chapman Iris 1998.

TICKLES (George Shoop, R. 1993). Sdlg. 89-59-1. SDB, 10" (25 cm), M. Deep pink self, F. lightly ruffled; beards tangerine pink; slight fragrance. 86-53: (Spring Dancer x Pink Caper) X 86-52: (Hug a Bunch x Pink Caper). Shoop 1993.

TICO TACO (Tom Magee, R. 1991). Sdlg. 8024. SDB, 15" (38 cm), L. S. ruffled amber, brown basal markings; style arms gold; F. amber, brown haft markings; beards amber gold. Visa X Dixie Pixie. Long 1993.

TIDELINE (Bob Bauer/John Coble, R. 1995). Sdlg. J86I-1. JI (6 F.), M. White, narrowly rimmed blue violet (RHS 90B); signals yellow, with long veins extending outward; style arms white, wide, with tailored crests edged blue. J83F-7: (Silver Cascade x Mai Ogi) X Light at Dawn. Ensata Gardens 1995.

TIDY (Austin Morgan, R. 1990). TB, 35" (89 cm), EML. S. blue white; F. rose violet, narrow blue white rim, white semi-circle around orange beard. Parentage unknown. Iris Test Garden 1983.

TIE DYED TYKE (Jim & Vicki Craig, R. 1993). Sdlg. C16W27. IB, 21" (53 cm), EM & RE. S. blended light blue, center and base darker; F. blended medium blue, center and base darker; beards light yellow, light blue at end; pronounced sweet fragrance. 26T5: (((En Route x unknown) x unknown) x 6H1: (Sacred Mountain x *I. aphylla*)) X 1R21: ((Light Fantastic x *I. aphylla*) x (Starchild x 6H1)). J. & V. Craig 1993.

TIFFANY LASS (Currier McEwen, SIB, R. 1988). Pope's Perennials, Seaways 1990.

TIFFANY TIME (Barry Blyth, R. 1990). Sdlg. J79-A. TB, 36-38" (91-97 cm), M. Lacy pale pink, slightly lighter area around bright coral beard. First Blush X Niswonger 12-77, Lilac Thrill sib. Tempo Two 1990/91.

TIGER BUTTER (Richard Ernst, TB, R. 1985). Correction of seedling number. Sdlg. S909-1.

TIGER CUB (B. Charles Jenkins, R. 1990). Sdlg. B30-11B. CA, 14" (36 cm), ML. Tan ground striped brown. Santa Rita X San Gegorio sib. Shepard Iris 1990.

TIGER HONEY (Brad Kasperek, R. 1993). Sdlg. 89-45D. TB, 38" (97 cm), EM. S. butterscotch (RHS 163B) with random golden yellow (15C) streaks; F. butterscotch and caramel (163A) stripes on golden yellow (15C) ground, off-white (155C) streaking; beards butterscotch; lightly laced, ruffled; slight fragrance. Desert Realm X Maria Tormena. Zebra 1994.

TIGER TAFFY (Donald Spoon, R. 1996). Sdlg. 92-25. BB, 27" (69 cm), M. Honey gold, F. with white area at end of beard, darker butterscotch haft venation; beards golden yellow, base white; ruffled, flared; slight fragrance. Nectar X (Delia's Child x Samurai Warrior).

TIGER TALK (Henry Rowlan, R. 1992). Sdlg. HR-87-TB-10. TB, 30" (76 cm), M. S. medium yellow; F. burnt gold, banded yellow, white stripes radiating out and down from golden yellow beard; lightly laced and ruffled; slight sweet fragrance. Gala Angel X Hindenburg. Comanche Acres 1993.

TIGGAH (Anne Blanco White, R. 1995). SPEC (*pseudacorus*), 48" (120 cm), M. S. and F. yellow; stems with aubergine ring at nodes. *I. pseudacorus* X *I. pseudacorus*. Stillingfleet Lodge 1995.

TIKI (Joseph Ghio, R. 1998). Sdlg. PC-169F2. CA, 14" (36 cm), EM. Deep henna self, hairline blue edge, F. with blue violet signal. PE-188H: (PG-173M: (San Felipe sib x Hot Blooded sib) x PG-142-I: (On the Wildside sib x Temblor)) X PE-189-I: (PG-177G: (PI-MIX-A, unknown, x Valet sib) x PG-154, Spanish Don sib). Bay View 1998.

TIKI TORCH (Oscar Schick, R. 1999). Sdlg. 92-43H05. TB, 38-40" (97-102 cm), M. Ruffled toasted orange (near RHS 168B); beards brown; slight musky fragrance. Fortunata X Orange Slices. Stockton 1999.

TILLIE REDD (Margaret Hale, R. 1996). Sdlg. H-90-69. MTB, 19" (48 cm), M. S. and style arms red; F. red, overtoned black; beards orange, lightly ruffled. Jungle Shadows X H-70-B, Jungle Eden sib.

TIMBERTONE (Kevin Nilsen, R. 1991). Sdlg. 70-84-1. TB, 31" (79 cm), EM. S. clear light yellow; F.

yellow base overlaid with deep red brown lines radiating from deep yellow beard; ruffled, fringed. White Lightning X Caramba. Iridescence 1991/92.

TIMBERWIND (James Burch, R. 1991). Sdlg. 44-4. TB, 36" (91 cm), M. S. barium yellow (RHS 10C); F. white, 1/4" barium yellow edge; beards cadmium orange (23A). Ballad of Dixie X Temple Gold. Burch Iris 1992.

TIM CLARK (Hooker Nichols, R. 1998). Sdlg. 9202B. TB, 36" (91 cm), ML. S. light blue, midrib washed deeper; F. light blue; beards yellow and white. Olympiad X Windsong West. Hillcrest 1998.

TIME AND AGAIN (Ben Hager, R. 1991). Sdlg. RE5020. TB, 36" (91 cm), M & RE (Aug.-frost/CA). S. cool white, base blended medium blue; F. cool white; beards pale yellow. T4229: ((Geometrics x (Ice Sculpture x Avalon Bay)) x Ron) X T4216: ((Silver Flow x Ruffled Ballet) x Mother Earth sib). Melrose 1991.

TIME KEEPER (John C. Taylor, R. 1990). Sdlg. OL 108-3. LA, 47" (120 cm), L. Violet (RHS 88D) edged violet blue (91D), yellow signal on all petals. Lucile Holley X Dazzling Star. Rainbow Ridge 1990/91.

TIMELESS THEME (Barry Blyth, R. 1996). Sdlg. A77-A. TB, 38" (97 cm), EM. Silvery blue white; beards silvery blue; slight fragrance. Silverado X Blues Brothers. Tempo Two 1996/97.

TIMESCAPE (Ben Hager, TB, R. 1989). Melrose 1990.

TIME'S TAPESTRY (Richard Ernst, R. 1993). Sdlg. F127-4. TB, 36" (91 cm), EM. Fluted cherry red and burgundy blend, bluish cast around beard; beards orange red, tipped burgundy. Jovial Vagabond X Danger. Cooley 1993.

TIME TOGETHER (Ben Hager, TB, R. 1989). Roris 1990.

TIME TO SHINE (Paul Black, R. 1998). Sdlg. B298AA. SDB, 14" (36 cm), L. S. and style arms medium blue violet; F. medium blue violet, darker diffused red violet spot around beard, white haft area veined red plum; beards light blue white at end changing to orange in throat; ruffled, upright S.; pronounced sweet fragrance. Tweety Bird X blue 91-321 sib: (87-149B, Unpretentious sib, x 86-382A: ((Oriental Blush x Gigglepot) x Stardate sib)). Mid-America 1998.

TIME TRAVELER (Darlene Pinegar, R. 1992). Sdlg. TG-2-2. TB, 36" (91 cm), EML. Lightly ruffled deep bright golden yellow; beards dark yellow orange, 1" yellow gold horn, sometimes with additional spoon or flounce; slight sweet fragrance. Tut's Gold X Spoontime. Spanish Fork 1993.

TIME WILL TELL (Richard Ernst, R. 1999). Sdlg. KF125-1-4. TB, 38" (97 cm), ML. S. blue plum, lighter midrib flush, dark berry rim; F. dark berry sanded plicata markings on white changing to solid dark berry on lower half; beards yellow; stalks purple. F125-1: (Edna's Wish x Wild Jasmine) X Chiffon Ruffles. Cooley 1999.

TIMPCALS (Tomas Tamberg, R. 1993). Sdlg. SSTT268. SPEC-X (cal-sib, tet.), 28" (70 cm), M. S. beige; F. light rose violet, signal area veined yellow. 8300: (Starting Calsibe x (Yellow Chrys x *I. innominata*)) X blue cal-sib hybrid of unknown parentage. Schoeppinger 1994.

TINA JOYCE (Jim Hedgecock, R. 1991). Sdlg. C-84-9-2. TB, 36" (91 cm), M. Laced and ruffled pale lilac, F. near-white around bright orange beard; pronounced sweet fragrance. 83-2: (Beauty Crown x Homecoming Queen) X 73-13, inv. sdlg. lines. Comanche Acres 1992.

TINA MARIE (Jim Hedgecock, R. 1992). Sdlg. C-82-4-A. TB, 36" (91 cm), M. Baby pink, F. paler around reddish pink beard; ruffled, laced; pronounced sweet fragrance. Choir Girl X Custom Made. Comanche Acres 1993.

TINDER BOX (Edwin Hill, R. 1995). Sdlg. ED 27-16-91. TB, 34" (86 cm), M. Red black self; beards bronze. Red Lion X Samurai Warrior. O'Brien Iris 1998.

TING TANG (Barry Blyth, R. 1998). Sdlg. D25-4. SDB, 12" (30 cm), ML. S. creamy apricot; F. creamy apricot, whitish area around and pink fleck at end of beard; beards lavender white at end, tangerine in throat; slight fragrance. Carats X B34-2, Little Bev sib. Tempo Two 1998/99.

TING TOY BOSS (Tom Burseen, R. 1999). Sdlg. 95-267B. TB, 35" (89 cm), M. S. cream, edges light yellow orange; style arms amber yellow (18A); F. white, amber yellow edges; beards indian yellow (17D), creamy yellow spoon; ruffled, laced; musky fragrance. All Aflutter X Open Arms.

TINK (John Durrance, R. 1991). Sdlg. D86-2. BB, 26" (65 cm), EM. S. lavender; F. gold; beards gold orange. Little Susie X Tinker-Tam. Long 1991.

TINTAGEL (Nora Scopes, SDB, R. 1985). British Iris Society 1989.

TINTINARA (Leslie Donnell, TB, R. 1988). Iris Acres 1993/94.

TINTINNABULATION (Lois Olson, R. 1992). Sdlg. 84-C-10. TB, 36" (92 cm), M. S. grape purple; F. deeper grape purple, fine white rays at hafts, hint of silver at crimped and laced edge; beards yellow in throat, shading to lavender at end, tipped white; slight fragrance. Gay Parasol X Pink Sleigh. Long 1994.

TINY BIT TIPSY (Albert Faggard, R. 1994). Sdlg. FWI-11-92. LA, 21" (53 cm), ML. Rich dark red wine, tiny green yellow pencil line signal hidden under dark red wine styles; slight sweet fragrance. Parentage unknown. Faggard 1995.

TINY FRECKLES (A. J. Farrington, MDB, R. 1986). British Iris Society 1987.

TINY LOU (B. Charles Jenkins, R. 1990). Sdlg. A28-11A. SPU, 26" (79 cm), E. Lightly ruffled blue, small yellow signal. Protege X Dawn Candle. Shepard Iris 1990.

TINY PIRATE (Lois Rich, R. 1990). Sdlg. R80-35B. AB (OGB), 6" (15 cm), M. Lavender purple bitone, inconspicuous veining on F., bold dark purple signal. Sdlg. inv. *I. antilibanotica*, *I. korolkowii* "Brown and Green", and Judean Cream X (*I. pumila* sdlg. 51-38 x Little Charmer). Aril Society, Melrose 1990.

TINY TEMPTRESS (A. & D. Willott, R. 1998). Sdlg. W 94-50. MDB, 4-5" (11-12 cm), EM. S. warm white; style arms white; F. blue white, blue flush at end of creamy white beard; lightly ruffled. Little Drummer Boy sib. Willott 1998.

TINY TIARA (A. & D. Willott, R. 1993). Sdlg. 92-141. MDB, 5" (14 cm), ML. Lightly ruffled icy white; beards white. Daisy Fresh X 79-13: (Greenlee GX-2: ((White Mite x self) x (*I. pumila alba* X Hanselmayer)) x Buttons). Willott 1994.

TIOMNAYA NOCH (Liudmila Mironova, R. 1999). Sdlg. 1-7-96. JI (6 F.), 40" (102 cm), L. Dark violet, yellow signal surrounded by white; style arms white, washed violet, crests violet. Sirenevaya Dymka X Vasili Alfiorov. DVO RAN 1999.

TIR NA NOG (Barry Emmerson, R. 1999). Sdlg. BE 92-16-9. TB, 37" (93 cm), M. S. white, midrib flushed pink, yellow veins and halo; style arms white, toasted peach center stripe and edge; F. toasted peach with orange glow, small white area under tangerine red beard; ruffled; slight fragrance. Love Chant X Scopes sdlg.

TIRRA LIRRA (Nora Scopes, SDB, R. 1985). British Iris Society 1987.

TIS A TIZZY (Allan Ensminger, R. 1998). Sdlg. 93-8. BB, 23" (58 cm), M. S. campanula violet (HCC 37/3); style arms, F. and beards deeper campanula violet (37/1); slight fragrance. 89-6: (86-29: (Christa x (Infatuation x Entourage)) x Shenanigan) X Iris Bohnsack. Varigay 1998.

TITANIC'S NEMESIS (David Miller, R. 1999). Sdlg. 93-27A. TB, 38" (97 cm), EM. White self, very light blue toning; style arms white; beards blue, hairs tipped white; slight musky fragrance. Honky Tonk Blues X Cuss a'Blue Streak.

TITANIUM (Lawrence Ransom, R. 1999). Sdlg. 90/433-2. TB, 38" (97 cm), M. Ruffled pure white self; beards white, lightly brushed yellow, orange in throat. Tide's In X 88/13-1: (Soap Opera x Opera Bouffe).

TITAN'S HORN (Jim Hedgecock, R. 1991). Sdlg. 85-42-1. TB, 38" (97 cm), M. Ruffled royal purple, F. velvety; self beards, short purple horn. Trick or Treat X Titan's Glory. Comanche Acres 1992.

TITAN'S TOY (William Maryott, R. 1995). Sdlg. T178PUR. SDB, 10" (25 cm), M. Medium purple self; beards purple. Pal Sam X Sigh. Maryott 1996.

TITLED (Barry Blyth, R. 1996). Sdlg. B60-2. SDB, 14-15" (36-38 cm), EML. S. rich burgundy; F. burgundy black, 1/4" burgundy edge; beards light mustard; slight fragrance. Thundercat X It's Love. Tempo Two 1996/97.

TIT WILLOW (Ben Hager, R. 1996). Sdlg. AMT5208GyBlSh. MTB, 22" (56 cm), EM. S. pale grey blue; F. light grey blue blend; beards pale yellow. AMT4891V: (New Wave x AMT3792Bl: (Ting-a-Ling x Dinky)) X AMT3790BlWh: (AMT2950, Ting-a-Ling sib, x Dinky). Adamgrove 1996.

TMAVÁ NOC (Zdeněk Seidl, R. 1997). Sdlg. 91-SDB-HF/3. IB, 27" (70 cm), M. S. and style arms dark purple; F. velvety blackish purple; beards purple, mustard in throat; slight sweet fragrance. Unknown purple SDB X Hell's Fire.

TOASTED WATERMELON (Joseph Hoage, R. 1993). Sdlg. H86-27. TB, 34-36" (84-91 cm), ML. Rosy brown blend; beards red. Mulled Wine X Lady Friend. Long 1994.

TODD (Mary Louise Dunderman, R. 1991). Sdlg. KK993 dark violet. MTB, 19" (48 cm), L. Dark violet blue (darker than RHS 90A), blue signal; beards blue, tipped white. EE375: ((Panda x Z589 dark purple) x sib) X EE503 violet: ((Blue Twinkle x Z588A purple) x (K188D blue x Surprise Blue)). Ohio Gardens 1995.

TOFF (Barry Blyth, R. 1993). Sdlg. A14-9. SDB, 15" (38 cm), VE-M. S. violet; F. plush violet black; beards violet, tipped tangerine; slight fragrance. Smoky Imp X Chanted. Tempo Two 1993/94.

TOKYO BLUES (Akihiko Terada, R. 1994). Sdlg. 36-13. TB, 36" (91 cm), M. S. white; F. deep blue; beards yellow, tipped blue. Edith Wolford X Royal Crusader. Roris 1995.

TOLDJASO (Sharon McAllister, R. 1993). Sdlg. 87-2-7. AB (OGB+), 28" (72 cm), M. S. buff ground, finely veined golden yellow; F. golden yellow ground, fine rust veins radiating from mustard beard. Child of God X Persian Embroidery. McAllister 1993.

TOM JOHNSON (Paul Black, R. 1996). Sdlg. A68A. TB, 35" (89 cm), E. S. and style arms dark purple; F. velvety purple black, narrowly edged dark purple; beards red orange; ruffled; slight spicy fragrance. Witches' Sabbath X In Town. Mid-America 1996.

TOMMYKNOCKER (Ray Lyons, R. 1992). Sdlg. LY 82-46-2. BB, 20½" (52 cm), M. Red black self; beards dark bronze. Parentage unknown. Long 1994.

TOM NGUYEN (Bob Thomason, R. 1993). Sdlg. BT 9073L. TB, 36" (91 cm), ML. Light lavender, F. ruffled; beards white; slight fragrance. Mary Frances X Snowy Wonderland.

TOMORROW MAY RAIN (Richard Ernst, R. 1994). Sdlg. JF169-1A. TB, 34" (86 cm), M. S. bright yellow; style arms yellow; F. yellow rim and shoulders, center flushed white; beards yellow orange; ruffled; pronounced sweet fragrance. F169-1A, Competitive Edge sib, X F104-1: ((Irene Nelson x Sun Fire) x Friday Surprise). Cooley 1995.

TONEGAWA (Toichi Ito by Society for Japanese Irises, R. 1999). JI (3 F.), E. S. red violet, much lighter edge; style arms red violet, much lighter crest edges; F. very light violet (near white), deep red violet halo and veining. Parentage unknown. Introduced in Japan prior to 1990.

TONGUE OF FIRE (Carl Boswell, R. 1995). Sdlg. 143-85-T. TB, 31" (78 cm), E. Red violet self; beards coral red. (Under Gleam x Focus) X Chapel Bells. Adamgrove 1995.

TONGUE TWISTER (Barry Blyth, R. 1991). Sdlg. X100-1. BB, 24" (61 cm), EM. Coral pink, heavily ruffled F. with gold hafts; beards vibrant saturn red, bushy. (Catalyst x Academy Awards) X Flaming Victory. Tempo Two 1991/92.

TONSY LOVE (Udo & Rudolf Wilkeneit, R. 1996). Sdlg. EW 16/1/94. MDB, 6" (15 cm), L. S. red maroon, flushed blue; F. blue; beards yellow to orange, hairs tipped blue; slight fragrance. Parentage unknown.

TON TON BANA (Society for Japanese Irises, R. 1993). JI (3 F.), 38" (97 cm), M. Near greyed erythrite red, signal yellow. Collected form of *I. ensata* from Mie Prefecture, Japan. Introduced in Japan prior to 1990.

TOO MANY FLOUNCES (Walt Dean, R. 1996). TB, 30-31" (76-79 cm), EM. Yellow, F. with rosy center blush; beards yellow, mixed yellow and rosy multiple flounces 2/3 width of F. stacked up to six high. Space Angel X Sky Hooks. Stanley Iris 1997.

TOON TOWN (Paul Black, R. 1997). Sdlg. B330D. SDB, 11" (28 cm), E. S. yellow ground, rose purple midrib blending to slight rose purple markings, brassy gold band; style arms yellow gold; F. gold hafts, butter yellow central area, blended red violet plicata margin, slight central dotting, 3/4" purple dart at end of beard; beards orange gold to violet; ruffled. Static sib X Wacko. Mid-America 1997.

TOO SWEET (Richard Ernst, R. 1994). Sdlg. HD175-D. TB, 36" (91 cm), M. Ruffled and laced pink, F. slightly lighter and with very slight paler flush at end of coral pink beard. D175: ((Cheesecake x (Sumptuous x Sandberry)) x Piping Hot) X sib. Cooley 1995.

TOOTH FAIRY (Bennett Jones, R. 1992). Sdlg. 440-1. MDB, 7" (18 cm), M. S. white; F. pumpkin orange, edged white; beards carrot red. 385-9: (((Melon Honey x Wright L32) x ((Roberts 65R11 x (pink IB x *pumila*)) x Melon Honey)) x Orange Tiger sib) X Orange Tiger. Bennett Jones 1993.

TOO TOO RIPE (Tom Burseen, R. 1990). Sdlg. 6-84B. TB, 36" (91 cm), EM. S. orange tan (near RHS 179D), pinkish maroon (181D) veining and wash; F. pinkish purple (181C) wash with heavy yellowish tan veining, faint yellow tan edge; beards bright gold; ruffled, laced; sweet fragrance. Lilac Laser X Villa Splendor. T.B.'s Place 1990.

TOOTSIE (Roger Nelson, TB, R. 1987). Iris Country 1990.

TOPAZ JEWEL (Lynda Miller, TB, R. 1989). Miller's Manor 1991.

TOP CAT (Chet Tompkins, R. 1998). Sdlg. 93-3B. TB, 38" (97 cm), EML-VL. S. white, flushed and bordered copper and violet brown; style arms blended violet brown; F. white, bordered coppery violet tinted brown; beards violet, hairs tipped brown. (Apollodorus x Changing Winds) X 89-14, inv. plicata line. Fleur de Lis 1998.

TOP COPY (Chet Tompkins, R. 1998). Sdlg. 94-25. TB, 37" (94 cm), ML-VL. Lemon cream, flushed milan yellow; style arms cream; beards medium blue, base blue white. (Hot Pinata x Magharee) X Revival Meeting. Fleur de Lis 1998.

TOP CREAM (Kevin Nilsen, R. 1992). Sdlg. 26-87-2. TB, 31" (79 cm), ML. S. cream blend, fringed and ruffled white edge; styles blended cream, crests fringed; F. white blended cream, deeper reverse, yellow hafts; beards light yellow white, few light violet hairs at end. Cloudburst X Wings of Dreams. Iridescence 1992/93.

TOP DOG (Chet Tompkins, R. 1998). Sdlg. 94-9. TB, 38" (97 cm), ML-VL. S. gold, dusted buff; style arms buff; F. dark cream, overlaid rich lilac blue; beards buff, blended blue. (((Intermission x Up and Coming) x (Ming Porcelain x Sheer Bliss)) x (Burning Bright x Up and Coming)) X Sheer Bliss. Fleur de Lis 1998.

TOP DRAWER (Chet Tompkins, R. 1998). Sdlg. 95-44K. TB, 40" (107 cm), ML-VL. Ivory and cream, blended lemon; F. cream to lemon. (((Cool Comfort x Comforting Thought) x (Primrose Path x Cool Comfort)) x ((Angel's Touch x Ming Porcelain) x (Iced Sunshine x Cascade Waters))) X (Candle Power x Ming Porcelain). Fleur de Lis 1998.

TOP HAND (Lin Flanagan, R. 1992). Sdlg. 85050-2. AB (OGB-), 26" (66 cm), M. S. light red brown blended amber; F. ruffled medium red brown blending to amber at edge; beards orange; slight fragrance. 78001-6: (Thunderstorm x Mayfest) X 79044-1: ((64060, red TB sdlg., x War Lord) x (61148, red TB, x 61212, red TB)). Aril Society 1993.

TOP JOVIAL (Ladislav Muska, R. 1997). Sdlg. S-LELL-05. SDB, 13" (33 cm), E. S. deep blue lilac; style arms blue lilac; F. blackish brown; beards azurine blue; heavily ruffled; slight fragrance. Little Episode X Laced Lemonade. Muska 1993.

TOP NOTCHER (Chet Tompkins, R. 1998). Sdlg. 94-36A. TB, 38" (97 cm), ML-VL. S. white; style arms white, tinted blue; F. bright blue; beards pale bluish white, tipped yellow. Inv. Progenitor, Whole Cloth, Emma Cook, Garden Path, Crown Point, River Hawk and sib, Fabulous Kate X inv. Madame Butterfly, Whole Cloth, Melody, Sass sdlgs. Fleur de Lis 1998.

TOPPED WITH CREAM (Sharon McAllister, R. 1992). Sdlg. 84-4B-13. AB (OGB), 28" (72 cm), EM. S. creamy white; F. pale chrome yellow with pale pinkish blush, U-shaped signal almost solidly veined burgundy; beards yellow orange, tipped burgundy. Desert Princess X Rose of Sharon. McAllister 1992.

TOP PICK (Tony Huber, R. 1998). Sdlg. 91-544 (sel. 94-102). SPEC-X, 39" (100 cm), ML. S. violet (RHS 86B); style arms pure white; F. violet (83B), large bright yellow signal bordered by deeper violet (83A) halo, reverse much paler, near-white; slight sweet fragrance. X-Dom 030: (Belle Promesse x Nouvel Age) X white *I. ensata*.

TOP SHELF (Chet Tompkins, R. 1998). Sdlg. 93-28. TB, 38" (97 cm), ML. S. and style arms pale colonial cream, flushed lemon cream; F. lilac, tinted orchid; beards white, tinted lime. (Swedish Spring x Lullaby of Spring) X Hushabye Time. Fleur de Lis 1998.

TOP START (John C. Taylor, R. 1990). Sdlg. OL 105-1. LA, 47" (120 cm), M. S. purple (RHS 76C); F. purple (76A), darker midrib, yellow signal; ruffled. Cammeray X L89: (Secret Spell x Helen Naish). Rainbow Ridge 1990/91.

TORA-TORA (Frederick Held, R. 1996). Sdlg. 06. JI (3 F.), 36" (91 cm), M. S. reddish purple, edged white; style arms dark purple, white at tip; F. center dark purple, dark purple veins extending into grey outer portion, bordered white. Parentage unknown, seed from Jelitto Staudensamen, Germany. Nature's Garden 1997.

TORCHED WITCH (Lynda Miller, R. 1997). Sdlg. 101491. BB, 27" (69 cm), ML. S. bright full orange; style arms full orange; F. burnt orange; beards dark orange. 2685A: (Far Corners x Marmalade) X Orange Star.

TORCHLIGHT TATTOO (Nora Scopes, TB, R. 1987). British Iris Society 1989.

TORNADO WATCHER (G. F. Wilson, R. 1992). Sdlg. 35-890TW-D. AB (OGB), 32" (81 cm), EM. S. orchid pink veined light blue, darker rib; F. tan and light rose blend, maroon haft dotting, large semi-circular maroon signal; beards grey cream; slight sweet fragrance. Onlooker X Tornado Warning.

TORO BLANCO (Frank Foster, R. 1998). Sdlg. 8707WH. IB, 19½" (49 cm), EM. White self, F. with turquoise blue lines around beard; beards cream white, base creamy yellow, small white horn. Sky Hooks X Sheer Energy.

TORQUE (Kevin Nilsen, R. 1995). Sdlg. 72-87-1. TB, 28" (72 cm), EM. S. amber brown; F. blackish red; beards deep yellow. Whoop 'em Up X Ken Ware. Iridescence 1995/96.

TOTAL IMAGE (Don Delmez, R. 1994). Sdlg. DLB-1. JI (6 F.), 36" (91 cm), M. Light blue with white lines, small white halo around yellow signal; style arms tipped blue, midrib white. "Sakuraku" X Kontaki-On. Delmez Gardens 1995.

TOTALLY COOL (J. T. Aitken, R. 1994). Sdlg. 87M67. SDB, 10" (25 cm), ML. S. white; F. white rim, blue spot with white veining around beard; beards white, tipped orange. ((B. Jones M346,

Pumpkin Center sib, x Greenwood yellow IB) x B. Jones M334-2: ((Solar Flight x M255) x (Wright L20 x Jones M255-1: (Melon Honey x M229)))) X Joe Cool. Aitken's Salmon Creek 1994.

TOTALLY WILD (John C. Taylor, R. 1996). Sdlg. UL 19-6. LA, 39" (100 cm), ML. S. cream, variably marbled purple; style arms cream, blushed purple; F. purple, yellow signal; ruffled; slight fragrance. Desert Jewel X Dural Dreamtime.

TOTAL OBSESSION (Chet Tompkins, R. 1993). Sdlg. 84-18. TB, 37" (94 cm), ML. S. pale to medium violet; F. deep violet blended with lighter areas, large white central area blending to pinkish orchid and pale blue. Inv. Dymia, Narain, Mountain Music, Fantasia, Dusky Dancer, Defiance, Twilight Sky, Camelot Rose, Distant Drums, Winner's Circle, Wandering Rainbow X Street Walker. Fleur de Lis 1993.

TOTAL RECALL (Ben Hager, R. 1992). Sdlg. RE5079SmkCrBi. TB, 34" (86 cm), EML & RE. S. light to medium yellow; F. white, edged yellow; beards light yellow; ruffled. Mother Earth X Bonus Mama. Melrose 1992.

TOTAL TEN (Tom Burseen, R. 1990). Sdlg. 6-166D. TB, 36" (91 cm), EM. S. bright lemon yellow; F. slightly darker; beards gold; ruffled; slight fragrance. Catalyst X Wings of Dreams. T.B.'s Place 1990.

TO THE POINT (Paul Black, R. 1998). Sdlg. C59B. TB, 36" (91 cm), M. Ruffled medium lavender self; beards gold with 1" horn, sometimes flounced; slight spicy fragrance. Lookout Point X Honky Tonk Blues. Mid-America 1998.

TOUCAN TANGO (Brad Kasperek, R. 1999). Sdlg. 93B-65. TB, 36-38" (91-97 cm), M. S. yellow (RHS 7A), streaked violet purple (77A) and white (155C), lightly banded yellow; style arms yellow and grape, streaked; F. yellow band, with broken color violet purple, center white with purple streaking; beards mustard yellow, hairs tipped purple; ruffled; style crests laced; slight fragrance. Hotdogs and Mustard X Grecian Goddess.

TOUCH AND GO (Barry Blyth, R. 1996). Sdlg. B34-3. SDB, 10" (26 cm), EM. S. soft pastel apricot, faint violet midrib flush; F. soft pastel apricot, bright violet chevron marking; beards white, lavender at exteme tip, tangerine in throat. Z15-4, Fairy Favours sib, X Z24-1, Volts sib. Tempo Two 1996/97.

TOUCHED BY ANGELS (William Maryott, R. 1997). Sdlg. R115A. TB, 37" (94 cm), M. Heavily ruffled pure white self; beards white; slight fragrance. White Linen X N148A: (Tide's In x Tide Crest). Maryott 1997.

TOUCH OF COLOR (Jim & Vicki Craig, R. 1991). Sdlg. 34T42. TB, 36" (90 cm), ML. S. nearly solid pale blue; F. white, very lightly marked blue around rim; heavily ruffled. Gentle Rain X 17M9: (Odyssey x (Stepping Out x Deborah Suzanne)). J. & V. Craig 1991.

TOUCH OF FROST (Lynn Markham, R. 1999). Sdlg. 92-1A. BB, 25-27" (63-69 cm), VE-EM. Ruffled cold white with green texture veining, S. with green midrib, faint green overlay in F. center; beards cold white, pale lemon in throat. 89-1A2: (84-5A3: (Angel Feathers x (Black Swan x Flaming Heart)) x Secret Weapon) X 8791-11A: (Carrara Marble x 64-2A2: (Little Lynn x *aphylla* "Dark Violet")).

TOUCH OF IRISH (Carl Boswell, R. 1995). Sdlg. 56-85-M. MDB, 6" (14 cm), L. Pale blue, F. with light chartreuse halo; beards blue. I'm Yellow X ((Garnet Star x Ruby Contrast) x Sapphire Jewel).

TOUCH OF LACE (B. Charles Jenkins, R. 1990). Sdlg. A20-11K. SPU, 45-56" (114-142 cm), M. Lacy pale bluish white, small yellow signal. Ila Crawford X Dawn Candle. Shepard Iris 1991.

TOUCH OF MAHOGANY (Barry Blyth, R. 1999). Sdlg. E123-2. TB, 36" (91 cm), ML. S. coffee brown, slight gold infusion; F. coffee brown, overlaid soft lavender around old gold beard, 1" burgundy hafts; pronounced sweet fragrance. Chestnut Avenue X Copatonic. Tempo Two 1999/2000.

TOUCH OF SCARLET (A. E. Cox, TB, R. 1975). Iris Acres 1993/94.

TOUCH OF SUNSHINE (Dale Satterwhite, R. 1993). Sdlg. 12-1. BB, 25" (64 cm), ML. Light lemon yellow, F. with large soft white blaze, lemon veining; lightly ruffled. Inv. sdlg. X Enterprise.

TOUCH OF WINTER (Dale Satterwhite, R. 1993). Sdlg. 18-618. TB, 32" (81 cm), EM. S. warm white, base slightly tinted lavender; F. warm white, very slightly tinted lavender on edge; beards white, tipped orange deep in throat; ruffled; slight sweet fragrance. Honky Tonk Blues X Skyblaze. Dale Satterwhite 1994.

TOULA THEOS (Ruth Goebel, R. 1995). Sdlg. T.T. TB, 30" (76 cm), E. S. yellow (RHS 11B); F. violet (88C) with dark haft thumbprints; beards mustard; ruffled. Betty Simon X ((O. T. Baker sdlg. x Chinese Coral) x Ballyhoo).

TOURBILLON (Jean Cayeux, R. 1990). Sdlg. 7914 B. TB, 36" (90 cm), ML. S. light blue white; F. bright violet; beards tangerine; waved. Condottiere X Metropolitan. Cayeux 1988.

TOWERING FINALE (Ben Hager, R. 1991). Sdlg. T4832TlVLcLa. TB, 42" (107 cm), VL. Lightly laced medium blue violet; lighter blue haze around white beard. T3965LcLvVyLa: ((T2590A: ((Babson M131-4 x Morning Breeze) x Dream Time) x Grand Waltz) x T3323BlWh: (Igloo x T2590A)) X Silver Flow. Melrose 1992.

TOWER STREET (Ron Busch, R. 1991). Sdlg. 7763/4. TB, 38" (97 cm), ML. S. light plum red; F. velvety plum red, edged lighter plum; beards orange wine. Latin Lover X Rich Melody. Busch 1992.

TOWN BELLE (Elyse Hill, R. 1998). Sdlg. EJ 5-8. CA, 8" (20 cm), M. Ruffled pinkish violet veined deep rose, F. with lighter rim and deep rose signal centered cream; cartwheel form. Bubbly X unknown.

TOWN GOSSIP (Barry Blyth, R. 1991). Sdlg. U101-1. TB, 36" (91 cm), ML. S. icy lavender; F. plush velvety violet black, 1/4" bright violet edge; beards bright red. Sooner Serenade X London Lord. Tempo Two 1991/92.

TOY CLOWN (Joseph Gatty, R. 1990). Sdlg. S48-1. SDB, 13" (33 cm), EM. S. greyed wine (M&P 8-A-5) 1/4"-1/2" edge, citron yellow (10-J-2) in center; F. cordovan to java brown (8-HI-8) 1/4"-3/8" edge, chrome lemon (8-K-1 to 9-K-2) ground paling toward beard; beards white, tinged violet yellow; pronounced sweet fragrance. L-1-5: (F-12-1: (((Dainty Royal x Golden Fair) x Zip) x Ginger Tart) x Baja) X Muchacha. Keppel 1991.

TOY KINGDOM (Barry Blyth, R. 1993). Sdlg. Z7-4. SDB, 10" (25 cm), L. S. champagne chartreuse, faint violet midrib infusion; F. white, 1/8" champagne chartreuse edge; beards lavender blue; slight fragrance. X16-1, Thundercat sib, X X25-5, Cupfull sib. Tempo Two 1993/94.

TOY STORY (Lynda Miller, R. 1996). Sdlg. 1793. SDB, 10" (25 cm), M. S. and style arms pale blue; F. pale blue, hafts chartreuse; beards deep blue; slight musky fragrance. Shy Violet X 1185E: (380: (Dove Wings x unknown) x Azure Gem). Miller's Manor 1997.

TRACE (Mary Dunn, R. 1990). Sdlg. M80-742C. TB, 34" (86 cm), M. White ground, small blue plicata markings; style arms violet; beards white; ruffled. Perfecta X Victoria Falls. M.A.D. Iris 1991.

TRACES OF ANTS (Ladislav Muska, R. 1999). Sdlg. 98-OFQG-06. TB, 36" (91 cm), M. S. blue lavender, washed lilac; style arms blue lavender; F. pale cream, nearly covered with blue lavender plicata patterning; beards light mustard; heavily ruffled, laced; slight fragrance. ((Orinoco Flow x Jesse's Song) x Spacelight Sketch) X (Queen in Calico x Graffiti). Muska 1999.

TRACEY ANN (J. Owings Rebert, R. 1999). Sdlg. CB-97-15. SIB, 28" (71 cm), M. Midnight blue, F. with gold line rim, gold signal. Parentage unknown.

TRACY'S SUNSHINE (Darlene Pinegar, R. 1998). Sdlg. DS-1D. TB, 33" (84 cm), M. S. white; style arms medium yellow; F. bright fuchsia blending to lighter fuchsia and pale blue at edge, hafts yellow, white by beard, with fuchsia marking; beards deep yellow orange; lightly ruffled; slight sweet fragrance. Double Scoop X Eagle's Flight. Spanish Fork 1999.

TRADING PLACES (James Gibson by Cooley's Gardens, R. 1994). Sdlg. 3-1A. TB, 35" (89 cm), EM. S. golden yellow, slight violet midrib infusion; F. white ground, burgundy plicata markings; beards gold; ruffled. Beyond X Broadway. Cooley 1995.

TRADITIONAL (Loleta Powell, R. 1995). Sdlg. 93-14. TB, 37" (94 cm), ML-VL. S. and style arms soft blue white; F. royal blue, edged blue white; beards blue white; pronounced sweet fragrance. Proud Tradition X Mary D. Powell's Gardens 1996.

TRAIL BOSS (Lin Flanagan, R. 1992). Sdlg. 83045-3. AB (OGB), 28" (71 cm), E. S. light red brown; F. red brown, dark red brown signal; beards dark brown; ruffled; slight fragrance. Springscape X Warrior's Mantle. Aril Society 1993.

TRAITOR (Mitch Jameson, R. 1993). Sdlg. 4-88. TB, 30-34" (76-86 cm), M. S. light blue green; F. light blue violet, edged light blue green; beards blue violet, tipped bronze. Gift of Dreams X Contrite. Knee-Deep in June 1994.

TRAJECTORY (Paul Black, R. 1997). Sdlg. 91207A. SDB, 13" (33 cm), M. S. dark purple; style arms white, edged purple; F. darker purple, white luminata patch; beards white; pronounced spicy fragrance. Black Star X 87130J: (Chubby Cheeks x 85319B: (Gentle Air x Chubby Cheeks sib)). Mid-America 1997.

TRAMP (Barry Blyth, R. 1994). Sdlg. A1-7. SDB, 10" (25 cm), VE-M. Burgundy red brown, deeper spot on either side of beard; beards mustard yellow, bright lavender on outer 1/4"; slight fragrance. Scat X X32-B: (Tricks x Yipee). Tempo Two 1994/95.

TRANCAS (Joseph Ghio, R. 1996). Sdlg. PE-202-C2. CA, 13" (33 cm), E. Smooth parchment pink, F. with soft mahogany signal, yellow center spear. PG-185Y: (PI-MIX-Y, unknown, x PI-MIX-A, unknown) X PG-172A: (PI-MIX-pink, unknown, x Herald). Bay View 1996.

TRANQUIL BEAUTY (O. D. Niswonger, TB, R. 1989). Cape Iris 1991.

TRANQUILINO (Gene Gaddie by Roger Nelson, R. 1999). TB, 35" (89 cm), M. S. wistaria violet (M&P 41-E-8); style arms slightly bluer (41-B-7); F. wistaria violet paling to silvery pallid blue (41-A-4); beards aureolin yellow (10-L-2), hairs tipped golden yellow (10-L-7) in throat; ruffled; sweet fragrance. Charisma X Carriage Trade. Iris Country 1995.

TRANQUIL PEACE (Adolph Vogt by John Wood, R. 1992). JI (6 F.), 38" (97 cm), M. Greyed white (RHS 155A), yellow (2A) signal; style arms greyed white. Token of Friendship X Powder and Paint. John Wood 1993.

TRANQUIL SUNSHINE (O. D. Niswonger, TB, R. 1989). Cape Iris 1990.

TRANSCRIBE (Paul Black, R. 1990). Sdlg. 87152AA. SDB, 12" (30 cm), M. S. white, heavy grape plicata markings and edge; style arms grape; F. white with grape plicata markings around wide grape margin; beards grape white, tipped mustard in throat. Peso X 85368: ((Melon Honey x Velvet Pride) x (Melon Honey x Soft Air)). Mid-America 1990.

TRANSIT (John C. Taylor, R. 1998). Sdlg. UL 32-2. LA, 39" (100 cm), ML. S. light yellow, veined; style arms light yellow; F. light yellow, veined, with yellow veined signal. Natural Wonder X Dancing Vogue. Rainbow Ridge 1998/99.

TRANS-ORANGE (O. D. Niswonger, R. 1999). Sdlg. 22-94. TB, 36" (91 cm), M. S. near-white, light orange midrib; style arms white, touched orange; F. orange, 1/8" white edge; beards orange. Apricot Frosty X 19-83: (Love Chant x Ambrosia Delight). Cape Iris 1999.

TRANSYLVANIA NATIVE (Eric & Bob Tankesley-Clarke, R. 1994). SPEC (aphylla), 13" (33 cm), E. Bright light violet self; beards pale blue; slight sweet fragrance. Collected at Turda, Romania; distributed by Randolph in 1962 and in commerce as *I. aphylla* 61-56A.

TRAPEL (Jean Segui, R. 1998). TB, 39" (100 cm), E. Violet (RHS 89B) self; beards bronze yellow (163A); purple-based foliage; pronounced fragrance. Navy Strut X Dark Allure. Iris de Thau 1982.

TREASURE MARK (Floyd Dyer, R. 1993). Sdlg. D-81-85-D. SDB, 12" (30 cm), M. Light blue, violet F. overlay; beards dark purple; musky fragrance. D-108-81-D: ((D-51-72-D: (Lilli-White x Papoose) x self) x Gingerbread Man) X D-112-81-D: (B. Jones M226-31 x self). Four Cedars 1993.

TREASURE TREAT (Floyd Dyer, R. 1992). Sdlg. D-101-89-B. BB, 26" (67 cm), M. S. light yellow; F. light violet, lightly ruffled yellow edge; beards yellow; pronounced musky fragrance. Touche X Brown Lasso. Four Cedars 1992.

TRECCIA D'ORO (Augusto Bianco, R. 1999). Sdlg. 476. TB, 33" (85 cm), EM & RE. S. cream, veined yellow; style arms cream and yellow; F. cream, hafts veined yellow; beards chrome yellow, cream base; pronounced spicy fragrance. Spirit of Memphis X Borderline.

TRENCAVEL (Jean Segui, R. 1998). TB, 32" (80 cm), E. S. purple (RHS 79B); style arms grey (177B); F. white, entirely striated purple; beards bronze yellow (163A); slight fragrance. ((Golden Years x (Rocket Rust x Radiant Apogee)) x (Wild Apache x Study in Black)) X Provencal. Iris de Thau 1990.

TRENDY (Evelyn Robarts, TB, R. 1986). Stahly 1994.

TRENWITH (R. E. Nichol, TB, R. 1985). British Iris Society 1989.

TRES (Mary Dunn, R. 1990). Sdlg. M83-817-BB. BB, 18" (46 cm), M. S. white, edge with slight violet plicata marking; F. white, deeper violet plicata markings at hafts and edge; beards white. Ghio 77-70: ((Premonition sib x Mystique) x Barletta) X Fancy Face. M.A.D. Iris 1992.

TRESCOLS (Franz Kurzmann by Jean Peyrard, SDB, R. 1989). Iris au Trescols 1991.

TRESCOLS FLASH (Lawrence Ransom, R. 1996). Sdlg. 90/321-7. SDB, 10" (25 cm), EM. S. cream, midrib deeper; style arms cream, flushed lavender; F. khaki yellow, cream centerline; beards grey lavender; ruffled. Hushpuppy X Trescols. Iris au Trescols 1996.

TREVAUNANCE COVE (R. E. Nichol, R. 1992). Sdlg. M137-2. TB, 36" (92 cm), M. S. tan; F. ivory cream shaded lemon, sanded tan, darker at hafts; beards tan; ruffled. (Rancho Rose x Keppel 77-111M, Gigolo sib) X (Nampara x Flamenco). V. H. Humphrey 1993.

TRIBAL FIRE (Heather Pryor, R. 1997). Sdlg. 29/93-D. LA, 40" (102 cm), M. S. and F. hot sunset

455

red, lemon rim and reverse, raised lime green steeple signal; style arms lemon, red basal blush; heavily ruffled. Volcanic Wildfire X Fashion World.

TRIBUNE (Franklin Carr, R. 1990). Sdlg. 84-6YT. TB, 37" (94 cm), EM. S. yellow to light brown ground, light violet midrib and veining; F. yellow white ground, light yellow brown halo, darker yellow brown on shoulders, light violet plicata markings, pale violet line from tip of yellow beard to edge; slight sweet fragrance. Burgundy Brown X Sterling Prince. Carr 1993.

TRICERABOTTOMZ (Brad Kasperek, R. 1998). Sdlg. 89F-6B. TB, 30" (76 cm), M. Light egyptian buff (RHS 19D), faint overlay of amethyst violet (84C) giving off-white effect; beards toffee (164B); foliage tricolored: medium green, light yellow green, white. Ensminger sdlg. X Capricious. Zebra 1999.

TRICERATOPS (David Spence, R. 1996). Sdlg. S82-106-2. TB, 38" (97 cm), L. Powder blue, F. with slightly darker center wash of blue violet, shoulders golden brown; beards light blue, yellow in throat, ending in 1/4" to 1/2" hairless to slightly hairy horn; ruffled. Pacific Mist X Trumpet Concerto.

TRICKS (Barry Blyth, SDB, R. 1987). Correction of parentage and date of introduction. P14-B: (Sniffs 'n' Sneezes x Hammered Copper) X Ashanti. Tempo Two 1987/88.

TRIFFID (Monty Byers, TB, R. 1989). Moonshine 1990.

TRIFLE (Ben Hager, R. 1996). Sdlg. AMD5494PlYVFth. MDB, 6" (15 cm), EML. S. light lemon yellow; style arms white, tipped yellow; F. creamy yellow, purple feather-like spot; beards whitish. Sib to Bugsy. Adamgrove 1997.

TRILLION (Elaine Bessette, R. 1996). Sdlg. EWMBS 92-12. TB, 36" (91 cm), ML. S. yellow (RHS 162B), darker toward edge, dark violet (83B) veining, red violet (77B) midrib wash; style arms yellow (162B), violet (85B) sides; F. blended rose brown (near 183D), raspberry violet (77A) wash from center to near edge, golden shoulder flush over white, violet (83B) streak from beard to edge; beards violet, tipped yellow, golden yellow in throat, 3/4" violet horn; ruffled; slight musky fragrance. Edith Wolford X M. Byers space-age sdlg.

TRIM THE VELVET (Marty Schafer/Jan Sacks, R. 1995). Sdlg. S86-8-2. SIB, 40" (102 cm), M. S. rich blue purple (slightly redder than RHS 89A); style arms same, small; F. rich blue purple, white wire rim, small white signal veined blue purple; lightly ruffled. Forrest McCord X Springs Brook. Joe Pye Weed 1995.

TRINCOMALEE (John D. Taylor by Carilla Taylor, R. 1990). Sdlg. Y45/1. BB, 24" (60 cm), L. Yellow, F. with darker rim; beards orange. Fosseway X Sun Miracle.

TRINY (Manfred Beer, R. 1998). Sdlg. MB 36/90A. TB, 32" (80 cm), M. S. and style arms greyed yellow (RHS 160A), stigmatic lip violet; F. violet (83D) with greyed orange (177D) edge; beards maize yellow (21B); ruffled; spicy fragrance. Edith Wolford X Sweet Musette. Ortenauer Staudencenter 1998.

TRIPLE DRAGON (Leo Barnard, R. 1997). Sdlg. L 91-76-ED. TB, 36" (91 cm), ML. S. light gold, faint light gold veining, base green gold; style arms light gold; F. light gold, more pronounced veining, brass yellow shoulders and veins beside beard; beards bright brass yellow, bushy, lighter at end, continuing as long brassy yellow horn, tip usually tri-forked; ruffled, laced; slight fragrance. Twice Thrilling X Borderline. Paradise Iris 1997.

TRIPLE HEART (B. Charles Jenkins, R. 1992). Sdlg. B21-32A. CA, 14" (36 cm), M. Purple self, F. with large heart-shaped ivory flash. Mission Santa Cruz X Spring Daze.

TRIPLE SOMERSAULT (Donald Spoon, R. 1997). Sdlg. 93-71A. TB, 32" (81 cm), M. S. lavender blue, darker veining at base and midrib; style arms lavender blue; F. lavender blue, prominent white and darker lavender shoulder striations, darker lavender center venation; beards lavender blue, hairs tipped yellow; lightly ruffled, flared. Busy Being Blue X English Cottage.

TRIPLE WHAMMY (Ben Hager, TB, R. 1989). Melrose 1990.

TRIPLICITY (John J. Taylor, R. 1992). Sdlg. AA-24-1. SPEC-X, 14-18" (35-48 cm), EM. S. coppery bronze, yellow near base, purplish near tip; F. slightly paler than S. with red purple (RHS 71B/C) wash on blade, fine brown haft reticulation; beards gold. P-17: (*I. imbricata* x M-3: (*I. timofejewii* x *I. reichenbachii* "Van Nes")) X M-3.

TRIVIA (Keith Keppel, IB, R. 1989). Keppel 1990.

TROIKA (Nora Scopes, R. 1993). Sdlg. 10LC8. SIB, 38" (97 cm), ML. S. light blue mauve; F. deep purple, upper part gold, veined brown. Floating Island X Silver Edge.

TROJAN'S POINT (Rosa Belle Van Valkenburgh, R. 1992). Sdlg. VV1-90. TB, 32" (81 cm), EM. S. dark blue purple; F. velvety dark blue purple, definite white patch ending in a point below white beard. Victoria Falls X Titan's Glory.

456

TROPEZIENNE (Jean Peyrard, R. 1995). Sdlg. K157. CA, 12" (30 cm), M. S. and style arms dark pink (RHS 58C); F. dark pink veined darker, flushed light blue around dark yellow signal. Parentage unknown; from Ghio seed. Lewisia 1996.

TROPICAL ENCOUNTER (Richard Ernst, R. 1998). Sdlg. F120-4. TB, 34" (86 cm), M. S. rose orchid; style arms rose orchid, cream crests; F. paler rose orchid, pale blue cast, rim rose, shoulders honey caramel; beards tangerine. Afternoon Delight X Gaulter 81-17, inv. Irene Nelson. Cooley 1998.

TROPICAL MAGIC (George Shoop, R. 1994). Sdlg. 86-12. TB, 36" (91 cm), M. S. peach pink; F. white, peach orange thumbprints beside tangerine beard; ruffled. Fantasy Lace X 84-19: ((((Mayview x Queen of Hearts) x China Dragon) x Early Surprise) x (Dream Affair x Blazing Light)). Keppel 1995.

TROPICAL MORN (Bernard Hamner by Shepard Iris, R. 1992). Sdlg. 87-24. TB, 36" (91 cm), EM. S. velvety soft golden yellow; F. darker golden yellow (RHS 20A); beards orange; laced. Golden Sparkler X Well Endowed. Hamner Iris, Shepard Iris 1992.

TROPICAL PARADISE (Donald Sorensen, R. 1999). Sdlg. S-96-24-1. TB, 33" (84 cm), M. S. coral pink (RHS 38D); style arms pinkish cream (27C); F. creamy chinese yellow (20D) blending to white in center; hafts peach (29C); beards indian orange (32A); heavily ruffled and laced; slight musky fragrance. Falling in Love X Bubble Up.

TROPICAL PEACH (A. & D. Willott, R. 1990). Sdlg. 89-66. IB, 18" (46 cm), EM. Ruffled light apricot, hafts deeper; beards coral orange. Coral Wings X Magic. Willott 1992.

TROPICAL PUNCH (J. T. Aitken, R. 1994). Sdlg. 84T27. BB, 26" (66 cm), ML. S. melon purple flushed papaya; F. papaya orange, rimmed melon purple; beards coral. Copper Classic X Shoop 82-9: ((Color Bash sib x pink amoena) x So Rare). Aitken's Salmon Creek 1994.

TROPICAL STORM (Bob Bauer/John Coble, R. 1996). Sdlg. J89F-7. JI (9-12 F.), 40" (107 cm), M. Red violet (shaded RHS 77A to 80A), veined darker in center, lighter (near-white) edges, signal dark yellow; style arms white, large crests veined violet. J86M-2: (Lace Ruff x Peloponnesus) X Hagoromo. Ensata Gardens 1996.

TROPICANA DOLL (Ladislav Muska, R. 1995). Sdlg. GFGE-02-2. TB, 39" (99 cm), ML. S. light nut; F. purple red; beards tangerine; laced. (French Gown x Geniality) X Krimhilde. Muska 1995.

TROUBADOUR'S SONG (Paul Black, R. 1991). Sdlg. 87137A. SDB, 11" (28 cm), M. S. white, heavily overlaid violet, diffusing out to tan grey band; style arms white; F. washed violet, edged grey, white luminata pattern around beard and hafts; beards yellow in throat, tipped white. Chubby Cheeks X 85319B: (Gentle Air x Chubby Cheeks sib). Mid-America 1991.

TRUE BELIEVER (Frederick Kerr, R. 1994). Sdlg. 88-29-05. TB, 32" (81 cm), M. S. honey tan, blue midrib infusion; F. medium blue, edges paler and touched yellow, hafts tannish gold; beards gold orange. Edith Wolford X Betty Simon. Rainbow Acres 1994.

TRUE LASS (Nora Scopes, R. 1991). Sdlg. 9S58. IB, 24" (61 cm), EM. Ruffled azure blue; beards pale yellow; sweet fragrance. 5/68D: (Song of Norway x Cobweb Morning) X 7/95: (Tirra Lirra sib x Skydrops). British Iris Society 1999.

TRUE QUEST (John C. Taylor, R. 1997). Sdlg. UL 22-7. LA, 35" (90 cm), ML. Ruffled purple, light tan edge and reverse, signals yellow green; style arms yellow, edged light tan. Gladiator's Gift X Dural Dreamtime. Rainbow Ridge 1999/2000.

TRUE REWARD (Mary Dunn, R. 1994). Sdlg. L169-2. LA, 36" (91 cm), M. S. purple violet, lighter toward center; style arms white; F. purple violet, edge lighter, white in heart, signal green gold. Plantation Beau X Easter Tide. Bay View 1995.

TRUE VALOR (Ed Roberts, TB, R. 1987). Ed Roberts 1993.

TRULY LOVELY (Kirk Strawn, R. 1993). Sdlg. CC-1985. LA, 35" (89 cm), M. S. dark violet purple (RHS 77A); style arms yellow (3D); F. dark red purple (59B), signal dark yellow orange (17A). Charles Arny III X Counterpoise.

TRUST (Leonard Michel, TB, R. 1989). Michel 1990.

TSA LA GI (Cleo Palmer, R. 1994). Sdlg. 8837. SDB, 13" (33 cm), EM. White, F. with large pale blue violet spot and light orange-toned shoulders; beards red, tipped white. Parentage unknown. Palmer's Iris 1994.

TSAREVICH DMITRI (V. & N. Gordodelovy, R. 1995). Sdlg. 296. TB, 35" (90 cm), M. S. brown, tinted pink; style arms yellow; F. red brown, yellow haft striations; beards orange; ruffled. Parentage unknown. Gordodelovy 1993.

TSARITSA YEKATERINA (V. & N. Gordodelovy, R. 1996). Sdlg. 95. TB, 28" (72 cm), E.

Ruffled white, base of S. and hafts greenish, shaded brown; beards red. Parentage unknown. Gordodelovy 1996.

TSITRON (Sergey Loktev, R. 1998). Sdlg. 94-L13-14E. SDB, 14" (36 cm), L. S. and style arms lemon yellow; F. pale lemon yellow, lemon mustard haft veining and small spot around beard; beards yellow, white at end and orange in throat. Easy Style X unknown. Loktev 1998.

TSLIL (David Shahak, R. 1992). Sdlg. S-T-81-127 I. AR (OH), 23" (58 cm), M. S. dark purple (RHS 77A); F. red purple (52A), signal yellow orange; beards black purple. *I. samariae* X (*I. mariae* x *I. hermona*). Aril Society, Tira Nurseries 1993.

TSUKI-NO-TAMAGAWA (Society for Japanese Irises, R. 1993). JI (3 F.), 36" (90 cm), M. S. white, edged red violet; style arms white, tipped red violet; F. red violet, large white center and white veining, signal yellow. Unknown parentage. Introduced in Japan prior to 1920.

TSUYUZORABARE (Shuichi Hirao by Society for Japanese Irises, R. 1993). JI (9-12 F.), 42" (107 cm), M. Near-white ground, sanded and finely veined light blue violet (RHS 98B to 83C), signals yellow; style arms sanded blue violet, edged and tipped red violet, anthers petaloid. Parentage unknown. Hirao prior to 1985.

TSUZUMI UTA (Shuichi Hirao by Society for Japanese Irises, R. 1994). JI (6 F.), 36" (90 cm), M. Silver violet, red violet halo and veins; style arms red violet, thinly edged silver. "I-no-Ichigo" X Cobra Dancer. Hirao 1968.

TSUZURE NISHIKI (Koji Tomino by Society for Japanese Irises, R. 1992). JI (3 F.), 36" (91 cm), EM. S. light orchid pink; F. light orchid pink, veined darker, signal yellow. "Shiranuhi" X self. Tomino 1953.

TSYGANOCHKA (Viacheslav Gavrilin, R. 1999). Sdlg. 96-212-1. TB, 31" (78 cm), M. S. wine rose, base lighter; style arms wine rose; F. wine rose, large whitish area around beard with whitish rays extending to edge; beards orange tangerine, end lighter; laced. Beverly Sills X Blue Chip Pink.

TUFF E NUFF (Lynda Miller, R. 1993). Sdlg. 2587A. SDB, 9" (22 cm), M. S. light blue; F. violet, plum hafts; beards blue, tipped yellow; slight fragrance. Crispin X 831B: (Petite Polka x unknown). Miller's Manor 1994.

TUHFATUL (Ladislav Muska, R. 1999). Sdlg. 98-ZQGB-02. TB, 36" (91 cm), M. S. blended brown and lilac; style arms light brown; F. ivory white ground, 3/4" lilac border; beards yellow mustard; sweet fragrance. ((Zuzana x Scattered Dots) x (Queen in Calico x Graffiti)) X Bed in Peppering. Muska 1999.

TULE AT DUSK (Ed Matheny III, R. 1999). Sdlg. J:00-20-94. JI (3 F.), 41" (104 cm), ML. S. purple; style arms white lightly brushed purple, edged darker, crests light purple; F. purple, yellow signal. Returning Tide X unknown.

TULE AT NIGHT (Ed Matheny III, R. 1999). Sdlg. J:00-01-94. JI (3 F.), 40" (102 cm), M. Purple, F. with yellow signal. Returning Tide X unknown.

TULE PLUM (Ed Matheny III, R. 1999). Sdlg. J:05-01-93. JI (6 F.), 36" (91 cm), M. Plum purple, yellow signal; style arms purple. My Heavenly Dream X Dark Enchantment.

TULE STORM (Ed Matheny III, R. 1998). Sdlg. J:04-03-93. JI (6 F.), 40" (102 cm), M. Reddish violet, signal yellow; style arms purple. Midsummer Reverie X Dark Enchantment. Ed's Iris 1999.

TULE STREAM (Ed Matheny III, R. 1999). Sdlg. J:00-13-94. JI (3 F.), 38" (97 cm), M. S. dark violet; style arms white, edges and crests light ultramarine; F. marine blue, yellow signal. Returning Tide X unknown.

TULE WINGS (Ed Matheny III, R. 1999). Sdlg. J:00-04-94. JI (3 F.), 41" (104 cm), M. S. violet; style arms white, brushed violet, crests white lightly veined violet; F. white, brushed blue lavender, yellow signal. Returning Tide X unknown.

TULKA GOLD (Colin Fidock, R. 1999). Sdlg. F98-1. AB (OGB), 20" (51 cm), E. S. pale icy lemon; style arms golden yellow; F. gold, lightly shot raspberry, raspberry signal with dark burgundy center; beards yellow, hairs tipped burgundy. Study in Amethyst X Edith Seligmann.

TULUM (Joseph Ghio, R. 1996). Sdlg. PE-196-B2. CA, 14" (36 cm), EM. S. rusty red; F. rusty red overlay on apricot base, violet red signal. PG-177-M2: (PI-MIX-A, unknown, x Valet sib) X PG-193-L2: (Herald x Valet sib). Bay View 1996.

TUMAN NAD OZEROM (Viktor Sheviakov, F. 1995). Sdlg. 3D 11. TB, 37" (95 cm), M. Smoky light blue blending to smoky cream, F. with brown haft striations, light blue stripe below light brown beard; musky fragrance. Allegiance X Pink Taffeta. Sheviakov 1995.

TUMBLEWEED WALTZ (Rob Stetson, R. 1997). Sdlg. RS93D1. TB, 42-46" (107-117 cm), M. S.

greyed pink (near RHS 186D), 1/4" old gold (163B) edge; style arms greyed pink, old gold crests; F. greyed pink edged old gold, with red violet overlay spreading from amber orange beard; ruffled, lightly laced; slight spicy fragrance. Ruth Porter Waring X Pacific Mist.

TUMBLIN' DICE (Roger Nelson, TB, R. 1985). Iris Country 1990.

TUMULTUEUX (Richard Cayeux, R. 1995). Sdlg. 89241 A. TB, 33" (85 cm), EM. S. pure yellow; F. violet blue, 1/3" bronze edge; beards clear bronze. Edith Wolford X Bold Accent. Cayeux 1995.

TURANDOT (Franklin Carr, TB, R. 1989). Carr 1992.

TURKISH HEART (Howard Shockey, AB (1/2), R. 1989). Arilian Acres 1990.

TURKISH HERALD (Howard Shockey, R. 1991). Sdlg. 88-157-A. AB (OGB), 29" (74 cm), M. S. light purple violet (near RHS 82D), midrib flushed buff; F. buff orange (near 24D), recurved, large sharply defined near-black signal; beards bronze; slight sweet fragrance. Turkish Pendant X 85-125-B: (Ruthie x Dawn Cascade). Arilian Acres 1992.

TURKISH PENDANT (Howard Shockey, AB (1/2), R. 1989). Arilian Acres 1990.

TURKISH TATTOO (Lois Rich by Eric Tankesley-Clarke, R. 1994). Sdlg. R65-13D. AB (OB), 12" (31 cm), EM. S. parchment tan to buff, blended lilac and maroon; F. parchment tan, heavily netted maroon, small brown black signal; beards cream, tipped buff. Bagdad Beauty X Knotty Pine. Adamgrove 1994.

TURKISH WARRIOR (G. F. Wilson, R. 1994). Sdlg. 45-89TTWM-F. AB (OGB), 28" (71 cm), EM. S. cream ground suffused blood red, heavy maroon veining; F. dark oxblood maroon deepening to black at maroon black beard. Turkish Tangent X Warrior's Mantle. Pleasure Iris, Potterton & Martin 1995.

TURNABOUT (Chet Tompkins, R. 1992). Sdlg. 83-101. TB, 38" (97 cm), ML. S. ivory white, hint of pink at base; F. light clover pink faintly flushed violet; beards deep red. Camelot Rose lines X (pink and red sdlgs. x (Twilight Skies x Defiance)). Fleur de Lis 1992.

TURNER MILLS (Harry Turner, R. 1996). Sdlg. 13-88. TB, 31" (79 cm), E. S. spectrum violet, base of midrib white; F. spectrum violet, 3/8" white blaze, slight brownish haft marking; beards yellow; slight fragrance. 13-83-1: (Loudoun Charmer x Broadway) X Brown Lasso. Quail Hill 1997.

TURN ON (Chet Tompkins, R. 1995). Sdlg. 93-18. TB, 34" (86 cm), ML. S. apricot pink, silvery undertone, F. slightly darker; beards orange apricot. (Pagoda Goddess x (Lux Aeterna x (Bonbon x Tinsel Town))) X Ming Porcelain. Fleur de Lis 1995.

TURQUOISE TOUCH (Jean Witt, R. 1992). Sdlg. PCN-10-92. CA, 15" (38 cm), M. S. light lavender blue, darker median streak; F. light lavender blue, darker blue "bleeding" halo, hint of turquoise at tip of yellow centerline. (*I. munzii* x *I. douglasiana*) X *I. douglasiana*.

TUTU MANGO (Michael Moller, R. 1999). Sdlg. BO/BO/RB-1. SDB, 13" (33 cm), ML. Bright tangerine orange (RHS 24B); beards red. Obligato X Orange Tiger.

TU YUNG (Duane Meek, R. 1995). Sdlg. JI41. JI (6 F.), 40" (107 cm), ML. White, lightly veined, speckled and sanded light to medium red violet, deeper near gold signal and bottom center, with narrow clean white rim; style arms white, sides flushed pale violet, veined deeper, curled red violet crests; ruffled. Parentage unknown. D & J Gardens 1995.

TWEETY BIRD (Paul Black, R. 1991). Sdlg. 89259A. SDB, 12" (30 cm), E. S. pastel yellow; style arms yellow; F. yellow with olive cast, orange overlay on hafts; beards bright orange; slight fragrance. Wake Up X 86384A: ((Oriental Blush x Gigglepot) x (Gigglepot x Chubby Cheeks sib)). Mid-America 1992.

TWICE BLUE (Bernard Hamner by Shepard Iris Garden, R. 1993). Sdlg. 87-07. TB, 38" (97 cm), M. S. icy light blue; F. deep royal blue; beards light blue, tipped yellow. Ruffled Ballet X Harbor Cruise. Hamner Iris, Shepard Iris 1994.

TWICE TOLD (William Maryott, R. 1994). Sdlg. L172D. TB, 34-36" (86-91 cm), M & RE. S. flesh to light beige, slight maroon at midrib; F. velvety medium red maroon; beards tangerine. H92B: (F154D: ((Latin Lover x Victorian Days) x Keppel 74-32E: ((Roundup x Artwork sib) x Osage Buff)) x E31D: ((Dream Fantasy x Pink Sleigh) x Heather Blush)) X Cameo Wine. Maryott 1994.

TWILIGHT BLAZE (Keith Keppel, R. 1991). Sdlg. 86-34D. TB, 30" (76 cm), EM. S. near bishops violet (M&P 44-G-10) paling (44-D-7) toward edge; F. steely violet (45-F-10) center, paling and greying (45-D-8 to 45-C-4) toward hafts blended honey beige (11-C-6); beards solid mandarin red (2-F-12); pronounced sweet fragrance. Skyblaze X Faraway Places. Keppel 1992.

TWILIGHT CARESS (Les Fort, TB, R. 1989). Fort Iris 1990.

TWILIGHT MODE (Barry Blyth, R. 1993). Sdlg. ET-4. SPU, 38" (97 cm), EM. S. navy blue; F. navy blue infused gold, giving muted gold effect. Ethic X self. Tempo Two 1993/94.

TWILIGHT MOONRISE (Donald Spoon, R. 1999). Sdlg. 93-81A. BB, 24" (61 cm), ML. Ruffled and laced light rose lavender, F. with darker 1/4" border, plum spot with fan-like whiskers, white sunburst around beard; beards tangerine, hairs tipped white at end. ((Condottiere x (Cherished x Dusky Evening)) x Ringo) X Yosemite Sam. Winterberry 1999.

TWILIGHT PASSAGE (J. T. Aitken, R. 1998). Sdlg. 91T32. BB, 25" (64 cm), ML. S. orchid; F. pink; beards tangerine pink. Lankow 8J85: (Abridged Version x Greensleeves) X Faraway Places. Aitken's Salmon Creek 1998.

TWILIGHT RAIN (Les Peterson by Ardi Kary, R. 1992). Sdlg. AK85-20BM. AB (OGB-), 29" (74 cm), M. Light violet with darker sprinkles; F. light violet washed purple violet; beards brown, tipped dark violet. ((Amanda Sings x Jealous Lover) x Stitched Beauty) X Heart Stealer. Kary Iris 1992.

TWILIGHT'S LAST GLEAMING (Jeanne Holley, R. 1999). Sdlg. 101-92. TB, 32" (81 cm), ML. S. smoky pinkish lavender; style arms gold; F. smoky pinkish lavender tan infused light blue, gold on hafts; beards gold; heavily ruffled and laced. Ruffled Surprise X Classic Edition.

#TWILIGHT THOUGHTS (Calvin Helsley, TB, R. 1978). Name released 1990.

TWILIGHT THOUGHTS (Calvin Helsley, R. 1990). Sdlg. 86-3. SIB, 24" (61 cm), M. S. light blue violet veined dark blue; style arms light blue, veined turquoise; F. medium blue veined darker, slightly darker blue violet edge, signal yellow in throat changing to creamy white; ruffled; slight sweet fragrance. Ruffled Velvet X unknown.

TWILIGHT WONDER (Jim Hedgecock, R. 1992). Sdlg. 84-60-2. TB, 36" (91 cm), M. Laced and ruffled pale blue, F. with darker blue haft veining; beards pale blue, gold in throat; slight sweet fragrance. Startler X Mary O. Mahoney. Comanche Acres 1993.

TWINKLE EYES (Lynda Miller, R. 1992). Sdlg. 1287. MDB, 3¾" (9½ cm), E. Off-white, F. with medium blue veined spot; slight fragrance. (Pansy Heart x Sky Dot) X 584: ((What Not x Sky Dot) x unknown).

TWIN LAKES (Joseph Ghio, R. 1992). Sdlg. PH-305A. CA, 16" (41 cm), ML. True medium blue, white heart and edge, yellow signal. Mists of Time X San Andreas. Bay View 1993.

TWO-SIDED COIN (Richard Ernst, R. 1996). Sdlg. HR8545-B1. TB, 37" (94 cm), ML. S. light yellow; style arms medium yellow; F. blue violet, yellow amber shoulders, lighter near gold beard; ruffled; slight spicy sweet fragrance. Edith Wolford X R8545: (inv. Afternoon Delight, Edith Wolford, C142-3: (Ringo x (Cranberry Ice x Grand Waltz))). Cooley 1996.

TWYLA (Chet Tompkins, R. 1998). Sdlg. 93-23. TB, 38" (97 cm), ML-VL. S. bone china white; style arms white, blended buckskin; F. true brown; beards cinnamon brown. Inv. Trudy, Post Script, Bayberry Candle, Cimarron Strip, The Chocolate Soldier, Louvois, etc. Fleur de Lis 1998.

TY BLUE (Tom Burseen, R. 1999). Sdlg. 95-266D. TB, 35" (89 cm), M. Ruffled pale lavender, F. sometimes splotched violet; beards white, hairs tipped tangerine, purple horn; flared; sweet fragrance. Hunk X Thornbird.

TYRIAN DREAM (Cy Bartlett, R. 1998). Sdlg. C91-41. IB, 24" (61 cm), M. S. pale grey, midrib tyrian purple; F. tyrian purple, edges paler; beards violet, tipped gold; ruffled. Gossip X C88-42: (Amadora x Wensleydale). Sutton 1998.

UCHU (Matsudaira Shoo by Society for Japanese Irises, R. 1993). JI (9 F.), 31" (80 cm), ML. Blue violet, white centers radiating white veins. Parentage unknown. Correction of entry in 1939 Check List listing cultivar as "Uchiu". Matsudaira Shoo ca. 1848.

UEBER DEN WOLKEN (Tomas Tamberg, R. 1993). Sdlg. SSTT174. SIB, 33" (85 cm), M. Light blue self. SSTT108: ((Tycoon x Limeheart) x Limeheart) X Signals Blue. Schoeppinger 1994.

UFFDOWN (John D. Taylor by Carilla Taylor, R. 1990). Sdlg. E18/3. TB, 30" (75 cm), M. S. white flushed violet with brown striations; crests white; F. creamy, with violet and brown markings; beards orange. unknown X Festive Skirt.

UGETSU (Zensaku Makino by Society for Japanese Irises, R. 1995). JI (3 F.), 35" (90 cm), M. S. medium to dark blue violet, edged white; style arms white, medium blue violet edge and crests; F. white, brushed blue violet. Parentage unknown. Introduced in Japan prior to 1980.

UGRIUM-REKA (Nina Miroshnichenko, R. 1996). TB, 35" (90 cm), M. Blue violet self; beards blue at end, yellow in throat; slight sweet fragrance. Parentage unknown. Miroshnichenko 1988.

UH-HUH (Allan Ensminger, R. 1991). Sdlg. 184-32. BB, 24" (61 cm), ML. Lavender rose (HCC 633/1); beards yellow; slight sweet fragrance. Color Brite X 78-21: ((Little Mark x (Dominocus sib x (Faydy Girl x sib))) x ((((Gypsy Baron sdlg. x Belle Meade) x Stepping Out) x 69-31) x (Doodle Strudel sib x 69-31))). Varigay 1993.

UKINEDORI (Shuichi Hirao by Society for Japanese Irises, R. 1993). JI (3 F.), 42" (107 cm), M. Flaring white, yellow signal; style arms white, tinted light yellow. Parentage unknown. Hirao prior to 1980.

ULTIMATE SUNTAN (Joseph Ghio, R. 1996). Sdlg. PF-188N. CA, 14" (36 cm), EM. Golden orange, overall red wash and veining, F. with red black signal. Eagle Eyes X PH-266K: (Las Lomas x Aftershock sib). Bay View 1996.

ULTIMATUM (Lawrence Ransom, R. 1993). Sdlg. 87/86-4. TB, 37" (94 cm), M. Lightly ruffled and laced apricot orange self; beards orange to red; sweet fragrance. Lady Friend X Opium. Iris au Trescols 1994.

ULTRALIGHT (A. & D. Willott, R. 1994). Sdlg. 90-77. IB, 20" (51 cm), EM. Ruffled white ground plicata, stitched light blue; beards light blue, yellow in throat. Everything Plus X 85-3: ((Kentucky Bluegrass x unknown) x unknown). Willott 1994.

ULTRA PRETTY (Alex Wintle, TB, R. 1976). Cooling's Nursery 1996.

ULTRA TREAT (Stan Dexter by Marie Ingersoll, R. 1995). Sdlg. 5-194A. TB, 38" (97 cm), L. S. pale lilac; F. rose violet, some haft markings; beards orange, pink tip; ruffled. Deming Glacier X Touch of Bronze. Ingersoll's Iris 1996.

ULYBKA (Viktor Koroliov, R. 1997). Sdlg. S80-93K. BB, 26" (65 cm), M. S. light yellow, heavily stitched brown; style arms yellow brown; F. milky white ground, bright claret violet plicata edge; beards yellow brown; slight sweet fragrance. Siva Siva X Cliffs of Dover. Koroliov 1997.

UMUNHUM (Joseph Ghio, R. 1998). Sdlg. PC-228X. CA, 16" (41 cm), VE. Bright sienna, underside deeper, F. with precise violet signal. Ultimate Suntan X PF-188H, sib. Bay View 1998.

UNBELIEVABLE LOVE (William Grise, R. 1995). Sdlg. AIX-9. TB, 36" (91 cm), ML & RE. S. violet blue (near RHS 91D); style arms violet blue, violet (86D) tip; F. violet blue (91D) blending gradually to dark violet blue (93A) dimple 3/8" below beard; dimple 1/4" long, 1/4" deep; beards bluebird blue (94B), golden yellow in throat; ruffled; slight musky fragrance. Carriage Trade X Silkwood. Parkwood 1998.

UNCHAINED MELODY (Clarence Mahan, R. 1992). Sdlg. 888-1. TB, 36" (91 cm), EM & RE. Ruffled white, F. flared; beards white, tipped yellow in throat. Harvest of Memories X Soap Opera. Friendship 1999.

UNCLAIMED TREASURE (Sharon McAllister, R. 1990). Sdlg. 81-3-1. AB (OGB), 29" (74 cm), EM. S. intense iridescent violet (RHS 87A); F. bright copper on inner half, blending to brown overlay on violet purple (77A) base toward outer edge, overall metallic sheen, veined maroon black signal; beards mustard, tipped maroon. Welcome Reward X Esther the Queen. Aril Society 1990.

UNCLE CHARLIE (Donald Spoon, R. 1997). Sdlg. 91-39B. TB, 34" (86 cm), ML. Ruffled pale lavender blue (RHS 97C) self; beards darker lavender blue, hair tips lighter, yellow deep in heart; flared; slight sweet fragrance. Honky Tonky Blues X Silverado. Winterberry 1999.

UNDERCOVER (John C. Taylor, R. 1996). UL 5-4. LA, 39" (100 cm), ML. Purple violet, F. with yellow signal; ruffled; slight fragrance. 'Bout Midnight X Rachel's Request. Rainbow Ridge 1998/99.

UNFINISHED BUSINESS (William & Martha Griner, R. 1998). Sdlg. 92-72A. TB, 46" (117 cm), M. S. and style arms pale violet, S. narrowly edged darker violet; F. rosy purple, lighter violet edge with outer rim white, hafts marked white and brown; beards orange, rosy purple spoons. Miss Pretty X Conjuration. W. & M. Griner 1999.

UNFORGETTABLE FIRE (Schreiner, R. 1991). Sdlg. T 1505-2. TB, 39" (99 cm), EML. Red; beards old gold; ruffled, flared. Distant Fire X Cayenne Pepper. Schreiner 1991.

UNICORN WONDER (Jim Hedgecock, R. 1992). Sdlg. 84-25-3. TB, 30" (76 cm), M. S. pale yellow; F. white, edges and hafts pale yellow; beards yellow orange, fuzzy white horn; pronounced sweet fragrance. Sunset Sonata X Sky Hooks. Comanche Acres 1993.

UNION PACIFIC (Connell Marsh, TB, R. 1989). C. Marsh 1990.

UNIQUE ONE (Stan Dexter by Marie Ingersoll, R. 1993). Sdlg. A10-7-158A. TB, 36" (91 cm), ML. Coral tan, F. center overlaid light brick red radiating toward edge, then shading to tan; beards pink orange. 82-138: ((Crandall 76-2 x Crandall 77-15B) x Crandall 77-15B) X 84-10: (Caramba x (69-26 x Flamenco)). Ingersoll's Iris 1994.

UNIQUE STYLE (Heather Pryor, R. 1998). Sdlg. 42/93-A. LA, 39" (100 cm), EM. S. soft lemon, edges blushed pink, pink line signal; style arms lemon, intensely feathered, horned at end, feathers and horns with pink tips; F. medium pink, veined deeper, rim pale lemon, raised lime green steeple signal. Charlotte's Tutu X Margaret Lee. Iris Haven 1999/2000.

UNIVERSAL PEACE (B. Charles Jenkins, R. 1990). Sdlg. B5-3D. SPU, 36-47" (91-119 cm), M. S. purple; F. purple lines over ivory ground. Equality X Crow Wing. Shepard Iris 1991.

UNJOBITO (Kakuta by Society for Japanese Irises, R. 1994). JI (3 F.), 38" (97 cm), ML. S. medium violet; F. light pink-tinted blue, yellow signal. Parentage unknown. Kakuta 1986.

UNPRETENTIOUS (Paul Black, R. 1991). Sdlg. 87149A. SDB, 14" (36 cm), L. Medium blue; beards blue white. Little Louie X Stardate. Mid-America 1991.

UNYORO (Ladislav Muska, R. 1997). Sdlg. ASAV-10. TB, 36" (91 cm), ML. S. vanilla apricot; style arms creamy caramel; F. mahogany red, wide light creamy vanilla rim; beards light orange; pronounced fragrance. (Aphrodisiac x Sweet Musette) X (Aphrodisiac x Vanilla Lace). Muska 1997.

UPAL S LUNY (Viacheslav Gavrilin, R. 1999). Sdlg. 96-2-66-11. TB, 30" (75 cm), ML. S. white; style arms light yellow; F. white, hafts yellow; beards orange red, white at end; heavily ruffled. Wedding Candles X Coral Joy.

UP CLOSE (Glenn Bowers, R. 1998). Sdlg. B40-1. TB, 34" (86 cm), EM. Lightly ruffled medium violet (Pantone 2622C), F. center lighter (2592C), hafts shaded rust bronze (471U); beards bronze (540U), violet at end; slight sweet fragrance. Wright Flyer X Suky.

UP DANCING (Barry Blyth, R. 1996). Sdlg. A70-3. TB, 38" (97 cm), M. Light lavender lilac, F. overlaid pastel lilac white; beards lemon yellow. Liqueur Creme X Taffeta Bow. Tempo Two 1996/97.

UPGRADE (John C. Taylor, R. 1998). Sdlg. 94-38. LA, 47" (120 cm), EM. S. and F. purple violet, edged lighter, yellow signal; style arms purple violet, edged buff; fluted. Parentage unknown. Rainbow Ridge 1998/99.

UP NORTH (Jack Worel, R. 1993). Sdlg. 19-20-3. TB, 34" (86 cm), M. S. medium to dark blue violet; F. lighter blue violet, fading to very light blue at edge; beards light blue. St. Louis Blues X Cosmic Dance. Holly Lane 1993.

UP PERISCOPE (William Maryott, TB, R. 1984). Correction of parentage. Scented Nutmeg X Victoria Falls.

UPSIDE DOWN (O. D. Niswonger, R. 1994). Sdlg. 34-84. TB, 33" (84 cm), M. S. lilac blue, midrib deeper; F. very pale lilac blue, near white; beards white, tipped red. Battle Fury X Lilac Lass. Cape Iris 1994.

UP TO SNUFF (Allan Ensminger, R. 1998). Sdlg. 94-22. IB, 24" (61 cm), ML. S. and style arms mimosa yellow (HCC 602/1); F. deeper mimosa yellow (602); beards canary yellow (2/1); slight fragrance. 489-33: (285-40: ((Peachy Creamy x Fresno Calypso) x Michel C-120-2: (Bride's Halo x Joyce Terry)) x sib) X Vavoom. Varigay 1998.

UPTOWN PINK (George Slade, R. 1990). Sdlg. 80-24-04. TB, 36" (91 cm), M. Pink orange; beards tangerine, white at end. Sunday Chimes X Summer Love. Wyle Wynde 1990.

UPTOWN PROPER (Richard Ernst, R. 1999). Sdlg. NJF168-2-3A2. TB, 36" (91 cm), ML. S. and style arms pink; F. peach; beards tangerine orange; ruffled. Sib to Just My Style. Cooley 1999.

URBAN STAR (Joseph Stien, R. 1996). Sdlg. S92-3-1. SDB, 10" (25 cm), ML. S. pale yellow, midrib greyed yellow; style arms pale yellow; F. champagne, large wine red thumbprint with feathered edges changing to brass yellow at hafts; beards white, hairs tipped orange in throat; slight sweet fragrance. Aqua Star X Urban Cowboy. Comanche Acres 1998.

URGENT (Hooker Nichols, TB, R. 1988). Hillcrest 1992.

URMIA (Lawrence Ransom, R. 1996). Sdlg. 89/165-2. AB (OGB+), 30" (76 cm), M. S. pale grey blue, fine darker blue veining, edge lightly blended tan; style arms cream, bluer rib; F. pale grey blue, small oval diffused blue purple signal; beards golden yellow, tapered, hairs tipped bronze; slight sweet fragrance. *I. hoogiana* X Tabriz. Iris au Trescols 1997.

URSULA WARLEGGAN (R. E. Nichol by Jean Nichol, R. 1998). Sdlg. S 290-5. TB, 36" (91 cm), M. S. very pale lilac pink (RHS 69B); style arms yellow; F. very pale lilac (76C), dark central blotch, yellow haft marking; beards bright yellow; lightly ruffled; slight fragrance. Sib to Julia Vennor.

URUSALLIMU (Ladislav Muska, R. 1998). Sdlg. CDSP-02. TB, 38" (97 cm), M. S. white, midrib flushed apricot; style arms apricot; F. white and deeper apricot shot silk effect; beards orange; slight fragrance. ((Chiffon Bonnet x "Donna Giala": (Tut's Gold x Sunshine Express)) x Lady Madonna) X Pani Ambra. Muska 1998.

USHIO-NO-KEMURI (Shuichi Hirao by Society for Japanese Irises, R. 1992). JI (multi-petal), 27"

(70 cm), EM. Blue violet, white streaks and splashes, yellow signals. Parentage unknown. Hirao 1958.

UTAH JAZZ (D. C. Anderson, AB (OGB), 1988). Brown's Iris Garden 1990.

UTRENNIAYA SVEZHEST (Viktor Koroliov, R. 1996). Sdlg. C19-89K. TB, 45" (115 cm), M. Lilac self; beards yellow, light at end shading to dark in throat; pronounced spicy fragrance. South Pacific X Jersey Beauty. Koroliov 1993.

UTRO TUMANNOYE (Adolf Volfovich-Moler, R. 1995). Sdlg. 134. TB, 47" (120 cm), E. Light lilac self; beards yellow, white at end; ruffled. Mary Frances X Rippling Waters. Volfovich-Moler 1996.

U-TURN (Carl Boswell, SDB, R. 1989). Adamgrove, Aril Patch 1991.

VABU (Ladislav Muska, R. 1996). Sdlg. FFKR-03/A. TB, 39" (99 cm), ML. S. vanilla amber; F. buff; beards orange; heavily ruffled and laced; sweet fragrance. (Faded Denim x "Fialovy Kvet": (Windsor Rose x Laced Cotton)) X (Krimhilde x Vanilla Lace). Muska 1996.

VAGABOND PEDDLER (Hooker Nichols, R. 1991). Sdlg. 8824A. SDB, 12" (30 cm), EML. Lightly ruffled olive green beige, pink violet highlights around beige lavender beards. Evening Event X Dixieland Delight. Hillcrest 1992.

VAGUE A L'AME (Jean Cayeux, R. 1990). Sdlg. 7477 B. TB, 38" (96 cm), VL. S. smooth pink beige; F. light violet; beards red. Barcelona X Condottiere. Cayeux 1986.

VAIL (Michael Moller, R. 1996). Sdlg. CYCWYB-1. TB, 36" (91 cm), ML. S. cream yellow to white; style arms white; F. cream white; beards yellow. Class Act X America's Cup. Long 1997.

VAIN FRIVOLITY (James Gibson by Cooley's Gardens, R. 1999). Sdlg. 10-3A. TB, 34" (86 cm), M. Pink self; beards pinkish orange. Beverly Sills X 48-3: ((Lorna Lee x (Tahiti Sunrise x (Tahiti Sunrise x Lorna Lee))) x ((Lorna Lee x Tahiti Sunrise) x (Tahiti Sunrise x Lorna Lee))). Cooley 1999.

VAL DE LOIRE (Richard Cayeux, R. 1998). Sdlg. 9099A. TB, 32" (80 cm), M. S. lilac white; F. smoky lavender; beards orange red. Coquetterie X 8780: ((Color Splash x Condottiere) x ((Condottiere x Metropolitan) x sib)). Cayeux 1999.

VALENTINE'S DAY (Vernon Wood, R. 1996). Sdlg. 92-49. TB, 34" (86 cm), VE. Ruffled pink (near RHS 56B) self; beards tangerine. Sib to Sly Fox. Stockton 1997.

VALERE CASTLE (Eric & Bob Tankesley-Clarke, R. 1994). SPEC, 10-12" (25-31 cm), E. Cream, F. veined and blended pale violet; beards yellow white; pronounced sweet fragrance. Collected at Valere Castle, Switzerland; distributed by Randolph prior to 1963 and in commerce as *I. lutescens virescens* S21C.

VALERIYA (Viktor Sheviakov, R. 1997). Sdlg. 21d15a. IB, 24" (60 cm), EM. White, shading to pale lilac at hafts and center; beards yellow, white at end; slight sweet fragrance. "Uroda" X Demon. Sheviakov 1997.

VALET (Joseph Ghio, R. 1991). Sdlg. PI-214P2. CA, 13" (33 cm), EML. Pinkish grape mauve, neon violet signal. Black Eye sib X PL-303C3: (((Gone Native x (Casa Pacifica x Las Flores)) x Montara sib) x (San Vicente x Casa Pacifica)). Bay View 1992.

VALLEY BLUE (Ben Hager, R. 1997). SPEC-X (evansia), 30" (76 cm), M. Light blue self, F. with deep yellow spear signal; frilled form. Origin unknown; has been found on several occasions growing in conjunction with Darjeeling, which it resembles closely except for color.

VALLEY OF DELIGHT (D. Steve Varner, SIB, R. 1985). Illini Iris 1991.

VALLEY SUNSET (Stan Dexter by Marie Ingersoll, R. 1993). Sdlg. B-7-232. TB, 36" (91 cm), M. S. yellow, purple midrib; F. rose purple edged yellow tan; beards yellow, tipped white. 83-80: ((Vanity x Focus) x Coral Surf) X In Concert. Ingersoll's Iris 1994.

VALSE BLUETTE (Clarence Protzmann, TB, R. 1988). Protzmann 1990.

VALS TSVETOV (V. & N. Gordodelovy, R. 1995). Sdlg. 8. TB, 39" (100 cm), E. S. light brown, tinted pink; style arms yellow, lilac center stripe; F. yellow, light brown rim and haft striations; beards yellow; lightly ruffled. Parentage unknown. Gordodelovy 1995.

VAMPIRE'S KISS (Chris Vizvarie, R. 1991). Sdlg. CRV 11-85A. TB, 36" (90 cm), M. S. rust red; F. dark rust red, lighter around yellow beard tipped orange; ruffled, laced; slight fragrance. Hombre X Peking Summer. Last Scent Farm 1991.

VANDA SONG (Barry Blyth, R. 1996). Sdlg. A144-3. TB, 36" (91 cm), ML. S. silvery blue, midrib infused deeper; F. silvery blue, shading to silvery white center; beards medium blue, tipped white; pronounced sweet fragrance. Just Magic X Honky Tonk Blues. Tempo Two 1996/97.

VANILLA BUTTERFLY (Ladislav Muska, R. 1999). Sdlg. 99-PPIB-07. TB, 38" (97 cm), L. Ruffled and laced vanilla cream; F. washed soft pink; beards red tangerine; sweet fragrance. (Pan-Pink x (Pan-Pink x Invocazione)) X Beverly Sills.

VANILLA FUDGE (Larry Lauer, R. 1998). Sdlg. 91-227-3. TB, 35" (89 cm), ML. S. golden tan, midrib lighter; style arms tan; F. reddish maroon, tan rim; beards orange; heavily ruffled; pronounced sweet fragrance. Busy Signal X L88-92: (L86-47: (Howdy Folks x Frances Gaulter) x Tiger Butter). Lauer's Flowers 1998.

VANILLA KISSES (Barry Blyth, R. 1997). Sdlg. D53-2. TB, 36" (91 cm), M. S. cream, deeper midrib; F. creamy white, hafts slightly deeper; beards mustard yellow; pronounced sweet fragrance. Dragon's Fancy X Hostess Royale. Tempo Two 1997/98.

VANILLA LACE (Ladislav Muska, R. 1997). Sdlg. MAEX-01. TB, 38" (97 cm), M. Ruffled, heavily laced deep vanilla, F. washed cream in center; style arms deep cream washed buff; beards sunflower yellow; sweet fragrance. ("Marcelina": (Miss Dolly Dollars x Grecian Gown) x ("Marcelina" x Extravagant)) X Extravagant. Muska 1995.

VANILLA ROUGE (Leo Barnard, R. 1995). Sdlg. L 91-76A. TB, 30" (76 cm), EML & RE. S. pearly white, very pale peach pink (RHS 36D) base; slight pink midrib veining; style arms pale peach pink; F. pearly white washed peach, deeper (36B) shoulders; beards white at end, white to tangerine in throat; ruffled; slight sweet fragrance. Borderline X Twice Thrilling. Paradise Iris 1995.

VANOZZA (Ladislav Muska, R. 1999). Sdlg. 98-CGSB-01. TB, 36" (91 cm), M. S. white, veined lilac; style arms buff tan; F. ivory white ground, 1" brown lilac peppering darkest at rim; beards tangerine; ruffled, heavily laced; slight fragrance. ((Cream With Gold x Spacelight Sketch) x (Graffiti x Scattered Dots)) X Bed in Peppering. Muska 1999.

VARIAG (Viktor Sheviakov, R. 1996). Sdlg. 10a6a. TB, 31" (78 cm), EML. Dark red violet, hafts black violet; beards brown violet, red violet at end; slight spicy fragrance. Tyrian Prince X Arabi Pasha. Sheviakov 1997.

VARIATION IN PINK (Currier McEwen, R. 1995). Sdlg. 89/34. JI (3 F.), 30" (75 cm), EML & RE. S. phlox purple (RHS 75C), paling (75D) with age; style arms white, edged and tipped phlox purple, paling to (75D); F. lavender pink (75B), paling to (75D), signal light yellow (7C). Miyoshino X Celestial Pink. Eartheart 1996.

VARIETE (Ladislav Muska, R. 1997). Sdlg. SACA-09. TB, 38" (97 cm), M. S. light lilac; style arms deeper lavender; F. deep burgundy red, wide brown rim; beards bright yellow; ruffled, heavily laced; spicy fragrance. ((Saturabico x Calitrix) x Tropicana Doll) X Sweeter Than Wine. Muska 1996.

VASIA-VASILIOK (Viktor Sheviakov, R. 1995). Sdlg. 22D 19A. TB, 28" (71 cm), M. Ruffled sapphire self; beards blue at end, merging from brownish blue to brown in throat; musky fragrance. Winner's Circle X Rippling Waters. Sheviakov 1997.

VASILI SHUKSHIN (Viktor Sheviakov, R. 1995). Sdlg. 12V 10A. TB, 32" (82 cm), M. S. light tan; F. light tan, hafts shaded light brown, light violet veining near yellow brown beard. Dancers Veil X Frost and Flame. Sheviakov 1995.

VAVOOM (Allan Ensminger, R. 1993). Sdlg. 288-8. SDB, 15" (40 cm), L. S. uranium green (HCC 633); F. canary yellow; beards white. 85-13: (People Pleaser x 83-4: (280-4, Jillaroo sib, x (78-4 x 78-18, Limpid Pools sib))) X sib. Varigay 1994.

VDOKHNOVENIYE (Adolf Volfovich-Moler, R. 1995). Sdlg. V-25. TB, 39" (100 cm), L. S. lilac; F. blended lilac, paler at edge; beards orange; ruffled, laced. Rippling Waters X Dancers Veil. Volfovich-Moler 1992.

VECHERNEYE PLATIYE (Adolf Volfovich-Moler, R. 1997). Sdlg. V-150. TB, 43" (110 cm), EM. Ruffled and laced violet purple, paler around beard; style arms bright lilac, edges paler; beards yellow, lavender at end; slight spicy fragrance. Pink Sleigh X Master Touch. Volfovich-Moler 1999.

VECHERNIAYA SKAZKA (Adolf Volfovich-Moler, R. 1997). Sdlg. V-148. TB, 39" (100 cm), E. Ruffled and laced blended purplish brown, F. with paler edge, brighter center; beards light lilac, hairs tipped yellow; pronounced sweet fragrance. Vdokhnoveniye X Pink Sleigh. Volfovich-Moler 1999.

VECHNY OGON (V. & N. Gordodelovy, R. 1996). Sdlg. 36. TB, 28" (72 cm), EM. Red brown self; beards brown; slight fragrance. Parentage unknown. Gordodelovy 1985.

VEE FOR VICTORY (Austin Morgan, R. 1991). Sdlg. 87/102. TB, 36" (91 cm), M. S. light blue; F. rose; beards lime. Stunning X Victoria Falls. Iris Test Garden 1991.

VEGAS HEAT (George Sutton, R. 1997). Sdlg. G-91. BB, 27" (68 cm), EM. S. and style arms empire yellow (RHS 11A); F. violet purple (87A), slightly redder at edge; beards mustard, 3/4" imperial purple horn; ruffled. F-63: (Edith Wolford x Gladys Austin) X Fly to Vegas. Sutton 1998.

VEGAS LIGHTS (A. & D. Willott, R. 1995). Sdlg. 92-208. IB, 21" (53 cm), ML. S. light yellow; F. white, narrowly edged light yellow, full yellow hafts; beards yellow to orange; ruffled. 88-102: (Vegas Showgirl x Raspberry Whip) X Beverly Sills. Willott 1995.

VEGAS WEEKEND (Hooker Nichols, R. 1991). Sdlg. 8742A. TB, 34" (86 cm), ML. Ruffled medium yellow, white area below gold beards. Oklahoma Sunshine X Academy Awards,

VEINED BANNER (Tony Huber, R. 1998). Sdlg. 94-003 (91-629). SPEC-X (versata), 32" (82 cm), EM. S. white, veined or lined violet blue (RHS 93C/D); style arms blue, bordered white; F. white, veined violet blue, signal bright yellow; slight sweet fragrance. 91-402 *versicolor* white X white 6-F. *ensata* sdlg.

VELVET HAMMER (Chris Vizvarie, R. 1994). SDB, 12" (31 cm), ML. Ruffled grape, F. with deeper grape thumbprint; beards orange, tipped yellow; slight sweet fragrance. Chubby Cheeks X Catani. Last Scent Farm 1994.

VELVET LADY (Norma Barnard, R. 1997). Sdlg. N 94-4P. CA, 14" (36 cm), ML. S. blended purple; style arms light purple; F. dark purple, small gold signal; ruffled. Lacylady X NB 91-305P. Paradise Iris 1997.

VELVET MEMORY (Richard Morgan, R. 1994). Sdlg. L662-RV. LA, 28" (71 cm), M. Dark red violet, F. with tan halo, medium green yellow steeple signal; lightly ruffled. Treasured Memories X L203-A: (Melon Time x Chowning 77-6: (Mockers Song x Ann Chowning)). Redbud Lane 1996.

VELVET UNDERGROUND (Larry Lauer, R. 1995). Sdlg. L-8-121-3. TB, 36" (91 cm), ML. S. and style arms red violet; F. dark velvety red violet; beards white. Royal Celebrity X L86-35: (Park Lane x Peppermint). Stockton 1996.

VENERA MILOSSKAYA (Viktor Sheviakov, R. 1996). Sdlg. 10c14a. TB, 30" (75 cm), ML. S. light cream pink; F. cream pink, veined rose; beards yellow brown; slight spicy fragrance. Heather Hawk X Pipes of Pan. Sheviakov 1997.

VENETIAN LOVE (Akihiko Terada, R. 1999). Sdlg. 91-10. TB, 34" (86 cm), M. S. white; F. deep burgundy, upper half sanded white, white rim; beards yellow. Theatre X Streetwalker. Roris 1999.

VENEVONGSOTH (Bob Thomason, R. 1991). Sdlg. BT 8804A. TB, 30" (76 cm), ML. Deep purple, lighter toward F. edge, lavender hafts veined red brown; beards orange, tipped white; slight fragrance. Sunset Sky X ((Stepchild x Stylelite) x Swift River). Okie Iris 1993.

VENEZIA LUSTRA (Ladislav Muska, R. 1996). Sdlg. MOCA-05/B. TB, 39" (99 cm), M. S. pale azurine blue, white midrib; F. pale azure blue, white central area; beards yellow; heavily laced; sweet fragrance. ((Monte Albano x (Chartreuse Ruffles x Frivolous Idea)) x (Carrara Lace x Nordic Seas)) X Song of Angels. Muska 1996.

VENUS AT TWILIGHT (Carl Boswell, R. 1991). Sdlg. 112-83-T. TB, 34" (86 cm), M. Blue violet, white star under violet beard. Nova at Midnight X Star Master. Adamgrove 1993.

VENUS BUTTERFLY (Barry Blyth, R. 1994). Sdlg. A63-6. TB, 38" (97 cm), ML. S. mulberry lilac infused light tan; F. mulberry lilac, mauve near beards, tannish hafts; beards white, tipped yellow in throat; pronounced sweet fragrance. Dance Man X Rembrandt Magic. Tempo Two 1994/95.

VENUS VORTEX (Heather Pryor, R. 1998). Sdlg. 50/93-A. LA, 45" (115 cm), M. Deep purple (RHS 77B), white spray pattern, rim and petal reverse; lime green signal radiating to white spray pattern; style arms pale lime green, white tips blushed purple; ruffled. Saturn Swirl X self. Iris Haven 1999/2000.

VERA-ANNE (Lawrence Ransom, R. 1995). Sdlg. 88/23-3. AB (RB), 18" (46 cm), EM. S. golden yellow, center cream yellow, wide grey white center on reverse; style arms greyed cream, crests yellow; F. wide golden yellow border, grey white in center, short lavender violet flash at tip of beard, red brown haft veining; beards lavender grey, tipped light orange in throat. Vera X -- Third Charm or Triplicate. Iris au Trescols 1996.

VERA-BEATRICE (Lawrence Ransom, R. 1995). Sdlg. 88/26-2. AB (RB), 16" (40 cm), EM. Medium blue violet, slightly darker diffused F. spot, red brown haft veining; beards light blue violet, tipped orange yellow in throat. Vera X -- Canary Isle or Hocus Pocus. Iris au Trescols 1996.

VERA HAYES (Kathy Millar, R. 1990). Sdlg. 87PC6A-17. CA, 14" (36 cm), E. S. pale lavender; F. pale lavender with dark purple veining, darker lavender halo around white signal, pale yellow centerline. Parentage unknown -- seed from Thompson & Morgan.

VERA-LOUISE (Lawrence Ransom, R. 1995). Sdlg. 88/26-1. AB (RB), 16" (40 cm), EM. S. golden yellow changing to light grey violet in center, midrib flushed darker violet; style arms light grey violet, yellow crests; F. golden yellow lower border, center light grey violet with wide darker violet centerline, red brown haft veining; beards grey blue to blue violet, tipped yellow in throat. Vera X -- Canary Isle or Hocus Pocus. Iris au Trescols 1996.

VERA-MARINA (Lawrence Ransom, R. 1997). Sdlg. 88/26-3. AB (RB), 17" (43 cm), ML. S. deep naples yellow changing to pale lavender center, reverse deeper; style arms lavender, crests yellow; F. old gold lower border, hafts veined darker, center light lavender purple with darker flash at tip of beards; beards lavender blue, hairs tipped mustard in throat. Vera X -- Canary Isle or Hocus Pocus. Iris au Trescols 1998.

VERA-OLIVIA (Lawrence Ransom, R. 1997). Sdlg. 88/23-2. AB (RB), 17" (43 cm), M. S. deep cadmium yellow, light lavender midrib flush darker and wider on reverse; style arms lavender, crests deep yellow; F. wide deep cadmium yellow border, rich maroon diffused spot and centerline, lavender blue flash; beards blue, hairs tipped orange brown in throat. Vera X -- Triplicate or Third Charm. Iris au Trescols 1998.

VERA-RUBY (Lawrence Ransom, R. 1995). Sdlg. 88/23-1. AB (RB), 17" (44 cm), EM. S. red brown changing to red violet in center, midrib flushed violet, wider violet flush on reverse; style arms red violet, brown violet crests; F. darker red brown border, red violet center, blackish red diffused spot and haft veining; beards light blue violet, hairs tipped bronze in throat. Vera X --Third Charm or Triplicate. Iris au Trescols 1996.

VERA'S LOVE (Stan Dexter by Marie Ingersoll, R. 1993). Sdlg. A19-6-129A. TB, 32" (81 cm), ML. Deep rose pink, center of F. lighter, rosy tan near deep pink beard. Freda Laura X Today's Fashion. Ingersoll's Iris 1994.

VERDE LUNA (Valeria Romoli, R. 1996). Sdlg. 2-F-90. TB, 31" (78 cm), EM. Tailored white, greenish overlay, F. with yellow green haft and shoulders; style arms white overlaid green, light yellow green crests; beards yellow green to greenish white, hairs tipped violet at end; pronounced sweet fragrance. 14A-87 X Evening Canticle.

VERHOOGA (Lawrence Ransom, R. 1997). Sdlg. 88/9-3. AR (RH), 21" (53 cm), ML. Mauve brown blend, edges browner, centers clearer mauve, with very fine overall veining; style arms lavender mauve, crests browner; beards tapered, light yellow, pale blue base; slight spicy sweet fragrance. *I. hoogiana alba* X Vera. Iris au Trescols 1998.

VERITY BLAMEY (R. E. Nichol by Jean Nichol, R. 1998). Sdlg. S 268-18. TB, 36" (91 cm), M. S. pale mallow purple (RHS 73D); style arms yellow; F. pale lilac, deep violet purple (77A) central blotch, white haft marking; beards pale gold; ruffled; slight fragrance. M 133-4: (Elizabeth Poldark x Loveday) X Kayleigh-Jane Louise. Kelways 1999.

VERKHNI IRTYSH (Leonard Venivitin, R. 1995). TB, 33" (85 cm), EM. White ground, blue edges; beards orange, tipped light blue; ruffled; sweet fragrance. Parentage unknown. Venivitin 1991.

VERMILION QUEEN (Richard Goula, R. 1992). Sdlg. G-87-G1. LA, 38" (97 cm), EM. S. pale cream; F. medium buttery gold, greenish gold signal; ruffled; slight spicy fragrance. Clara Goula X Gold Plaque. Gatewood Gardens 1993.

VERMILION SUNSET (Adolph Vogt, JI, R. 1989). Ensata Gardens 1992.

VERONA WIEKHORST (Frank Foster, R. 1999). Sdlg. 9218C. TB, 35" (89 cm), EM. S. cream buff, slight lavender infusion; style arms cream; F. reddish violet, faint lighter edge; beards orange yellow; lightly ruffled; slight sweet fragrance. Latin Hideaway X Best Bet.

#VERSICLE (H. R. Meyer, not. reg.) Marked as obsolete in 1949 Check List, no description or other data given. Name released.

VERSICLE (Marty Schafer/Jan Sacks, R. 1998). SPEC (*versicolor*), 15" (38 cm), M. S. clean white; style arms clean white, heart yellow; F. clean white veined pale blue, light yellow signal with pale blue veins; rounded, arched form. SP90-3-1: (Party Line x Little Rhyme) X Version. Joe Pye Weed 1998.

VERSIJACK (Jack Worel, R. 1999). SPEC (*versicolor*), 26" (66 cm), M. S. pinkish magenta rose; style arms slightly lighter; F. slightly darker magenta rose (RHS 64B), light yellow signal; foliage very stiff. Parentage unknown. Holly Lane 1999.

VERY CANARY (Ruth Goebel, SDB, R. 1989). Long 1993.

VERYL DWAYNE STONEKING (Ruth Goebel by Glenn Stoneking-Jones, R. 1998). Sdlg. CIR6-821-05-29-1993. TB, 30" (76 cm), EM. S. light blue; F. grape purple; beards dark blue, purple base, lighter at end; slight spicy fragrance. ("Acres Aglow" x Chinese Coral) X Dream Lover. Orin 1999.

VERY TRULY YOURS (Joseph Hoage, R. 1992). Sdlg. H82-10-2. TB, 34" (86 cm), ML. S. cream, flushed gold in center; style arms white, tipped gold; F. creamy white, white signal tipped gold, gold hafts and lacy edge, dark yellow reverse; beards dark yellow. Jeweled Starlight X Gold Trimmings. Long 1992.

VERY VARIED (Allan Ensminger, R. 1992). Sdlg. 86-59. BB, 24" (61 cm), M. Royal purple (HCC 834/3) streaked white; beards sulphur yellow (1/2); slight fragrance. Everything Plus X Batik. Varigay 1993.

VERY VICTORIAN (Robert Hollingworth, R. 1999). Sdlg. 90M3A3. SIB, 32" (81 cm), EM. Medium mauve, veined blue, F. with inconspicuous white signal veined blue; style arms light blue, edged mauve. 87Q4C13: (81C2C5: (Pink Haze x Wing on Wing) x 81A5C3: (7712: (Varner 067 x unknown) x Augury)) X 85G1B5: (Pas-de-Deux x Lavender Bounty). Windwood Gardens 1999.

VERY VIOLET (Bennett Jones, R. 1990). Sdlg. 399-1. SDB, 12" (30 cm), M. S. spectrum violet (HCC 735); F. lightly ruffled bright spectrum violet; beards pale blue; slight fragrance. Bedford Lilac X Pale Star. Bennett Jones 1991.

VESTALKA (Izidor Golob, R . 1996). Sdlg. 872-3. TB, 32" (80 cm), M. S. and style arms pink; F. orchid pink, veined darker pink; beards deep tangerine red; lightly ruffled; slight sweet fragrance. Vanity X (Mojca x Beverly Sills). Golob 1996.

VETER PUSTYNI (Nina Miroshnichenko, R. 1999). TB, 30" (75 cm), M. S. pale claret; style arms yellow; F. pale claret, brownish hafts, small lilac spot below yellow beard; slightly ruffled; pronounced spicy fragrance. Parentage unknown. Miroshnichenko 1993.

VIA DOMITIA (Jean Segui, R. 1998). TB, 32" (80 cm), L. S. white, light yellow in center; style arms white, edge and crests straw yellow (RHS 13C); F. lemon yellow (13B), edged white; beards darker lemon yellow (13A); pronounced fragrance. Sur Deux Notes X Gold Trimmings. Iris de Thau 1993.

VIBES (Barry Blyth, R. 1997). Sdlg. D21-8. SDB, 14" (36 cm), EML. Mushroom apricot, F. with deeper mushroom pink spot, rosy brown hafts; beards tangerine, end lavender blue; slight fragrance. Celsius X B34-2, Say Hello sib. Tempo Two 1997/98.

VIBRANT (Paul Black, R. 1999). Sdlg. C17A. TB, 34" (86 cm), EM. Ruffled bright yellow gold, F. with greenish tone around bright gold orange beard, inconspicuous whitish veins; slight spicy fragrance. Good Show X Goldkist. Mid-America 1999.

VIBRANT ROSE (Jean Witt, MTB, R. 1987). Kirkland Iris 1990.

VIBRATIONS (Mary Dunn, TB, R. 1989). Correction of parentage. B73-416: (M68-302: (Vaudeville x (Gracie Pfost x Melodrama)) x Gala Madrid) X Rancho Rose. M.A.D. Iris 1990.

VICKI ANN (Bee Warburton, SIB, R. 1989). Joe Pye Weed 1990.

VICTORIA CIRCLE (Frederick Kerr, R. 1994). Sdlg. 88-17-12. TB, 34" (86 cm), M. S. white; F. white, 1/2" sapphire blue edge, ivory near beard; beards white, tipped gold; slight sweet fragrance. Edith Wolford X Lullaby of Spring. Rainbow Acres 1994.

VICTORIAN CHARMER (Darlene Pinegar, R. 1994). Sdlg. V-1-1. BB, 26" (66 cm), EML. S. white with light pink midrib and veining; style arms white; F. creamy white overlaid light pink, veined medium pink; beards orange; lightly ruffled; slight sweet fragrance. Vanity X Marmalade Skies. Spanish Fork 1995.

VICTORIA PERFECT (Alphonse Van Mulders, R. 1990). Sdlg. 122-16/83. TB, 33" (84 cm), M. Ruffled deep royal blue purple. Ceremony Violet X Silver Point. Jardinart-Van Mulders 1989.

VICTORIA ROSE (John Durrance, R. 1992). Sdlg. D86-153. TB, 33" (84 cm), M. S. blush pink; F. white ground stitched plum violet, plum violet centerline; beards red. Capricious X Rancho Rose. Long 1992.

VIDTINKY NOCHI (Oleg Amekhin, R. 1996). Sdlg. SBS-1. SPEC-X (sib-tosa), 39" (100 cm), VE. Blue violet, white signal. *I. sibirica* X *I. setosa*. Amekhin 1996.

VIEL SCHNEE (Tomas Tamberg, R. 1990). Sdlg. SSTT177. SIB (tet.), 37" (95 cm), M. White. McEwen white tet. sdlg. X Tamberg white tet. sdlg. Schoeppinger 1988.

VIENNA WOODS (Joseph Ghio by Roris Gardens, R. 1993). Sdlg. 83-106-O4. TB, 36" (91 cm), M. Ruffled red brown, F. with yellow undertone in center; beards yellow. 80-122FF: ((Lady Friend sib x ((Malaysia x Carolina Honey) x 76-122Z: ((Hi Top x Travel On) x Peace Offering))) x (Lady Friend x (Act of Love x (Ballet in Orange x 76-122Z)))) X 81-130: (Praline x Lady Friend). Roris 1993.

#VIENTIANE (Bob Thomason, SDB, R. 1988). Stock destroyed; name released.

VIENTIANE (Bob Thomason, R. 1991). Sdlg. BT 8810A. SDB, 12" (30 cm), EM. Burnt gold, F. lighter with dark hafts and edge; beards orange, tipped blue; slight fragrance. Triplicate X Gingerbread Man. Okie Iris 1994.

VIGILANTE (Schreiner, R. 1990). Sdlg. W 872-A. TB, 36" (91 cm), ML. S. mustard yellow (RHS 163C); F. maroon black (187A); beards old gold. L 873-3, Peking Summer sib, X T 1576-B: (Gypsy Caravan x Cayenne Pepper). Schreiner 1991.

VIKTOR DRIAGIN (Irina Driagina, R. 1997). Sdlg. 115. TB, 49" (125 cm), E. White self, tinted light blue; beards orange yellow; pronounced sweet fragrance. Nezhnost X Christmas Time. Driagina 1977.

VIKTOR MIROSHNICHENKO (Nina Miroshnichenko, R. 1999). BB, 26" (65 cm), M. S. blue violet; style arms blue; F. blue violet, slightly lighter area near beard; beards blue, yellow at tip. Parentage unknown. Miroshnichenko 1993.

VILLAGE FLIRT (Barry Blyth, R. 1994). Sdlg. A44-12. SDB, 12-14" (30-36 cm), EML. Peachy salmon to light melon self; beards lavender blue; slight fragrance. V7-5, Gigolette sib, X Chanted. Tempo Two 1994/95.

VILLAGE GOSSIP (Barry Blyth, R. 1995). Sdlg. A161-1. TB, 34" (86 cm), EM. S. pastel mushroom champagne, flushed pink; F. red to rose burgundy, 1/4" edge matching S.; beards tangerine; ruffled, laced; pronounced spicy fragrance. Curacao X W126-A: (TL181-A: ((Tranquil Star x Coral Strand) x ((Latin Lover x Bayberry Candle) x ((Panoramic x Latin Lover) x Embassadora))) x T168-A, Behold a Lady sib). Tempo Two 1995/96.

VILLA MONTALVO (Joseph Ghio, R. 1991). Sdlg. PI-201P3. CA, 12" (30 cm), ML. S. apricot; F. apricot with wine rose overlay, violet signal. PK-321A: (((Banbury Candy x Simply Wild) x (Native State sib x Emigrant)) x (Elberta Peach sib x (Going West x Mission Santa Cruz))) X PK-331D3: (Cup of Tea x Wildman). Bay View 1992.

VILLANELLE (Bryce Williamson, R. 1995). Sdlg. B-11-2. TB, 33" (84 cm), ML. S. raspberry pink; F. lighter raspberry pink washed terracotta from hafts; beards coral red; heavily laced; slight musky fragrance. Love Poem X Mulled Wine. Stockton 1996.

VINACCIA (Stefano Gigli, R. 1998). Sdlg. 322/90. TB, 32" (80 cm), M. Violet self; beards orange; pronounced sweet fragrance. Parentage unknown.

VINHO VERDE (Cy Bartlett, R. 1994). Sdlg. C91-34. IB, 24" (61 cm), ML. S. lemon yellow; F. lemon yellow washed lime green; beards lemon, gold in throat; ruffled. Mrs. Nate Rudolph X Sunny and Warm. Sutton 1998.

VINH X. TRAN (Bob Thomason, R. 1991). Sdlg. BT 8629A. BB, 22" (56 cm), E. S. tan, lavender infusion; F. rose, tan edge, heavy rose haft veining; beards yellow; slight fragrance. Orchid Bouquet X (Oriental Blush x Rancho Rose). Okie Iris 1993.

VINNAYA YAGODA (Sergey Loktev, R. 1999). Sdlg. 94-R11-9D. TB, 32" (80 cm), EM. Red wine; style arms yellow, midrib and crests red wine; beards dirty yellow. Probably -- Siva Siva X Petite Posy. Loktev 1999.

VIN NOUVEAU (Richard Cayeux, R. 1995). Sdlg. 88127 A. TB, 33" (85 cm), ML. S. light mauve; F. velvety garnet; beards bright vermilion. Far Corners X 8512: (Marcel Turbat x (Flaming Light x Gold Galore)). Cayeux 1996.

VINO ROSSO (Augusto Bianco, R. 1999). Sdlg. 678. SDB, 10" (25 cm), ML. S. garnet ruby; style arms light ruby; F. garnet ruby; beards mustard; slight spicy fragrance. (Leprechaun's Gold x Chubby Cheeks) X Logo. Iride 1999.

VÍNOVÝ SEN (Josef Dudek, R. 1997). Sdlg. 91-ExRi-12. TB, 36" (90 cm), M. S. and style arms medium wine violet (RHS 77A); F. dark velvety wine (darker than 71A), narrow medium wine violet edge, veined white and wine around orange red beard; ruffled; pronounced spicy fragrance. Extravagant X Ringo. Seidl 1997.

VINTAGE PRESS (George Sutton, R. 1998). Sdlg. G-86-C. IB, 25" (64 cm), VE-EM & RE. Heavily ruffled apricot, S. with lavender shading on midrib, F. white around beard; beards apricot to orange, pale lavender at end; slight sweet fragrance. F-65: (Bubble Up x Sky Hooks) X Chanted. Sutton 1999.

VINTAGE ROSE (Bennett Jones, R. 1997). Sdlg. 494. SDB, 12" (31 cm), M. S. medium rose pink to dusty rose; F. lightly shaded rose pink, rose pink edge; beards pink and tangerine blend. 419-1: (Straw Hat x Orange Tiger sib) X 437-2: (Pink Prevue x Tillie). Aitken's Salmon Creek 1998.

VINTAGE VICTORIAN (Paul Black, R. 1997). Sdlg. 86178AA. TB, 33" (84 cm), L. S. dusty rose, blending to medium brown at margin; style arms dusty rose; F. violet rose and terracotta blend, hafts amber, edged rose brown; beards dark red orange; ruffled, laced; pronounced musky fragrance. Laced Daisy X Undersea Adventure. Mid-America 1997.

VINTNER (Marky Smith, R. 1994). Sdlg. 90-54A. TB, 35" (89 cm), ML. S. black garnet (darker, redder than RHS 79), shading to near-black edge, dark red violet midrib; F. same, blacker rim, dark brown shoulders, few pale orchid marks near beard; beards very dark violet (darker than 93); ruffled; slight spicy fragrance. Warrior King X 87-22A: (Back in Black x (Storm Center x Visual Arts)). Aitken's Salmon Creek 1996.

VIOLA MAGIC (Stan Dexter by Marie Ingersoll, R. 1994). Sdlg. A14-6-166A. TB, 36" (91 cm), ML. Viola orchid with silvery sheen; beards yellow to white, blue at end; tailored, wide form. Touch of Bronze X Sumas. Ingersoll's Iris 1995.

VIOLA MAY (Louise Smith, R. 1992). BB, 27" (69 cm), EM. Heavily ruffled yellow brown, F. with butterscotch stripes; beards gold; pronounced sweet fragrance. Parentage unknown.

VIOLET BLAZE (Jean Collins by Hec Collins, R. 1990). Sdlg. 84/S6. SIB, 30" (75 cm), ML. S. deep lavender with dark blue midrib; style arms deep lavender; F. violet with red infusion, center lighter, lined dark blue from hafts. Parentage unknown.

VIOLET BLUSH (John Marchant, R. 1990). Sdlg. 4587. CA, 12" (30 cm), ML. S. violet purple (HCC 733/3); F. red violet purple, deeper red violet and blue signal halo and veining. Sdlg. X sdlg. Portable Acres 1990.

VIOLET CORONATION (Bernard Hamner by Shepard Iris, R. 1992). Sdlg. 87-21. TB, 30" (76 cm), E. S. violet purple (RHS 82C); F. dark violet purple (82A), silver spray pattern radiating from beard; beards silver, yellow in throat; heavily ruffled. Bubbling Over X Blue Gloss. Hamner Iris, Shepard Iris 1992.

VIOLET CRESCENT (Connie Redgate by Hilmary Catton, R. 1992). SPEC (*unguicularis*), 15¾" (40 cm), E. S. very pale blue lavender; F. same with large white central area veined deep violet, dark violet crescent-shaped mark at end of bright gold signal. Parentage unknown; seed from Wisley, England. Roger Gillander 1995/96.

VIOLET DAWSON (O. D. Niswonger, R. 1993). Sdlg. 78-89. TB, 34" (86 cm), M. S. near-white to very pale yellow; F. pale yellow; beards light yellow. Echo de France X Tranquil Sunshine. Cape Iris 1993.

VIOLET EYES (A. & D. Willott, R. 1995). Sdlg. 93-36. IB, 21" (53 cm), EM. Full golden yellow self; beards deep violet; ruffled, lightly laced. Coral Wings X unknown. Willott 1995.

VIOLET GARTH (John Carter, R. 1991). SPEC (*laevigata*) (3 F.), 24" (61 cm), M. Deep violet. Parentage unknown. Rowden Gardens 1991.

VIOLET ICING (Cy Bartlett, R. 1993). Sdlg. BS.R.2. TB, 36" (91 cm), ML. S. white ground, violet plicata markings; F. white ground, slight violet markings mainly at haft; beards white, bluish in throat; ruffled. Blue Staccato X Raziza. V. H. Humphrey 1995.

VIOLET LACE (Akihiko Terada, R. 1997). Sdlg. S-121-89-1. TB, 35" (89 cm), M. White ground plicata, edges stitched blue; beards blue; slight sweet fragrance. Rare Treat X Centre Court. Roris 1997.

VIOLET LASHES (Carl Boswell, R. 1995). Sdlg. 165-85-S. SDB, 9" (23 cm), E. S. light cream, marginal red violet stitching; F. light cream, marginal red violet dotting and stitching, red violet eyelash pattern from yellow beard. Invasion in Pink X (Rare Edition x *I. balkana*). Adamgrove 1996.

VIOLET MINUET (Monique Dumas-Quesnel, R. 1992). Sdlg. 90-X-versata-05. SPEC-X, 40½" (105 cm), M. S. violet blue (RHS 90D); F. slightly darker violet blue (90C) with white lines at base, creamy yellow signal; slight sweet fragrance. VF-400, *versicolor* sdlg., X white *ensata* sdlg.

VIOLET MUSIC (Clarence Mahan, R. 1990). Sdlg. 85X9. TB, 40" (102 cm), VE-EM & RE. Ruffled uniform medium violet (RHS 86B), F. with white blaze; beards violet, tipped yellow; pronounced spicy fragrance. Violet Miracle X Victoria Falls. Iris Pond 1991.

VIOLET REPRISE (Walter Moores, R. 1993). Sdlg. 86-30-A. TB, 34" (86 cm), M & RE (Sept./MS). Slightly ruffled dark red violet, white spray pattern around beard; beards white, tipped pale yellow. Earl of Essex X Feed Back. Moores 1993.

VIOLET SHIMMER (Walter Moores, R. 1995). Sdlg. 88-28. TB, 34" (86 cm), M. S. and F. white ground plicata stippled blue violet; style arms blue violet; beards bronze, blue base; ruffled; slight sweet fragrance. Sterling Prince X Purple Pepper. Moores 1998.

VIOLET TIGER (Brad Kasperek, R. 1993). Sdlg. 89-54C. TB, 28" (71 cm), M. S. royal violet (RHS 83A), off-white (155C) ribs radiating outward; F. royal violet streaked off-white; beards medium blue violet, tipped orange. Dot and Dash X Painted Plic. Zebra 1994.

VIOLET TURNER (Larry Lauer, R. 1999). Sdlg. 91-158-1R. TB, 30" (76 cm), EM & RE. S. and style arms violet; F. velvety dark violet, light violet rim; beards mustard; ruffled; pronounced sweet fragrance. Sweet Reflection X Sweeter Than Wine. Lauer's Flowers 1999.

VIOLET WOOD (Carol Lankow, SDB, R. 1989). Kirkland Iris 1990.

VIPER (George Sutton, R. 1998). Sdlg. G-86-D. IB, 24" (61 cm), EM & RE. S. and style arms orient pink (RHS 36D); F. white, blushed french rose (49D); beards mars orange (31C), 1/2" pansy horn; lightly ruffled, edges serrate; slight sweet fragrance. F-65: (Bubble Up x Sky Hooks) X Chanted. Sutton 1999.

VIREVOLTE (Jean Cayeux, R. 1990). Sdlg. 8006 L. TB, 36" (91 cm), M. S. soft carnation pink; F. smooth mauve blue, center lighter; beards orange. Condottiere X Lunar Rainbow. Cayeux 1990.

VIRGA (Tom Burseen, R. 1995). Sdlg. 8-387A. TB, 36" (91 cm), M. S. and style arms white; F. white, purple violet (RHS 82C) wash concentrated on edges; beards light lemon; ruffled. Big Melt X Snowbrook. T.B.'s Place 1995.

VIRGINIA BAUER (Gerald Richardson, R. 1992). Sdlg. 85-12-1. TB, 34" (86 cm), EM. Ruffled and flared medium dark blue with violet toned royal blue cast; self beards; slight fragrance. Titan's Glory X 80-45-4: ((Bluebell Lane x (65-2-27 x Dress Suit)) x (Rockette x Blue Luster)). Rainbow's End 1993.

VIRGINIA LYLE (A. & D. Willott, R. 1994). Sdlg. 90-131. MTB, 24" (61 cm), M. Lightly ruffled medium violet blue; beards yellow orange. White Canary X Surprise Blue. Willott 1994.

VIRGINIA PINK (Donald Spoon, R. 1997). Sdlg. 91-254. TB, 31" (79 cm), M. Ruffled and laced orient pink (RHS 36B/C) self; beards orient pink, nasturtium red (30A/B) deep in throat; fluted, flared; slight sweet fragrance. Laced Artistry X Vision in Pink.

VIRGINIA PLAUCHE (Charles Arny, LA, R. 1989). Bois d'Arc 1991.

VIRGINIA RUDKIN (James McWhirter by Abram Feuerstein, R. 1997). Sdlg. J89-89-2. TB, 32" (81 cm), L-VL. S. yellow; F. amber orange, shoulders deeper; beards henna; slight sweet fragrance. Brandy X Enchanting. Stockton 1996.

VIRGINIA SMALL (Bob Thomason, IB, R. 1988). Okie Iris 1990.

VIRGINICA DE LUXE (Jennifer Hewitt, R. 1987). Re-registered as DARK AURA.

VIRUS IRIS (Tom Burseen, R. 1993). Sdlg. 8-40A. TB, 37" (94 cm), EM. S. peach (RHS 37C); F. creamy pink (29D), amber hafts; beards orange, bushy; heavily ruffled, flared; sweet fragrance. Lovely Glow X 5-262: (Dream Fantasy x Bay Rum). T.B.'s Place 1994.

VISIBLE DIFFERENCE (Bennett Jones, R. 1995). Sdlg. 505-5. SDB, 12" (31 cm), M. Fox red, F. with large mahogany spot; beards bright red orange. 434: (Painted Canary x 331-4: ((Wright L32 x 255: (Melon Honey x (Roberts 65-R-11 x 229))) x (Solar Flight x 255))) X 439-7: (Orange Dazzler x (Orange Tiger x 331-4)).

VISION OF SPRING (Robert Annand, R. 1999). Sdlg. 88-91C. TB, 34" (88 cm), EM. S. yellow, lavender midrib; style arms yellow, lavender blue midrib; F. lavender blue, 3/8" yellow gold edge, yellowish hafts; beards orange to yellow; ruffled. Edith Wolford X 82-8A: (Brown Lasso x Chartreuse Ruffles). Stockton 1999.

VISITOR'S CHOICE (Sharon McAllister, R. 1996). Sdlg. 88-1-3. AB (OGB), 28" (71 cm), M. S. pallid pinkish ivory, yellow midrib and faint veining; style arms soft yellow; F. soft yellow ground heavily veined, dotted and washed rust, brown stippling on yellow around beard, small brown signal; beards mustard brown. Red Earth X Whirlwind Romance. McAllister 1996.

VISOKOSNOYE LETO (Sergey Loktev, R. 1999). Sdlg. 94-R14-A10. IB, 24" (62 cm), M. S. white to pale lemon ground, pale lilac violet specks; style arms yellow, midrib pale violet; F. lemon, bright lilac violet specks on hafts and edge, narrow bright lilac centerline; beards dirty yellow, pale lilac base. Parentage unknown.

VISTA DOME (Stan Dexter by Marie Ingersoll, R. 1994). Sdlg. A39-6-168-B. TB, 38" (97 cm), ML. S. yellow cream, base darker; F. rose purple, silver tan edge, center near-white, heavily lined; beards brown, gilded yellow gold. American Beauty X 1981-46: (Leda's Lover x Condottiere). Ingersoll's Iris 1995.

VITALI (V. & N. Gordodelovy, R. 1995). Sdlg. 7. TB, 35" (90 cm), ML. S. golden yellow, base dotted light brown; F. golden yellow, white central spot; beards light yellow, yellow in throat, with small light yellow horn. Parentage unknown. Gordodelovy 1978.

VIVACIOUS VI (Sharon McAllister, R. 1993). Sdlg. 89-1-8. AB (OGB-), 30" (75 cm), M. S. pinkish white; F. reddish violet, rust on white veins over inner half; beards yellow gold. Sostenique X Tribe of Judah. McAllister 1993.

VIVA KUBA (Nina Miroshnichenko, R. 1996). TB, 43" (110 cm), ML. S. red, tinted brown; style arms yellow, tinted bronze; F. dark red brown; beards yellow; slight spicy fragrance. Parentage unknown. Miroshnichenko 1990.

VIVA MARIA (Jean Peyrard, R. 1998). Sdlg. PC 85/1. CA, 12-16" (30-40 cm), M. White, veined purple; style arms light purple. Candy Banner X unknown.

VIVA MEXICO (William Maryott, R. 1995). Sdlg. S240A. TB, 36-37" (91-94 cm), M. Heavily ruffled medium bright orange (RHS 28C); beards orange, large and bushy. Radiant Energy X Peach Bisque. Maryott 1996.

VIVA NOVA (Barry Blyth, R. 1999). Sdlg. E58-1. IB, 20-22" (51-56 cm), M. S. golden yellow; F. rich egg yolk yellow; beards orange yellow; slight fragrance. Moustache X Yes. Tempo Two 1999/2000.

VIVE LA DIFFERENCE (Mary Dunn, LA, R. 1989). Bay View 1990.

VIVE LA FRANCE (Jean Cayeux, R. 1993). Sdlg. 84109 E. TB, 36" (91 cm), ML. S. white; F. bright medium blue edge with large white center; beards red. (Condottiere x Delphi) X (Alizes x (Condottiere x Lunar Rainbow)). Cayeux 1994.

VIVID IMAGINATION (Sharon McAllister, R. 1996). Sdlg. 91-29-2. AB (OGB-), 30" (76 cm), M. S. ivory center blending to soft pinkish ivory (RHS 56D) edge, few greyed red (181D) basal dots, very fine mulberry veins at edge; style arms yellowed ivory, mulberry midrib flush; F. white ground, mulberry (186B) plicata-like markings, lilac veins flanking beard, spectrum violet (82B) linear signal; beards layered white and yellow. Boaz X Asha Michelle.

VIZIER (Joseph Ghio, R. 1997). Sdlg. 93-120-N2. TB, 36" (91 cm), EM. Deep raspberrry to cranberry garnet self; beards red. Reality X Star Quality. Bay View 1998.

VKUS MINDALIA (Sergey Loktev, R. 1999). Sdlg. 94-1-9B. SDB, 11" (29 cm), VE-EML. S. grey olive, base and midrib bordeaux; style arms olive lilac; F. grey olive, narrow greenish rim, large bordeaux brown spot, white haft marking; beards yellow. Bold Violet X unknown. Loktev 1999.

VLADIMIR VYSOTSKI (Viktor Sheviakov, R. 1995). Sdlg. 6A 3. TB, 32" (80 cm), M. S. and F. cream white ground, with yellow brown, reddish wine and purple violet dotting; beards yellow brown. Violet Harmony X Radiant Apogee. Sheviakov 1993.

VLAMINCK (Monique Dumas-Quesnel, R. 1992). Sdlg. 90-Mag-Extra-01. SPEC (*versicolor*), 27½" (70 cm), E. S. deep violet blue (RHS 90A) veined darker; F. velvety deep red purple (deeper than 71A); signal yellow, large white center area, veined. Krieghoff X self.

VODEVIL (Adolf Volfovich-Moler, R. 1999). Sdlg. V-158. TB, 32" (80 cm), EM. S. light cardinal red; style arms same, light orange edge and crests; F. scarlet red edged orange, cream brown pattern on hafts and around bright yellow beard; ruffled, lightly laced; pronounced sweet fragrance. Pink Sleigh X Marsianin.

VODOLEY (Sergey Loktev, R. 1998). Sdlg. 94-1-10K. SDB, 14" (35 cm), ML. S. violet; style arms rose, midrib and crest violet; F. violet, darker hafts and near beard; beards yellow, whitish blue at end. Bold Violet X unknown. Loktev 1998.

VODOPAD (Viacheslav Gavrilin, R. 1999). Sdlg. 92-213-1. TB, 36" (91 cm), M. S. light blue, striped lighter and darker; style arms light blue; F. blue violet striped light blue, hafts dark brown, narrow light blue rim; beards mustard yellow, light blue at end. Fiesta Time X Pledge Allegiance.

VOIE LACTEE (Franz Kurzmann by Jean Peyrard, R. 1990). Sdlg. EN85/1. MDB, 5" (12 cm), E. S. creamy white; F. white; beards yellow. Parentage unknown. Iris au Trescols 1992.

VOKALIZ (Viktor Koroliov, R. 1999). Sdlg. S95-96K. TB, 37" (93 cm), ML. Ruffled light lilac self; beards tangerine red; slight spicy fragrance. Champagne Music X Frost and Flame. Koroliov 1999.

VOLATILE (Jim & Vicki Craig, R. 1996). Sdlg. C37Z19. TB, 32" (81 cm), M. S. light blue, base slightly deeper; style arms medium blue; F. light blue, medium blue haft markings extending to end of pale blue beard; ruffled; slight sweet fragrance. Bold Crystal X C103X1: ((53L: (Odyssey x (Stepping Out x Deborah Suzanne)) x 51S1: ((Odyssey x (Shipshape x ((Rimfire x Cedarcrest) x (Lovely Letty x Pinwheel)))) x Patina)) x 51S1). J. & V. Craig 1996.

VOLCANIC WILDFIRE (Heather Pryor, R. 1994) Sdlg. 60/90-1. LA, 30" (76 cm), EM. Yellow (RHS 13B) base with brown red veining and wash, F. with additional thin yellow edge and red brown line signal surrounded by yellow area; style arms yellow; lightly ruffled. Gladiator's Gift X Desert Jewel.

VOL'S DELIGHT (Dora & Volma Cattanach, R. 1991). Sdlg. DVC 80-3. TB, 30" (76 cm), ML. S. blue black; F. velvety blue black; beards violet. Matinata X Basic Black.

VOLSHEBNY KASATIK (V. & N. Gordodelovy, R. 1995). Sdlg. 45. TB, 32" (80 cm), E. S. lilac, tinted pink, brown at base; F. pink, light lilac rim, brown haft striations; beards red, end pinkish white with small white horn; ruffled. Parentage unknown. Gordodelovy 1984.

VOLTAGE (Virginia Messick, R. 1992). Sdlg. M87-69. TB, 36" (91 cm), M. Ruffled orange self; beards red orange; slight fragrance. Black Hills Gold X Edna's Wish. Messick 1993.

VOLTS (Barry Blyth, R. 1993). Sdlg. Z24-3. SDB, 14" (36 cm), VE-EM. Light pastel muted pink, F. with very slight lavender flush; beards tangerine, tipped lavender; slight fragrance. X20-2: (Camarilla x Yipee) X Chanted. Tempo Two 1993/94.

VOLUPTUOUS (Cleo Palmer, IB, R. 1989). Palmer's Iris 1990.

VOLUTE (Jean Cayeux by Richard Cayeux, R. 1995). Sdlg. 88190 A. TB, 33" (85 cm), M. S. pale beige, flushed gold; F. bright lilac; beards orange vermilion, long. 86225: ((7915: (Casino Queen x (Pink Taffeta x Schiaparelli)) x (7706 A, Alizes sib, x Love Bandit)) x Adventuress) X 86167 A: (((7706 A x Love Bandit) x (Condottiere x Delphi)) x ((Condottiere x Delphi) x (Condottiere x Metropolitan))). Cayeux 1996.

VOODOO BEAT (Barry Blyth, R. 1998). Sdlg. F118-1. IB, 25" (63 cm), EM. S. and style arms muted lemon yellow; F. yellow, overall light tan brown overlay deepening toward beard; beards lavender, hairs tipped bronze gold; slight sweet fragrance. Silk Degrees X Celsius. Tempo Two 1998/99.

VOODOO QUEEN (Henry Rowlan, R. 1992). Sdlg. 91-LA-20. LA, 36" (91 cm), EML. Ruffled dark violet purple (RHS 77A), yellow line signal; slight spicy fragrance. Graceland X Mentida. Comanche Acres 1993.

*VOODOO RITE (Henry Rowlan, LA, R. 1989). Comanche Acres 1990.

VOODOO SPELL (Barry Blyth, R. 1995). Sdlg. A107-2. TB, 34" (86 cm), EM. S. cream, flushed mushroom, slightly deeper cream edge; F. mushroom coffee, deepening toward haft; beards pale lavender, heavily tipped bronze; ruffled; slight sweet fragrance. Imprimis X Electrique. Tempo Two 1995/96.

VOSMOYE MARTA (Nina Miroshnichenko, R. 1996). TB, 41" (105 cm), M. Ruffled pink self; beards red, pink at end; slight sweet fragrance. Parentage unknown. Miroshnichenko 1976.

VOSTOCHNY ORNAMENT (Adolf Volfovich-Moler, R. 1995). Sdlg. V-30. TB, 32" (80 cm), M. S. light orange; F. light crimson, edged pale orange; beards yellow; ruffled, laced. Rippling Waters X Pipes of Pan. Volfovich-Moler 1992.

VOT ETO DA (Sergey Loktev, R. 1998). Sdlg. 94-R14-84. BB, 26" (66 cm), M. S. claret violet; style arms yellow, claret midrib and crests; F. deep purple to black in center, hafts cream, small white area below beard; beards orange tangerine, whitish violet at end. Parentage unknown; seed from Ron Busch. Loktev 1998.

VOYAGE (Barry Blyth, R. 1993). Sdlg. A44-7. SDB, 12-14" (31-36 cm), VE-EM. S. smoky pink; F. white, 1/4" smoky pink stitched edge; beards white, tipped tangerine; slight fragrance. (Cupid's Cup x Yipee sib) X Chanted. Tempo Two 1993/94.

VOYAGER ONE (George Slade, TB, R. 1989). Wyle Wynde 1990.

VOZDUSHNY ZMEY (Sergey Loktev, R. 1999). Sdlg. 94-R11-4B. TB, 32" (82 cm), EML. S. lilac, base marked brown; style arms yellow, lilac midrib and crests; F. lilac, dark lilac marking below yellow beard, hafts marked brown, slight brown rim. Master Touch X Fiodor Shaliapin. Loktev 1999.

VSIO DLIA TEBIA (V. & N. Gordodelovy, R. 1995). Sdlg. 145. TB, 35" (90 cm), VL. Orange, tinted pink; beards bright red. Parentage unknown. Gordodelovy 1985.

WACKO (Paul Black, R. 1995). Sdlg. 91235A. SDB, 10" (25 cm), M. S. yellow ground, heavy plum brown plicata markings 3/4 way to center, brown midrib line; style arms yellow gold; F. yellow, plum brown plicata hafts and narrow band; beards old gold, end lavender; slight musky fragrance. Toasty X 89255B: ((((Buckwheat Honey x Sundance Kid) x sib) x (Pulse Rate x Mister Roberts)) x ((Oriental Blush x Sniffs 'n' Sneezes) x Pet)). Mid-America 1995.

WADATSUMI (Shuichi Hirao by Society for Japanese Irises, R. 1993). JI (6 F.), 36" (90 cm), EM. Red violet (RHS 82A) with white halo radiating soft white veining which quickly merges into ground color, signal yellow with green center; style arms pale cream tipped red violet; extra petal sometimes present. Parentage unknown. Hirao 1969.

WAFFLE TALK (Richard Ernst, R. 1994). Sdlg. JF169-3. TB, 34" (86 cm), M. S. pale lavender orchid, midrib infused tan; style arms lavender orchid, highlighted yellow; F. pale orchid (RHS 85D), dusty rose (34D) rim; beards butter yellow; lightly ruffled; slight sweet fragrance. From sdlgs. inv. Afternoon Delight. Cooley 1995.

WA HO HO (Jim Harper, R. 1991). Sdlg. A-7. MDB, 3½" (9 cm), VE. Lemon yellow, F. with brown signal patch; beards whitish. Parentage unknown; seed from SIGNA. Harper's Gardens 1990.

WAHUPA WA (L. J. Duffy, R. 1992). Sdlg. WI-31-80. SPEC (*setosa*), 30-36" (76-91 cm), E. White, some yellow at base of F.; style arms and buds white. Selection of *I. setosa interior* collected 1980, near Fairbanks, Alaska.

WAIHI WEDDING (Heather Pryor, R. 1999). Sdlg. 59/91-8. LA, 45" (114 cm), ML. White, lime green line signal on all petals; style arms lime green at base, white reflexed tips; pronounced fragrance. Dural White Butterfly X Sea Lord. Iris Haven 1999/2000.

WAITING FOR GEORGE (Barry Blyth, R. 1997). Sdlg. D41-1. TB, 36" (92 cm), M. S. white, rosy pink allover flush; F. cream white lightening toward center, 1/4" rosy pink plicata edge deeper at hafts; beards burnt tangerine; slight fragrance. Lemon Silence X K. Turner KH91-3-1: (Bama Berry x Holiday Lover). Tempo Two 1997/98.

WAKE UP CALL (Paul Black, TB, R. 1989). Mid-America 1990.

WAKE-UP DIANNE (Ken Mohr, R. 1993). Sdlg. Q-3-A. TB, 35" (89 cm), VE-EM. Ruffled yellow gold; self beards; slight fragrance. Catalyst X Speculator. Pacific Coast Hybridizers 1994.

WAKE WATER (Tom Burseen, R. 1995). Sdlg. 0-40A. TB, 35" (89 cm), EM. S. white, blue influence at midrib; style arms white, washed blue; F. light blue washed violet blue (RHS 95C), lighter edge, darker centerline; beards mustard; ruffled; spicy fragrance. Bluid X 8-463: (((Curtain Call x Galen) x (Porta Villa x Risque) x ((Holiday Spain x Porta Villa) x Mandolin)). T.B.'s Place 1996.

WALDMEISTER-BOWLE (Lothar Denkewitz, R. 1995). Sdlg. N-85-bic 1. SDB, 13½" (35 cm), L. S. smoky blue, yellow glint; style arms cream; F. golden ochre brown; beards clear blue, tips golden yellow; pronounced spicy fragrance. ((Adrienne Taylor x Snow Elf) x (Blueberry Muffins x (Toskanerprinz x Scot Cream))) X Irish Lilt. Von Zeppelin 1997.

WALKARA (Hyram Ames, R. 1996). Sdlg. A8710. TB, 30" (76 cm), M. Red black self; style arms red black, midrib bronze; beards maroon, hairs tipped bronze; ruffled, laced; slight spicy fragrance. Marauder X Queen of Spades. Zebra 1996.

WALKER ROSS (Walker Ross by Chuck Chapman, R. 1996). Sdlg. SW-W13. AB (OGB-), 30" (76 cm), EM. Cool white, dark violet blue veining from center to edge; style arms light violet; beards wide, bronze with dark blue base giving black effect. Spinning Wheel X W13 arilbred. Chapman Iris 1998.

WALLACE LINBAL BALLARD (Bob Thomason, R. 1992). Sdlg. BT 8902C. TB, 30" (76 cm), EM. Golden tan, F. with heavy plum haft veining, plum area around bright orange beard; slight musky fragrance. Autumn Leaves X Mysterious.

WALL FLOWER (Chet Tompkins, R. 1993). Sdlg. 84-83E. TB, 38" (97 cm), ML-VL. Blended heliotrope and grey, highlighted iridescent pink, orchid and pale blue; beards amber pink. Inv. sdlgs. Fleur de Lis 1993.

WALL'S GLORY (Jim Hedgecock, R. 1991). Sdlg. C-83-13-3. TB, 32" (81 cm), M. Ruffled wine red, large violet overlay below bright golden yellow beard. Hilow X Lady Friend. Comanche Acres 1992.

WALL STREET (John C. Taylor, R. 1997). Sdlg. SL 24-1. LA, 32" (80 cm), E. Ruffled purple violet, edged white; signals yellow, variable in S.; style arms lemon. OL 113-2: (Koorawatha x Dazzling Star) X OL 138-1: (Dazzling Star x Watch Out). Rainbow Ridge 1997/98.

WALL STREET BLUES (J. T. Aitken, R. 1995). Sdlg. 89 S-1. SIB (tet.), 36" (91 cm), M. Medium blue, minimal lighter signal area. Harpswell Happiness X Dear Dianne. Aitken's Salmon Creek 1995.

WALSTERWAY (Ralph & Fran Walster, R. 1990). Sdlg. 8-1986C. TB, 40" (102 cm), ML. Warm rosy amber, deep violet signal below bright tangerine beard. Klondike Kate X Gallant Moment. Walsterway Iris 1991.

WALT LUIHN (Leo Barnard, R. 1995). Sdlg. 87-44B. IB, 20" (51 cm), E. S. and style arms satiny black red, midrib darker; F. velvety black red, hafts veined mahogany; beards blue, bushy; lightly ruffled; slight sweet fragrance. Little Buccaneer X Adamsblack. Paradise Iris 1995.

WALTZ (Barry Blyth, R. 1993). Sdlg. Z23-2. SDB, 12" (31 cm), ML. Pastel smoky creamy pink; beards lavender; slight fragrance. (Oladi x Kandi Moon) X Chanted. Tempo Two 1993/94.

WANDA WOOD (Chet Tompkins, R. 1992). Sdlg. 86-196. TB, 38" (97 cm), ML-VL. Fluted, heavily ruffled light baby ribbon pink; beards deep pink. ((Pretty Please x Ovation) x (Quinella x Bonbon)) X ((Pink Taffeta x Cameo Coral) x (Royal Gold x Ovation)). Fleur de Lis 1992.

WANDERER (Barry Blyth, R. 1991). Sdlg. X25-9. SDB, 11-12" (28-30 cm), EM. S. champagne cream beige; F. light cocoa coffee cream, flared; beards vibrant lavender, tangerine in throat. (Oladi x Fifi) X (Peach Eyes x Kandi Moon). Tempo Two 1991/92.

WANDO (Allan Ensminger, R. 1992). Sdlg. 286-68. BB, 25" (64 cm), M. White ground, striped veronica blue (HCC 639); beards blue-tipped; slight fragrance. Go Around X 81-44: ((Doodle Strudel x (69-50: ((Valimar x (Patience x Apricot Luster)) x Peachy Creamy) x Royal Belle)) x (Dream Lover x (64-33: ((Champagne Velvet x Lake Tahoe) x Dutch Doll) x Rococo))). Varigay 1997.

WANGANUI GEM (Jean Stevens by Bay of Plenty Iris Group, R. 1999). MDB, 6-8" (15-20 cm), M & RE. S. dark mauve; F. purple; beards white, tipped yellow; slight fragrance; summer bloom taller, branched. Purple *chamaeiris* X Madonna. In commerce in New Zealand since ca. 1930 as "The Gem".

WANIKIYA (L. J. Duffy, R. 1992). Sdlg. WI-29-79. SPEC (*setosa*), 24-36" (61-91 cm), E. Pale lavender blue fading to near-white, sometimes veined or streaked blue and sometimes overtoned blue; style arms white; buds pale blue. Selection of *I. setosa interior* collected 1979, near Fairbanks, Alaska.

WANNABEE (Sharon McAllister, R. 1996). Sdlg. 88-5-1. AB (OGB-), 28" (71 cm), E. S. pallid blue violet (near RHS 97D); style arms yellowed ivory, crests greenish buff; F. pale greenish ivory, rust violet stippling and fine veining on inner half, heavily stippled signal; beards soft greyed yellow. Mohric Art X Heavenly Sunlight. McAllister 1996.

WANNA GOLD (Colin Fidock, R. 1999). Sdlg. F98-2. AB (OGB), 18" (46 cm), E. S. pale icy lemon; style arms golden yellow; F. gold, lightly shot raspberry, with diffuse dark raspberry signal; beards yellow, hairs tipped burgundy. Study in Amethyst X Edith Seligmann.

WANTED (Duane Meek, R. 1997). Sdlg. 91-7-0. TB, 35" (89 cm), ML. Lightly ruffled old rose flushed mauve, S. deeper in midrib, F. lightening with age; beards coral, end ivory. Spring Tidings X Glory Be. D & J Gardens 1997.

WARABE-UTA (Toyokazu Ichie by Currier McEwen, R. 1996). Sdlg. 8A-123. JI (3 F.), 36" (90 cm), EM. S. white, edged violet purple (RHS 77A); style arms white with light pinkish purple tufts; F. white center blending to violet purple at outer 3/4", signal rich aureolin yellow (12A); small flower type. HO-6, inv. small flowered sdlgs., X NAGA #14, from sdlg. at Nagai Ayame Park. Introduced in Japan prior to 1996.

WAR CHANT (Connell Marsh, TB, R. 1984). C. Marsh 1990.

WAR CHIEF (Schreiner, R. 1992). Sdlg. T 1503-A. TB, 37" (94 cm), EM. Red self (RHS 185A); beards yellow. Minisa X M 1005-A: (Sultan's Palace x Gallant Moment). Schreiner 1992.

WAR DRUMS (Sharon McAllister, R. 1996). Sdlg. 90-59-10. AB (OGB), 28" (71 cm), M. S. smoky grey touched violet, few faint yellow veins; style arms flame yellow, reddish violet brushing on midrib and veins on crests; F. deep reddish black; beards near black, red cast in sun. Deborah's Song X Turkish Tangent. McAllister 1996.

WARLEGGAN (R. E. Nichol, R. 1990). Sdlg. G39-2. TB, 37" (94 cm), M. S. pale blue, slight bleeding of F. color at midrib; F. blue violet (RHS 89C), beards matching; ruffled, flared. Song of Norway X Congratulations. V. H. Humphrey 1995.

WAR MARCH (Calvin Helsley, R. 1990). Sdlg. 86-4. SIB, 30" (76 cm), EM. S. deep red violet; F. slightly lighter deep red violet, lighter under gold and white signal; ruffled. Kismet X Thespian. Helsley 1999.

WARM BREEZE (Duane Meek, R. 1997). Sdlg. 902-1-1. TB, 36" (91 cm), ML. Lightly ruffled greenish gold, flushed brown to tan, F. with darker tan hafts, remainder lightening with age; beards bronze to brown. Envy X Green Prophecy. D & J Gardens 1997.

WARM MEMORIES (Ron Mullin, R. 1995). Sdlg. 84-133W. TB, 34" (86 cm), M. Rosy lavender orchid, F. with orchid blaze flushed rose; beards tangerine, tipped white. Simple Pleasures X Starcrest. M.A.D. Iris 1995.

WARM MY HEART (Duane Meek, R. 1992). Sdlg. 186-6-9. TB, 34" (86 cm), ML. S. soft lemon ground stitched brown; F. ivory, soft lemon down sides, narrow brown plicata border widening toward hafts; beards ivory, tipped nutmeg; heavily ruffled, fluted; slight fragrance. Patina X 11-1-5: ((Radiant Apogee x (Erika x Citrus Mist)) x Roundup). D & J Gardens 1992.

WARM PUPPY (Walter Moores, R. 1997). Sdlg. 91-10-B. IB, 18" (46 cm), E & RE. Lightly ruffled salmon pink self; beards salmon pink, end white; pronounced sweet fragrance. My Sheba X Pink Reprise. Moores 1999.

WARM TOUCH (Barry Blyth, R. 1997). Sdlg. D64-1. TB, 36-40" (91-102 cm), EM. S. grey champagne at top, flushed lavender, wide tan area radiating from midrib; F. light violet, tan hafts, tan violet 1/4" margin; beards white, heavily tipped tangerine. Plume d'Or X A153-5, Cafe Risque sib. Tempo Two 1997/98.

WARM WISHES (William Maryott, R. 1998). Sdlg. W183B. TB, 35" (89 cm), M. Medium yellow, F. with lighter center area; style arms yellow; beards yellow, bushy, large; slight sweet fragrance. Sunny Bubbles X S131A: (Honey Crunch x Juan Valdez). Maryott 1999.

WARP DRIVE (Donald Spoon, R. 1997). Sdlg. 93-68B. BB, 26" (66 cm), ML. S. and style arms purple; F. purple, lighter area across hafts; beards red, base white; ruffled, flared. Skyblaze X Stars and Stripes.

WARP SPEED (Chet Tompkins, R. 1998). Sdlg. 93-29A. TB, 36" (91 cm), EML-VL. S. blended copper buff, smoky brass and pale rose; style arms buff; F. wine red infused coppery plum and rose slate; beards white, flushed pale blue. (((Apollodorus x Smart Alec) x (Hot Pinata x Soaring Spirit)) x (Camelot Rose x Revival Meeting)) X (Megabucks x Supreme Sultan). Fleur de Lis 1998.

WARRIOR CHIEF (Sharon McAllister, R. 1990). Sdlg. 82-25-1. AB, (OGB+), 28" (72 cm), EM. Iridescent pansy purple (near RHS 77A), deep purple black signal; beards deep yellow, tipped white. Persian Pansy X Heart Stealer. Aril Society 1990.

WATCH FOR IT (John C. Taylor, R. 1995). Sdlg. RL 33-4. LA, 35" (89 cm), EM. S. veined violet (RHS 85D); style arms violet (85A); F. violet, darker (85A) around yellow signal, rim lighter. Watch Out X Margaret Lee. Rainbow Ridge 1995/96.

WATCHMAN (G. F. Wilson, R. 1991). Sdlg. 31-89OTW-B. AB (OGB), 33½" (85 cm), E. S. violet rose, lightly veined bright purple; F. deep rose, fine maroon lines and light dotting around large circular maroon black signal; beards pale cream, tipped purple; fragrant. Onlooker X Tornado Warning. Pleasure Iris 1993.

WATER BALLET (Joseph Ghio, R. 1992). Sdlg. 88-6T. TB, 36" (91 cm), ML. Azure blue self; beards cream. 86-14J: (Sea of Joy x 82-124-Z2, Inaugural Ball sib) X Altruist. Bay View 1993.

WATERDRAGON (Marky Smith, R. 1997.) Sdlg. 90-45D. TB, 38" (97 cm), M. S. bluebird blue (RHS 94B); style arms bluebird blue, sides grey blue; F. darker violet blue (93B); beards blue, hairs tipped grey to yellow, gold in throat; heavily ruffled; pronounced sweet fragrance. Swirling Seas X 88-31A: (85-12A: (Storm Center x Sapphire Hills) x Breakers). Aitken's Salmon Creek 1998.

WATERLOOSAEULE (Harald Moos, R. 1993). Sdlg. 86/6009A. TB, 32½" (80 cm), M. Ruffled light salmon pink; beards orange red. Muchas Gracias X Exhilaration. Schoeppinger 1993.

WATERS OF MIRABA (Bernice Miller, R. 1991). Sdlg. WOM 91. BB, 26" (66 cm), EM & RE (July-Nov./AL). S. light blue with slight lavender influence, veined darker blue; F. light blue, veined and evenly striped darker blue, small white spot at throat; beards pale blue; lightly ruffled; pronounced sweet fragrance. (True and Faithful x Sea Double) X sib. Garden of the Enchanted Rainbow 1991.

WATERWORLD (Larry Lauer, R. 1995). Sdlg. L89-134-7. TB, 37" (94 cm), M. S. white; style arms white, blue base; F. and beards lavender blue. Strictly Ballroom X Alaskan Seas. Stockton 1996.

WAUKEE PRIDE (Arthur Blodgett, R. 1993). Sdlg. 88-66. TB, 36" (91 cm), M. Ruffled campanula violet (HCC 37/1). F. center lighter, light tan below light yellow beards. (Fuchsia Frills x sib) X Glory Bound. Blodgett Iris 1994.

WAVECROFT GOLD (June Towe, R. 1990). Sdlg. J.T.5. BB, 24-27" (60-67 cm), EML. Tailored golden yellow; beards orange. Parentage unknown.

WAVELENGTH (A. & D. Willott, R. 1993). Sdlg. 89-50. SDB, 11" (28 cm), M. Lightly ruffled light violet self; beards violet. Vegas Showgirl X Raspberry Whip. Willott 1993.

WAVERLY DEBUT (John Wood, R. 1992). Sdlg. W-115-85. SIB, 26" (66 cm), EM. Red purple (RHS 72A) self; style arms lighter (72B). Eric the Red X Polly Dodge. John Wood 1993.

WAVES OF GRAIN (Monty Byers by Phyllis Dickey, R. 1994). Sdlg. F51-102. TB, 36" (91 cm), M & RE. S. medium golden yellow; F. golden yellow, darker golden yellow haft veining; beards deep golden yellow. Grace Thomas X C-71-1. Misty Hill 1994.

WAWONA (Jean Witt, R. 1995). Sdlg. 92-09-P4. MTB, 23" (58 cm), M. Medium rust orange brown; style arms yellow; beards orange; lightly ruffled. 84-01-45 rust: (Spanish Coins x unknown) X 70-06-GR 'red': ((Pluie d'Or x Golden Light) x ("Ruby Roundfall" x *I. reginae*)).

WAY OUT WEST (Hooker Nichols, TB, R. 1988). Hillcrest 1990.

WAYSIDE LYRIC (Schreiner, R. 1990). Sdlg. T 779-A. TB, 37" (94 cm), EM. S. cream (RHS 23D) with rosy veins; F. red (60A), cream rim; beards yellow. Timeless Moment X Bristo Magic. Park Seed Co. 1990.

WAYSIDE'S APRICOT DELITE (Schreiner, R. 1997). Sdlg. AA 1541-1. TB, 36" (91 cm), ML.

S. apricot (RHS 24D); F. magenta rose (186D); beards tangerine. Sweet Musette X Frances Gaulter. Wayside Gardens 1997.

WAYSIDE'S ELEGANCE (Schreiner, R. 1992). Sdlg. W 665-A. TB, 37" (94 cm), EM. Apricot pongee (RHS 22B); beards apricot, tipped yellow. S 635-1: (Skyfire x M 629-A) X S 676-1: (M 797-2: ((Son of Star x G 1070-B) x Sandberry) x Mandolin). Park Seed Co. 1992.

WAYSIDE'S JOY (Schreiner, R. 1993). Sdlg. T 427-A. TB, 33" (84 cm), M. Velvety red black (RHS 202A) self; beards yellow. Superstition X unknown. Park Seed Co. 1993.

WEBER POINT (James McWhirter by Abram Feuerstein, R. 1997). Sdlg. J89-126-1. TB, 33" (84 cm), M. Heavily ruffled medium blue self, whitish area below blue beard; pronounced sweet fragrance. Denney 81-5-1: ((Regents' Row sib x Winterscape) x Midnight Love Affair) X J87-77-2: (Winterscape x Larry Gaulter). Stockton 1997.

WEBMASTER (Keith Keppel, R. 1996). Sdlg. 92-11D. SDB, 12" (31 cm), M. S. port wine (lighter than M&P 56-J-12), slight citron yellow (10-J-2) center blending; style arms port wine and citron yellow; F. glossy port wine veining and marginal suffusion on dark lemon gold (darker, brighter than 9-L-2) ground; beards buckthorn brown (13-L-8); ruffled; slight fragrance. Firestorm X Quote. Keppel 1997.

WEDDED BLISS (Dana Borglum, R. 1992). SPU, 42" (107 cm), M. S. creamy white; F. bright yellow with irregular 1/4" creamy white edge, lightly ruffled. Parentage unknown; seed from SIGNA. Borglum's Iris 1995.

WEDDING DANCE (Schreiner, R. 1999). Sdlg. CC 948-2. TB, 36" (91 cm), EM. S. and style arms yellow (RHS 7A); F. white center, yellow band; beards yellow. Starlight Express X Coral Sunset. Schreiner 1999.

WEE BONNIE LASSIE (Bonnie Haney by Jim Hedgecock, R. 1995). Sdlg. 86-3A. SDB, 12" (31 cm), M & RE. S. white; F. light yellow; beards white; lightly ruffled; slight sweet fragrance. 83-2: (81-2: ((Summer Whitewings x Autumn Snowdrift) x Cascade Pass) x Marmalade Skies) X Marmalade Skies. Comanche Acres 1996.

WEE CAPERS (Floyd Dyer, R. 1990). Sdlg. D-9-82-D. MDB, 5½" (14 cm), M. Dark red violet; beards yellow; slight spicy fragrance. Joy Bringer X D-1-77-D, unknown. Four Cedars 1990.

WEE CHARMER (Floyd Dyer, R. 1990). Sdlg. D-91-87-D. MDB, 4½" (11 cm), M. Red violet, darker area around pale blue beards. I. aphylla X I. aphylla. Four Cedars 1990.

WEE DANDY (Floyd Dyer, R. 1991). Sdlg. D-51-87-D. MDB, 4½" (11 cm), M. S. light blue; F. light blue violet, red violet spot; beards yellow, tipped blue violet; slight musky fragrance. D-20-81-D: (Bloodspot x Gingerbread Man) X D-1-77-D, unknown. Four Cedars 1991.

WEE GHOST (A. & D. Willott, R. 1995). Sdlg. 91-61. MDB, 5" (13 cm), EM. S. white; F. blue white, green brown spots; beards white. Pittance X 79-13: (Greenlee GX-2: ((White Mite x self) x (I. pumila alba x Hanselmayer)) x Buttons). Willott 1995.

WEE LADY (Floyd Dyer, R. 1991). Sdlg. D-26-87-D. MDB, 6" (15 cm), M. Blue violet, F. with reddish center; beards yellow, tipped light blue; slight sweet fragrance. Sib to Wee Dandy. Four Cedars 1991.

WEE LASSIE (Roberta Shoop, R. 1990). Sdlg. 85-54. IB, 16" (41 cm), M. S. light bronzy cream; F. lavender with purple spot; beards yellow orange; ruffled; slight fragrance. 83-11: (Broadway x Dancin') X Peccadillo. Shoop 1990.

WEE MAGIC (Floyd Dyer, R. 1990). Sdlg. D-1-76-D. MDB, 5½" (14 cm), M. S. blue blending to violet at base; F. blue violet, dark violet haft markings and area at end of beard; beards yellow, tipped white. D-103-71-D: (Heart's Content x Wilma V) X self. Four Cedars 1990.

WEE ME (Ben Hager, R. 1999). Sdlg. AMD5182TyBrtPk. MDB, 4½"-6½" (11-16 cm), ML. Bright pink; style arms pink; beards bright red flame. AMD4971Y2: (AMD4468: ((((Shrinking Violet x Timmie Too) x Dinky) x (unknown x ((((Norah x Thisbe) x (Frenchi x Pagoda)) x sib) x Tulare))) x Ceremony) x Tiny Cherub) X SD4913Pk: (((3393: (2885Y: (Blonde Doll x (Pink Amber x Pink Cushion)) x ((Pink Amber x Pink Cushion) x Buttercup Charm)) x ((2563-0: (Pink Cushion x Roberts 65R28) x (Frosty Lemonade x Pink Cushion)) x Pet sib)) x SD4024PkPc: ((3393 x Pet sib) x (((2563-0 x (Pink Amber x Pink Cushion)) x 2885) x 3393))) x (Gigglepot x SD4024PkPc)). Adamgrove 1999.

WEE NOBLE (A. & D. Willott, R. 1996). Sdlg. 91-76. MDB, 5" (13 cm), ML. S. and style arms full purple; F. deep purple, deeper flush around light violet beard. Dark Vader X What Not. Willott 1996.

WEEROONA (Kevin Nilsen, R. 1996). Sdlg. 9-90-1. TB, 37½" (95 cm), VE-E. S. white ground, light blue edge, light purple dotting; style arms white, tinged violet; F. white, deeper violet purple stitching; beards white, yellow in throat. Asha Michelle X Elsedina.

WEE WINE SHADES (Floyd Dyer, R. 1995). Sdlg. D-2-93-M. MDB, 4½" (11 cm), M. S. light red violet; F. paler, violet veins around beard; beards yellow, end light blue. Van Nes *I. pumila* sdlg. X Cretica. Dyer's Garden 1995.

WELCOME ABOARD (Ben Hager, TB, R. 1988). Roris 1990.

WELCOME FRIEND (Lin Flanagan, R. 1997). Sdlg. 89026-1. AB (OGB-), 32" (81 cm), E. S. pale violet; style arms light violet; F. light yellow, irregular light violet marks; beards yellow; slight fragrance. Close Contact X New Moon. Aril Society 1998.

WELCOME HOME (Kevin Nilsen, R. 1992). Sdlg. 1-88-1. TB, 36" (91 cm), EM & RE. S. brown, wine red blush up center; style arms yellow, wine red and brown markings, crests fringed; F. light yellow ground stitched wine red on edge, peppered toward center; beards yellow; ruffled. Auric X Ken Ware. Iridescence 1992/93.

WELCOME INTRUDER (Tony Huber, R. 1998). Sdlg. 94-006 (90 Dom 090). SPEC-X, 37" (95 cm), EM. S. violet (83B); style arms violet (83B/C); F. violet (83A/B/C), yellow signal nearly hidden by style crest. 90-Dom F/3 090: (Nouvel Age x Belle Promesse) X Dom F/3 43: (Belle Promesse x self).

WELCOME STRANGER (Polly Black, R. 1992). Sdlg. SR2-4R. TB, 36" (91 cm), M. S. delicate pinkish orange; F. white ground stitched red violet, deeper veins; beards deep orange. Summer Silk X purple plicata sdlg. Polly Black 1992.

WELDER'S FLAME (O. D. Niswonger, R. 1995). Sdlg. SDB 22-92. SDB, 12" (31 cm), M. S. and style arms light blue; F. light blue, soft yellow at hafts; beards deep blue. Chubby Cheeks X unknown. Cape Iris 1996.

WELDON GIBBS (Monty Byers, TB, R. 1989). Moonshine 1990.

WELFENBRAUT (Marlene Ahlburg, R. 1992). SIB, 31½" (80 cm), M. S. cream; F. light yellow; ruffled, waved. Welfenprinz X Welfenschatz. Ahlburg 1994.

WELFENGOLD (Marlene Ahlburg, R. 1992). SIB, 31½" (80 cm), M. S. pale yellow; F. full yellow; ruffled, flared. Welfenprinz X Welfenschatz. British Iris Society 1999.

WELFENHERZOG (Marlene Ahlburg, R. 1992). SIB, 31½" (80 cm), M. S. white; F. yellow (RHS 9A/B). Welfenprinz X Welfenschatz. Ahlburg 1994.

WELFENPRINZ (Marlene Ahlburg, R. 1990). SIB, 27½" (70 cm), M. S. cream white; F. yellow. (McEwen sdlg. x Butter and Sugar) X ((Dreaming Yellow x Cambridge) x McEwen 69/70/7). Ahlburg 1991.

WELFENPRINZESSIN (Marlene Ahlburg, R. 1990). SIB (dip.), 29½" (75 cm), M. S. white; F. yellow (RHS 2B to 2D). (Welfe x McEwen 69/70/7) X McEwen sdlg. Ahlburg 1991.

WELFENSCHATZ (Marlene Ahlburg, R. 1990). SIB (dip), 21½" (55 cm), M. S. cream white; F. yellow (RHS 5B to 2B). (Welfe x McEwen 69/70/7) X McEwen sdlg. Mid-America 1996.

WELL DRESSED (John C. Taylor, R. 1991). Sdlg. OL 105-2. LA, 39" (100 cm), M. Mauve (RHS 84C), signal yellow. Cammeray X L89: (Secret Spell x Helen Naish). Rainbow Ridge 1992/93.

WELLS FARGO (Connell Marsh, BB, R. 1989). C. Marsh 1990.

WELL SUITED (Paul Black, R. 1990). Sdlg. 86370A. SDB, 12" (30 cm), M. S. medium purple; F. velvety black purple, narrow iridescent purple band; beards white, tipped purple; pronounced spicy fragrance. 83185A: ((Cindy Mitchell x Velvet Pride) x (Marie's Delight x P. Dyer C-5)) X 83179A: ((Clay's Caper x Crimson Velvet) x Nancy Alane). Mid-America 1990.

WEMBURY FRANCES (Marion M. Wood, R. 1998). Sdlg. 4/2/94. SPEC-X (cal-sib, tet.), 31½" (80 cm), L. S. and style arms violet purple (RHS 83C); F. deeper (83B), gold signal veined purple. S 8/2/90 purple: (induced tet. cal-sibs (WI x WII) from purple 40 chr. siberian x mixed CA pollen) X Tamberg blue tet. cal-sib.

WEMBURY SOPHIE (Marion M. Wood, R. 1998). Sdlg. 11/1/94. SPEC-X (cal-sib, tet.), 31½" (80 cm), L. S. and style arms buff, flushed and veined pale rose purple (RHS 75B); F. purple (77) edged paler, gold signal edged white, purple veins. S 3/1/90, from induced purple tet. cal-sibs, X Timpcals.

WENCH (Lynda Miller, R. 1991). Sdlg. 14188A. TB, 34" (86 cm), EM. S. pink; F. plum red violet, pink pencil edge, pink lines around tangerine beard. Colortart X Ringo. Miller's Manor 1993.

#WENGFU (Bob Thomason, SDB, R. 1988). Stock destroyed; name released.

WENGFU (Bob Thomason, R. 1991). Sdlg. BT 8736A. SDB, 10" (25 cm), EM. S. pale blue, deeper blue base infusion; F. blue white, brown haft markings; beards orange, tipped white; slight fragrance. Sapphire Gem X (Golly Molly x Angel Baby). Okie Iris 1993.

WENONAH MANNING (Labriano Anaya/Julian Wells by Santa Fe Iris Society, R. 1996). TB, 38" (97 cm), M. Vivid hot orange pink, F. with subtle red striping; beards red; ruffled; slight spicy fragrance. Almost Provocative X Crowd Pleaser. Iris Ranch 1992.

WENSLEYDALE (B.L.C. Dodsorth, TB, R. 1985) British Iris Society 1987.

WERCKMEISTER'S BEAUTY (Peter Werckmeister by Sharon McAllister, R. 1992). Sdlg. 1916-1. AR (RC), 20" (51 cm), EM. S. lavender grey, finely veined medium violet; F. lavender grey, intensely veined and dotted medium violet and washed violet, deep violet signal; beards orange yellow. "Bronze Beauty" X (Teucros x *I. susiana*). Aril Society 1992.

WES SILVA (Frederick Kerr, R. 1997). Sdlg. 910301B. TB, 42" (107 cm), ML. Heavily ruffled dark navy blue, F. with blue-veined white area beside and below beard; beards gold, white at end, wide; pronounced spicy fragrance. Rainbow Etude X Star Master. Rainbow Acres 1997.

WESTCLIFFE BEAUTY (Jerry Hall, R. 1999). Sdlg. 95-13-A. TB, 40" (102 cm), ML. Blue lavender to mauve self; F. with yellow gold haft marking; beards yellow, white at end; ruffled, laced; pronounced sweet fragrance. Honky Tonk Blues X Mystic's Muse.

WESTERLIES (Joseph Ghio, R. 1991). Sdlg. PI-180D2. CA, 14" (36 cm), EM. S. white; F. white, blue line pattern overall, small yellow signal. Ventana X Idylwild. Bay View 1992.

WESTERNAIRE (David Miller, R. 1998). Sdlg. 93-16C. TB, 34" (86 cm), M. S. and style arms empire yellow (RHS 11A); F. yellow ground, white spot at tip of yellow beard, wide red purple plicata band with 1/8" chocolate brown outer band; slight musky fragrance. Colorscape X 85-1B: (Roundup x Crinoline). Long 1999.

WESTERN BLUEBIRD (John Weiler, R. 1990). Sdlg. CAW-1. CA, 18" (46 cm), EM. Medium blue, slight lavender influence, turquoise flush through F. center. Roving Eye X Claremont Bluebird. Rialto 1991.

WESTERN CARNIVAL (Akihiko Terada, R. 1997). Sdlg. 50-1. TB, 34" (86 cm), M. S. yellow; F. dark maroon; beards yellow; slight spicy fragrance. Brown Lasso X Fanfaron. Roris 1997.

WESTERN CIRCLES (A. & D. Willott, R. 1993). Sdlg. 92-27. MDB, 6" (17 cm), EM. Medium yellow, brown spot covering 1/3 of F.; beards white, orange in throat. Daisy Fresh X Buzz Bee. Willott 1993.

WESTERN LEGEND (Akihiko Terada, R. 1995). Sdlg. 65-1. TB, 36" (91 cm), M. Ochre yellow, light greenish tint, F. white in center; beards blue, yellow base; ruffled. Treasured Love X Storm Center. Roris 1997.

WESTERN SAGE (Cleo Palmer, R. 1992). Sdlg. 9046. IB, 22" (56 cm), E. S. light lavender, base darker; F. light lavender, rimmed lavender pink, red violet haft veining; beards red; pronounced sweet fragrance. Starfrost Pink X Pink Jubilee. Palmer's Iris 1992.

WESTLAND ROSE (William Simon by Elizabeth Simon, R. 1995). Sdlg. 51-66-75. TB, 36" (91 cm), M. Violet rose, center of F. lighter; beards bright tangerine; ruffled, lightly laced. Parentage unknown. Stahly 1996.

WEST VALE (John D. Taylor by Carilla Taylor, R. 1992). Sdlg. D13/8. IB, 19" (48 cm), M. S. very pale purple, flushed and veined deeper, fading to white at center; F. cream, edged very pale purple; beards cream, tipped yellow, end paler. Westwell X Socialite. V. H. Humphrey 1997.

WET SILK (George Sutton, R. 1997). Sdlg. E-217 AR. TB, 31" (79 cm), ML. Ruffled and laced campanula violet (RHS 82C) self; beards burnt orange; slight sweet fragrance. Lace Artistry X Faraway Places. Sutton 1998.

WEYMOUTH BLUE (Norman Bennett, R. 1997). Sdlg. S215. SPEC (*laevigata*), 18" (46 cm), M. S. and F. (3) vivid violet blue (RHS 94A), small white center stripe; style arms solid violet blue. Parentage unknown. In commerce since 1985 as *I. laevigata* "Weymouth". Bennetts Water Garden 1985.

WEYMOUTH ELEGANT (Norman Bennett, R. 1997). Sdlg, S185. SPEC (*laevigata*), 18" (46 cm), M. S. white, some slight violet blue marking in central area; style arms white, violet blue center; F. white ground, deep violet blue (RHS 83B) markings on approximately half of petal, haft and central area unmarked. Parentage unknown. In commerce since 1985 as *I. laevigata* "Elegant". Bennetts Water Garden 1985.

WEYMOUTH MIDNIGHT (Norman Bennett by Clive Russell, R. 1996). SPEC (*laevigata*), 18" (46 cm), M. S. and F. midnight blue with white central blaze, all six petals hanging. Parentage unknown. In commerce since 1985 as *I. laevigata* "Midnight". Bennetts Water Garden 1985.

WEYMOUTH PURITY (Norman Bennett, R. 1997). Sdlg. S188. SPEC (*I. laevigata*), 18" (46 cm), M. S. and F. (3, large) pure white; style arms pure white. Parentage unknown. In commerce since 1986 as *I. laevigata* "Purity". Bennetts Water Garden 1986.

WEYMOUTH SURPRISE (Norman Bennett, R. 1997). Sdlg. S193. SPEC (*laevigata*), 18" (46 cm), M. F. (6) white ground, light violet blue mottling more pronounced toward edge; style arms white, light violet blue central stripe. Parentage unknown. In commerce since 1986 as *I. laevigata* "Surprise". Bennetts Water Garden 1986.

WHARFEDALE (B.L.C. Dodsworth, TB, R. 1989). British Iris Society 1990.

WHAT AGAIN (Allan Ensminger, R. 1990). Sdlg. 85-13. SDB, 10" (25 cm), ML & RE. S. wistaria blue (RHS 64D); F. straw yellow; beards wistaria blue. People Pleaser X 183-4: ((Tantara x Jungle Shadows) x (*I. pumila* x (Miss Region Twenty-One x Tumwater))). Rialto, Varigay 1991.

WHAT A MIXTURE (Graeme Grosvenor, R. 1999). Sdlg. V38-A. TB, 28" (71 cm), ML. S. white, irregularly splashed blue; F. blue, irregularly splashed white; beards blue white, small and tufted; flat flower form, broken color pattern. Patterns X Mixture. Rainbow Ridge 1999/2000.

WHATCOM CHIEF (Stan Dexter by Marie Ingersoll, R. 1990). Sdlg. 1983/141. TB, 38" (97 cm), M. Golden red brown, F. with blue red flash, yellow hash marks; beards yellow. 1980/97: (Distant Light x Mabel Helland) X Hombre. Ingersoll's Iris 1991.

WHAT MAGIC (Barry Blyth, R. 1993). Sdlg. X83-A. TB, 36" (91 cm), ML. S. light bright butterscotch; F. red brown, slight bluish white area around mustard beard. Shine on Wine X (Edge of Winter x London Lord). Tempo Two 1993/94.

WHAT'S WHAT (Joseph Ghio, R. 1991). Sdlg. PI-MIX-Z4. CA, 14" (36 cm), ML. Silvery mauve pink, signal deep mauve. Parentage unknown. Bay View 1992.

WHATTA DREAM (Tom Burseen, R. 1997). Sdlg. 93-341Y. TB, 36" (91 cm), EM. Heavily ruffled, laced mimosa yellow (RHS 8A), F. slightly lighter below yellow (7A) beard; style arms lemon yellow (7C); slight sweet fragrance. 9-395: (Sterling Stitch x (Trousseau Lace x Wings of Dreams)) X Easter Lace. T.B.'s Place 1998.

WHEEL AND DEAL (Austin Morgan, R. 1990). TB, 36" (91 cm), EM. S. pink, base yellow; F. red, narrow yellow rim, full length yellow glint line; beards yellow. Parentage unknown. Iris Test Garden 1990.

WHEELER DEALER (Chet Tompkins, R. 1992). Sdlg. 80-12B. TB, 40" (102 cm), ML-VL. S. ivory white ground, raspberry red border; F. ivory white, solid raspberry red border; beards violet. 74-80: ((Tinsel Town x Summer Sandman) x ((Jet Fire x Siva Siva) x High Life)) X 74-11: ((On the Go x Summer Sandman sib) x (Pleasure Cruise x Darktown Strutter)). Fleur de Lis 1992.

WHEN YOU WISH (Phyllis Dickey, R. 1998). Sdlg. 92LM1-1. TB, 31" (79 cm), M. Medium baby pink, F. with white wash; beards red orange, ending in large baby pink frilled flounce. Mesmerizer X unknown. Misty Hill 1998.

WHERE EAGLES DARE (Calvin Helsley, R. 1993). Sdlg. 89-3. SIB, 41" (104 cm), M. S. and style arms dark blue violet (RHS 89C); F. dark violet blue (89B) veined darker (89A), white signal turning gold in throat and veined dark violet blue (89A), large white spot on reverse. Mabel Coday X S. Varner S060: (Marlya x Steve). Helsley 1995.

WHERE THERE'S SMOKE (Tom Burseen, R. 1990). Sdlg. 6-287M. TB, 36" (91 cm), L. Ruffled smoky light violet (RHS 85D); beards bright golden orange; spicy fragrance. Formosa Spring X 4-54A: (Satin Glass x Glory Bound). T.B.'s Place 1991.

WHIMSICAL ARTIST (Terrell Taylor, R. 1997). Sdlg. 94-6. TB, 34" (86 cm), EM. S. yellow ochre (RHS 161A); F. white ground washed violet (83B), pansy violet (83A) edge; beards yellow; sweet fragrance. Theatre X Colortrak. Bonita Gardens 1997.

WHIN HILL (Revie Harvey, R. 1990). Sdlg. 83/HGC/11. TB, 38" (96 cm), M. Bright golden yellow, F. with finely etched light tan ray marks around deeper gold beard; slight fragrance. Spiced Honey X Gingerbread Castle. Catton 1991.

WHIP LASH (Chet Tompkins, R. 1990). Sdlg. 83-91A. TB, 38" (97 cm), ML. S. chrome yellow infused coppery flame; F. bright brass blended buccaneer brown and chrysanthemum brown with harvard red undertone; beards bronze. (Copper Capers x (Pretty Please x Gypsy Prince)) X ((Tanya x Milestone) x (Gypsy Lullaby x Milestone)). Fleur de Lis 1990.

WHIPPED HONEY (Mitch Jameson, R. 1995). Sdlg. 1-90-A. TB, 36" (91 cm), M. S. and style arms golden honey; F. pastel lavender orchid, edged golden honey; beards golden honey; heavily laced. Step Nicely X Easter Lace. Knee-Deep in June 1996.

WHIPPERSNAPPER (Virginia Del Judge by Peter DeSantis, R. 1997). Sdlg. 79-1R. TB, 40" (102 cm), EM. S. wistaria blue (RHS 91A), dark violet centerline; style arms wistaria blue; F. white ground, velvety plum purple (79C) markings, brown at haft; beards yellow, tipped purple; slight fragrance. Skylab X Going My Way.

WHIPSTITCH (Jim Hedgecock, R. 1991). Sdlg. 83-20-10. TB, 37" (94 cm), M. Ruffled white ground plicata, wide blue violet stitched band; style arms purple; beards blue violet, hairs tipped yellow in throat; slight sweet fragrance. Going My Way X Hey Looky. Comanche Acres 1992.

WHIRLING THUNDER (Sharon McAllister, R. 1990). Sdlg. 84-5-13. AB (OGB), 29½" (75 cm), EM. S. smoky violet (greyer than RHS 84A or 85A); F. smoky purple (darker than 186B), ruby red (59A to 60A) signal; beards mustard. Gethsemane X Ora J. Seale. McAllister 1992.

WHIRLWIND ROMANCE (Sharon McAllister, R. 1990). Sdlg. 82-26-2. AB (OGB+), 28" (72 cm), EM. S. pewter (between RHS 197D and 202D); style arms brass; F. brass, yellow orange (near 20A/B) ground washed grey orange, burnt orange (173A) signal; beards mustard, tipped rust. Persian Pansy X Arab Dusk. McAllister 1991.

WHIRLWIND TOUR (Sharon McAllister, R. 1993). Sdlg. 88-7-4. AB (OGB), 28" (72 cm), M. S. white, veined golden yellow; F. metallic gold, rust veins covering inner half, dime-size rust spot surrounding tip of mustard and rust beards. My Joy X Whirlwind Romance. McAllister 1993.

WHISKY (A. J. Farrington, MDB, R. 1986). British Iris Society 1987.

WHISPERED PROMISE (Heather Pryor, R. 1994). Sdlg. 40/90-6. LA, 30" (76 cm), EM. Apricot pink (RHS 173D), center flushed apricot, F. with yellow orange steeple signal; style arms apricot pink, midrib yellow; slightly reflexed, ruffled. Alluvial Gold X Gladiator's Gift. Iris Haven 1996/97.

WHISPERING (Melba Hamblen, TB, R. 1988). Roris 1990.

WHISPERING WATERS (Jim Hedgecock, R. 1999). Sdlg. A-32-7. TB, 36" (91 cm), M. S. pale blue white; F. medium blue, white wash halfway down from beard; beards pale blue, gold in throat; ruffled; pronounced sweet fragrance. 83-25: (Space Dragon x Tuxedo) X Sophistication.

WHISTLE TWICE (Lucille Pinkston, R. 1996). Sdlg. 90-1-A. TB, 39" (99 cm), ML. Lightly ruffled medium pink, F. with lighter haft area, darker pink haft markings; beards dark pink, tipped lighter pink; sweet fragrance. Parentage unknown. Sand Hollow 1997.

WHISTLING DIXIE (Mary Dunn, R. 1994). Sdlg. L122-4. LA, 38" (97 cm), M. Velvety red plum purple, small yellow signal; ruffled. L78-1: ((Blue Shield x Black Widow) x Full Eclipse) X Clara Goula. Bay View 1995.

WHITE BLEACH (Tony Huber, R. 1998). Sdlg. 91-616 (sel. 95-82). SPEC-X (versata), 28" (70 cm), EM. White, shaded lilac; style arms white with yellowish border. *I. versicolor* white 616: (white #12 x 89-402) X *I. ensata* 6 F. white sdlg.

WHITE BUFFALO (Jim Hedgecock, R. 1995). Sdlg. 84-85-7. TB, 34" (86 cm), M. S. pale blue white; F. blue white; beards white, yellow deep in throat; ruffled, laced. Emmanuel X Lacy Snowflake. Comanche Acres 1996.

WHITE CHINA (Chun Fan, R. 1994). Sdlg. F90-36. TB, 34-36" (86-91 cm), EM. Ruffled crystal white self; beards yellow, tipped white; slight sweet fragrance. F86-G-43: (Victoria Falls x Song of Norway) X Knots Landing. Fan's Iris 1999.

WHITE CHOCOLATE (Sharon McAllister, R. 1992). Sdlg. 86-1-2. AB (OGB), 28" (72 cm), EM. Creamy white, F. with fine dark chocolate brown dots surrounding dark chocolate beard. Promises to Keep X Seligmann EQ-TS: (Esther the Queen x Tuesday Song). McAllister 1993.

WHITE CLASSIC (J. R. Allen, R. 1992). Sdlg. P10A. TB, 32" (81 cm), M. White self; beards yellow; slight fragrance. Bosky Dell X Wedding Vow. Allen Iris 1997.

WHITE CROW (Ladislav Muska, R. 1999). Sdlg. PPMW-01. TB, 39" (99 cm), M. Ruffled and laced white; beards white, light yellow in throat; sweet fragrance. ((Perinbaba x (Laced Cotton x Monte Albano)) x White Window) X Perinbaba. Muska 1998.

WHITE DREAM (Harald Moos, R. 1991). Sdlg. 82/123B. TB, 33" (85 cm), M. Frilled pure white; beards red orange. Silver Shower X Lilac Treat. Schoeppinger 1992.

WHITE HAT HERO (Chet Tompkins, R. 1995). Sdlg. 91-116. TB, 38" (97 cm), ML. S. and style arms smoky lime with ochraceous flush; F. deep plum wine heavily undertoned orange; beards brownish orange. ((Candle Power x New Revue) x (Candle Power x Tulip Festival)) X (Comanche Drums x Wedding Candles). Fleur de Lis 1995.

WHITE HEAT (Keith Keppel, R. 1992). Sdlg. 85-57A. TB, 33" (84 cm), ML. White (M&P 43-A-1) with inconspicuous touch of empire yellow (9-K-3) on hafts; beards mandarin red (2-F-12); slight sweet fragrance. 80-13A: (Old Flame x (72-3C, Marmalade sib, x Bride's Halo)) X 82-89B: (Orangerie x Precious Moments). D & J Gardens 1993.

WHITE OLINDA (O. D. Niswonger, R. 1994). Sdlg. Sp 7 B. SPU, 42" (107 cm), M. Lightly ruffled white, yellow signal. Sp 1-80: (Blue Lassie x unknown) X Ila Crawford. Cape Iris 1995.

WHITEONE (Heather Collins, R. 1993). Sdlg. 2/1/87. CA, 19" (48 cm), M. S. clear white, deep yellow midrib; F. clear white, gold ray pattern edged grey surrounding deep yellow signal; edges fluted. Parentage unknown.

WHITE PANDA (James Waddick, R. 1994). SPEC (*japonica*), 24-36" (60-91 cm), E. S. white; F. white with faint yellow and lilac dots and lines near pale yellow signal. Selection of *I. japonica* var. *pallescens* collected in Woolong Valley, Sichuan, China in 1989.

WHITE PRELUDE (Currier McEwen, R. 1993). Sdlg. T(7)83/9. SIB (tet.), 36" (90 cm), VE-EML-VL & RE. S. white; F. creamy white with fine yellow veins extending from yellow (RHS 12B) signal to edge; ruffled and crimped. Again X (T(2)75/4(8): (Welcome Return x Soft Blue tet. sib) x T(5)75/90(8): inv. Fourfold White, Lavender Light, McGarvey pink sdlg.). Eartheart, Seaways 1993.

WHITE SHIMMER (B. Charles Jenkins, R. 1990). Sdlg. A20-11B. SPU, 35-49" (89-124 cm), E. Lacy white, yellow signal. Ila Crawford X Dawn Candle. Shepard Iris 1991.

WHITE SILENCE (Ladislav Muska, R. 1999). Sdlg. MOWC-02. TB, 38" (97 cm), M. Laced chalk white; beards tangerine, white at end; slight fragrance. ((Monte Albano x Laced Cotton) x (Christmas Time x White Window)) X Perinbaba. Muska 1998.

WHITE SNOW (Cloyd McCord, R. 1992). Sdlg. 76-10. TB, 34" (86 cm), M. Ruffled and laced white self; beards red; sweet fragrance. Startler X 76-13: (Beauty Crown x Homecoming Queen). McCord 1992.

WHITE STALLION (Polly Black, R. 1990). Sdlg. RDS25PF. TB, 36" (91 cm), M. White, F. with slight green area around white-tipped beard; lightly ruffled; slight fragrance. Parentage unknown. Pleasure Iris 1991.

WHITE TAIL (Ken Durio, R. 1992). Sdlg. LL #3. LA, 36" (91 cm), M. S. clean white, slight lavender cast, green signal; F. white, slight lavender cast, yellow green veining, large full yellow signal; heavily ruffled; pronounced spicy fragrance. Alibi X Clara Goula. Louisiana Nursery 1997.

WHITE UMBRELLA (John C. Taylor, R. 1990). Sdlg. OL 118-1. LA, 51" (130 cm), ML. Lightly ruffled white (RHS 155D), yellow green veining intensifying at center. L89-1: (Secret Spell x Helen Naish) X Dural White Butterfly. Rainbow Ridge 1990/91.

WHITEWASH (Heather Collins, R. 1994). Sdlg. 81-3. CA, 17" (44 cm), M. S. white, midrib orange; F. white, orange midrib and grey veining, white signal; petal edges serrate (S.) or frilled (F.), style arms fluted. Parentage unknown.

WHITE WEDDING (Akihiko Terada, R. 1996). Sdlg. 144-3. TB, 36" (91 cm), M. White self, pale blue influence; beards white. Tinted Crystal X Bubbling Over. Roris 1996.

WHITE WINDOW (Ladislav Muska, R. 1996). Sdlg. BNSJ-07. TB, 39" (99 cm), ML. S. light gold; F. white, gold band; beards orange, end white; heavily laced; pronounced fragrance. (("Bila Neha": (Lavender Petticoat x Silver Shower) x San Jose) x Monte Albano) X Cream With Gold. Muska 1996.

WHITE WINE (Jim & Vicki Craig, R. 1998). Sdlg. AH18C20. MTB, 21" (53 cm), M. Pale lavender blue, F. with shoulders smoothly marked bronzy green on near-white; beards pale yellow, shaded pale purple at end; pronounced sweet fragrance. 45X5: ((1R20: ((Light Fantastic x *I. aphylla* "Van Nes") x (Starchild x (Sacred Mountain x *I. aphylla* "Werckmeister"))) x 11R24, Reformation sib) x 11R24 X 72Z7: (34V11: (Abridged Version x ((Sacred Mountain x *I. aphylla* "Werckmeister") x Puppy Love)) x 20T29: (((En Route x Pink Taffeta) x (New Moon x (Sacred Mountain x *I. aphylla* "Werckmeister"))) x Puppy Love))). J. & V. Craig 1998.

WHOLESOME (Graeme Grosvenor, R. 1999). Sdlg. V13-5. TB, 34" (86 cm), M. Blue, F. with dark blue violet veining and violet hafts; beards blue violet; slight fragrance. Dewana X Work Ethic.

WHOOPER SWAN (B.L.C. Dodsworth, R. 1995). Sdlg. EB 127. TB, 40" (102 cm), M. White self, beards red. Princess X Vanity.

WHOOPING CHARLIE (Ken Durio, R. 1992). Sdlg. BEDA-WALK #3. LA, 36-40" (91-102 cm), M. S. very deep rose violet, veined deeper, deep red violet center stripe; F. deep rose violet, veined deeper, deep red violet center stripe, bright full yellow signal; pronounced spicy fragrance. Decoy X Bozo. Louisiana Nursery 1993.

WHO'S WHO (Mary Dunn, R. 1995). Sdlg. M1027-1. TB, 36" (91 cm), M. Clear pink self; F. with slightly paler center; beards deep pink, redder in throat; frilled. Pink Belle X Amour. M.A.D. Iris 1996.

WICHITA FAREWELL (James & Lucy Fry by James Waddick, R. 1995). SPEC (*lactea*), 22" (56 cm), M. S. clear medium violet blue; style arms and F. veined violet blue over white. *I. lactea* X *I. lactea*. Adamgrove 1997.

WICKED WAYS (Lynda Miller, R. 1996). Sdlg. 4385B. TB, 32" (81 cm), ML. Deep raspberry burgundy; style arms dark apricot; beards tangerine; slight musky fragrance. Far Corners X Marmalade. Miller's Manor 1997.

WIDDERSHINS (Merle Roberts, R. 1999). Sdlg. 1-103A. TB, 32" (81 cm), ML. S. rose brown; F. honey yellow, 1/2" burnt honey brown border, 1" white flash below beard; beards orange, base white, yellow at end; slight fragrance. Bogota X Chocolate Marmalade. Roberts Backyard 1999.

WIDE ALERT (Opal Brown, R. 1994). Sdlg. 82-18G. TB, 36-38" (91-97 cm), M. Peach (HCC 312/1) self; beards saturn red (13), wide. 78-4B1: (Dawn Light x Sittin' Pretty) X 78-10D5: Glass Slippers sib. Brown's Sunnyhill 1994.

WIDE BLUE EYES (Gene Gaddie, IB, R. 1989). Gaddies' Gardens 1990.

WIDE HIPS (Lyle Fort, TB, R. 1987). Fort Iris 1990.

WIDE HORIZON (Joseph Gatty, R. 1990). Sdlg. S23-1. TB, 39" (99 cm), EML. S. light lavender blue (M&P 43-AB-6) blended paler and greyer moonbeam (44-A-2); F. white flushed moonbeam; beards blue white, end light yellow; slight sweet fragrance. N57-2A, Royal Elegance sib, X Little Much. Keppel 1991.

WIDE MIRAGE (Stan Dexter by Marie Ingersoll, R. 1995). Sdlg. 7-225AA. TB, 39" (99 cm), M. S. bright yellow; F. tan purple, edged yellowish tan, yellow haft marking; beards yellow; ruffled. Edith Wolford X unknown. Ingersoll's Iris 1996.

WIDOW'S VEIL (Lynda Miller, R. 1993). Sdlg. 100291A. SDB, 11" (28 cm), E. S. red violet; style arms soft yellow, ribs purple; F. red violet, black area around beard raying out to edge; beards dark violet; ruffled; slight sweet fragrance. Dark Vader X Bantam. Miller's Manor 1994.

WIGGLE (Paul Black, R. 1998). Sdlg. D330E. MDB, 7" (18 cm), M. S. deep wine, slight yellow ground on either side of midrib; style arms deep wine; F. yellow ground, wine veins along orange gold beard, wide wine band with dots on inner edge; slight musky fragrance. Static sib X Wacko. Mid-America 1999.

WILD AT HEART (Barry Blyth, R. 1999). Sdlg. E164-1. SPU, 55" (140 cm), EM. S. smoky violet to violet black; F. bright yellow, brown veining except in signal area. "Touareg": (Just Reward x (Marilyn Holloway x Fort Ridge)) X Universal Peace. Tempo Two 1999/2000.

WILD BABY (Jim & Lucy Fry, MDB, R. 1988). J & L Iris 1991.

WILD CAJUN (Henry Rowlan, LA, R. 1989). Comanche Acres 1990.

WILDCAT PAJAMAS (O. D. Niswonger, R. 1995). Sdlg. SDB 13-92. SDB, 14" (37 cm), M. S. purple, small white central area; style arms purple; F. white ground, heavily marked purple; beards medium blue. Chubby Cheeks X Court Magician. Cape Iris 1996.

WILD COUNTRY (Marvin Granger, R. 1991). Sdlg. 88-14. LA, 18" (46 cm), M. S. medium blue violet; F. dark blue violet, short white lines radiating from under style arm; slight spicy fragrance. Parentage unknown.

WILD DANCER (Alex Wintle, TB, R. 1978). Cooling's Nursery 1996.

WILDERNESS AMOUR (John Wood, R. 1992). JI (6 F.), 38" (97 cm), EM. White ground with violet (RHS 80D) rays extending from yellow green (1A) signal, violet (80D) speckles on edge; style arms white, tipped violet (80D). Continuing Pleasure X Wilderness Snowball. John Wood 1993.

WILDERNESS CRINOLINE (John Wood, R. 1990). JI (6 F.), 35" (89 cm), ML. White ground infused pink and blue, giving mother-of-pearl iridescence, signal gold; style arms white. Icy Peaks X unknown. John Wood 1991.

WILDERNESS DEBUTANTE (John Wood, R. 1990). Sdlg. W-102-82. JI (6 F.), 35" (89 cm), M. Crimped, lightly ruffled pink (RHS 73B), signal gold; style arms white, tipped pink. Enchanting Melody X unknown. John Wood 1991.

WILDERNESS EXPANSE (Terrell Taylor, R. 1999). Sdlg. 96-19. TB, 32" (81 cm), EM. S. and style arms greyed orange (RHS 167C); F. light yellow (3B) ground, dotted and lined oxblood (183C), heaviest across upper area; beards bronze; ruffled; musky fragrance. (Rosarita x Burgundy Brown) X Jitterbug.

WILDERNESS FINALE (John Wood by Steve Smart, R. 1997). Sdlg. W-101-91. JI (6 F.), 32" (81 cm), ML. Violet purple (RHS 77A), canary yellow (9A) crest signal with white radiating area surrounded by blue purple (93B). Parentage unknown.

WILDERNESS INTRIGUE (John Wood, R. 1990). JI (3 F.), 30" (76 cm), ML. Petaloids purple (RHS 72A) veined lighter on border; style arms violet blue (89A); F. white ground, violet blue (89C) veining on border, signal yellow (5A). Ike-no-Sazanami X Prairie Velvet. John Wood 1991.

WILDERNESS WARRIOR (John Wood, R. 1992). JI (3 F.), 54" (137 cm), E. S. dark violet purple (RHS 77A), white blaze and rays; style arms white, tipped imperial purple (78B); F. dark violet purple (77A), white rays extending from gold (11A) signal. Parentage unknown. John Wood 1993.

WILDER THAN EVER (Joseph Ghio, R. 1992). Sdlg. PH-302L. CA, 18" (46 cm), EM. S. white ground, red purple ray pattern; F. same, solid red purple edge, signal yellow with solid blue purple halo. Los Californio X San Andreas. Bay View 1993.

WILDEST DREAMS (Keith Keppel, TB, R. 1989). Keppel 1990.

WILDEST IMAGININGS (Joseph Ghio, R. 1995). Sdlg. PF-173V. CA, 12" (31 cm), E. Apricot orange, washed and veined rosewood, F. with neon violet signal. PH-266K: (Las Lomas x Aftershock sib) X PI-201-O, See the Light sib. Bay View 1995.

WILDEYED (Joseph Ghio, R. 1995). Sdlg. PF-173G3. CA, 15" (38 cm), L. Peach, rosy blush, F. with precise red black signal. Sib to Wildest Imaginings. Bay View 1995.

WILD FRONTIER (Schreiner, R. 1999). Sdlg. EE 949-2. TB, 36" (91 cm), ML. S. hazel brown (RHS 165C) with rosy midrib; F. pansy violet (77B) with russet marginal band, 1/4" outer rim cinnamon, shoulders reddish brown; beards lavender at end, changing to tan. Probably -- Y 542-1: (S 694-12, Fancy Brass sib, x Spanish Leather) X BB 1257-1: (Syncopation x Bohemian). Schreiner 1999.

WILD HAIR (Paul Black, R. 1998). Sdlg. C133H. SDB, 14" (36 cm), L. S. dark black cherry, slight buff ground showing toward base; style arms black cherry; F. pearl ground washed orchid blending to purple, plum lined edge, heavier haft markings; beards gold, ice white at end; slight musky fragrance. 91260A, pod parent of Imperative, X 87138AA: (Chubby Cheeks x (Gentle Air x Chubby Cheeks sib)). Mid-America 1999.

WILD KNIGHT (Mary Dunn, R. 1995). Sdlg. M1014-BX. TB, 36" (91 cm), M. S. old gold, mahogany midrib stain; F. blended mahogany, cordovan and violet blue; beards deep orange. M662-2: (Charro x (Ponderosa x Tambourine)) X Freedom Road. M.A.D. Iris 1998.

WILD LAD (Barry Blyth, R. 1995). Sdlg. B98-1. IB, 18-20" (46-51 cm), VE-EM. S. tan apricot buff, purple midrib infusion; F. deeper rosy tan brown, purple haft infusion; beards bright purple, tipped bronze black. X25-3, Impish sib, X Electrique. Tempo Two 1995/96.

WILD PROSPECT (John C. Taylor, R. 1993). Sdlg. RL 42-1. LA, 59" (150 cm), E. S. light yellow; F. lemon ground, heavily veined and suffused rose purple, signal greenish yellow. Dawn Planet X OL 113-1: (Koorawatha x Dazzling Star). Rainbow Ridge 1995/96.

WILD RIDE (Tom Wight by Barbara Wight, R. 1997). Sdlg. 91-6. TB, 38" (97 cm), EM. Ruffled dark violet (RHS 89D) self; beards light purple to white; slight sweet fragrance. Watch Night X Titan's Glory. Wight's Iris 1998.

WILD SHARON (George Sutton, R. 1994). Sdlg. 84-14. TB, 36" (91 cm), EM. S. white; F. blue white with variable white striping; beards blue violet; ruffled. BL-SB/RR-P AR: ((Big League x Stitched Beauty) x (Ribbon Round x Phoenix)) X French Gown. Sutton 1994.

WILD SIDE (Chet Tompkins, R. 1993). Sdlg. 87-60. TB, 40" (102 cm), ML-VL. S. pinkish rose infused fuchsia; F. deep rose pink, cream center tinted pink surrounded by pale pink inner band; beards rich rose pink. (((sdlg. x (April Lost x Blushing Butterfly)) x (((Camelot Rose x Capricious) x April Lost) x Gigolo)) x ((Winner's Circle x Wandering Rainbow) x Apollodorus)) X (April Lost x Street Walker). Fleur de Lis 1993.

WILD SILK (Barry Blyth, R. 1994). Sdlg. A1-3. SDB, 12" (30 cm), EML. S. apricot pink, flushed lavender; F. deeper, brown rose on either side of beard; beards bright lavender, tangerine in throat; slight sweet fragrance. Scat X X32-B: (Tricks x Yipee). Tempo Two 1994/95.

WILD THING (Schreiner, R. 1995). Sdlg. 1987 #105. TB, 38" (97 cm), M. Heavily ruffled deep maroon claret (RHS 72A) self; style arms maroon claret and yellow; beards yellow, end purple; pronounced sweet fragrance. Parentage unknown. Schreiner 1995.

WILD TOUCH (D. L. Shepard, R. 1993). Sdlg. 8901. TB, 32" (81 cm), EML. S. bright rich yellow; F. white, bright yellow shoulders and edge; beards yellow, yellow flounce. Battle Star X Howdy Do. Shepard Iris 1993.

WILD VISION (Barry Blyth, R. 1993). Sdlg. Z51A-2. TB, 34-36" (86-91 cm), ML. S. grey flushed violet at midrib; F. plush black to plum black, precise 1/8" lavender lilac edge; beards dull mustard. (Street Dancer x Surf Lady) X Curacao. Tempo Two 1993/94.

WILD WILEY (Polly Black, R. 1992). Sdlg. NH4T. TB, 36" (91 cm), ML. S. yellow; F. purple, edged yellow; beards bright yellow. Touche X unknown. Polly Black 1992.

WILD WINGS (Keith Keppel, R. 1998). Sdlg. 93-72A. TB, 34" (86 cm), EM. S. and style arms dark violet (M&P 44-L-12); F. black, slight violet cast; beards rusty terracotta (5-CD-12); ruffled; pronounced sweet fragrance. 89-79D, Night Game sib, X Romantic Evening. Keppel 1999.

WILLIAM OF ORANGE (B.L.C. Dodsworth, R. 1999). Sdlg. EB 98 GG. TB, 38" (97 cm), M. Ruffled orange self; beards orange. Orange Order X Good Show.

WILLIAMSBURG HAT (Richard Sparling, R. 1991). SDB, 9" (23 cm), EM. S. violet (RHS 97D); F. violet (83B), edged violet blue (97D), yellow hafts; beards white, yellow in throat. Parentage unknown. Green Box 1991.

WILLOW (Jim Hedgecock, R. 1998). Sdlg. F-37-1. TB, 36" (91 cm), EM. Creamy mustard yellow, F. with lighter area by bright yellow beard; ruffled, lightly laced; pronounced sweet fragrance. Midnight Serenade X Swazi Princess. Comanche Acres 1999.

WILLOW MAID (Les Fort, R. 1990). Sdlg. 86-133-A. TB, 34" (86 cm), M. S. pink, lavender flush; F. light blue lavender, edge darker; beards light salmon, tipped white; ruffled, lightly laced; slight fragrance. Broken Silence sib X Song of Spring. Fort Iris 1992.

WILLOW MINT (Richard Morgan, R. 1992). Sdlg. L646-GY. LA, 30" (76 cm), E. Full yellow, center infused green, green signal and style arms. Heavenly Glow X Sunny Episode. Redbud Lane 1995.

WILLOW STREET (Roy Bohrer, R. 1992). Sdlg. 82-6B. TB, 32" (81 cm), ML. S. full yellow; F. dark red violet, edged tan; beards orange. Sheer Poetry X Show Biz.

WILLOW WARE (Allan Ensminger, IB, R. 1989). Varigay 1990.

WILLUNGA (Ivar Schmidt, R. 1995). Sdlg. PC 90-A4. CA, 10" (26 cm), ML. S. rich cream, midrib and veins magenta; style arms rich cream; F. magenta edged cream, very small yellow signal deep in throat surrounded by deep magenta halo bleeding into veins. Big Money X unknown. Iris Acres 1995/96.

WILLURAH (Robert Harding, R. 1991). Sdlg. 86-6. TB, 36" (91 cm), M. Golden yellow; beards gold. Solano X White Lightning.

WILOH'S WHITE MAGIC (Wiloh Wilkes by Sharon McAllister, R. 1992). Sdlg. MG22W7b. AB (OGB+), 28" (72 cm), EM. S. white; F. pale yellow, few fine rust dots at tip of light yellow beard. (Imam Ahmid x Kalifa Gulnare) X (W7 x I. benjaminii). Aril Society 1992.

WIMPLE (W. & A. Godfrey, R. 1999). Sdlg. JPVL. SDB, 12" (31 cm), M. Ruffled lavender pink fancy pattern, S. tinged muted gold on midrib; beards white, orange in throat. Jeepers X Violet Lulu. Hermit Medlars Walk 1999.

WINDOW SHOPPING (Richard Morgan, R. 1992). Sdlg. L248-BC. LA, 28-32" (71-81 cm), M. S. light yellow, red midrib; F. dark red, light yellow steeple signal. Simple Melody X Shines Brightly. Bois d'Arc 1993.

WINDRIDER (G. F. Wilson, R. 1992). Sdlg. 21-90TSOL-B. AB (OGB) 31" (79 cm), EM. S. clear pale blue lightly veined blue; F. pale violet lightly flushed yellow, light grey veining, large maroon signal and surrounding dotting; beards orange yellow; slight sweet fragrance. (Tuesday Song x Ho5) X Onlooker. Pleasure Iris 1994.

WINDS OF CHANGE (Ben Hager, R. 1992). Sdlg. RE4657LtBl. TB, 36" (91 cm), M & RE. Fluted and ruffled light sky blue; beards white, tipped yellow in throat. T3532LtBl: ((Geometrics sib x Ice Sculpture) x Avalon Bay) X Welcome Reward. Melrose 1993.

WIND SPIRIT (Barry Blyth, R. 1996). Sdlg. B91-2. IB, 20" (51 cm), ML. S. mauve, shot deep violet; F. deeper mauve, shot metallic bluish mauve violet; beards vibrant tangerine. Z7-3, Toy Kingdom sib, X Electrique. Tempo Two 1996/97.

WINDWOOD SERENADE (Robert Hollingworth, R. 1990). Sdlg. 82H3A5. SIB, 27" (69 cm), VE-E. Deep red violet, very small white blaze; ruffled F. Showdown X Indy. Windwood Gardens 1990.

WINE AND LILAC (G. F. Wilson, R. 1994). Sdlg. 63-91W-A. AB (OGB), 30" (76 cm), EM. S. clear lilac, midrib lightly veined blue; F. lilac lightly flushed rose, large burgundy rose signal; beards purple violet, wide. 28-90BBO-D: (Bionic Burst x Onlooker) X 35-89OTWD: (Onlooker x Tornado Warning). Pleasure Iris 1995.

WINE DYNASTY (Melba Hamblen, TB, R. 1989). Roris 1991.

WINE PUNCH (Nancy Bartlett, R. 1995). Sdlg. 89V8. TB, 36" (91 cm), EM. S. beige ground, heavily speckled maroon; style arms light maroon; F. beige ground speckled maroon, white center; beards orange. Wild Jasmine X 84E2: (Tawny Wings x Solano). Nancy Bartlett, Rancho de Los Flores 1996.

WINE SPRITZER (Virginia Messick, R. 1996). Sdlg. 91-29. SDB, 9" (23 cm), E. S. lavender rose; F. pinkish rose, wine spot; beards light blue; ruffled. (Sherlock x Inflamed) X Clay's Caper.

WINE STITCHING (Floyd Dyer, R. 1992). Sdlg. D-205-86-D. SDB, 14" (36 cm), M. White ground heavily stitched dark violet; beards yellow, tipped tan; slight musky fragrance. D-75-82-D:

((((Green Spot x Knotty Pine) x *I. chamaeiris*) x Splash o' Green) x (D-20-69-D: (Brassie x Green Spot) x (Brassie x *I. barthii*))) X D-76-82-D: ((((Tinkerbell x Knotty Pine) x Lillipinkput) x Toy Swan) x (((Heart's Content x Plickadee) x Bimbo) x (Easter Bunny x Snow Elf))). Four Cedars 1992.

WINE SUNDAE (Thom Ericson, R. 1995). Sdlg. 89GD-6. AB (OGB-), 25" (64 cm), EML. S. pale blue (RHS 97D), veined buckskin, spotted burgundy; style arms tannish yellow, rib red; F. buckskin, washed burgundy; beards golden brown; pronounced musky fragrance. ES 109-D: (yellow *pumila* x brown *pumila*) X Sheik.

WINE TIME (Virginia Messick, R. 1998). Sdlg. M 90-33. TB, 38" (97 cm), M. Burgundy wine; style arms wine; beards deep blue. Royal Celebrity X (Royal Ballet x Le Fleur). Messick 1998.

WING COMMANDER (George Sutton, R. 1997). Sdlg. G-17 ARSA. TB, 35" (89 cm), ML. S. wistaria blue (RHS 92D) infused and veined princes blue (105A) at base; style arms wistaria blue; F. princes blue, pale wistaria blue central area; beards orange, white base, end white tipped orange and with white arms ending with 1½" to 2" princes blue flounce; ruffled, laced; slight sweet fragrance. Mystic Lace X Let's Pretend. Sutton 1998.

WING MY CHIMES (Carl Boswell, R. 1993). Sdlg. 3-84-4-I. IB, 18" (46 cm), M. Pale blue lavender, F. with blue halo blending to brown wings; beards blue; slight sweet fragrance. Puppet Baby X Chapel Bells. Adamgrove 1993.

WINGS AND SKY (Carl Boswell, R. 1994). Sdlg. 3-84-3-I. IB, 18" (46 cm), M. Light lavender blue, F. with reddish brown hafts, blue halo; beards blue; slight sweet fragrance. Puppet Baby X Chapel Bells. Adamgrove 1994.

WINGS OF DOVES (Richard Ernst, R. 1990). Sdlg. 84x102. TB, 35" (89 cm), ML. Fluted, lightly laced icy white; beards white. S923: ((Mill Race x Cherry Jubilee) x (Millrace x Christmas Time)) X S915: (Modern Classic x R78-114). Cooley 1990.

WINGS OF GOLD (William Maryott, R. 1991). Sdlg. M101BSTCLR. TB, 39" (99 cm), M. S. pure white, very pale lemon midrib; F. smooth bright golden lemon (RHS 14B); beards lemon, tipped white; lightly ruffled, F. flared. Alpine Journey X H115A: (Tranquil Star x Frosted Buttercup). Maryott 1991.

WINGS OF LACE (Opal Wulf, R. 1998). Sdlg. 54-93-5. MTB, 25" (64 cm), EM. S. and style arms hyacinth blue (RHS 91A); F. darker violet (83B), heavily lace-patterned white; beards violet. Carol Lee X unknown. Wulf's Backachers 1998.

WINGS OF LOVE (A. & D. Willott, R. 1990). Sdlg. 89-96. IB, 20" (51 cm), M. S. light pink; F. pale apricot center, hafts and edge slightly deeper; beards deep orange, tipped blue. Coral Wings X Magic. Willott 1993.

WINGS OF MERCURY (Heather Pryor, R. 1999). Sdlg. 40/92-C. LA, 48" (122 cm), E. S. creamy white (RHS 158C), feathered edge; style arms soft lemon; F. slightly deeper creamy white (158A), fimbriated edge; yellow line signal on all petals, raised on F. Avoca Mist X Heather Pryor. Iris Haven 1999/2000.

WINGS OF NIGHT (Calvin Helsley, R. 1990). Sdlg. 86-8. SIB, 30" (76 cm), E. Ruffled, flared wine red with red violet area below signal; signal gold in throat, white on F.; style arms deep black wine. Kismet X Thespian. Helsley 1991.

WINGS OF PEACE (George Sutton, R. 1996). Sdlg. G-71-A. TB, 38" (97 cm), EM. Ruffled white self; beards white, hairs tipped yellow in throat, 1" wide white spoon; slight sweet fragrance. Skating Party X Twice Thrilling. Sutton 1997.

WINGS TO HEAVEN (Marie Murdy, R. 1992). Sdlg. D-6-89. BB, 24" (64 cm), M. Lightly ruffled white, golden shoulders; beards light orange, short frilled horn; slight fragrance. Parentage unknown.

WINI CONKLIN (James McWhirter by Abram Feuerstein, R. 1996). Sdlg. J89-104-2. TB, 36" (91 cm), ML. S. and style arms medium violet; F. slightly darker violet; beards violet; ruffled; slight sweet fragrance. Winterscape X Honky Tonk Blues. Stockton 1996.

WINNER TAKE ALL (Richard Ernst, R. 1993). Sdlg. HA103A-2. TB, 39" (99 cm), ML. S. white; F. white with light to medium blue plicata markings on edge and hafts, light blue center stripe; beards light blue, tipped white. A103-1: (Song of Norway x Inheritance) X R85-75, inv. Victoria Falls. Cooley 1993.

WINNING EDGE (Joseph Ghio, R. 1996). Sdlg. 92-120B3. TB, 36" (91 cm), ML. S. begonia pink; F. white, blended pink band; beards tangerine, end blue. 87-28N: (Birthday Greetings x 84-82-U2: (Romantic Mood sib x (Exhilaration x (Blushing Pink x (((Ponderosa x Debby Rairdon) x (Show Time x San Leandro)) x ((New Moon x ((Gracie Pfost x Ponderosa) x Ponderosa)) x Valentina)))))) X 90-22G: (Honeymoon Suite x 87-119: (((Just Married x Fortunata) x (Just Married x Exhilaration)) x (Designer Gown x Divinity))). Bay View 1997.

WINNING SMILE (Joseph Ghio, R. 1991). Sdlg. 85-48-BO. TB, 38" (97 cm), ML. S. cream with deeper halo; F. white, edged light yellow; beards cream. ((Social Whirl x Entourage) x ((Party Girl x Highness) x (Toasted Almond x (Carved Cameo x Louise Watts)))) X 82-156H2, pollen parent of Birthday Greetings. Bay View 1992.

WINNING TICKET (Lynda Miller, R. 1999). Sdlg. 4894. TB, 32" (81 cm), E. S. white, tinted blue; style arms lavender, edged cream; F. white ground, dark lavender border changing to stitching toward haft; beards gold, white base; slight musky fragrance. Pagan Pink X Acoma. Miller's Manor 1999.

WINSOME CURIO (Stan Dexter by Marie Ingersoll, R. 1993). Sdlg. 7-157. TB, 38" (97 cm), M. Cream white, F. overlaid yellow brown in center; beards red orange. Sculptress X Peach Spot. Ingersoll's Iris 1994.

WINSOME LOSE SOME (Allan Ensminger, R. 1994). Sdlg. 191-4. SDB, 10" (25 cm), ML. Off-white; beards yellow, tipped white; very few S., most flowers with five F., flat form. 85-3: (Do-Si-Do x 83-6: (Pied Pretty x Sno Jo)) X Chubby Cheeks. Varigay 1997.

WINTER ADVENTURE (Paul Black, R. 1991). Sdlg. 88137A. TB, 35" (89 cm), ML. S. violet blue (RHS 96C) veined darker; style arms violet blue; F. light blue fading to near white, violet blue veining throughout; beards pale blue, tipped pale gold; ruffled; slight musky fragrance. Edge of Winter X Undersea Adventure. Mid-America 1992.

WINTERBOURNE (J. T. Aitken, R. 1991). Sdlg. 82T40. TB, 37" (83 cm), ML-VL. S. white; F. cream, blushed yellow at edge; beards bright yellow; slight sweet fragrance. Old Flame X Joy of Springtime. Aitken's Salmon Creek 1991.

WINTER DANCE (William Maryott, R. 1998). Sdlg. X200A. TB, 37" (94 cm), M. Pallid orchid (RHS 76D), S. midrib slightly darker; beards deep orange, hairs tipped white; slight sweet fragrance. Viva Mexico X Bubble Up. Maryott 1999.

WINTER ETCHINGS (Barbara Roberts, R. 1999). Sdlg. EW 26-3. TB, 36" (91 cm), M. S. medium violet blue, base and midrib deeper; style arms medium violet blue; F. blue white, deeper blue violet lines radiating from haft and beard area; beards violet blue to blue white, yellow in throat; ruffled. Edge of Winter X Undersea Adventure.

WINTER HAZE (Marlyn Mulkey, R. 1990). Sdlg. M8590R. TB, 33" (84 cm), M & RE (Nov.-Dec./CA). S. buff, flushed orchid lavender inside; style arms chartreuse; F. ruffled white, center flushed orchid, 1/4" finely laced edge, olive buff lines around beard; beards light yellow, tipped white. Snow Goddess sdlg. X Frontier Marshall.

WINTERLAND (Monty Byers, TB, R. 1989). Moonshine 1990.

WINTER PALACE (Don Denney by James McWhirter, R. 1995). Sdlg. 81-47-11. TB, 34-36" (86-91 cm), M. Cool blue white self, S. midrib slightly deeper; beards blue white; slight sweet fragrance. Winterscape X Regents' Row. Roris 1995.

WINTER QUEEN (Herbert Holk, R. 1995). Sdlg. 2812. TB, 35" (89 cm), M & RE (Nov./CA). S. lavender violet (RHS 86C to 88C); F. lavender violet, lighter area near beard and haft, streaked lavender violet; beards shrimp; sweet fragrance. 76-5A: (Casino Queen x Dover Beach) X 2810: (Hazy Day x Eva J). Cal-Dixie 1995.

WINTER'S FROST (Henry Rowlan, LA, R. 1989). Comanche Acres 1990.

WINTER SONNET (Harold Stahly, R. 1992). Sdlg. 87-5. TB, 36" (91 cm), M. S. very pale blue (lighter than RHS 97D); F. cool white; beards light blue; ruffled; slight sweet fragrance. Deep Pacific X 81-9: ((Ivy League x River Patrol) x Navy Strut). Stahly 1992.

WINTER'S TALE (James McWhirter by Abram Feuerstein, R. 1995). Sdlg. J89-87-1. TB, 38" (97 cm), L. Ruffled white self; beards white; slight sweet fragrance. America's Cup X Alaskan Seas. Mountain View 1995.

WINTER SUN (George Sutton, R. 1996). Sdlg. G-33ARE. TB, 32" (81 cm), E & RE. S. and style arms cream, edged aureolin yellow (RHS 12A); F. cream, aureolin yellow hafts and edges; beards tangerine orange (24B), end cream tipped aureolin; ruffled. Banana Cream X Orange Popsicle.

WINTER'S WHIMSEY (Don Denney by James McWhirter, TB, R. 1989). Cottage 1990.

WIRRAL GOLD (Donald Patton, IB, R. 1971). British Iris Society 1995.

WISH COME TRUE (Phyllis Dickey, R. 1997). Sdlg. PB 58-2. TB, 32" (81 cm), EM. S. medium blue violet; F. dark blue violet, edge medium blue violet; beards yellow; slight sweet fragrance. Harvest of Memories X Star Master. Misty Hill 1997.

486

WISHCRAFT (Tom Burseen, R. 1991). Sdlg. 6-50C. TB, 35" (89 cm), EM. S. white, tinted lavender; F. dark violet blue (RHS 93A), hairline edge of S. color, white flash and streaks 1/3 down below golden yellow beard; ruffled; spicy fragrance. 4-235: (Condottiere x Night Edition) X Theatre.

WISHFUL FANCY (Richard Morgan, R. 1999). Sdlg. MTB 2-D. MTB, 23" (58 cm), E. S. and style arms very pale blue; F. violet, heavily lined and edged pale blue; beards yellow. Sparkling Chablis X Welch's Reward. Redbud Lane 1999.

WISHFUL THINKING (Keith Keppel, R. 1995). Sdlg. 90-66B. TB, 40-44" (107-112 cm), M. S. hyacinth blue (M&P 42-E-7) paling to vervain (42-B-6) edge, wood violet (42-K-10) texture veining; style arms vervain; F. paler silvery hyacinth (42-B-5 to 42-A-4), chartreuse yellow (12-G-1) blending on haft; beards aureolin yellow (10-L-2), end lavender white; ruffled; pronounced sweet fragrance. 88-162B: (((Vivien x Battle Fury) x Little Much) x Honky Tonk Blues) X Spring Tidings. Keppel 1996.

WISHING (Joseph Ghio, R. 1992). Sdlg. PH-274Z. CA, 14" (36 cm), ML. S. white ground, strong blue violet plicata markings; F. white ground, widely edged with blue violet lining and dotting, signal yellow. Enclosed X Los Californio. Bay View 1993.

WISH WALTZ (Barry Blyth, R. 1993). Sdlg. X58-1. TB, 38" (97 cm), ML. Pure white self; beards orange tangerine; spicy fragrance. Precious Moments X Town Clown. Tempo Two 1993/94.

WISP OF GREEN (Cleo Palmer, R. 1993). Sdlg. 8840. SDB, 13" (33 cm), M. S. very pale yellow, fading to near white at edge; F. chartreuse yellow with light olive green center flush; beards yellow, tipped blue violet; slight sweet fragrance. Parentage unknown. Palmer's Iris 1993.

WISTFUL WISTERIA (Opal Wulf, R. 1997). Sdlg. 55-93-1. MTB, 16" (41 cm), L. S. and style arms wistaria violet (RHS 90C); F. wistaria violet, upper third white with wistaria veining; beards gold; slight sweet fragrance. Lisette X Snickerdoodle. Wulf's Backachers 1998.

WITCHES' SABBATH (William Maryott, TB, R. 1982). Correction of description: beards old gold.

WITCHING (Barry Blyth, R. 1991). Sdlg. Y6-7. TB, 36" (91 cm), VE-E. S. sky blue; F. blue, overlaid tan, rose tan to golden tan shading; beards violet, tipped bronze. ((Inca Queen x (Tranquil Star x (Love Chant x Festive Skirt))) x Amber Snow) X ((Alpine Journey x Beachgirl) x ((Beachgirl x (Tranquil Star x Coral Strand)) x (Persian Smoke x Chimbolam))). Tempo Two 1993/94.

WITCH'S CAPE (Jim Hedgecock, R. 1992). Sdlg. 84-55-1. TB, 34" (86 cm), M. S. dark inky blue; F. satiny dark blue, hafts paler blue; beards dark blue, gold in throat; heavily ruffled. Sky Hooks X Superstition. Comanche Acres 1993.

WITH CASTANETS (Jayne Ritchie, R. 1991). Sdlg. 84-6-7. SDB, 13" (33 cm), EML. S. pale lemon yellow, midrib flushed deeper (near RHS 13D); style arms lemon; F. deep sulphur yellow (7A), 1/4" light yellow (13D) edge; beards cream; heavily ruffled; slight fragrance. 79-39-11, Loveshine sib, X 80-17-16, Model Child sib. Ritchie 1991.

WITH THIS RING (Joseph Ghio, R. 1997). Sdlg. PD-264K5. CA, 15" (38 cm), ML. S. apricot with orchid wash; F. apricot with orchid halo, black maroon signal. PF-188-O, Osocales sib, X PG-172A, Charter Member sib. Bay View 1997.

WITOTO (Ladislav Muska, R. 1996). Sdlg. TCLM-20. TB, 39" (99 cm), ML. S. light orchid; F. deep purplish red black; beards gold; ruffled; slight fragrance. Tomorrow's Child X ("Cipkovana Krinolina": (After All x Grand Waltz) x Lady Madonna). Muska 1995.

WIT'S END (Chet Tompkins, R. 1995). Sdlg. 92-33C. TB, 39" (99 cm), EML. S. blended powder blue and amethyst over chamois gold; style arms smoky blue; F. color of S., slightly more heavily infused gold, with powder blue blaze from beard to lower edge; beards slate blue, tipped bronze yellow. (Beijing x Dance Fever) X Hot Streak. Fleur de Lis 1995.

WIYANNA (L. J. Duffy, R. 1992). Sdlg. WI-3-72. SPEC (*setosa*), 30-36" (76-91 cm), E. Lavender pink with yellow and white markings at base of F.; style arms lavender pink, lavender overtoning at crests. Selection of *I. setosa interior* collected 1972 near Fairbanks, Alaska.

WIZARD OF AUSSIE (Heather Pryor, R. 1997). Sdlg. 45/92-A. LA, 45" (114 cm), EM. S. variable, deep red with yellow blotching, red veining, lemon reverse, red or yellow contrasting line signal dependent on petal color; style arms lime yellow, tips blushed red; F. deep red, yellow sunray veining from lime yellow line signal, reverse lemon; variable color combinations. Volcanic Wildfire X 62/90-1: (Frank Chowning x Desert Jewel). Iris Haven 1999/2000.

WIZARD'S RETURN (Richard Tasco, R. 1997). Sdlg. 91-46-13-RE. SDB, 12" (31 cm), M & RE. S. and style arms reddish violet; F. reddish violet, darker halo around beard; beards pale violet, tangerine in throat; sweet fragrance. Extra Charm X Tender Tears. Superstition 1999.

WOERTHERSEE (Eberhard Fischer, R. 1999). Sdlg. 12. TB, 32" (80 cm), E. Waved pale lavender blue self, F. with very small white area beside beard; beards white, yellow in throat. Victoria Falls X Sapphire Hills.

WOLFGANG MOZART (V. & N. Gordodelovy, R. 1995). Sdlg. 99. TB, 32" (80 cm), M. Ruffled rose lilac, F. with brown haft striations; beards red. Parentage unknown. Gordodelovy 1983.

WOLF WHISTLE (Nora Scopes, R. 1996). Sdlg. 03/150A. TB, 35-36" (89-91 cm), ML. S. dusky orange; F. petunia, bright orange flush in heart; beards ochre brown; ruffled. Thriller X ((Hula Hula x (Owlslight x (Lovely Peace x Gracious Living))) x Bobby Dazzler).

WOLKENTANZ (Robert Fabel-Ward, R. 1992). CA, 27" (69 cm), E. White, veined rose blue. Chimes X Agnes James.

WONDERFUL CHILD (Chet Tompkins, R. 1990). Sdlg. 83-28A. BB, 25" (64 cm), EML. S. jonquil yellow; F. deeper; beards bronze yellow. (((Cimbay x Latin Lover) x (Cimbay x Treasure Key)) x ((Cimbay x Latin Lover) x (Starburst x Cimbay))) X (((Ballyhoo x Cadenza) x (Buttercup Bower x Foggy Dew)) x (Wayward Angel x Elegant Era)). Fleur de Lis 1990.

WONDERVU (Ruth Goebel, TB, R. 1989). Long 1996.

WOOD SPRITE (Franklin Carr, R. 1991). Sdlg. 84-6. TB, 35" (89 cm), EM. S. light brown, infused light yellow and light violet; style arms light brown, infused light violet; F. light brown widely banded S. color, light brown and light violet plicata marking, violet centerline, light violet and white radiating from yellow beard; slight sweet fragrance. Burgundy Brown X 81-16F: (Flamenco x Daylight Splendor).

WOOD TENDER (Udo & Rudolf Wilkeneit, R. 1996). Sdlg. EW 1/11/94. MDB, 7" (18 cm), L. S. velvety violet red, maroon heart; F. light red violet; beards maroon; slight fragrance. Parentage unknown.

WOOING (Mitch Jameson, R. 1992). Sdlg. 1-85. BB, 22-27" (56-69 cm), ML. Pink self; beards pink. Pink Bubbles X Social Register. Knee-Deep in June 1993.

WORK ETHIC (Graeme Grosvenor, R. 1996). Sdlg. R6-4. TB, 37" (95 cm), M. S. pale blue; F. blue violet, edged blue; beards yellow, hairs tipped white; slight fragrance. Silverado X Snowbrook. Rainbow Ridge 1996/97.

WORLD PREMIER (Schreiner, R. 1998). Sdlg. FF 527-3. TB, 37" (94 cm), ML. S. and style arms blue white (RHS 92D); F. dark blue violet (89A), white rim; beards yellow, base blue; ruffled. Yaquina Blue X 1985 #25, unknown. Schreiner 1998.

WORLD TOUR (Frederick Kerr, R. 1994). Sdlg. 88-12-01B. TB, 38" (97 cm), M. Heavily ruffled medium blue self; slight fragrance. Lullaby of Spring X Breakers. Rainbow Acres 1994.

WORLD WIDE WEB (Sharon McAllister, R. 1996). Sdlg. 91-34-2. AB (OGB-), 30" (76 cm), M. S. white ground, heavily covered with network of fine mulberry purple (darker than RHS 70A or 186A) dots and veins; style arms soft yellow, purple midrib and crests; F. white ground, in throat shading to soft yellow, with mulberry purple network of dots and veins, linear purple signal; beards maroon purple, base mustard. Rose Colored Glasses X Hindu Magic. McAllister 1996.

WORTH WAITING FOR (Sharon McAllister, R. 1998). Sdlg. 91-54-1. AB (OGB), 28" (71 cm), M. S. opalescent blue, few blue violet veins; style arms yellow, pinkish midrib flush, crests tan; F. velvety very dark raisin purple, black signal; beards near-black. Holden Ht24-T, inv. *I. susiana, I. hermona, I. sari, I. iberica, I. camillae*, Andromache, Persian Pansy, Vulcanus, Baghdad Beauty, X Chinese Empress.

WORTHY DEED (Franklin Carr, TB, R. 1983). Carr 1991.

WOWZER (Tom Burseen, R. 1990). Sdlg. 4-135S. TB, 35" (89 cm), M. S. bright yellow; F. burgundy red (RHS 181A) washed over creamy yellow ground; beards yellow; heavily ruffled. Theatre X Fiji Dancer. T.B.'s Place 1991.

WRANGLER (Harold Stahly, R. 1997). Sdlg. 93-1. IB, 25" (63 cm), M. S. medium deep red brown; style arms yellow, violet midrib and crests; F. medium violet, medium deep red brown shoulders and distinct 3/8" marginal band; beards brown; heavily ruffled. Woodward Centennial X Plum Perfect. Stahly 1997.

WRATH OF ANDREW (Glenn Stoneking-Jones, R. 1999). Sdlg. CIR6-53911-06-02-1999. TB, 36" (91 cm), EM. Light blue, style arms medium blue; beards orange with white base to light blue, medium blue in throat; pronounced musky fragrance. (Ocean Pacific x Olympiad) X (Breakers x Exotic Melody).

WRIGHT FLYER (Horace Wright by Susan Wright, R. 1992). Sdlg. HA33. TB, 30" (76 cm), E & RE. S. white, base with hint of purple (RHS 76B/D); F. purple violet (82B), some white at white beard; slight fragrance. Grand Baroque X Orchid Cloud. Hall's Flower Garden 1992.

WRONG SONG (O. D. Niswonger, R. 1995). Sdlg. IB 15-92. IB, 25" (64 cm), M. S. violet, midrib shaded darker, brown infusion on outer edge; style arms light violet; F. brown, edged white; beards yellow bronze. Little Louie X unknown. Cape Iris 1996.

WUESTENPLANET (Georg Emke, R. 1996). TB, 30" (76 cm), M. Orange self; beards orange. Good Show X Santiago.

WUNDERKIND (Ben Hager, SDB, R. 1989). Melrose 1990.

WUNNERFUL WUNNERFUL (Carl Jorgensen, R. 1996). Sdlg. 92-LP-1B. TB, 32" (81 cm), EML. S. and style arms crimson (HCC 22/3); F. methyl violet (39/2); beards cadmium orange, saturn red (13) in throat; ruffled; slight fragrance. Sib to Majestic Summit.

WYCH WAY (Barry Blyth, R. 1993). Sdlg. Y4-2. TB, 40" (102 cm), VE-EM. S. violet, magenta cast; F. rose burgundy; beards mustard yellow; slight fragrance. W117-2: ((Alpine Journey x Beachgirl) x (Beachgirl x ((Tranquil Star x Coral Strand) x (Persian Smoke x Chimbolam)))) X V116-A: ((Inca Queen x (Tranquil Star x (Love Chant x Festive Skirt))) x Amber Snow). Tempo Two 1993/94.

WYCHWOOD (John D. Taylor by Carilla Taylor, TB, R. 1988). Correction of spelling from WYNCHWOOD.

WYCHWOOD'S MULTIFLORAL (R. J. Henley, R. 1994). SPEC (*pseudacorus*), 60" (153 cm), M. Golden yellow, light brown signal. *I. pseudacorus* "Tangarewa Cream" X unknown.

WYEVALE (Maureen Foster, TB, R. 1988). V. H. Humphrey 1995.

WYLE FLASH (George Slade, TB, R. 1989). Wyle Wynde 1990.

WYLE GYPSY (George Slade, TB, R. 1989). Wyle Wynde 1990.

WYLE LILAC (George Slade, TB, R. 1989). Wyle Wynde 1990.

WYLE ROSE (George Slade, TB, R. 1989). Wyle Wynde 1990.

WYLE SWAN (George Slade, TB, R. 1989). Wyle Wynde 1990.

WYNCHWOOD -- see WYCHWOOD

WYNNE ROGERS (Francis Rogers, R. 1998). Sdlg. C-308-A. TB, 36" (91 cm), L. S. violet blue (RHS 97C) shading to wistaria blue (92B); style arms violet blue; F. paler wistaria blue (92D), darker (92B) area radiating from beard; beards wistaria blue, yellow in throat; flared, ruffled; sweet fragrance. Honky Tonk Blues X Kathy's Joy. Meadowbrook 1999.

WYOMING COWBOYS (Floyd Wickenkamp, R. 1993). Sdlg. SP-89-8. SPU, 48" (122 cm), M. S. gold striped brown, brown reverse; style arms tipped brown; F. gold striped brown, darker brown rim. Headway X SP-83-2: (Burnished Brass x (Burnished Brass x Proverb)). Shepard Iris 1994.

WYUNA EVENING (Hilmary Catton, AB, R. 1987). Wyuna 1987.

WYUNA EVENSONG (Hooker Nichols by Hilmary Catton, SDB, R. 1987). Introduced as "Evensong". Wyuna 1987.

XANADU (Philip Edinger, TB, R. 1968). Correction of parentage. M. Hawkinson 57-11 cream/rose plicata, unknown, X L. Burbridge purple sdlg.: (Raven Wing x Majorette).

XANANA (Ladislav Muska, R. 1997). Sdlg. S-RLPS-09. SDB, 13" (33 cm), E. Ruffled, lightly laced mahogany red bitone; beards red orange; slightly fragrant. ((Red Devil x "Scarlet Smile": (Li'l Red Devil x Laced Lemonade)) x Li'l Red Devil) X "Purple Song": (Little Annie x Laced Lemonade). Muska 1997.

XANTHIPPE'S HALO (O. D. Niswonger, R. 1992). Sdlg. 57-79. TB, 34" (86 cm), M. Deep red violet, F. edged brown; beards yellow. Marquesan Sunset X Gladish 8-77: ((Denver Mint x Meghan) x Brown Lasso). Cape Iris 1992.

XAVIER (Bob Thomason, R. 1991). Sdlg. BT 8812B. SDB, 10" (25 cm), EM. Medium purple, hafts darker; beards light purple. Ja Wohl X Que Paso.

XEWE (Joseph Ghio, R. 1995). Sdlg. PF-170C3. CA, 13" (33 cm), L. S. copper russet, bordered gold; style arms gold; F. copper russet, border gold, signal neon violet. Mission Santa Clara sib X PI-MIX-S, unknown. Bay View 1995.

XOCHIPILLI (Ladislav Muska, R. 1997). Sdlg. BSSK-02. TB, 38" (97 cm), ML. Ruffled and laced light pink; F. center flushed light creamy brown; style arms rose cream; beards red tangerine; spicy fragrance. ("Belase Striebro" x Sky Hooks) X Geniality. Muska 1995.

YABBA DABBA DO (Chun Fan, R. 1994). Sdlg. F91-703. TB, 32" (81 cm), EM. S. greyed yellow, slightly darker speckles; F. bold canary yellow ground, cinnamon red streaks and speckles; beards golden yellow, small; heavily ruffled. Jitterbug X Flaming Sun.

YAE KATSUMI (Society for Japanese Irises, R. 1995). JI, 33" (85 cm), L. S. very small, deep red violet; F. white ground, heavily sanded red violet; extra petals (same color as F.) inside S. to give "hose in hose" form. Parentage and hybridizer unknown. Introduced in Japan prior to 1910.

YAEMOMIJI (Hiroshi Shimizu by Clarence Mahan, R. 1994). JI (6 F.), 35" (89 cm), EM. Red violet, streaked and mottled white, green signal at base turning to light yellow and extending to white; style arms white, edges and crests red violet; extra petaloids white, edged and tipped red violet. "Sakura-no-Sei" X Sekiyo. Draycott 1997.

YAGODNY KOKTEYL (Sergey Loktev, R. 1999). TB, 37" (94 cm) EML. S. claret violet; style arms yellow, midribs and crests lilac; F. slightly lighter claret violet, lilac area below ginger brown beard, hafts marked cream yellow. Parentage unknown. Loktev 1999.

YAK ATTACK (Brad Kasperek, R. 1997). Sdlg. 93M-5H. MDB, 6½" (17 cm), M. S. white (RHS 155B), midrib veined green; style arms white, some green veining; F. white, yellow (7A) spot; beards white on outer half, remainder orange; lightly ruffled; slight fragrance. Chubby Cheeks X Perfume. Miller's Manor 1998.

YAKO-NO-TAMA (Shuichi Hirao by Society for Japanese Irises, R. 1993). JI (6 F.), 36" (91 cm), M. Vivid blue violet, white halo and radiating white veins, yellow signal; style arms white, blue violet crest edges. Parentage unknown. Hirao ca. 1961.

YAMANOBE (Kamo Nursery by Society for Japanese Irises, R. 1999). JI (3 F.), 36" (91 cm), M. S. violet, edges darker; style arms white, suffused light violet; F. violet, white halo and veins. From Nagai type sdlg. Kamo Nursery 1985.

YAMATAIKOKU (Mototeru Kamo by Society for Japanese Irises, R. 1993). JI (3 F.), 42" (107 cm), M. S. deep red violet; style arms dark violet, feathered; F. deep red violet, very large and overlapped, lighter crinkled edge, signal yellow with prominent yellow ridge line. Parentage unknown. Kamo 1979.

YAMATO HIME (Shuichi Hirao by Society for Japanese Irises, R. 1992). JI (6 F.), 36" (90 cm), M. Pinkish lavender (RHS 77D), white center, signal yellow. Parentage unknown. Hirao 1957.

YANKALILLA (Ivar Schmidt, R. 1995). Sdlg. PC 89-AT. CA, 20" (51 cm), EM. S. cream, midrib golden; style arms cream; F. cream, heavily veined rosy violet fading to give blue effect, small yellow signal. Nayook X unknown. Iris Acres 1995/96.

YANKEE PRIDE (William Maryott, TB, R. 1988). Maryott 1989.

YANKULI (Galina Shevchenko, R. 1995). MDB, 8" (19-20 cm), E. S. lilac purple; F. purple, lilac edge; beards purple; slight sweet fragrance. From *I. pumila* sdlgs. Shevchenko 1992.

YANTARNY TALISMAN (Viktor Sheviakov, R. 1996). Sdlg. 20c18. TB, 30" (75 cm), M. Ruffled amber yellow orange; F. veined light brown violet in center; beards amber yellow; slight spicy fragrance. Rippling Waters X Limelight. Sheviakov 1997.

YAQUINA BLUE (Schreiner, R. 1992). Sdlg. W18-2. TB, 37" (94 cm), M. Ruffled medium blue (RHS 96B); beards yellow, tipped white. N59-A: (J78-3: ((Cup Race x Tufted Cloud) x Sailor's Dance) x I 38-A: (Sapphire Hills x (Parisian Blue x ((Blue Linen sib x (J 274-A x Violet Harmony)) x (Swan Ballet x Snowy Heron))))) X L 100-A: (I 144-G: (((((Black Onyx x N 371-1) x Grand Ball) x (Sterling Silver x (((Pierre Menard x (Blue Rhythm x Chivalry)) x Harbor Blue) x (Blue Sapphire x Harbor Blue)))) x unknown) x Neptune's Pool) x G 119-H, Royal Regency sib). Schreiner 1992.

YAQUI PRINCE (Bob Thomason, R, 1993). Sdlg. BT8613A. SDB, 10" (25 cm), EM. S. lemon yellow; F. golden, red brown spot; beards orange, tipped white; slight fragrance. Harlow Gold X Gingerbread Man.

YARILO (Viacheslav Gavrilin, R. 1999). Sdlg. 94-414-3. TB, 33" (83 cm), EM. Tan-tinted yellow, F. with darker edge and lighter area below beard; style arms yellow; beards orange yellow, yellow at end. Rustic Cedar X unknown.

YAROONA (Ivar Schmidt, R. 1995). Sdlg. PC 89-AD. CA, 16" (41 cm), EM. S. and style arms apricot cream; F. cerise, darker around yellow signal. Nayook X unknown. Iris Acres 1995/96.

YAROSLAV MUDRY (Nina Miroshnichenko, R. 1999). TB, 28" (72 cm), EM. S. blended yellow beige; style arms yellow; F. beige ground, heavy claret streaking, lilac spot below yellow beard, hafts marked yellow, narrow beige rim. Parentage unknown. Miroshnichenko 1996.

YASABOSHI (Shuichi Hirao by Society for Japanese Irises, R. 1993). JI (6-9 F.), 36" (91 cm), M. Deep red purple, heavily splashed white; signal yellow; extra F. (over 6) usually not completely formed. Parentage unknown. Hirao prior to 1980.

YASHMA (Adolf Volfovich-Moler, R. 1999). Sdlg. B58. TB, 28" (71 cm), EM. Ruffled and lightly laced orange brown blend, F. tinted mauve in center; beards yellow orange. Karmen Dance X Victoria Falls. Volfovich-Moler 1999.

YATA-NO-KAGAMI (Society for Japanese Irises, R. 1995). JI (6 F.), 36" (90 cm), M. Silvery white, veined and dusted amethyst; style arms white, amethyst edge and crests. Parentage and hybridizer unknown. Introduced in Japan prior to 1940.

YAT ROCK (O. D. Niswonger, R. 1993). Sdlg. SDB 20-90. SDB, 12" (30 cm), M. S. pale lilac blue; F. pinkish buff, beards tipped tangerine, white base. SDB 27-87: (Oriental Blush x unknown) X unknown. Cape Iris 1993.

YAYOI (Yoshio Mitsuda by Society for Japanese Irises, R. 1993). JI (6 F.), 36" (90 cm), M. Light to medium red violet heavily sanded over light ground, signal gold, white halo; style arms white, red violet crests. Parentage unknown. Mitsuda 1963.

YAYOI KAGAMI (Shuichi Hirao by Society for Japanese Irises, R. 1994). JI (3 F.), 36" (90 cm), E. S. pink; style arms and F. pinkish lavender. Parentage unknown. Hirao 1968.

YEARLING (Marky Smith, R. 1998). Sdlg. 93-05Z. SDB, 11" (28 cm), E. S. yellow (near RHS 159A), midrib blended pink; F. smoky gold at edge blending to smoked peach (near 173D) center; beards cream at end, changing to orange, tangerine in throat; heavily ruffled. Tweety Bird X Flaming Rhythm.

YEARS OF PLENTY (Graeme Grosvenor, R. 1999). Sdlg. V55-5. TB, 32" (81 cm), ML. S. yellow; F. white, edged yellow; beards yellow. Silverado X Berry Sherbert. Rainbow Ridge 1999/2000.

YELLOW BRICK ROAD (James Gibson by Cooley's Gardens, R. 1993). Sdlg. 49-9J. TB, 33" (84 cm), EM. S. golden amber; F. deep gold, center paling to white, amber brown plicata shoulders and stripe at end of beard; beards gold, tipped amber. 22-4A: ((CoCo Mocha x 83-6B, Summer Sunshine sib) x (Pink Ember x Smoke Rings)) X 72-4C, Golden Garnet sib. Cooley 1992.

YELLOW CONUNDRUM (Eric & Bob Tankesley-Clarke, R. 1994). SPEC, 8-10" (20-25 cm), E. Variable blend of yellow, chartreuse and grey, often streaked darker; beards yellow; slight sweet fragrance. Collected; distributed by Hanselmayer prior to 1960, and in commerce as *I. aphylla* H17.

YELLOWCOPTER (B. Charles Jenkins, R. 1994). Sdlg. BF13D. SPU, 35-40" (89-102 cm), M. Bright yellow self; flared F. Bali Bali X Cinnamon Stick. Shepard Iris 1995.

YELLOW DESIGN (Donald Spoon, R. 1997). Sdlg. 90-153A. TB, 32" (81 cm), ML. Intense bright yellow, F. with lighter area below yellow beard; style arms yellow; ruffled. (Stately Mansions x Bride's Halo) X Lora Kathleen. Winterberry 1997.

YELLOW FLIRT (Kenneth Fisher, R. 1997). Sdlg. 94-7. MTB, 20" (51 cm), L. Bright yellow self; beards orange. R-6: (18-54: ((Buenita x Amethyst Sunset) x Bellboy) x Chickee) X unknown. Aitken's Salmon Creek 1998.

YELLOW GIANT (Loleta Powell, R. 1992). Sdlg. 86-62. TB, 40" (102 cm), ML-VL. Soft yellow self; beards deep yellow. Parentage unknown. Powell's Gardens 1993.

YELLOW SPOON (Margaret Buckner, R. 1999). TB, 37" (94 cm), ML. S. medium butter yellow, midrib blended lemon; style arms butter yellow; F. butter yellow, paling to cream center; beards yellow orange, end cream, extending as lemon yellow spoon or flounce. Sky Hooks X unknown. Stockton 1999.

YELLOW STREAK (Pat Otterness, R. 1999). Sdlg. 9697-12x34-087. TB, 31" (79 cm), ML. White self; beards bright yellow; ruffled; slight sweet fragrance. Edith Wolford X Silverado.

YENI CAMI (Ladislav Muska, R. 1997). Sdlg. FFEX-02. TB, 38" (97 cm), M. Waved, heavily laced maroon rose, F. with lavender circle near light yellow beard; pronounced fragrance. Fabulous Frills X ((Extravagant x Don Epifano) x Don Epifano). Muska 1995.

YERMAK (Leonard Venivitin, R. 1995). TB, 32" (80 cm), M. Ruffled white self; beards orange yellow, tipped white. Parentage unknown. Venivitin 1992.

YES (Barry Blyth, R. 1995). Sdlg. B187-1. TB, 36" (91 cm), VE-EM. S. pure white; F. honey yellow; beards vivid tangerine. Road Song X Electrique. Keppel 1996, Tempo Two 1996/97.

YESAUL (Viktor Koroliov, R. 1999). Sdlg. STG15-95K. TB, 43" (110 cm), M. S. red violet; style arms light violet, crests violet; F. red violet, hafts marked creamy yellow violet, bright brown spots below haft area; beards violet, hairs tipped brown, all brown in throat; slight spicy fragrance. Titan's Glory X Lunar Fire. Koroliov 1999.

YES INDEED (Graeme Grosvenor, R. 1999). Sdlg. V104-C. TB, 30" (76 cm), M. S. white, dotted and edged light blue violet; F. white, rim dark blue violet; beards mustard, tipped violet. Yes Minister X Zipper Stitch.

YES MA'AM (Tom Burseen, R, 1991). Sdlg. 7-321B. TB, 37" (94 cm), EM. S. pinkish orange (RHS 28B); F. lighter, white blaze below beard; beards white, tipped tangerine; ruffled, laced; sweet fragrance. Black Hills Gold X Miss Jeanie. T.B.'s Place 1992.

YES MINISTER (Graeme Grosvenor, R. 1996). Sdlg. T16-1A. TB, 35" (88 cm), EM. S. white, edged sky blue; F. white, violet rim and centerline; beards blue; slight fragrance. N6-2: (Goddess x ((Elsedina x (Rondo x (Quetta x Ribbon Round))) x Bonifay)) X Seaport. Rainbow Ridge 1996/97.

YIPES STRIPES (Paul Black, TB, R. 1989). Mid-America 1990.

YIPPY SKIPPY (Paul Black, R. 1998). Sdlg. C133B. SDB, 12" (30 cm), M. S. medium dark lilac blend, cream yellow base; style arms white; F. medium lilac blend darker at edge, white wire rim, pale yellow to white luminata patch, white dart at end of beard surrounded by blue haze; beards yellow orange, white at end; ruffled; slight spicy fragrance. 91260A: ((Gentle Air x Chubby Cheeks sib) x (85418A: (Caesura x (Betsey Boo x (Antique Satin x Encanto))) x 84207A: (Gigglepot x Oriental Blush))) X 87138AA: (Chubby Cheeks x (Gentle Air x Chubby Cheeks sib)). Mid-America 1998.

YO (Allan Ensminger, R. 1992). Sdlg. 186-57. BB, 25" (64 cm), ML. Rhodamine purple (HCC 29/2) self; beards saturn red (13). Weiler sdlg., parentage unknown, X 82-3D: ((Malaysia x Shahrohk Mahrohki) x Copper Classic). Varigay 1993.

YOAKE MAE (Toyokazu Ichie by Society for Japanese Irises, R. 1995). JI (3 F.), 37" (95 cm), M. S. and F. mauve, veined darker, with very slight silver edge; style arms mauve violet. Parentage unknown. Introduced in Japan prior to 1990.

YODO-NO-KAWASE (Society for Japanese Irises, R. 1994). JI (3 F.), 36" (91 cm), M. S. white, intense blue violet rim; style arms white, rimmed blue violet; F. white, edged blue violet, signal gold. Parentage unknown. Introduced in Japan prior to 1980. Incorrectly listed in commerce as "Yodono Kawase", "Yodong Kawase", and "Yodano Kawase".

YOROI MUSHA (Shuichi Hirao by Society for Japanese Irises, R. 1993). JI (6 F.), 36" (90 cm), M. Ruffled rich deep violet, signal yellow. Parentage unknown. Hirao 1971.

YOSEMITE SAM (Donald Spoon, R. 1999). Sdlg. 90-162A. TB, 34" (86 cm), ML. S. rose pink; style arms rose pink, tangerine infusions; F. rose pink, plum central spot with rose pink centerline, prominent white sunburst pattern around tangerine beard; ruffled, lightly laced; pronounced spicy fragrance. Lorilee X Abigail Provides.

YOU BETCHA (George Slade, TB, R. 1989). Wyle Wynde 1990.

YOU'LL LOVE (Stan Dexter by Marie Ingersoll, R. 1992). Sdlg. 65-83-235-5. TB, 38" (97 cm), EM. S. pink; F. pink brushed gold; beards tangerine; ruffled. 80-132-C: (Pink Angel x Temple Gold) X Today's Fashion. Ingersoll's Iris 1993.

YOUNG BLOOD (Ben Hager, R. 1994). Sdlg. IB5451B. IB, 23" (58 cm), M. Fluted maroon red self; beards orange yellow. T4405B: (Red Lion x (((Bermuda High x ((Display x Savage) x Tall Chief)) x Mary Todd) x (Sun Worshiper x Golden Bonanza))) X SD4046RndDkRd: (Tempt Me x (((Sunny Heart x ((Evening Storm x Welch H501) x (Sulina x Melodrama))) x (Blueberry Muffins x Peanuts)) x Abracadabra)). Adamgrove 1995.

YOUNG MAN'S FANCY (Allen Harper, R. 1991). Sdlg. M21-20. TB, 35" (89 cm), M. S. light blue violet (RHS 97C); F. slightly darker (100D). Fuji's Mantle X Breakers.

YOURS FREE (Paul Black, R. 1998). Sdlg. A10A. TB, 36" (91 cm), ML. S. and style arms cameo pink; F. bright orchid, deeper toward edges and haft, smoky cameo pink rim, white haft veined plum to rose; beards blue violet at end, burnt orange in throat; ruffled, lightly laced; slight sweet fragrance. Enchanting X Ruth Black. Mid-America 1998.

YOZAKURA (Zensaku Makino by Society for Japanese Irises, R. 1995). JI (3 F.), 35" (90 cm), EM. S. and F. pale pink; style arms white, edged pink. Parentage unknown. Introduced in Japan, 1975.

YUHI (Bungo Miyazawa by Society for Japanese Irises, R. 1993). JI (6 F.), 36" (91 cm), M. White, washed pale pink (RHS 77C), signal yellow; style arms white, edged and tipped pink (77B); 7 or 8 petals sometimes present. Parentage unknown. Miyazawa 1920.

YUHO (Shuichi Hirao by Society for Japanese Irises, R. 1993). JI (6 F.), 36" (91 cm), EM. Creped red violet, blue violet halo, signal yellow; style arms medium blue violet, crests darker. Parentage unknown. Hirao prior to 1980.

YUKI ARASHI (Kamo Nursery by Society for Japanese Irises, R. 1999). JI (3 F.), 36" (91 cm), M. White; style crests elaborate. Parentage unknown. Kamo Nursery 1975.

YUKICHIDORI (Shuichi Hirao by Society for Japanese Irises, R. 1992). JI, 32" (80 cm), E. White, yellow signal; multi-petaled, usually 9 F. Parentage unknown. Hirao 1969

YUKIJISHI (Hiroshi Shimizu by Carol Warner, R. 1997). JI (9 F.), 34" (86 cm), M. White, small yellow signal; style arms white. "Sakura-no-Sei" X Sekiyo. Draycott 1997.

YUKI KEMURI (Hiroshi Shimizu by Society for Japanese Irises, R. 1993). JI (3 F.), 32" (81 cm), EM.

492

S. lavender pink; style arms white, tipped pink; F. lavender pink with white halo and rays, signal yellow. Parentage unknown.

YUKON FEVER (Schreiner, TB, R. 1986). Schreiner 1986.

YULOVIT (B. Charles Jenkins, R. 1992). Sdlg. B22-8D. CA, 14" (36 cm), ML. Very dark maroon self; style arms lighter. Montara X Deepening Shadows. Portable Acres 1992.

YUMMY (Ken Durio, R. 1992). Sdlg. HKR-JR #C. LA, 24-30" (61-76 cm), ML. S. full yellow, heavily veined violet blue with violet splashing; F. full yellow, heavily veined violet blue, signal dark yellow; slight sweet fragrance. Harland K. Riley X Uralba Gold. Louisiana Nursery 1995.

YUNDI (Ivar Schmidt, R. 1995). Sdlg. PC 89-AG. CA, 15" (38 cm), M. S. and style arms wistaria violet; F. deeper wistaria violet, veined purple, small gold signal surrounded by white halo. Nayook X unknown. Iris Acres 1995/96.

YUNOST (Irina Driagina, R. 1996). Sdlg. 4-09. TB, 33" (85 cm), L. Cream pink self; beards dark orange. Parentage unknown. Driagina 1970.

YURI LUZHKOV (Viacheslav Gavrilin, R. 1999). Sdlg. 96-48-96. TB, 33" (85 cm), M. Ruffled white, brownish yellow pattern on hafts; beards tangerine, white at end. Trevi Fountain X Coral Joy.

YURU-NO-NIJI (Shuichi Hirao by Society for Japanese Irises, R. 1993). JI (6 F.), 38" (97 cm), L-VL. Deep red violet with white veins, signal yellow; style arms dark red violet, white center. Parentage unknown. Hirao 1958.

YUSHO (Shuichi Hirao by Society for Japanese Irises, R. 1994). JI (6 F.), 38" (97 cm), M. Mulberry wine lightly veined white, signal yellow. Parentage unknown. Introduced in Japan ca. 1980.

YUZEN (Toyokazu Ichie/Kamo Nursery, R. 1997). Sdlg. 8A-146. JI (6 F.), 30" (75 cm), ML. White, 1/8" to 1/16" somewhat irregular violet purple (RHS 77A) rim and sparse dotting, signal canary yellow (9B); style arms white, tufts edged light violet (85B); strongly ruffled. Stippled Ripples X "Syusho". Kamo Nursery 1994.

YUZHANKA (V. & N. Gordodelovy, R. 1996). Sdlg. 74. TB, 41" (105 cm), VE. Flared bronze brown; beards orange; pronounced fragrance. Parentage unknown. Gordodelovy 1985.

YUZHNAYA NOCH (V. & N. Gordodelovy, R. 1995). Sdlg. 100. TB, 28" (71 cm), M. Blue, shaded black; style arms brown; beards brown. Parentage unknown. Gordodelovy 1985.

YUZHNY ALTAY (Piotr Hattenberger, R. 1995). Sdlg. 5. TB, 31-33" (80-85 cm), ML. S. wide dark violet edge on cream; F. wide near-black edge on cream ground; beards blackish violet; lightly ruffled. Seed from Altaiski Botanical Garden. Going My Way X unknown.

ZAGGERAN (Tom Burseen, R. 1997). Sdlg. 94-315A. TB, 35" (89 cm), M. Ruffled, heavily laced mauve (186C), F. slightly lighter in center; beards red orange, white horn; sweet fragrance. Flushed Delight X 91-278: (8-59: (Ace of Lace x (Snowy Wonderland x Formosa Springs)) x 8-18: (For Tirah x Feminine Wiles)). T.B.'s Place 1998.

ZAGREB BROWN MARY (Predrag Nemet, R. 1991). Sdlg. RW129MN82. TB, 32" (80 cm), E. Chocolate brown. Rippling Waters X Muriel Neville. Nemet 1991.

ZAGREB GOLD (Predrag Nemet, R. 1991). Sdlg. M164SK84. TB, 36" (90 cm), E. S. vivid yellow, edged gold yellow; F. white, edged gold yellow; beards bright gold. Margarita X Soaring Kite. Nemet 1991.

ZAGREB LADY (Predrag Nemet, R. 1991). Sdlg. RW29MN82. TB, 32" (80 cm), M. Violet pink; beards yellow. Rippling Waters X Muriel Neville. Nemet 1991.

ZAHLE (Lucy Fowler, R. 1997). Sdlg. 92-3. AB, 20" (50 cm), E. S. wine red, large and rounded; style arms wine; F. wine red, black velvet thumb print; beards dark wine; slight fragrance. Parentage unknown -- seed from America.

ZAKOPANE (Cy Bartlett, R. 1995). Sdlg. HHBR. SIB (tet.), 34" (86 cm), EM. S. deep blue purple; F. very deep violet purple, very small greenish brown signal; lightly ruffled. Harpswell Happiness X Berlin Ruffles.

ZAMBOANGA (Ben Hager, R. 1991). Sdlg. S969Br/VdGd. SPU, 34" (86 cm), ML. S. deep red brown; style arms light yellow, brown ridge; F. gold over-veined deep brown to narrow solid edge, small bright golden yellow signal; deep green erect foliage. S731: (Crow Wing x Forty Carats) X Walker Ferguson. Cordon Bleu 1992.

ZAMRIYANNY VALS (Nina Miroshnichenko, R. 1997). TB, 35" (88 cm), ML. S. rose, paling toward center, midrib lemon cream; style arms yellow; F. cream white, hafts pale lemon, edges stitched claret brown; beards yellow; pronounced sweet fragrance. Parentage unknown. Miroshnichenko 1996.

ZANDRIA (Don Nebeker, R. 1995). Sdlg. 1000-5. TB, 38" (97 cm), M. S. rose pink (HCC 427/2);

style arms rose pink, spotted violet purple (733) on top; F. violet purple, rose pink reticulation on upper portion; beards fire red (15); ruffled. Fancy Tales X Planned Treasure. Zebra 1996.

ZATON (Perry Dyer, R. 1998). Sdlg. 90-70A. TB, 36" (91 cm), ML. S. and style arms dark violet; F. and beards dark violet to black; ruffled. Houdini X Navy Chant. Contemporary 1999.

ZEBEDEE (Mitch Jameson, R. 1992). Sdlg. 7-87-A. TB, 30" (76 cm), ML. S. lemon; F. lavender; beards yellow gold. Edith Wolford X Song of Spring. Knee-Deep in June 1995.

ZEBLOUZ (Lawrence Ransom, R. 1995). Sdlg. 90/156-2. IB, 25" (64 cm), EM. Light powder blue, edges frosted silver, F. center paler, hafts lightly veined maroon violet; beards dark violet blue, hairs tipped bronze, bushy; slight sweet fragrance. 87/90-5: (Earl of Essex x (Mystique x Rococo)) X Leprechaun's Delight. Iris au Trescols 1996.

ZEBRA BLUSH (Brad Kasperek, R. 1993). Sdlg. 89-6A. TB, 34" (86 cm), EM. S. pale yellow (RHS 4C); F. light rose purple (75C); beards lavender rose; foliage dark green with white streaks and marbling, base red purple; slight fragrance. Ensminger sdlg. X Capricious. Zebra 1995.

ZEBRA HALO (Brad Kasperek, R. 1996). Sdlg. 91F-52A. TB, 36" (91 cm), M. S. yellowish white (RHS 158A); F. warm white (158C) center edged aureolin yellow (12C), deeper (12A) shoulders; beards orange, hairs tipped white; ruffled, heavily laced; foliage and stems variegated green and white. 89F-4H: (Ensminger sdlg. x Lady Madonna) X Lady Madonna. Zebra 1997.

ZEBRA NIGHT (Brad Kasperek, R. 1996). Sdlg. 91F-35A. TB, 35" (89 cm), M. Lightly ruffled dark violet (RHS 86A) self; beards orange, hairs tipped lavender; foliage and stems variegated green and white; slight fragrance. 89F-12A: (Ensminger sdlg. x Titan's Glory) X Into the Night. Superstition 1998.

ZEELAND (Nora Scopes, BB, R. 1984). British Iris Society 1987.

ZEFFIRO ROSA (Valeria Romoli, R. 1999). Sdlg. 34E-91. TB, 34" (86 cm), ML. S. and style arms pink; F. pink, shaded blue; beards carmine red, paler base and in throat; laced; pronounced sweet fragrance. Coral Touch X Goodbye Heart.

ZELENÝ POČÁTEK (Jiří Dudek, R. 1998). Sdlg. GELSC. TB, 35" (90 cm), M. Ruffled yellow green (RHS 195B), F. lighter below yellow beard, hafts brown; slight sweet fragrance. Green Eyed Lady X Storm Center. Jiří Dudek 1997.

ZELIONY OMUT (Viacheslav Gavrilin, R. 1999). Sdlg. 96-66-2. TB, 31" (78 cm), ML. S. and style arms cream yellow; F. green-tinted white, wide yellow rim and darker hafts; beards orange yellow, lighter at end; heavily ruffled. Wedding Candles X Coral Joy.

ZENDA (Hilmary Catton, R. 1990). Sdlg. C844-2. IB, 16½" (42 cm), M. S. clear old gold; F. old gold, bright mahogany ray pattern around bronze beard and on hafts. Captive Spirit X Hot Line. Catton 1991.

ZENNIE (Virginia Keyser, R. 1999). Sdlg. 93-9. TB, 32" (81 cm), EM & RE. White self; beards light yellow; slight sweet fragrance. Bonus Mama X Faux Pas.

ZEPHERINA (William Maryott, R. 1995). Sdlg. S195E. TB, 34-36" (86-91 cm), EM. S. light lavender (RHS 94C), midrib smoky maroon; F. medium velvety maroon (80C), shoulders deep brown (183A); beards yellow, tipped purple; slight sweet fragrance. Mariachi Music X Twice Told. Maryott 1996.

ZERO (Keith Keppel, R. 1997). Sdlg. 91-11D. SDB, 13" (33 cm), M. Ruffled white self; beards white, faintly tipped lemon deep in throat; pronounced sweet fragrance. Pure Allure X Favorite Angel. Keppel 1998.

ZERZURA (Ben Hager, AB (OGB), R. 1989). Melrose 1990.

ZESTFUL MISS (Bernard Hamner by Shepard Iris, R. 1994). Sdlg. 90-5-1. BB, 27" (70 cm), E. S. lavender; F. grape with heavy white spray pattern, 1/4" lavender edge; beards lavender, tipped yellow; ruffled. Flamenco Whirl X Wild Jasmine. Hamner Iris, Shepard Iris 1994.

ZHAQ (Bob Thomason, R. 1991). Sdlg. BT 8812C. SDB, 10" (25 cm), EM. Medium purple, iridescent hafts; beards lavender, orange in throat; slight fragrance. Ja Wohl X Que Paso. Okie Iris 1993.

ZHARKOYE LETO (Viktor Sheviakov, R. 1995). Sdlg. 22S 20B. BB, 24" (60 cm), M. S. bronze yellow; F. brick red, cream midrib, hafts with bronze yellow and white striations; beards yellow orange; ruffled. Siva Siva X Matinata. Sheviakov 1995.

ZHELANNY (Galina Shevchenko, R. 1995). MDB, 7½" (19 cm), EM. Lightly ruffled cornflower blue, F. darker; beards light blue at end, darker blue in center, brown in throat; slight musky fragrance. From *I. pumila* sdlgs. Shevchenko 1994.

ZHEMCHUZHINA (Viacheslav Gavrilin, R. 1999). Sdlg. 95-41-1. TB, 35" (88 cm), M. S. light pink;

style arms warm pink; F. light brownish rose purple, light pink patterning around beard; beards tangerine, light pink at end; ruffled. Pink Swan X Hello Hobo.

ZHOLTY VELIKAN (Irina Driagina, R. 1996). Sdlg. 021. TB, 49" (125 cm), EM. Light yellow self; beards yellow; pronounced sweet fragrance. Golden Planet X unknown. Driagina 1964.

ZIGGY (Virginia Keyser, R. 1997). Sdlg. 92-TR-21. TB, 29" (74 cm), EML & RE. S. straw yellow, faint lavender midrib base; style arms straw yellow, faint lavender midstripe; F. ivory ground, erratic broken-pattern splashes of bright purple; beards yellow; slight sweet fragrance. Autumn Bugler X Faux Pas.

ZILLIONAIRE (Barry Blyth, R. 1996). Sdlg. A63-8. TB, 38" (97 cm), ML. S. rich gold; F. deeper gold, faint tan shading; beards mustard gold; slight fragrance. Dance Man X Rembrandt Magic. Tempo Two 1996/97.

ZIMNEYE UTRO (Nina Miroshnichenko, R. 1996). TB, 31" (78 cm), E. S. white; F. white, hafts lemon yellow; beards tangerine; slight sweet fragrance. Parentage unknown. Miroshnichenko 1976.

ZINGLET (Kevin Nilsen, R. 1996). Sdlg. 58-91-1. BB, 20" (51 cm), E. S. white, veined and blushed yellow; style arms white, tinged yellow, yellow crests; F. mauve blue fading white, yellow edge, brown central pattern; beards white, hairs tipped deep yellow. Zing Me X Speculator.

ZING ME (Barry Blyth, R. 1990). Sdlg. V42-A. IB, 20" (51 cm), EM. S. cream to creamy lemon; F. creamy white, lemon edge, large brown circular area 2/3 down; beards brown, bushy. Jazzamatazz X (Embassadora x Evening Echo). Tempo Two 1990/91.

ZIP IT UP (Graeme Grosvenor, R. 1999). Sdlg. V96-2. TB, 33" (84 cm), ML. White overlaid blue violet; beards white; slight fragrance. Zipper Stitch sib X Work Ethic.

ZIPPER STITCH (Graeme Grosvenor, R. 1993). Sdlg. S86-1. TB, 36" (91 cm), EM. S. white; F. white, stitched blue violet; beards yellow, tipped white; ruffled. Momentum X Snowbrook. Rainbow Ridge 1997/98.

ZIRKO (Lucille Robinson, R. 1992). Sdlg. 6-S-3. TB, 30" (76 cm), M. S. cream ground veined lilac; F. upper half cream veined crystal rose, lower half cranberry with 1/4" ruffled rose edge; beards gold; slight sweet fragrance. Focus X unknown. Iris Acres 1993.

ZIV (David Shahak, R. 1992). Sdlg. S-T-81-127 II. AR (OH), 30" (76 cm), M. S. violet (RHS 85A) heavily dotted darker; F. red purple (59B) heavily dotted darker, black purple signal; beards dark purple. *I. samariae* X (*I. mariae* x *I. hermona*). Aril Society, Tira Nurseries 1993.

ZLATI ORNAT (Izidor Golob, R. 1996). Sdlg. R-856/8-A. TB, 41" (105 cm), E. S. lemon yellow; style arms yellow; F. gold yellow, veined rich brown; beards yellow, hairs tipped orange; pronounced sweet fragrance. (Gala Gown x Foxfire) X Kimba. Golob 1996.

ZLATOHLÁVEK (Zdeněk Seidl, R. 1997). Sdlg. 91-YFLC/9. TB, 36" (90 cm), M. S. and style arms dresden yellow (RHS 5C); F. paler, veined dresden yellow; beards orange, end yellow; ruffled; slight sweet fragrance. Yukon Fever X Laced Cotton. Seidl 1998.

ZLATÝ JACEK (Nikola Bolacká, R. 1999). Sdlg. PU 1/99. TB, 32" (80 cm), VE. Ruffled golden yellow self, white flash near tangerine beards; slight sweet fragrance. Parentage unknown.

ZLATÝ PALCÁT (Josef Dudek, R. 1999). Sdlg. 95-GSHR-1. TB, 33" (85 cm), M. Ruffled medium golden yellow, style arms deeper, F. with white blaze; beards golden yellow, white at end and yellow orange in throat; pronounced spicy fragrance. Golden Surrey X Heavenly Rapture.

ZLATÝ PRSTEN (Josef Dudek, R. 1999). Sdlg. 96-EIGS-1. TB, 39" (100 cm), M. S. and style arms creamy mimosa yellow (RHS 8B); F. white, mimosa yellow hafts, veins and 3/16" marginal band; beards lemon yellow, white at end and golden orange in throat; ruffled, laced; slight sweet fragrance. Elegant Impressions X Golden Surrey.

ZOLOTAYA ARFA (V. & N. Gordodelovy, R. 1995). Sdlg. 94. TB, 32" (80 cm), E. Ruffled golden yellow self; beards orange. Parentage unknown. Gordodelovy 1993.

ZOLOTAYA KORONA (Adolf Volfovich-Moler, R. 1998). Sdlg. V-163. TB, 35" (90 cm), M. Ruffled orange yellow; beards orange yellow; slight fragrance. Deep Fire X Christmas Time.

ZOLOTINKA (Galina Shevchenko, R. 1995). MDB, 5" (13 cm), VE. S. golden yellow; F. dark yellow; beards white gold at end, dark yellow midsection, orange in throat; pronounced spicy fragrance. From *I. pumila* sdlgs. Shevchenko 1992.

ZOLOTOYE SERDTSE (Sergey Loktev, R. 1998). Sdlg. 92-L13-7D. IB, 18" (45 cm), L. S. and style arms bright medium yellow; F. mustard yellow, lemon toward center; beards dark yellow at end changing to orange in throat. "Uroda" X Brasier. Loktev 1998.

ZOLOTOY ORFEY (Nina Miroshnichenko, R. 1996). TB, 37" (95 cm), EM. Golden yellow self; beards yellow; slight spicy fragrance. Parentage unknown. Miroshnichenko 1974.

ZOLOTOY TOPAZ (V. & N. Gordodelovy, R. 1995). Sdlg. 84. TB, 39" (100 cm), VE. Golden yellow, violet striations on F. near red beard. Parentage unknown. Gordodelovy 1985.

ZOOT SUIT (Ray Rogers, R. 1998). Sdlg. DCSF-2. TB, 36" (91 cm), ML. Dark purple blue self; beards light grey blue, hairs lightly tipped yellow, yellow in throat; ruffled, shoulders pleated; pronounced sweet fragrance. Dusky Challenger X Star Fleet.

ZORE (Ladislav Muska, R. 1997). Sdlg. LSML-07. TB, 39" (99 cm), M. S. light pinkish orchid; style arms light lavender; F. light lilac lavender; beards red orange; heavily ruffled, lightly laced; slight fragrance. (L'Ely x Sweet Musette) X L'Ely. Muska 1997.

ZOV PREDKOV (Sergey Loktev, R. 1997). Sdlg. L-III-8C. TB, 34" (85 cm), ML. Lilac violet self; beards yellow; pronounced sweet fragrance. Marina Raskova X Stepping Out. Loktev 1997.

ZOWO (Ladislav Muska, R. 1997). Sdlg. IB-PILA-01. IB, 22" (56 cm), M. S. pink; style arms creamy pink; F. pinkish vanilla; beards tangerine; lightly laced; slight fragrance. (Hazel's Pink x Queen in Calico) X Honey Lace. Muska 1996.

ZULA (Ken Fisher, MTB, R. 1989). Riverdale Iris 1990.

ZULU CHIEF (B. Charles Jenkins, R. 1992). Sdlg. B1-3C. SPU, 34-44" (86-112 cm), M. Glowing black purple, subdued gold signal. Ada Perry X Crow Wing. Shepard Iris 1992.

ZURICH (Monty Byers, TB, R. 1989). Moonshine 1990.

ZUYDER ZEE (Nora Scopes, SDB, R. 1972). British Iris Society 1987.

ZUZANA (Ladislav Muska, R. 1999). Sdlg. 99-QCDM-05. TB, 36" (91 cm), M. S. light yellow, heavily marked brown lilac; style arms light brown; F. yellow ground, wide brown lilac edge; beards honey yellow; heavily ruffled, laced; pronounced fragrance. ((Queen in Calico x "Fialovy Kvet": (Windsor Rose x Laced Cotton)) x (Ri-Sampei x Date Bait)) X Spacelight Sketch.

ZYDECO (Patrick O'Connor, R. 1999). Sdlg. 95-11. LA, 28-30" (71-76 cm), M. Burnt orange, F. with yellow lance signal outlined deeper burnt orange. 91-1: (Ann Chowning x President Hedley) X High Rank.

ZZYZX (Richard Richards, R. 1999). Sdlg. 10804. TB, 37" (94 cm), M & RE. S. yellow green (RHS 154D); style arms primrose yellow (4D); F. chartreuse green (1D), citron green (151C) at hafts; beards saffron yellow (21A); slight sweet fragrance. Irish Spring X Green and Gifted.

ABBEY GARDENS, 32009 S. Ona Way, Molalla, OR 97038
ABREGO, TOM & ELLEN, P. O. Box 693, Newberg, OR 97132
A & M PERENNIALS, 3371 Bowen Road, Elma, NY 14059
ACKERMAN, WILLIAM L., P. O. Box 120, Ashton, MD 20861
ADAMGROVE, 31642 Wieneke Branch Road, California, MO 65018
ADAMS, MARGARET, 1509 W. Glenn Ave., Springfield, IL 62704
AHLBURG, MARLENE, Hohes Feld 22, 38531 Roetgesbuettle, Germany
AITKEN, J. TERRY, 608 NW 119th St., Vancouver, WA 98685
AITKEN'S SALMON CREEK GARDEN, 608 NW 119th St., Vancouver, WA 98685
ALBERS, DONOVAN, 11133 Highway 707, Murrells Inlet, SC 29576
ALDRIDGE, DONNA, 7503 W. 54th Terrace, Overland Park, KS 66202
ALLEN, J. R., (deceased), New Braunfels, TX
ALLEN IRIS GARDEN, 1206 E. Common St., New Braunfels, TX 78130
ALLERY, PHILIP, 199 Walsall Rd., Aldridge, Walsall, West Midlands WS9 0BE, England, U.K.
AMBROSIA GARDENS, P. O. Box 1135, Vernon, BC, V1T 6N4, Canada
AMEKHIN, OLEG, kv. 1, d. 18, ul. Dalniaya, Lvov, 290022, Ukraine
AMES, HYRAM L., 3675 South 2110 East, Salt Lake City, UT 84109
AMES, JACK, 1111 N. 34th Ave., Yakima, WA 98902
ANAYA, LABRIANO, 1807 Church Street, Galveston, TX 77550
ANDERSON, C. M., 190 North 14 East, Mountain Home, ID 83647
ANDERSON IRIS GARDENS, 22179 Keather Ave. N., Forest Lake, MN 55025
ANFOSSO, LAURE, B. P. 53, 83402 Hyeres Cedex, France
ANFOSSO, PIERRE, B. P. 53, 83402 Hyeres Cedex, France
ANFOSSO, PIERRE-CHRISTIAN, B. P. 53, 83402 Hyeres Cedex, France
ANNAND, ROBERT, P. O. Box 550, Forest Ranch, CA 95942
ARILIAN ACRES, 4611 Rio Grande Lane NW, Albuquerque, NM 87107
ARIL PATCH, 3843 Concord Blvd., Concord, CA 94519
ARIL SOCIETY INTERNATIONAL;
    (1990-1992): c/o Pete McGrath, 4605 Cairo NE, Albuquerque, NM 87110
    (1993-1996): c/o Steve Walter, 208 South St., Brighton, IL 62012
    (1997-1999): c/o Harold Peters, 22048 Hickok Rd., El Dorado Hills, CA 95762
ARNY, CHARLES, JR., (deceased), Lafayette, LA
ATTENBERGER, EDWIN C., P. O. Box 307, Roscommon, MI 48653
AUSTIN, DAVID -- ROSES, Bowling Green Lane, Albrighton, Wolverhampton WV7 3HB, England,
    U.K.
AUSTIN, GEOFF, 6 Progress St., Kaniva, VIC 3419, Australia
AUSTLAND IRIS GARDEN, 6 Progress St., Kaniva, VIC 3419, Australia
AVONBANK GARDENS, Box 52444, Durham, NC 27717

BACON, CARL & MABEL K., 8619 E. ML Ave., Kalamazoo, MI 49001
BAILEY, A. R. J., 6 Leaze Road, Kingsteignton, Devon TQ12 3JR, England, U.K.
BALDWIN, JOHN O., 31 Schutt St., Newport, VIC 3015, Australia
BALL, MARION E., 25 Lucknow Road, Havelock North, New Zealand
BANGHART, ROBERT M., P. O. Box 1507, Cambria, CA 93428
BARKER, ROBERT C., 101 Royal Oaks Drive, O'Fallon, MO 63366
BAR K IRIS GARDEN, 4435 E. Nancy Ave., Garden City, KS 67846
BARNARD, LEO, (deceased), Paradise, CA
BARNARD, NORMA, 867 Buschmann Road, Paradise, CA 95969
BARR & SONS, Covent Garden, England, U.K.
BARROWS, ANN DEE, P. O. Box 82, Glencoe, OK 74032
BARRY, IAN, 2 Hope St., Dimboola, VIC 3414, Australia
BARRY, WAYNE J., 4265 County Road 99W -- Sp. 34, Orland, CA 95963
BARTLETT, C.E.C. (Cy), Old Mill House, Shurton, Bridgwater, Somerset TA5 1QG, England, U.K.
BARTLETT, NANCY, 3050 Estepa Drive, Cameron Park, CA 95682
BAUER, BOB, 9823 E. Michigan Ave., Galesburg, MI 49053

BAUMSCHULE H. MATTUSCHKA, Emmersdorfer Str. 86, A-9061 Woelfnitz b. Klagenfurt, Austria

BAUMUNK, LOWELL, 10918 N. Sunshine Drive, Littleton, CO 80125

BAUSCH, LYNN, 11530 N. Laguna Drive, Mequon, WI 53092

BAY OF PLENTY IRIS GROUP, c/o Merrilyn May, 26 Oxford Road, Rotoma, RD 4, Rotorua, New Zealand

BAY VIEW GARDENS, 1201 Bay St., Santa Cruz, CA 95060

BEAL, JOHN, Ashleigh, Barnsley Road, Scawsby, Doncaster DN5 8QE, England, U.K.

BEATTIE, RONALD J., 21380 NE Main, Aurora, OR 97002

BEER, MANFRED, Neue Strasse 17, 04420 Markranstaedt, Germany

BEGLEY, JAMES D., 980 Scenic Ave., Santa Rosa, CA 95407

BELARDI, LOIS, 209 Linden St., Santa Cruz, CA 95060

BELFORD, INDRA J., P. O. Box 503, Joseph City, AZ 86032

BELLAGAMBA, LOUISE, 5640 Independence Road, St. Charles, MO 63304

BELLA VISTA GARDENS, 11431 Old St. Charles Road, Bridgeton, MO 63044

BENCH, JANET L., 11232 Morocco Road NE, Albuquerque, NM 87111

BENNETT, NORMAN, Putton Lane, Chickerell, Weymouth, Dorset DT3 4AF, England, U.K.

BENNETTS WATER GARDEN, Putton Lane, Chickerell, Weymouth, Dorset DT3 4AF, England, U.K.

BERG, BARBARA, 140 Gordon Parkway, Syracuse, NY 13219

BERNARD, MIKE, 1079 Bird Ave., San Jose, CA 95125

BERSILLON, MICHÈLE, 17 rue du Reveillon, 54330 Vitrey, France

BERTINOT, NEIL, 282 Marigold Drive, Opelousas, LA 70570

BESSETTTE, M. ELAINE, 831 Alameda Ave., Tacoma, WA 98466

BETTS, T. J., 18 Princeton Court, Thornlie, W.A. 6108, Australia

BETZER, RON, 2090 Vincent Drive, San Martin, CA 95046

BIANCO, AUGUSTO, Via San Pietro 126, 15020 Gabiano (AL), Italy

BILLIE'S IRIS GARDEN, 638 Ash St., Walla Walla, WA 99362

BINGHAM, JAMES M., 5414 Woodburn-Allen Springs Road, Bowling Green, KY 42104

BIRCHWOOD GARDENS, 5000 Eleven Mile Road, Rockford, MI 49341

BISHOP, HARRY, 71 Basket St., Huntington, MA 01050

BLACK, LYNETTE, Box 7, Private Bag, Heriot 9155, West Otago, New Zealand

BLACK, PAUL W., P. O. Box 18278, Salem, OR 97305

BLACK, POLLY, P. O. Box 635, Hatch, NM 87937

BLAKEWAY-PHILLIPS, RICHARD J., Church Cottage, Clun, Craven Arms, Shropshire SY7 8JW, England, U.K.

BLANCO WHITE, ANNE, 72 South Hill Park, London NW3 2SN, England, U.K.

BLODGETT, ARTHUR G., 1008 E. Broadway, Waukesha, WI 53186

BLODGETT IRIS GARDENS, 1008 E. Broadway, Waukesha, WI 53186

BLOSSOM VALLEY GARDENS, 15011 Oak Creek Road, El Cajon, CA 92021

BLYTH, BARRY F., P. O. Box 1109, Pearcedale, VIC 3912, Australia

BLYTH, HEIDI, c/o Tempo Two, P. O. Box 1109, Pearcedale, VIC 3912 Australia

BOBAL, ANNE, 2831 S. Vaughn Way, Aurora, CO 80014

BOHRER, ROY, 1 Summer Court, O'Fallon, MO 63366

BOHRER'S IRIS GARDEN, 1 Summer Court, O'Fallon, MO 63366

BOIS D'ARC GARDENS, 1831 Bull Run Road, Schriever, LA 70395

BOLACKÁ, NICOLA, Dělnická 27, 74801 Hlučín, Czech Republic

BONITA GARDENS, 504 Bonita St., Safford, AZ 85546

BORBELETA GARDENS, 15980 Canby Ave., Faribault, MN 55021

BORGLUM, DANA, 2202 Austin Road, Geneva, NY 14456

BORGLUM'S IRIS, 2202 Austin Road, Geneva, NY 14456

BORO, MARILYN, 2133 Yosemite Drive, Milpitas, CA 95035

BOSWELL, CARL, 1821 Gross Lane, Concord, CA 94519

BOULDIN, ALICE W., (deceased), Elon College, NC

BOWERS, GLENN L., 221 Mountain Road, Dillsburg, PA 17019

BOXWOOD FARMS, Fox Creek Lane, Clarksville, MO 63336

BRADSHAW, HALL, 112 E. Encanto Drive, Tempe, AZ 85281

BRAYBROOK, ERIC, 57 Steele Road, Gisborne, New Zealand

BREHM, ANNE-RUTH & WALTER, St. Laurentiusstr. 31, 34550 Daun/Eifel, Germany

BRENNER, FRANCIS, Rt. 1, Box 1 -- 100 Southeast St., Dakota, IL 61018
BRIDGE IN TIME IRIS GARDENS, 10116 Scottsville Road, Alvaton, KY 42122
BRILE, FLORA, 1681 Ferry St., Anderson, CA 96007
BRITISH IRIS SOCIETY, c/o Derek Carver, 2 Birds Hill Rise, Oxshott, Surrey KT22 0SW, England, U.K.
BROADLEIGH GARDENS, Bishops Hull, Taunton, Somerset TA4 1AE, England, U.K.
BROOK, RICHARD, 48 Blacker Lane, Crigglestone, Wakefield, West Yorkshire WF4 3EW, England, U.K.
BROOMFIELD, R. W., 78 Court Road, Malvern, Worcs. WR14 3EG, England, U.K.
BROWN, B. J., (deceased), Charlotte, NC
BROWN, BOB, (deceased), Oakland, CA
BROWN, OPAL, (deceased), Milton-Freewater, OR
BROWN, R. C., Old Barn, Station Road, Fladbury, Pershore, Worcs. WR10 2QW, England, U.K.
BROWN'S IRIS GARDEN, 1186 W. Dallas St., Syracuse, UT 84075
BROWN'S SUNNYHILL GARDENS, Rt. 3, Box 102, Milton-Freewater, OR 97862
BRYANT, VIRGIL, 1301 SW Ward Road, Lee's Summit, MO 64081
BUCHHOLZ, ALBERT E., 941 Miller Ave., Cupertino, CA 94014
BUCKNER, MARGARET, 3165 Datsonville Road, Clarksville, TN 37042
BUMBLE BEE GARDENS, 801 Logan St., Wayne, NE 68787
BURCH, JAMES G., P. O. Box 146, Elora, TN 37326
BURCH, THOMAS C., 5800 Colonial Drive, Columbia, SC 29203
BURCH FIELDS, 740 Sharpe Road, Columbia, SC 29203
BURCH IRIS GARDEN, 205 Knox Drive, Huntsville, AL 35811
BURGE, THOMAS, Seftigenstr. 199, 3084 Wabern, Switzerland
BURGOYNE, ENID, (deceased), Kingsbridge, Devon, England, U.K.
BURNS, THOMAS J., 5100 E. Morada Lane, Stockton, CA 95212
BURR, FRED A., 195 Crawford Ave., Apt. 410-R, Windsor, ON, N9A 5C3, Canada
BURSEEN, TOM, 1513 Ernie Lane, Grand Prairie, TX 75052
BURTON, JOHN & LUCY, 188 Sagamore St., South Hamilton, MA 01982
BUSCH, RON W., 3 R. D., Leeston, Canterbury, New Zealand
BUSH, GEORGE C., (deceased), York, PA
BUSHNELL, HOWARD, 31 Washington Road, Princeton Jct., NJ 08550
BUTIUKOV, SERGEY, (deceased), Vladivostok, Russia
BUTLER, RICHARD, (deceased), Little Rock, AR
BYERS, MONTY, (deceased), Potter Valley, CA

CADD, ANNA & DAVID, 329 North St., Healdsburg, CA 95448
CAL-DIXIE IRIS GARDENS, 14115 Pear St., Riverside, CA 92508
CALLY GARDENS, Gatehouse of Fleet, Castle Douglas, DG7 2DJ, Scotland, U.K.
CAMEHL-GARTEN, 29399 Wahrenholz-Betzhorn, Germany
CAMICOT ACRES, Rt. 2, Box 8, Norton, TX 76865
CAMPBELL, FARRON, 5637 Saddleback Road, Garland, TX 75043
CAMPBELL, OREN, (deceased), North Little Rock, AR
CANNING, ROBERT & JANET, 45 Simpson Drive, Walnut Creek, CA 94596
CANNON, P. & D., by Jennifer Hewitt
CANTWELL, DOROTHY, 320 N. Ninth, Ponca City, OK 74601
CAPE IRIS GARDENS, 822 Rodney Vista Blvd., Cape Girardeau, MO 63701
CAPRICE FARM NURSERY, 15425 SW Pleasant Road, Sherwood, OR 97140
CAREY, DUANE, Box 95, Romney, IN 47981
CARPENTER, ELLIS L. W., 2 The Causeway, Boxford, Sudbury, Suffolk CO10 5JR, England, U.K.
CARR, FRANKLIN, (deceased), Bordentown, NJ
CARR, MARGARET, 30 Greenwood Drive, Bordentown, NJ 08505
CARROLL, CRAIG, 5A Kenneth Ave., Baulkham Hills, NSW 2153, Australia
CARSON, DUDLEY W., P. O. Box 556, Willamina, OR 97396
CARTER, JOHN R. L., Rowden Gardens, Brentor, nr. Tavistock, Devon PL19 0NG, England, U.K.
CASCADE BULB AND SEED, P. O. Box 271, Scotts Mills, OR 97375
CATTANACH, DORA & VOLMA, 8 Brassey Ave., Rosanna, VIC 3084, Australia
CATTON, HILMARY, (deceased), Havelock North, Hawkes Bay, New Zealand

CAYEUX, B. P. 35, 45501 Gien Cedex, France
CAYEUX, JEAN, B. P. 35, 45501 Gien Cedex, France
CAYEUX, RICHARD, La Carcaudiere, 45500 Poilly lez Gien, France
CELEBRITY IRIS, 1408 Hoffman, Richland, WA 99352
CELESTIAL GARDENS, 1613 Country Club Road, Reidsville, NC 27320
CHADWICK, KEITH, 14000 Oasis Road, Caldwell, ID 83607
CHAPMAN, CHUCK, RR 1 -- 8790 WR 124, Guelph, ON N1H 6H7, Canada
CHAPMAN, SYLVIA, RR 1 -- 8790 WR 124, Guelph, ON N1H 6H7, Canada
CHEHALEM GARDENS, P. O. Box 693, Newberg, OR 97132
CHERNISS, STANLEY, 3895 Windemere Lane, Oroville, CA 95695
CHILDS, JOHN LEWIS, (deceased), Flowerfield, NY
CLARK, BARRY, 20257 Clark Road, Covington, LA 70433
CLARK, BRUCE, The Elms, Panmure, VIC 3265, Australia
CLARK, LEO T., (deceased), Corning, CA
CLAUSSEN, C. T., 4201 S. Ellis Road, Sioux Falls, SD 57106
CLOUGH, WILLIAM HARRY, P. O. Box 196, Pittsfield, PA 16340
COBLE, JOHN, 9823 E. Michigan Ave., Galesburg, MI 49053
COCHRAN, HELEN, 272 Aztec Lane, Henderson, NV 89015
COLE, DEBORAH A., 7417 92nd Place SE, Mercer Island, WA 98040
COLLINS, HEATHER, Flat 2, 71 Cox St., Geraldine, New Zealand
COLLINS, HEC E., 6 Pyes Pa Road, R.D. 3, Tauranga, New Zealand
COLLINS, JEAN, (deceased), Tauranga, New Zealand
COLLINS, PHYLLIS, 8 Dakota Grove, Upper Hutt, New Zealand
COMANCHE ACRES IRIS GARDENS, 12421 SE State Rt. 116, Gower, MO 64454
COMBSIE'S GARDEN, 8138 S. College Ave., Whittier, CA
CONARTY, BERTHE, 9119 Smith Rd., Vernon, BC, V1H 1K2, Canada
CONTEMPORARY GARDENS, Rt. 5, Box 800, Blanchard, OK 73010
COOK, MARK, 9100 SW 202 Av. Rd., Dunnellon, FL 34431
COOK, PHILIP, P. O. Box 338, Underhill, VT 05489
COOLEY'S GARDENS, P. O. Box 126, Silverton, OR 97381
COOLING'S NURSERIES LTD., Rushmore Hill, Knockholt, Sevenoaks, Kent TN14 7NN, England,
    U.K.
COOPER'S GARDENS, 212 West County Road C, Roseville, MN 55133
COPELAND, JAMES A. JR., 25234 67th Avenue, Lawton, MI 49065
COPELAND, JAMES A. SR. & JILL, 78118 M-40, Lawton, MI 49065
CORDON BLEU FARMS, P. O. Box 2033, San Marcos, CA 92079
CORLEW, GLENN F., 2229 Ptarmigan Drive #4, Walnut Creek, CA 94595
COTSWOLD GARDEN FLOWERS, c/o CLM, Newtown, Offenham, Evesham, Worcs. WR11 5RZ,
    England, U.K.
COTTAGE GARDENS, 11314 Randolph Road, Wilton, CA 95693
COUTURIER, GERALDINE, 1724 Drinnen Road, Knoxville, TN 37914
COWDERY, LARRY, 11295 New Ave., Gilroy, CA 95020
COX, ALWYN, (deceaed), Burwood, VIC, Australia
COX, MRS. A. B., 1 Dundas St., Burwood, VIC 3215, Australia
CRAIG, JIM & VICKI, 16325 SW 113th Ave., Tigard, OR 97224
CRANDALL, FRED, (deceased), Seattle, WA
CROFTWAY NURSERY, Yapton Road, Barnham, Bognor Regis, West Sussex PO22 0BH, England,
    U.K.
CRONIN, ARTHUR B., 10920 Oakwood Road, Roscommon, MI 48653
CROSBY, LUZON, (deceased), Orem, UT
CROSS, LIBBY, 8907 Potts Creek Rd., Covington, VA 24426
CROSSPATCH GARDENS, 8907 Potts Creek Rd., Covington, VA 24426
CRUMP, J. GRIFFIN, 8924 Battery Road, Arlington, VA 22308
CRYSTAL PALACE PERENNIALS, P. O. Box 154, St. John, IN 46573
CUYAHOGA VALLEY IRIS GARDENS, 1065 Boston Mills Road, Peninsula, OH 44264

D & J GARDENS, 7872 Howell Prairie Road NE, Silverton, OR 97381
DANIELSON, HENRY, (deceased), Chaparral, NM

DANIELSON, LUELLA, 425 E. Luna Azul Dr., Chaparral, NM 88021
DAVID, REUBEN, 3414 Arbor Lane, Minnetonka, MN 55343
DAVIS, AARON, c/o Royal Botanic Garden, Kew, Richmond, Surrey TW9 3AB, England, U.K.
DAVIS, MARVIN, 226 E. County Road 340 South, Connersville, IN 47331
DEAN, WALTER J., 2334 Whittier Pl., Fairfield, CA 94533
DEEP SOUTH GARDENS, 1218 Duhon Road, Duson LA 70529
DELANEY, LUCY, (deceased), Richmond, Nelson, New Zealand
DEL JUDGE, VIRGINIA, 113 Victoria View Road, Sequim, WA 98382
DELMEZ, DONALD, 3240 Connecticut, St. Charles, MO 63301
DELMEZ GARDENS, 3240 Connecticut, St. Charles, MO 63301
DENKEWITZ, LOTHAR, (deceased), Hamburg, Germany
DENNEY, DONALD, (deceased), Sebastopol, CA
DeROSE, TONY, 21680 Upper Pleasant Ridge, Caldwell, ID 83605
DeSANTIS, PETER J., 7727 Rhea Ave., Reseda, CA 91335
DEXTER, STAN, (deceased), Everson, WA
DICKEY, PHYLLIS, 5080 W. Soda Rock Lane, Healdsburg, CA 95448
DILLARD, TOM, 12 Normandy Road, Little Rock, AR 72207
DODSWORTH, B.L.C., The Old Rectory, East Bridgford, Nottingham, NG13 8PE, England, U.K.
DODSWORTH, JILL R., The Old Rectory, East Bridgford, Nottingham, NG13 8PE, England, U.K.
DOEHNE, W. E., 1941 Castle Ave., Maplewood, MN 55109
DOMINION SEED HOUSE, Box 2500, Georgetown, ON, L7G 5L6, Canada
DONNELL, LESLIE J., (deceased), Brighton, VIC, Australia
DOONAN, SARA, 415 Green Acres Lane, Bosque Farms, NM 87068
DOW, WANDA GAINES, 5837 El Campo, Fort Worth, TX 76107
DRAYCOTT GARDENS, 16815 Falls Road, Upperco, MD 21155
DRIAGINA, IRINA V., ul. Matveevskaya, 42, k. 2, kv. 268, Moscow 119517, Russia
DROBNICH, OLGA A., Porechye, Mozhayski r-n, Moskovskaya obl., 143263, Russia
DUDEK, JIŘÍ, Cihelní 23, 748 01 Hlučín, Czech Republic
DUDEK, JOSEF, Kučoviny 23, 747 17 Darkovice, Czech Republic
DUFFY, L. J., Box 01462, Fairbanks, AK 99710
DUMAS-QUESNEL, MONIQUE, c/o W. H. Perron et Cie, 2914 Boul. Labelle, Chomedey, Laval,
    Quebec H7P 5R9, Canada
DUNCAN, ROGER W., 2536 Old Highway, Cathey's Valley, CA 95306
DUNDERMAN, MARY LOUISE, (deceased), Akron, OH
DUNN, MARY, (deceased), North Highlands, CA
DUNN, ROBERT, 4828 Jela Way, North Highlands, CA 95660
DURIO, KEN, 5853 Hwy. 182, Opelousas, LA 70570
DURRANCE, JOHN R., 4301 E. Cedar, Denver, CO 80222
DVO RAN BOTANICAL GARDEN, ul. Makovskogo, 142, Vladivostok, 690024, Russia
DYBVIG, CLARENCE, 24883 473rd Ave., Baltic, SD 57003
DYER, FLOYD M., (deceased), Wichita, KS
DYER, PERRY, Rt. 5, Box 800, Blanchard, OK 73010
DYER'S GARDEN, 9503 S. Hydraulic, Wichita, KS 67233

EARTHEART GARDENS, RR 1, Box 847, S. Harpswell, ME 04079
ECO GARDENS, P. O. Box 1227, Decatur, GA 30031
ED ALS IRIS, Rt. 5, Box 273, Cynthiana, KY 41031
EDELMAN, REGGIE, 708 N. Tenth St., St. Joseph, MO 64501
EDEN ROAD IRIS GARDEN, Wenatchee, WA
EDINGER, PHILIP W., P. O. Box 637, Cloverdale, CA 95425
ED'S IRIS GARDEN, 633 E. Chevy Chase Drive, Tulare, CA 93274
EHRCKE, LOU A., 2701 Brunswick Dr., Nashville, TN 37207
EICH, ROLLA, 1153 Richard St., Miamisburg, OH 45342
EIGHT MILE GROVE, P. O. Box 7225, Omaha, NE 68107
ELLIS, J. R., The Grove, Well End, Bourne End, Bucks. SL8 5NY, England, U.K.
EMKE, GEORG, Visbeker Damm 22, 49429, Visbek, Germany
EMMERSON, BARRY, 24 Seaward Ave., Leiston, Suffolk, IP16 4BB, England, U.K.
ENGELEN, KOEN, Wijnegembaan 1, 2520 Ranst, Belgium

ENNENGA, JAMES, 6913 Chartwell Road, Knoxville, TN 37931
ENNENGA'S IRIS GARDEN, 1621 N. 85th St., Omaha, NE 68114
ENSATA GARDENS, 9823 E. Michigan Ave., Galesburg, MI 49053
ENSMINGER, ALLAN, 5700 Fremont - #212, Lincoln, NE 68507
EPP, MICHAEL E., 25575 Coder-Holloway Road, Raymond, OH 43067
ERICSON, THOM, 3020 Hill Court, Grand Junction, CO 81504
ERNST, LARRY, P. O. Box 126, Silverton, OR 97381
ERNST, RICHARD C., P. O. Box 126, Silverton, OR 97381
EVANS, PAULINE, 'Peak Alone', P. O. Box 60, Cobargo, NSW 2550, Australia

FABEL-WARD, ROBERT D., 54 Belmont Drive, Little Rock, AR 72204
FACHGRUPPE IRIS der GdS, c/o Erhard Woerfel, Meisenweg 1, 65795 Hattersheim, Germany
FAGGARD, ALBERT C., 3840 LeBleu St., Beaumont, TX 77707
FAIRMOUNT GARDENS, 166 Fairmount St., Lowell, MA
FAITH, M. D., 210 W. Pleasure Ave., Searcy, AR 72143
FALCONER, HELEN, 57 Brandon St., Alexandra, Central Otago, New Zealand
FAN, CHUN, 14 Chestnut Drive, East Windsor, NJ 08520
FANKHAUSER, E. S., 17 Eastgate St., Pascoe Vale South, VIC 3044, Australia
FAN'S IRIS GARDEN, 14 Chestnut Drive, East Windsor, NJ 08520
FARRINGTON, BRIAN, 6969 Bennett Road, Nampa, ID 83686
FEDOROFF, IGOR, by Sylvain Ruaud
FENTON, MARGERY, R.S.D. 315, Baulch Road, Kerang, VIC 3579, Australia
FEUERSTEIN, ABRAM, P. O. Box 55195, Stockton, CA 95205
FIDOCK, COLIN HENRY, 1/13 Margaret Ave., Port Lincoln, S.A. 5606, Australia
FIELD, CYRIL, 44 Railway St., Gillingham, Kent ME7 1YF, England, U.K.
FIELDING, ROY, (deceased), San Gabriel, CA
FILLMORE, KEITH, (deceased), Garden City, KS
FISCHER, EBERHARD, Mitschurinsiedlung 9, 39164 Klein Wanzleben, Germany
FISHER, KENNETH W., 1 Penzance Drive, Bella Vista, AR 72714
FITZGERALD, JACK, (deceased), El Cajon, CA
FLANAGAN, LIN, 5700 Rockhill Road, Fort Worth, TX 76112
FLEMING, MARILYN, 82 Orion Road, Makarewa RD 6, Invercargill, New Zealand
FLEUR DE LIS GARDENS, 185 NE Territorial Rd., Canby, OR 97013
FLINT, JOY, 92 Moss St., Victoria, BC V8V 4L8, Canada
FOREST RANCH IRIS GARDENS, P. O. Box 550, Forest Ranch, CA 95942
FORT, DONA, 3702 E. Lattin Road, West Richland, WA 99352
FORT, LES ALAN, 3702 E. Lattin Road, West Richland, WA 99352
FORT, LYLE, (deceased), Richland, WA
FORT IRIS GARDEN, 2157 Hoxie, Richland, WA 99352
FOSTER, FRANK, 7647 Stayton Road NE, Turner, OR 97392
FOSTER, HARRY, (deceased), Crickhowell, Wales
FOSTER, MAUREEN, -- see PROBERT, MAUREEN
FOUR CEDARS, Rt. 2, Box 188, Augusta, KS 67010
FOUR SEASONS, Forncett St. Mary, Norwich, NR16 1JT, England, U.K.
FOWLER, LUCY, 32 Sterling Cres., Mosgill, Otago, New Zealand
FRAMKE, MABEL, (deceased), Canby, OR
FRANCOIS, JEAN-JACQUES, 14 allee des Buccollines, 78530 Buc, France
FRECH, AGNES, 3890 E. Townsend Ave., Fresno, CA 93702
FREUND, RICHARD, (deceased), Dubuque, IA
FRIENDSHIP GARDENS, 341 Schwartz Road, Gettysburg, PA 17325
FRIESLAND STAUDENGARTEN, Husumer Weg 16, 26441 Jever, Germany
FRY, JAMES & LUCY, (deceased), Wichita, KS
FULTON, CHANDLER, 21 Hillcrest Road, Weston, MA 02193

GADD, FRED W., (deceased), Wethersfield, CT
GADDIE, GENE, 913 S. First St., Norfolk, NE 68701
GADDIES' GARDENS, 601 Eighth St., Stanton, NE 68779
GAMLIN, BOB, by Marty Schafer & Jan Sacks

GARDEN OF THE EAST WIND, 11530 N. Laguna Drive, Mequon, WI 53092
GARDEN OF THE ENCHANTED RAINBOW, Rt. 4, Box 439-B, Killen, AL 35645
GARDENS LTD., 1890 Alfresco Place, Louisville, KY 40205
GARTENBAU BAENSCH, Nossener Str. 1, 09661, Etzdorf, Germany
GARTENCENTER KANIA GMBH, Ganghoferstr. 5, 14476 Neu Fahrland, Germany
GARTMAN, LILLY, (deceased), Los Gatos, CA
GASS, JOHN, 11692 Fir Road, Carthage, MO 64836
GATEWOOD GARDENS, 113 Acacia Dr., Lafayette, LA 70508
GATTY, JOSEPH A., (deceased), Stockton, CA
GAULTER, LARRY, (deceased), Castro Valley, CA
GAVRILIN, VIACHESLAV A., ul. Baramzinoy 14/4, kv. 39, Podolsk, 142100, Russia
GESSERT, GEORGE, 86070 Cougar Lane, Eugene, OR 97402
GHIO, JOSEPH J., 1201 Bay St., Santa Cruz, CA 95060
GIBSON, JAMES, (deceased), Porterville, CA
GIBSON, RICHARD E., (deceased), Roseville, CA
GIGLI, STEFANO, Loc. Pinzano 5, 50060 Pomino, Firenze, Italy
GILLANDER, ROGER, Waitaka Nursery, Gisborne, New Zealand
GILLESPY, DAGON, 408 S. Lafayette, Newton, IL 62448
GINTER, WILLIAM L., 102 West Field, Richmond, KY 40475
GLASSHOUSE WORKS, P. O. Box 97, Stewart, OH 45778
GLAZELEY GARDENS, Bridgnorth, Shropshire, England, U.K.
GLEBE COTTAGE PLANTS, Pixie Lane, Warkleigh, Umberleigh, Devon, EX37 9DH, England, U.K.
GLENLEIGH IRIS GARDENS, Orion Road East, Makarewa, R.D. 6, Invercargill, New Zealand
GODA, GINAN, by Society for Japanese Irises
GODFREY, WILLIAM & ADA, 9 Bradford Ave., Foxborough, MA 02035
GOEBEL, RUTH, (deceased), Denver, CO
GOERBITZ, SIEGMAR, Im Hain 4, 32760 Detmold, Germany
GOLDBECK, KLAUS, Waldemar-Bonsels-Weg 32a, 22929 Ahrensburg, Germany
GOLOB, IZIDOR, Sentilj 117/a, SLO-2212, Sentilj, Slovenia
GORDODELOVY, VITALI & NADEZHDA, ul. Internatsionalnaya 13, kv. 1, Essentuki, Stavropolski Kray, 357600, Russia
GORMLEY GREENERY, 6717 Martha Drive, Cedar Hill, MO 63016
GOTO, S., by Society for Japanese Irises
GOULA, RICHARD, 113 Acacia Drive, Lafayette, LA 70508
GRANDVIEW IRIS PATCH, 3613 Grandview Drive West, University Place, WA 98466
GRANGER, MARVIN, P. O. Box 838, Lake Charles, LA 70602
GRANT, JOSEPH B., 7851 Carmencita Ave., Sacramento, CA 95829
GREEN BOX IRIS GARDENS, 18016 Lafayette, Olney, MD 20832
GREENWOOD, DORIS, (deceased), Vancouver, WA
GREYSTONE, 6450 Delp Road, Muscoda, WI 53573
GRIFFITH, JOSEPH G., 407 Seventh St., Pacific Grove, CA 93950
GRINER, WILLIAM & MARTHA, 21 Chesterfield Rd., Bordentown, NJ 08505
GRISE, WILLIAM, 160 Parkwood Drive, Richmond, KY 40475
GROSVENOR, GRAEME, 8 Taylors Road, Dural, NSW 2158, Australia
GRUMBINE, MARK H. A., 1315 Pride Gap Cove, Cabot, AR 72023
GUILD, DOROTHY, N. 1100 Superior - #175, Spokane, WA 99202

HAGBERG, MARGUERITE, (deceased), Westmont, IL
HAGER, BEN R., (deceased), Stockton, CA
HALINAR, JOSEPH C., 2333 Crooked Finger Road, Scotts Mills, OR 97375
HALL, DAVID, (deceased), Wilmette, IL
HALL, EARL, 1495 Enterprise Road, West Alexandria, OH 45381
HALL, JERRY L., 6432 W. 75th Drive, Arvada, CO 80003
HALL'S FLOWER GARDEN, 1495 Enterprise Road, West Alexandria, OH 45381
HAHN, CLYDE & ANNA, 200 N. School St., Desloge, MO 63601
HAHN'S RAINBOW IRIS GARDEN, 200 N. School St., Desloge, MO 63601
HALE, MARGARET, R.R. 4, Yates Center, KS 66783

HAMBLEN, MELBA B., (deceased), Roy, UT
HAMNER, BERNARD, 960 N. Perris Blvd., Perris, CA 92571
HAMNER'S IRIS GARDEN, 960 N. Perris Blvd., Perris, CA 92571
HANEY, BONNIE, 1016 E. Tenth St., Carrollton, MO 64633
HANSEN, CONSTANCE, (deceased), Lincoln City, OR
HARDER, LARRY, P. O. Box 547, Ponca, NE 68770
HARDING, ROBERT, RMB 739, Nhill, VIC 3418, Australia
HARPER, ALLEN, (deceased), Iola, KS
HARPER, JIM, Rt. 1, Box 24A, Iola, KS 66749
HARPER'S GARDENS, Box 207, Moran, KS 66755
HARRIS, CHAD, P. O. Box 346, Washougal, WA 98671
HARRIS, GWENDA, R.D. 12 O, Oamaru, North Otago, New Zealand
HARRIS, JARED, 93 East 100 South, Logan, UT 84321
HARRISON COUNTY HISTORICAL SOCIETY, P. O. Box 411, Cynthiana, KY 41031
HARVEY, REVIE, c/o Marion Ball, 25 Lucknow Road, Havelock North, New Zealand
HARWOOD, CHERRY, 1429 Park Road, Te Awamutu, Waikato, New Zealand
HATTENBERGER, PIOTR F., ul. Primorskaya, 25, Goretovo, Mozhayski r-n, Moskovskaya obl.,
   143222, Russia
HAVEMAN, DAVID, 509 Oceanview Ave., San Mateo, CA 94401
HAYASHI, ISABURO, by Society for Japanese Irises
HAYMON, DORMAN, 1218 Duhon Road, Duson, La 70529
HAZZARD, ARTHUR, (deceased), Kalamazoo, MI
HEACOCK, MARY ANN, 1235 S. Patton Court, Denver, CO 80291
HEDGECOCK, JIM & LAMOYNE, 12421 SE State Rt. 116, Gower, MO 64454
HELD, FREDERICK W., 40611 Hwy. 226, Scio, OR 97374
HELSLEY, CALVIN, P. O. Box 306, Mansfield, MO 65704
HEMPEL, INGABORG, 6500 74½ Ave. N., Brooklyn Park, MN 55428
HENDERSON, ISABELLE BOWEN, (deceased), Raleigh, NC
HENLEY, R. J., Wychwood Carp Farm, Farnham Road, Odiham, Basingstoke, Hants. RG25 1HS,
   England, U.K.
HERMIT MEDLARS WALK, 3 Pierce St., Foxborough, MA 02035
HERMOSA GARDENS, 2724 First Ave., Safford, AZ 85546
HERZ, URSULA, by John Wood
HEUSS, WOLFGANG, Im Hummerholz 18, 71397 Leutenbach, Germany
HEWITT, JENNIFER, Haygarth, Cleeton St. Mary, Cleobury Mortimer, Kidderminster DY14 0QU,
   England, U.K.
HICKERSON, ALVA, (deceased), Tulsa, OK
HICKERSON, RILLA, 915 S. Canton, Tulsa, OK 74112
HILDENBRANDT'S IRIS GARDENS, 1710 Cleveland St., Lexington, NE 68850
HILL, COLIN, c/o Caroline Ryan-Chacon, 4747 Harlan, Apt. V, Wheat Ridge, CO 80033
HILL, DAMON, 4613 Maddocks Road, Sebastopol, CA 95472
HILL, EDWIN C. & ELYSE J., 4613 Maddocks Road, Sebastopol, CA 95472
HILL, HORACE M., (deceased), Lafontaine, KS
HILLCREST GARDENS, 3365 Northaven Road, Dallas, TX 75229
HILL'S IRIS & PEONY FARM, Lafontaine, KS
HIRAO, SHUICHI, by Society for Japanese Irises
HITE, HARRY, (deceased), Goshen, IN
HOAGE, JOSEPH H., 8425 W. Fifth Place, Lakewood, CO 80226
HOCHHEIMER STAUDENGARTEN, Nordenstaedter Str. 90, 65239 Hochheim, Germany
HOLDEN, MYRTLE, (deceased), by Glenn G. B. Stoneking-Jones
HOLK, HERBERT C., 14115 Pear St., Riverside, CA 92508
HOLLAND, MARTIN, 29106 Meridian E., Graham, WA 98338
HOLLAND GARDENS, 29106 Meridian E., Graham, WA 98338
HOLLEY, JEANNE, P. O. Box 255, Jackson, MO 63755
HOLLINGWORTH, ROBERT, 124 Sherwood Road East, Williamston, MI 48895
HOLLOW, JANE, Pounsley Plants, Pounsley Combe, Spriddlestone, Brixton, Plymouth PL9 0DW,
   England, U.K.
HOLLY LANE GARDENS, 10930 Holly Lane, Osseo, MN 55369

HORTICLUB, 2914 Boul. Labelle, Ville de Laval, Quebec, H7P 5R9, Canada
HOSSACK, MRS. D. J., Janian's Way, 28 Bruce St., Ngongotaha, Rotorua, New Zealand
HUBER, TONY, 4137, 2e rue, Laval, Quebec, H7W 2N2, Canada
HUBLAU, WILLY, Steenweg op Borgloon 37A, 3830 Wellen, Belgium
HULBERT, ELAINE, Rt. 3, Box 57, Floyd, VA 24091
HUMMEL, JIM, 801 Logan, Wayne, NE 68787
HUMPHREY, V. H., Westlees Farm, Logmore Lane, Westcott, Dorking, Surrey RH4 3JN, England, U.K.
HUNT, EUGENE, (deceased), Fallis, OK
HUTCHINSON, JANET, 15 Pymble Ave., Pymble, NSW 2073, Australia
HUTCHINSON, PETER, by Lorena Reid

ICHIE, TOYOKAZU, by Society for Japanese Irises
ILLINI IRIS, 1690 N. State St., Monticello, IL 61856
INGERSOLL, MARIE, 4288 Deming Road, Everson, WA 98247
INGERSOLL'S IRIS TO SEE, 4288 Deming Road, Everson, WA 98247
INNERST, STERLING, 6011 Mountain Road, Dover, PA 17315
I.POPPIN' IRISES, 4747 Harlan St., #V, Wheat Ridge, CO 80003
IRIDE, Via San Pietro 126, 15020 Gabiano (AL), Italy
IRIDESCENCE IRIS NURSERY, P. O. Box 583, Cowra, NSW 2794, Australia
IRIS ACRES, R.R. 4, Box 189, Winamac, IN 46996
IRIS ACRES, P. O. Box 248, Meadows, S.A. 5201, Australia
IRIS AU TRESCOLS, Trescols, 47340 Hautefage La Tour, France
IRIS COUNTRY, 6219 Topaz St. NE, Brooks, OR 97305
IRIS DE THAU, 14, rue des Logis, Loupian, 34140 Meze, France
IRIS EN PROVENCE, B. P. 53, 83402 Hyeres Cedex, France
IRIS GALLERY, THE, 33450 Little Valley Road, Fort Bragg, CA 95437
IRIS GARDEN, THE, Rt. 1, Box CW 21, Spencer, IN 47460
IRIS GARDEN, THE, 47 Station Road, Barnet, Herts EN5 1PR, England, U.K.
IRIS HAVEN, P. O. Box 83, Pennant Hills, NSW 2120, Australia
IRIS POND, THE, 7311 Churchill Road, McLean, VA 22101
IRIS RANCH, THE, P. O. Box 227, Cerrillos, NM 87010
IRIS TEST GARDENS, 1010 Highland Park Dr., College Park, WA 99324
IRISTOCRAT ACRES, 10800 W. Fletcher Ave., R.R. 20, Lincoln, NE 68524
ISHIYAMA, TEIKICHI, by Society for Japanese Irises
ISLES, RON, 50 Woodinville St., Christchurch 8001, New Zealand
ITO, TOICHI, by Society for Japanese Irises

J & L IRIS, 2640 N. Bluff, Wichita, KS 67220
JACKSON, PETER, 5/2 Jewell St., Oaklands Park, S.A. 5046, Australia
JACOBS, DON, Box 1227, Decatur, GA 30031
JAMES, BERYL, Mitchell Highway, Trangle, NSW 2823, Australia
JAMES, WILFORD, 1065 Boston Mills Road, Peninsula, OH 44264
JAMESON, MITCH, 1511 Boyd St., St. Joseph, MO 64505
JEANSELME, MARY, 594 - 30 Road, Grand Junction, CO 81504
JEFFRIES, ROBERT R., (deceased), Healy, KS 67850
JENKINS, B. CHARLES, 9426 E. Topeka Dr., Scottsdale, AZ 85255
JOE PYE WEED'S GARDEN, 337 Acton St., Carlisle, MA 01741
JOHNSEN, LAWRENCE, 9802 N. 40 Drive, Phoenix, AZ 85051
JOHNSON, ALAN, (deceased), Tongala, VIC, Australia
JOHNSON, BEN, 715 W. Stanford, Springfield, MO 65807
JOHNSON, DAVID L., 14940 Willemite St., NW, Ramsey, MN 55303
JOHNSON, JEAN, Findlay Road, Tongala, VIC 3621, Australia
JOHNSON, LARRY, P. O. Box 126, Silverton, OR 97381
JONES, BENNETT C., 5635 SW Boundary St., Portland, OR 97221
JONES, EVELYN, (deceased), Portland, OR
JONES, FRANK, (deceased), Crown City, OH
JORGENSEN, CARL J. C., 1445 Whedbee, Fort Collins, CO 80524

KAKATU, by Society for Japanese Irises
KALKWARF, EUGENE, 8521 West Haven Rd., Lincoln, NE 68528
KAMO, MOTOTERU, 110 Harasato, Kakegawa-shi, Shizuoka-Ken, 436-01, Japan
KAMO NURSERY, 110 Harasato, Kakegawa-shi, Shizuoka-Ken, 436-01, Japan
KANSAS RAINBOW GARDEN, Rt. 1, Box 51, Healy KS 67850
KARY IRIS GARDENS, 6201 E. Calle Rosa, Scottsdale, AZ 85251
KASPEREK, BRAD & KATHIE, 9130 N. 5200 W., Elwood, UT 84337
KATHE, FRANK, Gebauerstr. 20, 01189 Dresden, Germany
KAULEN, MARIYA, ul. Chertanovskaya, 48-1-37, Moscow 113570, Russia
KEGERISE, ELEANOR, 4306 Seventh Ave., Temple, PA 19560
KEGERISE, EVELYN, (deceased), Reading, PA
KEITH, A. D., (deceased), Washougal, WA
KELWAYS LTD., Barrymore Farm, Langport, Somerset TA10 9EZ, England, U.K.
KEPF, JOAN E., P. O. Box 492, 6100 Carroll Lake Road, Union Lake, MI 48387
KEPPEL, KEITH, P. O. Box 18154, Salem, OR 97305
KERR, FREDERICK J., P. O. Box 2191, North Highlands, CA 95660
KEY, FRANCIS SCOTT, -- IRIS SOCIETY, c/o J. Owings Rebert
KEYSER, VIRGINIA, 226 Harvest St., Salinas, CA 93901
KHIMINA, NATALIYA I., Varshawskoye shosse, 143-2-155, Moscow 113405, Russia
KICKAPOO GARDENS, 521 Kickapoo Trail, Frankfort, KY 40601
KINDERMANN, RICHARD L., 54441 Mound Road, Shelby Township, MI 48316
KING, C. R., 183 Padholme Road, Peterborough, Cambs. PE1 5JA, England, U.K.
KINNAMON, JOHN & HELEN, 15146 Galena Drive, Austin, TX 78717
KIRKLAND IRIS GARDEN, 725 - 20th Ave. West, Kirkland, WA 98033
KLEIN, CAROL, Glebe Cottage Plants, Pixie Lane, Warkleigh, Umberleigh, Devon EX39 9DH,
    England, U.K.
KNAUS, JOHN R., 2306 Quail Run, Rockford, IL 61103
KNEE-DEEP IN JUNE, 708 N. Tenth St., St. Joseph, MO 64501
KNEHANS, GERARD, JR., 1008 E. Springfield, Owensville, MO 65066
KNIGHT, HUGH, by John Wood
KNOEPNADEL, UWE, Husumer Weg 16, 26641 Jever, Germany
KNOWLES, F. I. L., (deceased), Sevenoaks, Kent, England
KNOWLES, RUTH, 9 Webbs Meadow, Akehurst Lane, Sevenoaks, Kent TN13 1JN, England, U.K.
KNUDTSON, JOHN P., 14533 Westchester Drive, Colorado Springs, CO 80921
KOMARNICKI, LECH, Rumunki Tupadelskie 23, 87-603, Wielgie, Poland
KONDRATAS, EDMUNDAS, Neries Krantine 24-13, LT-3026, Kaunas, Lithuania
KOROLIOV, VIKTOR M., ul. Perova 19, Enem, Takhtamukayski r-n, Adygeya, 385130, Russia
KRUG, ROY, 1009 Carr St., Lakewood, CO 80215
KUNDE, CLIFTON, 429 Presidential Lane, Madison, WI 53711
KURZMANN, FRANZ, (deceased), Vienna, Austria

LANDSEND GARDENS, 4326 Grandin Road SW, Roanoke, VA 24018
LANGE, ANTHONY W., Rt. 2, Box 8, Norton, TX 76865
LANGTHORNS PLANTERY, High Cross Lane West, Little Canfield, Dunmow, Essex CM6 1TD,
    England, U.K.
LANKOW, CARLA, 11118 - 169 Ave. SE, Renton, WA 98059
LANKOW, CAROL, (deceased), Kirkland, WA
LANTHELME, CHRISTIAN, Route de Beauregard, 26300 Jaillans, France
LAPHAM, NOEL W., P. O. Box 96, Mossburn, Southland, New Zealand
LAST SCENT FARM, P. O. Box 100, Newcastle, OK 73065
LAUER, LARRY, 11314 Randolph Road, Wilton, CA 95693
LAUER'S FLOWERS, 11314 Randolph Road, Wilton, CA 95693
LAURIE'S GARDEN, 41886 McKenzie Hwy., Springfield, OR 97478
LAWYER, INC., 4333 Oak Hill Road, Oakland, CA 94605
LAWYER, LEWIS O., 4333 Oak Hill Road, Oakland, CA 94605
LEAVITT, MEL, (deceased), Whitehouse, NJ
LEMMER, SANDRA, W162 N9917 Mayflower Drive, Germantown, WI 53022

LEWISIA, Le Maupas, 05300 Lazer, France
LIND, ALPHID, 1911 N. Cedar, Tacoma, WA 98406
LINEBERGER, EVERETTE, 2460 Compton Bridge Road, Inman, SC 29349
LLEWELLYN, ALLAN, 102 Victoria St., Eaglehawk, VIC 3556, Australia
LOGAN, AARON, (deceased), Tacoma, WA
LOKTEV, SERGEY, P. O. Box 54, Moscow, 129226, Russia
LONE STAR IRIS GARDENS, 5637 Saddleback Road, Garland, TX 75043
LONGAKER, SHAROL, 22179 Keather Ave., Forest Lake, MN 55025
LONG'S GARDENS, P. O. Box 19, Boulder, CO 80306
LOOMIS, PHILIP A., (deceased), Colorado Springs, CO
LOOP, JOANNE, 518 Persimmon Road, Walnut Creek, CA 94598
LOUISIANA NURSERY, 5853 Highway 182, Opelousas, LA 70570
LOVE, FRANCES E., 11 Frederick St., Carterton, New Zealand
LOVERIDGE, GORDON B., (deceased), Leura, NSW, Australia
LOWE, MICHAEL B., 12219 Zilles Road, Blackstone, VA 23824
LUCAS, ELSIE, 73 Connolly St., Geraldine, South Canterbury, New Zealand
LUKON BULBS, 503 61 Lovčice 30, Czech Republic
LYONS, RAY D., (deceased), Lakewood, CO

MACHULAK, AUDREY, W124 S10077 S. 124th St., Muskego, WI 53150
M. A. D. IRIS GARDEN, 4828 Jela Way, North Highlands, CA 95660
MAEDA, SHICHIRO, by Society for Japanese Irises
MAGEE, TOM, 6631 South Hill Way, Littleton, CO 80120
MAHALO IRIS GARDENS, 320 N. Ninth, Ponca City, OK 74601
MAHAN, CLARENCE, 7311 Churchill Road, McLean, VA 22101
MAKINO, ZENSAKU, by Society for Japanese Irises
MANCHESTER GARDEN, 614 Nandale, Manchester, MO 63021
MAPLE TREE GARDEN, P. O. Box 547, Ponca, NE 68770
MARCHANT, JOHN D., 1451 Springbrook, Walnut Creek, CA 94596
MARKHAM, LYNN & PETER, P. O. Box 154, Lunenburg, MA 01462
MARSH, CONNELL L. & BARBARA, 10800 W. Fletcher Ave., R.R. 20, Lincoln, NE 68524
MARX, WALTER, (deceased), Boring, OR
MARYOTT, WILLIAM R., P. O. Box 1177, Freedom, CA 95019
MARYOTT'S GARDENS, P. O. Box 1177, Freedom, CA 95019
MASTER CREATIONS, 3970 N. Hwy. 89, Prescott, AZ 86301
MATHENY, ED, III, 633 E. Chevy Chase Drive, Tulare, CA 93274
MATHES, HARALD, Husmannstr. 15, 45966 Gladbeck, Germany
MATTHE, VERA, Ilsenburger Str. 5, Zepernick/Berlin, 1297, Germany
MAY, MRS. M. P., Settlement Road, RD 2, Kaikawa, New Zealand
MAYNARD, PETER R., 43 Sea Lane, Goring-by-Sea, Worthing, Sussex BN12 4QD, England, U.K.
McALLISTER, SHARON, P. O. Box 112, Fairacres, NM 88033
McALLISTER'S IRIS GARDEN, P. O. Box 112, Fairacres, NM 88033
McCALL, MAXINE, Rt. 7, Box 311, Rocky Mount, NC 27803
McCORD, CLOYD, 10965 Malta St., Hanford, CA 93230
McCORD'S GARDEN, 10965 Malta St., Hanford, CA 93230
McCOWN, ELEANOR, (deceased), Holtville, CA
McEWEN, CURRIER, 1811 Harpswell Neck Road, Harpswell, ME 04079
McCRAE, MARGARET, 1685 Ruth, Walla Walla, WA 99362
McGRATH, PETE, 11208 Eagle Rock Ave. NE, Albuquerque, NM 87122
McKNEW, JANE, (deceased), Pasadena, MD
McMILLEN, JIM, R.R. 1, Norwich, ON, N0J 1P0, Canada
McMILLEN'S IRIS GARDEN, R.R. 1, Norwich, ON, N0J 1P0, Canada
McWHIRTER, JAMES P., (deceased), Stockton, CA
McVICKER, FRANCIS W., Rt. 1, Box 142-B, Crescent, OK 73028
MEADOWBROOK GARDENS, W269 N686 Meadowbrook Road, Waukesha, WI 53188
MEEK, DUANE & JOYCE, 7872 Howell Prairie Road NE, Silverton, OR 97381
MEININGER, LEROY, 50029 Sunflower Road, Mitchell, NE 69357
MELGERS, J. J., 9 Titoki St., Natamata, New Zealand

MELLIERE, SHANNON, 226 W. Woodland Ridge, Valmeyer, IL 62295
MELROSE GARDENS, 309 Best Road S., Stockton, CA 95215
MEMPHIS BOTANIC GARDEN, 750 Cherry Garden, Memphis, TN 38117
MERTZWEILLER, JOSEPH, (deceased), Baton Rouge, LA
MESSICK, VIRGINIA, 200 Pine Creek Road, Walnut Creek, CA 94598
MESSICK GARDEN, 200 Pine Creek Road, Walnut Creek, CA 94598
METCALF, J. P., Forncett St. Mary, Norwich NR16 1JT, England, U.K.
MICHEL, LEONARD, 77 Westbury Drive, Bella Vista, AR 72714
MID-AMERICA GARDEN, P. O. Box 18278, Salem, OR 97305
MIDDLETON, GARY, 101 Heathfield Road, Hitchin, Herts SG5 1TD, England, U.K.
MILDENBERGER, KARL, (deceased) Hamburg, Germany
MILLAR, KATHY, 8056 McLay Road, Rt. 3, Duncan, BC, V9L 2X1, Canada
MILL CREEK GARDENS, 210 Parkway, Lapeer, MI 48446
MILLER, ANNA MAE, Bronson Place, 1700 Bronson Way - #155, Kalamazoo, MI 49009
MILLER, BERNICE, Rt. 4, Box 439-B, Killen, AL 35645
MILLER, DAVID, 14425 W. 48th Ave., Golden, CO 80403
MILLER, LYNDA, 12788 E. 191st St., Noblesville, IN 46060
MILLER, MARY, 1122 E. Eleventh St., The Dalles, OR 97058
MILLER'S MANOR GARDENS, 12788 191st St., Noblesville, IN 46060
MILLHORN, HENRY O., 4308 Rhoric Road, Athens, OH 45701
MILLIKEN, CARL S., (deceased), Arcadia, CA
MILLIKEN GARDENS, 385 W. Colorado, Arcadia, CA
MILWOOD NURSERY, 2020 Main St., Susanville, CA 96130
MIRONOVA, LIUDMILA, Botanical Garden DVO RAN, ul. Makovskogo, 142, Vladivostok, 690068, Russia
MIROSHNICHENKO, NINA A., Ozdorovitelny per. 4, Zhitomir, 262005, Ukraine
MISSION BELL GARDENS, 2778 West 5600 South, Roy, UT 84067
MISSOULA GARDENS, 1309 Idaho St., Missoula, MT 59801
MISTY HILLS FARMS, 5080 W. Soda Rock Lane, Healdsburg, CA 95448
MITCHELL, SYDNEY B., (deceased), Berkeley, CA
MITSUDA, YOSHIO, by Society for Japanese Irises
MIYAZAMA, BUNGO, by Society for Japanese Irises
MOFFITT, JOHN, JR., (deceased), Unionville, VA
MOHR, DAVID, 8361 Country Oak Station, West Chester, OH 45069
MOHR, HUBERT C., (deceased), Dunwoody, GA
MOHR, KENNETH, 22321 Caminito Tecate, Laguna Hills, CA 92653
MOLDOVAN, STEVE, 38830 Detroit Road, Avon, OH 44011
MOLDOVAN'S GARDENS, 38830 Detroit Road, Avon, OH 44011
MOLLER, MICHAEL, 4702 Bentley Place, Duluth, GA 30096
MONASHEE PERENNIALS, RR 7, S-6, C-9, Vernon, BC, V1T 7Z3, Canada
MON JARDIN, Rue Denis Netgen, L-3801 Schifflange, Luxembourg
MONUMENT IRIS GARDEN, 50029 Sunflower Road, Mitchell, NE 69357
MOONSHINE GARDENS, 5080 W. Soda Rock Lane, Healdsburg, CA 95448
MOORE, RANDALL, 7608 Maehs Circle, Oklahoma City, OK 73162
MOORES, WALTER A., 1860 County Road 170, Oakland, MS 38948
MOORHEAD, GERALD, 16824 Rayen St., North Hills, CA 91343
MOOS, HARALD, Milanstr. 79, 30627 Hannover, Germany
MORGAN, AUSTIN, (deceased), College Park, WA
MORGAN, GRAEME, 'Avilion', Sterkstroom, C.P. 5425, R. South Africa
MORGAN, RICHARD, 271 Grandstaff Drive, Hot Springs, AR 71913
MORLEY, KEVIN, 8404 Cherry, Kansas City, MO 64131
MOSSBURN IRIS GARDEN, P. O. Box 96, Mossburn, Southland, New Zealand
MOUNTAIN VIEW IRIS GARDENS, 6307 Irwin Ave., Lawton, OK 73505
MUELLER, A. THEODORE, 3001 Ivy Drive, #307, North Newton, KS 67117
MUELLER'S GARDEN, 3001 Ivy Drive, #307, North Newton, KS 67117
MULKEY, MARLYN G., 485 Amoros Court, Santa Rosa, CA 95401
MULLIN, RONALD, Rt. 3, Box 84, Pawnee, OK 74058
MURDY, MARIE, 30 Oak Terrace, Howell, NJ 07731

MUSKA, LADISLAV, Jurigovo Nam. 1, 841 05 Bratislava, Slovakia
MY STARZ IRIS, 30 Oak Terrace, Howell, NJ 07731

NATURE'S GARDEN, 40611 Hwy. 226, Scio, OR 97374
NAYLOR, ERNEST, (deceased), Maidstone, Kent, England, U.K.
NAYLOR, THELMA J., 4 Amherst Close, Maidstone, Kent, ME16 0JB, England, U.K.
NEARPASS, D. C., (deceased), College Park, MD
NEBEKER, DON, 296 East 4500 South, Murray, UT 84107
NEILSON, JUDITH, Glenlogan, 7 R.D. Waihao Downs, Waimate 8791, New Zealand
NEJEDLO, PAVEL, 503 61 Lovčice 30, Czech Republic
NELSON, IRIS & JOHN, 19887 Merribrook Drive, Saratoga, CA 95070
NELSON, ROGER, 5735 Green Acres Drive, Anderson, CA 96007
NEMET, PREDRAG, Klanfari 1, Dramalj, HR 51265, Hrvatska - Croatia
NETHERBY GARDENS, Mandeville, R.D. 6, Gore, New Zealand
NEWBURN'S IRIS GARDENS, 1415 Meadow Dale Drive, Lincoln, NE 68505
NEWTON, MARY G., 104 S. Seals, Fort Stockton, TX 79735
NICHOL, JEAN, 25 Weymoor Road, Harborne, Birmingham B17 0RR, England, U.K.
NICHOL, R. E., (deceased), Birmingham, England, U.K.
NICHOLLS, DIANA, 4724 Angus Drive, Gainesville, VA 20155
NICHOLLS GARDENS, 4724 Angus Drive, Gainesville, VA 20155
NICHOLS, HOOKER, 3365 Northaven Road, Dallas, TX 75229
NICHOLSON, GORDON, P. O. Box 578668, Modesto, CA 95357
NICOLL, ALISON, 376 Hill St., Richmond, Nelson, New Zealand
NILSEN, KEVIN & PETER, Iridescence, Mary Road, Cowra, NSW 2794, Australia
NISBET, MR. & MRS. T., 12 Normdale Road, East Bentleigh, VIC 3165, Australia
NISHIDA, NOBUTSUNE, by Society for Japanese Irises
NISHIGUCHI, SHOJI, by Society for Japanese Irises
NISWONGER, O. DAVID, 822 Rodney Vista Blvd., Cape Girardeau, MO 63701
NORRICK, JACK E., 1120 E. County Road 800 N., Muncie, IN 47303
NORRIS, SAM, 3128 Settles Road, Owensboro, KY 42303
NORTH CASCADE GARDENS, Aurora, OR 97002

O'BRIEN, LOIS, 3223 Canfield Road, Sebastopol, CA 95472
O'BRIEN IRIS, 3223 Canfield Road, Sebstopol, CA 95472
O'CONNOR, PATRICK, 109 N. Gatehouse Drive, Apt. C, Metairie, LA 70001
OHIO GARDENS, 148 Alta St., Marietta, OH 45750
OHRSTROM, MAJ, Skiftesvagen 11, S 17550 Jarfalla, Sweden
OKIE IRIS GARDEN, P. O. Box 60673, Oklahoma City, OK 73146
OKKEN, CHARLES R., 2371 Princeton Drive, San Bruno, CA 94066
OLD DOUGLAS PERENNIALS, 6065 Old Douglas Road, Kalamazoo, MI 49007
OLLEY, ANN, West Cottage, Flimwell, Wadhurst, Sussex TN5 7PX, England, U.K.
OLSEN, MERCEDES, (deceased), Richland, WA
OLSON, LOIS J., 4875 E. Louisiana Ave., Denver, CO 80222
ORIN NATIONAL GROWERS, P. O. Box 140625, Edgewater, CO 80214
ORPINGTON NURSERIES, Reigate, Surrey, England, U.K.
ORTENAUER STAUDENCENTER, Windschlägerstr. 11, 77770 Durbach-Ebersweier, Germany
OSBORNE, MANLEY, 1199 Crandano Court, Sunnyvale, CA 94087
OSTHEIMER, RUSTY, 1831 Bull Run Road, Schriever, LA 70395
OSUGI, SHINNOSUKU & RYUICHI, by Society for Japanese Irises
OTEPOPO GARDEN NURSERY, R.D. 12 O, Oamaru, North Otago, New Zealand
OTTERNESS, PAT, 4664 Davis Creek Lane, Lovingston, VA 22949

PACIFIC COAST HYBRIDIZERS, P. O. Box 972, Campbell, CA 95009
PALMER, CLEO, (deceased), Geary, OK
PALMER'S IRIS GARDEN, Rt. 1, Box 152, Geary, OK 73040
PAQUET, SHIRLEY, 857 Circle H Woods Road, Prosperity, SC 29127
PARADISE IRIS, 507 Valley View Drive, Paradise, CA 95969
PARKHILL, TOM, 2822 Island Home Ave., Knoxville, TN 37920

PARK SEED COMPANY, INC., P. O. Box 31, Greenwood, SC 29647

PARKWOOD IRIS GARDENS, 160 Parkwood Drive, Richmond, KY 40475

PAV, SUSAN, 595 Eder Road, Stormville, NY 12582

PAYNE'S JAPANESE IRISES, 84 Whatley Ave., Merton Park, London, SW20 9NU, England, U.K.

PEARSON, HUGH, Kemptville College of Agricultural Tech., Kemptonville, ON, K0G 1J0, Canada

PECAN GROVE GARDENS, 1351 Chesnee Hwy., Gaffney, SC 29341

PEDERICK, BERYL G., 37 Newstead Road, Kojonup, W.A. 6395, Australia

PENNYROYAL GARDENS, 5414 Woodburn-Allen Springs Road, Bowling Green, KY 42104

PERENNIAL GARDENS, 258 St. Ronan St., New Haven, CT 06511

PERMIAN BASIN IRIS SOCIETY, c/o Ann Carnes, Rt. 3, Box 102A, Seminole, TX 79360

PERMIAN BASIN IRIS SOCIETY, c/o Claudette Carnes, 4605 Hendrick, Odessa, TX 79762

PEROMA, Sentilj 117/a, 2212 Sentilj, Slovenia

PERRON, W. H., 2000 Dubois, Boisbriand, Quebec J7E 4H4, Canada

PERRY, AMOS, (deceased), England

PERRY'S HARDY PLANT FARM, Middlesex, England, U.K.

PETERSON, LES, (deceased), Salt Lake City, UT

PEYRARD, JEAN, 101 av. de la Republique, 38170 Seyssinet, France

PHILLIPS, WILLIAM, (deceased), Ellicott City, MD

PHOENIX FLOWER FARM, 2620 Lamson Road, Phoenix, NY 13135

PICKIN, ED M., 48 Glendinning Way, Madeley, Telford, Shropshire TF7 5TB, England, U.K.

PIERCE, JOHN, 8464 Bazemore Road, Cordova, TN 38018

PIERCE COUNTY IRIS SOCIETY, c/o Al Lind, 1911 N. Cedar St., Tacoma, WA 98406

PINEGAR, DARLENE, 40 South 200 West, Spanish Fork, UT 84660

PINKSTON, LUCILLE, 706 Bates Ave., Parma, ID 83660

PIROGOV, YURI, P. O. Box 15, 119121 Moscow, Russia

PLEASURE IRIS GARDENS, 425 E. Luna Azul, Chaparral, NM 88021

PLOTNER, WILLIAM, P. O. Box 250, Molalla, OR 97038

POPE'S PERENNIALS, 39 Highland Ave., Gorham, ME 04038

PORTABLE ACRES, 18341 Paulson SW, Rochester, WA 98579

PORTERFIELD, GARY, 9608 Highway E, Bonne Terre, MO 63628

POTTERTON & MARTIN, The Cottage Nursery, Moortown Road, Nettleton, Caistor, Lincs. LN7 6HX, England, U.K.

POUNSLEY PLANTS, Pounsley Combe, Spriddlestone, Brixton, Plymouth PL9 0DW, England, U.K.

POWELL, LOLETA K., 9468 U.S. Highway 70 East, Princeton, NC 27569

POWELL, MARGE, 3412 Sunday St., Haltom City, TX 76117

POWELL'S GARDENS, 9468 U.S. Highway 70 East, Princeton, NC 27569

POWELL'S IRIS PATCH, 3412 Sunday St., Haltom City, TX 76117

POZNIAK, JOHN, 5004 Williams Road, San Jose, CA 95129

PRAVDYVY, BORYS, ul. Turgenevskaya, 67, kv. 12, Kiev 40050, Ukraine

PRICE, BRIAN P., High Trees, 5 Grange Close, Everton, Lymington, Hants. SO41 0TY, England, U.K.

PROBERT, MAUREEN, 26 Oakapple Close, Willowbridge, Bedlington, Northumberland NE22 7LL, England, U.K.

PROBST, ANN, (deceased), Kirkwood, MO

PROBST, RILEY, 418 N. Van Buren, Kirkwood, MO 63122

PROTZMANN, CLARENCE, (deceased), Milwaukee, WI

PRYOR, BERNARD & HEATHER, 5 Coolabah Ave., Turramurra, NSW 2074, Australia

PYBURN, ALTON, 109 CR 371, Sweetwater, TX 79556

PYE, CLARICE, 137 Main St., Pleasant Point, New Zealand

QUAIL HILL GARDENS, 2460 Compton Bridge Road, Inman, SC 29349

QUINN, LOLA, 522 Asbury Place, Colorado Springs, CO 80906

RAGLE, MARIAN JOYCE, 5216 Poplar Blvd., North Highlands, CA 95660

RAINBOW ACRES, P. O. Box 2191, North Highlands, CA 95660

RAINBOW CHASERS GARDEN, 11692 Fir Road, Carthage, MO 64836

RAINBOW HYBRIDIZING GARDENS, Placerville, CA

RAINBOW RIDGE NURSERY, 8 Taylors Road, Dural, NSW 2158, Australia
RAINBOW'S END GARDEN, 1109 Pine St., Richland, WA 99352
RANCHO DE LA FLOR DE LIS, Cerrillos, NM 87010
RANCHO DE LOS FLORES, 8000 Balcom Canyon Road, Moorpark, CA 93021
RANSOM, LAWRENCE, Trescols, 47340 Hautefage La Tour, France
REBERT, J. OWINGS, 152 Leisters Church Road, Westminster, MD 21157
REDBUD LANE IRIS GARDEN, 2282 N. 350th St., Kansas, IL 61933
REDGATE, CONNIE, by Hilmary Catton
REED, ROBERT L., 2726 Merrill St., Roseville, MN 55113
REID, HELEN, 16 Farnsworth St., Sunshine, VIC 3020, Australia
REID, LORENA, 41886 McKenzie Highway, Springfield, OR 97478
RETTIG, ANNA, 3371 Bowen Road, Elma, NY 14059
REYNA, OZ, 715 Central Canyon, Nampa, ID 83651
RHODES, CHARLES E., 3150 Miami St., St. Louis, MO 63118
RIALTO GARDENS, 1146 W. Rialto, Fresno, CA 93705
RICH, LOIS (JONNYE), (deceased), Roseville, CA
RICHARDS, RICHARD C., 5885 Cowles Mountain Blvd., La Mesa, CA 91942
RICHARDSON, GERALD, 1109 Pine St., Richland, WA 99352
RICHLIE, WAYNE, 1309 Idaho St., Missoula, MT 59801
RICHMOND IRIS GARDEN, 376 Hill St., Richmond, Nelson, New Zealand
RIGBY, COLIN, 18341 Paulson SW, Rochester, WA 98579
RILLALVA IRIS GARDEN, 915 S. Canton, Tulsa, OK 74112
RITCHIE, JAYNE, 24646 180th Ave. SE, Kent, WA 98579
RIVERDALE IRIS GARDENS, P. O. Box 524, Rockford, MN 55373
RIVERVIEW IRIS GARDEN, 21680 Upper Pleasant Ridge, Caldwell, ID 83605
ROBARTS, EVELYN, 215 E. Sherman St., Whittemore, MI 48770
ROBERTS, BARBARA, (deceased), Barre, MA
ROBERTS, ED, 3887 Ninevah Road, Frankfort, KY 40601
ROBERTS, JOAN, 341 Schwartz Road, Gettysburg, PA 17325
ROBERTS, MERLE, 101 Banks, Grand Coulee, WA 99133
ROBERTS BACKYARD IRIS GARDEN, 101 Banks, Grand Coulee, WA 99133
ROBINSON, LUCILLE, 29310 Lynn Road, New Carlisle, IN 46552
ROBINSON, MARGIE L., 558 N. Stratford, Wichita, KS 67206
RODERICK, ELVAN, 3862 Highway O, Farmington, MO 63640
RODERICK HILLVIEW IRIS GARDEN, 3862 Highway O, Farmington, MO 63640
RODIONENKO, GEORGE, Serdobolskaja 9-36, St. Petersburg, 197343, Russia
ROGERS, DOROTHY D., 30935 SW Magnolia, Wilsonville, OR 97070
ROGERS, FRANCIS & RUTH, W269 N686 Meadowbrook Road, Waukesha, WI 53188
ROGERS, RAYMOND, 503 Lee Avenue, North Brunswick, NJ 08902
ROMOLI, VALERIA PALLESI, Via de' Ceci 30, 50135 Firenze, Italy
RORIS GARDENS, 8195 Bradshaw Road, Sacramento, CA 95829
ROSS, WALKER, (deceased), Burlington, ON, Canada
ROWDEN GARDENS, Brentor, nr. Tavistock, Devon PL19 0NG, England, U.K.
ROWLAN, HENRY, (deceased), Little Rock, AR
RUAUD, SYLVAIN, 13 les Caves Simonneau, 37420 Beaumont en Veron, France
RUDOLPH, NATHAN, (deceased), Aurora, IL
RUSSELL, JOHN CLIVE, 47 Station Road, Barnet, Herts EN5 1PR, England, U.K.
RYAN-CHACON, CAROLINE, 4747 Harlan St., Apt. V, Wheat Ridge, CO 80033
RYDER, SHIRLEY, Toadshole Cottage, Old Road, Feering, Colchester, Essex CO5 9RN, England,
    U.K.

SACKS, JANET, 337 Acton St., Carlisle, MA 01741
SAGE, TERESA, 22652 Califa St., Woodland Hills, CA 91367
SAIA, JOE, (deceased), Helena, AR
SANDERS, JEAN, Rt. 4, Box 189, Winamac, IN 46996
SAND HOLLOW IRIS GARDENS, 14000 Oasis Road, Caldwell, ID 83605
SANTA FE IRIS SOCIETY, c/o Bill Huey, P. O. Box 381, Tesuque, NM 87574
SASS BROTHERS, (deceased), Omaha, NE

SATTERWHITE, DALE D., 3331 E. 4th St., Tulsa, OK 74112

SAZIO, VIVETTE, B. P. 53, 83402 Hyeres Cedex, France

SCARBOROUGH, TRUMAN D., 752 Maple Lane, Grenada, MS 38901

SCARBOROUGH'S BACKYARD GARDEN, 752 Maple Lane, Grenada, MS 38901

SCHAFER, MARTY, 337 Acton St., Carlisle, MA 01741

SCHALLER, MARLENE, P. O. Box 748, Altaville, CA 95221

SCHICK, OSCAR A., 1123 Berlin Ave., Henderson, NV 89015

SCHIFFERLI, GREGORY, 1211 McKinley Parkway, Lackawanna, NY 14218

SCHMIDT, IVAR, P. O. Box 248, Meadows, S.A. 5201, Australia

SCHOEPPINGER IRIS GARTEN, Buergerweg 8, 48624 Schoeppingen, Germany

SCHREINER'S GARDENS, 3625 Quinaby Road NE, Salem, OR 97303

SCOPES, NORA, Larch Cottage, 68 Somerset Road, New Barnet, Herts EN5 1JD, England

SEAWAYS GARDENS, 1811 Harpswell Neck Road, Harpswell, ME 04079

SEGUI, JEAN, 11 rue du Palais, 11000 Carcassonne, France

SEIDL, ZDENĚK, Vinohradská 57, 748 01 Hlučín, Czech Republic

SELIGMANN, GUSTAV, (deceased), Las Cruces, NM

SHAHAK, DAVID, Tirat Tsvi, Doar Na, Emek Beit Shean 10815, Israel

SHANNON, DAVID, RR 1, Box 116, Amboy, MN 56010

SHANNON GARDENS, RR 1, Box 116, Amboy, MN 56010

SHAPIRO, JOSEPH, 3205 W. Owasso Blvd., St. Paul, MN 55126

SHAWE, MERRICK, 6405 Fairborn Terrace, New Carrollton, MD 20784

SHEPARD, D. L., 3342 W. Orangewood, Phoenix, AZ 85051

SHEPARD IRIS GARDEN, 3342 W. Orangewood, Phoenix, AZ 85051

SHEVCHENKO, GALINA T., ul. Komsomolskaya, 102, kv. 2, Stavrapol, 35500, Russia

SHEVIAKOV, VIKTOR, ul. Stepana Razina 2, kv. 12, Nikolsk, Pensenskaya obl., 442680, Russia

SHIDARA, HO, Kawagoe Ayame Garden, 791-2 Imafuku, Kawagoe-shi, Saitama-Ken, 350-1151, Japan

SHIMIZU, HIROSHI, 3-6-21 Aihara, Sagamihara-shi, 229-1101 Japan

SHOCKEY, HOWARD, (deceased), Albuquerque, NM

SHOCKEY, IRENE, 4611 Rio Grande Lane NW, Albuquerque, NM 87107

SHOO, MATSUDAIRA, by Society for Japanese Irises

SHOOP, GEORGE, (deceased), Beaverton, OR

SHOOP, ROBERTA, 4521 Broadway, Portland, OR 97213

SHORT, RUBY I., Rt. 1, Box 69, Broadview, NM 88112

SIDES, GARY D., 4601 Packard Drive - #A313, Nashville, TN 37211

SILVERBERG, DAVID, 32009 S. Ona Way, Molalla, OR 97038

SIMON, ELIZABETH, 33310 Jefferson Ave., St. Clair Shores, MI 48082

SIMON, WILLIAM, (deceased), Westland, MI

SIMPSON, ISOBEL, 241 Kenilworth Road, Hastings, New Zealand

SINDT, DAVID, (deceased), Chicago, IL

SLADE, GEORGE D., 305 E. Pike St., Cynthiana, KY 41031

SLAMOVA, H. VALMAR, (deceased), El Monte, CA

SLOAN, RICHARD, 118 E. Walnut, Alma, AR 72921

SMART, STEVE W., 1351 Chesnee Hwy., Gaffney, SC 29341

SMITH, IAN, 8 Wicket Road, Kinson, Bournemouth, Dorset, BH10 5LT, England, U.K.

SMITH, LOUISE CLAY, (deceased), Williamsburg, VA

SMITH, MARKY D., 1014 Crest Acres Place, Yakima, WA 98908

SMITH, MARLE D., 861 Parry Drive, Chadron, NE 69337

SMITH, RAYMOND G., (deceased), Bloomington, IN

SNELLVILLE IRIS GARDEN, 2645 Eldorado Place, Snellville, GA 30278

SOBEK, ROBERT, 37 River St., Box 3125, Westford, MA 01886

SOCIETY FOR JAPANESE IRISES, c/o Clarence Mahan, 7311 Churchill Rd., McLean, VA 22101

SORENSEN, DONALD R., 5000 Eleven Mile Road, Rockford, MI 49341

SPANISH FORK IRIS GARDEN, 40 South 200 West, Spanish Fork, UT 84660

SPARLING, RICHARD, 796 Hampton Road, Pomfret Center, CT 06259

SPARROW, DORA, 16 Idris Road, Christchurch 5, New Zealand

SPEICHERT, C. GREG, P. O. Box 154, St. John, IN 46373

SPENCE, DAVID R., 3970 N. Hwy. 89, Prescott, AZ 86301

SPENCER, M. J. R., Croftway Nursery, Yapton Road, Barnham, Bognor Regis, West Sussex, PO22 0BH, England, U.K.

SPICER, SHIRLEY, 29 Caius Ave., Wanganui, New Zealand

SPOON, DONALD, 1225 Reynolds Road, Cross Junction, VA 22625

SQUIRES, BETTY, 15906 Chase St., North Hills, CA 91343

STADLER, J. D., 6900 Foxworth Dr., Charlotte, NC 28226

STAHLY, HAROLD L., 8343 Manchester Drive, Grand Blanc, MI 48439

STALLCOP, JEAN, 3084 W. Hwy. 40, Greencastle, IN

STANEK, TIMOTHY J., 23329 Ellington Ave., Glenwood, IA 51534

STANLEY IRIS GARDENS, 3245 N. Wing Road, Star, ID 83669

STEEL, JOHN, by Roger Nelson

STEELE, KATHARINE, 2121 Sedley Road, Charlotte, NC 28211

STEINHAUER, W. W., (deceased), Audubon, NJ

STETSON, ROBERT E., II, 2501 S. Cherokee St., Denver, CO 80223

STEVENS, JEAN, (deceased), Wanganui, New Zealand

STEVENS, STEPHEN, P. O. Box 136, Crystal City, MO 63019

STIEN, JOSEPH, 7907 Scott Lane, Machesney Park, IL 61115

STILLHAMMER, JAN, Kamilkova 2, 83106 Bratislava, Slovakia

STILLINGFLEET LODGE NURSERY, Stillingfleet, York YO4 6NW, England, U.K.

STOCKTON IRIS GARDENS, P. O. Box 55195, Stockton, CA 95205

STONEKING-JONES, GLENN G. B., 584 Castro St. - PMB 690, San Francisco, CA 94114

STORNOWAY GARDENS, 2755 Bella Vista, Santa Barbara, CA 93108

STRAWN, KIRK, 1005 Ashburn, College Station, TX 77840

STROHMAN, ROBERT L., 1830 Alfresco Place, Louisville, KY 40205

SUMMERILL, MARGARET, Sutherland Gardens, Alma & Young St., Bombala, NSW 2632, Australia

SUNNYRIDGE GARDENS, 1724 Drinnen Road, Knoxville, TN 37914

SUNSET IRIS GARDEN, 269 Sunset Road SW, Albuquerque, NM 87105

SUPERSTITION IRIS GARDENS, 2536 Old Highway, Cathey's Valley, CA 95306

SUTTON, GEORGE, 16592 Road 208, Porterville, CA 93257

SUTTON'S GREEN THUMBER, 16592 Road 208, Porterville, CA 93257

SYLVIA, SHIRLEY, Box 382, Merbein, VIC 3505, Australia

T & H GARDEN, 1105 Sproles Drive, Fort Worth, TX 76126

TAMBERG, TOMAS, Zimmerstr. 3, 12207 Berlin, Germany

TANKESLEY-CLARKE, ERIC & BOB, 31642 Wieneke Branch Road, California, MO 65018

TASCO, RICHARD, 2536 Old Highway, Cathey's Valley, CA 95306

TAYLOR, CARILLA, Harestock Cottage, 47 Harestock Rd., Winchester, Hants. SO22 6NT, England, U.K.

TAYLOR, F. TERRELL, 504 Bonita St., Safford, AZ 85546

TAYLOR, JOHN C., 8 Taylors Road, Dural, NSW 2158, Australia

TAYLOR, JOHN D., (deceased), England

TAYLOR, JOHN J., 3747 E. Kent Drive, Phoenix, AZ 85044

T.B.'S PLACE, 1513 Ernie Lane, Grand Prairie, TX 75052

TELL'S IRIS GARDENS, 691 W. 8th North, Provo, UT

TEMPO TWO, P. O. Box 1109, Pearcedale, VIC 3912, Australia

TERADA, AKIHIKO, Roris Gardens, 8195 Bradshaw Road, Sacramento, CA 95829

TERRA NOVA GARDENING, Box 19149, Diamond Lake Station, Minneapolis, MN 55419

THOMAS, HENRY F., (deceased), East Bentleigh, VIC, Australia

THOMASON, BOB, Box 60673, Oklahoma City, OK 73146

THOMPSON & MORGAN, Poplar Lane, Ipswich IP8 3BU, England, U.K.

THRUMAN, DANIEL, (deceased), Oregon, WI

THURMAN, HUGH & MARY, 521 Kickapoo Trail, Frankfort, KY 40601

TIFFNEY, SARAH, (deceased), Sharon, MA

TOMINO, KOJI, by Society for Japanese Irises

TOMPKINS, CHET W., (deceased), Canby, OR

TOPNOTCH GARDENS, Chesterton, IN

TOWE, JUNE, Wychwood, Aynall Lane, Little Hereford, Ludlow, SY8 4BA, England, U.K.

TRANQUIL LAKE NURSERY, 45 River St., Rehoboth, MA 02769

TRINDER, A. J., 72 Audley Road, Alsager, Stoke-on-Trent ST7 2QN, England, U.K.

TUBBS, MARY, 9 Lingfield Road, Wimbledon Common, London SW19 4QA, England, U.K.

TUNNEY, JO, RMB 438, Kojonup, W.A. 6395, Australia

TURLEY, ROBERT M., 755 Caloosa Estates Dr., LaBelle, FL 33935

TURNER, HARRY, 2645 Eldorado Place, Snellville, GA 30078

TURNER, KERRYN, c/o Tempo Two Nursery, P. O. Box 1109, Pearcedale, VIC 3912, Australia

UEKI, HISAHARU, by Society for Japanese Irises

UNDERWOOD, SANDRA, by Louise Smith

UPWARD, PRIMROSE, c/o R. C. Brown, Old Barn, Station Road, Fladbury, Pershore, Worcs. WR10 2QW, England, U.K.

VAGABOND GARDENS, 4023 E. Pikes Peak, Colorado Springs, CO 80909

VAN MULDERS, ALPHONSE, Rue du Plangelois 17, B-5310 Taviers, Belgium

VAN VALKENBURGH, ROSA BELLE, 212 Longwood Drive SE, Huntsville, AL 35801

VARIGAY GARDENS, 7909 Cornhusker Hwy., Lincoln, NE 68507

VARNER, D. STEVE, 1690 N. State St., Monticello, IL 61856

VARNER, W. TERRY, 148 Alta St., Marietta, OH 45750

VAUGHN, KEVIN, P. O. Box 350, Stoneville, MS 38776

VENIVITIN, LEONARD L., ul. Utepova, 31/1, kv. 62, Ust-Kamenogorsk, 492085, Kazakhstan

VIETTE, ANDRE, FARM AND NURSERY, Rt. 1, Box 16, Fishersville, VA 22939

VINE AND BRANCH PERENNIAL GARDENS, 11026 Steele Creek Rd., Charlotte, NC 28273

VIZVARIE, CHRIS, Box 100, Newcastle, OK 73065

VOGT, ADOLPH, (deceased), Louisville, KY

VOLFOVICH-MOLER, ADOLF, (deceased), Tashkentskaya obl., Uzbekistan

VON ZEPPELIN, STAUDENGARTNEREI GRAFIN, 79295 Sulzburg-Laufen, Germany

VOSSEN, CAROLE, P. O. Box 7, Igo, CA 96047

WADDICK, JAMES W., 8871 NW Brostrom Road, Kansas City, MO 64152

WADEKAMPER, JULIUS, (deceased), Parkdale, OR

WAECHTER-GARTEN, 25421 Pinneberg, Germany

WAGONTRAIL ACRES, Rt. 5, Box 1363, Sioux Falls, SD 57106

WAIMATE IRIS GARDEN, 4 Durham St., Waimate, South Canterbury, New Zealand

WALLACE, R. & CO., Tunbridge Wells, England, U.K.

WALSTER, FRAN & RALPH, 19923 Broadway, Snohomish, WA 98290

WALSTERWAY IRIS GARDENS, 19923 Broadway, Snohomish, WA 98290

WARBURTON, BEE, (deceased), Westborough, MA

WASMUNDT, MILDRED R., 2730 S. Newland St., Denver, CO 80227

WATSON, ANNE, Ashfield House, Austfield Lane, Monk Fryston, Leeds LS25 5EH, England, U.K.

WAYSIDE GARDENS, Hodges, SC 29695

WEEKS, JEFF, by Farron Campbell

WEIKLE, DARRELL W., P. O. Box 175, Shawsville, VA 24162

WEIKLE'S WONDERLAND, P. O. Box 175, Shawsville, VA 24162

WEILER, JOHN, 1146 W. Rialto, Fresno, CA 93705

WEINREICH, ALFRED, STAUDENGARTEN, 39326 Wolmirstedt, Germany

WELLS, JULIAN, 1807 Church St., Galveston, TX 77550

WERCKMEISTER, PETER, (deceased), Geisenheim/Rhein, Germany

WHITE, CLARENCE G., (deceased), Redlands, CA

WHITE, EDWARD W., 193 Jackson Hill Road, Minot, ME 04258

WHITE, JOHN W., 193 Jackson Hill Road, Minot, ME 04258

WHITE FLOWER FARM, Litchfield, CT 06759

WHITEHOUSE PERENNIALS, R. R. 2, Almonte, ON, K0A 1A0, Canada

WHITELY, JAMES, 3843 Concord Blvd., Concord, CA, 94519

WICKENDEN, MICHAEL, Cally Gardens, Gatehouse of Fleet, Castle Douglas, DG7 2DJ, Scotland, U.K.

WICKENKAMP, FLOYD W., 10521 Bellarose Drive, Sun City, AZ 85351

WICKERSHAM, PAUL, (deceased), Urbana, OH

WIGHT, BARBARA J., 367 Giano Ave., La Puente, CA 91744
WIGHT, JOHN C., P. O. Box 4717, West Covina, 91791
WIGHT, TOM, (deceased), La Puente, CA
WIGHT'S IRIS, P. O. Box 4717, West Covina, CA 91791
WILCOX, JOYCE D., 717 Westowne Ave., Waukesha, WI 53188
WILDER, RUTH, 802 Camellia Drive, Anderson, SC 29625
WILD MOUNTAIN THYME, 486 Skiff St., North Haven, CT 06473
WILDWOOD GARDENS, P. O. Box 250, Molalla, OR 97038
WILKENEIT, UDO & RUDOLF, Wiesenstr. 44, 60385 Frankfurt/Main, Germany
WILKES, WILOH, (deceased), Tujunga, CA
WILKERSON, BETTY, 936 Shive Lane, Lot 9, Bowling Green, KY 42103
WILKINSON, DARLYN SPRINGER, 85 River Road, Topsfield, MA 01983
WILLIAMS, ELMER V., 3200 Winfield Ave., Odessa, TX 79764
WILLIAMSON, BRYCE, P. O Box 972, Campbell, CA 95009
WILLOTT, ANTHONY & DOROTHY, 26231 Shaker Blvd., Beachwood, OH 44122
WILLOWWOOD, P. O. Box 445, Parkdale, OR 97041
WILSON, G. F., Little Garth, Main Road, Utterby, Louth, Lincs. LN11 0TQ, England, U.K.
WILSON, NELL, 23 Nelson St., Albany, W.A. 6330, Australia
WINDWOOD GARDENS, 124 Sherman Road East, Williamston, MI 48895
WINKELMANN, ARTUR, Zieglerweg 13, 86447 Aindling, Germany
WINSPEAR, SUZ, 63 Park Ave., Barbourne, Worcs. WR3 7AJ, England, U.K.
WINTERBERRY GARDENS, 1225 Reynolds Road, Cross Junction, VA 22625
WISE, EILEEN, 197 The Parkway, Iver Heath, Slough, Bucks. SL0 0RQ, England, U.K.
WISE, R. A., (deceased), Iver Heath, Slough, Bucks., England, U.K.
WITT, JEAN, 16516 25th NE, Shoreline, WA 98155
WOERFEL, ERHARD, Meisenweg 1, 65795 Hattersheim, Germany
WOLFF, MYRTLE I., 26 Judith Lane, Waterloo, IL 62298
WOLFORD, HARRY, 9215 State Route 19, Galion, OH 44833
WOOD, JOHN, (deceased), Mooresboro, NC
WOOD, MARION M., Woodlands, Wembury Road, Hollacombe, Devon PL9 0DQ, England, U.K.
WOOD, VERNON, 2568 Henry Ave., Pinole, CA 94564
WOODLAND IRIS GARDENS, P. O. Box 578668, Modesto, CA 95357
WOREL, JACK, 10930 Holly Lane, Osseo, MN 55369
WRIGHT, HORACE, (deceased) Xenia, OH
WRIGHT, SUSAN, 2460 Spahr Road, Xenia, OH 45385
WULF, OPAL M., 7172 S. 70th, Lincoln, NE 68516
WULF'S BACKACHERS, 7172 S. 70th St., Lincoln, NE 68516
WYLE WYNDE NURSERY, Rt. 2, Box 84, Cynthiana, KY 41031
WYSS, BETTY, 1413 S. Liberty, Independence, MO 64055
WYUNA IRIS GARDEN, Panapa Road, Hastings, New Zealand

YOSHIDA, YOSHITERU, by Society for Japanese Irises
YOSHIE, KIYORO, by Society for Japanese Irises
YOSHIE, SEIRO, by Society for Japanese Irises
YOSHINO-EN, by Society for Japanese Irises
YUNKER, NADINE M., N61 W16039 Hawthorne Drive, Menomonee Falls, WI 53051

ZABAYKALSKI BOTANIC GARDEN, Chita, Russia
ZEBRA GARDENS, 9130 North 5200 West, Elwood, UT 84337
ZEPHYRWUDE IRISES, 48 Blacker Lane, Crigglestone, Wakefield, West Yorkshire WF4 3EW, England, U.K.
ZIMMERLY, ELEANOR DuBOIS, P. O. Box 151, Turner, OR 97392
ZINOVIYEVA, GALINA N., ul. Nechayeva, 35-10, Chita, 672012 Russia
ZLIOBIENE, V., c/o Edmundas Kondratas
ZURBRIGG, LLOYD, Box 52444, Durham, NC 27717

ABBREVIATIONS FOR THE AMERICAN IRIS SOCIETY AWARDS
Cited in the following List of Garden Awards

LOWER AND INTERMEDIARY AWARDS

HM HONORABLE MENTION (Awarded to selected irises which have been officially registered and introduced. This is a prerequisite for all other awards listed.)

AM AWARD OF MERIT (Awarded to all classes of irises. This is a prerequisite for all Medal Awards).

CGW CLARENCE G. WHITE MEMORIAL AWARD (Awarded to Aril and Arilbred irises with ½ or more Aril breeding. Equivalent to AM.)

Mitch SYDNEY B. MITCHELL AWARD (Awarded to Californicae irises. Equivalent in value to AM.)

Mohr WILLIAM MOHR MEMORIAL AWARD (Awarded to Arilbred irises with at least ¼ but less than ½ Aril breeding. Equivalent in value to AM.)

Payne W. A. PAYNE AWARD (Awarded to Japanese irises. Equivalent in value to AM.)

Nies ERIC NIES AWARD (Awarded to Spuria irises. Equivalent in value to AM.)

W-W WILLIAMSON-WHITE AWARD (Awarded to Miniature Tall Bearded irises. Equivalent in value to AM.)

MEDAL AWARDS

Cap-W CAPARNE-WELCH MEDAL (Awarded to Miniature Dwarf Bearded irises. Eligible after receiving AM.)

CGW CLARENCE G. WHITE MEDAL (Awarded to Aril and Arilbred irises with ½ or more Aril breeding starting in 1993. Eligible after winning A.M. or equivalent award).

Cook COOK-DOUGLAS MEDAL (Awarded to Standard Dwarf Bearded irises. Eligible after receiving AM).

DeB-M MARY SWORDS DEBAILLON MEDAL (Awarded to Louisiana irises. Eligible after receiving AM).

Knowl KNOWLTON MEDAL (Awarded to Border Bearded irises. Eligible after receiving AM).

Mitch SYDNEY B. MITCHELL MEDAL (Awarded to Californicae irises starting in 1993. Eligible after winning A.M. or equivalent award).

Mohr WILLIAM MOHR MEDAL (Awarded to Arilbred irises with at least 1/4 but less than 1/2 Aril breeding starting in 1993. Eligible after winning A.M. or equivalent award).

Mor-W MORGAN-WOOD MEDAL (Awarded to Siberian irises. Eligible after receiving AM).

Payne W. A. PAYNE MEDAL (Awarded to Japanese irises starting in 1993. Eligible after winning A.M. or equivalent award).

Nies ERIC NIES MEDAL (Awarded to Spuria irises starting in 1993. Eligible after winning A.M. or equivalent award).

Sass HANS AND JACOB SASS MEDAL (Awarded to Intermediate Bearded irises. Eligible after receiving AM).

W-W WILLIAMSON-WHITE MEDAL (Awarded to Miniature Tall Bearded irises starting in 1993. Eligible after winning A.M. or equivalent award).

Wister JOHN C. WISTER MEDAL (Awarded to Tall Bearded irises starting in 1993. Eligible after receiving A.M.)

Dykes DYKES MEMORIAL MEDAL (Highest award any iris can receive. All classes of irises eligible after receiving preliminary medal for class).

GARDEN AWARDS OF THE AMERICAN IRIS SOCIETY
1990 - 1999

(As voted by Accredited Garden Judges)

Compiled by Sara Marley and David Silverberg

VARIETY	HYBRIDIZER	H.M.	A.M. OR EQUIVALENT	MEDAL AWARDS
Aaron's Shield	Rich, J.	'98		
Abba Alias Abba	Ensminger, A.	'97		
Abbey Road	Silverberg, D	'96	'98	
Abraco	Innerst, S.	'97		
Abstract Art	Keppel, K.	'92	'95	
Acadiana Sunset	Goula, R.	'98		
Acadian Miss	Arny, C.			DeBM '90
Acapulco Sunset	Nichols, H.	'95	'97	
Acey Deucey	Ensminger, A.	'97		
Ack-Countable	Ackerman, W.	'94		
Acoma	Magee,T.	'92	'94	Wister '97
Advance Design	Jones, B.	'96		
Aegean Storm	Nichols, H.	'96		
Affirmation	Corlew, G.	'94		
Afternoon Delight	Ernst, R.		'93	
After the Ball	Hager, B.	'96		
After the Dawn	Ernst, R.	'97		
After the Storm	Innerst, S.	'94	'96	
Age of Innocence	Kerr, F.	'97		
Age of Chivalry	Ghio, J.	'95		
Ain't Misbehavin'	Ernst, R.	'98		
Air Show	Belardi, L.	'99		
Alabaster Unicorn	Sutton, G.	'99		
Aladdin's Flame	Messick, V.	'95	'97	
Aladdin's Treasure	Pinegar, D.	'96	'98	
Alaskan Seas	McWhirter, J.	'94	'96	
Alene's Other Love	Dean, W.	'96		
Alexander's Ragtime Band	Gaulter, L.	'96		
Alice Briscoe	Briscoe, H.	'90		
Alice Goodman	Roderick, E.	'90	'93	
Ali Khan	Shockey, H.	'98		
Allendale	Sparling, R.	'91		
Alley Cat	Willott, A. & D.	'91		
All Right	Hager, B.	'90		
All That Glitters	McAllister, S.	'95		
All the Way	Danielson, H.		'94	
All Together	Gatty, J.	'95		
Almaden	Maryott,W	'92		
Almeria	Wolford, L.	'91		
Almost Heaven	Niswonger, D.	'99		
A l'Orange	Gartman, L.	'98		
Alphaspu	Jenkins, B.C.	'95	'97	
Alpine Twilight	Durrance, J.	'98		
Alright Already	Seligmann, G.	'99		
Altruist	Schreiner		'91	
Amadeus	Tompkins, C.	'93		
Amazon Bride	Hager, B.	'90		
Amber Tambour	Ernst, R.	'93		
Ameila Bedeila	Innerst, S.	'95		

VARIETY	HYBRIDIZER	H.M.	A.M. OR EQUIVALENT	MEDAL AWARDS
American Classic	Schreiner	'98		
America's Cup	McWhirter, J.	'91	'93	
Amethyst Wings	Ackerman, W.	'92		
Anacrusis	Mathes, H.	'95	'99	
Ancient Scrolls	Rich, L.	'92		
Ancient Scrolls	Rich, L.	'92		
Angel Echo	Ennenga, J.	'90		
Angel's Halo	Miller, L.	'94		
Angels In Flight	Messick, V.	'97		
Angel's Star	Danielson, L.	'91		
Ann	Lineberger, E.	'92		
Anna Glitsch	Nichols, H.	'91		
Ann Blocher	Blocher, C.	'92		
Anne Gaddie	Gaddie, G.	'93		
Anne Murray	Moller, M.	'98		
Annick	McEwen, C.	'90		
Answered Prayers	Keppel, K.	'97		
Aplomb	Ghio, J.	'94	'98	
Apollo's Touch	Nichols, H.	'93	'95	
Apricot ala Mode	Boswell, C.	'91		
Apricot Drops	Aitken, T.	'98		
Apricot Frosty	Niswonger, D.	'94	'96	
Apricot Topping	Black, P.	'99		
April Angel	Nichols, H.	'95		
April Fog	Nichols, H./Niswonger, D.	'92		
April Fresh	Brizendine, M.	'90	'95	
April In Paris	Wood, V.	'94	'97	
Aquatic Alliance	Reid, L.	'97	'99	
Aqua Whispers	Miller, A.M.	'90	'92	Mor-W '95
Arabian Archer	Rich, L.	'95		
Arabian Midnight	Rich, L.	'91		
Arbee	Wood, J.	'92		
Arctic Express	Gatty, J.	'98		
Arctic Rebloomer	Lankow, Carla	'97	'99	
Aril Reverie	Moores, W.	'92		
Arizona Convention	Niswonger, D.	'90		
Armada	Keppel, K.	'90		
Around Midnight	Schreiner	'97		
Art Deco	Schreiner	'99		
Artesian Lady	Lyons, R.	'90		
Art Faire	Schreiner	'95		
Art Nouveau	Messick, V.	'94		
Art School Angel	Vizvarie, C.	'93		
Ascent of Angels	Bernard, M.	'98		
Ashley Michelle	Mertzweiler, J.	'91	'94	
Asian Alliance	Witt, J.	'93	'95	
Ask Alma	Lankow, Carol		'91	Sass '94
Astra Girl	Varner, T.	'92		
Atten	Shockey, H.	'96	'99	
Aunt Shirley	Mertzweiller, J.	'96		
Aura Light	Blyth, B.	'98		
Auroralita	Weiler, J.	'94		
Aurora's Blush	Willott, A. & D.	'96		
Austrian Garnets	Maryott, W.	'93		
Autumn Circus	Hager, B.	'94		
Autumn Maple	Weiler, J.	'96		

VARIETY	HYBRIDIZER	H.M.	A.M. OR EQUIVALENT	MEDAL AWARDS
Autumn Tryst	Weiler, J.	'97		
Avalon Sunset	Schreiner	'96		
Awakening	Meek, D.	'96		
Baboon Bottom	Kasperek, B.	'96	'98	
Baby Bengal	Sutton, G.	'92		
Baby Blue Marine	Denney, D.		'91	
Baby Boom	Byers, M.	'94		
Baby Grand	Meek, D.	'97		
Babylonian Fires	Rich, L.	'95		
Baby Red Mohr	Boswell, C.		'95	
Baby Sister	McEwen, C.	'91		
Bagdad's Folly	Rich, L.	'95		
Bajazzo	Dunn. M.			DeB '92
Balch Springs	Nichols, H.	'96		
Bali Bali	Jenkins, B.C.	'91		
Balkana Baby	Boswell, C.	'90		
Ballerina Princess	Stadler, J.D.	'94		
Ballet Lesson	Niswonger, D.	'96	'99	
Ballet Slippers	Willott, A. & D.	'92		
Baltic Star	Stahly, H.	'96	'98	
Banded Rogue	Boswell, C.	'92		
Band of Angels	Hollingworth, R.	'99		
Bangles	Miller, L.	'97	'99	
Bantam	Varner, S.		'92	
Basso	Ensminger, A.	'92		
Batik	Ensminger, A.		'90	Knowl '92
Battle Royal	Ghio, J.	'98		
Baubles and Beads	Miller, L.	'99		
Bayou Dawn	Rowlan, H.	'97		
Bayou Mystique	Dunn, M.	'93	'95	DeB '98
Bay Ruffles	Warburton, B.	'91	'93	
Beach Baby	Tasco, R.	'97		
Be a Dream	Niswonger, D.	'94		
Beautiful Vision	Schreiner	'94		
Bedford Lilac	Jones, B.	'93	'95	Cook '97
Bee Early	Miller, L.	'91		
Before the Storm	Innerst, S.	'91	'93	Wister '95 Dykes '96
Beguine	Keppel, K.	'92		
Be Happy	Aitken, T.	'94		
Being Busy	Hager, B.	'95		
Belissinado	Corlew, G.	'91		
Bella Bella	Boswell, C.	'90		
Bellender Blue	Bauer, R./Coble, J.	'96	'98	
Bells Are Ringing	McWhirter, J.	'96		
Bernard McLaughlin	McEwen, C.	'90		
Berry Rich	Ensminger, A.		'92	
Bertwistle	Innerst, S.	'92	'96	
Best Bet	Schreiner	'90	'93	
Betty Cooper	McCown, E.			Nies '93
Betty Dunn	Niswonger, D.	'98		
Betty Frances	Mahan, C.	'91		
Betty My Love	Wickenkamp, F.	'91		
Between the Lines	Schafer, M./Sacks, J.	'94	'96	
Bewilderbeast	Kasperek, B.	'97	'99	
Big Bird	Magee, T.	'96		

VARIETY	HYBRIDIZER	H.M.	A.M. OR EQUIVALENT	MEDAL AWARDS
Big Easy	Dunn, M.	'99		
Big Money	Ghio, J.		Mitch '90	
Big Victory	Burch, J.	'92		
Billie the Brownie	Burton, J.	'95	'97	W-W '99
Bimini	Brown, R.		'92	
Bionic Flash	Danielson, H.	'90	'95	
Bionic Focus	Danielson, H.	'94	'98	
Birthday Greetings	Ghio, J.	'96		
Birthday Surprise	Maryott, W.	'95		
Bite Size	Miller, L.	'90		
Bit More	Miller, L.	'92		
Bit o' Magic	Miller, L.	'94		
Bitsy	Hager, B.	'93	'95	
Bitsy Blue	Miller, L.	'94	'96	
Bittersweet Joy	Miller, L.	'96		
Black as Night	Meek, D.	'94	'96	
Blackbeard	Weiler, J.	'91	'93	
Blackbeard's Ghost	McAllister, S.	'96		
Blackberry Jam	Willott, A. & D.	'97		
Black Cherry Delight	Niswonger, D.	'95		
Black Falls	Nebeker, D.	'98		
Black Flag	Stahly, H.		'90	
Black Suede	Willott, A. & D.	'98		
Black Tie Affair	Schreiner	'95	'97	
Blast	Hager, B.	'96		
Blenheim Royal	Schreiner,	'92	'94	
Blink	Miller, L.	'98		
Blitz	Weiler, J.	'92		
Blonde Bombshell	Ghio, J.	'99		
Blood Covenant	Nichols, H.	'93		
Blowtorch	Byers, M.	'90		
Blue Aristocrat	Schreiner	'90		
Blue Ballet	Keppel, K.	'93		
Bluebird In Flight	Niswonger, D.	'90	'93	
Blue Bubbles	Hamner, B.	'92		
Blue Chip Pink	Niswonger, D.	'92	'94	
Blue Embers	Bauer, R./Coble, J.	'97		
Blue Eyed Blond	Ensminger, A.	'91	'93	Sass '95
Blue-Eyed Maiden	Willott, A. & D.	'95		
Blue Line	Jones, B.		'91	
Blue Moment	Meek, D.	'97		
Blue Montana Skies	Nelson, R.	'98		
Blue Neon	Black, P.	'92		
Blue Nymph	Gaddie, G.	'90		
Blue Suede Shoes	Schreiner	'98		
Bogota	Ghio, J.	'92		
Bohemian	Schreiner	'91		
Bold and Beautiful	McAllister, S.	'94		
Bold Look	Schreiner	'96		
Bold Sentry	Peterson, L.		Mohr '90	
Bold Stroke	Jones, E.	'95	'99	
Boogie Woogie	Nichols, H.	'95	'97	Wister '99
Boom Boom Bunny	Miller, L.	'97		
Border Bandit	Black, P.	'91	'93	
Boss Tweed	McWhirter, J.	'95	'98	
Bottled Sunshine	Nichols, H.	'97		

VARIETY	HYBRIDIZER	H.M.	A.M. OR EQUIVALENT	MEDAL AWARDS
Bountiful Harvest	Hager, B.	'93		
Boxwink's Golden Dream	Steinhauer, W.	'96		
Boy o' Boy	Ghio, J.		'90	
Boy Next Door	Black, P.	'96		
Boysenberry Buttercup	Lauer, L.	'99		
Bozrah	Gadd, F.	'92	'94	Mohr '98
Braggadocio	Keppel, K.	'99		
Brash	Gatty, J.	'98		
Brave New World	Feuerstein, A.	'98		
Brazilian Holiday	Schreiner	'99		
Breakers	Schreiner		'90	
Bridesmaid's Apparel	Danielson, L.	'96		
Brighten the Corner	Ensminger, A.	'99		
Brighten Up	Hager, B.	'92		
Brindled Beauty	Ensminger, A.	'96	'99	
Broad Grin	Lankow, Carol	'90		
Broadway Baby	Gatty, J.	'92	'94	
Brocaded Gown	Tompkins, C.	'90		
Bronze Art	Jenkins, B.C.	'95		
Bronze Falcon	Danielson, L.	'90	'95	
Bronzette Star	Kegerise, Ev.	'94	'96	
Brownberry	Willott, A. & D.		'91	
Brownie Boy	Brizendine, M.	'91		
Brown Imp	Fry, J. & L.	'90		
Bubble Dancer	Ghio, J.	'97		
Bubble Up	Ghio, J.	'91		
Bubbling Along	Ghio, J.	'96		
Buckeye Belle	Willott, A. & D.	'92		
Bugleboy Blues	Sutton, G.	'99		
Bugles And Horns	Sutton, G.	'99		
Bugsy	Hager, B.	'96	'98	
Bumblebee Deelite	Norrick, J. & G.		W-W '90	W-W '93
Bunnicula	Innerst, S.	'95		
Bunny Hop	Black, P.	'90		
Burgundy Blues	Gaddie, G.		'91	
Burra Sahib	Hager, B.	'93		
Busy Being Blue	Denney, D.	'92	'96	
Butterflies in Flight	Aitken, T.	'94	'96	Payne '98
Butterfly Mode	Reid, L.	'95	'97	
Butter Pecan	Hager, B.			Sass '91
Bye Bye Blues	Sutton, G.	'99		
Cabot Cove	Lauer, L.	'96		
Cafe Ole'	Ghio, J.	'95		
Cairo Lady	Lyons, R.	'93		
Cajun Angel	Rowlan, H.	'98		
Cajun Beauty	Schreiner	'94		
Cajun Cookery	Hager, B.	'94	'97	
Cajun Queen	Miller, L.	'98		
Cajun Rhythm	Schreiner	'98		
Cajun Spices	Maryott, W.	'97		
Cajun Sunrise	Mertzweiller, J.	'96	'98	
Cajun Sunset	Granger, M.	'97		
Calamari	Copeland, Jill	'98		
Calico Cat	Lankow, Carol	'91	'93	Knowl '95
Calico Kid	Ensminger, A.	'95	'97	
Calico Kitten	Tompkins, C.	'97		

VARIETY	HYBRIDIZER	H.M.	A.M. OR EQUIVALENT	MEDAL AWARDS
California Style	Jones, B.	'92	'94	
Calling Card	Messick, V.	'94	'96	
Calm Sea	Hager, B.	'94		
Can Can Dancer	Lauer, L.	'99		
Candle Lace	Jenkins, B.C.	'92	'95	
Can Do	Ensminger, A.	'97		
Candy Floss	Keppel, K.	'92		
Candy Fluff	Miller, L.	'90	'93	
Candyland	Byers, M.	'90		
Candystriper	Warburton, B.	'94	'96	
Cannington Bluebird	Bartlett, C.	'95		
Cannonball	Schreiner	'96		
Can't Elope	Miller, L.	'94		
Capaneus	Innerst, S.	'90	'95	
Caprician Butterfly	Marx, W.		Payne '90	Payne '94
Captain's Joy	Schreiner	'96		
Captive Sun	Jones, B.	'96	'98	
Caracas	Ghio, J.	'93		
Caramel and Honey	Hahn, C.	'93		
Careless Sally	Schafer, M./Sacks, J.	'99		
Car Hop	Black, P.	'90		
Caribbean Dream	Schreiner	'92	'96	
Carmel Mission	Ghio, J.	'97		
Carmen Jean	Helsley, C.	'99		
Carnival Song	Schreiner	'96		
Carol Lee	Fisher, K.	'91	'93	
Carol's Dream	Dunderman, M.	'92	'95	
Carriwitched	Innerst,S.	'96		
Cascade Creme	Reid, L.	'95		
Cascade Crest	Aitken, T.	'90	'93	Payne '95
Cascade Spice	Reid, L.	'91		
Cascade Spring Dress	Reid, L.	'96		
Cascade Springs	Schreiner	'96		
Cascade Storm	Reid, L.	'96		
Cascade Velvet	Halinar, J.	'98		
Casper's Shadow	Niswonger, D.	'92		
Castle Stronghold	Nichols, H.	'90		
Cathy Childerson	Johnson, D.	'90	'93	
Cat Nap	Tompkins, C.	'90		
Cee Cee	Innerst, S.	'98		
Cee Jay	Lankow, Carol	'94	'96	Sass '98
Celebration Song	Schreiner	'95	'97	
Centering Point	Ghio, J.	'93		
C'est Bonne	Dunn, M.	'90	'94	
C'est Fantastique	Dunn, M.	'94	'96	
Champagne Elegance	Niswonger, D.		'91	
Champagne Frost	Keppel, K.	'99		
Champagne Waltz	Schreiner	'96	'98	
Champagne Wishes	Keppel, K.	'94		
Change Artist	Corlew, G.	'90		
Change of Pace	Schreiner	'93	'97	
Change Your Ways	Ernst, R.	'98		
Chantilly Lace	Maryott, M.	'95		
Chapter	Innerst, S.	'92		
Chardonnay	Smith, M.	'98		
Charming Darlene	Miller, A.M.	'90		

VARIETY	HYBRIDIZER	H.M.	A.M. OR EQUIVALENT	MEDAL AWARDS
Charming Image	Flanagan, L.	'93		
Charter Member	Ghio, J.	'99		
Chatter	Ghio, J.	'95		
Cheating Heart	Keppel, K.	'96	'98	
Cheery Lyn	Miller, A.M.	'95		
Cher	Nelson, R.	'94		
Cherokee Heritage	Nichols, H.	'95		
Cherokee Nation	Hedgecock, J.	'96		
Cherry	Dunderman, M.	'91	'94	
Cherry Cup	Morgan, R.	'93	'96	
Cherry Flirt	Aitken, T.	'93		
Cherry Glen	Maryott, W.	'97		
Cherry Lane	Corlew, G.	'95		
Cherry Tart	Aitken, T.		'92	
Chez Michelle	Dunn, M.	'99		
Chief Quinaby	Schreiner	'93		
Chief Sequoia	Weiler, J.	'94	'96	Mitch '99
Child Bride	Miller, L.	'92		
China Peach	Lankow, Carol	'99		
China West Lake	Waddick, J.	'99		
Chinese New Year	Ghio, J.	'99		
Chippewa Brave	Rogers, F.	'93		
Chocolate Cupcake	Jeffries, R.	'91	'94	
Chocolate Fudge	Niswonger, D.	'90	'93	Nies '96
Chocolate Marmalade	Fort, Les	'93		
Choose A Juice	Burseen, T.	'99		
Christmas	Gatty, J.	'93	'96	
Chubby Cheeks	Black, P.			Cook '91
Chubby Cherub	Aitken, T.		'90	Cap-W '92
Churchill Downs	Mohr, K.	'92		
Cimarron Rose	Nichols, H.	'92	'94	
Cinnamon Apples	Black, P.	'92	'94	Cap-W '96
Cinnamon Stick	Niswonger, D.		Nies '90	Nies '95
Circus Circus	Sutton, G.	'99		
Circus Jewel	Albers, D./Nichols, H.	'90		
Circus World	Schreiner	'97		
Citron Frommage	Rogers, F.	'99		
City Lights	Dunn, M.	'93	'95	
City of Paris	McWhirter, J.	'96		
Clara Ellen	Jenkins, B.C.	'97		
Clarence	Zurbrigg, L.	'95	'97	
Classic Bordeaux	Ernst, R.	'99		
Classic Look	Schreiner	'94	'96	
Classmate	Keppel, K.	'95		
Classy Babe	Miller, L.	'92		
Classy Chassy	Osborne, M.	'93		
Clear Creek	Jones, B.	'98		
Clear Morning Sky	Ernst, R.	'95		
Close Contact	Flanagan, L.	'93		
Close Shave	Meek, D.	'98		
Cloud Ballet	Fort, Lyle	'93		
Clue	Wood, V.	'97		
Coalignition	Burseen, T	'97		
Colette	Brown, B.	'94		
Coloradoan	Magee, T.	'98		
Color Curls	Gaddie, G.	'92		

VARIETY	HYBRIDIZER	H.M.	A.M. OR EQUIVALENT	MEDAL AWARDS
Color Focus	Jenkins, B.C.	'92	'96	
Color Me Blue	Schreiner	'99		
Comandante	Ghio, J.	'97		
Comeback Trail	Nichols, H.	'93	'95	
Coming Up Roses	Gatty, J.	'94	'96	
Competitive Edge	Ernst, R.	'93	'95	
Confectionery	Ernst, R.	'94		
Conjuration	Byers, M.	'91	'94	Wister '98 Dykes '98
Conspiracy	Messick, V.	'99		
Continuity	Innerst, S.	'98		
Contrast In Styles	Hollingworth, R.	'91	'95	
Cool Melodrama	Nichols, H.	'91		
Cool Treat	Lankow, Carol	'97		
Copper Trident	Hager, B.	'96		
Coral Shell	Jones, B.	'91		
Coral Sunset	Schreiner	'93	'97	
Corona Gold	Maryott, W.	'99		
Coronation Anthem	Hollingworth, R.	'92	'94	Mor-W '97
Cote d'Or	Schreiner	'93	'95	
Cotton Plantation	Dunn, M.	'97		
Countess Zeppelin	Hager, B.		'93	Nies '97
Country Dance	Jones, E.	'99		
Country Gentleman	Bellagamba, L.	'96		
Coup de Grace	Dunn, M.	'94		
Coup D'Etat	Dunn, M.	'93	'95	
Coup de Ville	Dunn, M.	'94		
Court Magician	Nichols, H.	'90	'95	
Cozumel	Ghio, J.	'99		
Cranapple	Aitken, T.	'97	'99	
Cranberry Cooler	Dunn, R.	'99		
Cranberry Crush	Aitken, T.		'90	
Cranberry Delight	Aitken, T.	'97	'99	
Cream and Peaches	Niswonger, D.	'96		
Cream Cake	Niswonger, D.	'93		
Credit Line	Ghio, J.	'98		
Crispin	Miller, R. & L.	'90		
Cross Current	Keppel, K.	'97		
Crowned Heads	Keppel, K.	'99		
Cruise Control	Lauer, L.	'97		
Crystal Dreams	Shockey, H.	'91		
Crystal Ruffles	Dunderman, M.		W-W '91	
Crystalyn	Dunn, R.		'90	
Cum Laude	Ensminger, A.	'90		
Cuss a'Blue Streak	Miller, D.	'95	'98	
Cust	Niswonger, D.	'91		
Cute Orange Horn	Sutton, G.	'90		
Cute Stuff	Boswell, C.	'90		
Cutting Edge	Ghio, J.	'96		
Dainty Bianca	Witt, J.	'90		
Daisy Fresh	Willott, A. & D.	'90		
Dakota Moon	Schreiner	'95		
Dance Away	Hamblen, M.	'92		
Dance Hall Dandy	Maryott, W.	'99		
Dance Hall Dolly	Maryott, W.	'96		
Dances With Wolves	Loop, J.	'94		

VARIETY	HYBRIDIZER	H.M.	A.M. OR EQUIVALENT	MEDAL AWARDS
Danube Waltz	Nichols, H.	'97		
Daredevil	Keppel, K.	'90		
Dark Crystal	Byers, M.	'92		
Darkness	Hager, B.	'97		
Dark Rings	Gatty, J.	'95	'99	
Darkside	Schreiner		'91	
Dark Vader	Miller, R. & L.		'91	Cook '93
Dark Waters	Aitken, T.	'94	'97	
David Keith	Stadler, J.D.	'94		
Davy Jones	Hager, B.	'92		
Dawning	Ghio, J.	'97	'99	
Dawn of Change	Ernst, R.	'96		
Day Glow	Keppel, K.	'99		
Dear Dorothy	Roderick, E.	'91		
Dear Jean	Kerr, F.	'99		
Debbie Reynolds	Schick, O.	'98		
Debrenee	Maryott, W.	'98		
Dee Mouse	Danielson, H.		CGW '90	
Deep Blue Sea	Ghio, J.	'95	'98	
Degas Dancer	Schreiner	'96	'98	
Delta Belle	Dunn, M.	'90		
Delta Blues	Schreiner	'96	'98	
Delta Twilight	Dunn, M.	'99		
Desert Attire	Shockey, H.	'99		
Desert Celebration	Flanagan, L.	'98		
Desert Diamond	Hager, B.	'90		
Desert Finery	Rich, L.	'92		
Desert Fury	Shockey, H.	'96	'98	
Desert Joy	Flanagan, L.	'99		
Desert Jubilee	Flanagan, L.	'99		
Desert Melody	Flanagan, L.	'92	'96	
Desert Mirage	Rich, L.	'91		
Desert Moonlight	Rich, L.	'93		
Desert Orange	Jones, B.	'95		
Desert Plum	Hager, B.	'95		
Desert Spring	Flanagan, L.	'90		
Desert Thunder	Flanagan, L.	'94		
Desert Trumpet	Flanagan, L	'94	'97	
Designing Woman	Gatty, J.	'92	'94	
Devil's Dream	Schafer, M./Sacks, J.	'93		
Diabolique	Schreiner	'99		
Dianne's Daughter	McEwen, C.	'91		
Diddler	Nichols, H.	'96		
Different Approach	Innerst, S.	'94		
Dimity Butterfly	Reid, L.	'96	'98	
Diomedes	Innerst, S.	'95	'97	
Dirigo Debutante	White, J.	'98		
Dirty Devil Canyon	Durrance, J.	'98		
Discovered Gold	Jones, E.	'98		
Distant Roads	Keppel, K.	'93		
Divine	Dunn, M.	'90		
Dodge City	Lauer, L.	'98		
Doll	Keppel, K.		'91	
Dorothea Marquart	Innerst, S.	'97		
Dorothy Davis	Innerst, S.	'99		
Dorothy Howard	Palmer, C.	'91		

VARIETY	HYBRIDIZER	H.M.	A.M. OR EQUIVALENT	MEDAL AWARDS
Dorothy Palmer	Stevens, S.	'90		
Dot Com	Jones, B.	'99		
Dotted Doll	Fry, J. & L.		'93	
Dotted Line	Reid, L.	'95	'97	
Dottie Joy	Witt, J.	'92		
Double Agent	Maryott, W.	'92		
Double Banded	Boswell, C.	'90		
Double First	McEwen, C.	'90		
Down Payment	Danielson, H.	'90		
Dracula's Shadow	Hedgecock, J.	'93		
Drambuie	Willott, A. & D.	'91		
Dream Catcher	McAllister, S.	'96		
Dreamsicle	Schreiner	'97		
Dream Waltz	Willott, A. & D.	'92		
Dress Circle	Hager, B.		Nies '92	
Drive You Wild	Ghio, J.		Mitch '91	Mitch '94
Drum Roll	Hager. B.	'94		
Dumpling	Hager, B.	'90		
Dunsmuir	Brown, B.	'94		
Dusky Challenger	Schreiner		'90	Dykes '92
Dusky Thief	Nichols, H.	'91		
Dynamite	Schreiner	'99		
Eagle's Flight	Schreiner		'91	
Earthquake	Ghio, J.	'95	'97	
Earth Song	Kegerise, Ev.	'97		
Easter	Keppel, K.	'98		
Easter Lace	Byers, M.	'90		
Ebb and Flow	Hirao, S.	'91		
Edge of Frost	Dienstbach, M.	'90	'93	Payne '96
Edith P. Wheeler	McWhirter, J.	'97		
Edith Wolford	Hager, B.		'90	Dykes '93
Egret Snow	Sindt, D.		'91	
Egyptian Lullaby	Nichols, H.	'91		
Elainealope	Kasperek, B.	'98		
Electric Avenue	Nelson, R.	'93		
Electric Glow	Aitken, T.	'95	'98	
Electric Rays	Aitken, T.	'92	'94	Payne '97
Electric Shock	Messick, V.	'99		
Elegant Impressions	Schreiner	'95		
Elfin Magic	Willott, A. & D.	'92	'95	
Elisabeth McEwen	White, J.	'99		
Elizabeth Marrison	Nichols, H.	'91		
Elizabeth Poldark	Nichol, R. E.	'94		
El Niño	Ghio, J.	'97		
Elsie Richardson	Richardson, G.	'95		
El Torito	Jones, B.	'99		
Elusive Butterfly	Ghio, J.		'90	
Emperor Moon	Jensen, E.	'93		
Emperor's Concerto	Wood, V.	'97		
Emperor's Delight	Schreiner	'99		
Emu Zing	Kasperek, B.	'99		
Energizer	Shockey, H.	'98		
Engraved Invitation	McAllister, S.	'96		
Enhancement	Ghio, J.	'99		
Ensign	Tankesley-Clarke, E.	'96		
Envogue	Dunn, M.	'94		

VARIETY	HYBRIDIZER	H.M.	A.M. OR EQUIVALENT	MEDAL AWARDS
Epicenter	Ghio, J.	'96	'98	
Epimetheus	Innerst, S.	'96		
Erect	Black, P.	'92		
Ermine Doll	Dexter, S.	'97		
Escalona	Ghio, J.	'98		
Esmeralda	Ghio, J.	'90		
Evelyn Harris	McWhirter, J.	'94		
Even Handed	Dunn, M.	'99		
Evening Gown	Ghio, J.		'93	
Evening Magic	Schreiner	'93		
Evening Silk	Aitken, T.	'94		
Everything Plus	Niswonger, D.			Dykes '91
Exquisite Lady	Owen, A.		'91	
Extra	Palmer, C.	'92		
Extraordinaire	Dunn, M.	'95	'98	
Exuberant Chantey	McEwen, C.	'93		
Faded Jeans	Bishop, H.	'99		
Fairy Fingers	Willott, A. & D.	'96		
Fallen Angel	Meek, D.	'97		
Fall Fiesta	Schreiner	'94		
Fancy Stitches	Burch, J.	'96		
Fancy Woman	Keppel. K.	'97	'99	
Fanfaron	Hager, B.	'90		
Far and Away	Dunn, M.	'96		
Faraway Places	Keppel, K.	'90		
Fashion Designer	Keppel, K.	'97		
Fashion Statement	Gatty, J.	'99		
Fatal Attraction	Kerr, F.	'98		
Fathom	Smith, M.	'99		
Fat 'n Sassy	Gaddie, G.	'92		
Fault Zone	Ghio, J.	'94		
Faux Pas	Keppel, K.	'92	'94	
Favorite Angel	Jones, B.	'92		
Feature Attraction	Schreiner	'96	'98	
Feminine Fire	Ernst, R.	'94		
Femme Fatale	Gatty, J.	'91		
Festive Glow	Willott, A. &. D.	'99		
Festive Mood	Schreiner	'95		
Fickle Storm	Gadd, F.	'91		
Fiddle Faddle	Hager, B.	'91		
Field of Dreams	Denney, D.	'93		
Fiesta Song	Wood, V.	'95		
Filibuster	Ghio, J.	'97		
Film Festival	Keppel, K.	'95		
Finalist	Gatty, J.	'96		
Finally Free	Jenkins, B.C.	'91		
Finsterwald	Innerst, S.	'98		
Firebreather	Schreiner	'94		
Firebug	Gatty, J.	'96		
Fire on Ice	Weiler, J.	'93		
Firestarter	Willott, A. & D.	'99		
Firestorm	Smith, M.	'96	'98	
First Interstate	Schreiner	'93	'95	
First Sergeant	Danielson, L.	'91		
Five o'Clock World	Nelson, R.	'99		
Fixed Star	Hager, B.	'92		

VARIETY	HYBRIDIZER	H.M.	A.M. OR EQUIVALENT	MEDAL AWARDS
Fjord	Nelson, R.	'99		
Flashy Flirt	Guild, D.	'92		
Flights of Fancy	Keppel, K.	'95	'98	
Flivver	Innerst, S.	'90		
Flower Shower	Weiler, J.	'93		
Fly With Me	Aitken, T.	'93		
Foothill Banner	Lawyer, L.	'92	'95	
Footloose	Schreiner	'95		
Forbidden Fruit	Gartman, L.	'97		
Foreign Intrigue	Bauer, R./Coble, J.	'98		
Foreign Statesman	Ernst, R.	'95		
Forever In Love	Mahan, C.	'99		
Forge Fire	Ernst, R.	'94		
Fort Bragg	Denney, D.	'91		
Forte	Black, P.	'90		
Fort Point	Wood, V.	'90	'93	
Frank Chowning	Rowlan, H.		'91	DeB '93
Freckled Sunshine	Black. P.	'93		
French Toast	Sindt, D.	'94		
Friday Blues	Lankow, Carol	'99		
Friday Harbor	Lankow, Carol	'91		
Frilly Milly	Witt, J.	'91		
Fringe Benefits	Hager, B.	'90	'92	
Frizzy Lizzy	Weiler, J.	'91		
Frosted Cranberry	Miller, A.M.	'94	'96	Mor-W '98
Frosted Plum	Rich, L.	'99		
Frosted Velvet	Fisher, K.	'91	'93	W-W '95
Frostico	Gartman, L.	'94		
Frosting	Gatty, J.	'95	'99	
Frothingslosh	Innerst, S.	'96		
Frozen Blue	Ernst, R.	'98		
Fruit Cocktail	Keppel, K.	'99		
Fruit Salad	Miller, L.	'91		
Fuji Skies	Tompkins, C.	'93		
Fuji's Snowcap	Bush, G.	'92		
Full Moon Rising	Mohr, D.	'93		
Fun Fest	Brown. O.	'92		
Funny Face	Brizendine, M.		'90	Cap-W '94
Funny Girl	Gibson, J.	'97		
Gala Performance	Miller, A.M.	'93		
Galilee Prince	Danielson, L.	'95		
Gallant Rogue	Blyth, B.	'94	'96	
Galway	Keppel, K.	'99		
Garden Gnome	Black, P.	'91		
Geisha Doll	Matheny III, E.	'98		
Geisha Eyes	Arny, C.	'96	'99	
Geisha Obi	Rich, L.	'91	'95	Payne '99
Gemstar	Smith, M.	'96	'98	
Gentle Dragon	Miller, L.	'90		
Gentle Showers	Sprowls, H.	'91		
Getup and Go	Tompkins, C.	'93		
Ghost Dancer	McAllister, S.	'95		
Ghost Gossip	Nichols, H.	'98		
Giraffe Kneehiz	Kasperek, B.	'98		
Girl Next Door	Black. P.	'93		
Giuseppe	Jenkins, B.C.	'99		

VARIETY	HYBRIDIZER	H.M.	A.M. OR EQUIVALENT	MEDAL AWARDS
Glad Choice	Pierce, J.	'99		
Glitz 'n Glitter	Black, P.	'90	'92	
Glory Story	Weiler, J.	'92		
Gnu	Kasperek, B.	'96	'98	
Gnu Again	Kasperek, B.	'96	'98	
Gnu Blues	Kasperek, B.	'96	'98	
Gnu Rayz	Kasperek, B.	'99		
Gnus Flash	Kasperek, B.	'98		
Gnuz Spread	Kasperek, B.	'98		
God's Handiwork	Ghio, J.	'93		
Golden Edge	McEwen, C.	'97		
Golden Galaxy	Weiler, J.	'92		
Golden Gusto	Gaddie,G.	'92		
Golden Muffin	Niswonger, D.		'90	
Golden Sculpture	Rich, L.	'93		
Gold Frosting	Niswonger, D.	'95		
Goldkist	Black, P.	'95	'99	
Gold Speculator	Williamson, B.	'97		
Good and True	Ensminger, A.	'90		
Goodbye Girl	Schreiner	'97		
Goodbye Heart	Schreiner	'91		
Good Doctor	Mertzweiller, J.	'97		
Good Guy	Hager, B.	'93		
Good Looking	Schreiner	'97		
Good Show	Hager, B.	'91	'95	
Good Vibrations	Schreiner	'99		
Gordola	Ghio, J.	'99		
Gordonville Cream	Niswonger, D.	'98		
Grapelet	Aitken, T.	'91	'93	Cap-W '97
Graphique	Dunn, M.	'98		
Grateful Citizen	Innerst, S.	'97		
Gratuity	Hager, B.	'93		
Great Gatsby	McWhirter, J.	'97	'99	
Greeting Card	Ghio, J.	'99		
Guadalajara	Ghio, J.	'91	'95	
Guadalupe	Maryott, W.	'96		
Gull's Wing	McGarvey, W.	'92		
Guru	Keppel, K.	'97		
Gypsy Romance	Schreiner	'96	'98	
Gypsy Woman	Schreiner		'91	
Gyro	Aitken, T.	'91	'93	
Hafnium	Innerst, S.	'90		
Halfway To Heaven	Niswonger, D.	'98		
Halo In Cream	Niswonger, D.	'95		
Halo In Gold	Niswonger, D.	'95		
Halo In Orange	Niswonger, D.	'91		
Halo In Pink	Niswonger, D.	'92		
Halo In Rosewood	Niswonger, D.	'95	'97	
Halo In Yellow	Niswonger, D.	'91		
Handshake	Ghio, J.	'94	'98	
Hanky	Magee, T.	'91		
Harlem Nocturne	Willott, A. & D.	'97		
Harpswell Chanteuse	McEwen, C.	'96		
Harpswell Snowburst	McEwen, C.	'96		
Harpswell Velvet	McEwen, C.	'95	'97	
Harry Hite	Hite, H.	'90	'93	

VARIETY	HYBRIDIZER	H.M.	A.M. OR EQUIVALENT	MEDAL AWARDS
Harvest King	Schreiner	'94		
Haute Couture	Gatty, J.	'98		
Heavenly Rapture	Schreiner	'93		
Helen Cochran	McWhirter, J.	'99		
Helen Leader	Innerst, S.	'99		
Helga's Hat	Nichols, H.	'92	'94	
Helicopter	Shidara, H.	'90		
Heliotrope Bouquet	Hollingworth, R.		'90	
Hellcat	Aitken, T.			Sass '90
Hello Darkness	Schreiner	'94	'96	Wister '98 Dykes '99
Hello-Goodbye	Nelson, R.	'95		
Hers	Ensminger, A.	'94		
Hey There	Lankow, Carol	'95	'98	
Hidden Oasis	Rich, L.	'93		
Highborn Kinsman	Nichols, H.	'90		
High Drama	Gatty, J.	'95		
Highline Coral	McCown, E.		Nies '91	
Highline Snowflake	McCown, E.	'94	'96	
High Standards	Hollingworth, R.		'92	
Hi Ho Silver	Byers, M.	'93		
Hilo Surf	Durrance, J.	'94		
Hippo'z Tutu	Kasperek, B.	'98		
His	Ensminger, A.	'92		
Hissy-Fit	Innerst, S.	'91		
Holden's Child	Tiffney, S.	'94	'96	
Holiday Flame	Schreiner	'90		
Holly Golightly	McWhirter, J.	'99		
Hollywood and Vine	McWhirter, J.	'96		
Hollywood Blonde	Gatty, J.	'91		
Holy Night	Mohr, K.		'91	
Honeymoon Suite	Ghio, J.	'93		
Honky Tonk Blues	Schreiner	'90	'92	Wister '94 Dykes '95
Honky Tonk Hussy	Meek, D.	'93	'95	
Hoodlum	Keppel, K.	'99		
Hoopla	Danielson, L.	'91		
Horatio	Hager, B.	'93	'97	
Hot	Byers, M.	'94		
Hot Buttons	Aitken, T.	'98		
Hot Chocolate	Ghio, J.	'97		
Hotdogs and Mustard	Kasperek, K.	'97	'99	
Hot Fudge	Hager, B			Sass '92
Hot Pink	Weiler, J.	'93		
Hot Spice	Aitken, T.	'91	'93	Sass '97
Hot Spot	Boswell, C.		'95	
Hot Streak	Ghio, J.	'90		
Hottentot	Smith, M.	'97	'99	
Hot to Trot	McWhirter, J.	'93		
Hot Wheels	Black, P.	'92		
Hubbub	Ensminger, A.	'91		
Huckleberry Fudge	Gibson, J.	'99		
Hug a Bunch	Shoop, G.	'90		
Hula Hoop	Shoop, G.	'98		
Iapetus	Innerst, S.	'90	'94	Payne '97
Ice and Indigo	Willott, A. & D.	'94	'97	

530

VARIETY	HYBRIDIZER	H.M.	A.M. OR EQUIVALENT	MEDAL AWARDS
Iced Tea	Lauer, L.	'96		
Icy Peaks	Vogt, A.	'91		
Idylwild	Ghio, J.	'92	'94	Mitch '96
Ignition	Stahly, H.	'92		
Ila Remembered	Hager, B.	'95	'97	
I'll Fly Away	Michel, L.	'99		
Illini Dame	Varner, S.	'90		
Illini Fountain	Varner, S.	'97	'99	
Illini Glory	Varner, S.	'91		
Illini Purple Pepper	Varner, S.	'91		
Illini Ruby	Varner, S.	'92		
Imaginarium	Meek, D.	'95		
Immortality	Zurbrigg, L.		'90	
Impressionist	Ghio, J.	'90		
Inaugural Ball	Ghio, J.	'90		
Incendiary	Smith, M.	'99		
In Depth	Hager, B.	'90	'94	
Indian Beauty	Weiler, J.	'95		
Indigo Princess	Schreiner	'94	'97	
Indiscreet	Ghio, J.	'90		
Indulge	Nelson, R.	'97		
Indy	Hollingworth, R.		'91	
Infernal Fire	Richardson, G.	'97		
Infini	Corlew, G.	'96		
Ink on Ice	Aitken, T.	'97	'99	
Inky Dinky	Black,	'93		
Inky Elf	Willott, A. & D.	'99		
Inland Princess	Hamner, B.	'90		
Inner Fires	Witt, J.		'93	
In Person	Hager, B.	'93		
In Reverse	Gatty, J.	'95	'97	
Instructor	Innerst, S.	'90	'94	
In the Money	Ghio, J.	'91		
In Toto	Boswell, C.	'95		
Into the Night	Schreiner	'91		
In Town	Blyth, B.	'90		
Irish Moss	Jones, B.	'96		
Isabelle	Warburton, B.	'91		
Island Dancer	Shoop, G.	'94		
Island Sunset	Schreiner	'94		
Island Surf	Aitken, T.	'97		
Isn't This Something	Ensminger, A.	'95		
It's Magic	Maryott, W.	'98		
It's Wild	Ghio, J.	'93		
Jaciva	Harris, C.	'95		
Jade Jewels	Aitken, T.	'91		
Jade Maid	Aitken, T.	'98		
James Bond	Smith, M.	'98		
James P.	Dunn, M.	'97		
Jamita	Gadd, F.	'90		
Japanese Pinwheel	McEwen, C.	'90		Payne '92
Japanese Princess	McEwen, C.	'90		
Jazzebel	Ensminger, A.	'90		
Jazzed Up	Schreiner	'96		
Jazz Festival	Schreiner	'93		
Jazz Me Blue	Schreiner	'95		

VARIETY	HYBRIDIZER	H.M.	A.M. OR EQUIVALENT	MEDAL AWARDS
Jean Erickson	Rigby, C.	'96	'98	
Jean Hoffmeister	Gatty, J.		'90	
Jeri	Bertinot, N.	'90	'92	DeB '94
Jesse Lee	Lankow, Carol	'91		
Jesse's Song	Williamson, B.			Dykes '90
Je t'Aime	Gartman, L.	'96		
Jet Stream	Danielson, L.	'93		
Jeweler's Art	Lankow, Carol	'95	'97	
Jewelled Crown	Hollingworth, R.		'91	Mor-W '93
Jewel of Omar	Boswell, C.		Mohr '91	Mohr '93
Jillaroo	Ensminger, J.		'92	
Jitterbug	Keppel, K.	'90		
Joan Moritz	Hagberg, M.	'94		
Jocasta	Innerst, S.	'90	'94	
Joe Cool	Aitken, T.	'93		
John	Ensminger, A.	'92	'94	
John Kearney	Innerst, S.	'96		
Johnny Reb	Nelson, R.	'97		
Jolly Jim	Dunderman, M.	'90		
Jolt	Weiler, J.	'90		
Jonnye's Magic	Rich, L.	'94	'97	
Joy Joy Joy	Ensminger, A.	'98		
Joy Peters	Ackerman, W.	'92	'95	
Juan Valdez	Maryott, W.	'95		
Judean Magic	Shockey, H.	'90		
June Rose	Blodgett, R.	'91		
Jungle Kitten	Breth, T.	'91		
Jungle Princess	Aitken, T.	'91		
Jungle Warrior	Aitken, T.	'93		
Jurassic Park	Lauer, L.	'97	'99	
Just Helene	Mertzweiller, J.	'94		
Just Jennifer	Taylor, J.D.	'90		
Kalamazoo	Hazzard/Bauer/Coble	'91	'93	Payne '96
Kalifa's Horn	Annand, R.	'97	'99	
Kalifa's Robe	Hager, B.	'92	'94	CGW '98
Kathleen Kay Nelson	Hager, B.	'95	'97	
Katmandu	Ghio, J.	'94		
Katy Lynn	Kegerise, Ev.	'90		
Katy Mendez	McEwen, C.	'91		
Kay Nelson	Granger, M.	'90	'92	DeB '95
Kelley's Choice	Morgan, R.	'96		
Kentucky Cajun	Norris, S.	'99		
Kentucky Woman	Schreiner	'99		
Kermit	Ensminger, A.	'92		
Kevin's Theme	Kerr, F.	'97		
Khyber Pass	Kidd, K.			CGW '94
Kid Stuff	Hager, B.	'92		
King Clovis	Tankesley-Clarke, E.&B.	'98		
Kingly Dignity	Niswonger, D.	'93		
King of Kings	Varner, S.			Mor-W '90
King Tush	Kasperek, B.	'99		
Kiosk	Hager, B.	'91		
Kissing Circle	Stevens, S.	'91		
Kitt Peak	Wickenkamp, F.		'94	
Kiwi Capers	Niswonger, D.	'93	'95	
Kiwi Slices	Niswonger, D.	'92	'94	

VARIETY	HYBRIDIZER	H.M.	A.M. OR EQUIVALENT	MEDAL AWARDS
Klondike Lil	Wood, V.	'97		
Knock 'em Dead	Ernst, R.	'96		
Kona Blush	Aitken, T.	'92		
Kona Nights	Aitken, T.	'94		
Kuniko	Gatty, J.	'91		
Lace Artistry	Aitken, T.	'90		
Lace Legacy	Greenwood, D.	'94		
Laced Coffee	Rowlan, H.	'90		
Lacy Primrose	Hoage, J.	'97		
Lady Bird Johnson	Mahan, C.	'98		
Lady Butterfly	Jenkins, B.C.	'99		
Lady Di	Varner, T.	'91		
Lady Juliet	Nichols, H.	'96	'99	
Lady of Marietta	Varner, T.	'90		
Lady Vanessa	Hollingworth, R.		'90	Mor-W '92
Laguna Creek	Ghio, J.	'93		
Lake Keuka	Borglum, D.	'97	'99	
La Mer	Richardson, G.	'98		
Lancer	Shockey, H.	'97	'99	
Larcenist	Burch, J.	'93		
Lark Ascending	Hager, B.	'98		
Larry Gaulter	Brown, B.	'90		
La Selva Beach	Ghio, J.	'97		
Latin Hideaway	Nichols, H.		'90	
La Valse	Hager, B.	'97		
Lavender Lemon	Danielson, L.	'90	'94	
Learn	Innerst, S.	'94		
Lee's Blue	Bauer, R./Coble, J.	'98		
Lemon Blossom	Magee, T.	'91		
Lemon Chess	Moores, W.	'98		
Lemon Fever	Maryott, W.	'91		
Lemon Pop	Lauer, L.	'92	'94	Sass '96
Lemon Up	Magee, T.	'96	'99	
Lemon Whip	Lankow, Carol	'95	'98	
Lenora Pearl	Nichols, H.	'92	'94	Knowl '96
Leprechaun's Eyelash	Boswell, C.	'91	'95	
Letmentertainu	Burseen, T.	'99		
Levity	Aitken, T.	'93	'95	
Liberty Hills	Miller, A.M.	'91	'93	
Life of Riley	McWhirter, J.	'95		
Lighten Up	Miller, L.	'93		
Lightning Bolt	Ghio, J.	'95		
Lightning Streak	Gibson, J.	'96		
Lights of Arabia	Rich, J.	'97		
Lilac Peaks	Vogt, A.		Payne '91	
Lima	Ghio, J.	'99		
Lime Mist	Willott, A. & D.	'90		
Lime Smoothy	Aitken, T.	'99		
Linda Mary	Cooper, J.	'92		
Lion King	Bauer, R./Coble, J.	'99		
Lion's Share	Jameson, M.	'94	'98	
Little Big Horn	Byers, M.	'91		
Little Blue Eyes	Weiler, J.	'95	'98	
Little Brown Jug	Meek, D.	'90		
Little Dazzler	Pinegar, D.	'91		
Little Drummer Boy	Willott, A. & D.	'99		

VARIETY	HYBRIDIZER	H.M.	A.M. OR EQUIVALENT	MEDAL AWARDS
Little Green Eyes	Boswell, C.		'91	
Little Jazz Man	Guild, D.	'91		
Little John	Spoon, D.	'99		
Little Mary Sunshine	Roderick, E.	'98		
Little Me	Hager, B.	'90		
Little Mermaid	Magee, T.	'96		
Little Misty	Craig, J. & V.	'92		
Little O Chris	Shepard, D.	'90		
Little Rascal	Fry, J. & L.	'93	'96	
Little Rhyme	Schafer, M./Sacks, J.	'95	'98	
Little Showoff	Hall, E.	'91	'94	Cook '98
Little Snowball	Vogt, A.	'92		
Little Snowman	Vogt, A.	'92	'96	
Little Sunrise	Craig, J. & V.	'90		
Little Who	Hager, B.	'90		
Little You	Hager, B.	'90		
Live Coals	Niswonger, D.	'96		
Lively One	Jenkins, B.C.	'91		
Local Color	Keppel, K.	'98		
Logo	Keppel, K.		'90	
Londonderry	Keppel, K.	'98		
Lonesome Dove	Kerr, F.	'96		
Long's Peak	Durrance, J.	'98		
Look Lively	Hager, B.	'90		
Lorena Cronin	Cronin, A.	'99		
Los Californio	Ghio, J.	'93		
Los Coyotes	Burseen, T.	'97		
Loskeha	Gadd, F.	'91		
Love Blush	Shockey, H.	'94		
Love's Tune	Ensminger, A.	'90		
Low Ho Silver	Byers, M.	'91	'94	
Low Life	Aitken, T.	'98		
Low Spirits	Keppel, K.	'96	'98	
Loyalist	Schreiner		'92	
Lucille Richardson	Richardson, G.	'95		
Lucky Devil	Ghio, J.	'90		
Lucky Lilac	McEwen, C.	'90		
Lullaby of Spring	Schreiner		'93	
Lumalite	Aitken, T.	'98		
Lunar Frost	Keppel, K.	'98		
Lyme Tyme	Messick, V.	'99		
Mabel Coday	Helsley, C.			Mor-W '91
Mabel Wing	Jeffries, R.	'90		
Macarena	Messick, V.	'99		
Macumba	Hager, B.	'92		
Madame Bovary	Lauer, L.	'96		
Mad Magenta	Warburton, B.	'90		
Magic Bubbles	Willott, A. & D.	'97	'99	
Magician's Apprentice	Maryott, W.	'94		
Magic Show	Keppel, K.	'96		
Magnificent Obsession	McAllister, S.	'95	'97	
Maharishi	Keppel, K.	'93		
Maid of Orange	Aitken, T.	'91	'94	
Mallow Dramatic	Gatty, J.	'98		
Managua	Ghio, J.	'96		
Mango Tango	Ghio, J.	'99		

VARIETY	HYBRIDIZER	H.M.	A.M. OR EQUIVALENT	MEDAL AWARDS
Manisses	Varner, T.	'90		
Mantra	Ghio, J.	'96		
Manuscript	Burch, J.	'93		
Marcy Michelle	Lauer, L.	'98		
Margaret Beaufort	Burton, L.	'97		
Marge Hagberg	Albers, D.	'92		
Mariah	Schreiner	'99		
Maria Tormena	Ensminger, A.		'93	
Mariposa Skies	Tasco, R.	'98		
Maritima Gem	Hager, B.	'93		
Marjan	Bishop, H.	'96	'98	
Martha's Gold	Aitken, T.	'94		
Marthella	Nichols, H.	'97		
Marvell Gold	Waddick, J.	'96	'99	
Mary Ellen Nichols	Nichols, H.	'92		
Master Plan	Keppel, K.	'97		
Master Sleuth	Nichols, H.	'95		
Maui Gold	Aitken, T.	'94	'98	
Maui Magic	Aitken, T.	'93	'95	
Maui Moonlight	Aitken, T.		'91	Sass '93
Maui Surf	Aitken, T.	'92	'94	
Mauve Snowtop	Reid, L.	'99		
McKenzie Sunset	Reid, L.	'91		
Megabucks	Tompkins, C.	'94		
Megglethorp	Innerst, S.	'95		
Melba Hamblen	Hager, B.	'94		
Melted Butter	Fan, C.	'96	'99	
Memoirs	Ghio, J.	'90		
Merci Beaucoup	Dunn, M.	'97		
Merit	Fisher, K.	'99		
Mesa Pearl	Coble, J./Bauer, R.	'97		
Mesmerizer	Byers, M.	'93	'96	
Michelle Stadler	Stadler, J.D.	'95		
Michio	Miller, A. M.	'91		
Midnight Dancer	Schreiner	'93		
Midnight Fragrance	Stevens, S.	'93		
Midnight Mist	Black, P.	'98		
Midnight Rival	Johnsen, L.	'98		
Midnight Stars	Aitken, T.	'90		
Mimsey	Wood, V.	'90	Mitch '92	Mitch '93
Mind Reader	Keppel, K.	'96	'98	
Mini Minx	Fry, J. & L.	'91		
Mini Pearl	Street, S.		'92	
Mini Wabash	Probst, R.	'98		
Mississippi Gambler	Dunn, M.		'91	
Miss Nellie	Burch, J.			Knowl '90
Missouri Blue	Niswonger, D.		'93	
Missouri Clouds	Niswonger, D.	'99		
Missouri Lakes	Niswonger, D.	'98		
Missouri Rivers	Niswonger, D.	'92	'94	Nies '98
Missouri Springs	Niswonger, D.	'97	'99	
Missouri Sunset	Niswonger, D	'99		
Mist of Blue	Palmer,C.	'91	'93	
Modern Times	Gatty, J.	'94		
Mohric Art	Peterson, L.	'90		
Moonlight Madness	McAllister, S.	'99		

VARIETY	HYBRIDIZER	H.M.	A.M. OR EQUIVALENT	MEDAL AWARDS
Moon Silk	Stahly, H.	'94	'96	
Morning's Blush	Jones, E.	'96		
Morning Show	Ensminger, A.	'90	'92	
Mostest	Durrance, J.	'92		
Mother Earth	Hager, B.	'91		
Mother's Little Helper	Ernst, R.	'98		
Motto	Gatty, J.	'96		
Mountain Majesty	Ghio, J.	'97		
Much Obliged	Hager, B,	'96		
Mulberry Punch	Schreiner	'94		
Muse	Smith, M.	'99		
My Shadow	Magee, T.	'93		
My Sheba	Hager, B.	'91		
Mystic's Muse	Schreiner	'97		
Nancy Glazier	Hamblen, M.	'90		
National Anthem	Ghio, J.	'95	'99	
Nautical Flag	Black, P.	'91		
Navajo Jewel	Weiler, J.		'90	
Navajo Rose	Shepard, D.	'98		
Navy Blues	Dunn, R.	'96	'98	
Nectar	Keppel, K	'92	'95	
Nefertiti's Daughter	Niswonger, D.	'93		
Neon Pixie	Miller, L.	'92		
Neon Troll	Nichols, H.	'96		
Neptune's Cloak	Hager, B.	'94		
New Centurion	Schreiner	'95		
New Kid	Shoop, G.	'90		
New Melody	Peterson, L.	'90		
Nigerian Raspberry	Kasperek, B.	'97	'99	
Night Attack	Ghio, J.	'95		
Night Editor	Ghio, J.	'92	'95	Mitch '97
Night Fires	Innerst, S.	'96		
Night Flame	Aitken, T.	'94		
Night Game	Keppel K.	'98		
Night Ruler	Schreiner	'92	'94	
No Bikini Atoll	Ernst, R.	'98		
Noble House	McWhirter, J.	'90		
Nora Eileen	Richardson, G.	'97		
Nordica	Maryott, W.	'95	'98	
Nordic Ice	Shockey, H,	'95	'99	
Norma Jean	Durrance, J.	'94		
North Coast	Willott, A. & D.	'91		
Northwest Pride	Schreiner	'95		
Northwest Progress	Schreiner	'99		
Notable	Ghio, J.	'95		
Nothing But Net	Niswonger, D.	'98		
Notorious	Ghio, J.	'93		
Nursery School	Ghio, J.		'91	
Nut Ruffles	Lankow, Carol	'94	'96	
Oba Oba	Dunn, M.	'94		
Obligato	Stahly, H.	'90	'92	
Oh Jamaica	Schreiner	'97		
O.K.Corral	Black, P.	'96		
Oklahoma Crude	Black, P.	'91	'94	
Oklahoma Jubilee	Palmer, C.	'90		
Oklahoma Kitty	Granger, M.	'97		

VARIETY	HYBRIDIZER	H.M.	A.M. OR EQUIVALENT	MEDAL AWARDS
Oktoberfest	Maryott, W.		'91	
Old Black Magic	Schreiner	'98		
Oklahoma Kitty	Granger, M.	'97		
Old Fashioned Girl	McAllister, S.	'97	'99	
Ol' Man River	McEwen, C.	'90		
Omar's Gold	Boswell, C.	'98		
Omar's Torch	Boswell, C.		Mohr '92	Mohr '94
Omar's Valor	Boswell, C.	'97		
Omar the Tentmaker	Boswell, C.	'91	'94	Mohr '97
Ominous Stranger	Innerst, S.	'95	'97	
Onco G Plus	Boswell, C.	'94	'98	
One Little Pinkie	Durrance, J.	'96		
Opal Brown	Meek, D.	'98		
Opening Act	Lauer, L.	'93		
Orange Chips	Aitken, T.	'92		
Orange Dazzler	Jones, B.	'94	'96	
Orange Embers	Shockey, H.	'95		
Orange Jewelius	Miller, D.	'94		
Orange Jubilee	Schreiner	'95		
Orange Outrage	Jones, B.	'97		
Orange Petals	Niswonger, D.	'93		
Orange Slices	Niswonger, D.		'91	
Orange Tiger	Jones, B.	'90	'92	Cook '94
Oregold	Jones, B.	'92	'95	
Oregon Skies	Schreiner	'93,	'95	
Oriental Classic	McEwen, C.	'90	'95	
Oriental Eyes	Vogt, A.			Payne '93
Oro de Sonora	Wickenkamp, F.	'94	'97	
Osaka	Ghio, J.	'96		
O'So Pretty	Kegerise, Ev.	'95		
Outrageous	Fry, J & L.	'90		
Outrageous Fortune	Schreiner	'91		
Over Easy	Lankow, Carol	'92		
Over In Gloryland	Hollingworth, R.	'96	'98	
Overjoyed	Gatty, J.	'96	'98	
Overnight Sensation	Schreiner	'97		
Owyhee Desert	Pinkston, L.	'99		
Ozark Dream	Fisher, K.	'94	'96	
Ozark Evening	Fisher, K.	'93	'95	
Ozark Jewel	Fisher, K.	'94	'96	
Ozark Sky	Fisher, K.	'92	'95	
Pacer	Aitken, T.	'91		
Pacific Cloud	Lauer, L.	'99		
Pacific Destiny	Lauer. L.	'95	'99	
Pacific Red Velvet	Reid, L.	'99		
Pacific Rim	Jones, B.	'94	'96	Mitch '98
Pacific Snowflake	Shoop, G.	'98		
Pacific Starprint	Reid, L.	'95	'97	
Pagan Goddess	Miller, L.	'97		
Pagan Pink	Byers, M.	'90		
Paint It Black	Schreiner	'96		
Pale Moon Rising	Harper, J.	'92		
Panama Hattie	Begley, J.	'97		
Pardner	Fisher, K.	'95	'98	
Paris Blues	Dunn, M.	'93		
Party Line	Warburton, B.	'93	'95	

VARIETY	HYBRIDIZER	H.M.	A.M. OR EQUIVALENT	MEDAL AWARDS
Party Paleface	Reid, L.	'96	'98	
Pas-de-Deux	Hollingworth, R.	'90	'94	
Pastel Delight	Willott, A. & D.	'90		
Patacake	Black, P.	'91		
Patches on Parade	Aitken, T.	'90		
Patio Rose	Bellagamba, L.	'98		
Pat Loughran	Durrance, J.	'93		
Patriot's Gem	Gadd, F.	'95	'97	Mohr '99
Pawnee Princess	Jones, E.	'94	'96	
Payoff	Craig, J. & V.	'91	'95	
Peace and Harmony	Ghio, J.	'94		
Peach Cooler	Aitken, T.	'97		
Peach Ice Cream	Lankow, Carol	'95		
Peach Petal Pie	Niswonger, D.	'96	'99	
Peach Petals	Niswonger, D.		'92	
Peach Picotee	Schreiner	'93		
Pebble Brook	Gadd, F.	'90		
Peignoir	Markham, L.	'99		
Pele	Aitken, T.	'95	'97	Cook '99
People Pleaser	Ensminger, A.		'90	
Perfect Gift	Keppel, K.	'99		
Perfect Pitch	Gatty, J.	'94		
Perfume	Byers, M.	'92		
Persephone	Innerst, S.	'99		
Persian Padishah	Shockey, H.	'90	'93	CGW '95
Petite Ballet	Keppel, K.	'94	'96	Knowl '99
Petite Blush	Boushay, J.	'91		
Petite Doll	Rowlan, H.	'93		
Petite Jewel	Albers, D.	'91	'93	
Petite Lady	Rowlan, H.	'92		
Petite Monet	Steele, K.	'92	'94	W-W '96
Phaeton	Smith, M.	'99		
Phil Edinger	Hager, B.	'94	'96	
Picacho Peak	Wickenkamp, F.	'90		
Picante	Ghio, J.	'99		
Picotee Princess	Reid, L.	'95	'97	
Piece of Cake	Hager, B.	'91		
Pieces of Ice	Nelson, R.	'92		
Pilgrims' Choice	Willott, A. & D.	'92		
Pink Betterment	Peterson, L.		'94	
Pink Blink	Aitken, T.	'96	'99	
Pink Blue Genes	Niswonger, D.	'93		
Pink Charming	Ghio, J.	'96		
Pink Cupid	Wood, V.	'96	'98	
Pink Dace	Copeland, Jill	'96		
Pink Dimity	Reid, L.		'94	
Pink Empress	Palmer, C.	'92		
Pink Gala	Wood, V.	'93		
Pinkie Paws	Miller, L.	'94		
Pink Peaks	Schafer, M./Sacks, J.	'93	'95	
Pink Pele	Aitken, T.	'98		
Pink Quartz	Wood, V.	'98		
Pink Ringlets	Aitken, T.	'98		
Pink Sapphire	Hamblen, M.	'94		
Pink Starlet	Wood, V.	'95	'97	
Pippi Longstockings	Innerst, S.		'90	

VARIETY	HYBRIDIZER	H.M.	A.M. OR EQUIVALENT	MEDAL AWARDS
Pirate's Patch	Black, P.	'97		
Pirate's Quest	Schreiner	'94		
Pittance	Miller, L.	'90		
Pixie Flirt	Willott, A. & D.	'91	'95	
Pixie Pirate	Willott, A. & D.	'99		
Plantation Belle	Dunn, M.	'99		
Pleasant Earlybird	Harris, C.	'99		
Pleasures of May	Schafer, M./Sacks, J.	'99		
Plum Lucky	Lankow, Carol	'96		
Plum Wine	Weiler, J.		'91	
Poem of Ecstacy	Hager, B.	'99		
Poetic	Ghio, J.	'94		
Point In Time	Innerst, S.	'91		
Point Made	Innerst, S.	'90		
Polar Seas	Keppel, K.	'91		
Pond Lily	Jones, E.	'97	'99	
Popular Demand	McEwen, C.	'92		
Power Surge	Ghio, J.	'93		
Prairie In Bloom	Gaddie, G.	'92		
Prairie Thunder	Black, P.	'92	'94	Mohr '98
Praline Festival	Haymon, D.	'95	'99	
Premier Edition	Schreiner	'92		
Prestige Item	Hager, B.	'95		
Pretty Beginning	Jones, E.	'93		
Pretty Is	Mullin, R.	'97	'99	
Pretty Quirky	Probst, A.	'95	'97	W-W '99
Pretty Woman	Maryott, W.	'94	'97	
Prince George	Shoop, G.	'99		
Prince of Burgundy	Niswonger, D.	'95	'97	Sass '99
Princess Bluebeard	Willott, A. & D.	'93		
Prism	Smith, M.	'97		
Private Reserve	Aitken, T.	'96		
Private Stock	Hamblen, M.	'95		
Private Treasure	Shoop, G.	'95		
Privileged Character	Black, P.	'93	'96	
Professor Barbara	Mertzweiller, J.	'95		
Professor Fritchie	Mertzweiller, J.	'98		
Professor Jim	Mertzweiller, J.		'93	DeB '96
Professor Marta Marie	Mertzweiller, J.	'96		
Professor Neil	Mertzweiller, J.	'95	'97	DeB '99
Professor Sigmond	Mertzweiller, J.	'90		
Progressive Attitude	Innerst, S.	'96		
Promenade Lady	Flanagan, L.	'91		
Prom Night	Schreiner	'91		
Protocol	Keppel, K.	'98		
Proud Tradition	Schreiner	'92	'94	
Pumpin' Iron	Black, P.	'92	'94	Cook '96
Pumpkin Center	Jones, B.	'91	'93	
Pumpkin Cheesecake	Niswonger, D.	'97		
Punkin Patch	Denney, D.	'92		
Puppet Baby	Boswell, C.			Cap-W '91
Pure Allure	Ritchie, J.	'90		
Pure As Gold	Maryott, W.	'95	'99	
Pure-As-The	Innerst, S.	'91	'94	
Purgatory	Moores, W.	'90		
Purple Pepper	Nearpass, D.C.		'92	

VARIETY	HYBRIDIZER	H.M.	A.M. OR EQUIVALENT	MEDAL AWARDS
Purple Pleaser	Lineberger, E.	'99		
Pussytoes	Willott, A. & D.			Cap-W '90
Queen Bee	Dunn, M.	'98		
Queen of Angels	Schreiner	'97	'99	
Queen's Gambit	Johnson, D.	'91		
Queen Sheba	Shockey, H.	'95	'97	CGW '99
Quicken	Aitken, T.	'93		
Quiet Elegance	Aitken, T.	'97		
Quiet Place	Varner, T.	'91		
Quito	Ghio, J.	'95	'97	
Quote	Gatty, J.	'96		
Radiant Energy	Maryott, W.	'90		
Rainbow Goddess	Ernst, R.	'96		
Rainbows	Miller, L.	'92		
Rainbow Sherbet	Weiler, J.	'92		
Rainbow Tour	Black, P.	'94		
Raindance Kid	Aitken, T.	'92		
Rain Man	Meek, J.	'96		
Raku Blaze	Aitken, T.	'99		
Ramblin' Rose	Schreiner	'95		
Ramona Howard	McWhirter, J.	'93		
Ranchipur	Moores, W.	'90		
Rapscallion	Miller, L.	'97		
Rapture In Blue	Schreiner	'92	'94	
Rare Occasion	Gatty, J.	'96		
Rare Treat	Schreiner		'92	
Raspberry Cheesecake	Dickey, P.	'99		
Raspberry Dazzler	Wood, V.	'99		
Raspberry Fudge	Keppel, K.	'91	'93	
Raspberry Gem	Miller, A.M.	'91		
Raspberry Glow	Aitken, T.	'97	'99	
Raspberry Lace	Pinegar, D.	'93		
Raspberry Punch	Ennenga, J.	'90		
Raspberry Rascal	Protzmann, C.	'92		
Raspberry Splendor	Niswonger, D.	'97		
Rat-A-Tat	Bohrer, R.	'92		
Raven Rock	Carr, F.	'90		
Raven's Quote	Ernst, R.	'96		
Razzleberry	Nelson, R.	'98		
Razzle Dazzle	Gaddie, G.		'90	
Rebus	Gatty, J.	'98		
Recherche	Hager, B.	'92		
Red Echo	Rowlan, H.		'90	
Red Hawk	Schreiner	'97		
Red Rooster	Durrance, J.	'92	'95	Knowl '98
Red Sands	Shockey, H.	'96		
Regal Affair	Shoop, G.	'93		
Regency Belle	McEwen, C.	'90		
Reminiscence	Mahan, C.	'98		
Reprise	Warburton, B.	'90	'93	
Respectable	Ghio, J.	'91		
Response	Corlew, G.	'92		
Rhett	Dunn, M.			DeB '91
Rhinemaidens	Magee, T.	'92		
Rhonda Fleming	Mullin, R.	'95	'97	Wister '99
Rich and Famous	Dunn, M.	'97		

VARIETY	HYBRIDIZER	H.M.	A.M. OR EQUIVALENT	MEDAL AWARDS
Rich Jewel	Morgan, R.	'99		
Rich Man	Lineberger, E.	'99		
Ride the Wind	Schreiner	'93	'96	
Rikugi Sakura	Shidara, H.	'92		
Rill	Bellagamba, L.	'96	'98	
Ringer	Keppel, K.	'99		
Rinky-Dink	Keppel, K.	'95	'97	
Ripple Chip	Aitken, T.	'91		
Rippling River	Schreiner	'97		
Rita Kinsella	Briscoe, H.		'91	
Rite of Spring	Hager, B.	'98		
Riverboat Blues	Schreiner	'93	'95	
Roaring Jelly	Schafer, M./Sacks, J.	'95	'97	Mor-W '99
Robin Goodfellow	Mahan, C.	'96	'98	
Robin's Egg	Sindt, D.	'95		
Rock Star	Byers, M.	'94		
Rodeo Clown	Nichols, H.	'93		
Rogue	Ghio, J.	'99		
Rokki Rockwell	Haymon, D.	'95		
Role Model	Denney, D.	'90	'94	
Romantic Evening	Ghio, J.	'98		
Romantic Interlude	Varner, T.	'99		
Romanticist	Keppel, K.	'92		
Romantic Mood	Ghio, J.	'90		
Rosalie Figge	McKnew, J.	'96	'99	
Rosa Nova	Schreiner	'93		
Rosarita	Keppel, K.	'93		
Rose Caper	Guild, D.	'92		
Rose Frappe	Miller, A.M.	'91		
Rosemary's Dream	Dunderman, M.			W-W '94
Rosette Wine	Schreiner	'91	'93	
Rosewater	Bauer, R./Coble, J.	'99		
Rose World	Reid, L.	'91		
Royal Dolly	Reid, L.	'98		
Royal Elegance	Gatty, J.	'91		
Royal Gossip	Nichols, H.	'96		
Royal Intrigue	Schreiner	'93		
Royalist	Dunn, M.	'90		
Roy Bohrer	Briscoe, H.	'90		
Ruby Locket	Niswonger, D.	'92		
Ruby Star	Aitken, T.	'94		
Ruby Tuesday	Maryott, W.	'95		
Ruby Wilson	Denney, D.	'91		
Ruffled Copper Sunset	Gibson, J.	'95		
Ruffled Feathers	Innerst, S.	'93		
Ruffled Goddess	Tasco, R.	'95	'97	
Rumbleseat	Innerst, S.	'95		
Rustler	Keppel, K.	'90	'92	
Rusty Dusty	Hager, B.	'91		
Rusty Nail	Messick, V.	'95		
Ruth Black	Black, P.	'99		
Ruth Sloan	Sloan, R.		'90	
Sailor	Smith, M.	'98		
Sam	Aitken, T.	'90		
Samson	Aitken, T.	'96		
San Lorenzo Valley	Ghio, J.	'97		

VARIETY	HYBRIDIZER	H.M.	A.M. OR EQUIVALENT	MEDAL AWARDS
Santa Cruz Beach	Ghio, J.	'90		
Santiago	Ghio, J.	'94		
Sass With Class	Black, P.	'91		
Saturday Night Live	Schreiner	'98		
Scandia Delight	Schreiner	'92		
Scarlet Embers	Begley, J.	'97		
Screen Play	Keppel, K.	'99		
Scruples	Miller, L.	'97	'99	
Sea Admiral	Wood, V.	'98		
Seabright Cove	Ghio, J.	'96		
Sea Cadet	Aitken, T.	'95		
Sea Gal	Belardi, L.	'97	'99	
Sea Jewel	Albers, D.	'90		
Seakist	Schreiner	'99		
Sea Monster	Miller, L.	'96		
Seaport	Keppel, K.	'93		
Sea Quest	Shoop, G.	'94		
Season Ticket	Gatty, J.	'97		
Sea Urchin	Aitken, T.	'90	'93	
Second Opinion	Bausch, L.	'90		
See the Light	Ghio, J.	'95		
Select Circle	Ghio, J.	'99		
Semper Fi	Ames, H.	'90		
Señor Frog	Aitken, T.		'92	
Seraph's Jewel	Shockey, H.	'94	'96	
Serenade In Blue	Waite, K.	'90		
Serendipity Elf	Niswonger, D.	'95		
Serenity Prayer	Dyer, P.	'91	'93	Cook '95
Shaker's Prayer	Warner, C.	'92	'94	Mor-W '96
Sheba's Beauty	Nichols, H.		'93	
Sheba's Jewel	Shockey, H.	'96	'98	
She Devil	Black, P.	'98		
Sheer Class	Miller, L.	'91		
Shenanigan	Keppel, K.			Knowl '91
Shirley M.	Kegerise, Ev.	'97		
Shooting Sparks	Black, P.	'91		
Shopper's Holiday	McWhirter, J.	'93		
Show Me Yellow	Anderson, D.	'92		
Shrimp Boat	Gatty, J.	'94		
Shy Violet	Jones, B.	'91		
Sierra Dell	Lawyer, L.	'90	'93	Mitch '95
Sierra Grande	Schreiner	'94,	'96	
Sigh	Black, P.	'92		
Sighs and Whispers	Black, P.	'92	'95	
Silent Tears	Peterson, L.	'93	'96	
Silhouette	Dunn, M.	'93		
Silicon Prairie	Stanek, T.	'93		
Silk Silhouette	Gartman, L.	'94		
Silverado	Schreiner		'91	Wister '93 Dykes '94
Silverband	Bauer, R./Coble, J.	'92		
Silver Fox	Wood, V.	'92	'95	
Silver Illusion	Johnson, D.		'91	
Silver Rose	Warburton, B.	'90		
Simply Wild	Ghio , J.			Mitch '94
Sinfonietta	Raabe, R.	'90	'92	

VARIETY	HYBRIDIZER	H.M.	A.M. OR EQUIVALENT	MEDAL AWARDS
Sinister	Denney, D.	'93		
Sixteen Candles	Byers, M.	'91		
Skiddle	Innerst, S.	'98		
Skipalong	Ghio, J.	'98		
Skyblaze	Keppel, K.		'93	
Sky Blue Pink	Niswonger, D.	'96		
Sky Echo	Dyer, F.	'91		
Skylash	Belardi, L.	'98		
Skylark's Song	Schreiner	'98		
Sky Mirror	Warburton, B.	'92		
Skywalker	Schreiner	'98		
Slam Dunk	Niswonger, D.	'98		
Slap Bang	Niswonger, D.	'94		
Sleepy Time	Schreiner	'90		
Sly Fox	Wood, V.	'99		
Smart	Innerst, S.	'95		
Smart Aleck	Gatty, J.	'91		
Smart Move	Keppel, K.	'97		
Smell the Roses	Byers, M.	'90	'94	
Smiling Gold	Ernst, R.	'94		
Smitten Kitten	Aitken, T.	'93	'95	
Smoke With Wine	Boswell, C.			Mohr '95
S'more	Aitken, T.	'94	'97	
Smuggler's Cove	Wood, V.	'91	'94	
Sneezy	Keppel, K.	'98		
Snickerdoodle	Wulf, O.	'96		
Snoopy	Lankow, Carol	'98		
Snowbelt	Keppel, K.	'94		
Snowbrook	Keppel, K.		'91	
Snow Bunny	Brown, O.	'93		
Snow Burst	Hamner, B.	'94		
Snow Hawk	Corlew, G.	'90		
Snow Prince	Tiffney, S.	'92	'95	
Snow Season	Jones, E.	'95		
Snow Shoes	Osborne, M.	'99		
Snow Tree	Sobek, R.	'94		
Snowy Mountain	Johnson, D.	'91		
Snowy River	Willott, A. & D.		'90	
Snugglebug	Schreiner	'97		
Snuggles	Miller, L.	'90	'94	Cap-W '98
Social Event	Keppel, K.	'93	'97	
Social Lady	Rowlan, H.	'90		
So Fine	Schreiner	'98		
Soft Caress	Gatty, J.	'93		
Solar Eclipse	Slade, G.	'90		
Soloist	Ernst, R.	'96		
Solomon's Glory	Nichols, H.		'93	Mohr '96
Solomon's Wisdom	Rich, J.	'97		
Somersault	Ghio, J.	'98		
Song of Angels	Schreiner	'95		
Sonja's Selah	Ensminger, A.	'91	'93	Knowl '97
Son of Sun	Wickenkamp, F.			Nies '94
Sonoran Caballero	Wickenkamp, F.	'92	'95	
Sonoran Senorita	Wickenkamp, F.	'91	'94	
Sonoran Skies	Wickenkamp, F.	'96	'99	
Sonoran Sunset	Wickenkamp, F.	'96	'98	

VARIETY	HYBRIDIZER	H.M.	A.M. OR EQUIVALENT	MEDAL AWARDS
Southern Son	McEwen, C.	'92		
Space Psalms	Nichols, H.	'92		
Spanish Fireball	Jones, B.	'97		
Sparkling Sapphire	Vogt, A.	'92		
Sparky	Aitken, T.			Cap-W '93
Speed Limit	Lauer, L.	'94	'96	
Spellbreaker	Schreiner	'94	'96	
Spiced Cider	Sexton, N.	'91		
Spiced Tiger	Kasperek, B.	'98		
Spin Doctor	Davis, M.	'99		
Spirit World	Keppel, K.	'96	'98	
Splash Dance	Shepard, D.	'90		
Splash of Raspberry	Hoage, J.	'98		
Splash of Red	Niswonger, D.		'93	
Split Decision	Hobbs, E.	'92		
Spot of Tea	Black, P.	'91	'93	Cap-W '95
Spring Fresh	Keppel, K.	'99		
Spring Parasol	Ernst, R.	'95		
Springs Brook	Warburton, B.	'91	'93	
Springtime Showers	Reid, L.	'90		
Sprinkles	Bauer, R./Coble, J.	'98		
Squeeze Louise	Nichols, H.	'90		
Squiggles	Miller, L.	'97		
Stairway To Heaven	Lauer, L.	'95	'97	Wister '99
Standing Tall	Johnson, D.	'91		
Starbaby	Smith, M.	'95	'97	
Stardust Memories	Schreiner	'94		
Star Fleet	Keppel, K.	'95		
Starlight Express	Schreiner	'96		
Starlit Velvet	Stahly, H.	'93		
Star Power	Dunn, M.	'98		
Star Sailor	Schreiner	'97		
Status Seeker	Gartman, L.	'93		
Steffie	Fisher, K.	'97	'99	
Step Aside	Danielson, L.	'95		
Stolen Dreams	Hager, B.	'94		
Stop and Go	Dunn, M.	'99		
Stratagem	Ghio, J.	'92		
Strawberry Cream	Boushay, J.	'91	'94	
Strawberry Fair	Hollingworth, R.	'97	'99	
Strictly Ballroom	Lauer, L.	'96		
Strike It Rich	Ernst, R.	'95		
Striped Moonbeam	Shepard, D.	'93		
Striped Pants	Fisher, K.	'91	'94	W-W '98
Sudden Impact	Tasco, R.	'99		
Suky	Mahan, C.	'93	'95	
Sultan's Ruby	Hollingworth, R.	'90	'92	Mor-W '94
Sultan's Sash	Niswonger, D.	'92	'95	Nies '99
Sultry Mood	Schreiner	'91		
Summer Moon	Rich, J.	'99		
Sun Cascade	Huber, T.	'98		
Suncatcher	Ensminger, A.	'96		
Sun Doll	Jones, B.		'90	Cook '92
Sunflight	Jensen, E.	'92		
Sunkist Delight	Niswonger, D.	'99		
Sunkist Frills	Palmer, D.	'90		

544

VARIETY	HYBRIDIZER	H.M.	A.M. OR EQUIVALENT	MEDAL AWARDS
Sunny Bubbles	Maryott, W.	'96		
Sunny Dawn	Jones, B.	'91	'93	
Sunny Shoulders	Hager, B.	'94		
Sunny Song	Willott, A. & D.	'90		
Sunray Reflection	Ernst, R.	'95		
Sunrise in Missouri	Niswonger, D.	'98		
Sunrise in Sonora	Wickenkamp, F.	'97		
Sunshine Boy	Foster, F.		'90	
Supreme Sultan	Schreiner	'90	'92	
Swazi Dame	Danielson, H.	'94		
Sweeter Than Wine	Schreiner	'90	'94	
Sweet Musette	Schreiner		'91	
Swing and Sway	Messick, V.	'96	'99	
Swingtown	Schreiner	'98		
Swirling Lavender	Miller, A.M.	'90		
Sylvia's Masquerade	Eddy, S.	'91		
Syrian Jewel	Shockey, H.		CGW '91	CGW '93
Syrian Princess	Shockey, H.	'90	'93	CGW '96
Tact	Keppel, K.	'97		
Tall Ships	Aitken, T.	'95		
Tangueray	Dunn, M.	'97		
Tan Man	Aitken, T.	'99		
Tantrum	Keppel, K.	'99		
Tanzanian Tangerine	Kasperek, B.	'97	'99	
Tattler	Keppel, K.	'98		
Tchin-Tchin	Gatty, J.	'90	'92	
Telegraph Hill	McWhirter, J.	'97		
Temperence	Maryott, W.	'94		
Temper Tantrum	McGarvey, W.		'90	
Tempting	Ghio. J.	'95		
Tempting Fate	Meek, D.	'95		
Tennessee Gentleman	Innerst, S.	'93	'95	
Tennessee Vol	Niswonger, D.	'95		
Tennessee Woman	Innerst, S.	'93	'95	
Tennison Ridge	Begley, J.	'91	'93	
Test Pattern	Ghio, J.	'93		
Texas Glory	Nichols, H.	'96		
Thai Orange	Ernst, T.	'98		
Theda Clark	Nichols, H.	'90	'93	
Thornbird	Byers, M.	'91	'93	Wister '96 Dykes '97
Thriller	Schreiner	'90	'92	
Thrillseeker	Ernst, R.	'96		
Throb	Weiler, J.	'93		
Thumkin	Corlew, G.	'98		
Thunder Mountain	Schreiner	'93		
Thunder Spirit	Schreiner	'98		
Tickled Peach	Lankow, Carol	'97		
Tideline	Bauer, R./Coble, J.	'99		
Tide Mark	Hummel, J.	'90		
Tiffany Lass	McEwen, C.	'92		
Tiger Honey	Kasperek, B.	'96	'98	
Tillie	Shoop, G.	'90		
Timberwind	Burch, J.	'95		
Timescape	Hager, B.	'92	'96	
Tink	Durrance, J.	'93	'97	

VARIETY	HYBRIDIZER	H.M.	A.M. OR EQUIVALENT	MEDAL AWARDS
Tinted Crystal	Hager, B.	'91		
Tintinnabulation	Olson, L.	'98		
Tiny Apricot	Hager, B.		'91	
Tiny Cherub	Hager, B.	'90	'92	
Tiny Lou	Jenkins, B.C.	'92		
Titanic Gem	Danielson, L.	'92		
Toasted Watermelon	Hoage, J.	'97	'99	
Tom Johnson	Black, P.	'98		
Tommyknocker	Lyons, R.	'97		
Tomoko	Nelson, R.	'93		
Toon Town	Black, P.	'99		
Tooth Fairy	Jones, B.	'95	'97	Cap-W '99
Top Gun	Gaulter, L.	'90		
Totally Cool	Aitken, T.	'97		
Total Recall	Hager, B.	'96		
Touched By Angels	Maryott, W.	'99		
Toy Boat	Black, P.	'93		
Toy Clown	Gatty, J.	'94		
Trajectory	Black. P.	'99		
Trancas	Ghio, J.	'99		
Transcribe	Black, P.	'94		
Tri Blue	Johnson, D.	'91		
Trim The Velvet	Schafer, M./Sacks, J.	'98		
Triplet	Keppel, K.	'90		
Triple Whammy	Hager, B.	'92	'95	
Trivia	Keppel, K.	'92		
Tropical Fruit	Black, P.	'91		
Tuffet	Magee, T.	'90		
Tumblin' Dice	Nelson, R.	'94		
Turkish Heart	Shockey, H.	'92	'96	
Turkish Herald	Shockey, H.	'94	'97	
Turkish Pendant	Shockey, H.	'92	'95	CGW '97
Turkish Tattoo	Rich, J.	'96		
TuTu Turquoise	Black, P.	'91	'93	
Tweety Bird	Black, P.	'94	'96	
Twilight Blaze	Keppel, K.	'94		
Unforgettable Fire	Schreiner	'93	'97	
Up All Night	Ghio, J.	'92		
Upper Echelon	Ghio, J.	'93		
Urgent	Nichols, H.	'95		
U-Turn	Boswell, C.	'94		
Valentine's Day	Wood, V.	'99		
Variation in Pink	McEwen, C.	'99		
Vavoom	Ensminger, A.	'96	'98	
Vegas Showgirl	Willott, A. & D.	'90		
Velvet Underground	Lauer, L.	'99		
Venus and Mars	Nelson, R.	'90		
Veracity	Hummel, J.	'90		
Very Varied	Ensminger, A.	'96		
Very Violet	Jones, B.	'93	'96	
Vibrant Rose	Witt, J.	'92		
Vibrations	Dunn, M.	'92	'96	
Vicki Ann	Warburton, B.	'93	'95	
Victorian Frills	Black, P.	'92		
Victorian Lace	Schreiner	'92		
Viewer's Wish	Peterson, L.	'91		

VARIETY	HYBRIDIZER	H.M.	A.M. OR EQUIVALENT	MEDAL AWARDS
Vigilante	Schreiner	'93	'95	
Vintner	Smith, M.	'98		
Violet Lulu	Warburton, B.	'90		
Violet Tiger	Kasperek, B.	'97		
Vitality	Ritchie, J.	'90		
Viva Mexico	Maryott, W.	'98		
Vive La Difference	Dunn. M.	'93		
Voltage	Messick, V.	'95	'97	
Voodoo Magic	Rowlan, H.	'91	'93	DeB '97
Voodoo Queen	Rowlan, H.	'96		
Wacko	Black, P.	'98		
Wake Up	Black, P.	'91		
Walkara	Ames, H.	'99		
War Chief	Schreiner	'95		
Warm Memories	Mullin, R.	'99		
Warrior Chief	McAllister, S.	'94		
Water Ballet	Ghio, J.	'97		
Waterworld	Lauer, L.	'98		
Waverly Pink	Lineberger, E.	'91		
Webmaster	Keppel, K.	'99		
Wee Folk	Willott, A. & D.	'90		
Wee Magic	Dyer, F.	'92		
Welch's Reward	Welch, W.	'90	W-W '92	
Well Suited	Black, P.	'92	'94	
Wench	Miller, L.	'95	'97	
Westerlies	Ghio, J.	'97		
Western Bluebird	Weiler, J.	'94	'97	
What Again	Ensminger, A.	'93	'96	
What's What	Ghio, J.	'97		
Where There's Smoke	Burseen, T.	'95		
Whipped Honey	Jameson, M.	'99		
Whirlwind Romance	McAllister, S.	'95		
Whispering	Hamblen, M.	'94		
Whistling Dixie	Dunn, M.	'99		
White Chapeau	Blodgett, R.	'91		
White Chocolate	McAllister, S.	'97		
White Heat	Keppel, K.	'95		
White Triangles	Warburton, B.	'91		
Wide Blue Eyes	Gaddie, G.	'92		
Wide Hips	Fort, Lyle	'92		
Widow's Veil	Miller, L.	'97		
Wild Cajun	Rowlan, H.	'93		
Wild Jasmine	Hamner, B.		'90	
Wilderness Rubies	Wood, J.	'92		
Wilderness Snowball	Wood, J.	'91		
Wilder Than Ever	Ghio, J.	'96	'99	
Wild Thing	Schreiner	'98		
Willow Mint	Morgan, R.	'98		
Willow Ware	Ensminger, A.	'92		
Winds of Change	Hager, B.	'97		
Windsong West	Nichols, H.	'90	'93	
Windwood Serenade	Hollingworth, R.	'92	'94	
Wings of Gold	Maryott, W.	'93		
Wini Conklin	McWhirter, J.	'98		
Winifred Ross	Hamblen, M.	'90		
Winner Take All	Ernst, R.	'96		

VARIETY	HYBRIDIZER	H.M.	A.M. OR EQUIVALENT	MEDAL AWARDS
Winning Edge	Ghio, J.	'99		
Winter Adventure	Black, P.	'94		
Winter's Whimsey	Denney, D.	'92		
Winterland	Byers, M.	'94		
Wishful Thinking	Keppel, K.	'98		
Wishing	Ghio, J.	'98		
Witch's Wand	Blyth, B.	'90		
Wizardry	Hollingworth, R.		'92	
World Class	Hager, B.	'92		
Wunderkind	Hager, B.	'94		
Wyoming Cowboys	Wickenkamp, F.	'98		
Xanthippe's Halo	Niswonger, D.	'94		
Yaquina Blue	Schreiner	'94	'96	Wister '98
Yellow Brick Road	Gibson, J.	'94		
Yes	Blyth, B	'98		
Zamboanga	Hager, B.	'97		
Zandria	Nebeker, D.	'98		
Zebra Blush	Kasperek, B.	'97		
Zebra Halo	Kasperek, B.	'99		
Zepherina	Maryott, W.	'99		
Zerzura	Hager, B.	'92		
Zimbek	Gadd, F.	'90		
Zinc Pink	Ensminger, A.		'91	Knowl '93
Zinger	Stevens, S.		'90	Knowl '94
Zula	Fisher, K.	'92	'94	W-W '97
Zulu Chief	Jenkins, B.C.	'96	'98	

WALTHER CUP

(Awarded to the iris receiving the greatest number of HM votes)

1990	Honky Tonk Blues	TB	Schreiner
1991	Frosted Velvet	MTB	K. Fisher
1992	Shaker's Prayer	SIB	C. Warner
1993	Tennessee Gentleman	TB	S. Innerst
1994	Hello Darkness	TB	Schreiner
1995	Boogie Woogie	TB	H. Nichols
1996	Feature Attraction	TB	Schreiner
1997	Fancy Woman	TB	K. Keppel
1998	Protocol	IB	K. Keppel
1999	Diabolique	TB	Schreiner

DYKES MEDAL WINNERS

AMERICAN

1990	JESSE'S SONG	(B. Williamson)
1991	EVERYTHING PLUS	(D. Niswonger)
1992	DUSKY CHALLENGER	(Schreiner)
1993	EDITH WOLFORD	(B. Hager)
1994	SILVERADO	(Schreiner)
1995	HONKY TONK BLUES	(Schreiner)
1996	BEFORE THE STORM	(S. Innerst)
1997	THORNBIRD	(M. Byers)
1998	CONJURATION	(M. Byers)
1999	HELLO DARKNESS	(Schreiner)

AUSTRALASIAN

1990	JAZZ BALLET	(J. C. Taylor - Australia)
1991	PENCHANT	(R. Harding - Australia)
1992	FIRST MOVEMENT	(G. Grosvenor - Australia)
1993	DURAL WHITE BUTTERFLY	(J. C. Taylor - Australia)
1994	EMMA RIPEKA	(F. Love - New Zealand)
1995	TEMPTONE	(G. Grosvenor - Australia)
1997	HILLS DISTRICT	(G. Grosvenor - Australia)
1998	RIBANDS	(G. Grosvenor - Australia)
1999	MOVE ON	(G. Grosvenor - Australia)

BRITISH

1990	HIGH PEAK	(B. Dodsworth - UK)
1991	WHARFEDALE	(B. Dodsworth - UK)
1994	ORINOCO FLOW	(C. Bartlett – UK)
1997	WHOOPER SWAN	(B. Dodsworth - UK)
1999	BERLIN RUFFLES	(T. Tamberg - Germany)

INTERNATIONAL IRIS COMPETITION

FLORENCE, ITALY
"PREMIO FIRENZE"

1990	SKYBLAZE	(K. Keppel - USA)
1991	PRINCE CHARMING	(B. Williamson - USA)
1992	SIGHS AND WHISPERS	(P. Black - USA)
1993	CONJURATION	(M. Byers-USA)
1994	STEADFAST LOVE	(F. Carr - USA)
1995	IKAR	(A. Volfovich-Moler - Uzbekistan)
1996	CELEBRATION SONG	(Schreiner - USA)
1997	CHAMPAGNE WALTZ	(Schreiner - USA)
1998	HELEN DAWN	(G. Grosvenor - Australia)
1999	SETTIMO CIELO	(V. Romoli - Italy)

No winner for years not listed in all of the above awards.